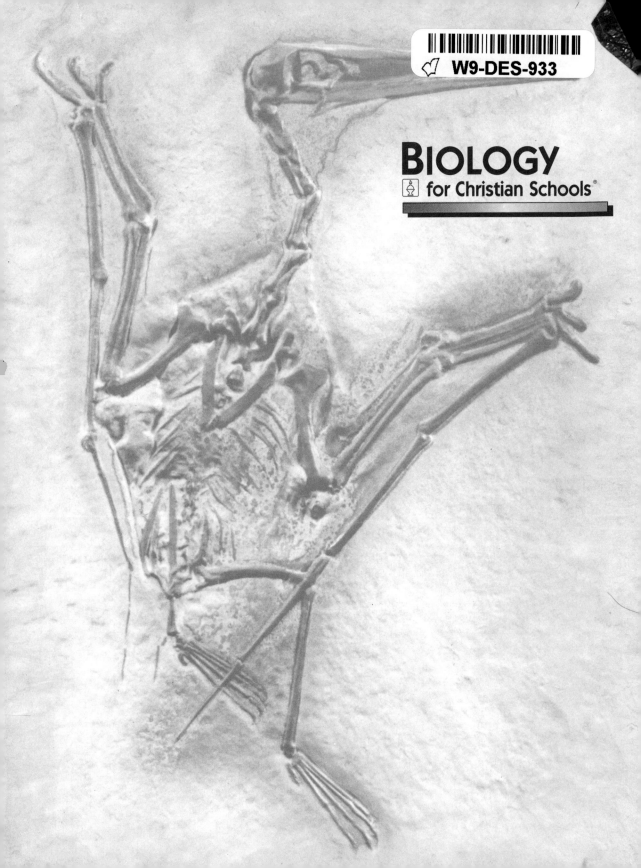

BIOLOGY
for Christian Schools®

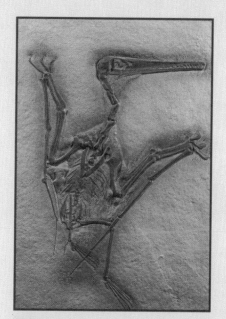

BIOLOGY
🔯 for Christian Schools®
Second Edition

William S. Pinkston, Jr.

Bob Jones University Press
Greenville, South Carolina 29614

NOTE:
The fact that materials produced by other publishers may be referred to in this volume does not
constitute an endorsement of the content or theological position of materials produced by such
publishers. Any references and ancillary materials are listed as an aid to the student or the
teacher and in an attempt to maintain the accepted academic standards of the publishing
industry.

BIOLOGY for Christian Schools®
Second Edition

William S. Pinkston Jr., M.Ed.

Produced in cooperation with the Bob Jones University Division of Natural Science
of the College of Arts and Science, the School of Religion, and Bob Jones Academy.

for Christian Schools is a registered
trademark of Bob Jones University Press.

© 1991, 1999 Bob Jones University Press
Greenville, South Carolina 29614
First Edition © 1980 Bob Jones University Press

Printed in the United States of America
All rights reserved

ISBN 1-59166-608-2

15 14 13 12 11 10 9

Contents

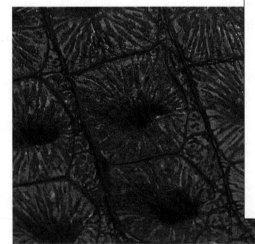

Introduction for the Student

BIOLOGY for Christian Schools® is a high school textbook for Bible-believing Christians. Those who do not believe that the Bible is the inspired, inerrant Word of God will find many points in this book puzzling. This book was not written for them.

Between true science (those things that can be accurately observed and measured) and the Bible there are no contradictions. After all, the One who wrote the Bible also created the things that scientists can observe. Men, however, can make mistakes in their observations, or they may reach a faulty conclusion from what they observe.

The people who have prepared this book have tried consistently to put the Word of God first and science second. To the best of the author's knowledge, the conclusions drawn from observable facts that are presented in this book agree with the Scriptures. If a mistake has been made (which is probable since this book was prepared by humans) and at any point God's Word is not put first, the author apologizes.

The position expressed by Dr. Bob Jones, Sr., as he said, "Whatever the Bible says is so; whatever man says may or may not be so," is the only one a Bible-believing Christian can take, but it does present some problems for a Christian high school biology student. Some of the conclusions a Christian must reach differ from those expressed by worldly sources. If your teacher assigned you to prepare a report on grasshoppers, an encyclopedia would be a logical place to begin. As you find out about the legs and wings of grasshoppers, how far these insects jump, their life cycle, how much damage they cause each year, and what type of insecticides are used to control them, you are gleaning scientific material.

The same encyclopedia article may state that the grasshopper evolved 70 million years ago. You may find a "scientific" explanation of the Biblical locust (grasshopper) plague in Egypt. You may find a description of the insects that the grasshoppers evolved from, and what insects evolved from the grasshoppers. These statements are conclusions based on "supposed science." If the conclusions contradict the Word of God, the conclusions are wrong no matter how many scientific facts may appear to back them.

The problem for the Christian biology student is not only to find information, but to consider the information in light of the Word of God. The task is not easy, but is, however, a task at which Christians need skill, not only in the sciences, but also in all areas of their lives. Keep these guidelines in mind as you start:

❑ *The Christian must know the Word of God.* This knowledge involves more than familiarity with Bible stories and some passages that are considered useful or interesting. The knowledge of the Bible needed to make good decisions comes only with years of studying the Bible and listening to good preaching and teaching. It comes only after meditating upon what God says in His Word.

❑ *The Christian must evaluate the source of the statement.* Scientific statements must be based on observation or else they are mere guesses. There is nothing wrong with a guess, as long as it is clearly labeled a guess or a belief. But Christians must disregard those guesses and beliefs that contradict the Bible.

Format of the Text

Notice the Table of Contents. This book is divided into three units. *Biology: The Science of Life* deals with topics basic to all biological studies. Much of this material concerns philosophy and theory (guesses) and covers the area in which many of the biological discoveries that most affect our lives are made. *Biology: The Science of Organisms* is a survey of the major groups of living things on our planet. This unit takes the traditional "classificational" approach to studying organisms. *Biology: The Study of Human Life* includes human anatomy, physiology, and Christian philosophy related to our physical, mental, and spiritual selves.

Each of these units is divided into chapters. Each chapter is divided into sections, which are lettered (for example: 1A, 1B, 1C, 2A, 2B). The chapter sections are divided into subsections by large type like the "Format of the Text" above. Finally, the subsections are divided into parts by headings like "Biological Terms" below. These headings should give you insight into what you are going to read. Do not skip over them, but use them as "pause-and-gather-your-thoughts" points before going on in the text.

Biological Terms

An important part of any study is the vocabulary of the subject. Several vocabulary learning aids are incorporated into *BIOLOGY for Christian Schools.* If you use these aids, you will not only make better grades, but will also glean material useful in other areas of life. Usually the biological terms considered most important are printed in

dark type, called **boldface.** Once a term has appeared in boldface, it will appear in *italic type* if it is stressed again in that chapter or in following chapters. Many biological terms of secondary importance appear in *italic type.* Italic type is also used for *emphasis* and for *scientific names.*

Every chapter section ends with a list of boldfaced terms that have appeared in the chapter. This list, called "Biological Terms," is arranged in the order the terms appear in the text. After you have read a section, you should be able to define the terms in this list. For special help and review, the **Glossary,** which begins on page 648, contains selected definitions for many terms used in this book. Unfamiliar terms used in this text often have a self-pronouncing spelling immediately following their appearance in the text.

Etymology* (ET uh MAHL uh jee) is the study of the history of words. It is useful because after you have learned a number of the common root words you should be able to figure out the meaning of some words you may not be familiar with. This text gives etymologies for certain words, each of which is marked with an **asterisk (*).** The etymology is found on the bottom of that page or the adjacent page. The first time the root is used in a chapter, it is defined. After that, only the root is given. Sometimes, if it is not obvious, the *combining form* (the prefix or suffix in current use) is given in parentheses by the root word.

Pronunciation Key

The pronunciations given in this text are designed to be self-evident and should give the average reader an acceptable pronunciation of the word as he reads it from the page. For accurate pronunciations, consult a good dictionary. This sample pronunciation key may help those who have difficulty with the symbols used.

Stressed syllables appear in large capital letters. Syllables with secondary stress and one-syllable words appear in small capital letters. Unstressed syllables are in lower case letters. Most consonants and combinations of consonants (ng, sh) make the sounds normally associated with them.

Some Symbol Key Words and Examples

a	cat KAT, laugh LAF	i-e	might MITE
a-e	cape KAPE,	ih	pity PIH tee
	reign RANE	o	potion POH shun
ah	father FAH thur	o-e	groan GRONE
ar	car KAR	oh	own OHN
aw	all AWL, caught KAWT	oo	tune TOON
ay	neigh NAY,	oy	toil TOYL
	paint PAYNT	th	thin THIN
e	jet JET		nothing NUH thing
ee	fiend FEEND	th	then THEN
eh	rebel REH bul,	u or uh	above uh BUV
	care KEHR	ur	person PUR suhn
eye	ivory EYE vuh ree	wh	where WHEHR
i	women WIM un	y	mighty MY tee

---

etymology: etymo- (Gk. ETUMOS, true) + -logy (Gk. LOGIA, word)

Facets of Biology and boxes

A new feature in this edition is the **Facets of Biology** which you will find scattered through the book. *Facets* contain material which is related to the content of the chapter. Some of them contain interesting examples, others have additional information, and some deal with practical or Biblical applications of scientific material. Some *Facets* contain terms which are listed in the *Biological Terms* section of the chapter while others do not.

Another new feature is the **boxes.** *Boxes* are found scattered in the text and in *Facets*. Generally the *boxes* contain additional information about or examples of the scientific material being discussed in the text. Your teacher will inform you what *Facets* and *boxes* you are expected to read and which ones contain material you may be tested over.

Other study helps

Every few pages you will find a list of **Review Questions.** After carefully reading the preceding material, you should be able to answer the Review Questions. Only when you can answer these questions have you really comprehended the significant material. Some students find it profitable to read the Review Questions before they read the material. This alerts them to the most important points. When preparing for tests, you will find the Review Questions and the list of Biological Terms valuable in directing study.

The **Thought Questions** are designed to direct your attention to significant concepts that may require more knowledge than the text presented. Often you must draw from material covered in other chapters. (You may need to use the Index, pages 683-700.) Other times it will require the use of other sources such as encyclopedias, other textbooks, and, frequently, the Bible.

In the back of this book are several appendixes (pages 648-666) with which you should become familiar. Although you may not need their help every time you read this text, using these materials will often make your study of biology easier.

The *figures, tables,* and *illustrations* in this book have been designed to help you. Consider these carefully as you read the text. Some of the material in the tables and figures is reference material. You will not, of course, be expected to memorize this type of material. Your teacher will point out which tables and figures contain material you must remember and which are reference material.

At this time, check to see how well you have read this introduction by defining the following terms and answering the following questions:

Biological Terms

boldface	etymology	Review Questions
italic type	asterisk	Thought Questions
Biological Terms	Facets of Biology	
Glossary	boxes	

Review Questions

1. For what group of students was *BIOLOGY for Christian Schools* written?
2. What two points should a Christian student keep in mind as he considers any source of information other than the Bible?
3. List the topics of the three major units of this text?
4. In this text what is the significance of (a) boldface type and (b) italic type?
5. Why is the study of etymologies significant?

Thought Questions

1. Write a single paragraph to explain why you are studying biology.
2. Does Scripture have anything to say regarding the study of biology? If so, what?
3. Why would it be advantageous for a Christian young person to study biology from a Christian textbook? Would it be equally advantageous to have a "Christian encyclopedia?" Why or why not?

• Truth, facts, and fallacies • A Christian philosophy of science • What
• Do genes determine what you are and can be? • Genetic engineering

I

THE SCIENCE
OF LIFE

? What is spiritual life? • Cells: the building blocks of life • Cellular processes: building up and tearing down
re hope or nightmare?

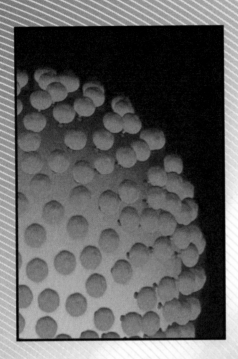

THE SCIENCE OF LIFE AND THE GOD OF LIFE

ONE

1A-God and Science

Today a disease which was virtually unknown in the 1970s is a worldwide medical concern. Each year AIDS (Acquired Immune Deficiency Syndrome) kills thousands of people. Although there are good methods for preventing this disease, it is spreading rapidly.

Cancer claims thousands of lives every day. Despite claims, there seems to be little you can do to prevent many forms of cancer, and practicing one preventive measure does not mean you

will not get some other form of cancer. Although there are treatments which easily cure some cancers, the treatments for other cancers are often not successful.

Most people believe that someday medical scientists will discover a prevention or a cure for AIDS and cancer. Through scientific pursuits man learned to control the Black Death which wiped out large portions of Europe's population in the 1300s. Smallpox, polio, malaria, and many other fatal diseases have been brought under control in much of the world. Is it not logical to think that someday man will conquer AIDS and cancer?

The recent population explosion has resulted in millions of people on the earth. By using fertilizers and selected plants, scientists can obtain crop yields of ten times more per acre than was possible ten years ago. It seems that if the governments of the world could settle their differences, agricultural knowledge could be used to produce enough food for all mankind.

Scientists have worked out the intricate details of sending a man to the moon and bringing him back. It cannot be long before other scientists will be able to correct a malfunctioning human heart or, if the heart is beyond repair, replace it with some adequate apparatus.

Almost every day you can find something in the news about environmental pollution. Toxic wastes, harmful chemicals in drinking water, smog, oil spills, acid rain, and trash disposal that spoils the environment are real concerns. Most people assume, however, that if we just give scientists enough money they will come up with answers before the problems get too bad. Then, if we all work together and do what the scientists say we should, somehow everything will be fine.

AIDS, cancer, crowding, heart disorders, and pollution are but a few of the biological problems facing us today. Scientists are looking for

1A-1 *The ocean was thought to be so large that trash could be put into it and forgotten. Recently some beaches have been contaminated by washed up trash.*

1A-2 *The Black Death, a major killer of the past, is prevented by modern sanitation and medical practices.*

solutions, and since they have often been successful in the past, most people seem confident that a better life is just around the corner. But is it?

The Bible states, "Ye have the poor always with you" (Matt. 26:11). There will be sickness, suffering, and death until Christ returns for His thousand-year reign on the earth (Isa. 35:5-10; Matt. 24:5-14; Rev. 21:4). Man must now earn his bread by the sweat of his brow because of God's curse upon the earth (Gen. 3:19).

The Bible teaches that things are getting worse and that God is the source of all that is good. Some people claim that scientific efforts are improving man's existence and will continue to do so. These two statements appear to contradict each other. Which should we believe? Is one true and the other false? Are they both true? Are they both partly true? To answer these questions, one must look closely at what science is and what we know about God.

A Definition of Science

Science can be defined as a body of facts that man has gathered by observing the physical universe. (There are many other possible definitions of science, some of which will be discussed later in this chapter.) One question arises immediately from this definition of science: what are facts? A **fact** is something that is *true*. What is *truth,* and how does one know that a supposed fact is *true?* This concept has kept man's mind busy for thousands of years. Some commonly accepted theories about truth are discussed here.

Truth: what everybody believes?

Some facts are established according to what everybody does. The rules of grammar and spelling and the meanings of words are based on how educated people commonly write and speak. But language is manmade and man-governed. Is truth simply what everybody believes? Let us examine an idea that everybody believed to be true for hundreds of years.

Hippocrates (hih PAHK ruh TEES), a Greek physician who lived about 350 B.C., believed in the **Doctrine of Humors,** which states that living things are composed of four fluids, or ''humors.'' These humors had certain properties and were produced by specific organs. A person was healthy and happy, it was thought, when these four humors were correctly proportioned and well-mixed in the body. If, however, a person had too much or too little of one or several of these humors, his temperament (humor) was affected. For example, a person with too much blood would be warm, ruddy, friendly, and happy. If a person had too much black bile, he would be warm, sad, and melancholy.

Each individual supposedly tended toward one of these four humors. Hippocrates believed that the fluids were affected by the season, winds, temperature, sunshine, food, manner of living, age, and many other things. In winter, phlegm would dominate. If a person tended to have too much phlegm, in the winter he would be sluggish and indifferent. Severe cases of too much phlegm produced disorders such as pneumonia, dropsy, diarrhea, or dysentery. Hippocrates, who is still called ''the Father of Modern Medicine,'' believed that counteracting the predominant fluids would cure a sick person. If cold, moist phlegm entered the blood, resulting in chills, the person was to be kept warm and dry.

The Doctrine of Humors was the accepted medical practice for centuries. Today the Doctrine of Humors seems quaint or silly, yet it described

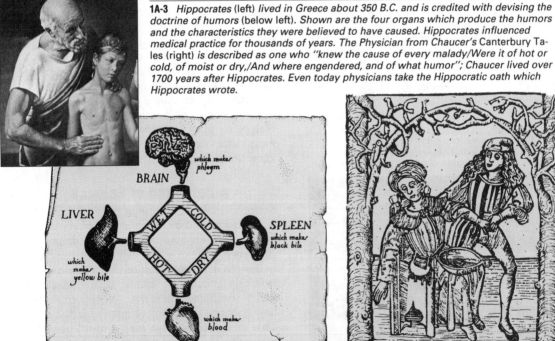

1A-3 *Hippocrates* (left) *lived in Greece about 350 B.C. and is credited with devising the doctrine of humors (below left). Shown are the four organs which produce the humors and the characteristics they were believed to have caused. Hippocrates influenced medical practice for thousands of years. The Physician from Chaucer's* Canterbury Tales (right) *is described as one who ''knew the cause of every malady/Were it of hot or cold, of moist or dry,/And where engendered, and of what humor''; Chaucer lived over 1700 years after Hippocrates. Even today physicians take the Hippocratic oath which Hippocrates wrote.*

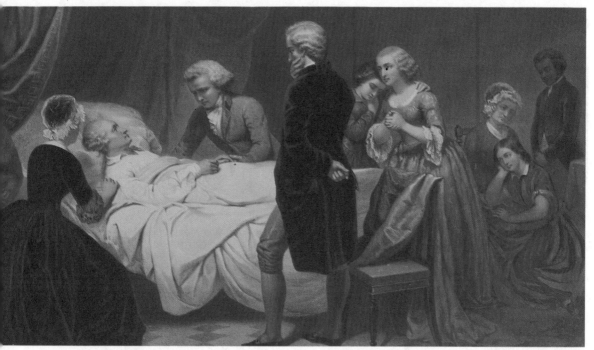

1A-4 *In 1799, George Washington's medical doctors believed that his fever was caused by too much blood. They prescribed bleeding several pints of blood. Because they believed in the Doctrine of Humors, the first President of the United States was bled to death.*

human health satisfactorily for the Greeks. Until just a few hundred years ago, almost everyone who was educated believed it. But is it *true?*

Truth: a hunch that works?

In a mathematics class, using the right method to compute a problem is sometimes considered more important than merely finding the right answer. If a student performs a series of mathematical steps with given numbers and produces the correct answer, he may assume that he followed the proper procedure, but in fact he may have made errors which were compensated for by other errors. He arrived at the correct answer but did so by mistake. The incorrect steps *worked.* Does this mean the incorrect steps are a valid method of discerning *truth?*

The ancient Babylonians used the **Doctrine of Signatures** to prescribe remedies for various ailments. In the fourteenth and fifteenth centuries Europeans promoted this doctrine to its height. They believed that when God cursed man with diseases, He mercifully left in the physical world signs (signatures) of cures for these diseases. Scriptural basis for this belief does not exist.

Medieval doctors prescribed a yellow, papery lichen (a small plantlike growth found on rocks) as a cure for a yellow condition of the skin called jaundice. The similar yellow appearance was believed to be God's sign that the lichen was the remedy. A small plant that looks like the lobe of a liver was used to cure liver infections. The plant still has the name liverwort ("liver plant"). In 1540, Dorstenius gave directions for a preparation of lungwort, a lichen that looks like a lung, as a cure for diseases of the respiratory system.

Dog's tooth lichen resembles the teeth of a dog; hence, it was thought effective against diseases related to dogs. In 1741, Dr. Richard Mead recommended it for treating rabies in humans.

> Let the patient be blooded at the arm, nine or ten ounces. Take of the herb called in Latin, *Lichen cinereus terrestris* [dog's tooth lichen] . . . clean'd, dry'd, and powder'd half an ounce. Of black pepper powder's two drachms. Mix these well together and divide the Powder into four Doses, one of which must be taken every Morning, fasting; for four Mornings successively in half

1A-5 *The bladder wort (a) has tiny insect-catching bladders growing on its underwater root system. The liverwort (b) has structures shaped somewhat like a liver. The hairy cap moss (c) reminded the ancients of hair on a person's head. The dogtooth lichen (inset) looked like a dog's teeth. All of these organisms were used to treat human disorders according to the Doctrine of Signatures.*

a Pint of Cow's Milk, warm. After these four doses are taken, the Patient must go into a cold bath, or a cold Spring or River, every Morning fasting, for a Month. He must be dipt all over but not stay in (with his head above water) longer than half a minute, if the Water be very cold. After this he must go in three Times a week for a Fortnight longer.*

It is recorded that when dog's tooth lichen was served to several of the Duke of York's best dogs, they were cured of being mad.

The Doctrine of Signatures sounds absurd to the modern mind. But the medical books of the Middle Ages indicate that these remedies had cured patients (usually in "other countries" or in "olden times"). It is understandable that a medieval gentleman who had been bitten by a rabid dog would reason that if the dog's tooth lichen had cured the Duke of York's dogs and was reported to have cured a few people, it was at least worth a try. Besides, it was the only thing he could do, and to him it was probably better than doing nothing.

Scientists quickly point out that maybe these dogs and people who were reportedly cured were never really sick, or possibly their symptoms were caused by a lesser disease, a disease from which they would have recovered without the lichen-and-pepper mixture.

In the 1940s, however, it was found that some lichens do manufacture antibiotics that are effective in stopping the growth of some tuberculosis bacteria. Lichen antibiotics have been marketed commercially and have been found effective in treating wounds and burns. Is it possible that some people in the Middle Ages were actually aided by the antibiotics recently discovered in some lichens? If so, this aid could have strengthened a mistaken belief in the Doctrine of Signatures. Just because something works or appears to work, is it *true?*

Truth: repeated observations?

Some people feel that ideas are established as true by repeated observations. If a phenomenon happens over and over again, they feel it is safe to assume that it will happen again.

If a pencil is picked up and released a few inches above a table, it will fall. This falling, which happens every time, is the effect of gravity. If you were to watch a magician seemingly suspend a person on nothing and repeat this trick several times, would this force you to alter your belief about the truth of gravity? Would observing blimps or satellites affect the truth of gravity? Are repeated observations a sure guide to truth?

The **spontaneous generation** of life from nonliving materials was believed, on the basis of observations, as early as eight hundred years before Christ. The ancients were of course familiar with

---

Quoted in John H. Bland, *Forests of Liliput: The Realm of Mosses and Lichens* (Englewood Cliffs, New Jersey: Prentice-Hall, Inc., 1971), p. 111.

birds hatching and the birth of many animals, but some of the less familiar animals were believed to generate spontaneously whenever conditions were acceptable. In the Middle Ages, frogs and fish were thought to be formed during storms and then rained to earth. Insects supposedly came

NAW, HONEY! IT'S JUST DRIZZLIN'!

from the soil, while maggots and worms developed from dead and decaying flesh. A fallen leaf of certain plants could develop into a fish or snake, depending on where it landed. A toad could form out of a lump of mud.

If an **infusion*** (in FYOO zhun), made by boiling animal or plant material in water, is left standing for a period of time and is then examined under a microscope, it will reveal quantities of small organisms called **microbes.*** According to most scientists from the 1700s until the mid-1800s, the microbes found in infusions spontaneously generated as the mixture began to ferment (spoil).

Some scientists held the theory that microbes came from the air; therefore, if the air were cut off, they would not develop. In 1749, John Needham, an English priest and scientist, performed a set of experiments to prove the spontaneous generation of microbes. He filled a number of glass

vials with an infusion of mutton, stoppered them tightly, and heated them "violently" in hot ashes. He reasoned that the stoppers would prevent airborne microbes from entering the vials, and that any microbes already in the gravy would be destroyed by the heat. If there were any organisms found in his infusions, they would have had to generate spontaneously. After a few days, each of his vials was found to be teeming with microbes.

Over and over again scientists were able to demonstrate (they thought) that organisms, especially the smaller ones like microbes, would just "happen" if conditions were right. The fact that someone had not seen fish lay eggs that hatch into small fish but had over and over seen fish in a pond does not prove spontaneous generation. Nor did Needham's "scientific" experiments, however often he repeated them. He had made a mistake, an error in his reasoning, that was not obvious to him. (Needham's errors will be discussed along with other aspects of spontaneous generation later in this chapter.)

Just because you observe something repeatedly, does that make it *true*? Often the senses are fooled, or observations are made from faulty experiments.

Truth: that which is logical?

Logical reasoning constitutes truth to some people. If it makes sense, or if it can be figured out, they feel it is true. Since mathematics is logical, some would say it is true. 2 + 2 = 4. If we define 2, +, =, and 4, we see the truth of this mathematical statement. But numbers can be made to give inaccurate descriptions of what exists. By "juggling the figures" a company can be made to look profitable when it is nearly bankrupt. What may appear to be logical mathematically may not be true.

Logical reasoning is usually classified as inductive or deductive. **Inductive reasoning** begins with a number of observed facts and derives from them a general conclusion. After seeing many particular objects fall and roll downhill, one perceives by induction the general principle of gravity. Scientists often repeat experiments and observations over and over to arrive at a *scientific*

---

infusion: (L. INFUSUS, to pour in)

microbe: micro- (Gk. MIKROS, small) + -be, -bi, -bio, or -bios (BIOS, life)

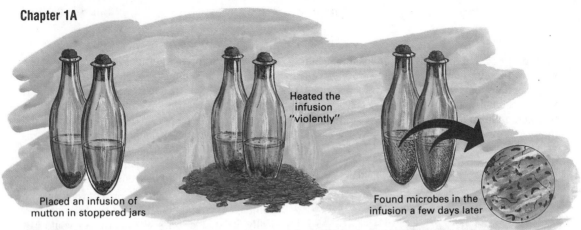

1A-6 *Needham's experiment. The presence of microbes in the infusion supported Needham's belief in spontaneous generation.*

principle. But repeated observations may be faulty and cause one to arrive at an untrue principle. The fact that something can be reasoned inductively does not make it *true*.

Deductive reasoning begins with general principles assumed to be true and draws conclusions about particulars. One of the first recorded illustrations of deduction is attributed to Aristotle, describing his teacher:

Statement 1: All men are mortal.
Statement 2: Socrates is a man.
Conclusion: Socrates is mortal.

If the statements in logical reasoning are not exclusive enough, the conclusion may exhibit faulty logic and be false.

In the early 1600s, Jean Baptist van Helmont, a Belgian chemist and physician, experimented to prove that soil changed into the material that makes up plants. A large pot was filled with exactly 200 lb. of dry soil. He planted a 5-lb. willow tree in the pot and covered the pot with a shield that admitted water but excluded dust and new soil.

At the end of 5 yr. the tree was carefully removed. Its final weight was 169 lb. 3 oz., a gain of 164 lb. 3 oz. Next van Helmont dried the soil and found that only 2 oz. was missing. Obviously the entire 164 lb. 3 oz. gained by the plant had not come from the 2 oz. of soil. He concluded that the additional 164 lb. 1 oz. that the tree had grown must have come from the only other substance he knew of which the plant could get:

water. Van Helmont's logic, although somewhat faulty, proceeded along these lines:

Statement 1: Plants, when growing in only soil and water, gain weight.
Statement 2: Plants gain much more weight than is taken from the soil.
Conclusion: Weight gain of plants comes almost entirely from water.

1A-7 *Jean Baptist van Helmont and his tree experiment*

He observed that air is a mixture of gases, and he isolated CO_2, but he failed to recognize it in this experiment.

Start
Tree: 5 lb.
Soil: 200 lb.

End
Tree: 169 lb. 3 oz.
Soil: 199 lb. 14 oz.

Although inaccurate in this experiment, van Helmont contributed much to science.

Van Helmont's statements are *true,* but his conclusion is false. His logical, well-designed, and carefully conducted experiment resulted in a faulty conclusion, even though the numerical information obtained was correct. Van Helmont did not take into account that plants use carbon dioxide and water to make sugar, the basic material from which plants can make other substances. The process by which plants convert water and carbon dioxide into sugar was not discovered until long after van Helmont's death. The fact that something is logical and seems to make sense does not mean it is true.

Truth: that which is accepted by faith?

What a person believes can be called his **faith.** It has been said that whatever a person believes to be true will be truth for him. A person acts because of his faith–what he believes. When you cross a bridge, you must have faith that the bridge will hold you. If you doubt the bridge's strength, you lack faith in it and probably will not cross it. However, your faith in a bridge does not mean that it is strong enough to hold you. Men may have faith in something that is not true and may act wrongly in light of their belief. If they do, they must suffer the consequences of believing something that is false.

A person going to a medical doctor has faith in that doctor. But if the doctor practices the Doctrine of Signatures, the patient may die of the cure prescribed, whether or not he believes the doctrine to be true. The patient has faith, but he believes in something that is wrong. A person may be affected by his faith or lack of faith, but does faith or lack of faith affect truth? If you do not believe there is a hell, does hell no longer exist because of your disbelief?

Truth: the Word of God

Our God is a God of truth. Christ said "I am . . . the truth" (John 14:6) and later called the Holy Spirit the "Spirit of truth" (John 14:17, 15:26, 16:13). What the God of truth says must be true. Thus Scripture, the Word of God, is truth (John 17:17). Logic, observations, workability, and common beliefs or personal faith cannot disprove these claims of the Bible.

It is true that a person must accept the truth of the Bible by faith, but that faith is not blind. The physical world around us testifies to the power of God that created and sustains it. Thus repeated, accurate observations of the world help to support the truth of the Bible (Ps. 19:1). The historical accuracy and fulfilled prophecy of the Scriptures also testify to its truth.

Our God is a God of logic. Although His ways are often beyond our understanding, "God is not the author of confusion" (I Cor. 14:33). What He does makes sense, which is the essence of logic after all.

To some people these testimonies to the truth of God's Word are not conclusive enough to justify their faith. Such people often spend time picking apart what the Bible says, looking for errors. But to those who are willing to have faith in God and His Word, these testimonies help to support their belief that God's Word is **Truth.**

Review Questions 1A-1

1. According to the Doctrine of Humors, what conditions were necessary for a person to be happy and healthy? What could happen to a person to make him ill? What could be done to cure him?
2. On what assumption is the Doctrine of Signatures based? According to the Doctrine of Signatures, what could be done to cure an illness?
3. What evidence did those who believed in spontaneous generation offer to support their belief?
4. Give (a) an example of inductive reasoning and (b) an example of deductive reasoning.
5. Describe van Helmont's tree experiment, and tell why his conclusions were false.
6. Why is faith not a good method of determining truth?
7. List six ways man has tried to decide what is true and what is false.

FACETS OF BIOLOGY

How God Communicates to Man

God walked and talked with Adam in the Garden of Eden. In the Bible God spoke to some people directly and to others in dreams. Sometimes He sent angel messengers. He even wrote on tablets of stone to communicate His law to His people. But today even the best of Christians may never hear the voice of God or have a divinely sent dream or see an angel while they are in this flesh. Does God no longer speak to us? Is God now silent, leaving us to make it on our own?

Ever since the apostles finished writing the New Testament, there have been people who have claimed to have revelations from God. A well-known example happened in the 1830s. Joseph Smith, a New York farmer's son, claimed he was visited by the angel Moroni. Moroni showed him golden plates inscribed with a strange writing. Smith used special stones in silver bowls to translate these plates into Elizabethan English (the language of the King James Version).

The plates told of Christ's coming to North America and dealing with the American Indians, of how the priesthood should be reestablished, and of how God evolves into man and man evolves into God. In time, Joseph Smith and his followers were forced to leave New York and several other places because of their beliefs (which included a belief that a man may have several wives). Finally, under the leadership of Brigham Young, the group settled in Utah. Today they are called the Church of Jesus Christ of Latter-day Saints, or Mormons (after the angel Moroni).

Was Joseph Smith's revelation from God? Based on Scripture, one must say no! The Apostle Paul tells us that if anyone (including Paul himself or even an angel) comes and preaches any other gospel, he is to be accursed (Gal. 1:8). The Bible also condemns the adding of doctrine to the Scripture (Rev. 22:18). In other words, any additional communication of God to man will not contradict the Bible, nor will it add to the Bible.

The Bible, comprising the Old and New Testaments, is the complete written Word of God to man. It contains all the spiritual truth we need to know to live in this world. The Bible, then, is God's primary communication to us. But does God only communicate to us through the reading, studying, and preaching of His Word? No. Scripture teaches us that there are two other methods God uses to communicate to all Christians.

Luke by Guido Reni, Bob Jones University Collection of Sacred Art.

The Italian painter Guido Reni (ca. 1600) depicted the Gospel writer Luke seeking inspiration from heaven.

❑ *Nature* is a testimony of the power of God. The very existence of our world and the universe demands belief in a Designer, Creator, and Sustainer. The more one studies the creation, the more one knows of the Creator (Ps. 19). This is one of the reasons a Christian should study science.

❑ *The inner testimony of the Holy Spirit,* given to those who in faith have found the Lord of creation, persuades the believer that God is the ultimate Truth of the universe. This testimony of the Holy Spirit can take many forms. Often it is God directing a Christian's thoughts, bringing to his mind things he should do, not do, or change in accordance with the Bible. It is the testimony of the Holy Spirit that makes the Scriptures the *living* Word of God in the Christian's heart.

But what about dreams? Could God use them to communicate to us today? The Bible records several instances when God spoke to men in dreams. Joseph, Daniel, Samuel, Ezekiel, Jacob, Peter, and Paul are men of God who had dreams from the Lord. Pharaoh and Nebuchadnezzar also had dreams from the Lord.

Occasionally we hear of a missionary who had a dream, acted on it, and escaped great harm. We hear of other Christians who responded to dreams and were able to lead someone to Christ or received great blessing as a result. The Bible does not tell us that God will not communicate to Christians in dreams. But before we start trying to assign spiritual significance to every dream, let us consider some important aspects of sleep and dreams.

Scientists estimate that we spend about half our sleeping time dreaming. Most of our dreams last only seconds, although the actions that take place in them seem to take long periods of time. We actually remember only what we are dreaming as we wake up. It is

safe to assume that God does not speak to us in every dream, for if He did, most of what He said in dreams would be lost. Most dreams, it appears, are normal functions of our mind. Such dreams lack spiritual significance.

In the past, dreams with spiritual significance have been recognized as unusual by the dreamer. When God communicates with people, He is clear and consistent. God may send these dreams to people, but He does not reveal new truth to us in dreams (Heb. 1:1-2). A God-sent dream will never contradict the principles and commands of Scripture.

The Word of God is complete. It is God's message to us, and it is forever settled in heaven. "God is not the author of confusion" (I Cor. 14:33). The testimony of nature, the Holy Spirit in our hearts, or even God-sent dreams may speak to us, but they never contradict or add to Scripture. If such communciations seem to, someone is seeking to deceive us.

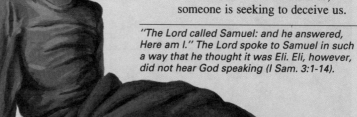

"The Lord called Samuel: and he answered, Here am I." The Lord spoke to Samuel in such a way that he thought it was Eli. Eli, however, did not hear God speaking (I Sam. 3:1-14).

Review questions on page 13.

God's Truth and Science

Some Christians have difficulty understanding the facts and claims of science in the light of the facts of God's truth revealed in Scripture. Let us try to put these facts in their correct places. God has directly revealed some truth to man in His Word, the Bible. This direct revelation is usually about spiritual matters–God Himself, the sinful nature of man, and the plan of redemption. But He speaks of the physical world in language and illustrations that man can understand and is accurate as He does so. After all, the same One who created the physical world inspired the Bible.

The Bible is a spiritual handbook, not a scientific textbook. It does not reveal all possible knowledge about creation. Man needs God to tell him about spiritual things which he cannot examine and experiment with. But God gives men senses and minds to observe and work with the physical truths of nature. This, then, is the **realm of science:** man's observations of the physical

1A-8 *The flat-earth theory was once thought to be a Scriptural "fact." Careful examination of Scripture and scientific observations have shown it to be a fallacy.*

world. That water runs downhill is easy to observe and does not need to be dealt with in the Bible. The fact that the energy in the falling water can be used to turn the grindstones of a mill and make flour or to turn the turbines of an electric generator and supply the energy necessary to bake bread was left for man to figure out.

A classification of truth

Understanding God's relationship to truth may be easier if truth is classified first as God views it and then as man looks at it. From God's viewpoint a statement must be in one of three categories:

❑ **Revealed truth:** those truths which God recorded in Scripture;

❑ **Unrevealed truth:** those truths, the natural laws, that God established but did not reveal in Scripture; or

❑ **Fallacy:** any statement not part of revealed or unrevealed truth.

When man looks at a statement, whether based on repeated observations, a hunch, logic, or even faith, it must fit under one of four categories:

❑ **Revealed truth:** that which is revealed in Scripture, whether or not man has scientifically proved it. If it is in the Bible, it is already true, without other proof.

❑ **Theory:** that which is thought to be true, is not revealed truth, but may be part of unrevealed truth.

❑ **Fallacy:** that which is contradicted by God's revealed truth, no matter how scientific, how commonly believed, or how apparently workable it may seem; or that which is contradicted by scientific evidence.

❑ **Truth by definition:** that which is true because man has defined it, as in mathematics, grammar, spelling, and meanings of words. For example, because man can define numbers, he can arrive at mathematical conclusions which are based on logic and by definition are true. To the extent that man correctly uses his tools (be they rulers or calculators), such fields as measurements and geometry can be considered true by definition.

No amount of work on the part of man can make a theory part of God's revealed truth. But some theories, such as the Doctrine of Signatures or the Flat Earth Theory, were once thought to be supported by Scripture since they were "hinted at," it seemed, in the Bible. The Scriptures used, however, were taken out of context. A Christian must be very careful not to take verses out of context or to take a passage he does not understand and try to make it say what he wants. Because all truth is not revealed in the Bible, a Christian should not try to make the Bible deal with all topics.

Science, then, is man's attempts to observe and describe the natural processes God established to govern the universe.

Biological Terms

A Definition of Science	spontaneous generation	deductive reasoning	revealed truth
science	infusion	faith	unrevealed truth
fact	microbe	truth	theory
Doctrine of Humors	logical reasoning	*God's Truth and Science*	fallacy
Doctrine of Signatures	inductive reasoning	realm of science	truth by definition

Review Questions 1A-2

1. What is revealed truth? What is unrevealed truth?
2. What is the difference between revealed truth and man's theories? Can a theory become part of revealed truth if enough supporting evidence is obtained? Why or why not?
3. List two ways a theory can be shown to be a fallacy.
4. What types of statements can be true by definition? List several statements that can be considered true by definition.

Facet 1A-1: How God Communicates to Man, pages 10-11

1. List the three major ways that God communicates to all Christians.
2. If someone claims that something is a teaching of God, how can you know if what the person says is truly from God?
3. Some people say that God does not communicate to humans by dreams in this present age. Is this true? Why?

Thought Questions

1. Classify the following statements as either (a) part of revealed truth, (b) possibly part of unrevealed truth, or (c) fallacy.
    (1) Man evolved from apes.
    (2) What goes up must come down.
    (3) An Ice Age in which all the earth will experience extreme cold is coming.
    (4) Water runs downhill.
    (5) Sentences end with periods, exclamation points, or question marks.
    (6) If a man is hot and flushed, he should be treated by bleeding.
    (7) The earth will never be completely flooded by water.
    (8) All things that are physically alive must die.
2. Classify the statements given in number one above as either (a) revealed truth, (b) a theory, (c) a fallacy, or (d) true by definition.
3. It has been said, "Only what I believe can be true for me." Can something be true if a person does not have faith to believe it? Give examples to prove your position.
4. Give two examples of modern beliefs which are not true.
5. "The Bible does not deal with modern science; therefore, science is of the devil." Give reasons to contradict or support this statement.
6. Physical phenomena (plants, mountains, gravity, animals, life, etc.) cannot be completely defined. Manmade phenomena (numbers, spelling, grammar, etc.) can be defined completely. Explain how the ability to be defined limits man's ability to know truth.

1B–The Scientific Method

For some people the thought of a scientist using the scientific method produces visions of a man in a white coat, with a clipboard, looking at dials and flashing lights on a large console, surrounded by a complex system of glass tubes and flasks, doing things difficult to be understood even when he tries to explain them in simple language. Most people who have these mental pictures have great respect, even awe, for scientists who can use the scientific method.

Scientists may sometimes wear white coats, use elaborate equipment, and perform experiments that are difficult to explain, but none of these makes a scientist different from other skilled persons. The **scientific method** is not a "magical," miracle-working formula which will solve all man's problems. It is, rather, a method of reasoning that you use daily.

The scientific method is simply a logical procedure for choosing an answer to a question. For example, after examining hundreds of ripe oranges, a person could use deductive reasoning to say, "Ripe oranges are orange in color and nearly round." Such deductive reasoning is characteristic of what scientists often do, and of what you do to employ the scientific method.

Using the Scientific Method

Although there is no set order of activities, you will usually do all the following preliminary steps at one point or another when using the scientific method of collecting information.

❏ *Define the problem.* Before the actual experiment begins, you will state the specific question or problem to be solved. It must be limited sufficiently so that it can be dealt with conveniently. The question "What makes plants grow?" is too broad and indefinite; but "Do geraniums grow better in dim or bright light?" is limited enough to be answered by experimentation.

❏ *Do preliminary research.* Once the problem has been stated, you should **research** to become familiar with the relevant area of science. Perhaps your problem has already been solved by someone else; if so, experimentation would be unnecessary. In any case, research in books and magazines and conversations with knowledgeable people will help you understand your problem better and avoid foolish mistakes.

❏ *Form the hypothesis.* Once you have stated the question and researched it completely, you will usually formulate a **hypothesis *** (hye PAH thuh sis)–an educated guess which attempts to answer the problem. You will then devise activities to see whether that hypothesis is correct.

Steps of the scientific method

The activities used to test a hypothesis can be an experiment or a survey. If an **experiment** is to be used, you must tailor it to answer the problem precisely. When the problem asks what exists in a particular area or what is common practice, a **survey** is necessary. For example, which pain

---

hypothesis: hypo- (Gk. HUPO, beneath) + -thesis (TITHENAI, to place)

1B-1 *Can you determine which steps in the scientific method are being used in each illustration?*

remedy doctors recommend most or what kind of tree is most common in a certain area would be answered by surveys, not experiments.

Once the experiment or survey has been constructed, you will go through the following steps:

❏ *Observe* the experiment or survey carefully.

❏ *Collect* information from the experiment or survey and record it accurately. The recorded information is the **data** you will use to solve the problem.

❏ *Classify* the data into a logical order or into logical groups.

❏ *Analyze* the data to determine what it reveals about the problem.

❏ *Choose* from among the several answers suggested by the data the one that best answers the question. (In some cases the data may suggest only one answer.) If the data point to an answer different from the original hypothesis, then the original hypothesis should be discarded.

❏ *Verify* the chosen answer by repeating the experiment. The more often a well-designed experiment is repeated and produces similar results, the more valid and reliable is the answer.

❏ *Predict* what will happen in similar situations. The goal of using the scientific method is to be able to draw conclusions that can be applied to similar cases.

Controlled experiments

An ideal scientific experiment is sometimes called a **controlled experiment.** In a controlled experiment there are two identical groups, and the difference between the two groups is a single factor called the **experimental variable.***

The group not exposed to the experimental variable is the **control group,** and the group exposed to the experimental variable is the **experimental group.** As an example, consider two sets of mice grown in identical cages in the same room with the same diets. If one group has a vitamin dissolved in its water, it would be the experimental group, and the vitamin would be the experimental variable; the other group of mice would be the control group.

Normally, *multiple variables* in a controlled experiment are unacceptable. If an experiment has more than one variable, you would not know which variable was responsible for the observed results. If the experimental group of mice was given larger cages than the control group, the results obtained might be caused by the added space (or both the added space and the vitamins) rather than just the vitamins.

Fewer variables give more *valid* (accurate and reliable) results. That is, if you repeated the experiment, you would get the same (or very similar) results. If you do not get the same or very similar results each time, your results are not considered valid. To insure valid results, scientists often repeat experiments. If the results are the same a significant number of times, the insignificant results are blamed on some uncontrolled variable in the experiment, and those results are often ignored.

If in the mice-and-vitamin experiment 99 of the 100 mice in the experimental group grew longer fur than the mice in the control group, you have data, but it may not be valid. If you repeated this experiment fifty times and each time 95 to 100 of the experimental group had longer fur and only 1 to 5 of the control group had longer fur, your results have a good level of validity. The more you repeat your experiment with similar results, the more valid are your results.

Review Questions 1B-1

1. List and describe the activities involved in the scientific method.
2. What types of cases are best investigated with a survey rather than an experiment?
3. A problem that is investigated by the scientific method must have what two limitations? Why is each of these limitations necessary?
4. Why must an experiment or a survey be controlled? What is the difference between the control group and the experimental group in a controlled experiment?

The Limits of Science

The very nature of the scientific method greatly limits science. Although some people attribute godlike capabilities to science, science is actually little more than what man can sense around him. No matter how often an experiment or survey is repeated, no matter how carefully observed, no matter how accurately recorded, no matter how well it works and how valid it appears, a scientific "fact" can, and often has been wrong. To understand why, you must recognize the limitations of science.

Limitations inherent in the scientific method

Scientific investigations must deal with physical phenomena* (fih NAHM uh nuh), because experiments or surveys must have *observable, measurable* data to support a conclusion. A problem investigated by the scientific method is generally stated so that it can be answered with a yes, a no, or a number (such as a percent or ratio). Questions

---

variable: (L. VARIUS, changeable)   **phenomena:** (Gk. PHAINEIN, to show)

Using the Scientific Method

Many people use the scientific method of thinking every day. That is not to say that it is always used well. Often the limitations of the method, the controls, or the repetitions needed to obtain valid workable results are not considered.

Consider the following example: Assume that a family is planning a trip to Detroit and wonders which way is quicker: the expressway, which takes a roundabout route but promises rapid travel; or the back roads, which take a more direct route. Since time is measurable, the problem is within the scope of science. Using a map, a ruler, and a pencil, one could come up with a good hypothesis. To make sure the hypothesis is correct, however, experimentation is necessary. A member of the family could obtain data by driving to Detroit on one route, carefully recording the time and the mileage, and then taking the other route when coming home, again recording the time and mileage.

He must be careful to record exact times for every stop. Having to decide, "I guess it took us about half an hour to eat," would destroy the validity of the results. The traffic jam on the interstate in Toledo and the road work along the country road will affect the validity of the results by adding other variables. If he travels one route in the early morning and the other late at night, there would be more variables: the route and the time of day. It would be best if the experiment could be *controlled* so that there is only one variable (in this case, the route).

Controls on all the possible variables along hundreds of miles of roads would be difficult, if not impossible. To have more valid results, the experiment should be repeated many times and the results averaged. If the results of three round

trips indicate that one route averages five minutes less than the other, is the conclusion valid? Since it is based on such a small number of repetitions, the five minutes difference could easily be the result of variables other than route.

But when Mother states that she likes the back roads because they are more scenic, the scientific method can no longer be applied. Science cannot deal with beauty or other value judgments, because such are not measurable physical phenomena. The number of bumps in the road and the number of restaurants on the route could be determined by surveys. The amount of gasoline necessary for each route or the wear on the tires could be determined by experimentation. These are within the scope of science. No experiments can be devised, however, to test the beauty of one route as compared to another. When it comes to which route the family *wants* to travel, science yields to the authority of man's will.

using how or why are not measurable and are therefore beyond the scope of science. The scientific method cannot *explain* a phenomenon.

Measurable, observable results require the use of most if not all of man's senses. The phenomenon must be seen, felt, heard, tasted, or smelled. Man's senses, of course, are often not accurate and can be fooled. If the phenomenon cannot be observed, a device capable of measuring the phenomenon must be used. Man cannot sense X-rays,

for example, but photographic plates and other devices can measure the presence of X-rays. Using more devices to make observations introduces more variables which then increase the possibility of mechanical errors.

The beginning of life, what is in the future, and spiritual concepts such as heaven, angels, man's soul, and hell cannot be observed or measured; thus they are beyond the domain of science. These things are part of a person's faith.

1B-2   The Limitations of Science

- Science must deal with observable, measurable phenomena.
- Science can only describe not explain.
- No experiment can be completely controlled.
- Observations may be faulty.
- Man's beliefs affect his judgment.
- Science must deal with repeatable results.
- Science cannot deal with values or morals.
- Science cannot prove a universal statement.
- Science cannot establish truth.

What scientifically could be said about these?

Another problem scientists often have is being biased. A **bias** is what someone wants to believe. A scientist employed by a tobacco company to research the effects of smoking would tend to emphasize results that would please his employer and overlook results that would show tobacco harmful. Since a scientist must choose an answer, his answer will likely reflect his bias.

Limitations of the results of the scientific method

Since it is impossible to limit the variables completely in any experiment or survey, the *exact* answer (absolute answer) is not obtainable. Even if you did obtain the exact answer, it would be so hidden in a group of other answers that it would be unrecognizable. Scientists then must *choose* the best answer to a problem. A valid choice is one which is usable because it is supported by repetitions of the experiment and because it can be used to predict future answers in similar situations. But just because an answer is valid does not make it correct.

Information gained by the scientific method is *workable* if it can be used in other circumstances. If a piece of information cannot be used to predict outcomes in similar situations, the information lacks **workability.** For example, if laboratory experiments support the hypothesis that a certain type of plant needs "chemical X" to grow, but in a field these plants grow equally well with or without "chemical X," the results of the experiment are not workable. The results may be valid for plants grown in the laboratory, but in the field some factor (something in the soil or air, or some other condition) causes the plants to grow without "chemical X." In this case the scientist has a piece of information that may be valid but cannot be used to predict the plant's growth in other situations. His information lacks workability.

Suppose it is necessary to find out how much water people in the United States drink per day. This fact is to be used to help project the country's water needs for the next twenty years. A survey is taken of one hundred people living in the Chicago area. If the survey is taken several times in that area with similar results, the results can be called valid. But there is still a good chance that the workability of the information is low. Without many other surveys in other areas, no one can be sure that Chicago is typical of the whole country. Highly valid results of a survey or experiment may be unworkable if the survey or experiment is not typical or if it included conditions that were not measured.

1B-3 *A survey could be used to determine water usage in a city.*

FACETS OF BIOLOGY

1B-1

Spontaneous Generation and the Scientific Method

Spontaneous generation, the concept that organisms come to life from nonliving substances (see pages 6-7), was considered an acceptable scientific theory by many people until the mid-1800s. Let us look at two reasons that this belief held on for so long.

In Genesis 1 God spontaneously created organisms out of the earth. Many people assumed that God continued to do so ever since. Those who did not believe in spontaneous generation were accused of doubting God's Word, bordering on heresy. Even today, many people similarly try to use Scripture to support their purposes. We must conform our beliefs to the Bible, not conform the Bible to our beliefs. The supporters of spontaneous generation ignored the Scripture passages that tell us that God finished creation (Gen. 2:1-3) and that organisms reproduce after their own kind (Gen. 1:24-25).

Another reason that some people continued to believe in spontaneous generation of some organisms was the faulty use of the scientific method. To better understand the scientific method and its proper application, we will now consider examples of its use and misuse. The following examples describe some of the more interesting experiments dealing with spontaneous generation and also with **biogenesis,*** the concept that only living things can generate living things.

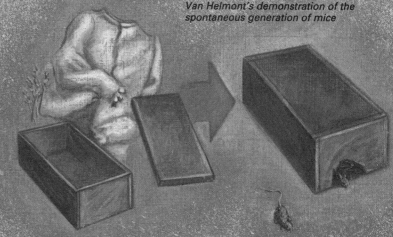

Van Helmont's demonstration of the spontaneous generation of mice

Jean Baptist van Helmont

Jean Baptist van Helmont (ca. 1600) proposed that mice could be spontaneously generated in at least 21 days by putting a sweaty shirt and grains of wheat in a dusty box. The sweat supposedly supplied the *active principle* which caused the wheat grains and dust in the box to become mice. Every time van Helmont conducted the experiment, he found mice gnawing out from the box within 21 days.

The design of the experiment, however, was faulty. Van Helmont failed to take into account that the mice might be gnawing *into* the box. What could van Helmont have done to limit the number of variables? He was attempting to support his widely-accepted belief. Since his results supported his belief, he did not see the need to restructure his experiment.

Francesco Redi

Francesco Redi (ca. 1600), a poet and physician, also considered the concept of spontaneous generation. Aristotle's statements that maggots and flies spontaneously arose from rotting flesh and slime were contrary to what Redi had observed in nature. Redi believed that the decaying matter and slime served only as the material in which the organisms were growing and that the animals thought to be spontaneously generated were actually the results of biogenesis.

In order to support his belief, Redi devised a set of experiments. Redi placed dead fish, veal, dead eels, and pieces of snake in eight jars. He then placed paper covers securely over one set of jars (the experimental group) and left the other set open (the control group). The two sets of jars were alike ex-

---

biogenesis: bio- (life) + -genesis (GENESIS, beginning)

Francesco Redi (right) and his experiment to disprove the spontaneous generation of flies

First experiment: Redi used a set of open and a set of closed jars.

Second experiment: Redi used a set of jars covered with nets.

cept for a single variable: the covers which prohibited the entrance of flies. In a few days, flies and maggots were found in the open jars, but no flies or maggots were found in the sealed jars. Redi's experiment supported his hypothesis.

If Redi had been satisfied and had stopped his experiment at this point, he would have been criticized. Supporters of spontaneous generation would have said that since air (which they believed necessary for spontaneous generation)

had been cut off by sealing the jars, Redi had prevented spontaneous generation. Redi's experiment had a double variable: the presence of flies and the presence of air. Redi therefore conducted other experiments. He set up the jars as before, but this time, rather than sealing the experimental jars, he covered them with "fine Venetian net" which would permit air but not flies into the jars. In a few days the open jars had flies and maggots in them. Although flies were attracted to the closed jars and had even laid eggs on top of the net, no maggots or flies were inside the jars.

Redi repeated his experiment in different locations, using different substances in the jars, but he always obtained the same results.

Evidence against the spontaneous generation of flies was shown by these simple, well-designed experiments. Nothing was conclusively proved; no absolute truth was gained; but the experiments produced valid support for biogenesis.

John Needham and Lazzaro Spallanzani

John Needham's experiments, which supported his ideas about spontaneous generation, were described earlier in this chapter. The growth of microbes in infusions that Needham assumed to be *sterile* (without living material present) was held to be proof of the spontaneous generation of these tiny organisms. After all, he reasoned, where could the microbes have come from? They were not like Redi's flies; they could not have traveled into the infusion.

About 25 yr. after Needham's experiments, the Italian scientist Lazzaro Spallanzani (ca. 1700) pointed out weaknesses in them. Needham had not boiled the broth long enough to destroy all the microbes that were already in his flasks, and the stoppers were not tight enough to prevent air-borne microbes from entering. Spallanzani was convinced that these two oversights were not enough to account for the microbes in Needham's infusions.

To support his opinion, Spallanzani conducted a series of experiments. He placed various infusions in glass flasks and sealed the flasks by heating them and fusing the tops. He then placed the sealed flasks in boiling water for one hour to sterilize them. After several days he opened each flask, and none of the infusions contained living organisms.

Spallanzani's experiment, however, was challenged. Since he had boiled the infusions for a long time, some who still believed in spontaneous generation said that he had destroyed the "active principle" in the infusions. Spallanzani then devised another set of experiments. He made several infusions and divided them into four identical groups. One group he boiled for half an hour; another group, for an hour; the third group, for an hour and a half; and the last group, for two hours. All of them he left open. If boiling destroyed the active principle, he should find the fewest organisms in the infusions that were boiled the longest.

After eight days he examined the infusions. Microbes were present in all of them; but the numbers and types of organisms varied. In all but one of them he found that

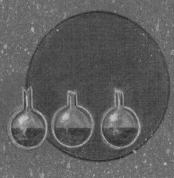

Lazzaro Spallanzani (left) experimented to show the weaknesses in Needham's experiment. After a period of time he found no microbes in the sealed jars that he had boiled long enough to sterilize the infusion.

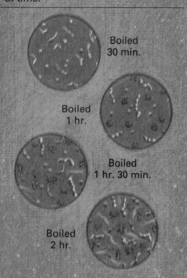

Boiled
30 min.

Boiled
1 hr.

Boiled
1 hr. 30 min.

Boiled
2 hr.

the infusions that were boiled the longest had the most organisms. Rather than destroying the active principle, longer boiling had dissolved more of the material, making the infusion better for the growth of microbes.

For the next century those who believed in the spontaneous generation of microbes ridiculed those who believed that the microbes in an infusion came from microbes in the air, or their "seeds," as Spallanzani had called them. Since microbes in the air were invisible, most people assumed that there were none there.

Most of the respected scientists of the 1600s and the 1700s believed in spontaneous generation, but few, if any, devised experiments to support it. They were content to believe in spontaneous generation and quoted one another and the ancients to support their beliefs.

Louis Pasteur

Louis Pasteur (ca. 1800), a French chemistry professor, became interested in the spontaneous generation controversy. Pasteur believed that spontaneous generation was a myth; so he devised a series of experiments which to this day are of unquestioned validity.

One series of experiments was designed to support the idea that microbes are carried in the air. Pasteur prepared several sets of infusions and sealed them in flasks. He then sterilized the infusions by boiling. He opened one set of infusions along a dusty road, another set in a forest, and other sets in other different places. Later, Pasteur examined the infusions and found that those opened in dusty places contained abundant and varied microbes. Those that were exposed to "cleaner air," like the set opened on a mountain, had fewer and different microbes. These results supported his belief that microbes are carried in the air.

Louis Pasteur working with a swan-necked flask

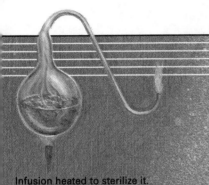

Infusion heated to sterilize it.

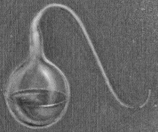

Air entered but microbes were trapped in neck. Infusions remained microbe-free for years.

When flask tilted, microbes in trap entered infusion.

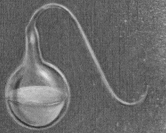

The infusion would support biogenesis.

Pasteur's famous swan-necked flask experiment dealt the final blow to the belief in the spontaneous generation of microbes. Pasteur prepared a sugar-and-yeast infusion, put it in a flask, and then bent the neck of the flask so that it formed a long S-shaped curve. He then heated the infusion to sterilize it. The boiling forced air and water vapor out of the flask, but air was able to return freely through the open neck. Pasteur reasoned that the dust and microbes that entered with the air would be trapped in the lower bend of the long neck.

His reasoning was correct, for he found that infusions prepared in this way would remain sterile for over a year. If, however, the flasks were tipped so that the dust particles trapped in the neck could enter the infusion, microbes developed quickly. Though the infusion was still capable of supporting life, life did not spontaneously generate in it.

Spontaneous generation today

After Pasteur's swan-necked flask experiment and thousands of other experiments supporting biogenesis, one might expect most people to reject spontaneous generation. Yet many scientists who believe in biogenesis also believe in evolution and thus are forced to accept the concept of spontaneous generation.

Even today many scientists attempt to prove that the various substances found in living things are formed outside a living organism; if these substances can be brought together and properly arranged, they will form a living thing that can reproduce and evolve into the various organisms now alive. These scientists are trying to obtain data to support the supposed spontaneous generation of life. They would be quick to agree that spontaneous generation is not taking place today, but they are working hard to try to make it

SPONTANEOUS GENERATION OR NOT, IT STUNK!!

happen in a laboratory. If they can create life, they think they can support their belief in life's beginning without God. But spontaneous generation has never been successfully demonstrated, not even in a laboratory.

Review questions on page 24.

Things that cannot be done using the scientific method

People sometimes expect to be able to use science to make decisions. Science may, for example, be used to devise a chemical that, if put into a city's water supply, would kill everyone who drank it. Deciding to put the chemical in a city's water, however, is not in the realm of science. Value judgments and moral decisions must be made by men, not science.

Scientific investigations cannot prove a universal statement. A universal statement includes a word such as "all," "always," "no," or "never" which makes the statement impossible to prove through experimentation. To say, for example, that all wooly mammoths are extinct cannot be proved. Every place in the world would have to be checked at the same time, since the wooly mammoths could change locations. The more limited statement that no living wooly mammoths were in your backyard at noon yesterday may be valid, depending on the size of your yard and how many people were observing.

Science cannot be used to establish truth. The fact that man can observe something and measure it, and do so repeatedly, does not *prove* his hypothesis. The results of the scientific method may only *support* or *not support* a hypothesis. The more support a hypothesis has, the more valid it is assumed to be. But no amount of scientific experimentation, or any other type of work, can prove beyond doubt any statement.

Review Questions 1B-2

1. Why is workability an important criterion for scientific knowledge?
2. Why can science not prove a universal statement?
3. What is the difference between the term *valid* and the term *proved?* (Hint: Scientists are seeking *predictable* and *workable* answers to problems.)
4. List and describe eight limitations of science.
5. List two areas of human concern in which the scientific method of problem solving is useless and explain why.
6. Why is a large problem more difficult to deal with than a small one when using the scientific method?

Facet 1B-1: Spontaneous Generation and the Scientific Method, pages 19-23

1. List several reasons why people living before the 1900s believed in spontaneous generation.
2. What could van Helmont have done to obtain more valid results from his experiment with the spontaneous generation of mice? How would these adjustments have altered his results?
3. Why was Redi's second set of experiments with the spontaneous generation of flies necessary? Could he have eliminated the first experiments and still obtained the same validity for the second experiments? Explain.
4. Why was Spallanzani's first experiment with spontaneous generation of microbes challenged? In what way did his second experiment add validity to his first set?
5. Explain how Pasteur's first experiment (open sterile infusions in different places) was significant in supporting biogenesis.

Science and the Christian

In the first part of this chapter, science was defined as a body of facts that man has gathered from observing the physical universe. Such a simple definition is not really adequate to define science and its many ramifications. Other possible definitions of science include these:

❏ the organized total of man's knowledge gained through observation;
❏ knowledge obtained through investigation;
❏ man's efforts to understand God's creation.

These valid definitions of science overlap, but each shows aspects of science not seen in the others. They should all probably be used together. The important thing is not to have a series of words to parrot when asked what science is but to have a *working understanding* of what science is, what it can do, and what it cannot do. It is important for the Christian to realize what science is and the limitations of science so that he can see the proper relationship between science, God, and His Word.

Scripture's scientific challenge

No matter how much we Christians look forward to heaven, God has placed us on earth to do His will faithfully while the Lord Jesus prepares our eternal home. Part of doing His will is to "preach the gospel to every creature" (Mark 16:15). Other tasks involve worshiping and praising God, praying, and believing in His name. But the first recorded duty of man was a scientific one. In Genesis 1:28 God told man to subdue the earth and to have dominion over it.

There are two basic methods of subduing and having dominion over anything. If a ruler wants to subdue and dominate a city, he can send his army to destroy the entire city. The city will be subdued, and he will dominate it. But what would he rule? A mass of rubble has no great value. It is better to subdue and dominate without destroying. The better methods may take more time, but they can be just as effective and produce better returns.

Second to the Bible, science is man's principal source of the knowledge that he needs to subdue and to have dominion over the earth without destroying it. Mankind will never completely dominate the earth. Not only does science have many limitations, but also man is a sinful creature and cannot perfectly rule the earth. Not until Christ returns for His thousand-year reign will the earth be completely subdued and dominated. This does not mean that we should not try to properly subdue the earth, but that we should do the best that we can while realizing our limitations.

Consider the problem of heating a home. Man can cut and burn trees to supply his home with warmth, but if man had done so without care, he would have depleted the earth's natural forests long ago. Of course, man has replanted trees to supply future generations with wood to heat their homes. When, where, and how to plant which

1B-4 *Block cutting of timber in Olympic National Forest. One of the modern methods of logging which helps man to obtain lumber without destroying the forest, a renewable resource.*

Science: Pure or Applied

Scientific activities can be classified as pure or applied science. This is not a value judgment regarding rightness, but a judgment of how *workable* that science has become in our society.

Pure science is knowledge that scientific activities have produced. A scientist may, through experimentation, discover that a particular plant requires a certain nutritive element in order to produce fruit in maximum numbers and size. That knowledge, as well as the work behind its discovery, is pure science.

Applied science is *using* knowledge gained through scientific activities. When a person uses the knowledge of the nutritive requirements of a plant in order to supply the proper amounts of that nutrient to a field of plants to obtain a more abundant harvest, the knowledge has become applied science.

Two different types of scientific activities have been involved in the above example. The first scientist used the **research method.** He recorded, classified, and analyzed data; chose an answer and verified it; and then made predictions about the nutritive element and the plant. He is a *research scientist* and has used the scientific method of thinking to discover knowledge.

The person who follows the instructions of the research scientist in order to apply the correct amount of nutrient to a field of plants is a *technician.* A technician, in this case, uses the techniques prescribed by the research scientist to predict the nutrient needs of a particular field of plants. The use of prescribed techniques to obtain information about a particular example is the second type of scientific activity, called the **technical method.**

A research scientist may devise a test to determine the presence of a certain chemical in human urine. The person in the laboratory who follows the instructions of the research scientist to test human urine samples is a *laboratory technician.* Both research scientists and technicians are necessary. Without research, scientific knowledge is not gained. Without technicians, scientific knowledge is not used.

Study these pictures. Can you tell which of these people are using the research method and which are using the technical method? Can you tell which illustrates pure science and which illustrates applied science? The answers are on page 29.

1B-5 *This computer of the 1950s contained about 800 transistors and, although an improvement over large vacuum tube computers, was less powerful than computers found in many homes today. As man gains the use of better tools, his scientific accuracy may improve, but wise use of information happens only as he bases decisions on God's Word.*

trees for quickest production of lumber is information not given in Scripture. Yet man, using his God-given intelligence, can determine how best to grow trees.

As world population continues to grow, however, man could run out of wood despite reforestation. Other sources of energy, such as natural gas, oil, solar power, or electricity made from flowing water or nuclear power, have been used to heat homes in scientifically advanced countries. Less than a hundred years ago these heating methods were only ideas. Today, through scientific endeavors, they are commonplace.

God expects man to use science

The physical world is made of substances which operate under God-ordained laws. Scripture teaches that God created the world and sustains it. Man is to subdue and have dominion over it. If he uses his God-given intelligence, he can subdue and have dominion over the world without destroying it. If he ignores what science can teach,

he will have wasted two God-given gifts: the earth and his intelligence.

God has revealed in the Bible all the *spiritual* knowledge we need. But God did not reveal all the *scientific* knowledge mankind would need in order to exist on the earth until His return. God, according to His timing, permits man to discover scientific knowledge. For example, beasts of burden, such as horses and donkeys, cannot do the things trains can do. Moreover, trains by themselves are not able to do what trucks and cars do today. God has *permitted* man, through science, to discover the knowledge he needs to build things he can use.

Some people feel that science is basically bad and attempt to return to "natural" methods of doing things. Some people even feel that returning to the old ways is more godly. But the old way of doing things is not necessarily the best way. For example, the fact that our great-grandfathers used candles and torches for light does not make those light sources better than electric lights. In previous times candles and torches were the best methods that man's knowledge had devised, but scientific investigation has supplied additional knowledge about illumination. There is nothing wrong with our using that information. Running from scientific ideas and returning to old methods of doing things is not turning back to God. Instead, it is the burying of scientific talents, much like the burying of spiritual talents spoken of in Matthew 25:14-30.

Some improper attitudes of Christians toward science

A wrong attitude toward science is to believe that science is anti-God. Since science is the discovering of usable information about God's creation, science is not inherently bad. Scientific information can be used for good or bad purposes, but science does not decide how information is used. Men do. Science is not evil just because men have abused scientific knowledge.

It is interesting that when cars were first becoming widely used, some Christians condemned them, saying that these new-fangled scientific inventions were going to cause man to sin. A person *can* sin by using a car, but simply *having* the car is not sin; it is man's *sinful use* of the car that can be wrong. A car, rightly used, can be a tool of blessing. The same is true of most modern conveniences, like television and record players.

It is wrong for a Christian to think that scientific achievements will replace faith in God. Although scientific investigations cannot supply all the answers man wants when he wants them, and although the answer may be wrong and may need changing as more information is obtained, science can and does supply workable answers. That fact may cause some people to place their faith in science rather than God. They look to science to solve all their problems, but it cannot do that. Science supplies information which can solve *physical* problems. The problems with which science cannot deal are man's real problems: science cannot solve the guilt problem caused by sin; science cannot save a man from hell. Only faith in the Lord Jesus Christ and the salvation He offers can solve man's sin problems. A person

who believes that man's wisdom can solve these problems is believing something which Scripture says is not true (I Cor. 3:19).

A proper Christian attitude toward science

Since science is a tool used by man to discover useful knowledge about God's creation, science itself is not good or bad. Men use or abuse knowledge gained by scientific investigations. It is wrong, therefore, for a Christian to condemn science as being anti-God or to fear science, believing it can destroy man's faith in God. It is also wrong for a Christian to ignore science. Man's intelligent use of God's creation is part of subduing and having dominion over the earth.

The psalmist states in Psalm 19:1, "The heavens declare the glory of God; and the firmament sheweth his handywork." God's power and majesty are revealed in what He has created. The person who looks carefully at creation can know more about the God Who created it.

1B-6 *"The heavens declare the glory of God; and the firmament sheweth his handywork." (Psalm 19:1)*

True **worship** can be defined as man's recognizing his insignificance and turning his thoughts in love, reverence, adoration, and obedience to the almighty God. Worship does not require a church building, a preacher, or soft organ music. All too often worship does not take place even with all these helps. Worship takes place when *you* seek to *know* and *obey* God. Worship can and does take place when men look at the creation and see the God who designed, created, and sustains it. True scientific knowledge can enhance your worship by giving you more insight into the wonders of God's creation.

Answer to questions on page 26 All scientists on these pages could be using the technical method and therefore would be technicians. However, if the data they obtain is recorded, classified, and analyzed in order to choose an answer which will then be verified–or if the data is used to verify some previously chosen answer to a problem or survey, they are using the research method and therefore would be research scientists. In other words, the activity itself is not as important as the purpose for the results in determining the difference between research and technical methods.

Biological Terms

scientific method

Using the Scientific Method
research
hypothesis
experiment
survey
data

controlled experiment
experimental variable
control group
experimental group

The Limits of Science
bias
workability

Science and the Christian
pure science
applied science
research method
technical method
worship

Facet
biogenesis

Review Questions 1B-3

1. List five points that could be considered in developing a proper Christian attitude toward science.
2. In what way can scientific knowledge aid a person in his worship of the Creator?
3. What is the relationship between pure science and applied science? Give an example of each.
4. What is the relationship between the research method and the technical method of science?

Thought Questions

1. Why cannot the scientific method be used to make a judgment of values or morals?
2. Why is it important to have a single variable between a control group and an experimental group? What happens if there is more than one variable?
3. Science can only describe, not explain. Why is this statement true?
4. Occasionally it is reported that a scientist has performed an experiment which *proves* a passage of Scripture. Is this possible? Why or why not?
5. Some people look to science as a god. Since scientists have supplied the knowledge to heal many diseases and have used scientific information to produce many conveniences, they look to science to cure all their problems. Why is this view of science unacceptable to a Christian?
6. Some Christians turn away from anything that appears scientific. Since they do not understand science and cannot find most scientific facts in the Bible, they believe that science is anti-God. Give five Biblically based reasons that these Christians should reconsider their opinions.

1C–Biology and the Study of Life

Biology is often defined by its Greek word origin: *bios,* which means "life" or "living," and *logos,* which literally means "word" but has come to mean "study of" or "science of." The previous sections of this chapter have discussed the term *science.* We now turn our attention to the other portion of the definition of the term *biology: living.* What does it mean to be alive? Just as there is no set definition for *science,* no set definition can be given which will adequately describe life.

The Attributes of Life

Rather than study definitions, let us look first at a list of the *attributes of life.* This list does not include all the attributes, but it does present the major characteristics of living things. Since these attributes describe a very complex phenomenon—the **living condition**–they necessarily contain overlapping ideas.

Do not think that anything that possesses a few of these attributes is alive. Living things have *all* these attributes. Nonliving things, such as machines, computers, light bulbs, and chemicals, may have one or several of these attributes, but only those things which have all of them are alive.

❑ **Movement**   Normally one thinks of movement as motion from one place to another. Actually, moving from place to place is *locomotion.* Plants, most fungi, many bacteria, and even some animals cannot carry on locomotion, but they are alive and do exhibit movement.

Movement may be **internal movement** as well as locomotion. Even when you are perfectly still, blood is moving in your veins. Until you die, small structures will constantly be moving inside the cells of your body, even when your body is at rest. Plants move water internally, dissolve minerals, and process foods. Even a stationary, single-celled organism carries on internal movement.

❑ **Growth**   Though rocks or buildings may be said to grow, they are nonliving things and grow only in the sense that more material is added to them. But in order to increase the size of a brain,

one cannot similarly add more brain substance directly into the skull. Living things do not grow that way. Organisms grow by **assimilation*** (uh SIM uh LAY shun)–assembling the component parts which make up their living material. Growth is *achieved by* an organism, not *done to* an organism.

Growth does not always affect the size of an organism. Growth is often the replacement of worn-out cells. An adult, as a rule, does not continue to grow in size but does grow new cells and parts of cells to replace older cells until he dies.

❑ **Reproduction**   At one time or another during its life span, every normal living thing is capable of reproduction. **Reproduction** is the making of another organism which has characteristics and limitations similar to the original. Splitting a rock in two is not reproduction since the two halves cannot become like the original. Some small organisms do reproduce by splitting in two. But unlike the rock, each new organism has the capability to become like its parents, just as a puppy becomes like its parents. Puppies are not "half dogs." They are small dogs that have inherited a dog's characteristics and limitations.

Although a puppy has been nourished by its mother's body, very little of the puppy (only the

---

assimilation: (L. ASSIMULARE, to make similar to)

1C-1 *The coyote pup will be similar to, but not exactly like its mother. There are limits to the amount of possible variations it can have.*

original egg and sperm cells) was actually part of the mother and the father. After growing, the puppy will be similar to its parents.

Reproduction of living things is not making duplicates from a mold. A mother dog is not a mold for her puppies. She and the father dog have given the puppies the genetic information necessary for them to grow into dogs.

❏ **Comes from similar preexisting life** As a result of careful observations of controlled experiments and natural conditions, *biogenesis* is now generally accepted. Since all organisms reproduce, there is no need for spontaneous generation.

The idea that life comes from *similar* life is important: oak trees reproduce oak trees, and cats reproduce cats. The idea of oak trees reproducing cats is absurd. (However, in a roundabout way, this idea is similar to what evolutionists believe.) It is true that no kitten will be exactly like its parents. Some kittens may be slightly larger or smaller or have different colors, depending on the genetic information given to them by their parents. These differences, some minor and unobservable and some very noticeable, are termed **variations.** But variations are limited. The eventual adult size of a kitten, for example, is limited to a certain range. The genetic information inherited by a kitten (along with its diet, exercise, and physical surroundings) will determine what point in that range it will attain.

❏ **Similar chemical make-up** All living things are made up of the same basic chemical elements in similar compounds. Since all organisms move,

grow, reproduce, and come from preexisting life, the idea that all living things have a similar chemical make-up is not surprising.

The substances which living things produce contain varying amounts of carbon and are called **organic** chemicals. The living material of an organism is **protoplasm.** Many organisms, however, produce substances which are nonliving and often remain long after the protoplasm has deteriorated. These nonliving substances are organic but are not alive. The shell of a snail, the hair of your head, and the hoof of a cow are examples of *organic dead* materials. Of course, the body of an organism that has just died can also be considered organic dead material before it decomposes. Those things that are not alive and have never been alive, such as rocks, water, steel, and glass, are considered **inorganic.**

❏ **Made up of cells** Every living thing is made of either a single cell or many cells. Cells, discussed in Chapters 3 and 4, are units of protoplasm which are limited by the membranes they manufacture.

❏ **Irritability** All living things respond somehow to various forces in their environment. **Irritability** is the capacity to respond to stimuli. For example, human beings are highly sensitive to light and respond not only to its intensity, direction, and color but also to the object from which it comes. An earthworm, on the other hand, does not have eyes but merely light-sensitive areas. Though human beings need to respond to what they see, an earthworm merely needs to know if it is in the light or not; in its burrow seeing is not important. Sensing the light, however, the earthworm is aware that it is not in its protective hole and can do something about it. God designed each organism to be sensitive to those conditions in the environment that affect that organism.

❏ **Requires energy** All living things require a constant supply of energy. Humans obtain energy from food. Plants and some other organisms obtain their energy directly from the sun and store it for future use. **Food** can be defined as an organic, energy-containing substance. The energy that plants *store* is in the form of a food. Since many organisms, like plants, do not eat food, it is not accurate to list "eating" or "requires food" as an attribute of life. Organisms require energy.

❑ **Maintains a high level of organization** Being alive requires that a collection of molecules be *highly organized.* This organized complex of molecules forms the structures of living things. Energy is required to keep these molecules in that organized condition that permits life. As soon as energy is no longer expended to keep the organization, the molecules fall into disorder, and the organism begins to die. Think of it this way: in part, you are a self-assembled mass of what you have eaten; you are being held together in complex order by the energy you have obtained from your food. The Bible puts it this way, "Dust thou art, and unto dust shalt thou return" (Gen. 3:19).

❑ **Faces death** All things that are alive will die. Actually, parts of all living organisms are constantly dying–that is, they are no longer being held in the organized state that permits life to continue. Today thousands of cells in your body will die, and parts of all cells will wear out and cause the cells to die eventually. You are still

Christ on the Cross, Bob Jones University Collection of Sacred Art.

1C-2
Christ's death paid the price for our sins, so we can have spiritual life.

alive because your body is expending large amounts of energy to produce new cells and to keep alive and in good repair most of the others. If the Lord tarries, however, there will come a time when enough of one type of cell in your body–heart cells, brain cells, liver cells, or whatever kind of cells–will die, and the other living cells in your body will not be able to carry on.

The living condition

Physical life is not some special element or compound that some objects have and others do not. Life is a *condition,* a state in which something exists. **Life** can be defined as a highly organized cellular condition which is derived from preexisting life; requires energy to carry on processes such as growth, movement, reproduction, and responses; and faces death. It is more important, however, to understand what life is than to memorize a definition.

In the Bible *spiritual life* is often compared to physical life, and the comparison makes sense. The Christian's spiritual life, for example, comes from God's pre-existing spiritual life. Spiritual growth requires the strength (energy) we receive from God as we read and meditate on His Word. We also need His power to reproduce spiritually–that is, to witness to others and bring them into God's family. Our spiritual life is highly organized; we are to do God's will as prescribed for us in the Scripture. We grow in the Spirit only when we are responsive to God's leading.

One of the most notable exceptions to the parallels between our spiritual life and physical life is that Christians do not face spiritual death. Christ has conquered spiritual death; so those who know the Lord will live eternally with Him. Our physical bodies will die and return to dust, for "it is appointed unto men once to die" (Heb. 9:27). But our spiritual, glorified bodies will know no age and face no death.

Review Questions 1C-1

1. List and briefly describe the attributes of life.
2. Why is life best described as a condition?
3. List several characteristics of physical life and parallel characteristics of spiritual life as presented in Scripture.

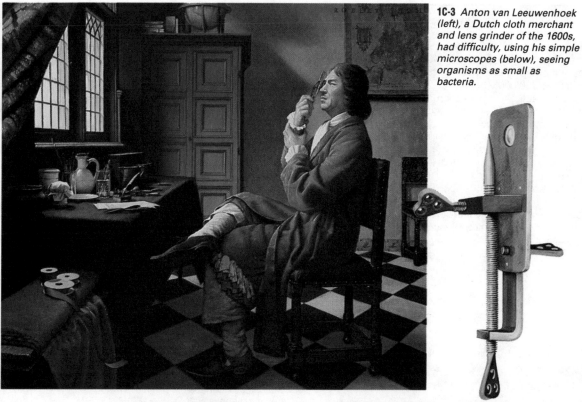

1C-3 *Anton van Leeuwenhoek (left), a Dutch cloth merchant and lens grinder of the 1600s, had difficulty, using his simple microscopes (below), seeing organisms as small as bacteria.*

The Study of Life

Studying life has always been difficult. Life is a state of being which can cease, leaving the investigator with a set of dead chemicals. Studying these chemicals may reveal what life *has done* but not what *it is*. Finding out what chemicals make up a living body does not reveal much about the life which the body had before the chemicals were separated. Diagrams of a watch can tell an engineer how the watch works; but careful descriptions of the size, shape, color, and even chemical make-up of the various structures of living things tell us little about life processes. A complete set of diagrams of the human body is simply inadequate to describe how it works.

In this section we will look at some of the tools and techniques scientists use to study living things and some of the difficulties they experience as they study life.

The microscope: a tool for biological study

Although a description of an organism's structures is not adequate by itself to explain life, a knowledge of the structures is essential. Unassisted human vision, however, cannot see millions of microbes or the parts of cells which make up an organism. **Microscopes*** aid in studying these tiny structures.

The first microscopes were probably made in the first century A.D. by filling glass balls with water. Glass lenses that were used to magnify structures were introduced in the Middle Ages. A single lens constitutes what is called a *simple microscope*. In about 1590, two Dutch eyeglass makers, the Janssen brothers, mounted two lenses in a set of adjustable tubes. The lens closer to the observer's eye magnified the already enlarged image of the lens closer to the object being observed. Such a microscope, consisting of two lenses or

---

microscope: micro- (small) +
-scope (to view)

Biological Measurements

When you use most light microscopes, you can easily see things 100X to 1,000X larger than they really are. Some electron microscopes magnify objects 1,000,000X but about 250,000X is the highest practical magnification. You can quickly get into hundredths, thousandths, millionths, and billionths of an inch. Just as you deal in miles and light years rather than millions and billions of inches when you study long distances, you also deal with different units of length as you get smaller.

A **centimeter*** (cm) is about 1/2 in. (2.54 cm. = 1.0 in.). If a centimeter is divided into ten equal parts, each part is a **millimeter*** (MIL uh MEE tur) (mm). A millimeter scale is often shown on

man body cells are about 20 μm and human red blood cells average only 7.5 μm across. To make these structures clearly visible, 400X is necessary. Most medium-sized bacteria are about one micrometer. These require 1,000X on the light microscope to be seen.

If a micrometer is divided into 1,000 equal parts, each part is a **nanometer*** (NAN uh MEE tur) (nm). Some small bacteria are about 100 nm, and the mumps virus is approximately 115 nm.

	m	cm	mm	μm	nm	Å
m	1	0.01	0.001	0.000001	0.000000001	0.0000000001
cm	100	1	0.1	0.0001	0.0000001	0.00000001
mm	1,000	10	1	0.001	0.000001	0.0000001
μm	1,000,000	10,000	1,000	1	0.001	0.0001
nm	1,000,000,000	10,000,000	1,000,000	1,000	1	0.1
Å	10,000,000,000	100,000,000	10,000,000	10,000	10	1

To appreciate the smallness of these measurements, consider the following. If a meter were enlarged to the distance between Spokane, Washington, and Washington, D.C., then
• a millimeter would be the distance around the Indianapolis 500,
• a nanometer would be the thickness of 2 nickels, and
• an angstrom would be the thickness of a paper clip.

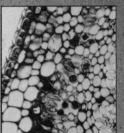

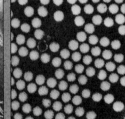

human finger (2.5X)   leaf cells (35X)

crab louse claw (100X)   polio virus (100,000X)

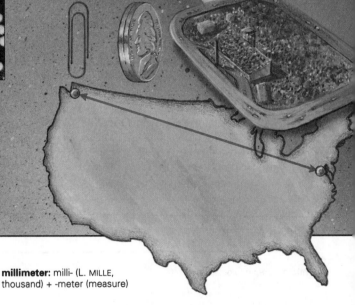

rulers and a single millimeter unit can easily be seen with the unaided eye. Some large microbes can be measured in millimeters.

If a millimeter is divided into 1,000 equal parts, each part is a **micrometer*** (my KRAHM ih tur) (μm). Most microbes, like amebas and algae cells, are approximately 100 μm long. To see things of this size, one must magnify the image at least 100X on a light microscope. Many hu-

centimeter: centi- (L. CENTUM, hundred) + -meter (Gk. METRON, measure)

millimeter: milli- (L. MILLE, thousand) + -meter (measure)

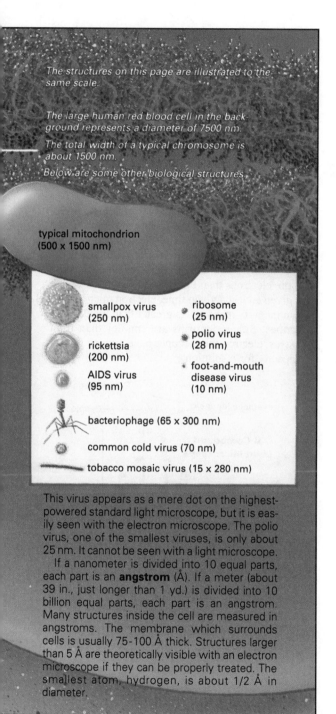

The structures on this page are illustrated to the same scale.

The large human red blood cell in the background represents a diameter of 7500 nm.

The total width of a typical chromosome is about 1500 nm.

Below are some other biological structures.

typical mitochondrion
(500 x 1500 nm)

smallpox virus
(250 nm)

ribosome
(25 nm)

polio virus
(28 nm)

rickettsia
(200 nm)

foot-and-mouth
disease virus
(10 nm)

AIDS virus
(95 nm)

bacteriophage (65 x 300 nm)

common cold virus (70 nm)

tobacco mosaic virus (15 x 280 nm)

This virus appears as a mere dot on the highest-powered standard light microscope, but it is easily seen with the electron microscope. The polio virus, one of the smallest viruses, is only about 25 nm. It cannot be seen with a light microscope.

If a nanometer is divided into 10 equal parts, each part is an **angstrom** (Å). If a meter (about 39 in., just longer than 1 yd.) is divided into 10 billion equal parts, each part is an angstrom. Many structures inside the cell are measured in angstroms. The membrane which surrounds cells is usually 75-100 Å thick. Structures larger than 5 Å are theoretically visible with an electron microscope if they can be properly treated. The smallest atom, hydrogen, is about 1/2 Å in diameter.

two sets of lenses, is called a *compound microscope*. Because of the distance necessary between the lenses, early compound microscopes were often over 0.6 m (2 ft.) long.

The best known microscopist is probably Anton van Leeuwenhoek (LAY wun HOOK), a Dutch merchant who had a hobby of lens grinding in the early 1600s. Leeuwenhoek used simple microscopes rather than the cumbersome compound microscopes of his day. Some of Leeuwenhoek's lenses were smaller than a pinhead, and he had to push the lenses almost into his eye in order to see anything.

Leeuwenhoek made over 200 different microscopes, which had various mountings to view many types of specimens. Some of his discoveries include circulation of fluids in the tiny vessels of a living fish's tail, thousands of microbes, blood cells, sperm, and even various human tissue structures. For most of his long life Leeuwenhoek sent his observations of "very many wretched little beasties all cavorting about very nimbly" to the Royal Society of London. Leeuwenhoek, who is called "the Father of Microscopy," never saw an object magnified more than 160 times. Today, even the microscopes commonly used in high schools can magnify 400 times (400 times can also be written 400X in which the "X" means *times larger*).

The compound light microscope

The *compound light microscope* is commonly used in classrooms and laboratories today. It consists of one set of lenses to magnify an object and another set to serve as a telescope to further enlarge the image and permit the observer to look at it from a convenient distance. In a light microscope the two sets of lenses are located in the **objective** and the **ocular*** (AHK yuh lur) or eyepiece. Many microscopes have a *revolving nosepiece* which permits several objectives with different magnifications to be used.

When you look *through* the microscope, you see light that has passed through the specimen on the **stage,** through the objective lens, through the **body tube,** and through the the eyepiece lens. Actually, you are seeing the "shadow" of the

---

micrometer: micro- (small) +
-meter (measure)

ocular: (L. OCULUS, eye)

nanometer: nano- (L. NANUS, dwarf)
+ -meter (measure)

1730

1686

1744

1C-4 *Old compound microscopes*

specimen since you observe light that has passed *through* it and not light that is reflected from it. Microscopes are focused by moving the objective lens closer to or farther from the specimen.

Many modern microscopes have two eyepieces. Some of these microscopes (especially higher-powered ones) give the same image to both eyes. Others, however, are *stereoscopic microscopes* that provide two slightly different views of the same object, similar to the images one gets when looking at an object with both eyes. These slightly different views result in depth perception. A number of these stereoscopic microscopes are low-powered and use light reflected from the specimen which is placed relatively far from the objective lens. Microscopes of this nature are frequently used for dissecting small specimens.

The electron microscope

One of the most useful tools for biological investigation developed in the twentieth century is the **electron microscope.** The electron microscope replaces light rays with electrons which are exceptionally small and straight-traveling. Because more electrons than light waves can pass through a given area at a given time, electron microscopes can magnify many times greater than light microscopes. Since electrons are smaller than light waves, electron microscopes have a much greater capacity for resolution.

1C-5 *A comparison of a light microscope and an electron microscope*

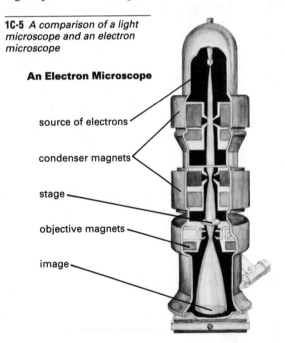

An Electron Microscope

source of electrons

condenser magnets

stage

objective magnets

image

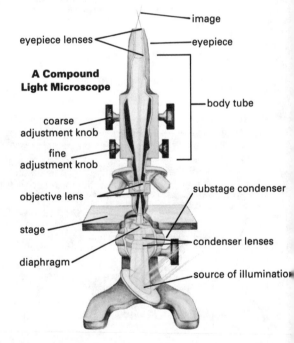

image

eyepiece lenses

eyepiece

A Compound Light Microscope

body tube

coarse adjustment knob

fine adjustment knob

objective lens

substage condenser

stage

diaphragm

condenser lenses

source of illumination

Principles of Light Magnification

Normally the **reflection** of light from the surface of an object makes it visible to the eye. If, however, a lens is placed between the object and the eye, the light waves will be bent. The wavy patterns seen through some window glass or the apparent bend in a drinking straw placed in water are results of light waves being bent as they pass through the transparent substances. This bending of light as it passes through a substance is called **refraction**. The refraction of light as it passes through a curved lens either enlarges or shrinks an image.

There are limits to magnification. Since only a certain amount of light reflects from or passes through a specific point at one time, no image is visible if these waves are spread too far apart. The ability to distinguish fine detail is called **resolution**. The unaided human eye can distinguish two points 0.1 mm apart, but points closer than that appear as a single point. If two points 0.1 mm apart are magnified 100X, however, they will *appear* 10 mm apart. When an image is magnified, the resolution increases.

There is, however, a limit as to how close two points can be and still appear as two individual points when magnified with a light microscope. In part, the ability of a lens to clearly separate two points depends on the quality of the lens. Due to the size of light waves, points too close together become distorted as they are magnified. Even the highest quality lens, therefore, has resolution limits.

Refraction causes the pencil to appear bent and enlarged.

Electrons do not pass through any substance very easily; in fact, the specimen in an electron microscope must be in a vacuum because the electrons would be affected by the air molecules. Specimens viewed on an electron microscope must be sliced extremely thin. They must also be treated with relatively harsh chemicals which do not permit electrons to pass. These electron-dense substances sometimes change or damage the specimen.

A lens does not bend the paths of electrons but does stop almost all of them. So, rather than lenses, electromagnets of various charges and strengths pull or push on the electrons, either condensing or separating them. Although electrons cannot be seen by the human eye, they can affect photographic plates and can be detected by electron-sensitive devices which transfer images of the electrons to a screen like a television tube. *Electron micrographs,** the pictures produced by an electron microscope, have no color but only light and dark areas where electrons passed or did not pass through the stained specimen.

The *scanning electron microscope*, a special kind of electron microscope, is used to obtain

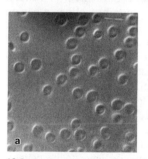
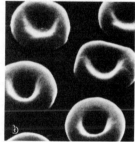

1C-6 *Comparisons of (a) a light micrograph and (b) an electron micrograph of red blood cells*

A scanning electron micrograph of a louse

---

micrograph: micro- (small) +
-graph (Gk. GRAPHEIN, to write)

images of the surfaces of structures. After an electron-dense substance is applied to the surface of a specimen, this special electron microscope produces images up to 20,000X.

The electron microscope can magnify from 1,500X to 250,000X. In other words, it starts at the highest magnification possible on a light microscope and can magnify that image about 160X.

Review Questions 1C-2

1. Who is called "the Father of Microscopy," and how did he earn this title?
2. Describe how a lens magnifies an image.
3. Why must you use a thin specimen when viewing with a light microscope?
4. What structures of an electron microscope are comparable to the following requirements for the light microscope: (a) light waves, (b) lenses, (c) viewer's eye, (d) mirror or light source?
5. Give the size relationships between a meter, centimeter, millimeter, micrometer, nanometer, and an angstrom. (Example: 100 cm in a meter)
6. Give an example of something that would easily be measured by using each of the following units: meter, centimeter, millimeter, micrometer, nanometer, and angstrom.

Variables in biological studies

Because God designed life to function in a certain range of environmental conditions, it is difficult to experiment with living things. When a person wants to measure the amounts of oxygen and hydrogen needed to produce a certain amount of water, the experiment can be repeated over and over with the same results. An experiment to determine how much weight a horse can pull, however, would be affected by many variables including type of horse, its age, health, and size. Some of these factors could be controlled by using the same horse for all experiments, but then fatigue and boredom would have to be considered. The results of such an experiment could not be applied to all horses.

A student conducting an experiment for a science fair project put hamsters into two groups of five hamsters each. His hypothesis was that hamsters on a diet of seeds and carrots would gain weight and be happy and healthy, while hamsters being fed cake and cookies would lose weight and become sickly. All the seed-and-carrot hamsters remained the same weight and appeared happy and healthy. Most of the cake-and-cookie hamsters also kept the same weight, but two of them gained a considerable amount of weight. All, however, still appeared happy and healthy.

Because the science fair was close at hand, the student began to draw conclusions about cake, cookies, and hamsters. The day of the fair, though, he found two litters of baby hamsters in the cake-and-cookie hamster group along with two considerably slimmer hamsters. His conclusions had been wrong because there was a factor he had failed to take into consideration.

You may smile, but eminent, qualified scientists have made the same type of mistakes over and over again. All the variables involved in a living condition are almost impossible to control; therefore, reliable experimentation on living things is difficult.

The validity of biological studies

From this discussion about some of the tools and techniques biologists use to study life, one thing should be evident: studying life itself is not easy. There are far too many variables to control.

❑ Errors can be made by the biologist in his observations.

❑ Errors can result if the specimen is not typical.

❑ Errors can be made when the techniques used are crude.

To overcome these problems, a scientist testing a living organism must usually repeat his work many times with a high percentage of similar results before considering a conclusion valid.

FACETS OF BIOLOGY

1C-1

Biological Research Techniques

Today's scientists have many sophisticated tools which allow them to observe, often indirectly, many things which would have been impossible to know about in the past. Some of the techniques described below are used in the medical profession to aid in making diagnoses. Others are used primarily in researching the structure and function of microscopic living things.

❏ *Staining* Although some cellular components are specific colors, most are clear. Scientists often use stains to make various substances visible. Because stains only color specific chemicals, the presence of those chemicals can be detected by the use of those stains. Some stains can be used on living cells, but most stains must be used on dead materials.

❏ *X-rays* X-rays easily pass through thin materials, but pass less slowly through dense materials. By exposing a structure to X-rays and then catching the rays that pass through the structure on photographic film, scientists can learn about the internal structures without cutting into the structure. Since many structures in living things are similar in density, scientists often must use substances that make the structures more dense. To view the structures of the digestive system, people are often asked to drink an X-ray dense substance (a substance which blocks X-rays). The X-ray pictures then show the digestive system's structures.

❏ *Computerized Axial Tomography Scan (CAT or CT scan)* X-rays are passed through a single area from different angles and are picked up by a detector. The information is fed into a computer,

The physician prepares a patient to enter the CAT scan machine.

compared, and made into a picture. A CAT scan machine is about 100 times more sensitive than a conventional X-ray machine and does not use X-ray dense material to identify structures.

❏ *Ultrasonography** (UHL truh suh NAWG ruf fee) Ultrasound is much like the sonar used by ships. A device which releases sound and then picks up the echoes of that sound that bounce off internal structures is moved slowly on the surface of the body near the structures. The resulting data is fed into a computer which produces a picture based on the speed and quality of the echo. The pictures are not as accurate or precise as CAT scans or X-rays, but are quite useful in observing unborn children, who can be harmed by X-rays. Ultrasound pictures are useful also in studying the heart, which is often

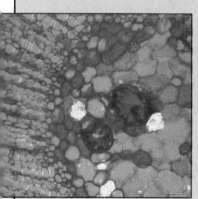
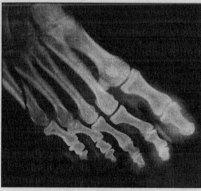

A micrograph of plant stems that are stained to show different tissues (left). An X-ray reveals a broken bone in a person's foot (right).

ultrasonography: ultra- (L. ULTRA, beyond) + -sono- (SONORUS, sound) + -graphy (to write)

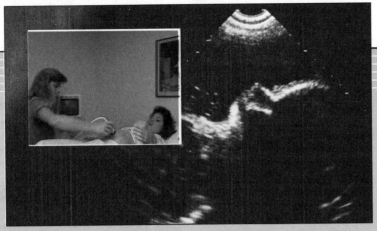

Ultrasound being used (inset) to generate this picture of the unborn child

difficult to observe with X-rays because heart muscle is soft tissue.

□ *Cellular fractionation* Cellular fractionation (FRAK shuh NAY shun) is used to remove structures from inside a cell in sufficient quantity to be analyzed chemically. After a cell has been physically broken and placed in a solution in a tube, it can be put in a *centrifuge* (SEHN truh FEWJ). The centrifuge spins the material at extremely high speeds which causes dense materials to settle to the bottom of the tube and forces lighter materials to the top. In between are layers of cellular pieces of various densities. By taking a layer of material from the centrifuged tube and repeating the process several times, an almost pure collection of structures of a certain density can be obtained and then chemically analyzed. This process permits scientists to determine what chemicals comprise cellular structures.

□ *Autoradiography* A technique used to study the chemical activity of a structure is autoradiography* (AW toh RAY dee AWG ruh fee). A chemical made with a radioactive element is supplied to a living cell. Since radioactivity affects the photographic plates used in electron microscopes, the presence of this chemical can be pinpointed. For example, if radio-active hydrogen in the form of water (called deuterium) is supplied to a cell, a series of photographs taken through an electron microscope can reveal how fast the water enters the cell and into what cellular structures the water goes.

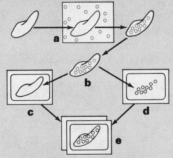

A representation of autoradiography: (a) Material containing a radioisotope (red dots) is supplied to a cell. The cell absorbs and uses the radioisotope. (b) The cell is then killed, (c) photographed, and (d) exposed to other photographic film which is affected by the radioisotope (black dots). (e) The two photographs are combined to locate the radioisotope.

□ *Chromatography* Scientists often use chromatography* (CROH muh TAWG ruh fee) to separate substances in a solution. An absorbing material (often a strip of special paper) is placed in the solution, and the various materials go up, like water being picked up by a paper towel. The various materials in the solution are different weights and thus go to different heights on the absorbing material. Bands containing different substances from the solution are formed on the absorbing material.

Paper chromatography

□ *Endoscopy* Endoscopy * (en DAH skuh pee) is a name for using a hollow tube or a fiber optic cable to look inside a structure. Often the tube will have devices in it which permit the scientist to supply light to the dark area, remove specimens, perform surgery, or pump air into the structure so that it can be seen more clearly. Different endoscopes are designed for looking at various structures. Some endoscopes are inserted through natural body openings such as the mouth or nose; others enter through incisions made by a physician or scientist.

Review questions on next page.

autoradiography: auto- (Gk. AUTO, self) + -radio- (L. RADIARE, to emit beams) + -graphy (to write)

chromatography: chroma- (Gk. KHROMA, color) + -graphy (to write)

endoscopy: endo- (Gk. ENDON, within) + -scopy (SCOPEIN, to view)

The conclusion must also agree with other scientific information about the topic before it can be considered valid. A scientist performing electron microscope observations may conclude that a certain molecule is box-shaped. Another scientist performing experiments on the chemical make-up of the same molecule may conclude that it is ball-shaped. There are several possible explanations for these contrasting results.

❏ Possibly the molecule can change its shape as it is prepared for electron microscope viewing or as it is analyzed chemically.

❏ Possibly one or both scientists are wrong in their observations or conclusions.

❏ Possibly the molecule is both box- and ball-shaped.

In any case, further study is necessary.

Models

Earlier it was noted that science cannot *explain* things. Science only *describes*. This is true because of the nature of science. However, one often finds *explanations* in scientific materials. Descriptions of *how* things operate is a major part in the study of biology or any other science. An explanation of how something works is called a **model.**

Scientists devise models to explain the data they have obtained. A series of different experiments can tell much about a process. Putting all the experimental information together so that it "works" logically can produce a model. Further experimentation often reveals more information. If the results of these additional experiments agree with the model, the model is assumed to be more valid. If these results do not support the model, then either that data is in error, or the model must be greatly changed or discarded.

Despite the fact that models are often changed, they are the only method man has to describe *how* something functions. Knowing how a process operates is often crucial for man to effectively use the process he is ordained of God to use. As you study various models in this book, however, recall that any explanation is merely *man's guess* at how *God ordained* something to operate.

Biological Terms

biology	organic	*The Study of Life*	objective	resolution
The Attributes of Life	protoplasm	microscope	ocular	model
living condition	inorganic	centimeter (cm)	stage	
internal movement	irritability	millimeter (mm)	body tube	
assimilation	food	micrometer (μm)	electron microscope	
reproduction	life	nanometer (nm)	reflection	
variation		angstrom (Å)	refraction	

Review Questions 1C-3

1. Why is a description of the structures found in a living organism not adequate to describe life?
2. Why is studying living organisms difficult?
3. List several problems that can affect the validity of experiments with living things.
4. What is a scientific model, and why do scientists construct them?

Facet 1C-1: Biological Research Techniques, pages 39-40

1. List and describe five techniques used by scientists to enhance their ability to observe various structures.
2. List and describe four techniques used by scientists to determine the chemical make-up of a structure.

Thought Questions

1. Based on an analysis of the attributes of living things, could a robot with a highly sophisticated computer attached to it be considered alive? Why or why not?
2. Why are models important in science? Why can no model be accepted as a completely valid explanation of a phenomenon?

THE CHEMISTRY OF LIFE

TWO

2A- Basic Chemistry

Biology was once almost entirely *natural history;* that is, learning to recognize organisms and discovering where they lived constituted most of the study of biology. Then came *descriptive biology.* Scientists, armed with hand lenses and microscopes, described in minute detail the structures of everything that grew, crept, or flew, as well as a few things that were not even alive.

Today, however, biology is mostly the study of *how* structures function. Whether in a test tube or in a living cell, the same substances behave according to God-ordained rules. This is why one must first understand **chemistry*** (the study of those substances and the rules that govern their behavior) in order to understand biology.

Matter

It is not always easy to distinguish the two basic components of the physical universe, matter and energy, because they exist and work together. For the sake of simplicity, though, this study of basic chemistry will consider each of them separately.

chemistry: chem-, chemi-, or chemo- (Gk. KHEMEIA, alchemy, *hence,* chemistry or chemicals)

The simple definition of matter (although scientists are modifying it as they learn more about the physical universe) will suffice here: **matter** is anything which occupies space and has mass. Normally there are three *states of matter:* solid, liquid, and gas. Actually, these states of matter are the result of varying amounts of energy possessed by that matter. If heat, a form of energy, is added to solid water (ice), the water will enter the liquid state; and if more heat energy is added to the water, it becomes a vapor, the gaseous state.

Elements and atoms

Matter is composed of over 100 known elements. Occasionally, scientists synthesize another element in the laboratory, but usually these elements are highly unstable. **Elements** are those substances that cannot be broken down into simpler substances by ordinary chemical reactions.

According to the atomic theory, cutting a piece of pure gold (one of the elements) in half, and then in half again, and again, and again, in time would yield a piece that could not be cut again and still be gold. That piece would be an **atom,** the smallest unit of an element that is still that element. Although nuclear reactions can break atoms apart, the products of these reactions are no longer the original element. Scientists now isolate atoms and detect their presence by using specialized electron microscopes, but no one has yet clearly seen individual atoms. Our notions of their existence and what they are like are only workable theories.

The *periodic table of the elements* is an arrangement of the elements according to the structure of their atoms. This table displays the *element symbols* (usually the first letter or letters of the chemical names in Latin or English). The common elements found in living organisms are listed along with their symbols in table 2A-1. The first four elements listed are essential to all life in large amounts. The next seven elements are essential to all life in smaller amounts. The rest of the elements in the table are *trace elements,* which are essential to some organisms only in tiny amounts.

An atom is not solid (like a marble). One model pictures an atom somewhat like our solar system: a central part and outer moving parts with much space in between. In the center of the atom, clustered into a group called the *nucleus,* are **protons,** the positively charged particles, and **neutrons,** which have no charge. In a constant state of circling motion within levels or shells around the nucleus are the **electrons***–particles with negative charges. There are other subatomic particles that need not be discussed here.

2A-1	The Elements of Life	
Symbol	Element	Abundance in Human Body (% Weight)
O C H N Ca	Oxygen Carbon Hydrogen Nitrogen Calcium	65 18 10 } 98% 3 2
P K	Phosphorus Potassium	0.5-1.0 each
S Cl Na Mg	Sulfur Chlorine Sodium Magnesium	0.1-0.5 each
Cu F Fe I Zn	Copper Fluorine Iron Iodine Zinc	less than 0.1 each

▇ Essential   ☐ Trace

---

electron: (Gk. ELEKTRON; amber, which when rubbed produces electricity; hence, electricity).

The nucleus of the atom is relatively distant from the electron shells. If a single oxygen atom were the size of a football field, the nucleus would be the size of a tennis ball in the center, and the electrons would be the size of pinheads circling the field at the distance of the goal posts. Most of matter, then, is empty space between the nucleus and the electrons of atoms. The matter which makes this book is quite solid, even though it is made of atoms which are mostly space. Strong forces hold the atoms of this book together so that they form a solid substance.

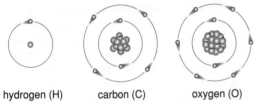

hydrogen (H)   carbon (C)   oxygen (O)

What forces hold electrons and protons together as atoms, and what forces bind atoms together? Scientists believe that the opposing charges of the electrons (−) and the protons (+) cause them to stay together as an atom. To understand what binds one atom to another, we need to know more about the atom's make-up.

Atoms of different elements differ in their number of subatomic particles (electrons, protons, and neutrons). In a single atom, however, the number of electrons is always the same as the number of protons. If there is 1 proton in the nucleus and 1 electron in its shell, the atom is hydrogen. The atom with 8 protons (with the proper number of neutrons) in the nucleus and 8 electrons is oxygen. The *atomic number* in the periodic table indicates the number of protons in the atoms of that element.

If the number of electrons and protons in an atom decreases or increases, the atom becomes a different element. Normally, the number of protons in an atom does not change except in nuclear reactions, as in atomic bomb explosions, nuclear power reactors, or stars.

Chemical bonding: ionic

Most atoms are unstable and will normally bond with other atoms to become more stable. An atom is stable when its outermost electron shell is full. The innermost electron shell, which is the first to be filled, can contain only 2 electrons. The second shell can hold 8 electrons. The next shell has the potential to hold 18 electrons but acts as if it were full when it has 8. The shells farther out hold

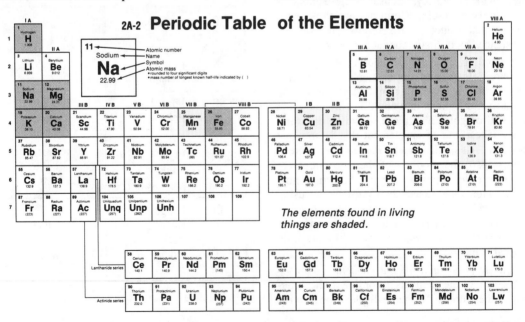

2A-2 **Periodic Table of the Elements**

The elements found in living things are shaded.

larger numbers, but all behave as full when they have 8.

Those atoms with full shells are quite stable (the noble gases: helium, neon, argon, and so forth). Other atoms, especially if their outermost shells lack 1 or 2 electrons or if they have only 1 or 2 electrons, seem quite willing to give, get, or share electrons in order to have a full outermost shell. Atoms that give, get, or share electrons to become more stable are *chemically active*.

For example, an atom of chlorine, a chemically active nonmetal, has 17 electrons: 2 in the first shell, 8 in the second shell, and 7 in the third shell. If it gets 1 more electron, it will have a full outermost shell. Sodium, a chemically active metal, is the opposite. It has 11 electrons: 2 in the first shell, 8 in the second, and 1 in the third. If it gives its outermost electron, it will have a full second shell. When these 2 elements meet, sodium gives its outermost electron to chlorine, which takes it readily and fills its outermost shell. When these 2 elements meet, they combine to form a *compound*–table salt. Salt is more chemically stable than the 2 elements which form it.

Since one atom gives and the other gets an electron, the atoms of sodium and chlorine in salt each have *unequal* numbers of electrons and protons. An atom with a charge (not having an equal number of protons and electrons) is called an **ion*** (EYE un). Since the sodium in salt is missing an electron, it is a *positively charged ion*. In other words, it has more positive charges (protons) than it has negative charges (electrons). The chloride ion, however, is a *negatively charged ion*. It has more electrons than protons. The giving and taking of electrons, forming ions, is called **ionic** (eye AHN ik) **bonding.** Since all cells are surrounded by and contain ions, the study of ions and ionic bonding is significant to biological studies.

Chemical bonding: covalent

Another type of chemical bonding involves the *sharing* of electrons. The forming of a water molecule is a good example. Hydrogen has only 1 electron and requires another to fill its first shell. Oxygen has 8 electrons: 2 in its first shell and 6 in its second shell. Two more electrons would complete the second shell of the oxygen atom. One oxygen atom will therefore combine with 2 hydrogen atoms. The oxygen shares 1 electron from its second shell with each of the 2 hydrogen atoms so that each hydrogen atom has a filled shell. The 2 hydrogen atoms share their electrons with the oxygen so that the oxygen has a filled outer shell.

Two hydrogen atoms bonded to an oxygen atom form a water molecule. These atoms *share* the electrons involved in this bond. This sharing of electrons is called **covalent** (koh VAY lunt) **bonding** and is a strong chemical bond. Covalent bonds do not separate easily.

2A-3 *Two types of chemical bonding*

ionic bonding

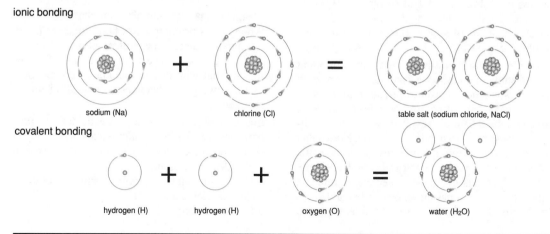

sodium (Na)   chlorine (Cl)   table salt (sodium chloride, NaCl)

covalent bonding

hydrogen (H)   hydrogen (H)   oxygen (O)   water (H₂O)

---

ion: (Gk. ION, something that goes)

Not all chemical bonds are ionic or covalent. Many other bonds are somewhere between the two and often form substances which behave like both *ionic compounds* and *covalent compounds*. Those which form ions easily are ionic, but some ionic compounds do not form ions easily. Likewise, all covalent bonds are not equally strong.

Compounds

In the examples given above–water and salt–different elements combined to form different substances called **compounds.** Sodium is a highly reactive metal which in its pure state reacts violently with water producing flammable hydrogen. Chlorine is a very poisonous gas which, when dissolved in water, is used to kill bacteria in swimming pools. Separately, sodium and chlorine are harmful to living things. But bonded together, they form a crystal that is essential to most living organisms.

Hydrogen is a highly combustible gas, and oxygen is a gas necessary for combustion. In compound form, however, they become water, which is used for putting out fires!

Compounds may be made of only a few atoms, as the ones described above, or they may be made up of many atoms. **Molecular formulas** express clearly the number and type of atoms in a compound. The empirical formula for sodium chloride is NaCl. This shows that 1 molecule of table salt contains 1 atom of sodium (Na) and 1 atom of chlorine (Cl). H_2O indicates that there are 2 atoms of hydrogen and 1 of oxygen. $C_6H_{12}O_6$ is the molecular formula for the simple sugar glucose. There are 24 atoms represented in this formula: 6 carbons, 12 hydrogens, and 6 oxygens.

A **structural formula** is often more important in the study of a compound and its reactions with other compounds than an empirical formula. Note in figure 2A-4 the structural formulas for glucose. In a structural formula scientists see where a molecule could bond to another molecule. Notice that there are two different structures that a molecule of glucose can take. Galactose is another simple sugar which has the same molecular formula as glucose because it has the same number and kinds of atoms. In galactose those atoms are bonded

Molecules

When atoms bond, a molecule is formed. A **molecule** is the smallest unit of a substance that is still that substance in a natural state. Most molecules are compounds such as water, carbon dioxide, sugar, fat, and propane. A carbon atom bonds with 2 oxygen atoms, for example, to form a carbon dioxide molecule (CO_2).

Some molecules, however, contain atoms of only a single element. The oxygen you breathe is not in the form of single oxygen atoms. Atmospheric oxygen is 2 oxygen atoms bonded together forming a molecule of oxygen (O_2). Similarly, other gases, such as nitrogen, hydrogen, and chlorine, combine with themselves to form molecules.

together in a different configuration. Its structural formula, therefore, is different. Because of its different structure, galactose has properties slightly different from the properties of glucose.

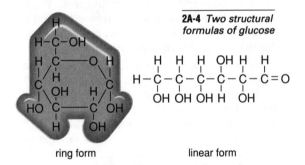

2A-4 *Two structural formulas of glucose*

ring form   linear form

Chemical changes and physical changes

When atoms or compounds bond together (react chemically), there is a **chemical change.** A chemical change takes place when the atoms of a substance bond with different atoms or compounds. The following are characteristics of all chemical changes:

❏ Chemical changes take place in definite proportions. Ten hydrogen atoms can make only 5 water molecules, no matter how many oxygen molecules are present.

❏ New compounds are formed, and/or there is a release of elements.

❏ Energy is involved.

FACETS OF BIOLOGY

2A–1

Acids, Bases, and Buffers

Most substances, when dissolved in water are either an acid or a base. Most chemical reactions, especially those that take place in living things, are affected by whether they are taking place in an acid or a base and by how strong the acid or base is.

Acids and bases are really opposites which, when they get together, do not fight, but destroy each other. An **acid** is a compound which releases *hydrogen ions* (H^+) when dissolved in water. A **base** is a compound which releases *hydroxyl ions* (OH^-) when it is dissolved in water.

When an acid and base are put together they **neutralize** each other, forming a salt and water. For example, sodium hydroxide and hydrochloric acid will combine to form sodium chloride (table salt) and water.

$$NaOH + HCl \rightarrow NaCl + H_2O$$

The *acidity* (amount of hydrogen ions) or *alkalinity* (amount of hydroxyl ions) of a solution is usually expressed in terms of a number called **pH** (which stands for "potential of hydrogen"). For biologists, the useful pH scale goes from 0 (very acidic) to 14 (very alkaline). A pH reading of 7 is neutral, meaning the solution has no excess H^+ or OH^- ions.

Living things and pH

The pH surrounding living things is crucial. If you breathe an acid dissolved in the water of the air, you will gag. If the acid is strong enough or you breathe it long enough, you could harm your lungs. pH is especially critical for aquatic organisms. Some fish that normally live in water with a pH of 6.5 will begin to show signs of distress when placed in water with a pH of 6.0, and if placed in water with a pH of 5, they die.

The internal pH of living things is also important. The human stomach enzymes work best if the pH of the stomach is between 1.6 to 2.4. Sometimes a person's stomach may secrete too much acid for too long causing "an acid stomach." If the acid is neutralized by destroying the walls of the digestive system the person has a burning sensation (often called "heartburn" even though it has nothing to do with the heart). One method of dealing with an acid stomach is to eat basic foods (milk, crackers, bread) or to take medicines that contain bases (sometimes called antacids) to neutralize the "excess stomach acid" forming salts and water.

In many living systems there are buffers which keep the pH within a tolerable range. A **buffer** is a substance that will combine with H^+ if it is in abundance or with OH^- if it is in abundance.

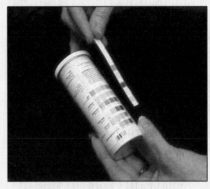

A test strip has indicators to determine the presence of various substances in urine. One of the indicators shows the pH.

Your blood, for example, maintains a pH between 7.35 to 7.45 using buffers. If an acidic substance enters your blood the buffers will quickly pick up the excess H^+ ions. The reverse would happen if an alkaline substance gets into your blood.

There are, of course, limits. If someone gets too much of an acid in his blood the buffers may not be able to handle all the ions. His blood pH would go down, and he would end up in a coma; if it goes too far, he would die. The brain cells tolerate only small pH fluctuations beyond the normal range.

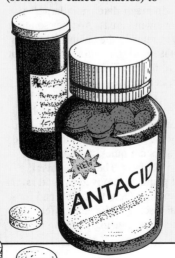

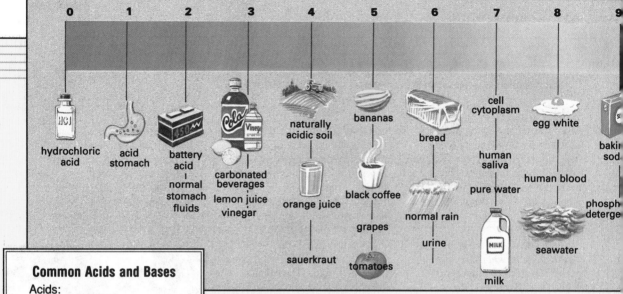

pH scale:

| 0 | 1 | 2 | 3 | 4 | 5 | 6 | 7 | 8 | 9 |

- hydrochloric acid (0)
- acid stomach (1)
- battery acid / normal stomach fluids (1)
- carbonated beverages / lemon juice / vinegar (2–3)
- naturally acidic soil (4)
- orange juice (4)
- sauerkraut (4)
- bananas (5)
- black coffee (5)
- grapes (5)
- tomatoes (5)
- bread (6)
- normal rain (6)
- urine (6)
- cell cytoplasm (7)
- human saliva (7)
- pure water (7)
- milk (7)
- egg white (8)
- human blood (8)
- seawater (8)
- baking soda (9)
- phosphate detergent (9)

Common Acids and Bases

Acids:
- hydrochloric acid–HCl
- sulfuric acid–H_2SO_4
- carbonic acid–H_2CO_3

Bases:
- sodium hydroxide–NaOH
- calcium hydroxide–Ca(OH)$_2$

Acid rain

Some metal statues and some stone buildings appear to be melting. In some crystal clear lakes and streams there are no longer any fish. The cause: acid rain. Normal rain is slightly acidic (pH 5.6 to 6) because it picks up carbon dioxide from the air which dissolves to form carbonic acid.

$$H_2O + CO_2 \longrightarrow H_2CO_3$$

Under normal circumstances any mildly acidic rain is neutralized by basic substances in the water or soil where it falls.

Automobile exhausts and the burning of coal and oil in industry release compounds containing sulfur and nitrogen. When these substances dissolve in atmospheric water, they form **acid rain.** When small amounts of these substances are put into the air, the harmful ef-

fects are seen near the industry that produced the pollution. To solve the problem, taller smokestacks are built. This puts the chemicals higher in the atmosphere and causes them to spread over greater distances before they fall as acid rain.

For a while the natural buffers in the soil and water could deal with the excess H$^+$ ions. Today, however, major industrial areas put so much acidic substances into the atmosphere that acid rain comes down in sufficient quantity to do major damage in large, downwind areas. Another solution is to remove the chemicals that cause acid rain before they are put into the air. This process, however, is expensive.

Today in some places rain has a pH of 2 (near that of automobile battery acid). With such high acidity the natural buffers in soils and waters are quickly used up, and the pH falls. The waxy covering of plants is removed by acid rain, exposing them to insects and fungal diseases. The acids affect soil nutrients, causing plants to die of

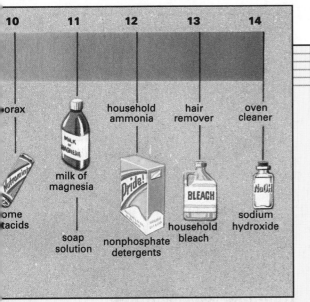

10   11   12   13   14

orax

household
ammonia

hair
remover

oven
cleaner

milk of
magnesia

BLEACH

NaOH

ome
tacids

soap
solution

nonphosphate
detergents

household
bleach

sodium
hydroxide

Not all changes in matter are chemical changes. Adding heat to ice causes it to change its state. Such a change is a **physical change**–the process of altering the state of something, its appearance, or its combination with substances, but involving no change in electron sharing or giving.

A **mixture** is formed when two substances are combined without chemical bonding. Forming a mixture involves only a physical change. Since they are not chemically bonded, mixtures can be separated by heating or by mechanical methods. Water and sand do not have definite proportions as do chemically bonded compounds. You can have as much or as little sand in your water as you like. Mixtures keep the properties of the components of which they are made, not any of the new properties that would result if the components were united chemically.

Review Questions 2A-1

1. Why is an understanding of chemistry important for an understanding of biology?
2. Define the two components of the physical world.
3. What elements are essential to life? What are their element symbols?
4. Describe an atom. What is the significance of its electron configuration?
5. Name and describe the two primary types of chemical bonding.
6. Define and compare the following: an atom, an ion, a molecule, a compound, a mixture.
7. What things can a scientist determine (a) by studying a molecular (empirical) formula of a compound and (b) by studying a structural formula of a compound?
8. List and compare the characteristics of a chemical change and a physical change.

Facet 2A-1: Acids, Bases, and Buffers, pages 47-49.

1. Describe acid and base; also explain what happens when the two are mixed together.
2. What unit of measurement tells the acidity or alkalinity of a substance? What range of readings indicate an acid solution? an alkaline solution? a neutral solution?
3. What are the causes and effects of acid rain, and why is acid rain a difficult problem to solve?

The effects of acid rain. Some kinds of trees are more acid tolerant than others. If the soil becomes too acidic, they will die.

mineral starvation. As soil pH falls the kinds of organisms in the soil change, and in time the acidity gets so high that few organisms can live in the soil.

In freshwater lakes and streams, acidity causes the bones in many living fish to lose calcium. As muscles pull on the weakened bones, the fish become deformed. The eggs or young of some aquatic animals cannot survive the high acidity. In such places only an adult population of certain organisms exist. When these adults die there will be no replacements. In some beautiful, clear, blue lakes nothing lives except rare forms of algae.

Since what goes up in one country often falls in another, the acid rain problem is international. To be good stewards of the natural resources the Lord has given us, we must be concerned enough to do our part to help solve this environmental problem (see pages 483-97).

Review questions on right.

Energy

Energy can be defined as the ability to do work. For our purposes, there are two types of energy: *kinetic**(kih NET ik) and *potential*. **Kinetic energy** is the energy of motion, such as falling, heat, light, and electricity. **Potential energy** is stored energy, like the energy found in a rock sitting at the top of a cliff, in a log waiting to be burned, or in a battery ready to be connected to a light bulb.

In each of these examples, potential energy can be converted into kinetic energy. Pushing the rock, igniting the log, or connecting the battery will start the change from potential to kinetic energy.

Kinetic energy can also be converted into potential energy. One of the most important conversions to take place on our planet is the one in which green plants absorb light energy from the sun and convert it into the potential chemical energy that is stored in sugar. Later, the plant and other organisms, including humans, will convert the stored chemical energy in sugar into the other forms of energy needed to carry on life.

The laws of thermodynamics*(THUR moh dye NAM icks) are man's statements of how energy

2A-5 *Sunlight is converted from kinetic energy into the stored energy of a sugar molecule by kelp, a large algae.*

changes occur. The *first law of thermodynamics* states that in any process energy is neither created nor destroyed. Energy can change from one form to the other, but there is always as much at the end as there was at the beginning of the process. The *second law of thermodynamics* states that whenever energy is used (changed from one form to the other), some of it is wasted (though not destroyed). That is, not all energy put into something is still there at the end of the transfer. Some of the energy radiates out of the object, usually as heat or light. Eventually this wasted energy goes into space. But because of the vastness of space, all the energy that has gone into it has not yet diminished its darkness or even raised the temperature of outer space to even near the freezing point of water.

A natural corollary, or parallel, to the second law of thermodynamics is the *law of degeneration:* in all natural processes there is a net increase in disorder and a net loss of usable energy. For reactions such as burning a piece of wood, it is easy to see that the end products (carbon dioxide, water vapor, and ashes) contain much less energy and are in a much more random arrangement of molecules than before the burning took place. This increase in randomness and loss of usable energy is an increase in **entropy** (EN truh pee).

---

kinetic: (Gk. KINEIN, to move)

thermodynamics: thermo- or therm- (Gk. THERME, heat) + -dynamics (DUNAMIS, power)

Some reactions, however, appear to contradict the law of degeneration. Green plants use sunlight energy to make sugar from water and carbon dioxide. This conversion of kinetic energy to potential energy and of simple substances to a larger more orderly substance requires more energy than is left in the new molecule, and is a result of the *law of conservation*. This process permits the growth and reproduction of plants.

At first glance, the law of degeneration and the law of conservation appear to be in contradiction. Actually, however, they work in God-ordained harmony. For example, living things build complex substances according to the law of conservation. In time, the living organism will either use the energy stored in the molecule or release the energy in the form of heat or motion. When the organism dies, energy is released as its molecules decompose. The use or release of the energy by the organism is in keeping with the law of degeneration. This balance will be discussed in more detail throughout this text.

Kinetic molecular energy
Are you surprised to be told that each of the molecules that make up this book is wiggling? Unless you are in a room at absolute zero ($-273.15°$ C or $-459.7°$ F), all the molecules which make up the substances around you have a certain amount of heat, the energy of motion. Even solid substances, therefore, are composed of moving molecules.

The amount of heat in a substance determines how fast its molecules are moving and its physical state. In ice, for example, molecular motion is slight; the individual water molecules are barely moving. In liquid water, however, the movement is greater because the substance has more heat. And when water molecules are heated to 100° C (212° F–the boiling point of water), they are so active that they leave the surface of the fluid as water vapor, a gas.

The fresh air you are breathing is an example of a mixture of gases (oxygen, carbon dioxide, nitrogen, water vapor, and others) which are not chemically bonded to one another. At room temperature the moving molecules press against each other, against the walls, and all surrounding objects. If the temperature drops sufficiently (reducing the movement of the molecules), some of the molecules will settle out. First, the water vapor leaves the mixture and condenses. If the temperature drops further, carbon dioxide (heavier than most of the other gases) will begin to form a layer near the floor of the room as its molecules move less and less. If the temperature were low enough and if the pressure were sufficiently increased, carbon dioxide would turn to a liquid, just as the water vapor did. At various lower temperatures the other gases would also become liquids. The mixture of gases called air would then be separated by the physical process of cooling.

Diffusion
Diffusion* is the net movement of molecules from an area of higher concentration of a substance to an area of lower concentration of that substance. *Net movement*, in this definition, means the number of molecules that moved from the higher concentration area *minus* those that moved back into the higher concentration area. When there are no longer places of higher and lower concentrations, a state of **equilibrium*** (EE kwuh LIB ree um) has been reached, and diffusion stops. Let us consider an example.

If a bottle of perfume is left open in the center of a room, the molecules of the perfume will diffuse: they will leave the fluid and enter the air. A few of the molecules of perfume will leave the air and return to the perfume in the bottle. These molecules are going from an area of lower concentration to an area of higher concentration and thus are not part of the diffusion; they are not part of the *net movement*.

At first, the area around the perfume bottle will have a strong odor because this area will have the greatest concentration of perfume molecules. In time, however, even the farthest corners of the room will have perfume molecules. If left alone, the perfume will completely evaporate as all the perfume molecules enter the air, and the entire room will eventually be filled evenly with the scent of the perfume. Equilibrium will have been reached.

---

diffusion: dif- (L. DIS, apart) + -fusion (FUNDERE, to pour)

equilibrium: equi- (L. AEQUUS, equal) + -librium (LIBRA, balance)

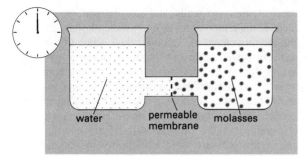

In the above diagram water has been placed on one side of a cloth and molasses on the other. Because the water side has no molasses molecules and the molasses side has relatively few water molecules, the **concentration gradient** (GRAY dee unt) is high for water on one side and high for molasses on the other. The concentration gradient is the difference between the numbers of one type of molecule in two adjacent areas. A high concentration gradient indicates that the difference is very great; a low concentration gradient indicates that there is little difference.

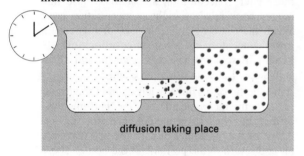

The **diffusion pressure,** based on the relative concentrations of water and molasses molecules, is very high in the above figure. Diffusion occurs rapidly when the diffusion pressure is high. Since the molecules of both water and molasses can easily pass through the cloth, diffusion happens in both directions.

After a period of time, the number of water molecules and the number of molasses molecules on each side even out, and diffusion slows. The individual molecules are not slowing down, though; they continue to move because of the heat they possess. As long as the temperature remains the same, the molecules will continue to move at the same rate. Diffusion slows down as the concentration gradient decreases.

As diffusion continues, the number of molecules moving out of the areas of high concentration approaches the number of molecules moving *into* the areas of high concentration. That is, about the same number of molasses molecules are entering and leaving the molasses side. The same is true for the water molecules. Diffusion, you re-

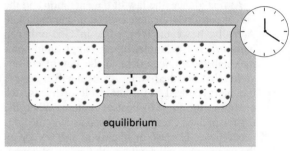

call, is the *net movement*. Although these molecules continue to move, the *gain* in number on the lower concentration side is not as great as it was. As the concentrations of water and molasses get closer, diffusion presssure decreases, and diffusion slows down. In time, equilibrium will be reached.

Osmosis

Suppose that instead of cloth, a membrane having very small pores was placed between the molasses and water in the example of diffusion discussed previously. If the membrane's pores are so small that they will permit the water molecules to pass through but will not permit the larger molasses molecules to pass through, it is a **semipermeable*** (SEM ee PUR mee uh bul) **membrane** (or *selectively permeable membrane*) be-

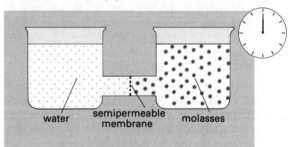

---

semipermeable: semi-
(L. SEMIS, half) + -permeable
(PERMEARE, to pass through)

cause it is permeable to some things but not to others. Living organisms have many selectively permeable membranes.

If the water and molasses are separated by a semipermeable membrane, the concentration gradients for both water and molasses are very high. Water molecules move into the molasses. Diffusion of water molecules through a semipermeable membrane is **osmosis*** (ahz MOH sis). The large molasses molecules, however, are not able to move into the water because of the small size of the pores in the semipermeable membrane. The water level falls as water molecules move to the molasses side, forcing the level higher on the molasses side.

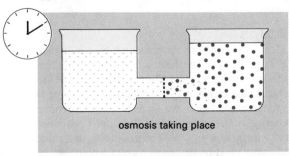

osmosis taking place

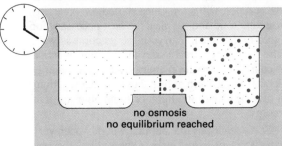

no osmosis
no equilibrium reached

Will this unequal movement of water molecules into the molasses ever produce an equal concentration of molasses and water molecules on each side? That type of equilibrium is impossible in this case. Nor can the water molecules continue going through the membrane until all the water has moved to the molasses side even though a continuous concentration gradient exists because the molasses cannot enter the water. The *net movement* of water molecules into the molasses will decrease. Gravity pulling down on the

molasses side, along with other forces, will in time equalize the diffusion pressure of the water molecules. At that point osmosis, the *net movement* of water molecules through a semipermeable membrane, will cease, even though the concentrations are not equal. Molecules of water will continue to move back and forth across the membrane, but there will be no net gain or loss.

Diffusion and osmosis are two of the most important physical processes that affect organisms. The materials of a cell exist as a colloid inside a semipermeable membrane. The proper concentration of **solutes*** (dissolved substances) inside and outside that membrane is highly critical to the existence of the cell. A good example of this fact is the effect on a person who drinks seawater. The concentration of ions in the salt water is higher than the ionic concentration of substances inside the cells of the human digestive tract. The diffusion of salt ions into, and the osmosis of water out of, these cells soon kills the cells. If too many cells in the digestive system are affected, it can cause serious disorders and even death.

STUDY METHODS BASED ON A FAULTY UNDERSTANDING OF OSMOSIS.

Potential energy of a molecule

The energy required for diffusion and osmosis and the energy which keeps the particles of a solute in solution are kinetic energy. It is the movement of molecules which gives diffusion and osmosis, as well as solutions, many of their qualities. Each molecule, however, also has potential energy held in its chemical bonds. A discussion of chemical reactions is necessary to understand this.

Chemical reactions fall into 2 basic groups: those that require or absorb heat are called *endothermic,** and those that give off heat are called

---

osmosis: osmos- or osmot- (Gk. OSMOS, thrust)   **solute:** (L. SOLUTUS, to loosen)   **endothermic:** endo- (within) + -thermic (heat)

exothermic.* Heat is required to make cake batter solidify into the cake you eat; this is an endothermic reaction. A piece of wood gives off heat (as well as light) as it burns; this reaction is exothermic.

Let the letters "A" and "B" represent two elements or compounds before they chemically react with one another, and let "C" and "D" be the compounds that are the result of the chemical reaction. The reaction would be written like this:

$$A + B \longrightarrow C + D$$

This chemical equation is read, "A plus B yields the products of C plus D." The energy given off or absorbed in a reaction is often represented in a chemical equation. If the reaction between A and B is exothermic–giving off energy–the reaction is written like this:

$$A + B \longrightarrow C + D + energy$$

Assume that the reaction between "W" and "X" requires energy to become "Y" and "Z." This endothermic reaction is written:

$$W + X + energy \longrightarrow Y + Z$$

But where does the energy required for baking a cake (or for any other endothermic reaction) go? In the endothermic reaction above, energy does not appear on the products side of the arrow. Does all the energy therefore escape into the atmosphere? No. The products *contain* some of the energy. From where does the energy given off by a burning piece of wood (or from any other exothermic reaction) come? In an exothermic reaction the energy released was *contained* in the substances that entered the reaction.

Whenever atoms get, give, or share electrons, energy changes occur. Large molecules are usually formed by combining smaller molecules, and this requires energy. Generally, in living things, to have the molecules combined by sharing electrons, energy is supplied to some of those electrons. With the exception of the energy which escapes, the energy supplied is actually still there as chemical bond energy.

Think again of the cake. The substances mixed together to form the batter need to combine in order to become a cake. This requires heat energy.

When molecules break apart, the bond energy is released. When wood burns, the large molecules are being broken down to carbon dioxide, water, and other small molecules. This breaking apart of molecules releases large amounts of energy as heat and light.

In the previous chapter, the need for a constant supply of energy was listed as one of the attributes of life. One of the reasons for this requirement is that living organisms must constantly make large, complex molecules. These molecules are the very substance of the organism itself. The food you eat supplies you not only with the energy you use to move but also with the energy necessary to build the complex molecules which form your cells.

Catalysts

Many reactions are spontaneous; that is, whenever the proper substances contact one another, the reaction immediately takes place. For instance, the combining of sodium and chlorine is spontaneous. Other reactions, however, require energy to start them. Paper does not burn when only oxygen is present. The molecules in a piece of paper must be heated to a certain point before the reaction will start. Once started, this reaction is exothermic and supplies the heat necessary for other molecules to carry on the reaction as well. The heat necessary to start the burning reaction is called the **activation energy.** Activation energy is often in the form of heat, but for other reactions it may be electricity, light, or some other form of energy.

Some reactions like burning wood happen very rapidly, even explosively. Others, like iron and oxygen forming rust, happen slowly. In order to control reactions, scientists use **catalysts*** (KAT uhl ists)–substances which affect the rate of a reaction but are not changed in the reaction. Catalysts seem to affect reactions by changing the activation energy required for the reaction.

Specific chemicals serve as catalysts for specific reactions, so there is not one catalyst for speeding up all reactions and another for slowing down all reactions. Many chemical reactions have no known catalyst. In a chemical equation, the

---

exothermic: exo- (Gk. EXO, outside of) + -thermic (heat)

catalyst: (Gk. KATALUEIN, to dissolve)

FACETS OF BIOLOGY

2A–2

Solutions, Suspensions, and Colloids

Living things are mostly water. The average human body contains 12 gal. of water. The other substances that make up protoplasm are in some way dissolved or suspended in water. The characteristics of the watery combinations that make up living things are vastly different, depending on what is in the water. Some things, like oils and large carbohydrates, do not mix well with water, while others, like sugars and salts, mix very well. Many proteins have some Jell-O-like properties when they are mixed with water.

Solutions

When sugar is dissolved in water, it forms a **solution.** A solution is a

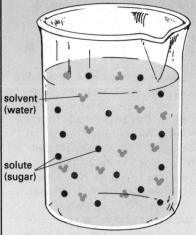

solvent (water)

solute (sugar)

A solution of sugar water

homogeneous* (HOH muh JEE nee us) mixture of one or more substances in another substance. A homogeneous mixture is one that is the same throughout. The sugar

molecules, for example, are small enough to be separated by water molecules. The sugar will not settle out, and the mixture will be homogeneous. Sugar water is, therefore, a solution.

The substance which is dissolved (sugar) is called the **solute,** and the substance in which it is dissolved (water) is called the **solvent.** Solutes are generally made of ions or small molecules, and often several different solutes will be in a single solution. Because water is the solvent in many solutions it is sometimes called the *universal solvent.*

The quantity and kinds of solutes in water are significant for aquatic organisms. Freshwater has fewer solutes than salt water. Most freshwater organisms if put in salt water will have problems with the higher solute concentration, and many will die. The reverse is true when putting saltwater organisms in fresh water.

Organisms must also maintain a specific internal solute/solvent ratio. Any injection into your blood stream must have the same solute/solvent ratio as your blood or your tissues may be damaged. When a person is fed by putting sugar into his blood stream the solute/solvent ratio of sugar and water going in must be the same as his blood or he may die.

Solutions put into a person's blood must have the same concentration of solutes as blood.

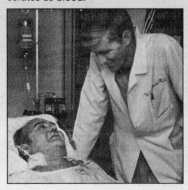

homogeneous: homo- or homeo- (Gk. HOMOIOS, same) + -geneous (GENOS, stock, race, or kind)

Suspensions

A **suspension*** can be made by placing flour in water. After the mixture is stirred, flour is suspended in the water; but if the mixture is allowed to stand, the flour will soon settle to the bottom. In a suspension the molecules of the suspended material do not form a homogeneous mixture. They are so large that the molecular movement of the solvent is not sufficient to keep them up; so they settle to the bottom.

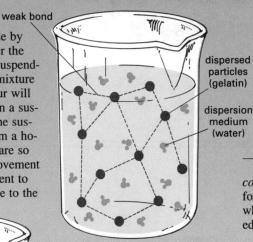

weak bond

dispersed particles (gelatin)

dispersion medium (water)

A colloid in gel phase

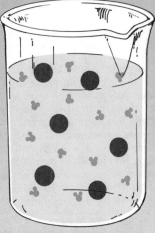

A suspension of flour water

Some of the substances and structures in protoplasm are suspended particles. Living protoplasm is constantly moving which keeps the solution "stirred up" and the particles suspended.

Colloids

Protoplasm itself, however, is not just a solution with some suspended materials in it. Protoplasm is a specialized mixture called a **colloid.*** The size of the particles of a colloid is somewhere between

that of the particles in a true solution and the particles in a suspension. In a colloid the solvent is properly called the *dispersion medium,* and the solute makes up the *dispersed particles.* In a colloid the dispersed particles are not small enough to be a solution nor large enough to settle out quickly. Colloids are often in one of two different stages: the semisolid state called the **gel phase** or the fluid state called the **sol phase.**

Gelatin mixed in water (such as in Jell-O) is a common colloid which is affected by temperature. Lower temperature causes the gelatin's dispersed particles to line up and form weak bonds. The gelatin becomes a semisolid gel. Heat breaks the bonds between the particles, and the colloid enters the sol phase. In other colloids, substances such as salt or factors such as pressure, pH, or concentration of other ions can change the substance from one phase to another.

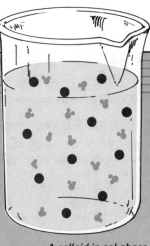

A colloid in sol phase

Gelatin is a *reversible phase colloid:* it can change back and forth between sol and gel. Egg white is a colloid that, when heated, is changed into the gel phase.

But egg white is a *nonreversible phase colloid:* once the dispersed particles have become bonded and it is a gel, it does not return to the sol phase.

All living materials are colloids. The protoplasm that makes up a cell is a complex reversible phase colloid. This can be easily demonstrated. Put your hand over a muscle and flex the muscle. The firmness you feel is the gel phase of your muscle colloid. Now relax. The muscle enters the sol phase.

Temperature and many other factors can change the protoplasmic colloid from one phase to another. Electric shock causes muscles to become gels and forces your body to jerk as it does so. Heat can cause the protoplasmic colloid to enter the sol phase.

Review questions on next page.

---

suspension: sus- (L. SUB-, under) + -pension (L. PENDERE, to hang)

colloid: coll- (Gk. KOLLA, glue) + -oid (EIDOS, form or shape)

catalyst is indicated over the arrow. A chemical reaction for which much energy is required is written:

$$A + B + \textbf{Energy} \longrightarrow C + D$$

With a catalyst the same reaction might look like this:

$$A + B + energy \xrightarrow{\text{catalyst x}} C + D$$

You have often heard of a person "burning" up his food or "burning" off fat. You may have thought these expressions were merely figures of speech, but they are accurate. The food you eat is combined with oxygen for the release of energy, almost as if you had set your food on fire. The

difference, which prevents you from cooking yourself as you digest your dinner, is a complex system of organic catalysts. These catalysts lower the activation energy required for the reaction and slow down the reaction so that the energy is released in small, usable amounts. The process could be written like this:

Food burning: $O + P \longrightarrow \textbf{ENERGY} + Y + Z$

Digestion: $O + P \xrightarrow{\text{catalyst a}} energy + Q + R$
$Q + R \xrightarrow{\text{catalyst b}} energy + S + T$
$S + T \xrightarrow{\text{catalyst c}} energy + U + V$
$U + V \xrightarrow{\text{catalyst d}} energy + W + X$
$W + X \xrightarrow{\text{catalyst e}} energy + Y + Z$

Biological Terms

chemistry	ionic bonding	*Energy*	semipermeable	neutralize	colloid
Matter	covalent bonding	energy	membrane	pH	gel phase
matter	compound	kinetic energy	osmosis	buffer	sol phase
element	molecular formula	potential energy	solute	acid rain	
atom	structural formula	entropy	activation energy	solution	
proton	molecule	diffusion	catalyst	homogeneous	
neutron	chemical change	equilibrium	*Facet*	solute	
electron	physical change	concentration gradient	acid	solvent	
ion	mixture	diffusion pressure	base	suspension	

Review Questions 2A-2

1. Name, describe, and give examples of two basic forms of energy.
2. What are the first and second laws of thermodynamics?
3. Describe how heat affects the molecules of a substance.
4. Describe diffusion and give two examples of how it occurs in the home.
5. List two main differences between diffusion and osmosis.
6. Where does the energy needed for the movement of molecules in diffusion and osmosis come from?
7. According to the heat energy involved, what are the two basic types of chemical reactions?
8. List two attributes of a catalyst.

Facet 2A-2: Solutions, Suspensions, and Colloids, pages 55-56.

1. List and compare the characteristics of a solution, a suspension, and a colloid.
2. What is meant by a reversible phase colloid and a nonreversible phase colloid?

Thought Questions

1. Give an example of the law of conservation and the law of degeneration working opposite each other.
2. Does the death of an organism result in increased or decreased entropy? Explain.
3. Give two reasons living things need energy and describe how they illustrate the law of conservation.
4. List several examples of diffusion and several examples of osmosis.
5. When something diffuses to the state of equilibrium, is that an example of an increase in entropy? Explain.
6. Does a catalyst help or hinder an increase in entropy? Explain.

2B–Organic Chemistry

Living organisms make **organic** compounds. Many of these compounds are very large, complex molecules. Though some of the simpler ones are synthesized in laboratories, under normal circumstances most organic compounds are the result of **biosynthesis,*** the putting together of substances by living things.

Biosynthesis is essential to life. If a sculptor wants his statue to be larger, he adds more clay, bronze, or whatever makes up his statue. But if a living organism is to grow, it cannot just apply more of the material of which it is made. You do not spread layers of raw meat on your body in order to increase your physical size. That meat must be broken down into its component parts (digested) and then put back together so that it is your flesh, not the flesh of some other organism.

Headlines occasionally say that life has been created in a test tube. Those misleading headlines are written to get attention. A close reading of the article (if it is written accurately) reveals that the new development falls far short of creating life in a test tube. Usually a scientist has simply manufactured another organic compound in the laboratory. Examination often reveals that an elaborate apparatus was used. To duplicate biosynthesis–even of small organic substances–man must use large amounts of energy and special procedures and equipment. Each time a scientist employs sophisticated techniques to synthesize an organic compound, he indicates how unlikely it is that life could *spontaneously* generate in a test tube, much less in a legendary prehistoric pond.

Not only must *one* organic compound be made, but literally thousands of different ones must be made in large quantities, all at the same time (for many of them are very unstable), and all in the same place. Then they have to be given life. Will life just happen if all the chemicals are right? Even those scientists who attempt to create life in a test tube admit that their chemicals need some special "starting" force. In the evolutionist's prehistoric pond, a bolt of lightning is supposed to have started life. Regardless of thunderbolts or special startings, life is more than the proper

2B-1 *Chemistry is a vital part of biology.*

alignment of the correct chemicals. **Vitalism*** is the theory that life is more than the chemicals which make up living things.

Is it possible for a living thing to be assembled from nonliving substances in a laboratory? At the time of this writing it has not been done. Many people who believe in vitalism believe it cannot be done. Life, the Scriptures tell us, is the creation of God. But the Bible does not tell us that man will not be able to put together a living thing. If, by using elaborate equipment and special manmade chemicals, scientists do form a structure that can be considered alive, does this support spontaneous generation and evolution? No. The use of the equipment, the manmade chemicals, and man's intelligence to form the living structure actually support the concept of a special creation of life by God, not a happenstance origin of life.

Organic compounds

Organic chemistry is often called carbon chemistry. Every organic compound has carbon in it, usually in conjunction with large quantities of hydrogen, and frequently with oxygen. Carbon, having only four electrons in its outermost shell, can form bonds with four other atoms. Often these

---

biosynthesis: bio- (life) + -synthesis (Gk. SUNTITHENAI, to put together)

vitalism: (L. VITA, life)

FACETS OF BIOLOGY

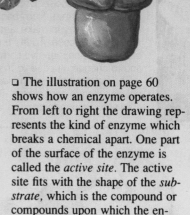

Enzymes - The Keys to Life

To some people **enzymes*** are those things which digest their food and somehow eat dirt in their laundry. It is true that a series of digestive enzymes break down foods to soluble nutrients that can be carried in your blood. Also, enzymes produced by various bacteria are used in detergents to break apart types of "grease and grime" so that they can be carried away in rinse water. Enzymes are even used in paper making, medicines, manufacturing textiles, clearing fruit juices, making sugars, forming cheeses, baking bread, tenderizing meats, and making soft-centered candy.

All living things must carry on thousands of chemical reactions, each one requiring or giving off energy. Living things must repeat these reactions many times. The amount of energy given off by the total of some of these reactions would cook the organism. Other reactions would require the heat of a flame to have them happen. Enzymes permit these reactions without the dangerous energy levels.

Generally, enzymes are proteins which serve as *organic catalysts*. By affecting the activation energy, catalysts slow down or speed up chemical reactions. Enzymes affect the energy levels needed or given off by chemical reactions in living things.

❑ The illustration on page 60 shows how an enzyme operates. From left to right the drawing represents the kind of enzyme which breaks a chemical apart. One part of the surface of the enzyme is called the *active site*. The active site fits with the shape of the *substrate*, which is the compound or compounds upon which the enzyme will react. The combination

Characteristics of Enzymes

❑ *Enzymes are proteins.* Although there are exceptions, most enzymes are proteins. Proteins as enzymes are discussed on pages 64-65.

❑ *Enzymes are highly specific.* The enzyme that catalyzes the reactions between two sugar molecules will deal only with those two sugar molecules or with molecules that are almost identical to them.

❑ *Many enzymes require energy to perform their functions.* Without the proper supply of energy, enzyme reactions cease; therefore, life ceases.

❑ *Many enzymes release energy as they perform their functions.* Normally, the amount of energy released in a single enzymatic reaction is small. This energy can therefore be trapped and temporarily stored for use in reactions that require energy. Because the amount of energy released during enzymatic reactions is controlled, cells are not destroyed by too much heat energy being released at one time.

❑ *Enzymes often require coenzymes.* All **coenzymes** are nonprotein substances which fit into or affect the active site so that it accepts the substrate properly. Without an adequate supply of coenzymes, enzymes do not function. Some important coenzymes are vitamins.

❑ *Enzyme action is affected by heat, radiation, pH, chemicals, and other things.* Any of these can cause the enzyme to function improperly or not at all, thereby causing illness or death.

❑ *Enzymes most often work in series.* A molecule of sugar, for example, is broken down by dozens of different enzymes in succession. Each one may break off or add an atom or molecule or change the shape of the substrate.

enzyme: en- (Gk. EN-, in) + -zyme (ZUME, leaven)

Enzymes That Make Soft Drinks Sweet

Enzymes are used commercially in the making of soft drinks. Glucose, the most widely available sugar, is not sweet enough to satisfy human taste buds. Fructose, a different arrangement of the same atoms found in glucose, tastes twice as sweet as glucose. Until scientists found ways to obtain enzymes from bacteria, there was no economical way to make large quantities of fructose from glucose. Today enzymes are used to break down inexpensive corn starch into glucose and to change glucose to fructose.

The first enzyme, α-amylase, breaks apart the polysaccharide corn starch. This makes the thick corn syrup much thinner because the molecules which make up the solution are shorter. Next, the enzyme glucoamylase breaks apart the long chain of glucose molecules which make up corn starch. The fluid becomes a solution of glucose in water. The third enzyme, glucose isomerase, converts the glucose to fructose. This process is continued until there are about equal amounts of each in the solution.

The fructose-glucose solution can then be added directly to soft drinks or other foods. Each year the United States soft-drink industry saves over $1 billion by using sweeteners made from domestic corn rather than importing other forms of sugar.

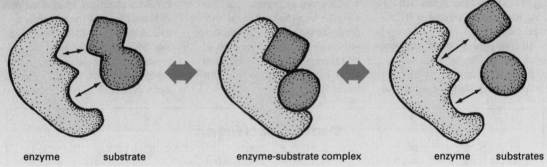

enzyme   substrate   enzyme-substrate complex   enzyme   substrates

of the enzyme and substrate is called the *enzyme-substrate complex*. While they are together, the enzyme breaks the substrate apart. The changed substrate is called the *product*. Notice that the enzyme is unchanged at the end. It has merely helped the reaction to take place.

❑ For most enzymes the process is reversible. In other words, the illustration can also be read from right to left. In that case the enzyme would put two substances together to form a larger product. Often it is the concentration of the substrate that determines whether the enzyme puts the substance together or takes it apart. If there is an abundance of the small molecules, the enzyme will put them together; if there are more of the large molecules, the enzyme will take them apart.

Enzymes are the essential keys to life. Every reaction a living thing carries on is catalyzed by an enzyme. Every organic substance that makes up an organism is manufactured by enzymes. The larger and more complex the structures of an organism are, the more enzymes it must be able to produce and the larger the quantity of each kind of enzyme it must have. But even the smallest organisms must be able to produce thousands of different enzymes and thousands of copies of each just to remain alive.

Review questions on next page.

bonds involve other carbon atoms in chains or rings, which form the backbone of most organic molecules. Sometimes a carbon atom will form two bonds with the same carbon atom to form a double bond. Occasionally two atoms will even form a triple bond. In the cholesterol molecule below, the carbon backbone has been drawn in red. The double-bonded carbon atoms have two

2B-2 *A cholesterol molecule with its carbon backbone in red*

lines drawn between them. Note the carbon rings and the carbon chain.

Organic compounds perform various functions for living organisms and can be categorized as follows:

❑ *Structural:* those compounds that are used as building blocks of a cellular or extracellular structure;

❑ *Enzymatic:* those compounds that are **enzymes** or that help enzymes in their functions; and

❑ *Storage:* those compounds that store either energy, substances, or information for future use.

Many organic compounds perform combinations of these functions.

The large number and variety of organic compounds make grouping them difficult. They are often classified into four main groups: carbohydrates, lipids, proteins, and nucleic acids.

Review Questions 2B-1

1. List several attributes of organic compounds which distinguish them from inorganic compounds.
2. What chemical element is found in all organic compounds?
3. List three functions an organic compound may have in living organisms.

Facet 2B-1: Enzymes-The Keys to Life, pages 59-60

1. List several characteristics of enzymes.
2. Why is it accurate to say that enzymes are essential to physical life?

Carbohydrates

Carbohydrates (KAR boh HYE drates) are organic compounds that contain carbon, hydrogen, and oxygen. They have the same ratio of hydrogen to oxygen as water does: twice as many hydrogen atoms as oxygen atoms. Carbohydrates are both structural and energy storage compounds.

Simple sugars

The basic units of carbohydrates are **monosaccharides*** (MAHN nuh SAK uh RIDES), simple sugars. A monosaccharide may contain as few as 3 carbon atoms. The monosaccharides that contain 5 or 6 carbon atoms are most important as building blocks of

other organic compounds. A common 5-carbon sugar is *ribose,* a component of nucleic acids.

Glucose* (a most common simple sugar manufactured by plants) is a 6-carbon sugar that is transported to the cells by the blood in humans. Two other simple 6-carbon sugars are important in biology: *galactose** and *fructose.**

2B-3

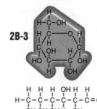

glucose

galactose

fructose

---

monosaccharide: mono- (Gk. MONOS, single) + -saccharide (L. SACCHARUM, sugar)

glucose: (Gk. GLUKUS, sweet)

galactose: galact- (Gk. GALAKT-, milk) + -ose (Fr. -OSE, carbohydrate or sugar)

fructose: fruct- (L. FRUCTUS, fruit) + -ose (sugar)

2B-4 *Forming monosaccharides and disaccharides*

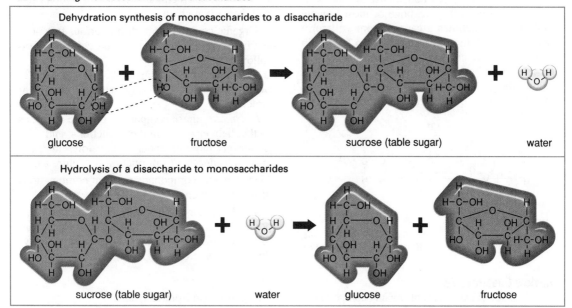

Dehydration synthesis of monosaccharides to a disaccharide

glucose   fructose   sucrose (table sugar)   water

Hydrolysis of a disaccharide to monosaccharides

sucrose (table sugar)   water   glucose   fructose

Monosaccharides can be joined together by enzymes to form a **disaccharide*** (dye SAK uh RIDE). In figure 2B-4 a glucose and a fructose molecule are combining by **dehydration* synthesis** (DEE hye DRAY shun ◊ SIN thuh sis). The glucose molecule loses a hydroxyl group (-OH) from one of its carbon atoms. The fructose gives up a hydrogen atom. The reaction gives off a water molecule and combines the glucose and fructose molecules to form the disaccharide **sucrose,*** the common sugar found in most foods and often called table sugar.

Because the process gives off a water molecule, it is a *dehydration* reaction. Because two substances are put together to form another substance, the reaction is called a *synthesis*. Two glucose molecules can combine by dehydration synthesis to form *maltose* (malt sugar); glucose and galactose form *lactose** (milk sugar).

When a cell needs the monosaccharides from which a disaccharide is made, enzymes will combine with the disaccharide and a water molecule. The two monosaccharides separate, the water molecule is broken down, and the hydrogen and hydroxyl group are attached to the appropriate carbon atoms of the monosaccharides. This process is termed **hydrolysis*** (hye DRAHL ih sis) because a large molecule is broken down by adding a water molecule.

Polysaccharides

A **polysaccharide*** (PAHL ee SAK uh RIDE) is a large, complex bonding of monosaccharides. Using specific enzymes, living things can build up or break down polysaccharides. Three types are particularly significant:

❑ **Starch** is one of the primary substances plants store as food. Corn starch and potato starch, as well as starches found in wheat, rice, and other grains, constitute the major source of food energy for humans.

❑ **Glycogen** is often called animal starch. The starches a person eats are broken down to simple sugars and, along with the other sugars in his diet, are then taken to the liver where they are made into glycogen for temporary storage. Glycogen is a branching chain of glucose molecules.

---

disaccharide: di- (Gk. DI, two) + -saccharide (sugar)

dehydration: de- (L. DE, from) + -hydra-, or -hydro- tion (Gk. HUDOR, water)

sucrose: sucr- (Fr. SUCRE, sugar) + -ose (sugar)

lactose: lact- (L. LACT-, milk) + -ose (sugar)

hydrolysis: hydra- or hydro- (water) + -lysis (Gk. LUSIS, a loosening)

 ❑ **Cellulose** (SEL yuh LOHS) molecules are much larger than starch molecules. They are made of long chains of glucose molecules bonded in an alternating arrangement. The long cellulose molecules account for the strength of plant cell walls. Plant fibers that form cotton, wood, paper, and many other products contain large quantities of cellulose.

Cellulose is nondigestible to most animals because they do not have the proper enzymes for breaking apart the bonds between its glucose molecules. The energy contained in the glucose molecules that make up cellulose is not directly available to animals. Cellulose is a primary part of the nondigestible portion of our diet called *bulk* or *roughage*. Certain bacteria, fungi, and protozoans, however, do produce enzymes for digesting cellulose.

Review Questions 2B-2

1. What substances make up carbohydrates? What characteristics do carbohydrates have?
2. Compare and contrast hydrolysis and dehydration synthesis.
3. List several monosaccharides, several disaccharides, and several polysaccharides.

Lipids

Lipids* are a group of organic substances which are only slightly soluble in water but are very soluble in organic solvents such as alcohol, ether, acetone, and chloroform. Lipids are most often structural, but they also store energy. A gram of lipid contains much more potential energy for organisms than does a gram of carbohydrate. Because lipids occupy less space than starches, animals store their excess energy as lipids. Plants, however, add to their size by storing starches.

Fats

The most abundant lipids are **fats**, and two fatlike substances, oils and waxes. Fat molecules consist of three *fatty acid molecules* bonded to the 3 carbon atoms of a 3-carbon alcohol called *glycerol* (glycerin). As each fatty acid molecule bonds to the glycerol molecule, a water molecule is released. Fat molecules are formed by a *dehydration synthesis* reaction. Fats can, of course, be broken apart by *hydrolysis* with proper enzymes. Fats are generally found in animal tissues and in dairy products.

The fatty acids of living things are chains usually composed of 14-18 carbon atoms. Fatty acid molecules can be broken into many 2-carbon molecule pieces. Each of these molecules may eventually release usable cellular energy, making fatty acids a good energy source.

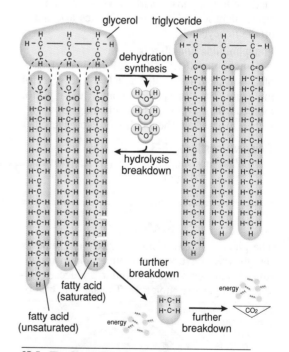

2B-5 *The formation of a fat (triglyceride) from fatty acids and glycerol. A comparison of saturated and unsaturated fatty acids.*

polysaccharide: poly- (Gk. POLUS, many) + -saccharide (sugar)

lipids: (Gk. LIPOS, fat)

If each of the carbon atoms in a fatty acid molecule (except the end ones) has 2 hydrogens attached to it, the fatty acid is *saturated*. If one or more of the carbon atoms are double bonded, not permitting as many hydrogen atoms to be attached to the carbon chain, the fatty acid is *unsaturated*. The double-bonded carbons of an unsaturated fat require additional enzymes to break apart. The controversy regarding the nutritional value of saturated and unsaturated fats results from this difference in the number of hydrogen atoms that the fatty acids of a fat molecule contain.

Lipids that are liquid at room temperature are called *oils*. Corn oil, olive oil, peanut oil, and coconut oil are examples of vegetable oils. *Waxes* result when several fatty acids join to alcohols made of long chains of carbon. Waxes commonly cover plant leaves and stems. Waxes also make up the honeycomb.

Phospholipids and sterols

A **phospholipid** (FAHS foh LIP id) is composed of 2 fatty acid molecules attached to a glycerol molecule. The third carbon atom of the glycerol molecule has a phosphate-containing group attached to it. Most phospholipids also have other

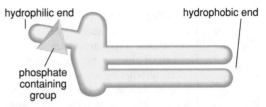

2B-6 *A phospholipid*

substances attached to them. *Lecithin* (LES uh thin), a common phospholipid, is a major component of cellular membranes.

Phospholipids, like all fatty acids, have a *hydrophilic** (HYE druh FIL ik) end and a *hydrophobic** (HYE druh FOH bik) end. If a phospholipid is dropped on the surface of water, the molecules will align themselves with the hydrophilic ends in the water and the hydrophobic ends away from the water. This characteristic is important in the forming of cell membranes, which is discussed later.

Sterols are made of 4 carbon rings and a side chain of carbons. They often combine with other substances to form hormones and other compounds. *Cholesterol,* a common sterol, is found along with phospholipids in the membranes of animals and human cells.

Review Questions 2B-3
1. What substances make up a lipid? What characteristics do lipids have?
2. List several lipids.

Proteins

The glucose in one plant is exactly the same as the glucose in every other plant and in every animal. No matter where you find it, a glucose molecule is a glucose molecule. The same is true of

all carbohydrates and lipids (fats) as well. The amounts may vary, but the carbohydrates and lipids in an organism are just like the same carbohydrates or lipids in any other organism. Proteins, however, are different.

2B-7 *The formation of a polypeptide chain of amino acids*

amino acid —

peptide bonds

dehydration synthesis

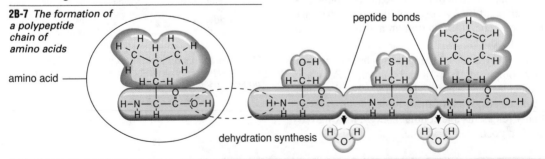

hydrophilic: hydro- (water) + -philic (Gk. PHILEIN, to love)

hydrophobic: hydro- (water) + -phobic (Gk. PHOBOS, fear)

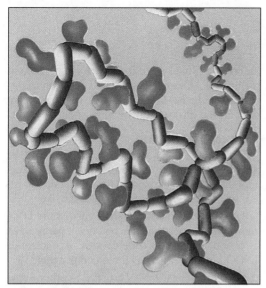

2B-8 *The twisting and bonding of a polypeptide chain of amino acids gives it a three-dimensional shape, which is characteristic of proteins.*

Although there is overlapping of the types of proteins in organisms, many proteins are different in each group and even in each individual organism. For example, human insulin, a protein that helps in food metabolism, is virtually identical to the insulin found in animals. Human hair protein, on the other hand, is different from the protein found in animal hair. Yet despite the fact that one person's hair proteins are similar to another's, they are not identical. Proteins, it may be said, are the things that make you unique.

Proteins come in a wide variety and are used either as enzymes or as structural building blocks. Some are very small, but some are large enough to be seen under high-powered microscopes.

Proteins consist primarily of carbon, hydrogen, oxygen, and nitrogen; but they sometimes include phosphorus, sulfur, and a few other elements. The basic building blocks of a protein are **amino** (uh MEE NOH) **acids.** There are about 20 different amino acids. An amino acid contains an amino group ($-NH_2$) and a carboxyl group ($-COOH$), both attached to a carbon. Different side groups (some simple, others complex) attach to the carbon of the amino acid. As few as 50 or as many as several thousand amino acids can line up in a specific sequence to make a protein.

When 2 amino acids line up and the proper enzymes are present, dehydration synthesis occurs, removing a water molecule and forming a *peptide** (PEP TIDE) *bond*. A peptide bond is one which links the carboxyl and the amino groups of two amino acids. A protein, then, begins as a **polypeptide** (PAHL lee PEP TIDE) **chain** of amino acids.

When the proper sequence of amino acids is arranged, the chain twists and then folds back upon itself. Certain amino acids bond together in a specific pattern that is determined by the sequence of the acids. The polypeptide chain of amino acids now has a 3-dimensional arrangement. It is this shape that forms the active sites of enzyme proteins.

If some of the amino acids are out of sequence, the shape of the protein molecule may be altered. Should this change of shape affect the active site of an enzyme, the enzyme may not react properly with the substrate. Heat, radiation, ion concentrations, and other factors can also affect the bonding of amino acids to other parts of the amino acid chain. When the bonds break between the amino acids that give the protein its three-dimensional shape, the shape of the protein molecule may change. If this change affects the active site of an enzyme, it may no longer function as an enzyme. The ability of a protein to fit in as a cellular building block may also be affected by these changes in shape.

Proteins often work together with other proteins or other substances. Enzyme proteins may require coenzymes in order to function. Some proteins combine with lipids, carbohydrates, or even other proteins to form a structural component. Hemoglobin, the red pigment in human blood which carries oxygen, is made of 4 polypeptide chains. Attached to each chain is an iron-containing heme group. Many hormones are lipids joined with proteins.

Review Questions 2B-4
1. Describe the relationship between amino acids and proteins.
2. What gives a protein molecule its 3-dimensional shape?

---

peptide: (Gk. PEPTEIN, to digest)

polypeptide: poly- (many) + -peptide (to digest)

Nucleic Acids

Although scientists have long known that proteins are different in various organisms, they did not discover until just before World War I that **nucleic** (noo KLEE ik) **acids,** not proteins, are the material of heredity. In other words, to transmit its characteristics to another cell, a cell must pass nucleic acids to that cell.

Nucleic acids, found in the nucleus* (NOO klee us), direct the activities of a cell by guiding the formation of both structural and enzymatic proteins. Because they contain the information necessary for the manufacture of the organism's proteins, nucleic acids determine its characteristics. In other words, nucleic acids form *genes.* The way the nucleic acids direct protein manufacture and the exact method of transmitting this information to the next generation of cells are important concepts for later chapters. At this point we shall examine what nucleic acids are.

DNA, deoxyribonucleic (dee AHK see RYE boh noo KLEE ik) acid is the primary nucleic acid in most organisms. About the time of World War II, scientists analyzed the components of DNA but were confused about their exact arrangement. To determine how DNA functions, it was necessary to form a working model of its components. In 1953, James D. Watson, an American biologist, and F. H. C. Crick, a British biophysicist, assembled information about DNA's components. Using information obtained from X-rays of DNA, they created a DNA model. Watson and Crick

2B-9
*Watson
and Crick
in the 1950s*

received a Nobel prize in 1962 for their accomplishment. Although since then it has been slightly modified, the basic model is still consistent with all the information we have about DNA.

The structure of DNA

Watson and Crick's model is a double helix, or spiral, consisting of two strands attached at regular intervals. Visualizing a flexible ladder, twisted, gives a good idea of what it looks like.

For study purposes we shall untwist the DNA molecule and examine its component parts. DNA is a double chain of **nucleotides.** A nucleotide (NOO klee uh TIDE) has three components:

❏ *sugar* (the sugar in DNA is the 5-carbon sugar deoxyribose),

❏ *phosphate* (the phosphate in a nucleotide is a small molecule made of phosphorus and oxygen atoms), and a

❏ *base* (each nucleotide will have one of these four bases: *adenine, thymine, guanine,* or *cytosine*).

The nucleotides line up so that the sugars and phosphates form one long side piece of the ladder, and the bases point off to one side, forming one half of each rung (step) of the ladder. The other half of the ladder is likewise formed by nucleotides.

Figure 2B-10 illustrates a typical DNA molecule. Note carefully the bases. Each adenine is bonded with a thymine by 2 hydrogen bonds, and each cytosine is bonded with a guanine by 3 hydrogen bonds. When there is a thymine on one side, there is an adenine on the other; and when there is a guanine on one side, there is a cytosine on the other.

DNA replication

The sequence of the bases in the DNA molecule can be compared to the sequence of letters in this sentence. In one order the letters make words and have meaning. In another order they may make different words and mean something else. In other arrangements the letters may make words in another language, or they may be senseless. The sequence of bases in DNA is the code which, through a series of steps, directs the sequence of

nucleus: nucle- or nucleo- (L. NUX, central part)

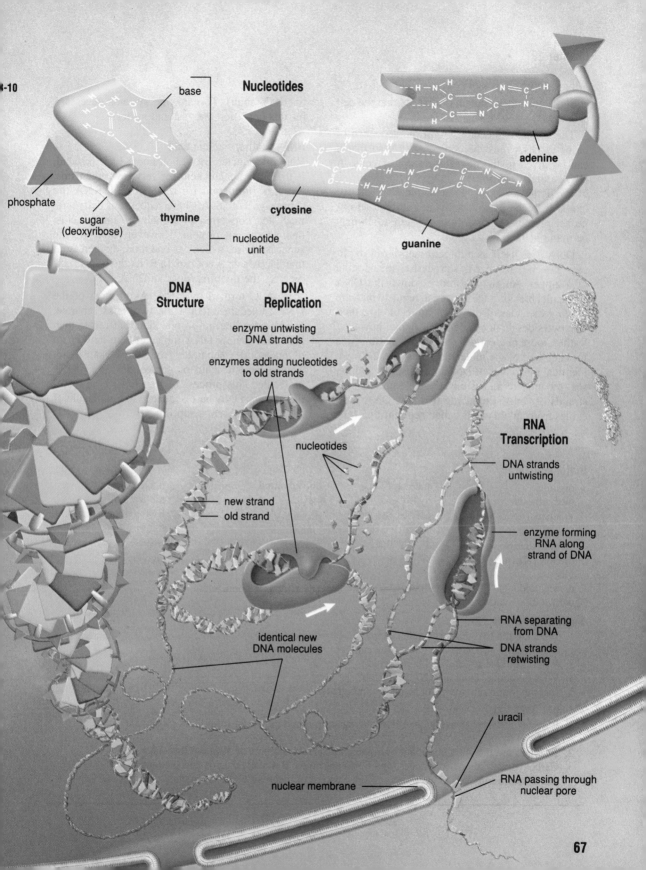

Nucleotides

base

phosphate

sugar (deoxyribose)

thymine

nucleotide unit

cytosine

guanine

adenine

DNA Structure

DNA Replication

enzyme untwisting DNA strands

enzymes adding nucleotides to old strands

nucleotides

new strand

old strand

identical new DNA molecules

RNA Transcription

DNA strands untwisting

enzyme forming RNA along strand of DNA

RNA separating from DNA

DNA strands retwisting

uracil

RNA passing through nuclear pore

nuclear membrane

amino acids in the protein molecules that the cell produces.

The message encoded within the sequence of bases in DNA must be copied *exactly* so that it can be given to the next generation of cells. A DNA molecule must be able to make a duplicate of itself that is exact, even to the *sequence* of bases. If the base sequence is not correct, an improper protein–or possibly no protein at all–may be manufactured.

DNA uses itself as a direct blueprint in duplicating itself. Visualize this process as the opening of a zipper. An enzyme moves down the DNA molecule, breaking the hydrogen bonds which are holding the sides of the DNA molecule together. The two sides do not close like a zipper, however. Rather, loose nucleotides replace the missing side for each half of the molecule. There are then two identical molecules of DNA. The sequence of bases is complete and is exactly the same in both strands of DNA. Producing two new DNA molecules from an old one is called **replication*** (REP

lih KAY shun). The enzyme systems necessary for this operation are vast and intricate.

RNA–another nucleic acid

RNA, ribonucleic (RYE boh noo KLEE ik) acid, is the basic nucleic acid for very few organisms, but it is important for all. Through RNA the "message" of DNA's base sequence is delivered, read, and converted to a chain of amino acids, thus producing protein. However, in RNA the sugar is ribose, which has one more oxygen atom than DNA's deoxyribose. In RNA the base *uracil* replaces the thymine found in DNA.

RNA is formed by DNA. As an area of the DNA molecule uncoils, the two sides separate. Nucleotides line up on one side, but rather than becoming a new DNA molecule, the new chain of nucleotides separates from the DNA strand. This separated chain of nucleotides is an RNA molecule. This process of transferring the complementary DNA base sequence to a molecule of RNA is called **transcription.***

Biological Terms

organic	sucrose	phospholipid	nucleotide
biosynthesis	hydrolysis	*Proteins*	replication
vitalism	polysaccharide	protein	RNA (ribonucleic acid)
Carbohydrates	starch	amino acid	transcription
carbohydrate	glycogen	polypeptide chain	
monosaccharide	cellulose		*Facet*
glucose		*Nucleic Acids*	enzyme
disaccharide	*Lipids*	nucleic acid	coenzyme
dehydration synthesis	lipid	DNA (deoxyribonucleic	
	fat	acid)	

Review Questions 2B-5

1. What are the two primary nucleic acids?
2. Describe the structure of a DNA molecule.
3. What is unique about a DNA molecule?
4. What is unique about an RNA molecule?
5. List the four main groups of organic compounds.

Thought Questions

1. If a scientist were to assemble a living thing from nonliving parts, would this disprove the Bible? Why or why not?
2. Enzymes are the most important of organic chemicals. Support or disprove this statement.
3. Carbohydrates are carbohydrates, and lipids are lipids. But nucleic acids and proteins they manufacture truly constitute the organism. Support or disprove these statements.

---

replication: re- (L. RE-, back) + -plication (PLICARE, to fold)

transcription: trans- (L. TRANS, across) + -scription (SCRIBERE, to write)

INTRODUCTION TO CELLS
CYTOLOGY PART I

3A – The Structure of Cells
   page 69

3B – The Living State of Cells
   page 83

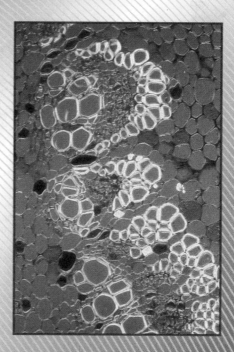

THREE

3A–The Cellular Structure

Cytology* (sye TAHL uh jee), the study of cells, can be traced back 300 years to the English scientist Robert Hooke. In 1665 he published *Micrographia,* a report of his use of simple compound microscopes capable of magnifying only about thirty times. He described his observation of a thin slice of cork: the neat rows of little boxes reminded him of rows of cells in a prison or a monastery; he therefore named what he was looking at "cells." Although Hooke saw only the dead, empty walls of those "boxes," and we now know that those boxes have vastly different sizes, shapes, and arrangements in other organisms, they are still called *cells.**

At first the walls or boundaries of cells were of interest, primarily because they were almost all that man could see. As microscopes and microtechniques improved, however, scientists recognized the contents of the cell as the primary substances of living organisms. In 1840 J. E. Purkinje first used the term **protoplasm*** (PROH tuh PLAZ um) to refer to the entire substance of cells.

---

cytology: cyto- (Gk. KUTOS, hollow or cell) + -logy, -logi, or -logo (Gk. LOGOS, word, *hence, the study of*)

cells: (L. CELLAE, chambers)

protoplasm: proto- (Gk. PROTOS, first) + -plasm (PLASSEIN, to mold)

3A-1 *In 1665 Robert Hook used the microscope illustrated to draw cork cells (inset).*

Although it had been recognized before, in 1833 Robert Brown set apart the *nucleus** as a special structure found in all cells. His and other studies attached significance to the role of nuclei during cellular division and to the nuclei of egg and sperm cells.

The year 1838 brought a startling and daring statement from a German botanist, Matthias Schleiden (SHLY den). After observing much botanical material under the microscope, he said that all plants are composed of cells. Most scientists who did not use microscopes ridiculed him. But the next year Theodore Schwann (SHVAHN), a German zoologist, made a similar statement about animals.

The Cell Theory

After 200 years of investigation, the **cell theory** was formulated in the late 1800s. Continued research in cytology in the past 100 years, including recent discoveries, have confirmed the scientific accuracy of the three basic principles of the cell theory.

❑ Cells are the units that make up all living things.
❑ Cells are the units that carry on the functions of all living things.
❑ Cells come from preexisting cells.

Today cytology is divided into several overlapping areas of study, which include the structures in cells, the molecules which make up those structures, and the functions of those structures and molecules. Someone has suggested that more has been learned about cells in the past 10 years than in the 200 years before the cell theory was formulated. Let us examine the three principles of the cell theory.

3A-2

Cellular Functions and Processes

Nutrition	Absorption:*	transport of dissolved substances into cells to serve as building blocks or energy sources
	Digestion:*	enzymatic breakdown of substances to secure building materials or energy
Internal Functions	Synthesis:	putting together organic compounds from smaller units obtained from digestion, absorption, or some other synthesis reaction in the cell. Synthesis results in a cell's growth, secretion, or replacing worn out cellular parts.
	Respiration:	breakdown of food (usually glucose) with the release of energy
	Movement:	movement of the cell itself (*locomotion*) or the *internal movement*, the movement of substances and structures inside the cell
	Irritability:	ability to respond to external factors that affect the operations of the cell; that is, the response or reaction of the cell to its environment
Releasing Materials	Excretion:*	removing soluble waste materials from cells
	Egestion:*	eliminating nonsoluble, nondigestible wastes from cells
	Secretion:	synthesizing and releasing materials from a cell
Continuing Existence	Homeostasis:	maintaining a steady state in a cell, thus permitting its existence
	Reproduction:	formation of new cells

---

nucleus: (L. NUX, nut or kernel, *hence, central part*)

absorption: (L. ABSORBERE, to absorb)

digestion: di- (L. DIS, apart) + -gestion (GERERE, to carry)

excretion: (L. EXCERNERE, to separate)

egestion: (L. EGERERE, to carry out)

Cells—units of living things

The size of most organisms does not indicate the size of its cells but rather the number of its cells. For example, although a mouse and an elephant have cells of about the same size, their quantity of cells is different.

Not all of the organism is made of cells. Those parts of an organism that are not composed of cells are made of materials that cells manufacture. An insect's body covering is a *secretion* of some of the cells of the insect. It is interesting also that much of the materials composing our bones are cellular secretions.

Cells—functions of living things

Cells are responsible for all the functions of any living thing. Because the things cells do are so various and overlapping, it is impossible to easily describe those functions. The cellular functions given in Table 3A-2 are more a list of the processes of life than a list of what cells do. Not all cells perform all these functions. In a complex organism like the human body, some cells perform a few of these functions almost to the exclusion of other functions.

Cells of an organism are *specialized* for particular functions. Most multicellular organisms have

Levels of Cellular Organization

Many organisms consist of only one cell. These organisms are called **unicellular.** Bacteria, as well as many protozoans, algae, and fungi, are unicellular. **Multicellular** organisms are made up of many cells. Some algae and fungi, as well as all plants and animals, are multicellular.

Some organisms are **colonial.** A colonial organism is a collection of similar cells living together. Except for certain reproductive cells, each of these similar cells could, if separated from the others, carry on the processes of any cell in the organism. Colonial organisms include many algae and fungi. A mushroom, for example, is a colonial, highly structured organism. Evolutionists often call unicellular and colonial organisms the "first" or "early" organisms. These terms are not accurate, however, since all life was created at the same time.

Most multicellular organisms are made up of **tissues**—similar cells that are grouped together and perform similar functions. Tissue cells normally depend upon other tissues to supply some of their needs. In other words, various tissues carry on different tasks to keep the organism alive. The muscle cells of our body compose tissues whose. primary function is movement. Muscles, however, depend upon the blood tissue to bring them oxygen, the tissues of the digestive tract to prepare food for their ready use, and the nervous tissues to regulate when and how much they contract. Tissues are specialized to perform certain functions and cannot exist under normal conditions by themselves. Scientists have been able, however, to grow tissues in special laboratory conditions.

Many multicellular organisms have **organs.** Tissues grouped together to perform a specific function form an organ. For example, the stomach includes tissues that strengthen it, cover it, compose its glands, make it churn, and perform other functions. All these different tissues work together to digest food, the major purpose of the stomach. Yet no single tissue that is part of the stomach is capable of digesting food by itself.

Organs in many organisms are arranged into **systems**—groups of organs working together to accomplish life functions. Your brain, eyes, ears, and taste buds, and the nerves that connect these structures are organs. These and a few other organs together compose the nervous system, which enables you to sense and respond to your environment, coordinate your activities, think, remember, and perform other related functions.

unicellular organism

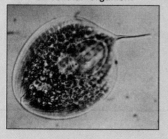

colonial organism

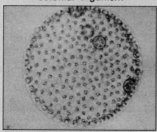

tissue

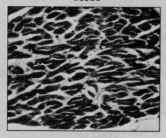

been designed with cellular *division of labor*. Each tissue or group of cells performs only a few of the processes of a living organism, but somewhere in the organism other cells are accomplishing the other functions.

In order for the organism to be alive, collectively the cells must be accomplishing *all* these functions. That they do so is not as surprising as the fact that unicellular and colonial organisms accomplish *all* these functions in one cell. Unicellular and colonial organisms are occasionally called the "simple organisms." Considering that in the space of a single cell these organisms do all the same basic functions that many organisms accomplish with billions of cells, the term "simple" seems inappropriate.

Review Questions 3A-1

1. List the three concepts of the cell theory.
2. Give the differences between a colony and a tissue.
3. Give two examples of (a) organs in the human body and (b) systems in the human body.
4. List ten of the primary functions of cells.

Cells–reproduction of living things

For most cells the biosynthesis of materials results in maintenance and growth of the cell. The science fiction cell "that grew so large it swallowed New York," however, is not possible. When most cells reach a particular size, they either slow down their synthesis of materials, secrete certain synthesized materials, or divide. The built-in control of a cell (the DNA) can control only so much; therefore, cell division after a limited amount of growth is essential for most cells.

Cells reproduce by dividing. Cellular division results in a new organism (if the organism is unicellular), more cells in the same organism, or a sex cell, like an egg or sperm. Processes of cellular reproduction are discussed in Chapter 5.

Structures of the Cell

Cells are so diverse in their functions and structures that finding a "typical" cell is impossible. There appear to be only a few different types of cellular structures, but each of these structures has a great variety of forms in various cells. Cytologists regularly discover new attributes of cellular structures. As they have learned more about cellular biology, some concepts of cell structure and function have changed. The materials presented here are generalizations of the concepts accepted as true by most cytologists today. In the next few years, as more information is discovered, some concepts will change.

The parts of a cell can be put into the following three categories:

❑ *Boundaries,* which include the plasma membrane, and cellular coverings like the cell wall, capsules, and sheaths;

❑ *Cytoplasm,* which includes the cytoplasmic matrix and organelles; and

❑ *Nucleus,* which includes the nuclear envelope, chromatin material (DNA and other substances), nucleolus, and nuclear matrix.

Two types of cells

Cells are easily divided into two groups. **Eucaryotic*** (yoo KEHR ee AHT ik) cells, the first group, are those which have a true nucleus with a set of membranes around it and also have specialized structures called *cytoplasmic organelles** (OR guh NELZ), which accomplish the cell's

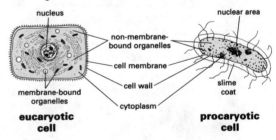

3A-3 *A comparison of a procaryotic and a eucaryotic cell*

eucaryotic: eu- (Gk. EUS, good) + -caryotic (KARUOTIS, with a central part)   **cytoplasmic:** cyto- (cell) + -plasm (to mold)   **organelle:** (L. ORGANUM, organ)

72

functions. Organelles with membranes around them are called *membrane-bound organelles.* Others lack membranes and are called *non-membrane-bound organelles.* Plants, animals, and several other groups have eucaryotic cells.

The various structures of eucaryotic cells will be discussed individually in the next sections of this chapter. Note figures 3A-5, a typical animal cell, and 3A-9, a typical plant cell. Remember, there is no such thing as a *typical* cell. These diagrams are included to help you visualize the structures of eucaryotic cells as you read about them. Returning often to them will be helpful.

Bacteria, blue-green algae, and some similar organisms are composed of **procaryotic** (proh KEHR ee AHT ik) cells, the second group. These cells lack a true nucleus and have only non-membrane-bound organelles. Procaryotic organisms and their cellular structures will be discussed in greater detail in Chapter 9.

Cell boundaries

Technically the outer boundary of the cell which is still a part of the cell is the *plasma membrane.* Many cells, however, have structures outside of their plasma membranes which are not actually part of the cell. We will consider cellular *capsules, sheaths, coats,* and *cell walls* as part of the boundaries of a cell even though they are really outside the cell.

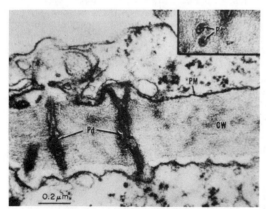

3A-4 *An electron micrograph of a cell wall* **(CW)** *showing plasma membrane* **(PM)** *and connective structures passing through the pores* **(Pd)** *(27,400X)*

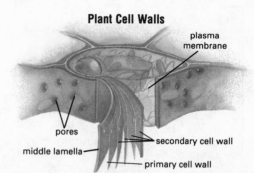

Plant Cell Walls

Cell walls in plants, as well as in many other organisms, are made primarily of cellulose. The *primary cell wall* is made when the cell is first forming and has not reached its full size. A plant's primary cell wall is made of about 20% to 30% cellulose fibers randomly arranged, about 70% water, and a variable amount of pectin–a jellylike substance which solidifies cellulose. It is found in abundance in some fruits and serves as the solidifying agent in jelly. The softness and flexibility afforded by the loosely bonded, random arrangement of cellulose fibers allows some cellular growth.

When the plant cell reaches maturity, it forms a *secondary cell wall* inside the primary cell wall but outside the cell membrane. The secondary cell wall has a higher percentage of cellulose, and the fibers are arranged in layers of almost parallel rows, each layer going a different direction. Additional pectin, hardening substances such as *lignin,* and a decreased amount of water make the secondary cell walls more rigid than the primary wall. Plant fibers (such as cotton) and wood are predominantly cell walls. These various cells demonstrate the strength of their cellular structures.

Cells that have cell walls have a barrier between the environment and their plasma membranes. In order for materials to enter and leave the cell, it is necessary for the cell wall to have *pores.*

Plasma membranes

Every cell, whether procaryotic or eucaryotic, has a **plasma membrane** (or *cell membrane*) which serves as the outermost boundary of the cell itself. The plasma membrane is the only thing that separates some cells from their environment. The cells of your body are like this. For your individual cells, though, other body cells are insuring

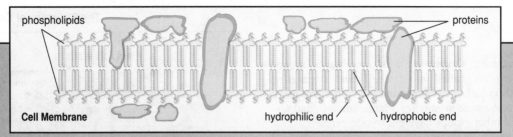

phospholipids

proteins

Cell Membrane

hydrophilic end   hydrophobic end

The Membranes Found in Cells

Would it be confusing to say that a cell is a fluid that contains fluids for structure, that it is encased in a fluid, and that it is surrounded by fluids? It might, unless you understand something about the unusual fluid membranes found in and around all cells.

Cellular membranes are the membranes found in and around cells. Cellular membranes can be put into the following two groups:

❑ **The plasma membrane** The plasma membrane, sometimes called the *cell membrane,* surrounds the cell's cytoplasm, separating the cell from its environment. (Be careful not to confuse cellular membranes [all the membranes in a cell] and the specific cellular membrane called the cell membrane.)

❑ **The internal cellular membranes** The internal cellular membranes form many of the structures in the cytoplasm.

Although cellular membranes may differ greatly within a single cell and even more greatly between cells, all of the membranes found in cells have some common characteristics. One thing that cellular membranes have in common is that they are composed of lipids. In fact, it is the unusual properties of lipids in water that give cellular membranes their "fluid" characteristic. For example, normally, lipid molecules do not dissolve in water. Thus if a drop of lipid is placed in water it will form a thin film on the surface of the water. This film of oil on water is an example of a *fluid* membrane.

Normally, cellular membranes are made of phospholipids (see page 64), which have hydrophobic and hydrophilic ends. In water, phospholipids form a little ball, called a *micelle,* or a *lipid bilayer.* The hydrophilic ends in these structures point outward and the hydrophobic ends point inward. One of the differences in cellular membranes is the combinations of various phospholipids and other lipids (such as cholesterol, which is found in all animal and human cellular membranes). Some lipids have longer fatty acid tails, and some have bent fatty acids which help to make the membrane stronger.

All cellular membranes also have proteins. In the past, various "sandwiches" of proteins and fats have been proposed to describe the structure of cellular membranes. Today most scientists agree that the various proteins that make up different cell membranes are found scattered through the lipid bilayer.

Different proteins also give various membranes distinct properties. Some of the proteins permit various substances through the membranes and some prohibit others from passing. Other membrane proteins are enzymes. These are called *membrane-bound enzymes,* and many important cellular processes happen along these membranes. Some proteins are structural in that they add strength or rigidity to the membrane. Some of these proteins have polysaccharides or other substances attached to them and give the membrane other properties.

Cellular membranes are *self assemblable.* If the molecules of such a membrane are physically separated, they will realign themselves as a membrane because of the hydrophilic and hydrophobic properties of the lipids and their attraction for the proteins. Some of the more complex enzyme-containing membranes take longer to reassemble than the simpler membranes.

If you were to take a fine glass needle and puncture the plasma membrane, does all the cytoplasm flow out of the cell? No. Disrupting the line-up of a portion of the fluid lipids and proteins that form the plasma membrane is a temporary problem. The membrane is self-assemblable. In short order the molecules reassemble into a membrane around the fluid cytoplasm, separating it from its fluid surroundings. See, it is not so confusing.

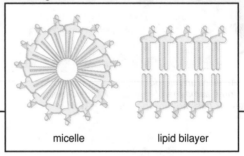

micelle   lipid bilayer

that the environment in which the individual cells exist has the correct temperature, pH, food supply, and every other condition suitable for maintaining life. Cells that do not have similar protection must have other forms of protection.

Cell walls and capsules

Although every cell has a plasma membrane, not every cell has a **cell wall.** Procaryotes, plants, algae, fungi, and many protozoans have some type of cell wall, but animal cells do not. The cell wall is a rigid or nearly rigid structure surrounding the cell. It is manufactured by the cell and assembled outside the plasma membrane. Since a cell wall is organic material that has been *secreted* by the cell, a cell wall is not alive, but it is still a necessary structure for those cells that have one.

Many unicellular or colonial organisms have a **capsule** or **sheath** in addition to (or occasionally in place of) a cell wall. Sometimes the capsule is called a *slime coat.* Capsules are made of cellular secretions (often polysaccharides and lipids) of varying thickness and are made without definite structures. Capsules give clusters of bacteria and algae their shiny appearance and slimy feel. They protect the cell because material entering it must first either dissolve the capsule or pass through it.

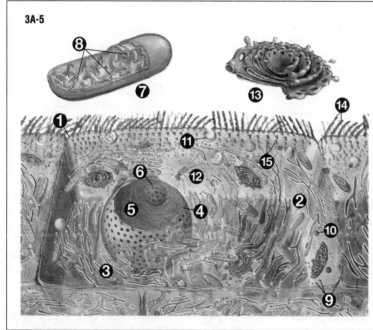

3A-5

Structures in a Typical Animal Cell

1. plasma membrane
2. endoplasmic reticulum, smooth
3. endoplasmic reticulum, rough
4. nuclear envelope
5. chromatin material, nucleoplasm
6. nucleolus
7. mitochondria
8. cristae
9. ribosome
10. lysosome
11. vacuole
12. centrioles and microtubules
13. Golgi body
14. cilia
15. basal body

Review Questions 3A-2

1. List the three basic parts of a cell.
2. Compare the structures of procaryotic cells and eucaryotic cells.
3. What are the two main kinds of cellular membranes?
4. What is the difference between a cell membrane and a cellular membrane?
5. What are the two main components of cellular membranes? What characteristics do each of these components give to the cell membrane they make?
6. What property of phospholipids permits them to form micelles and lipid bilayers?
7. Describe the structure of a cellular membrane.
8. Compare a plasma membrane with a cell wall.

Cytoplasm

The term **cytoplasm** (SYE tuh PLAZ uhm) refers to all the material inside the plasma membrane, excluding the nucleus. The cytoplasm appears as a semisolid, yet fluid, substance with small granules suspended in it. Even high magnification with the light microscope reveals only the largest of these granules clearly.

The **cytoplasmic matrix** is the watery substance in which the granules are suspended. It is a colloid made of proteins, fats, carbohydrates, ions, and small compounds in combinations that differ from cell type to cell type. It is a reversible phase colloid that is capable of *cytoplasmic streaming,* a flowing inside the boundaries of the cell. This movement involves the changing of the matrix from sol to gel and back again. Cytoplasmic streaming rearranges the cell's contents for particular purposes. In some plant cells, for example, cytoplasmic streaming moves the structures responsible for catching light and making sugar. The structures are moved in a circular pattern and thus all of them are exposed to the area of the cell that receives the most direct light.

Cytoplasmic organelles are structures in the cytoplasm which can be compared to the organs of the human body: each accomplishes a different function, and each must function properly in order to maintain a healthy condition. A survey of some of the primary cytoplasmic organelles and their functions follows. Some will be discussed in greater detail in later chapters.

Ribosomes and endoplasmic reticulum

A **ribosome** is a non-membrane-bound organelle found in both procaryotic and eucaryotic cells. These small units are actually strands of RNA with proteins attached to them. Some of these proteins constitute the enzyme system necessary for protein synthesis.

With the invention of the electron microscope, cytologists found that the cytoplasmic matrix of many cells has folds of cellular membranes running through it. These folded membranes are called **endoplasmic*** (EN doh PLAZ mik) **reticulum*** (rih TIK yuh lum), abbreviated ER.

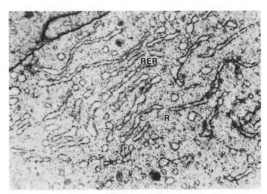

3A-6 *An electron micrograph showing rough endoplasmic reticulum* **(RER)** *and ribosomes* **(R)** *(27,400X)*

In some cells the ER is continuous with the membranes around the nucleus. Some ER is dotted with ribosomes and is called *rough ER.* Endoplasmic reticulum lacking ribosomes is called *smooth ER.* ER helps to give the cytoplasm a flexible yet structured shape. The ER also has membrane-bound enzymes and thereby functions in the synthesis of complex compounds. Much rough ER is found in cells that secrete protein-containing materials. Cells that secrete sterols contain much smooth ER. ER also serves as a channel for the movement of substances.

Mitochondria

Nicknamed "the powerhouse of the cell," these typically bean-shaped organelles are responsible for the respiration of sugars to release *usable* cellular energy. **Mitochondria** (MYE tuh KAHN dree uh) are double-membrane-bound, with the inner membrane having folds called *cristae.* On the inner surface of the inner membrane, which

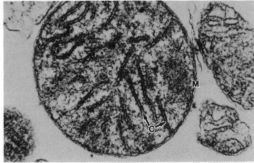

3A-7 *An electron micrograph showing a mitochondrium in cross section. The double membrane* **(M)** *and cristae* **(C)** *are visible. (27,500X)*

endoplasmic: endo- (in) + -plasmic (to mold)

reticulum: (L. RETE, net)

is considerably lengthened by the cristae, are many membrane-bound enzymes necessary for the process of *cellular respiration.*

The *mitochondrial matrix*–the fluid which is in the mitochondria–contains other enzymes for respiration. Depending upon the energy demands, mitochondria may be large and numerous with many cristae, as in muscle cells, or they may be small and relatively few with only a few cristae.

Plastids

Plastids are membrane-bound organelles found in the cells of plants, algae, and a few other organisms, but not in animals. Plastids are either *leucoplasts** (LOO kuh plasts), colorless structures used as storehouses, or *chromoplasts** (KROH muh PLASTS), structures that contain pigments and usually serve in synthesis processes. Leucoplasts are found in the fleshy storage areas of plants. Potatoes, root crops, and many fruits have leucoplasts containing starches and, occa-

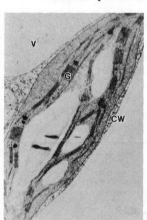
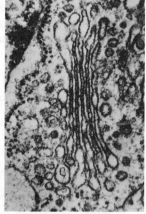

3A-8 *Electron micrographs of a chloroplast (left) showing grana* **(G),** *the cell wall* **(CW),** *and a vacuole* **(V)** *(8400X); and of a Golgi body (right) (27,400x)*

sionally, oils. Chromoplasts contain pigments that give plant parts their color (e.g. flowers).

The most common and best-known chromoplast is the **chloroplast,*** a green, sugar-manufacturing organelle. Chloroplasts are various sizes and shapes in various organisms. Some chloroplasts are cup-shaped and are nearly as large as the cells that hold them. Others are flat or even

spiral-shaped. The most common chloroplasts are round or football-shaped.

Chloroplasts contain a fluid called *stroma* and flattened sacs called *thylakoids** (THYE luh koydz). A stack of thylakoids, which resembles a stack of coins, is a **granum**. The membranes of the grana hold the green pigment *chlorophyll,* which catches light energy and uses it to start the synthesis of sugar. The making of sugar is completed in the stroma.

Golgi bodies

In 1898, Camillo Golgi (GOLE jee) first described a cellular structure which has since been found in one form or another in almost all eucaryotic cells. The **Golgi body** (or Golgi apparatus) is important in the synthesis of complex polysaccharides. In the flat, often curved *saccules** (SAK yoolz) of the Golgi body, complex polysaccharides, lipids, and proteins are processed. These substances are then sealed in small sacs whose membranes appear to be made by pinching off the membrane of the saccule.

Most cells that secrete materials have many Golgi bodies, and the secretions can be traced to these sacs and the Golgi body. The cellulose and polysaccharides found in cell walls and capsules, for example, are assembled in the Golgi bodies.

Lysosomes

Most often when an organelle is seen, its function is discovered only after additional investigation. Exactly the opposite was the case for the **lysosome** (LYE so SOHM). Enzymes capable of digesting proteins were known to exist in cells, but scientists speculated that they could not be free in the cytoplasmic matrix, or they would digest parts of the cell itself. Careful investigation revealed the existence of small, membrane-bound organelles named lysosomes which contained these enzymes.

Normally lysosomal enzymes digest invading substances or large food substances. These enzymes help in breaking down complex structures and preparing the materials for reuse, but occasionally they destroy old or useless cellular structures. For example, lysosomes function in the *absorption* of a tadpole's tail.

---

leucoplast: leuco- (Gk. LEUKOS, white or clear) + -plast (to mold)

thylakoids: (Gk. THYLAKOS, a sack)

chromoplast: chromo- or chroma- (color) + -plast (to mold)

saccule: (L. SACCUS, a bag)

chloroplast: chloro- (Gk. KHLOROS, greenish yellow) + -plast (to mold)

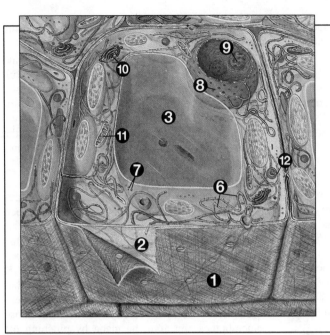

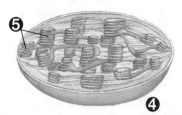

Structures in a Typical Plant Cell
1. cell wall
2. plasma membrane
3. central vacuole
4. chloroplast
5. grana
6. endoplasmic reticulum
7. ribosomes
8. nucleus
9. nucleolus
10. Golgi body
11. mitochondria
12. plastid

3A-9

Vacuoles and vesicles

Vacuoles* (VAK yoo ohlz) can be compared to various household containers–different boxes, bags, and jars which have in common only the fact that they hold something. A vacuole is a membrane-bound sac which contains food, water, wastes, or other materials. A vesicle* (VES ih kul) is a small vacuole, but there are no distinctly defined size differences between vacuoles and vesicles. The best way to learn about vacuoles and vesicles is to examine some of the more common and important types.

❑ **Phagocytic vacuole** When certain cells contact solid food that is too large to absorb, they engulf it. The cytoplasm flows around the food. As the plasma membranes meet, they fuse, leaving the substance in a *food vacuole*. This process, called **phagocytosis*** (FAHJ uh sye TOH sis), has been described as cellular eating. In the case of phagocytic vacuoles, the *vacuolar membrane* was originally a part of the plasma membrane. Amebas and white blood cells carry on phagocytosis.
❑ **Food vacuole** Food vacuoles are formed by phagocytosis or other processes and serve as sites of cellular **digestion.** Lysosomes fuse with the vacuolar membrane, releasing their digestive enzymes into the food vacuole. The enzymes break down the food into substances which will pass through the vacuolar membrane into the cytoplasm.

❑ **Waste vacuole** After the lysosomal enzymes have completed their task, the nondigestible materials remain in a waste vacuole (residual body).

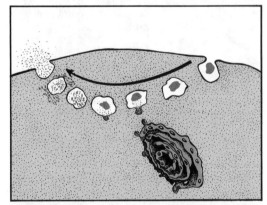

3A-10 *Cellular digestion. A food vacuole is formed. A Golgi-apparatus-formed lysosome fuses with the vacuole. The food is digested and absorbed into the cytoplasm. The wastes are then egested.*

---

vacuole: (L. VACUUS, empty)   **vesicle:** (L. VESICULA, little bladder)   **phagocytosis:** phago- (Gk. PHAGEIN, to eat) + -cyto- (cell)

Cytoskeletons

In the past biologists thought of the cytoplasm as a soup in which the chunks of meat and vegetables were the organelles and the broth was the cytoplasmic matrix. Although this may have been a good comparison, today biologists realize that cytoplasm requires a more complex structure than soup does.

Eucaryotic cells have been demonstrated to have a **cytoskeleton.** A cytoskeleton is made of proteins arranged as one of several structures. Two of the most common are the following:

❑ **Microfilaments*** are tiny flexible strands. In many cells the microfilaments form a branching internal network through the cytoplasm. In plant cells the microfilaments are arranged in patterns that direct the motion of organelles during *cytoplasmic streaming.* Often microfilaments contain *actin,* a protein involved in contraction. (Your muscle cells, for example, contain large quantities of actin microfilaments.)

❑ **Microtubules*** are proteins arranged into a tubular shape. These protein units are able to assemble and disassemble rapidly, making the microtubule longer or shorter. Microtubules just inside the plasma membrane help to give shape to many cells. In growing plant cells microtubules probably help to arrange the cellulose strands as they are deposited in the cell wall.

A number of organelles are made of microtubules joined and arranged into particular configurations. A basal body, for example, has 9 sets of 3 joined microtubules arranged in a circle with other proteins, causing a cross section of this structure to look like a pinwheel. Basal bodies are attached to each other by microfilaments which are believed to coordinate the movements of multiple flagella or cilia.

Each cilium or flagellum attached to the basal body usually has 9 sets of 2 microtubules arranged around a separated pair of single microtubules. From each pair of microtubules, reaching toward the next pair, are tiny arms made of the protein *dynein.* Dynein is able to bend and grab protein molecules in the next microtubule. As the dynein pulls on the proteins, the microtubules slide along each other, bending the flagellum or cilium.

Another organelle which is made of microtubules is the centriole. Centrioles have the same

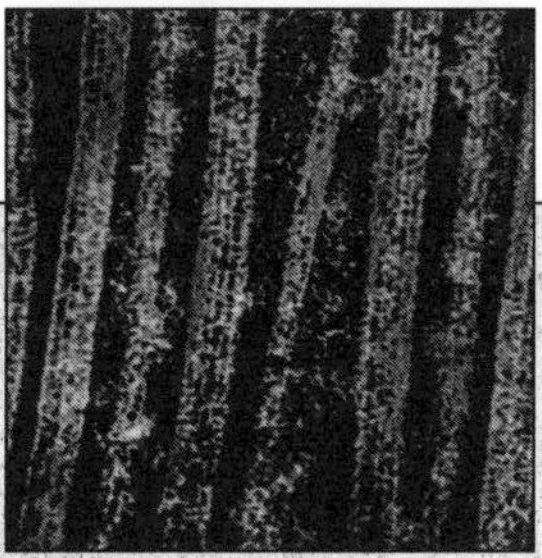

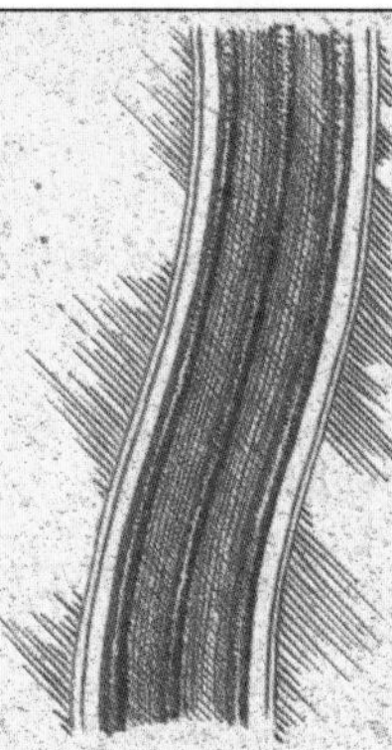

The micrograph above shows a group of microtubules.
A cross section of a microtubule (right).
A model of a microtubule (below) illustrates the spiral arrangement of proteins.

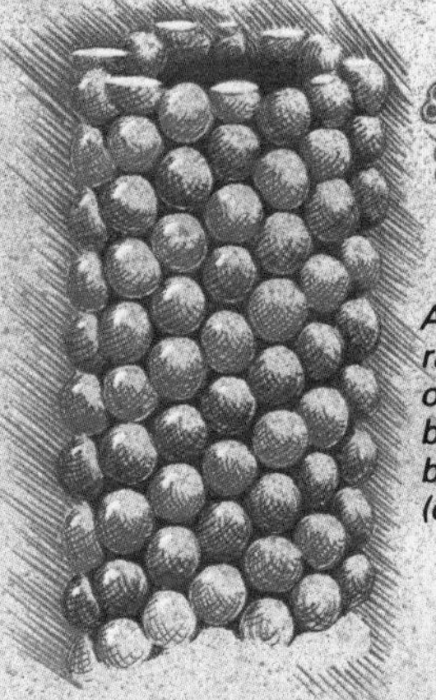

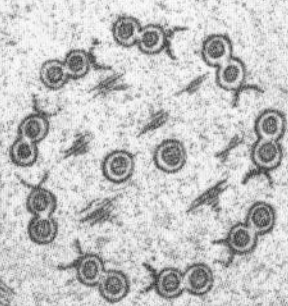

The microtubule arrangement in flagella (c.s.).

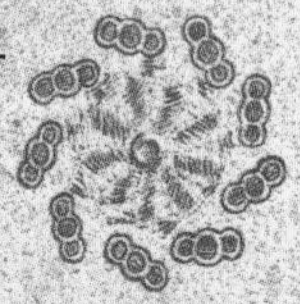

A wheel arrangement of microtubules in a basal body (c.s.).

A diagram showing the bent and unbent characteristic of microtubules in a cilium

microtubule pattern as the basal bodies and are found in pairs positioned at right angles to each other just outside the nucleus of animal and human cells. As part of cell division, a cluster of microtubules forms around the centrioles. These microtubules look like a star and are called the *aster.** During cell division the microtubules of the aster play significant roles in moving the chromosomes.

---

microfilament: micro- (small) + -filament (L. FILUM, thread)

microtubule: micro- (small) + -tubule (L. TUBULE, tube)

aster: (Gk. ASTER, star)

Cytoplamic streaming moves the waste vacuoles to the plasma membrane where they fuse with it, releasing the nondigested insoluble wastes. The release of such wastes is called *egestion*.

❑ **Secretion vesicle** These vesicles are usually formed by the endoplasmic reticulum or Golgi body. They take the materials made by these structures to the plasma membrane. When the vesicle membrane and plasma membrane unite,

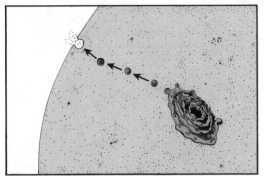

3A-11 *Secretion. A secretion vesicle formed by a Golgi-apparatus migrates to the plasma membrane and releases materials from the cell.*

the material is *secreted*. Many secreted substances, including human hormones and the cellulose for cell walls, are released by secretion vesicles.

❑ **Pinocytic vesicle** If phagocytosis is cellular eating, **pinocytosis*** (PIN uh sye TOH sis) is cellular drinking. Some cells form tiny pockets in their cell membranes when they confront mole-

3A-12 *Pinocytosis. Small substances collect in pockets of the cell membrane, which then pinch off to become vesicles.*

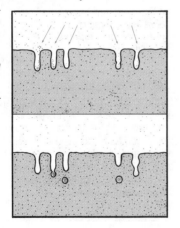

cules too large to be absorbed. The tip is pinched, sealing the molecules in a fluid-filled vesicle.

❑ **Central vacuole** Found in most plant and algal cells, this large vacuole is filled with water. Because of a high concentration of solutes in the fluid of the vacuole, water from outside the cell moves into the vacuole by osmosis. An internal pressure is then exerted on the vacuolar membrane, which in turn pushes on the cytoplasm, which then pushes against the cell wall. This cellular fullness because of water pressure in the central vacuole is called **turgor*** (TUR gur) **pressure.** The difference between crisp and wilted lettuce is the result of the plant cells being turgid (crisp) or lacking turgor (wilted).

❑ **Contractile vacuole** Many unicellular organisms that exist in water environments do not have cell walls. These cells, it seems, should burst since water molecules quickly come through the plasma membrane to equalize the concentration difference between the cytoplasm and the water outside. But under normal circumstances the cell collects these water molecules in contractile vacuoles. The contractile vacuoles, after reaching a certain size, fuse with the plasma membrane and release the water.

Centrioles, flagella, and cilia

Centrioles* (SEN tree OHLZ) usually occur in pairs arranged at right angles to each other near the nucleus in many eucaryotic cells. Centrioles appear to function in cell division, which is discussed later.

A **flagellum*** (fluh JEL um) (pl., flagella) is a long, tubular extension of the plasma membrane surrounding a set of tiny tubes. Flagella are often longer than the cell and usually exist singly but sometimes occur in pairs or groups of 3, 4, or 5. **Cilia*** (sing., cilium) are similar to flagella but are usually shorter and frequently cover either the entire cell or a section of the cell.

At the base of each cilium or flagellum is the *basal body,* which resembles a centriole. The basal bodies or *kinetosomes** (kuh NET uh SOHMZ) help to control the action of the cilia or flagella. Cilia and flagella in eucaryotic cells beat in specific patterns. A flagellum acts somewhat like a

---

pinocytosis: pino- (Gk. PINEIN, to drink) + -cyto- (cell)

turgor: (L. TURGERE, to be swollen)

centriole: (L. CENTRUM, center)

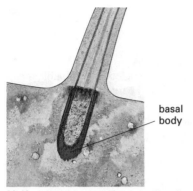
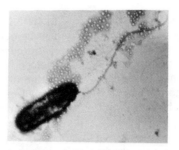

3A-13 *A basal body (left) and a flagellum (middle) and cilia (right) on microbes*

propeller, and cilia usually move in waves like a series of oars. The coordination of cilia or flagella is a function of the basal bodies.

Cilia and flagella do move unicellular organisms–the function they are most often associated with–but they are also quite common in multicellular organisms, where they often move the substances around the cell. The cells that line most of the human respiratory tract, for example, have cilia which move mucus and dust.

Review Questions 3A-3

1. Describe the cytoplasmic matrix.
2. Where are ribosomes found? Give the function(s) of ribosomes.
3. Describe and give the function(s) of the endoplasmic reticulum.
4. What are the two primary types of plastids? What are their functions?
5. Describe and give the function(s) of the Golgi body.
6. Why are the substances in a lysosome *not* released into the cytoplasmic matrix?
7. List several types of vacuoles and vesicles and give the functions of each.
8. What two structures contribute to the cytoskeleton?
9. Describe a microfilament and list several uses it has in cells.
10. Describe a microtubule and list several places it is found in cells. List several functions of microtubules.
11. What is the relationship between cilia (or flagella) and the basal body (kinetosome)?

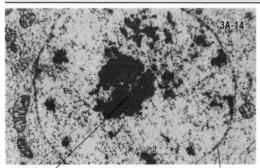

3A-14

nucleolus / nuclear envelope

Nucleus

The **nucleus** (pl., nuclei) is sometimes called the control center of the cell. Because it contains DNA, the nucleus has the coded information for protein manufacture. Proteins are used as building blocks and enzymes which enable cells to make and use all the other substances necessary for cell life. DNA indeed permits the activity of the cell. However, the DNA does not "decide" what a cell is to do or become. DNA cannot "decide."

The DNA that a cell has is a replicated copy of the DNA that was in the cell from which it came. Although a cell can make more DNA, this new DNA is only a copy of the cells original DNA. Since the cell has only a certain DNA with a certain structure, it is capable of making only certain proteins. When the need arises, a cell can stop making some proteins and start making others for which it has the DNA code. But it cannot make a protein for which it does not have the DNA code.

flagellum: (L. FLAGELLUM, little whip)
cilia: (L. CILIUM, eyelid)

kinetosome kineto- (Gk. KINEIN, to move) + -some (body)

A cell's nucleus can be compared to the plant manager of a cloth mill. He may order the production of different kinds of fabric, depending upon various conditions and what fibers he can obtain. But he cannot have his plant produce cars. A cloth mill has the machinery to produce only cloth. If it made cars, it would not be a cloth mill.

Similarly, the nucleus of a cell directs the manufacture of proteins based on the DNA it has, but it cannot make protein for which it lacks DNA. Plant cells have the enzymes for manufacturing cellulose; animal cells do not. The DNA that the cell has, not a "decision" by the DNA or nucleus, makes the difference.

A cloth mill can make several kinds of cloth, depending on the fibers and the machinery. Likewise, a cell can adjust itself within the limits of its DNA. Not all the DNA in a cell is being used all the time. The "turning on" and the "turning off" of DNA in a cell account for the different cells which make up your body. All your cells have the same DNA, but not all of the DNA is functioning in each of your cells.

Structure of the nucleus

In eucaryotic cells the nucleus has a double membrane around it called the **nuclear envelope.** This envelope has large pores which permit the easy passage of material between the cytoplasm and the *nuclear sap,* the protein-rich fluid inside the nuclear envelope. In some cells this envelope is continuous with the endoplasmic reticulum.

Most cellular DNA is in the nucleus, where proteins appear to protect the long DNA molecule. The DNA and the proteins are the **chromatin***(KROH muh tin) **material.** If a growing cell is stained for nucleic acids, the chromatin material appears as a fuzzy mass in the nuclear sap.

In most cells stained to make the chromatin material visible, a darker area indicating high concentration of nucleic acids and associated proteins also appears. It is the **nucleolus** (noo KLEE uh lus), which contains relatively large amounts of RNA. Depending on the cell type, there may be no nucleolus, one nucleolus, or several nucleoli. The nucleolus appears to be involved with the transcription of the RNA found in ribosomes.

Biological Terms

cytology	egestion	*Structure of the Cell*	mitochondria	pinocytosis
protoplasm	secretion	eucaryotic	plastids	turgor pressure
The Cell Theory	homeostasis	procaryotic	chloroplast	centriole
cell theory	reproduction	plasma membrane	granum (pl., grana)	flagellum (pl., flagella)
absorption	unicellular	cell wall	Golgi body	cilia (sing., cilium)
digestion	multicellular	capsule (sheath)	lysosome	
synthesis	colonial	cytoplasm	vacuole	*Nucleus*
respiration	tissue	cytoplasmic matrix	phagocytosis	nucleus (pl., nuclei)
movement	organ	cytoplasmic organelle	cytoskeleton	nuclear envelope
irritability	system	ribosome	microfilament	chromatin material
excretion		endoplasmic reticulum	microtubule	nucleolus

Review Questions 3A-4

1. It has been said that the nucleus of a cell is its control center. In what ways is this true, and in what ways is this not true?
2. List and describe the structures of a typical eucaryotic nucleus.

Thought Questions

1. In what sense would it be acceptable to call a unicellular or colonial organism a "simple organism"? In what sense is it unacceptable to do so? Is it acceptable to call these organisms "early organisms"? Why or why not?
2. In what ways are the plasma membrane, the cell wall, capsules, and sheaths really only the outer limits of a cell and not really the cell's boundaries?
3. Compare the human brain to the nucleus of a cell.

---

chromatin: chroma- (color)

3B–The Living State of Cells

In Chapter 1 life was defined as a delicate balance of operations which faces death. We who live and are surrounded by living things often lose an appreciation for the narrow set of conditions in which every living thing must exist if it is to maintain the **homeostasis*** (HOH mee oh STAY sis) of life. *Homeostasis* means "steady state," but actually it is a *dynamic equilibrium,* meaning something that has to be worked at to remain the same.

When conditions are unfavorable, an organism must work harder to maintain the homeostasis of life. Consider a muscle cell in your arm that the body calls upon to contract and move your arm. If for some reason your body temperature has risen too high, the cell will not be able to function normally. Enzymes, for example, change as the temperature changes. Thus, as the temperature rises, some cellular processes will happen too fast, others too slowly. The muscle cell will be forced to slow down or stop certain of its normal processes. The change in temperature forces the muscle cell to alter its normal operations in order to restore its homeostasis. When it is called upon to contract, the cell may not be able to do so because of damage caused by the increased temperature. If the temperature gets too high or continues for too long, the cell will die.

Optimal point and range of tolerance

Scientists call the point at which something functions best its *optimal*** point for a particular factor. The optimal point for temperature in your muscle cells is 37° C (98.6° F).

Most things have an *optimal range*. Within the limitations of the optimal range, an organism's or a cell's performance is about equal. Most human muscle cells, for example, will function equally well in temperatures within a degree or so from 37° C. The optimal range for a muscle cell is quite narrow when compared to the range of temperatures which are optimal for your body. You can function well and comfortably in rooms with temperatures from 16° C (60° F) to about 27° C (80° F), depending on the humidity, air currents, your clothing, and your activities. Despite this range

of temperatures, your body maintains a constant temperature for its muscle cells.

If a muscle cell in your body is exposed to temperatures above or below its optimal range, your body tries to return it to its optimal range. Your body will shiver, perspire, channel your blood to different areas of your body, and use other means to keep your muscle cell at or very near 37° C. This is an example of an organism's working to maintain its homeostasis.

When the muscle cell gets warmer or cooler than its optimal range, it enters its *range of tolerance* for temperature. The range of tolerance is that range in which a cell or an organism will remain alive but not function properly. The farther from the optimal range the living thing is, the more poorly it functions. When at last it reaches its *limit of tolerance,* it dies.

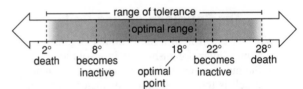

3B-1 *Temperature (C) tolerance for a soil microbe*

The range of tolerance for heat and cold for a muscle cell is only a few degrees, quite narrow when compared to the range of tolerance for skin cells. Skin was designed to deal with the more extreme temperature fluctuations in the environment. Nerve cells, on the other hand, were not. They have a very narrow range of tolerance for temperatures; it is almost the same as their optimal range. Brain cells are extremely specialized nerve cells and must be kept within their optimal range for normal activity.

A cell, whether it is a unicellular organism or part of a multicellular organism, is able to tolerate certain fluctuations. All living things were designed with ranges of tolerance which cover the different conditions in their normal environments. This concept accounts for banana trees growing well in rainy tropics but growing poorly in deserts or on chilly mountaintops. It also explains why

---

homeostasis: homeo- (same) + (Gk. STASIS, a standstill)

optimal: (L. OPTIMUS, best)

houseplants that do well in a kitchen window may not grow well in a window on the other side of the house.

There are organisms (and cells) that live in environments that change drastically in the course of a year. An organism whose environment normally fluctuates beyond its optimal range may enter a period of *dormancy** to survive unfavorable conditions. Adjustments made by some organisms (such as trees) in order to live through the winter are examples of dormancy. Winter-dormant organisms, however, will die if the temperature gets too cold and exceeds their limits of tolerance.

3B-2 *Freezing temperatures during a tree's growing period would kill the tree. During its dormancy freezing temperatures are within the tree's range of tolerance.*

Review Questions 3B-1
1. Why is homeostasis called an equilibrium? Why is homeostasis called dynamic?
2. Compare and contrast the optimal point, the optimal range, the range of tolerance, and the limit of tolerance.

The Solutions Around Cells

Whether a cell is in a multicellular organism or is a unicellular organism, it is in a solution. One of the most critical influences upon the existence of a cell is the concentration of materials in the solution around it. Of course, poisons or harmful substances in the solution affect the cell's homeostasis. Most cells cannot tolerate fat-soluble substances such as ether, alcohol, or chloroform because they dissolve the fats of the cellular membranes, enter the cell rapidly, and affect the normal functions of the cell's use of fats. Even weak concentrations of these substances take cells beyond their optimal range, and a slightly stronger concentration takes the cells beyond their range of tolerance and causes death. This is one reason that drinking alcohol is harmful.

Cells may have problems with normal and valuable substances like water, ions, and food dissolved in their environments. Too much of a good thing may harm cells as easily as too little.

Cells in solutions
The red blood cells in your bloodstream are good examples of cells in a completely controlled solution. The cytoplasm of the blood cells and the blood plasma (the fluid portion of the blood that surrounds the cells) have identical concentrations of solutes dissolved in them. The red blood cells of your body are in an **isotonic*** (EYE suh TAHN ik) **solution.** The solutes in the red blood cells are of a different nature than those in the plasma, but the ratio of solutes to water is the same inside and outside the cell membrane. Because there is no concentration gradient, there is transfer of molecules across the membrane, but there is no net osmosis.

If red blood cells are put in pure water, a concentration gradient is established. The outside of the cell has a higher concentration of water molecules and a lower concentration of solutes than

isotonic   hypotonic   hypertonic

3B-3 *Blood cells in various solutions. In which is cytolysis about to take place? In which has plasmolysis taken place?*

---

dormancy: (L. DORMIRE, to sleep)   **isotonic:** iso- (Gk. ISOS, equal) + -tonic (TONOS, tone or tension)   **hypotonic:** hypo- (Gk. HUPO, under) + -tonic (tension)

the inside. These red blood cells are in a **hypotonic*** (HYE poh TAHN ik) **solution.** The larger solutes, however, are unable to move out through the selectively permeable cell membrane. Water molecules, since they are very small and move freely through all cellular membranes, will rapidly diffuse into the red blood cells, causing them to expand and eventually burst. A cell's bursting from internal pressure is **cytolysis*** (sye TAHL ih sis).

If red blood cells are placed in a fluid with a concentration of solutes higher than that of the cells, the cells are in a **hypertonic*** (HYE pur TAHN ik) **solution.** In hypertonic solutions, water molecules will diffuse out of the cells. As the cell loses its water, it shrinks. Putting a cell in a hypertonic solution results in **plasmolysis*** (plaz MAHL ih sis)–a collapse of the cell's cytoplasm.

Red blood cells depend upon other parts of the body to keep the solutes in the blood plasma at exactly the right concentration. They therefore do not have mechanisms within them to adjust to different plasma-solute concentrations. Since these cells lack these mechanisms, an intravenous feeding solution or an injection must have the same solute concentration that the blood plasma does. If it does not, plasmolysis or cytolysis of the blood cells may occur, resulting in death.

If a physician wants to administer a large quantity of some medicine, he cannot give an extremely concentrated injection. He must instead give the medicine in a special amount of a solution which matches the concentration of the blood plasma.

Because most cells in multicellular organisms are in nearly constant isotonic solutions, they have few, if any, mechanisms to deal with hypotonic and hypertonic solutions. For many colonial or unicellular organisms, however, hypotonic or hypertonic solutions are a constant environment.

Cells in hypotonic solutions

Since fresh water has fewer dissolved substances than the cytoplasm of a cell does, a unicellular organism that lives in fresh water exists in a hypotonic solution. The unicellular and colonial organisms found in such aquatic environments must therefore either deal with the concentration gradient that is around them or die.

Many cells that live in aquatic environments have rigid cell walls which prevent cytolysis. The physical strength of the cell wall serves as a pressure against the concentration gradient. Once a certain amount of water has diffused into the cell and into the central vacuole, the cell becomes *turgid* (TUR jid). When the cytoplasm is pushing against the rigid cell wall, there is a physical pressure set up. Although the concentration gradient may favor water molecules moving into the cell, the pressure caused by the presence of the cell wall opposes them. This pressure against water entering the cell stops osmosis and prevents cytolysis.

Many cells in hypotonic solutions, though, must have a flexible membrane. A cell wall would restrict the movement and food-getting processes of many protozoans. Since many protozoans do not have cell walls, they must have other methods

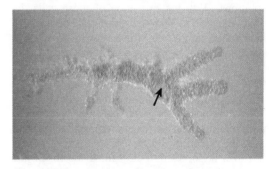

3B-4 *The clear area near the dark nucleus is a contractile vacuole.*

to survive their hypotonic environment. To do so, many of them have **contractile vacuoles.** As water molecules diffuse into the cell, they are collected in little vesicles or in arms of the contractile vacuole. The vesicles or arms then pass the water to the contractile vacuole. Once the contractile vacuole has collected enough water and reached a certain size, it fuses with the plasma membrane and forces the water outside the cell. This process requires the cell to expend energy.

---

cytolysis: cyto- (cell) + -lysis (a loosening)

hypertonic: hyper- (Gk. HUPER, over or beyond + -tonic (tension)

plasmolysis: plasmo- (to mold) + -lysis (a loosening)

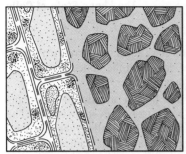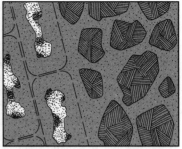

3B-5 *Fertilizer burn.* (left) *Normal conditions;* (middle) *The addition of fertilizer increases the solute concentration outside the cell, resulting in the movement of both water and solutes;* (right) *Solutes entering and water leaving the cell result in plasmolysis and possibly death of the plant.*

If a cell with a contractile vacuole is placed in water that has a lower concentration of solutes than the water it is accustomed to, the contractile vacuole begins to work faster. If a cell with a contractile vacuole is placed in nearly pure water, the diffusion of water molecules into the cell is so rapid that, despite the rapid working of the contractile vacuole, cytolysis will soon occur.

Cells in hypertonic solutions

Most cells are not equipped to deal with hypertonic solutions as well as they deal with hypotonic solutions. With the exception of those cells directly exposed to seawater, most cells do not find themselves naturally in situations with hypertonic solutions. Man, however, occasionally puts cells in hypertonic solutions and then wonders why they do not thrive.

For example, some homeowners, thinking that "if a little is good, a great deal must be better," put more fertilizer on the soil around their plants than the directions on the package suggest. The fertilizer dissolves into the soil. If too much has been applied, the root cells may be in a hypertonic solution. As the ions of the fertilizer enter the cell and the water leaves the cell to equalize the con-

centration gradient, the cell first loses its turgidity and then experiences plasmolysis, which results in cellular death. If this occurs to enough root cells, the plant may die and turn brown. The plant requires the ions found in fertilizers, but it cannot use too much.

Plant cells are sometimes temporarily short of water. Hot days can cause water to evaporate from leaves more rapidly than it is replaced from the roots. The results are the same as if a hypertonic solution surrounded the cells. Water molecules leave the cells and enter the atmosphere. This causes the cells to lose their turgidity, and the plant wilts. Under normal situations a cooler evening and night will permit the plant to restore turgidity by obtaining water from the soil without losing it by evaporation. If the wilting continues because of a lack of water in the soil or because of damage to the plant, the cells will experience plasmolysis and die.

The drooping of cut flowers and the limpness of lettuce is caused by the loss of turgor due to the situations similar to hypertonic conditions. Abundant, cool, fresh water will restore turgor to a salad or bouquet–unless plasmolysis has already occurred.

Review Questions 3B-2
1. Compare and contrast isotonic, hypotonic, and hypertonic solutions.
2. List two methods some cells have for withstanding hypotonic solutions and explain how they operate.

How Substances Enter Cells

Most of what we have discussed thus far about materials entering cells can be explained as diffusion through the semipermeable plasma membrane. In their fight for homeostasis, however, cells must often move substances against the concentration gradient. Some substances are not permitted into and others not permitted out of the cytoplasm, even though those substances should, it seems, diffuse through the membrane easily.

Some substances enter cells rapidly, others slowly. The ability of a substance to enter the membrane of various cells may be vastly different. Cells unable to ingest certain nutrients surrounding them will starve. Yet other cells in the same solution may grow rapidly because they are able to utilize the nutrients.

Cells are designed for specific environments. Some cells may not be able to adjust to a situation foreign to them even though these same conditions might be ideal for other cells.

Passive transport across membranes

Molecules often pass through a plasma membrane without expending cellular energy. **Passive transport** is the movement of molecules through a

---

3B-6   Factors Which Determine Whether a Molecule Will Pass Through a Cellular Membrane

- concentration of the molecule (diffusion pressure)
- size and weight of the molecule
- shape of the molecule
- charge of the molecule
- fat-solubility of the molecule
- permeability of the membrane

---

membrane *with* the concentration gradient. Kinetic energy of the molecule, not the cell, supplies the force behind passive transport.

One factor is the concentration of the molecule on both sides of the membrane. If the diffusion pressure is high, the molecule travels more rapidly across the membrane. Size is another factor. Very small molecules such as water and gases (oxygen, carbon dioxide, and nitrogen) seem to pass easily through almost all cellular membranes. Some other very small molecules and ions, however, pass through membranes slowly.

The properties of a substance and the permeability of the membrane to that substance determine which molecules will pass through and how rapidly. The shape of the molecule affects its permeability. Some long thin molecules pass slowly through membranes while round molecules of the same size and mass do not pass. Fat-soluble molecules appear to dissolve the phospholipids of a membrane and penetrate more quickly than molecules that are not fat-soluble.

Small molecules like monosaccharides, amino acids, fatty acids, and glycerols penetrate slowly through plasma membranes. Disaccharides and molecules that are physically larger (such as polysaccharides and proteins) penetrate even more slowly. Lipids barely penetrate membranes at all.

Passive mediated transport across membranes

For years scientists were baffled that some cells permit the penetration of certain large molecules (usually specific carbohydrates or proteins) but exclude the passage of other molecules of similar size and properties. The large molecules that penetrated were varied in different cells.

This is a passive transport since it requires no cellular energy and goes either into or out of the

---

3B-7 *In passive mediated transport, molecules are being moved across the membrane by a membrane factor. Passive mediated transport goes with the concentration gradient.*

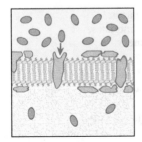 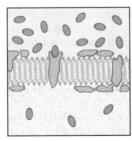 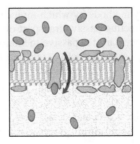 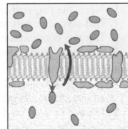

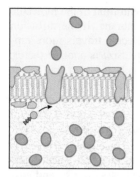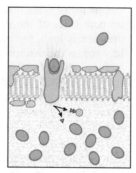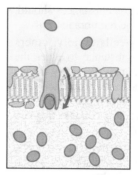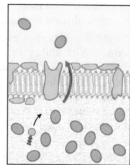

3B-8 *Active transport requires cellular energy and moves molecules across a membrane against the concentration gradient.*

cell, depending on the concentration gradient. But this transport does require the presence of a factor in the membrane; therefore, it is called **passive mediated transport.**

In passive mediated transport the combination of the molecule with the membrane factor permits the molecule to move across the membrane. Although most of these membrane factors are proteins, other molecules may be used as well. Scientists believe that some antibiotics work this way; that is, they change membrane permeability by supplying or affecting factors for passive mediated transport.

Active transport across membranes

Enzymes in the plasma membrane carry on **active transport,** the movement of molecules across membranes *against* the concentration gradient. Since these enzymes require energy to function, active transport involves the expenditure of cellular energy. The entry of nutritive substances or the elimination of molecules in the cell's environment is often done by active transport.

For example, active transport occurs when mineral ions are absorbed by root cells of plants. These ions exist in lower concentrations in the water outside the root than inside the root cells. However, live cells must expend energy by the active transport of ions into the cell. If oxygen, which is necessary for most cells to expend their stored energy, is absent, active transport stops. Because the ions can no longer be absorbed, the cell dies.

Biological Terms

homeostasis	cytolysis	*How Substances Enter Cells*
The Solutions Around Cells	hypertonic solution	passive transport
isotonic solution	plasmolysis	passive mediated transport
hypotonic solution	contractile vacuole	active transport

Review Questions 3B-3

1. Name the two primary methods by which molecules enter cells through membranes.
2. List several factors affecting passive transport of molecules through plasma membranes.
3. List two conditions necessary for passive mediated transport across a membrane.
4. List the conditions necessary for active transport across a membrane.

Thought Questions

1. Give three examples of how your body adjusts to maintain your homeostasis when your environment changes.
2. If a person were to drink salt water, what type of solution would the cells of the digestive system be in? Would this result in cytolysis or plasmolysis? Explain.

CELLULAR PROCESSES
CYTOLOGY PART II

4A– Cellular Energy
page 89

**4B– Cellular Metabolism
and Protein Synthesis**
page 102

Facet:
Interrelated Metabolisms–Living Things Change Things
(page 105)

FOUR

4A–Cellular Energy

Although cells also depend upon many other conditions in the environment, a constant supply of energy is necessary for cells to carry on all their cellular processes. Cells constantly use energy to maintain their homeostasis, even when they are in the most favorable environments. Energy is used to manufacture needed substances and to tear down others. Expenditure of energy is a primary attribute of life. When cells stop using energy, they are dead.

Cells use amino acids and other substances over and over again in making large different molecules. Energy, however, is a one-time commodity; every time it is used, some escapes and becomes useless. Cells must use energy to make energy-storing molecules. Since some energy escapes with every energy transaction, more energy is needed to *build* an energy-storing molecule than is *stored* in the molecule. To make any large molecule, cells need large quantities of energy.

Stored energy in large molecules is of value to the cell primarily when it is being used. Every time a large molecule is broken apart by the cell to get this stored energy, some of the energy escapes. As a result, the amount of *usable* energy in an energy storage molecule is considerably less than the total amount of energy in the molecule.

Cells constantly battle to maintain a supply of energy. Energy—crucial for all life—is the one commodity that is stored (but not without considerable loss), is used (but never reused), and escapes constantly. Yet *all* living cells need energy at *all* times.

Autotrophs and heterotrophs

Organisms can be classified into two groups, depending on how they obtain their energy. Organisms that make their own food are called **autotrophs.*** Plants, algae, and other organisms are able to capture light energy and make their own food. These are the primary autotrophs. Organisms that depend on other organisms for their energy are called **heterotrophs.*** These include animals, fungi, and most bacteria.

Photosynthesis, the process used by most autotrophs in storing energy (making their food), will be discussed in the next paragraphs. Cellular respirations, the processes all organisms (including autotrophs) use to release energy from storage, will be discussed in the next section.

Photosynthesis

On our planet the sun is the ultimate source of energy used by living things. The sun heats our planet. But warmth, though essential, is not the energy needed to keep living things alive. Chemical energy is necessary for the reactions that maintain the life.

But the sun's energy does not come as chemical energy. Instead, certain organisms are capable of absorbing light energy and converting it into stored chemical energy. This process is called **photosynthesis.*** Green plants and algae, the primary photosynthetic organisms, perform this essential energy transformation not only for themselves but also in large enough quantities to supply stored chemical energy for almost every

living thing. Because it is the essential step between solar energy and life, photosynthesis is one of the most important biological processes.

History of man's knowledge of photosynthesis

Man has long recognized his dependence upon plants for his food. Even the meat you eat comes from animals that ate plants. Before the seventeenth century people believed that plants obtained their substance from the soil. Van Helmont's famous tree experiment (see page 8) demonstrated that most of a plant's substance does not come from the soil. Van Helmont drew the conclusion that virtually all the substance of a plant is water. He was only partly right.

In 1772 Joseph Priestly conducted experiments with air. He discovered that if he burned a candle in a closed jar, the resulting ''impure air'' would kill a mouse put into the jar. He also noted that if a sprig of mint was placed in the jar, the air apparently changed so that the mouse would not die. About seven years later it was discovered that the plant in the jar must be exposed to light in order for this change in the air to take place.

4A-1 *Priestly's experiments with air*

The basic information was clear: green plants use water, affect the air, require light, and make organic matter. In the next hundred years scientists used refined techniques to uncover other facts about the process and formulate the basic concept of photosynthesis.

$$CO_2 + H_2O + \overset{light}{energy} \longrightarrow C_6H_{12}O_6 + O_2\uparrow$$

carbon dioxide   water   sugar   oxygen
(glucose)

---

autotroph: auto- (Gk. AUTOS, self) + (TROPHE, nourishment)

heterotroph hetero- (Gk. HETEROS, other) + -troph (nourishment)

photosynthesis: photo- (Gk. PHOS, light) + -synthesis (to put together)

ATP – The Energy Currency in Cells

Imagine going to a vending machine, reaching into your pocket for a quarter, but finding that all the money you have is a $10 bill. You have enough money for the item that you want, but you cannot get it because you do not have the amount in a usable form.

Similarly, a cell may have many molecules of starch or lipids, but there is *too much* energy in these molecules to be used all at once. If all the energy in a molecule of starch or lipid were released in a cell at one time, that area of the cell would be destroyed. The energy from these molecules must be converted to smaller, usable units. In living organisms, that smaller unit is the energy that is stored in a molecule of **ATP-adenosine triphosphate** (uh DEN uh SEEN ◊ try FAHS FAYT). ATP, you could say, is the penny of cellular energy currency.

ATP is a molecule composed of adenosine (made of a simple sugar and adenine) and three phosphates. Between the phosphates are *high energy bonds*. Although these bonds are unstable, they contain a usable quantity of chemical bond energy. When one phosphate breaks off an ATP molecule, the reaction produces **ADP-adenosine diphosphate** (uh DEN uh SEEN ◊ dye FAHS FAYT), a phosphate, and energy from the bond. The reaction can be written as follows:

$$ATP \rightarrow ADP + P + energy$$

ATP molecule:

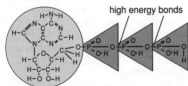

high energy bonds

adenosine + phosphate + phosphate + phosphate

The amount of energy transferred in this reaction is adequate to accomplish many cellular functions requiring energy. Occasionally two or more ATPs supply the energy for a single reaction. Active transport, biosynthesis of molecules, cellular movement, and locomotion are all possible because of energy released from ATP molecules.

Your muscles use ATP energy to contract. But ATP cannot be brought to muscles through the

blood. ATP is very unstable. The flow of blood would break ATP down to ADP plus a phosphate long before it reached your muscles. ATP is a temporary, unstable energy-storage molecule and must constantly be manufactured by every cell as long as it is alive.

An ATP molecule that has given off its energy and has become an ADP plus a phosphate can be reused. With the proper enzymes and an adequate supply of energy, the ADP and a phosphate can recombine to form ATP. The reaction can be summarized as follows:

$$ADP + P + energy \rightarrow ATP$$

A normal adult male uses about 2,800 kilocalories (or 2,800 cal.) of energy a day. That converts to about 5,250 oz. (150 kg) of ATP a day. In a person's body at any given time there is only about 0.175 oz. (0.005 kg) of ATP. Your body must constantly make ATP from ADP and energy if you are to stay alive.

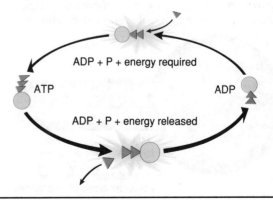

ADP + P + energy required

ATP

ADP

ADP + P + energy released

Until the 1900s it was believed that the process of photosynthesis happened all at once as the equation indicates. Work by Dr. Melvin Calvin in the middle of this century, however, indicated that photosynthesis is actually a series of steps. Calvin exposed a unicellular algae to radioactive isotopes of carbon and oxygen in the form of carbon dioxide or water. He exposed the algae to varying periods of light and then killed the algae. The radioactive water and carbon dioxide were traced into the various products formed during photosynthesis. Much of our present knowledge of the process of photosynthesis is the result of Calvin's work, which earned him a Nobel Prize in 1961.

4A-2 *Dr. Melvin Calvin and the "lollypop" that he used to discover information about photosynthesis*

Review Questions 4A-1

1. What is the primary need of all cells?
2. What are the two major groups of organisms, based on how they obtain their energy?
3. Describe an ATP molecule. What is its function?
4. What is the difference between ADP and ATP? Which holds more energy?
5. What is the primary reason for photosynthesis?
6. List (a) the materials necessary for and (b) the materials produced by photosynthesis.

Chlorophyll and light

Chlorophyll* (KLOHR uh fil), a green-colored pigment, is the primary catalyst of photosynthesis. It has a head portion containing a single magnesium atom and a tail containing a carbon chain. A chlorophyll molecule does not contain iron, but iron appears to be necessary for its formation. In fact, chlorophyll is made only when the cell has a supply of iron and is exposed to light. Plants grown in reduced light or in iron-poor soils lack chlorophyll and appear pale yellowish or whitish.

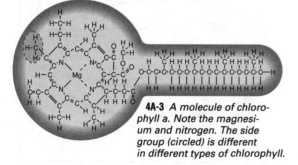

4A-3 *A molecule of chlorophyll a. Note the magnesium and nitrogen. The side group (circled) is different in different types of chlorophyll.*

Other Plant Pigments and Photosynthesis

There are at least four different types of chlorophyll, designated chlorophylls *a*, *b*, *c*, and *d*. Chlorophyll *a* is a bright blue green and has the formula $C_{55}H_{72}O_5N_4Mg$. Chlorophyll *b*, which often accompanies chlorophyll *a* in seed plants, differs only slightly in the amount of hydrogen and oxygen: $C_{55}H_{70}O_6N_4Mg$. Chlorophyll *b* appears a yellow green.

Other pigments often coexist with chlorophylls in many photosynthetic cells. Although these other pigments are usually in considerably lower quantities than the chlorophylls, they often are abundant enough to alter the color we see. Neither these pigments nor chlorophylls *b*, *c*, and *d* carry on photosynthesis. Rather, they absorb wavelengths of light energy that are not absorbed by chlorophyll *a* and pass that energy to chlorophyll *a* to be used in photosynthesis. In this way plants in dim light can use more wavelengths of the available light.

---

chlorophyll: chloro- (green) + -phyll (PHULLON, leaf)

Chlorophyll and other light-capturing pigments are found in the grana of the chloroplasts in photosynthetic eucaryotic cells. The chlorophyll appears to replace a number of the lipids in the membranes of the grana.

White light has wavelengths of all the colors of light. A prism can separate the wavelengths into a spectrum of color. Actually, when something appears red, it is reflecting red light waves

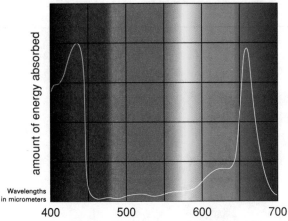

4A-4 *Colors of light absorbed by chlorophyll a*

and absorbing all the others. This should tell you what wavelengths, or colors, of light are necessary for photosynthesis.

Since chlorophyll *a* is a blue green pigment, it is safe to assume that it reflects the blues and the greens, and absorbs the violets and the reds. Chlorophyll *b* is yellow green and therefore absorbs some of the same colors as chlorophyll *a,* but it also absorbs some of the blues not absorbed by chlorophyll *a* and rejects a few of the yellow-greens that chlorophyll *a* absorbs.

The process of photosynthesis

In some of Calvin's photosynthesis experiments with algae, he used water and carbon dioxide molecules that contained the radioactive isotope oxygen-18. This radioactive isotope degenerates, releasing radiation which can affect photographic paper. By taking ''pictures'' of the algae that had been exposed to radioactive water or carbon dioxide, Calvin learned what happened to these two different molecules during photosynthesis.

In one set of experiments Calvin exposed the algae to normal carbon dioxide and radioactive water. He found that the oxygen which was given off by the process of photosynthesis was all oxygen-18. None of the sugar produced had any oxygen-18 in it. Note the following equation for photosynthesis:

$$12\,H_2O^* + 6\,CO_2 + \underset{energy}{light} \xrightarrow{\text{chlorophyll}} C_6H_{12}O_6 + 6\,H_2O + 6\,O_2^* \uparrow$$

The oxygen-18 which Calvin used is indicated by an asterisk (*). The 12 molecules of water on the left supply the 12 atoms of oxygen (6 oxygen molecules, O_2) given off. The water on the right side of the equation is new water. You cannot reduce the formula by canceling 6 water molecules from each side since the water molecules on one side are not the same water molecules on the other side. Later studies demonstrated that the oxygen in the glucose molecule came from the carbon dioxide. This, then, indicates that water is a by-product of photosynthesis.

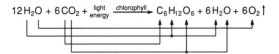

Further experiments with carbon-14 helped to establish the accuracy of this simplified equation. The equation of photosynthesis given above is balanced, as the arrows beneath the substances indicate.

What has happened to the light energy put in on the left side? No energy is expressed on the right side. Some energy, of course, has been lost. Energy was used to make the new water and to put together the glucose molecule. In other words, the energy that did not escape is now in the molecules which have been made by the process. The energy in the product's water and oxygen is of little use to the organism, but the energy stored in the glucose molecule will be used to carry on cellular processes.

Conditions for photosynthesis

Adequate supplies of the right wavelengths of light are necessary for photosynthesis. If they do

A Closer Look at Photosynthesis

Experiments have revealed that photosynthesis actually occurs in two separate, yet closely related, steps. The first is called the **photo phase**, or *light reactions,* of photosynthesis. The photo phase takes place in the membranes of the grana of the chloroplast, where the chlorophyll and other necessary enzymes are. In the photo phase the light energy is absorbed and energizes a chlorophyll *a* molecule.

Energized chlorophyll *a* molecules use their energy to do two things: break apart water molecules and form ATP molecules from ADPs plus phosphates. The breaking apart of a water molecule by energized chlorophyll is called **photolysis*** (fo TAHL uh sis). The oxygen is released, and if cellular concentrations of oxygen become sufficiently high, the excess oxygen diffuses into the atmosphere. The hydrogen and some electrons from the water pass from one carrier molecule to another. As this happens, energy is released, allowing ATP to be made. The energy held in the ATP molecules as well as hydrogen and electrons will be needed in the second phase of photosynthesis.

The **dark phase**, or *dark reactions,* of photosynthesis takes place in the stroma of the chloroplast, where the necessary enzymes and products are located. The dark reactions may take place either in the dark or in the presence of light but require the products of the light reactions. When the photo phase stops, the dark reactions may continue for a short time, but soon they will run out of

Light Phase of Photosynthesis

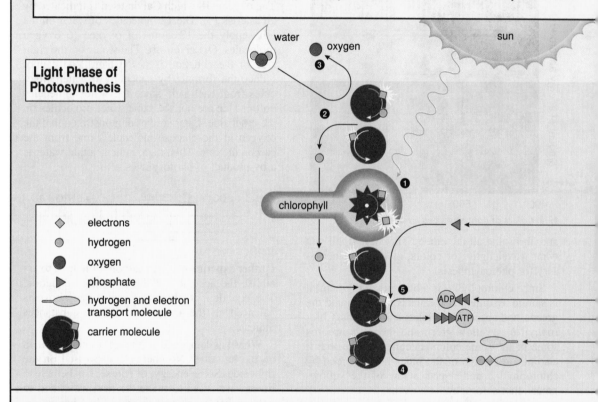

Key:
- ◇ electrons
- ● hydrogen
- ● oxygen
- ▷ phosphate
- ⬭ hydrogen and electron transport molecule
- ● carrier molecule

The Process of Photosynthesis

❶ *Chlorophyll absorbs light energy.* Light absorbed by chlorophylls and by other pigments is passed to chlorophyll *a*, which becomes *energized chlorophyll.* As energized chlorophyll releases its energy, it becomes normal chlorophyll.

❷ *Photolysis occurs.* Some of the energy from the energized chlorophyll is used to break apart a water molecule.

❸ *Oxygen is released.* The oxygen from the water molecule is released into the cytoplasm and is used, or it escapes into the environment. Two oxygen atoms combine, forming atmospheric oxygen (O_2).

❹ *Hydrogen and electrons are bonded.* Rather than diffusing out of the cell, hydrogen and electrons are passed from one carrier molecule to another. They will be used in the dark phase.

❺ *An ATP molecule is made.* Some of the energy from the energized chlorophyll molecule is used to manufacture an ATP molecule from an ADP plus a phosphate.

❻ *Carbon dioxide is fixed.* A carbon dioxide molecule which has diffused into the cell bonds to RuDP (ribulose diphosphate). RuDP is a five-carbon sugar with two phosphates bonded to it. The resulting six-carbon sugar is very unstable and

photolysis: photo- (light) + -lysis (a loosening)

necessary materials. Because in the dark reactions carbon dioxide is combined with the products of the light reaction to synthesize glucose, the dark reactions are sometimes called the *synthetic phase*.

Note that all the products of the light phase are either used in the dark phase or given off. All the products of the dark phase either are end products of photosynthesis or are reused in the photo or dark phases. The dark phase of photosynthesis must therefore happen at the same time as the light phase. If the dark phase did not happen along with the photo phase, all the cell's transport molecules would soon have hydrogen and electrons attached to them, and photolysis would stop. The dark phase, however, can continue in the dark only as long as the products of the light

phase are available. When all the hydrogen and electrons affixed to the hydrogen transport molecules have been used, the dark phase must stop until the light phase supplies it with more hydrogen and electrons.

During the dark phase **PGA (phosphoglyceric acid)** accepts hydrogen and electrons and the energy and phosphate from an ATP molecule to form **PGAL (phosphoglyceraldehyde)**, which is the preliminary product of photosynthesis. Several PGALs combine to form glucose and **RuDP (ribulose diphosphate)**—the carbon dioxide-fixing molecule of the first of the dark phase. If the dark phase does not run, the cell soon runs short of RuDP. The entire process of photosynthesis must continue, or it must stop completely.

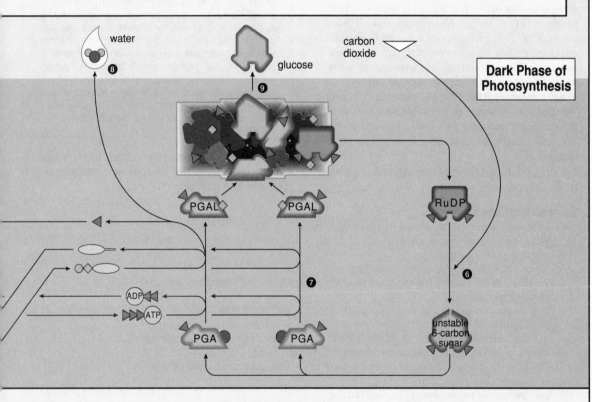

Dark Phase of Photosynthesis

breaks apart to form two molecules of PGA (phosphoglyceric acid). PGA is a three-carbon sugar with a phosphate attached to it.

❼ *PGA is converted to PGAL.* PGA is energized by the energy and a phosphate from an ATP molecule and then receives hydrogen and electrons from a transport molecule. Using these products of the photo phase, PGA forms PGAL (phosphoglyceraldehyde). The transport

molecule and ADP released during the formation of PGAL may be used again in the photo phase.

❽ *Water is given off.* In the conversion of PGA to PGAL, a "new water" is released into the stroma.

❾ *PGAL is converted to glucose.* PGAL can be, and often is, used directly by the cell. PGAL, however, is not an efficient storage molecule. If PGAL ($C_3H_5O_3{\sim}(P)$) were doubled, it would need to obtain only

two hydrogen atoms and to release two phosphates (indicated by the ${\sim}(P)$ in the formula) to be glucose. Actually, several PGAL molecules with hydrogen (from the light phase) combine, release phosphates, and thus form molecules of glucose and RuDP. The RuDP can then be used in the fixing of carbon dioxide as the dark phase begins again.

not absorb enough energy, chlorophyll *a* molecules cannot become energized enough to carry on photosynthesis. The cell must be able to absorb sufficient carbon dioxide. This is seldom a problem since carbon dioxide normally accounts for about 0.03% of the atmosphere by volume. A greenhouse with improper ventilation or with drastic temperature changes can affect the supply of carbon dioxide, and photosynthesis may cease.

Proper temperatures for photosynthesis vary from plant to plant. For most plants room temperature (21° C or 70° F) is about right. Above about 32° C (90° F), however, many of the plant's enzymes do not function properly for photosynthesis. In midday during hot summer months, many plants do not carry on photosynthesis. The lower temperature limit for photosynthesis is near freezing for some plants, but more moderate temperatures are required by others. In most plants the functioning of chlorophyll is temperature dependent.

Occasionally a lack of water will cause a plant to stop photosynthesis. On hot, dry summer days

---

Chemosynthesis: Other Autotrophs

There are, however, a few bacteria that are capable of obtaining energy from inorganic chemicals they break apart, a process called **chemosynthesis*** (KEE moh SIN thih sis). These bacteria can then use that energy to synthesize sugar. Since chemosynthetic bacteria do not depend on other organisms for their food, they are autotrophs.

Chemosynthetic bacteria often grow in dark areas with little organic matter in their environment. Some of these bacteria change ammonia to nitrites and nitrites to nitrates; others use iron compounds. Probably the best-known chemosynthetic bacteria use sulfur compounds and produce sulfur dioxide. A walk through a swamp may disturb some collections of this gas that are trapped underwater. The rotten egg odor of sulfur dioxide that bubbles to the surface may have been produced by chemosynthetic bacteria.

---

sufficient water may not be absorbed by the roots and transported up the stem to maintain photosynthesis in the leaves.

Review Questions 4A-2

1. Describe chlorophyll *a* and tell its function. What colors of light does it absorb?
2. What are the functions of chlorophylls *b, c,* and *d,* and other plant pigments that do not carry on photosynthesis?
3. Write a chemical equation for photosynthesis.
4. What inputs are needed for and what products are made by the photophase of photosynthesis?
5. What inputs are needed for and what products are made by the dark phase of photosynthesis?
6. Tell the function in relation to photosynthesis of the following substances: chlorophyll, hydrogen and electron transport molecules, PGAL, and RuDP.
7. Tell how the photo and dark phases of photosynthesis are dependent upon each other.
8. Why is *the dark phase* a misleading name?
9. List the conditions necessary for photosynthesis.
10. What are the two types of autotrophs? List an example of each.

Cellular Respiration

You probably think of respiration as *breathing*—air being taken into and forced out of your lungs. Breathing is only the first step in your body's respiration. Oxygen obtained by breathing is transported to your cells where **cellular respiration** takes place. Cellular respiration is the breaking down of a food substance into usable cellular energy in the form of ATP. In most cells glucose

---

chemosynthesis: chemo- (chemistry or chemical) + -synthesis (to put together)

is the food substance; but lipids, other monosaccharides, and even proteins can be used.

Cellular respiration may be **aerobic*** (eh ROH bik) (requiring oxygen) or **anaerobic*** (AN uh ROH bik) (not requiring oxygen). Most cells carry on aerobic respiration. Many cells which normally carry on aerobic respiration can, when necessary, operate anaerobically. There are some bacteria and fungi which carry on only anaerobic respiration. We will discuss the primary aerobic cellular respirations first and then a couple of important anaerobic respirations.

Aerobic cellular respiration

Aerobic cellular respiration can be compared to burning. If you hold a lighted match to a sugar cube, the match will supply the activation energy necessary to set the sugar on fire. The burning sugar releases large amounts of energy as heat and light. Carbon dioxide and water vapor are also released, even though you cannot see them.

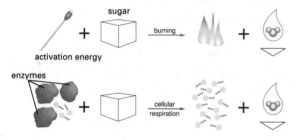

4A-5 *A comparison of burning and cellular respiration*

If you were to cover the flame in an airtight chamber, the fire would soon be extinguished because of a lack of oxygen.

In aerobic cellular respiration, the sugar glucose requires a small amount of activation energy

to begin a series of enzyme-controlled chemical changes that release energy which is then trapped in ATP molecules. Carbon dioxide and water molecules are released in cellular respiration, as in burning. Cells cannot carry on aerobic respiration if they do not receive oxygen, and in time many will die.

Aerobic cellular respiration is the opposite of photosynthesis. Photosynthesis combines water, carbon dioxide, and light energy to form glucose. Aerobic cellular respiration breaks down glucose to form water, carbon dioxide, and energy. The materials which are needed for the one are the products of the other.

Photosynthesis can be generalized thus:

$$H_2O + CO_2 + \underset{energy}{light} \xrightarrow{chlorophyll} C_6H_{12}O_6 + O_2$$

Cellular respiration can be generalized thus:

$$C_6H_{12}O_6 + O_2 \longrightarrow H_2O + CO_2 + ATP \text{ (energy)}$$

These processes, however, are not the reverse of each other. For example, chlorophyll is not used in cellular respiration. Although some chemicals function in both processes, they proceed down different enzyme paths. These differences are necessary because the purposes of the two processes are different. Photosynthesis captures *light* energy and converts it to *stored chemical energy*. Respiration takes *stored chemical energy* and converts it to a *ready-to-use chemical energy* (ATP).

The light energy harnessed by a chlorophyll molecule during photosynthesis is made useful to all cellular processes by cellular respiration. The atoms of oxygen, carbon, and hydrogen are essentially the same after these processes, but the

4A-6 *A comparison of photosynthesis and aerobic cellular respiration*

aerobic: aero- (Gk. AER, air) + -be (life)

anaerobic: an- (Gk. AN-, without) + -aero- (air) + -be (life)

A Closer Look at Aerobic Cellular Respiration

Aerobic cellular respiration can follow several different paths. Here we will look at the steps of the most common form of breaking down a glucose molecule to water, carbon dioxide, and ATP energy.

Aerobic cellular respiration can be divided into three phases. The first, called **glycolysis*** (glye KAHL uh sis), involves the breakdown of glucose to **pyruvic acid**. Glycolysis takes place in the cytoplasm, which contains the enzymes necessary for this series of reactions. Because glycolysis does not require oxygen, it is considered anaerobic. The products of glycolysis (pyruvic acid, hydrogen, and electrons) are shuttled to the mitochondria to continue aerobic cellular respiration.

The next two main steps in aerobic respiration of glucose are the **citric acid cycle (Krebs cycle)** and the **hydrogen and electron transport system.** Both of these processes happen in the mitochondria. The enzymes of the citric acid cycle are found in the fluid inside the inner membrane of the mitochon-

Glycolysis

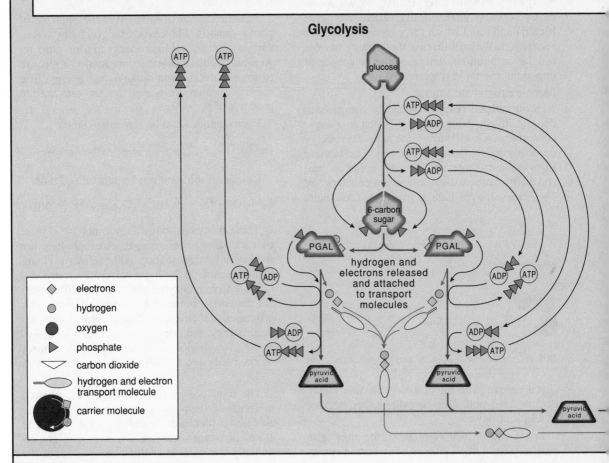

I. Glycolysis

Two molecules of ATP supply the activation energy necessary to start glycolysis. After receiving energy and phosphates from ATP molecules, a six-carbon sugar splits into two molecules of PGAL. Each molecule of PGAL releases a hydrogen and two electrons (held temporarily by a transport molecule) and supplies the energy to form two ATP molecules. A total of four ATP molecules are made from the energy given off by the breakdown of one glucose molecule to two pyruvic acid molecules. Glycolysis, then, yields a net gain of two ATP molecules.

II. Citric Acid Cycle (Krebs Cycle)

The second stage of aerobic cellular respiration starts with pyruvic acid and converts it to acetyl coenzyme A (acetyl CoA). This process gives off carbon dioxide, hydrogen, and electrons. The carbon dioxide diffuses into the cell and, if concentrations in the cell become high enough, into the environment. The hydrogen and electrons are held temporarily by a transport molecule. Acetyl

glycolysis: glyco- (sweet) + -lysis (a loosening)

dria. The enzymes of the hydrogen and electron transport system are part of the inner membrane of their mitochondria.

Both the citric acid cycle and the hydrogen and electron transport system are considered aerobic—that is, they require oxygen. Although the citric acid cycle reactions require no oxygen, the hydrogen and electron transport system does. If no oxygen is present, the final enzyme cannot release its electrons to receive the next set of electrons that comes down the system; thus the system stops operat-

ing. Without oxygen it does not take long for all the molecules in the transport system to have electrons attached to them, waiting to pass them on. If the transport system backs up, the hydrogen and electron transfer molecules in the cycle soon become filled. Without these acceptors, the citric acid cycle cannot operate. A lack of oxygen, then, eventually backs up both the hydrogen and electron transport system and the citric acid cycle. Since both processes ultimately require oxygen, they are aerobic.

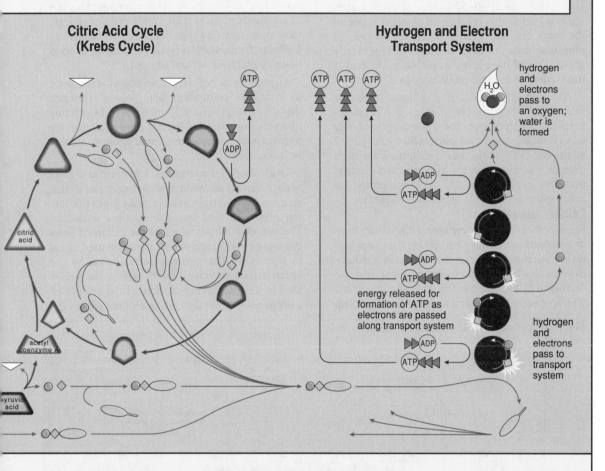

Citric Acid Cycle (Krebs Cycle)

Hydrogen and Electron Transport System

hydrogen and electrons pass to an oxygen; water is formed

H_2O

energy released for formation of ATP as electrons are passed along transport system

hydrogen and electrons pass to transport system

citric acid

acetyl coenzyme A

pyruvic acid

III. Hydrogen and Electron Transport System

coenzyme A is then converted to citric acid (one of the primary substances found in citrus fruits) and enters the citric acid cycle. This cycle is a series of enzymatically controlled steps that give off carbon dioxide, hydrogen and electrons (to a transport molecule), and sufficient energy to make an ATP molecule indirectly. The enzymes of the citric acid cycle are found in the mitochondria.

The third step in aerobic cellular respiration is a transport system for hydrogen and electrons. The energy-containing transport molecules with their hydrogen and electrons received during glycolysis and the citric acid cycle enter this transport system. The hydrogen and electron transport system is a series of enzymes and carrier molecules bound to the membrane of the cristae of the mito-

chondria. As electrons pass from one enzyme to another, energy is lost. Occasionally, these energy losses are enough to form an ATP molecule. The final enzyme of the transport system allows oxygen, which diffuses from outside the cell, to combine with hydrogen and electrons to form water.

energy involved has been changed several times, and much of it has been lost.

ATP energy from a glucose molecule

The aerobic cellular respiration of glucose traps, in the form of ATP molecules, approximately 50-60% of the energy that was in the glucose molecule. Although a 40-50% loss of energy may seem wasteful, this breakdown of sugar is one of the most efficient energy processes known. In most manmade machines (cars, for example) only about 20% of the energy available in the fuel is used. Most of the rest radiates as heat.

Although glycolysis of 1 glucose molecule makes 4 ATP molecules, it takes 2 ATP molecules to start glycolysis. There is a net gain of only 2 ATP molecules. In the citric acid cycle, only 2 additional ATP molecules are formed for each glucose molecule. But the hydrogen and electron transport system forms 32 ATP molecules for every glucose molecule in cellular respiration.

Cellular fermentation

Some cells exist in environments that do not have available oxygen. Many bacteria in the lower layers of swamps, lakes, or the ocean do not have oxygen available in their environment and are destroyed by exposure to free oxygen. Other cells which operate best with a supply of oxygen can occasionally operate without oxygen. For example, when you engage in strenuous physical activity, you may begin to breathe heavily but still be unable to supply enough oxygen for your muscle cells. Your muscles will then not carry on sufficient aerobic cellular respiration to supply the needed ATP. If cells in these circumstances are to supply themselves with usable cellular energy, they must carry on a type of cellular fermentation. **Cellular fermentation** is the breakdown of food (usually glucose) without oxygen.

Glycolysis in cellular fermentation is the same as in cellular respiration: one glucose is broken down to two pyruvic acid molecules. Depending upon the organism and the enzymes available, the pyruvic acid is usually converted to either alcohol or lactic acid.

In **alcoholic fermentation**, a pyruvic acid molecule gives off a carbon dioxide molecule; it then receives the hydrogen and electrons given off during glycolysis and forms an alcohol molecule. The use of the hydrogen and the electrons frees the transfer molecule so that it can be used again in glycolysis. This process is carried on by the bacteria used to make liquors and by the yeasts used in breads. Baking evaporates the alcohol of a bread dough, and the carbon dioxide causes the

4A-7 *A comparison of cellular fermentations*

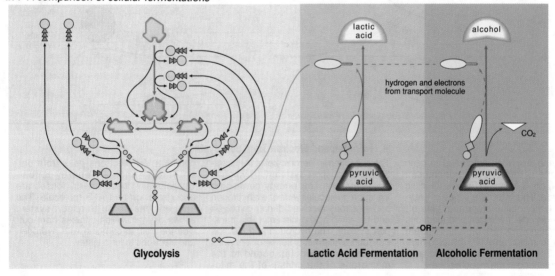

Glycolysis Lactic Acid Fermentation Alcoholic Fermentation

dough to rise. Some plants can use this form of fermentation when necessary.

Lactic acid fermentation is used by some microorganisms (such as bacteria that form yogurt and cottage cheese) and, when necessary, by many animal cells. Pyruvic acid takes the hydrogen and electrons from glycolysis, freeing the transfer molecule. The resulting *lactic acid* contains much energy. When ample oxygen is available, some cells, especially in multicellular animals, have the ability to convert lactic acid back to pyruvic acid, which can then be used in aerobic cellular respiration. Cellular fermentation supplies no ATP energy beyond that obtained from glycolysis. Cellular fermentation, therefore, produces only a net gain of two ATP per glucose molecule.

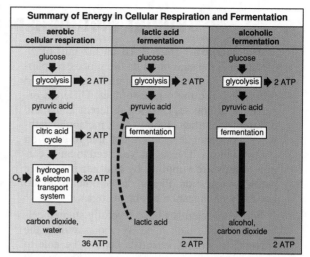

4A-8

Biological Terms

autotroph	PGA (phosphoglyceric acid)	pyruvic acid
heterotroph	PGAL (phosphoglyceraldehyde)	citric acid cycle
ATP (adenosine triphosphate)	RuDP (ribulose diphosphate)	hydrogen and electron
ADP (adenosine diphosphate)	chemosynthesis	transport system
Photosynthesis	*Cellular Respiration*	cellular fermentation
photosynthesis	cellular respiration	alcoholic fermentation
chlorophyll	aerobic	lactic acid fermentation
photo phase	anaerobic	
photolysis	aerobic cellular respiration	
dark phase	glycolysis	

Review Questions 4A-3

1. What is the difference between cellular respiration and breathing?
2. Name the two types of cellular respiration and list organisms that carry on each type.
3. Give a chemical equation for aerobic cellular respiration.
4. Where do each of the following occur: glycolysis, citric acid cycle, hydrogen and electron transport system?
5. What is required to activate glycolysis? What is produced by glycolysis?
6. What is required to activate and what is produced by the citric acid cycle?
7. What is required to activate the hydrogen and electron transport system? What is produced by the hydrogen and electron transport system?
8. Glycolysis is anaerobic because it does not require oxygen. The citric acid cycle does not require oxygen but is considered aerobic. Why?
9. List two forms of cellular fermentation. Give the beginning substances and the end products of each.

Thought Questions

1. Why must cells have a continual supply of energy?
2. Compare and contrast (a) photosynthesis and aerobic cellular respiration and (b) aerobic cellular respiration with alcoholic fermentation and with lactic acid fermentation.

4B–Cellular Metabolism and Protein Synthesis

The **metabolism*** (muh TAB uh LIZ um) of an organism is the sum of all its life processes: photosynthesis, movement, respiration, growth, and everything else the organism does. Different organisms, of course, carry on different kinds and different quantities of the various metabolic pathways. For example, you are not able to carry on photosynthesis. The sugars you need to build carbohydrates are supplied by another metabolic pathway: digestion. Plants, on the other hand, do not carry on digestion to obtain sugars.

For years scientists have carefully studied cellular metabolic pathways. By understanding the chemical reactions, scientists hope to be able to correct metabolic problems that are either causing disease or environmental harm. For example, if scientists determine that a disease is caused by certain cells making too much of a chemical, they have a better chance of developing a treatment if they know how the cell makes that chemical. Suppose high temperatures and abundant nitrogen in a pond cause algae to make a chemical that kills fish. Scientists have a better idea of how to control the chemical manufacture if they understand the metabolic processes cells use to make it.

The understanding of cellular metabolism has permitted scientists to encourage certain processes that are profitable to us and to discourage those that are harmful. At one time scientists had hoped to greatly alter a cell's metabolic pathways, and even introduce different metabolisms to various cells. (Some people hope to save on their grocery bills by introducing photosynthetic metabolism to their children. The cosmetic effects, however, are not the only drawbacks to this scheme.) The cell's metabolism can be slightly altered, but major changes are prohibited by the complexities of, and the interrelations between, metabolic pathways in the organism and its cells.

Before discussing how some of the metabolic pathways relate to each other, we need to discuss what some scientists consider the most important one, the one which controls and permits all the others: protein synthesis.

Protein Synthesis

The discovery of how proteins are made was a major breakthrough in the understanding of life. An organism's ability to manufacture proteins enables it to carry on its life processes. Since what a cell can and cannot do depends upon its *enzymes,* cells are controlled by enzymes, which are proteins. In addition, almost every cellular and extracellular substance made by a cell is a *structural protein* or contains a structural protein.

The mechanism for protein manufacture needs to be exceptionally flexible, able to produce the several thousand different proteins found in every cell. But the process must also be stable. When the amino acids of a particular protein line up, they must be in the same sequence every time. If the sequence alters as much as one amino acid, the protein will often not function properly. Thus the process of protein synthesis must manufacture a vast number of different proteins, but it must also manufacture thousands of exact copies of these proteins.

A protein, you will recall, is a twisted and looped *polypeptide chain* of amino acids. Several of the amino acids in this chain may be bonded to other specific amino acids within the chain. Thus, proteins have a specific shape. Not all proteins are a single chain of amino acids. Some proteins are a bonding of several different amino acid chains. Lipids or carbohydrates or inorganic materials combine with some amino acid chains to form functional proteins.

The code of life

The sequence of the four bases found in cellular DNA determines the sequence of the approximately 20 different amino acids found in that cell's proteins. It is important that you understand the code before we discuss the mechanism responsible for the lineup of amino acids.

Do you realize that you speak in a code? Each word in our language is a symbol for something. The 26 letters of the alphabet make hundreds of thousands of different English words. The words

---

metabolism: meta- (Gk. META, change) + -bolism (BALLEIN, to throw)

express even more ideas when arranged into sentences.

The code of life uses the same basic format. The four bases–adenine (AD uh NEEN), *thymine* (THY MEEN), *guanine* (GWAH NEEN), and *cytosine* (SY toh seen)–can be called the alphabet of life. These "letters" are arranged in groups as "words" that may be interpreted as amino acids. All the "words" in the DNA code are 3 letters long. Three bases then become the code for a particular amino acid. The code of life, then, is formed of *triplets of bases* called **codons.** When many of these codons are in a particular sequence, they are read to form a chain of amino acids.

A series of words in a sentence has more meaning than just the words alone. The polypeptide chain of amino acids also becomes more than just a string of amino acids. It twists and bonds and combines with other amino acid chains or other substances to become functional proteins.

4B-1	Messenger RNA Codons for Amino Acids				
first letter	**second letter**				**third letter**
	U	C	A	G	
U	phenylalanine	serine	tyrosine	cysteine	U
	phenylalanine	serine	tyrosine	cysteine	C
	leucine	serine	stop	stop	A
	leucine	serine	stop	tryptophan	G
C	leucine	proline	histidine	arginine	U
	leucine	proline	histidine	arginine	C
	leucine	proline	glutamine	arginine	A
	leucine	proline	glutamine	arginine	G
A	isoleucine	threonine	asparagine	serine	U
	isoleucine	threonine	asparagine	serine	C
	isoleucine	threonine	lysine	arginine	A
	(start) methionine	threonine	lysine	arginine	G
G	valine	alanine	aspartate	glycine	U
	valine	alanine	aspartate	glycine	C
	valine	alanine	glutamate	glycine	A
	valine	alanine	glutamate	glycine	G

The first base of the messenger RNA codon is found on the left, the second base in the middle, the third on the right. Thus, UGG codes for tryptophan, the only codon for that amino acid. Many codons code for the same amino acid. For example, GGU, GGC, GGA, and GGG all code for glycine. AUG, methionine, is the beginning amino acid and UAA or UAC or UGA is the last codon, indicating a stop of the polypeptide chain.

In DNA each of the 3 characters that make a word (codon) can be any one of the 4 letters representing the 4 bases. Therefore, the total number of possible combinations of 4 letters making a 3-letter codon is 64. Because there are about 20 amino acids, some amino acids are coded with more than one codon. There are some special codons believed to start and stop the process of lining up amino acids. You may consider them as punctuation marks in the DNA code.

Three types of RNA

Three different types of RNA are necessary to interpret the sequence of bases in a DNA molecule into the sequence of amino acids in a polypeptide chain. The first type is *messenger RNA.*

DNA, you may recall, is capable of manufacturing RNA by *transcription.* Transcription places the DNA code into the sequence of bases in an RNA molecule. (Recall that thymine in DNA is replaced by uracil in RNA.) The RNA molecule that contains the code for a polypeptide chain of amino acids is called **messenger RNA*** (mRNA). The mRNA carries the code from the DNA in the nucleus to the ribosomes in the cytoplasm, where the code is "read." The mRNA contains the proper sequence of codons to be interpreted as a chain of amino acids.

Amino acids are not assembled into proteins directly by the mRNA. Instead, the amino acids are attached to **transfer RNA** (tRNA) molecules, the second type of RNA. The tRNA molecules, about 80 nucleotides long, are formed in the nucleus. The chain of nucleotides forms several loops, taking a cloverleaf shape. At one loop of this configuration are 3 unattached bases called the **anticodon.** The anticodons will combine with the codons of the mRNA. If mRNA has the codon GAC, the tRNA that lines up on that codon will have the anticodon CUG. Anticodons, then, consist of bases which are the complements of the bases in the codon with which they align.

The free end of the cloverleaf stem of most tRNA molecules has the 3 nucleotide bases CCA. Using a high energy bond an amino acid attaches to the final base (adenine) of this sequence. The bonding of an amino acid to a tRNA requires the

Messenger RNA is also called *template RNA.*

energy of one ATP molecule. This energy is temporarily stored in the high energy bond. The particular amino acid which bonds to a specific tRNA molecule does not depend upon the final nucleotide bases, but upon different enzymes in the cytoplasm that bond each of the amino acids to the proper tRNA.

Ribosomal RNA (rRNA), the third type, is also manufactured by the DNA of the nucleus. The rRNA, however, does not come from the same area of a DNA molecule as does the mRNA. But rRNA combines with various proteins to form ribosomes. Some of the proteins located around rRNA are enzymes necessary for reading the codons of mRNA. Others proteins are enzymes for joining amino acids. Only at the point where mRNA is in contact with the ribosome are amino acids lined up to manufacture a polypeptide chain.

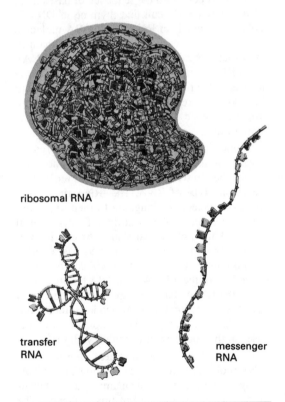

4B-2 *Three types of RNA*

The Manufacture of Messenger RNA

The mRNA was once believed to be a simple copy of one side of a DNA molecule. Today scientists believe the transcription process is only the first step. The RNA manufactured by transcription is actually longer than the number of nucleotides needed to code for the polypeptide chain of amino acids it produces. The transcribed RNA contains **exons** and **introns.** The *exons* are the sections of RNA that are actually needed in the mRNA. Exons are read as codons when making the protein. The *introns* are sections of transcribed RNA that must be cut out. They are not read when making the protein. Although the process is not completely understood, it appears

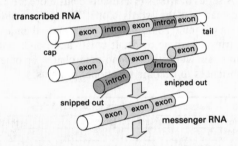

that introns are "snipped out" and the exons "glued" together as mRNA is formed.

During transcription an RNA *cap* is attached to one end of the mRNA. The cap is believed to deal with the mRNA lining up on the ribosome. On the other end a *poly-A tail* is attached. The tail is made of many adenine (poly-A) nucleotides. Scientists are not yet sure the function of the poly-A tail.

The discovery of exons and introns has opened up considerable speculation. Does it ever happen that an intron is kept? Are some exons ever left out? Does this result in different proteins? What might cause a cell to keep an intron it used to leave out, or leave out what once was an exon? Is this a possible form of natural genetic variation? Could this process cause additional genetic material needed by some cells as they spontaneously form cancer cells? Do exons and introns have anything to do with antibody formation and immunity? Do these RNA sections account for some of the protein differences seen in cells as they age? Only additional experimentation will tell.

FACETS OF BIOLOGY

4B-1

Interrelated Metabolisms–Living Things Change Things

How often have you heard statements like "Eat your meat; you need the protein" or "Don't eat those french fries; they are loaded with fats" or "That soft drink is loaded with sugar, and no one needs extra sugar." All of these statements may be true, but they often lead to a false conclusion: fats are always fats, proteins are always proteins, and sugars are always carbohydrates. Such is not the case.

A quick, superficial glance, such as the one presented here, will likely cause the various cellular processes to appear distinct. They are not, however. The end products of the various cellular processes are related and can be changed from one to another.

Most cells also have the ability to transform substances within one process to another process. By the

Plants produce carbohydrates by photosynthesis and manufacture the lipids and proteins they need from carbohydrates.

interrelationship of cellular processes, cells can change whatever organic substance they have in abundance into almost any other organic substance that they normally produce. This is essential for cells that do not have in their environment all the substances they need.

Plant cells, for example, produce abundant carbohydrates but obtain few or no lipids or proteins from their environment. Plants cannot eat and digest protein and lipid substances as humans do. They must, therefore, be able to convert the sugars they produce into the lipids and proteins necessary to form their cellular structures. Another example: humans do not have to eat fats to get fat (store excess lipids). One can eat too many carbohydrates and store the energy as lipids around the waist. (It is easier, however, to gain excess energy by eating lipids because fats have twice as much energy per unit of weight than carbohydrates.)

Carbohydrate and lipid metabolisms

One of the most important anabolic processes is *photosynthesis,* by which water, carbon dioxide, and energy are combined to form glucose. With the proper enzymes, glucose can easily be changed into other monosaccharides. With other enzymes monosaccharides can be converted into disaccharides, starches, cellulose, or any other

natural carbohydrate. Some cells do not have the enzymes to make every one of these carbohydrate conversions because the cells do not normally require all the various carbohydrates. Cells usually have the enzymes necessary to convert the carbohydrates they have to the glucose and glucose back to the carbohydrates. One notable exception, however, is cellulose in plant cell walls. Once cellulose is made, most plant cells cannot break it down.

PGAL is the first stable product of photosynthesis, the build-up of sugar, and is also involved in *glycolysis,* the breakdown of sugar. PGAL can also be converted to *glycerol,* one of the components of most lipids. Through a series of steps, simple sugars can be converted into fatty acids. Most cells, therefore, can make carbohydrates into fats and fats into carbohydrates. If a human diet does not include sufficient fats, the liver can synthesize fats from carbohydrates. Fats, however, are not as easily converted to sugars. Generally this conversion occurs only when a person is dieting or starving.

Cellular respiration changes glucose and oxygen to water, carbon dioxide, and ATP energy. That is not all that cellular respiration does. Fatty acids can be synthesized from *acetyl* (uh SEET uhl) *coenzyme A* (acetyl CoA), and the reverse is also true: most cells can also break long fatty acid mol-

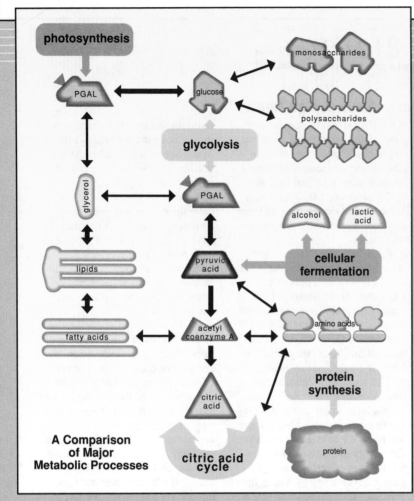

photosynthesis

monosaccharides

PGAL

glucose

polysaccharides

glycolysis

glycerol

PGAL

alcohol

lactic acid

lipids

pyruvic acid

cellular fermentation

fatty acids

acetyl coenzyme A

amino acids

protein synthesis

citric acid

A Comparison of Major Metabolic Processes

protein

citric acid cycle

not require the same essential amino acids. Those that are essential for one organism may be easily synthesized by another.

Amino acids can also enter the citric acid cycle and be broken down to carbon dioxide, water, and ATP energy. Some amino acids can be converted to acetyl CoA or to pyruvic acid and then broken down as energy sources. Long before a person starves to death, his body will begin to convert proteins, including muscle proteins, into usable ATP energy. It is better to be thin, weak, and alive than it is to be muscular, strong, and dead from lack of energy.

Nucleic acid metabolism

Nucleic acids are formed of nucleotides. Usually a nucleotide can be used over and over again. As messenger RNA falls apart with use, its component nucleotides can be resynthesized into more RNA or DNA. If a cell is to grow and expand its protein-manufacturing abilities or if the cell is to replicate its DNA and divide to form two cells, it will need additional nucleotides. A nucleotide is composed of a sugar, a phosphate, and a nitrogen-containing base. The sugar can be supplied by carbohydrate metabolism. The phosphate is an inorganic substance which most cells absorb easily. The nitrogen-containing base is similar to some of the amino acids. A cell with the proper enzymes can synthesize nucleotides.

Review questions on page 108.

ecules into pieces of 2 carbons and then use these 2-carbon molecules to make an acetyl CoA that can be used in the *citric acid cycle*.

For each acetyl CoA entering the citric acid cycle, there is a net gain of 16 ATP molecules. An 18-carbon fatty acid can produce 128 ATP molecules by way of the citric acid cycle and the *hydrogen and electron transport system*. Using the same catabolisms, 18 carbons in the form of sugar (3 glucose molecules) can produce only 108 ATP molecules.

Protein metabolism

The amino acids necessary for protein synthesis may be obtained by digestion and absorption, or they may be manufactured by the cell. Certain amino acids can be made from substances at certain steps in the citric acid cycle, from pyruvic acid, or from acetyl CoA. Some organisms, however, cannot manufacture a few of the amino acids by these processes. These are called *essential amino acids* because organisms must obtain them. All organisms, however, do

In the chart above, the large dark arrows indicate usual metabolic pathways. Light arrows indicate possible metabolic pathways. Colored blocks indicate processes that have been studied in Chapter 3 or 4.

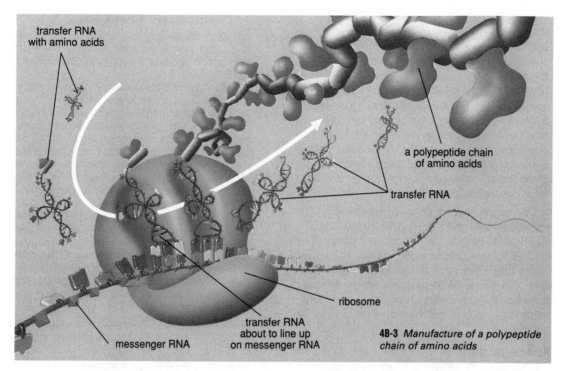

transfer RNA
with amino acids

a polypeptide chain
of amino acids

transfer RNA

ribosome

transfer RNA
about to line up
on messenger RNA

messenger RNA

4B-3 *Manufacture of a polypeptide chain of amino acids*

The manufacture of an amino acid chain

The mRNA leaves the nucleus with the DNA's triplet code by passing through a pore in the nuclear envelope. A ribosome lines up on one end of the mRNA. The ribosome has an active site which puts a mRNA codon at the proper place where a tRNA anticodon can line up with it. If the mRNA codon is AUG, a tRNA with the anticodon UAC will line up at that position. The tRNA has the amino acid methionine attached to its opposite end.

Once the codon and the anticodon have lined up, the ribosome moves down the mRNA, and the next codon is in place to be read. Suppose the next codon is UUU. The tRNA with anticodon AAA will join it, and the amino acid phenylalanine will now be right next to methionine, and they will bond together. Methionine and phenylalanine are now in the proper sequence for this polypeptide chain. Their sequence was dictated by the sequence of bases in the mRNA.

Ribosomal enzymes cause the amino acids lined up on the mRNA to form a peptide bond (see pages 64-65). The energy to form the bond holding the amino acids together was in the bond between the first amino acid, methionine, and the tRNA that brought it to the ribosome.

After the bonding of the amino acids (methionine to phenylalamine in our example), the first tRNA is no longer bonded to an amino acid. The tRNA that brought the first amino acid (which was temporarily bonded to the mRNA), leaves the ribosome and enters the cytoplasm as the ribosome slides down the mRNA to reach the next codon. (Soon another amino acid bonds with the tRNA, and it can be used again.) The process of reading new codons, bonding amino acids, and releasing empty tRNA's continues forming a polypeptide chain of amino acids.

The codon AUG, which codes for methionine, is called a *start codon*. Since methionine bonds on only one side it can start the polypeptide chain. Certain codons do not code for any amino acids. The codons UAA, UAG, and UGA are termed *stop codons* since they do not correspond to any amino acids and thus end the amino acid chain.

Ribosomes, then, start at a particular codon of the mRNA, travel along the mRNA, permitting the codons to be read by the lining up of tRNA with the appropriate amino acids, then end at a particular codon. The result is a polypeptide chain of amino acids which forms a protein. Occasionally a single mRNA may have several ribosomes all reading its messages at the same time. All evidence seems to indicate that a strand of mRNA is used repeatedly. When it breaks apart, the nucleotides may be used again to form more mRNA or any other nucleic acid.

One of the smaller proteins, ribonuclease (an enzyme which breaks apart RNA strands), is 124 amino acids long and is bonded in 4 places. The mRNA for this protein must be over 372 nucleotides long since each amino acid requires a codon of 3 bases. Most proteins, however, range from hundreds to thousands of amino acids long, requiring strands of mRNA with 3 times as many nucleotides.

Mitochondria–A Different Genetic Code

Not all of the genetic information found in a cell is located in the nucleus. Mitochondria have DNA, and organelles in other cells also appear to have DNA.

Mitochondrial DNA is a loop of DNA (similar to the DNA found in procaryotic cells) that manufactures RNA and appears to be responsible for the manufacture of some proteins used in the mitochondria. The code, however, is slightly different. UGA is usually a stop codon, but in the mitochondrial DNA of many organisms it is translated as the amino acid tryptophan. In plants, however, UGA is a stop codon in mitochondrial DNA.

New mitochondria are made in the cytoplasm by division of old mitochondria. In order to function each new mitochondrion must get a copy of the mitochondrial DNA. Mitochondrial DNA does not have the code for all the proteins needed for a mitochondrion to grow and reproduce and function. It must also have proteins made by the DNA of the nucleus.

Review Questions 4B-1

1. Compare the structures which make up the code of our language (letters, words, sentences, punctuation) to corresponding parts of the code of protein synthesis.
2. List the three types of RNA. Describe each and give its function.
3. What are exons and introns?
4. Describe the process of making a mRNA.
5. The following processes take place either in the nucleus, in the cytoplasm, or on the ribosome. Indicate where each process takes place.
   (a) transcription of a DNA molecule
   (b) reading of a mRNA molecule
   (c) lining up of a codon and an anticodon
   (d) replication of a DNA molecule
   (e) attachment of two amino acid molecules
   (f) attachment of a mRNA molecule to a ribosome
   (g) attachment of an amino acid to a tRNA molecule
6. What are start codons and stop codons?
7. Determine the codons and anticodons for the sequence of bases on the mRNA molecule given below. Then, using Table 4B-1, determine the sequence of amino acids in the section of a protein for which this mRNA would code:
   AUGUUCGUUAACGACCAAAUUUAA
8. Other than the nucleus, where is DNA located in eucaryotic cells?
9. What is unusual about mitochondrial DNA?

Facet 4B-1: Interrelated Metabolisms–Living Things Change Things, pages 105-6

1. Describe how carbohydrate and lipid metabolisms relate to each other.
2. How does protein metabolism relate to carbohydrate and lipid metabolisms?
3. Tell where the various components of a DNA nucleotide come from.

Metabolism and Homeostasis

The functioning of an organism is its metabolism. When an organism functions to maintain a stable condition, its metabolism is causing its *homeostasis*. An organism does not constantly face exactly the same situation; so the metabolic activities of cells change to maintain homeostasis. For example, cells require ATP energy constantly. If the environment is favorable, the cell may grow rapidly and therefore use large quantities of energy to carry on the necessary processes to supply substances for growth. The same cell in an unfavorable environment will not grow but may still use the same amount of ATP to maintain its life. The metabolic rate under these two conditions will be the same. The homeostasis–that is, the steady state of life–will in each case be maintained, but the metabolic processes used will be different.

Metabolic rate

Some organisms have a higher *metabolic rate* than others. A rapidly growing young organism, be it a bacterial cell or a child, usually builds large quantities of substances and therefore has a higher metabolism than when it is mature and no longer growing. Plant cells in sunlight carry on photosynthesis and respiration, but in darkness it carries on only respiration. During the day, then, the rate of metabolism is higher.

Members of a school's athletic teams force their bodies to engage in higher metabolic activity than a person who spends most of his out-of-school time reclining in front of a television. But a young person can change his daily metabolic totals, and many do so as they participate in different activities. Rates of metabolism vary even during sleep. If one is sick and feverish, his metabolism will be higher as his body reacts to the disease. But resting metabolisms are not the same even among healthy people.

For some organisms the rate of metabolism depends on the environment. The amount of available light or water may determine the amount of photosynthesis. The presence or absence of certain vitamins (to serve as coenzymes) may affect one's health. Biological reactions seem to happen twice as fast for each increase of

10° C. Most enzymes of living systems, however, have optimal ranges. At higher or lower temperatures, they begin to function improperly rather than just faster or slower.

Increasing your internal temperature 10° C will kill you. The *desert pup fish* can exist from 10° to 40° C but does not function well at either extreme. Increasing a fish's body temperature will increase its metabolism, but there is a limit. The *Antarctic fish,* for example, flourishes in water from −2° to +2° C. As the temperature reaches 0° C, the fish is active. As the temperature rises, its metabolism slows down. At about +2° C it

4B-4 *An Antarctic fish*

becomes immobile because of heat prostration. If temperatures continue to increase, the fish will die. God designed this fish for the constant near-freezing water temperatures of the Antarctic; so its metabolism is specialized.

Anabolism and Catabolism

Metabolism can be divided into two types: ❑ **anabolism*** (uh NAB uh LIZ um), those processes which build molecules and store energy, and ❑ **catabolism*** (kuh TAB uh LIZ um), those processes which break molecules down and release energy. Many cellular processes involve both anabolism and catabolism, but there is usually a net gain or loss. To grow, for example, a cell must break some substances down in order to build others up. But in growth there is a net gain of molecules; so growth is usually referred to as anabolism.

The cell is an awesome chemical factory. Not only can it take raw materials and put together the substances it needs, but also it can take its own substances and re-form them when necessary. It can, within limits, change the course of its operations in keeping a constant supply of needed materials and in maintaining the internal homeostasis that permits its life. It is truly amazing what God has wrought in even the tiniest cell.

---

anabolism ana- (Gk. ANA, up) + -bolism (to throw)

catabolism cata- (Gk. KATA, down) + -bolism (to throw)

Cellular Digestion

One of the important methods by which cells obtain substances is digestion. Many cells obtain materials for digestion by *phagocytosis* and *pinocytosis*. Those materials are then broken down by enzymes in **intracellular* digestion.** Enzymes, often supplied by lysosomes, break down the materials in food vacuoles to soluble carbohydrates, fatty acids, amino acids, salts, and other substances. These products of digestion diffuse through the vacuolar membrane into the cytoplasm and enter cellular processes.

Not all cells carry on digestion in food vacuoles. Some cells secrete enzymes which carry on **extracellular* digestion.** The soluble products of extracellular digestion are then absorbed by the cell. Most cells in multicellular organisms do not carry on digestion but rely on a supply of predigested food in their environment. The cells of your digestive system carry on extracellular digestion and supply the nutrients in a soluble form for all your body's cells.

Some cells carry on a "remodeling" process called **autophagy*** (aw TOHF uh jee). The cell forms a membrane around a damaged, worn out, or no longer needed cellular structure. Lysosomes join with the autophagic vacuole membrane and empty their enzymes into the vacuole. The cellular substances within the autophagic vacuole are then broken down to soluble materials which are absorbed into the cytoplasm. Substances in cellular structures can thus be recycled.

intracellular digestion	extracellular digestion	autophagy
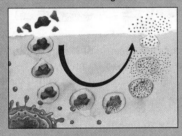	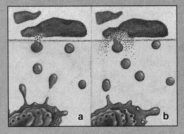	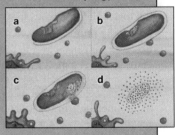

Biological Terms

metabolism

Protein Synthesis
codon
messenger RNA (mRNA)

transfer RNA (tRNA)
anticodon
ribosomal RNA (rRNA)
exon

intron

Metabolism and Homeostasis
anabolism
catabolism

intracellular digestion
extracellular digestion
autophagy

Review Questions 4B-2

1. Compare and contrast homeostasis and metabolism.
2. List several factors which may affect metabolic rates.
3. What are the two basic types of metabolism? Briefly describe each.
4. What are the two basic ways that cells can digest a substance?

Thought Questions

1. List several attributes which the process of protein synthesis must have. Explain why each attribute is necessary.
2. Since it is the proteins which make the differences between various organisms and individuals, discuss the possibility of DNA's being the genetic material.
3. For maturing into a frog, a tadpole relies heavily on the process of autophagy. Explain how this process is useful in the change in the frog's physical structures.
4. The interrelationship of the life processes (briefly outlined in this chapter) is carefully balanced while the organism is alive. Explain how this balance illustrates the first two laws of thermodynamics and the laws of conservation and degeneration.

---

intracellular: intra- (L. INTRA, within) + -cellular (cell)

extracellular: extra- (L. EXTRA, outside) + -cellular (cell)

autophagy: auto- (self) + -phagy (to eat)

GENETICS
THE CONTINUITY OF LIFE
PART I

FIVE

5A– Genes and Chromosomes

Humans resemble one another. They usually have two eyes, two ears, a nose, and a mouth. Their hands are basically the same. Internal human features such as stomachs, livers, kidneys, and bones are about the same size, shape, and location in different humans. Even human cells have basic chemical and structural similarities. For example, most human cells have 46 chromosomes. Characteristics that every member of a species has are called **species characteristics.**

A brown-haired man with a blond-haired son is not unusual. The boy probably inherited his hair color from his mother rather than his father. But actually a child's hair color is determined by both parents. Characteristics such as eye, hair, and skin color; body build; intelligence; and other features that distinguish people are called **individual characteristics.** What you are depends in part on the species characteristics and in part on the individual characteristics that you inherit.

111

Did you inherit *all* your characteristics from your parents? Do the hundreds of thousands of genes you inherited so control you that you just mechanically live out what you inherited? Both questions must be answered yes and no. Your genes determine your species characteristics and individual characteristics. But the *extent* to which these characteristics can express themselves in many ways depends upon your *environment,* the second major physical factor that determines what you are. For example, if a person inherited genes for being over six feet tall but had a poor diet, insufficient rest, and little exercise as he matured, he would likely not reach his genetic potential. This happens often in underdeveloped countries. Intelligence potential, most geneticists believe, is also inherited. If an individual's environment gives little stimulation, though, his intellect will not become what it could be.

As a human you are more than just the sum of your inherited genetic potential and your environment. You have a spiritual nature, a soul that will live forever. Your spirit, if permitted to remain in Satan's control, uses your inherited physical traits and your environment to sin and glorify the Devil. If, however, you are saved by Jesus Christ, you are born into the heavenly family. If your will is yielded to God, He will direct your environment and use your genetic potential to develop in you the fruit of the Spirit and to glorify Himself (Rom. 8:28; Phil. 4:13).

The Mechanism of Heredity

Genetics, the study of heredity, is both one of the oldest and one of the newest of the biological sciences. In the Old Testament the Jews were commanded, "Thou shalt not let thy cattle gender [mate to produce offspring] with a diverse kind" (Lev. 19:19). This type of selective breeding, which has been engaged in for thousands of years is, in essence, practical genetics.

Men have always been interested in how the characteristics of one generation are passed on to the next. The ancient Greeks believed that each offspring was a mixture of elements from the parents' bodies. Aristotle proposed the *particulate theory* of reproduction: particles of the par-

ents' blood mix and then join to form the offspring. From this belief came the terms "pure blood" and "blood relative."

A later group of people, called *preformationists,* believed that there were little, completely formed organisms in the sperm which merely grew up when planted in the egg. One early microscopist actually reported having seen tiny people in human sperm. Most preformationists also believed that inside the tiny person in that sperm are other sperm which contain smaller people, which contain sperm with even smaller people *ad infinitum.* In other words, inside Adam was *all* mankind, just waiting to grow up.* The impossibility of such decreasingly tiny people was part of the "miracle" of reproduction.

In the middle of the 1800s Gregor Mendel, who will be discussed later, performed a series of experiments with garden peas. Mendel advanced the understanding of genetics by proposing that there are pairs of *factors* in organisms and each parent gives a single set of these factors to its offspring.

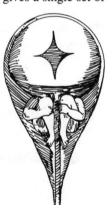

Mendel's report collected dust in libraries until the early 1900s, when it was rediscovered. By that time microscopy had advanced beyond the blood particle and preformation theories. Mendel's theories were applied to the new cellular knowledge as modern theories of genetics began to take shape.

In 1953 Watson and Crick described the DNA molecule, which was determined to be the genetic material. From the years 1953 to 1963 the amount

5A-1 *A drawing of a human sperm by a preformationist. Preformationists cited Scripture out of context to support their theory.*

One Scripture misapplied to support the preformationist view was "For as in Adam all die." (I Cor. 15:22).

of known genetic information doubled. Today genetic knowledge doubles in less than two years. Truly, man is now in the Genetic Age.

Characteristics of a Gene

For years before scientists had determined what a gene was, they knew the characteristics it must have. Consider these characteristics of a gene.

❑ Genes are fundamentally identical in both kinds and amount in the cells of an organism. For example, virtually all of your cells have the same number and kinds of genes.

❑ Genes are fundamentally identical in both kinds and amount in the cells of each organism of a species. For example, a normal human has the same number and kinds of genes as other normal humans.

❑ Genes are chemicals which can function as individual units–that is, they are different chemicals, each of which can do a different thing.

❑ Genes are able to carry information for the formation of organic chemicals–that is, they are responsible for biosynthesis.

❑ Genes are able to reproduce themselves–that is, they are able to make copies of the information they have.

❑ Genes are able to be passed on to the next generation.

❑ Genes are found in the cell's nuclear material.

The *nucleic acids* (DNA and RNA) are the only substances known to possess all of these characteristics.

Genes

The common term *gene* is hard to define. Mendel called the pairs of particles involved in passing on inherited characteristics *factors;* today we call them genes. But what is a gene?

Scientists now define a **gene** as a section of DNA that produces a particular polypeptide chain of amino acids (a protein or a section of protein) and thereby causes a trait. Not all traits are as visible and discernible as blue eyes or brown hair. Many genes produce structural or enzymatic pro-

teins which perform functions that you do not see. The enzymes of the citric-acid cycle, for example, are traits for which your genes have the code. If at conception you had lacked these genes, you would not be alive.

Some people find it hard to believe that genes carry all the information needed to produce the physical traits you possess. Your DNA is tightly compressed; the DNA from all your cells would fit into a 1-inch cube. But if all the DNA in one human cell were uncoiled and stretched out, it would form a thin string about 2 yards long. Some believe that the information found in the DNA of *one* human cell is equal to the information in 1,000 books containing 600 pages each. The nucleus of one human cell is a huge library of chemicals.

Chromosomes

Mendel had envisioned the factors floating around somewhere inside the organism. In fact they do not. Your genes are not even floating around independently inside the nuclei of cells. Each DNA strand in a nucleus actually comprises many genes. These long strands of DNA are associated with proteins and are called **chromosomes.** The proteins help to support and protect the long, thin strands of DNA and also help in DNA *replication* or in *transcription* of RNA.

In an active, nondividing cell most of the chromosomes appear as a fuzzy, tangled mass in the nucleus called the *chromatin material.* Some of the genes are active, producing RNA. Others are not being used and are often tightly coiled.

The number of chromosomes in a cell is a species characteristic. Humans have 46 chromosomes in the nuclei of most of their cells. Fruit flies have 8; certain species of goldfish have 100; crayfish have 200. Do not get the idea that the number of chromosomes determines the species. It is the genes on the chromosomes that make the organism. But every normal cell in a particular organism, as well as every normal organism of that type, has the same number of chromosomes.

Review Questions 5A-1
1. What are the three factors that contribute to the make-up of an individual?
2. List (a) several species characteristics and (b) several individual characteristics of dogs.
3. List seven characteristics a gene must possess.

Mitosis

When a cell divides, it is not essential that an equal amount of cytoplasm and an equal number of organelles be in each of the new cells. If the new cell has a complete set of genes, it can manufacture what is missing. The division of the nuclear material in such a way that each new nucleus has a complete identical copy of the genetic information from the parent cell is called **mitosis** (mye TOH sis).

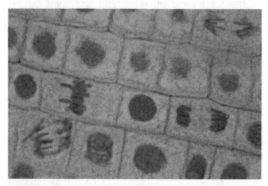

5A-2 *Cells dividing in onion root tips. The chromosomes are the dark masses in the center of each cell. All the phases of mitosis are illustrated. Can you find them?*

Scientists have divided the *process* of mitosis into phases:

❏ **Interphase**   The period of time between cellular divisions–interphase–is not actually a phase of mitosis. The cell carries on normal metabolism. The double *centriole* is just outside the nucleus. Inside the nucleus the chromatin material is producing RNA. Toward the end of interphase all the chromosomes are completely replicated. These DNA duplicates are attached to one another by the **centromere.** Each DNA duplicate is called a **sister chromatid.** The fuzzy appearance of the chromatin material hides these structures during interphase. A cell that is ready to begin mitosis is called a **mother cell.**

❏ **Prophase**   The first phase of mitosis is prophase, during which the centrioles divide and migrate to opposite sides of the nucleus. Around each centriole the **aster** becomes prominent. Some of the aster fibers form the **spindle** between the centrioles. The nuclear chromosomes get short and thick as they coil up, becoming visible as individual chromosomes composed of two sister chromatids that are pinched together at the site of the centromere. The nuclear membrane disintegrates, and the nucleolus disappears.

❏ **Metaphase**   At the end of prophase the chromosomes (sister chromatid pairs) migrate to the center of the spindle. Metaphase is the stage when the centromeres are on the *equatorial plane*–the imaginary line at the middle of the spindle. During metaphase the sister chromatids appear to repel each other, taking the shape of an ''X.''

❏ **Anaphase**   Metaphase ends as the centromeres separate. Anaphase is the period of time during which the centromeres appear to pull the **daughter chromosomes** (separated sister chromatids) along the spindle fibers toward opposite poles.

❏ **Telophase**   When the daughter chromosomes reach the end of the spindle, telophase begins. At each centriole a new nucleus begins to form. The daughter chromosomes begin to uncoil, the nucleoli reappear, and the nuclear membranes reform. The spindle disappears, leaving only a small aster around each centriole. The plasma membrane constricts at the center of the cell, and the cytoplasm divides, a process called **cytokinesis*** (SYE toh kih NEE sis).

❏ **Daughter cells**   The two cells resulting from mitosis (followed by cytokinesis) are daughter cells. Daughter cells are actually cells entering interphase.

Under normal conditions, daughter cells get a copy of the mother cell's DNA with exactly the same genes as the mother cell and have the same genetic potential.

Variations of mitosis

Not all cells go through mitosis in the same way. Figure 5A-3 shows the cytokinesis of animal cells. Animal cells *invaginate* (in VAJ uh NATE) (pinch in). Plant cells, because of their cell walls, cannot invaginate. Rather, they form a *division plate* near the equatorial plane of the spindle. The division plate, made of two cell membranes separated by a primary cell wall, begins to form in

---

cytokinesis: cyto- (cell) + -kinesis (to move)

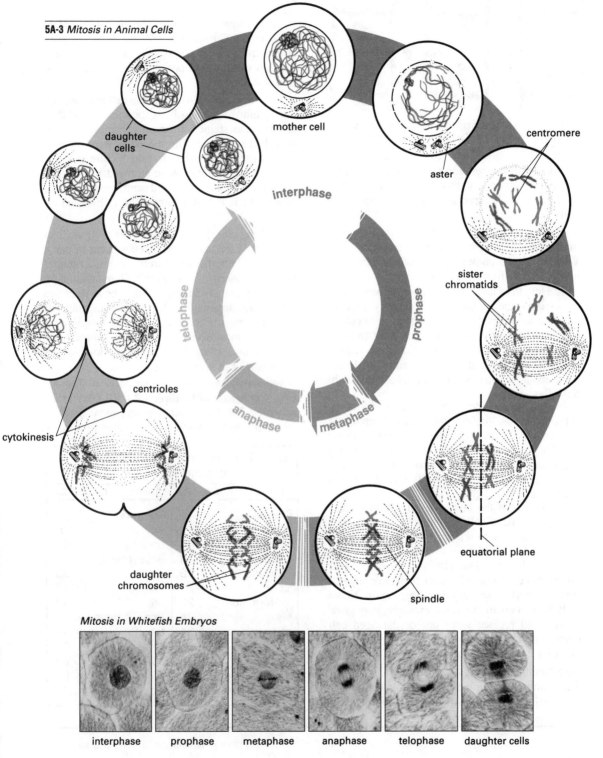

5A-3 *Mitosis in Animal Cells*

mother cell

daughter cells

centromere

aster

interphase

telophase

prophase

sister chromatids

centrioles

cytokinesis

anaphase

metaphase

equatorial plane

daughter chromosomes

spindle

Mitosis in Whitefish Embryos

interphase　　prophase　　metaphase　　anaphase　　telophase　　daughter cells

115

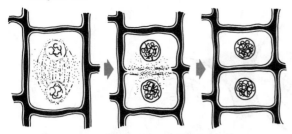

5A-4 *Cytokinesis in plants:* (left) *the end of mitosis,* (center) *the formation of a division plate,* (right) *daughter cells*

the middle of the cell and grows outward until it separates the two daughter cells. Another difference between plant and animal cell mitosis is that plant cells usually lack centrioles.

In some unicellular organisms all the phases of mitosis happen within the nuclear membrane. When mitosis is complete, the nuclear membrane invaginates to form two nuclei.

The length of time necessary for mitosis differs for various types of cells. Some procaryotic cells are able to complete a cell division in about 10 min. and are ready to divide again after an additional 10 min. of growth. Most plant cells require about 30 min. for mitosis. Some animal cells require about 3 hr. to pass from interphase to daughter cells.

Interphase may be extremely short for some cells. Embryos, for example, must form many cells rapidly. Almost as soon as the nuclei in the daughter cells have formed, the two nuclei may begin another prophase, even before cytokinesis is complete. Later these cells will grow and specialize.

Most cells in the body will divide to replace damaged or dead cells. Skin cells, for example, divide constantly to replace the skin we rub and wash off. Bone cells can divide, although much more slowly than skin cells, and grow to repair broken bones. Some cells, once they have reached maturity, will never carry on mitosis again. Nerve cells in the human brain, for example, may grow in size and replace worn out or damaged cell parts, but they will not divide. When brain cells die, they cannot be replaced.

Chromosome numbers

The number of chromosomes within an organism's cells is one of its species characteristics. If evolution were true, it would be logical to assume that the smaller species with the least complex structures would have smaller and fewer chromosomes. But this is not the case, as you can see in Table 5A-5.

Look at figure 5A-6. A human cell was stopped during mitosis by dissolving the spindle, and then the cell was stained to reveal chromosomes and squashed so that the chromosomes were separated. It was photographed and the picture was cut, and the chromosomes were arranged into groups according to their length and centromere location. The result is called a **karyotype** (KEHR ee uh TYPE).

Looking closely at the karyotype in figure 5A-6, you will see that chromosomes occur in pairs. There are 2 number one chromosomes, 2 number two chromosomes, and so forth. Humans actually have 23 pairs of chromosomes. These pairs are called **homologous** (hoh MAHL uh gus) **pairs of chromosomes.** Each member of a *homologous pair of chromosomes* is called a **homologue** (HAHM uh LAWG). In a karyotype homologues are arranged in *homologous pairs.*

When a cell has homologous pairs of chromosomes, it is said to be **diploid*** (DIP LOYD) (abbreviated *2n*). Most common organisms are diploid. The diploid number of an organism is its

5A-5	Diploid Chromosome Numbers in Some Organisms		
Name	**Number (2n)**	**Name**	**Number (2n)**
Plants		**Animals**	
pea	14	fruit fly	8
red clover	14	housefly	12
onion	16	honeybee	32
cabbage	18	cat	38
corn	20	mouse	40
watermelon	22	rat	42
lily	24	Rhesus monkey	42
tomato	24	rabbit	44
white pine	24	cattle	60
cotton	26	donkey	62
African violet	28	horse	64
white clover	32	crayfish	200

diploid: (Gk. DIPLOOS, double)

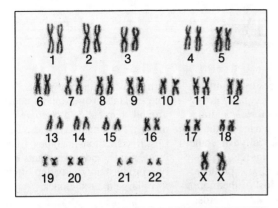

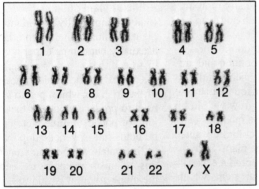

5A-6 *Human karyotypes: female (above) and male (below)*

Uses of mitosis

Mitosis results in two cells that have the same DNA. In other words, they both contain the same genetic information. The most obvious uses of mitosis are growth, repair, and replacement of cells in multicellular organisms. For example, your 10 trillion cells are the result of repeated mitosis of your original cell. Also, injured parts of your body are repaired by the growth of new cells to replace the damaged ones. Often cells are needed to replace those that wear out naturally.

Many organisms are able to carry on reproduction by undergoing mitosis. Any form of reproduction which involves only mitotic cell divisions is called **asexual reproduction.** For example, if a unicellular organism goes through mitosis, the organism has reproduced asexually.

Many colonial organisms are able to reproduce asexually by *fragmentation.* Breaking a simple colony in two and then permitting additional mitosis to replace missing cells will result in asexual reproduction. Many algae, fungi, and bacteria reproduce asexually by fragmentation.

Some multicellular organisms can, by producing a large number of cells in a certain area, produce a new, small organism on the side of the parent. This is called *budding.* Some plants, like the strawberry, carry on a similar process and produce small plants on the ends of special stems or on other plant parts.

Many multicellular organisms are able to reproduce asexually by forming spores. A **spore*** is a cell (sometimes cells) with a hard protective covering. Often a species is kept alive because the organism forms spores that live in an inactive state through a dry, cold, or otherwise unfavorable period. Spores of some molds can remain alive for over 50 years. Many organisms such as mosses and fungi reproduce and are spread predominantly by spores.

number of chromosomes. The human diploid number is 46 (2n = 46).

Both homologues in a pair have genes for the same characteristics. In other words, humans have 2 of almost every gene, 1 on each homologue of the pair. Assume, for instance, that humans have a gene for tongue length on chromosome number one.* Since humans have a homologous pair of chromosome number one, everyone has 2 genes for tongue length. We will discuss later the significance of having pairs of genes.

Review Questions 5A-2
1. Describe a chromosome. Distinguish between a chromosome and a chromatid.
2. List in sequence the phases of mitosis and describe each.
3. What is the difference between mitosis and cytokinesis?
4. What is the normal human diploid chromosome number?
5. List several types of asexual reproduction and describe each.

---

spore: (L. SPORA, seed)

This is a hypothetical example. Scientists are not sure on which chromosome many human genes are located.

FACETS OF BIOLOGY

5A-1

Clones and Cloning

If you speak of cloning, many people think of a scientist working on diabolical experiments to make exact duplicates of himself. People are relieved to learn that such activities are, at least at present, beyond the scope of scientific possibility. That does not mean that clones are rare. In fact, many clones are common in nature. Many manmade clones have existed for centuries. Even human clones exist and have been common for a long time.

A **clone** is a group of genetically identical individuals. If an organism reproduces using only mitosis, the result is a clone. For example, if a unicellular protozoan or alga goes through mitosis and forms 2 cells, both of those cells are members of a clone. As they grow and divide repeatedly, the clone gets larger.

Natural clones

Asexual reproduction that an organism carries on by itself produces *natural clones;* thus, unicellular organisms form clones as they reproduce. Any multicellular organism that reproduces by fragmentation, budding, or asexually produced spores also forms natural clones. Some organisms in the animal kingdom, like jellyfish, some worms, and some insects, reproduce asexually and thus produce natural clones. Most of the more familiar animals, like fish, birds, and mammals, normally reproduce sexually and thus do not form natural clones.

In the plant kingdom natural clones are more common and are even commercially beneficial. If a strawberry grower found a strawberry plant which grew well in his climate and had the qualities of taste, texture, and color he wanted, he would clone the plant. Strawberries naturally reproduce asexually by *runners* (thin stems which grow tiny plants on their ends). In time the farmer would be able to fill his field with clones of the desirable strawberry.

Cattail seeds may carry the species to a new pond, but once established, asexual reproduction

forms a new clump of plants. These plants grow from an underground stem called a *rhizome* making them natural clones. Tulips, irises, onions, peonies, lilies, ferns, mints, and other plants easily reproduce asexually and often form large natural clones.

Artificial plant clones

Many economically important plants do not naturally reproduce asexually but can be either helped or forced to do so. For example, the "eyes" of desirable varieties of the Irish (or white) potato are used to produce clones of that kind of potato. In time there can be fields full of genetic duplicates of this potato. Since man cloned this organism and helps to keep the clone going, it is said to be an *artificial clone.*

Planting the seeds of a seedless banana does not get more seedless banana plants. Banana plants are grown by planting the cut up pieces of their large underground stems. The genetic change which caused a seedless banana has been kept alive by cloning. Today seed-filled bananas are unknown to most people.

A similar situation is true of seedless grapes. Grape vines are woody plants and can be *grafted.* A stem of a seedless grape can be grafted into the root system of another grape plant. The grafted-in branch has the genetic make-up that will determine the kind of fruit produced. Since the branch has genes for seedless fruit, the

The Word "Clone"

The word "clone" as a noun means a group of individuals produced asexually from a single parent or only one individual from such a group. The word "to clone" as a verbal means to produce clones.

Consider this riddle: The scientist cloned his prize clone. From the clone he took a choice clone and gave it to his identical twin saying, "This clone on my clone was cloned for you, clone."

An orchid bud is removed and sterilized. (a) A few cells from the bud are grown on sterile media. (b) Rotation encourages growth. (c) Eventually many small orchid plants can be placed in soil and grown to produce identical flowers.

plant is essentially a clone. Repetitions of this procedure result in a vineyard filled with a clone that produces seedless grape plants.

The grafting process is used to produce almost all named varieties of fruits and ornamental woody plants whether they produce seeds or not. Because of genetic recombinations happening each time the sexual reproduction necessary to produce a seed takes place, a seed from a Bartlett pear will not produce a Bartlett pear tree. The genetic traits that produce a Bartlett pear become scrambled as the seed is made. Bartlett pear trees

All Bartlett pear trees are members of a large clone. From the original tree the clones were produced by grafting.

are all members of a graft-sustained clone, as are all Granny Smith apples, Tiffany roses, and Georgia Bell peaches.

Artificial animal clones

Artificial animal clones can be produced easily in only a few groups of organisms like sponges, jellyfish, corals, some worms, and insects. Often this type of cloning is done by forcing an organism to *regenerate* missing parts. A starfish, for example, can be cut into several pieces, each one of which can become a complete organism by regenerating its missing parts.

Today the technology is available to clone some other animals. Frogs were used in some of the original successful experiments with cloning from the zygote stage. When the zygote became two cells, scientists separated the cells. Each cell then developed into a genetically identical individual–a 2-member clone. Scientists discovered that the zygote could also be separated at later stages into a larger number of individual cells and thus produce larger clones. There was a limit, however. The more cell divisions the zygote went through before the cells were separated, the less likely the

Starfish regenerating ray

cells were to develop into frogs. The size of the clone was thus limited.

Because frogs produce large ova, frogs were also used as experimental animals in another form of artificial animal cloning. Scientists are able to use ultra-fine needles to remove the nucleus from a frog's ovum, without destroying the cytoplasm's structure. They can then take a nucleus from a cell of another frog (originally cells from the intestine were used) and implant them into the "empty ovum." This artificial zygote can develop into a frog. If several artificial zygotes are all prepared with nuclei from cells of the same frog, a clone of frogs can be developed. The number of individuals in such a clone is theoretically unlimited.

The processes used to obtain clones of animals are expensive, and thus not profitable except for scientific experimentation where genetically identical individuals are essential. There are also limits to our current technology. At this time, needles and other devices needed for handling nuclei of small ova are not available. The cloning of mammals which have small ova (compared to those of a frog) is being worked on.

Human clones

Natural human clones exist: identical twins are naturally occurring clones of only 2 individuals. Identical twins have the same genetic make-up because they are the result of 1 fertilized zygote dividing into 2 cells which then separate. Normally these cells remain together and develop into a single individual, but in the case of identical twins each of the 2 cells implants itself in a different place in

the womb (uterus) and develops into an individual. There are a few examples of identical triplets, and some rare examples of identical quadruplets. As with the dividing

of the frog zygote, there appear to be limits as to how many individuals can be cloned by the division of a single zygote.

The artificial cloning of humans will be as difficult as cloning mammals, for the ova are similar in size. (The artifical implanting of a zygote into a womb for development has already been accomplished. See pages 162, 165.) Scientists predict that the technology needed to clone humans by using the implanting of nuclei into ova will be developed within your lifetime.

Although some Christians may disagree, many Christian scholars believe that each member of an artifical human clone would have a soul. Identical twins are natural clones, and they do not share one soul. Although they are genetically identical, they sin independently, and they must be saved individually. Using this logic, it appears that if man develops enough technology to produce a human clone, each would still have an individual human soul in need of salvation just like everyone else.

But who should be cloned, and for what purpose? Cloning people who are very intelligent, talented, athletic, healthy, or who have other outstanding characteristics seems desirable at first glance. Most Christians would object to such cloning because it presents

too many potential spiritual problems. For example: such a costly procedure would probably have to be done by government(s), especially those in countries with undesirable or declining populations. Also a shortage of certain "types" of people may make cloning desirable. It is not impossible to imagine governments selectively cloning strong, docile people with low intelligence to serve as a work force. (Governments have done worse things with human life in the past!)

If the state pays for the cloning, who "owns" the child? Most governments will not want a child that they "paid for" brought up in the "nuture and admonition of the Lord" (Eph. 6:4). In fact, having the cloned individual even aware of any form of "religion" may make him less able to serve the government as desired.

The Bible teaches us that "children are an heritage of the Lord" (Ps. 127:3) given to the parents to raise according to God's precepts. Christians need to stand against the improper use of scientific knowledge and the government's assumption of rights it does not have. (Additional Biblical principles regarding this and similar considerations are discussed on pages 160-67 and 638-43.)

Review questions on page 124.

Meiosis

Simple mathematics tells you that if a father's **sperm*** contained 23 pairs of chromosomes (46), and a mother's **ovum*** (OH vum) (pl., ova) contained 23 pairs of chromosomes (46), the number of chromosomes in their baby's cells would be 46 pairs (92). Normal human cells, however, have only 23 pairs of chromosomes. As the parents' sperm and ovum were forming, the chromosome number of each was reduced to the **haploid*** (HAP LOYD) number (abbreviated n). A haploid cell is one that has only one chromosome from every pair. In humans the haploid number is 23 (n = 23). When the two haploid gametes (n) from the parents united, a diploid cell called a **zygote*** (n + n = 2n) was formed. After countless mitotic divisions, their baby entered the world.

Think about the cell division necessary to form a haploid cell. It cannot be a random dividing of chromosomes. A haploid cell must have 1 of every homologous chromosome pair. Under normal circumstances a gamete does not have 2 of one pair of chromosomes and none of another pair. If it did, the zygote it formed might not be diploid even though it had the right number of chromosomes. It might have none, 1, 3, or 4 of a homologue rather than a pair. If a zygote does not have all its chromosomes in pairs, it may lack genes that are on the chromosomes for which it has only one homologue. Or it may have too many of the genes that are on the chromosomes for which it has 3 or 4 homologues. Either case can be harmful.

To form a haploid cell (gamete), **meiosis** (mye OH sis) must occur. Meiosis is the reduction of a cell's chromosome number from diploid to haploid by two consecutive cell divisions.

The first division of meiosis

❑ *Prophase and metaphase* The prophase and metaphase of the first division of meiosis is similar to that of mitosis with one major difference. For metaphase not only the sister chromatids but also the *homologous pairs of chromosomes* line up together on the equatorial plane. Since both of the chromosomes in the homologous pair have replicated, there are 2 pairs of sister chromatids together. The 4 chromatids are called a *tetrad*.

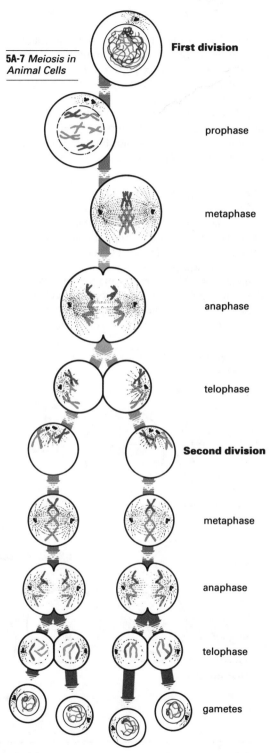

5A-7 *Meiosis in Animal Cells*

First division

prophase

metaphase

anaphase

telophase

Second division

metaphase

anaphase

telophase

gametes

---

sperm: sperm-, sperma-, or spermato- (Gk. SPERMA, seed)
ovum: (L. OVUM, egg)

haploid: (Gk. HAPLOS, single)
zygote: (Gk. ZUGON, yolk)

❑ *Anaphase* Rather than the sister chromatids separating as in mitosis, the homologous pairs separate, and the sister chromatids of each pair remain together. The homologues then travel to the ends of the spindle.

❑ *Telophase* The telophase of the first division of meiosis is the same as in mitosis, except that the chromosomes usually do not uncoil. The 2 new cells enter directly into the second division of meiosis.

The second division of meiosis

❑ *Prophase and metaphase* Usually the spindles in the 2 cells form in the opposite direction from the spindle in the original cell. The chromosomes (composed of a set of sister chromatids) line up on the equatorial planes.

❑ *Anaphase* The sister chromatids separate, and the resulting daughter chromosomes travel on the spindle fibers toward opposite poles.

❑ *Telophase* The 4 haploid cells reform their nuclei.

5A-8 *A comparison of spermatogenesis (top) and oogenesis (bottom)*

Gametes

Gametes* are those haploid cells which, when they unite, form a diploid cell called a zygote, the first cell of a new individual. The process of forming a zygote–the union of gametes–is called **fertilization.**

Some organisms produce gametes which are all alike, called **isogametes*** (EYE soh guh MEETS). Usually isogametes move by cilia or flagella. Fertilization occurs when 2 isogametes unite. Many algae and fungi produce isogametes.

Humans, all animals, many plants, and a few other organisms produce **heterogametes*** (HET uh roh gah MEETS). A heterogamete is usually either a sperm formed by a male, or an ovum formed by a female. Sperm are usually smaller than ova and can move. The ovum, if it moves, must be moved by structures around it. (An ovum is sometimes called an egg. The term *egg,* however, properly applies to the ovum with accessory structures–like a shell–such as a bird egg.)

The forming of sperm is called **spermatogenesis*** (spur MAT uh JEN ih sis). Notice that in

Spermatogenesis

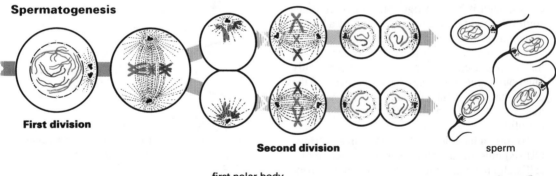

First division Second division sperm

Oogenesis

first polar body

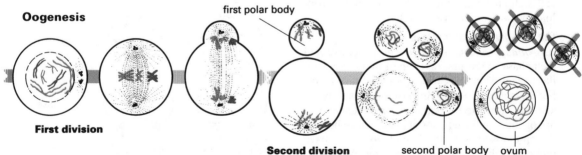

First division Second division second polar body ovum

---

gamete: (Gk. GAMETE, spouse)

isogamete: iso- (same) + -gamete (spouse)

heterogamete: hetero- (Gk. HETEROS, other) + -gamete (spouse)

pollen

After Plant Meiosis

Although meiosis in most plants is similar to the meiosis that occurs in animals, what follows plant meiosis is distinctly different. Unlike animals in which sperm and egg development directly follow meiosis, in plants pollen and egg development are not necessarily the next step.

In plant life cycles, the haploid cells produced by meiosis are technically considered to be a separate plant(s). Pollen or egg development does not have to directly follow meiosis in plants. In some cases this haploid generation may consist of only four cells; in other cases it may actually appear as a visible, leafy, green plant. In this case, mitotic cell divisions of the haploid cells produced the visible plant. Eventually the haploid plant, small or large, produces what in animals would be called egg or sperm. The sperm nuclei inside a pollen grain are an example. (See page 332.)

spermatogenesis, 4 functional gametes are formed. If you follow the chromosomes, you will notice that actually there are 2 pairs of identical sperm. In human sperm, as in sperm of other species, the cells formed by meiosis lose most of their cytoplasm and form a flagellum. The compressed DNA in the nucleus of the sperm is then moved toward the ovum by the flagellum.

The forming of an ovum is called **oogenesis*** (OH uh JEN uh sis). During the cytokinesis of the first meiotic division, 1 of the 2 cells receives most of the cytoplasm. The cell that receives the small amount of cytoplasm is called the *first polar body.* When the large cell divides the second time, again 1 of the 2 cells gets the majority of the cytoplasm and forms the ovum. The cell which gets very little cytoplasm is the *second polar body.* The first polar body often goes through the second meiotic division, forming 2 more polar bodies. Oogenesis therefore results in 1 ovum and 3 polar bodies.

In humans and animals the polar bodies soon disintegrate. The large quantity of cytoplasm in the ovum is necessary for the development of the zygote. The stored food and the cellular structures of the ovum's cytoplasm will be used during the period of rapid cell division at the beginning of the embryo's life.

Sexual reproduction

The union of haploid gametes, resulting in a diploid zygote, is **sexual reproduction.** It results in offspring which are not genetically identical to either parent. In sexual reproduction one of every homologous pair of chromosomes comes from one parent, and the other homologue comes from the other parent. The offspring, therefore, have one chromosome of every pair from each parent.

Inevitably one parent does not have exactly the same genes for a particular characteristic as the other parent has. Since each organism receives one gene of each set from each parent, the offspring will not have exactly the same genetic make-up as either parent.

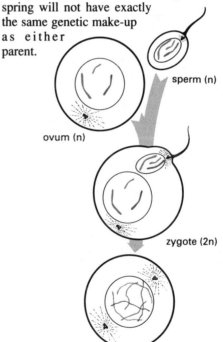

sperm (n)

ovum (n)

zygote (2n)

5A-9 *In sexual reproduction two haploid cells unite to form a zygote.*

spermatogenesis: spermato- (seed) + -genesis (beginning)

oogenesis: oo- (Gk. OION, egg) + -genesis (beginning)

Biological Terms

species characteristic
individual characteristic

The Mechanism of Heredity
genetics
gene
chromosome

Mitosis
mitosis
interphase
centromere
sister chromatid
mother cell
prophase
aster
spindle

metaphase
anaphase
daughter chromosomes
telophase
cytokinesis
daughter cells
karyotype
homologous pair of chromosomes
homologue
diploid
asexual reproduction
spore

Meiosis
sperm
ovum (pl., ova)

haploid
zygote
meiosis
gamete
fertilization
isogamete
heterogamete
spermatogenesis
oogenesis
sexual reproduction

Facet
clone

Review Questions 5A-3

1. Distinguish between a set of sister chromatids and a homologous pair of chromosomes.
2. List (a) several human cells that would contain the diploid chromosome number and (b) the human cells that would contain the haploid chromosome number.
3. What happens to the chromosomes during (a) the first division of meiosis and (b) the second division of meiosis?
4. Name the two types of meiosis that are carried on by humans.

Facet 5A-1: Clones and Cloning, pages 118-20

1. What is meant by the term *clone* (noun) and *to clone* (verbal)?
2. What is the difference between natural clones and artificial clones?
3. In what way is cloning economically advantageous in the plant kingdom? Give several examples of plants that are cloned commercially.
4. Describe the two methods used to clone larger animals (like amphibians, fish, birds, and mammals).
5. What is the difference between identical twins and fraternal twins? Which are clones? Explain.
6. List several Biblical principles (teachings) that may be violated by human cloning.

Thought Questions

1. What are the advantages and disadvantages of asexually reproducing apple trees as opposed to sexually reproducing them?
2. What advantages would a clone of an organism (like a fruit tree) have for a farmer?
3. What would be the advantages and disadvantages of cloning humans?

5B–Basic Genetics

Gregor Mendel was born in 1822 on a farm in Heinzendorf, Austria. At age 21 he entered the Augustinian order of the Roman Catholic church. As a monk he studied science at the University of Vienna and became an excellent mathematician. Later, as a schoolteacher, he engaged in many scientific activities. He recorded sun spots, read Darwin (with whom he disagreed), and maintained 50 beehives in which he tried to mate various European, American, and Egyptian types of bees. In 1857 Mendel began a program of selective breeding of peas in a small plot in the vegetable garden of Konigster monastery near Brunn, Moravia.

Mendel's experience in breeding and raising plants and animals on his father's farm, along with his mathematical and experimental science background from the university, equipped him well to investigate heredity. After 8 years of raising thousands of pea plants and recording and classifying many pages of notes, Mendel wrote a paper which presented a set of conclusions now called **Mendelian genetics.** In 1868 Mendel became the abbot of the monastery, and political problems forced him to give up most of his scientific work. In 1884 he died of a kidney disorder.

Gregor Mendel's paper on heredity in peas was published in 1865 but lay unnoticed in libraries for about 35 years. In 1900, after scientists had learned much about the cell, they rediscovered the paper and recognized its worth. Mendel became known as "the Father of Genetics." To understand modern genetic theories, you must understand what Mendel discovered about heredity.

Mendelian Genetics

Mendel ordered 34 varieties of pea seeds, planted them, and observed their characteristics. From those varieties he chose 7 *sets of opposing characteristics.* For example, he noted that peas are either about 6 ft. tall or about 2 ft. tall. Tall and short are a set of opposing characteristics. Pod color is either green or yellow, another set of opposing characteristics. Peas are round or wrinkled.

5B-1 *Gregor Mendel (left) and a summary of the sets of characteristics he observed in peas (below).*

dominant trait	tall plants	axial flowers	green pods	inflated pods	yellow peas	round peas	colored seed coat
	X	X	X	X	X	X	X
recessive trait	short plants	terminal flowers	yellow pods	constricted pods	green peas	wrinkled peas	white seed coat
F₁ generation	all tall plants	all axial flowers	all green pods	all inflated pods	all yellow peas	all round peas	all colored seed coat
F₂ generation	787 tall: 277 short (2.84:1)	651 axial: 207 terminal (3.14:1)	428 green: 152 yellow (2.82:1)	882 inflated: 229 constricted (2.95:1)	6022 yellow: 2001 green (3.01:1)	5474 round: 1850 wrinkled (2.96:1)	705 colored: 224 white (3.15:1)

The flower of the pea plant made it ideal for genetic experimentation. The petals are arranged so that the pollen (which contains the male gamete) naturally fertilizes the pistil (which contains the female gamete) of the same flower. This is called **self-pollination.** If Mendel wanted to **cross-pollinate** it, he had to tear open the petals and remove the pollen sacs before they matured. When the pistil was to be fertilized, he could supply pollen from another pea flower.

5B-2 *The pea flower:* (left) *closed, resulting in self-pollination;* (right) *opened, ready to be cross-fertilized*

Mendel began his experiments with peas that had been self-pollinating and breeding *true:* in other words, the tall plants always produced tall plants, the short plants always produced short plants, and so forth. He called these the parent plants and used the symbol P_1 to represent them. One of Mendel's experiments involved cross-pollinating a tall pea plant with a short pea plant. He called the offspring of this cross the **first filial* generation** (F_1). All the F_1 plants were tall. He allowed F_1 plants to self-pollinate and produce the **second filial generation** (F_2). Of the 1,064 plants in Mendel's F_2 generation, 787 of them were tall, and 277 of them were short.

Mendel's concepts

To explain the outcome of this experiment and similar results he obtained when he crossed peas with other sets of opposing characteristics, Mendel proposed several concepts. His concepts have been validated as scientists have observed similar results in other organisms and the cellular structures responsible for heredity. The following concepts are illustrated in the crosses described in figure 5B-3.

❑ **The concept of unit characteristics** Mendel stated that an organism's characteristics are caused by units which he called *factors* (now called *genes),* which occur in pairs. In pea plants

the tall parent has two genes for being tall, which are represented by *TT;* and the short parent has two genes for being short, *tt.* Remember that genes (made of DNA) are responsible for inherited characteristics, that genes are located on chromosomes, and that most organisms have homologous pairs of chromosomes. Thus most normal organisms have *pairs* of genes in their cells.

❑ **The concept of dominant and recessive** Since the short plant of the P_1 could give only a short gene *(t),* and the tall plant only a tall gene *(T),* the F_1 generation was *Tt.* But rather than being medium-sized as expected, all the F_1 generation were tall. Mendel called a trait that expressed itself when factors for two opposing traits are present the **dominant trait** (caused by a *dominant gene).* The trait that is masked (hidden) when two genes for opposing traits are present is the **recessive trait** (caused by a *recessive gene).*

❑ **The concept of segregation** Mendel reasoned that when a cell forms gametes, the genes separate (segregate) so that there is only one gene for each characteristic in each gamete. Our knowledge of the behavior of *chromosomes* in meiosis indicates that Mendel's description of gamete formation is accurate.

These concepts are also illustrated by the self-pollination which produced Mendel's F_2 generation of tall and short plants. Since the F_1 generation were all *Tt,* half of their pollen should contain a *T* gene and the other half a *t* gene. Half of the ova they produce should contain a *T* gene and the other half a *t* gene. This illustrates the concept of segregation.

The recessive gene *(t)* was not destroyed or altered when it was masked by the dominant gene in the F_1 generation; therefore, in the F_2 generation there are some short pea plants. Whenever both parent plants gave the recessive gene, the offspring expressed the recessive trait. This illustrates the concept of unit characteristics.

Notice the possible unions of the various gametes of the F_1 as illustrated in figure 5B-3. Three-fourths of the possible gamete combinations in the F_2 have at least one dominant gene; only 1/4 of them have two recessive genes. This, combined

---

filial: (L. FILIUS, son)

with the fact that Mendel's F_2 generation results were 787 tall to 277 short (which is about 3/4 to 1/4), lends support to the concept of unit characteristics.

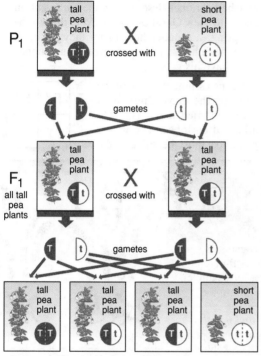

P_1

tall pea plant $T|T$ **X** crossed with   short pea plant $t|t$

T T gametes t t

F_1 all tall pea plants

tall pea plant $T|t$ **X** crossed with   tall pea plant $T|t$

T t gametes T t

tall pea plant $T|T$ tall pea plant $T|t$ tall pea plant $T|t$ short pea plant $t|t$

F_2 787 tall and 277 short pea plants

5B-3 *A summary of Mendel's crosses of tall and short pea plants.*

Genetic terms

Knowing the following genetic terms will help in our discussion of genetic principles:

❑ **Phenotype*** (FEE nuh TYPE)   The expression of an organism's genes; what an organism is like (tall, green, constricted); not all genes result in a visible trait. For example, you inherited genes for digestive enzymes which are not seen but must work for you to be healthy. Expressing these genes is part of your phenotype.);

❑ **Genotype*** (JEN uh TYPE)   The genes that the organism has (often expressed by letters such as *TT, Tt, tt,* and so forth);

❑ **Allele** (uh LEEL)   One pair of genes which has equivalent positions on homologous (paired) chromosomes; these are often expressed by letters–for example, *T* or *t;*

❑ **Homozygous*** (HOH moh ZYE gus)   The condition of both alleles in a cell (organism) being the same–for example, *TT* or *tt;*

❑ **Heterozygous*** (HET uhr oh ZYE gus)   The condition of both alleles in a cell (organism) *not* being the same–for example, *Tt;*

❑ **Monohybrid*** (MAHN oh HYE brid) **Cross**
A cross that deals with only 1 set of alleles–that is, with 1 set of opposing characteristics.

Suppose a man with the dominant phenotype (free earlobes) knows that he is homozygous for the trait. His genotype is *FF.* His wife has the recessive phenotype. What kind of earlobes does she have? The only genotype a person with the recessive phenotype can have is *ff.* (If she had a dominant allele, her phenotype would be different.) All the man's sperm contain the dominant allele *(F),* and all the woman's ova the recessive allele *(f).* All their children, therefore, would have the heterozygous genotype *(Ff).* What would be the phenotype of these children?

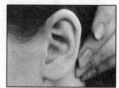
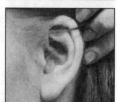

5B-4 *Attached (top) and free (bottom) earlobes.*

Review Questions 5B-1

1. Who is ''the Father of Genetics?'' What did he do to earn this title?
2. Describe the (a) concept of unit characteristics, (b) the concept of segregation, and (c) the concept of dominance.
3. The gene for yellow peas is dominant over the gene for green peas. What is the difference between homozygous yellow peas and heterozygous yellow peas?
4. Compare and contrast the genotype and phenotype of an organism.
5. What is the difference between a gene and an allele?

---

phenotype: pheno- (to show) + -type (Gk. TUPOS, type)

genotype: geno- (beginning) + -type (type)

homozygous: homo- (Gk. HOMOS, same) + -zygous (ZUGOS, yoked)

heterozygous: hetero- (other) + -zygous (yoked)

monohybrid: mono- (single) + -hybrid (L. HYBRIDA, offspring of different parents)

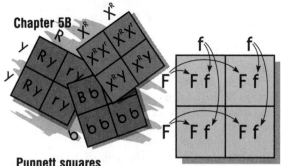

Punnett squares

Geneticists often use **Punnett squares** to depict genetic crosses and to determine the probability of the offspring's being a particular genotype or phenotype. On the top of a Punnett square the *possible gametes* of the female are listed, and down the left side the *possible gametes* of the male are listed. The gametes are then combined in each of the boxes within the square to give the *possible gamete combinations* (the possible genotypes) of the offspring. On the left is the Punnett square for the man and woman with the free and attached earlobes described in the paragraph just above Review Questions 5B-1. Note that all their offspring, no matter how many they have, will have the father's phenotype, even though none of them have his genotype.

Let us assume that one of the sons of the cross spoken of above married a woman with attached earlobes. The man's genotype must be *Ff*, and the

	f	f
F	Ff	Ff
f	ff	ff

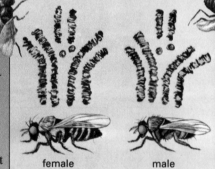

The Key to Genetics—Fruit Flies

In the early twentieth century the tiny **fruit fly** captured the attention of the scientific world—not because of major crops it destroyed (this insect normally consumes small amounts of overripe fruit) or diseases it carried (it is rarely involved in transporting any disease). What caused some of the most brilliant scientists at major universities to begin spending countless hours and millions of dollars was this insect's genetics.

For several reasons scientists found *Drosophila melanogaster* (droh SAHF uh luh ◊ MEL uh noh GAS tur), the tiny fly often found around ripe fruit, ideal for genetic investigations.

❏ *Abundant offspring* One mating will produce hundreds of offspring, enough to show genetic ratios without waiting for additional matings.

❏ *Short life span* Fruit flies reach maturity in about 16 days. The F_2 generation can be reached in about a month. In many organisms a scientist must wait years for a characteristic (baldness, for example) to express itself even in the F_1 generation.

❏ *Ease of keeping and handling* Their size and temperament permit hundreds of them to be kept in a small bottle. A small amount of mashed fruit will feed them for their entire lives. Even the study of small laboratory animals like mice requires much more effort.

❏ *Noticeable differences* Unlike the sexes of many small organisms, fruit fly sexes appear different. They also have many contrasting traits which can be observed easily.

Karyotype of fruit flies

❏ *Four pairs of chromosomes* A small number of chromosomes makes the manufacture of karyotypes and the study of chromosomes and their behavior relatively easy.

Because of the ease with which these tiny insects can be studied, many of the genetic concepts which are accepted today were either verified by or originated with observations of fruit flies. Early in their study the idea that genes

---

Red eye (normal) and white eye of the fruit fly

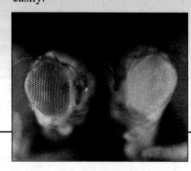

only genotype the woman could have is *ff*. Note the Punnett square for this couple earlier in this paragraph. One-half the boxes within the square have the dominant allele and will produce individuals with free earlobes, and 1/2 the boxes are homozygous for recessive alleles and will produce individuals with attached earlobes. Each child of these two individuals, therefore, will have a 50% chance of having attached earlobes and a 50% chance of having free earlobes.

If this couple were to have 12 children, the probability of 6 having free earlobes and 6 having attached earlobes is very good. Of course, if they have only 3 children, it will be impossible for

them to express the expected 50/50 ratio. In fact, it is quite possible that all of this couple's children will have the same trait. *Each child* has a 50/50 chance for either trait.

Assume that two individuals who are heterozygous for earlobe attachment marry and have a child. What are the child's chances for attached earlobes? Make a Punnett square for this cross. (Check your square with the answer on page 141.)

The Punnett square has 1 homozygous recessive combination *(ff)*. Since the homozygous dominant *(FF)* and the 2 heterozygous *(Ff)* combinations will produce individuals with the dominant phenotype (free earlobes), the child has a

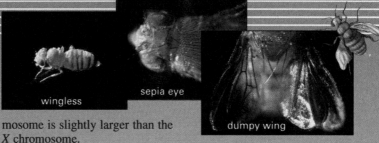

were located on a chromosome (a concept called **gene linkage** or *chromosome linkage*) was verified.

Because of the hundreds of thousands of crosses involving many generations that have been performed on these organisms, scientists were able to work out "chromosome maps" which tell the loci of various genes on the insect's chromosomes.

By doing karyotypes of fruit flies scientists verified the inheritance of sex by sex chromosomes. Fruit flies have 3 pairs of autosomes and 1 pair of sex chromosomes, and the inheritance of sex is similar to that in humans: *XX* is a female, and *XY* is a male. In fruit flies, as in many organisms (but unlike humans), the *Y* chro-

mosome is slightly larger than the *X* chromosome.

Fruit flies have been exposed to various kinds and amounts of radiation and substances which have caused changes in their genetic information or *mutations*. Scientists have carefully tended flies with curly, wrinkled, and otherwise deformed wings; odd colors and shapes to their eyes; abnormal antennas; and various other conditions that would cause them to die in nature.

Through the study of the inheritance of these mutations and other

characteristics, scientists have learned much about the mechanisms of genetics. Without the multiplied billions of fruit flies that have been bred, our knowledge of how traits are inherited would still be "waiting for results." But because of the ease with which scientists have been able to use the fruit fly for genetic experiments, we know more about this tiny insect's genes than we do about human genes.

Review questions on page 131.

A gene map of one of the three larger fruit fly chromosomes

aristaless antenna / star eyes / dumpy wings / clot eyes / black body / reduced bristles / purple eyes / vestigial wings / lobe eyes / curved wings / plexus wings / brown eyes / speck body

75% chance of having free earlobes. If the couple has 12 children, there should (statistically speaking) be 9 with free earlobes and 3 with attached earlobes. Of course, the ratios may not work out perfectly for *individual* families.

Genetic ratios in monohybrid crosses

The probability of offspring having or not having a particular gene or trait is usually expressed as a

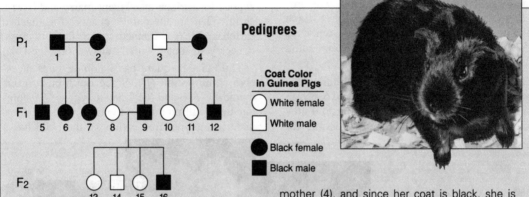

Pedigrees

Coat Color in Guinea Pigs

○ White female
□ White male
● Black female
■ Black male

A **pedigree** is a chart which geneticists use to show the presence or absence of a trait in a number of generations. Pedigrees often use symbols to indicate sex, marriage (or matings of animals and plants), offspring, and other related factors. Phenotypes are often indicated by symbols, shading, or colors.

Note the pedigree of coat color in guinea pigs. In the P_1 generation individuals 1 and 2 have black fur but one of their offspring, number 8, has white fur. You should be able to determine that black is the dominant characteristic *(B)*, and that individuals 1 and 2 are heterozygous for the trait. This is determined as follows: since 8 must be homozygous for white fur *(bb)*, she must have inherited a recessive allele from both parents. But since both parents have black fur, they must also have the dominant allele. Thus 1 and 2 must be heterozygous *(Bb)*. (If you do not understand that, try working it on a Punnett square.)

Now try another. Individual 9 must be heterozygous. You can determine that by looking at his parents or by looking at his offspring. First, look at his parents. Because his father (3) has the recessive phenotype, the father must also have the recessive genotype *(bb)*. The father can give his son only a recessive allele, since that is all he has. Since the son has the dominant phenotype (black) he must be heterozygous *(Bb)*. He must have received the dominant allele from his

mother (4), and since her coat is black, she is able to pass this trait on to her son.

Now determine the genotype of 9 by looking at his offspring. He is mated with a white female (8) who must have the genotype *bb*. Since three of their offspring are white, he must be able to give the recessive allele to his offspring, even though he must have the dominant allele to be black. Thus, he must be heterozygous *(Bb)*.

In this pedigree the genotypes can be determined for every individual except 5, 6, and 7. Geneticists would say there are "blanks" for these individuals. We know they have the dominant allele *(B)* but cannot be sure of the second allele. Their parents (1 and 2) are both heterozygous and thus can produce 2 different genotypes for black coats: *BB* and *Bb*. Some students think that since there are 4 boxes in a Punnett square from mating their parents *(Bb x Bb)* and since there are 4 offspring, each offspring must be one of the genotypes in the Punnett square. Remember that a Punnett square shows *possible* genotypes of the offspring in the ratio they are *expected* to occur. Based on the pedigree we cannot be sure of the genotypes of individuals 5, 6, and 7 without running test crosses.

Today geneticists create pedigrees to predict the possibilities of certain traits in offspring. Although not significant for many characteristics such as hair color and height, the information can be useful when it involves inherited disorders or diseases.

ratio. Corn kernel color clearly illustrates genetic ratios since on each ear of corn there are enough individual kernels to present an accurate ratio. In corn the gene for purple kernels *(P)* is dominant over its allele for yellow kernels *(p)*. If pollen from a homozygous yellow plant is applied to the developing ear of a homozygous purple plant, the ear of corn will develop all purple kernels. The Punnett square indicates 4 boxes with the heterozygous genotype *(Pp)* and none with any other genotype. The genotypic ratio for the F_1 generation is 4:0, or 4 heterozygous *(Pp)* to none of the other 2 types. In this case the phenotypic ratio is 4:0, or 4 purple to none of any other type. (Usually such ratios are reduced to 1:0, but both are accurate.) In phenotypic ratios the number of dominant individuals is listed first. The F_2 generation of this cross, however, will have different ratios.

	P	P
p	Pp	Pp
p	Pp	Pp

PP × pp
ratios:
genotypic 4:0
phenotypic 4:0

When 2 heterozygous corn plants are cross-pollinated, the F_2 phenotypic ratio will be 3:1; that is, 3 purple kernels will occur for every 1 yellow kernel. The genotypic ratio, however, will be 1:2:1—that is, 1 homozygous dominant, 2 heterozygous, and 1 homozygous recessive. (Always list the number of homozygous dominant, then hetero-

	P	p
P	PP	Pp
p	Pp	pp

Pp × Pp
ratios:
genotypic 1:2:1
phenotypic 3:1

5B-5 *This corn cob has the phenotypic radio of 3 purple to 1 yellow. Can you determine what the genotypes of the parents must have been?*

zygous, and then homozygous recessive individuals when giving this type of genotypic ratio.)

If a heterozygous plant is mated with a homozygous yellow plant, what will be the expected genotypic and phenotypic ratios? (See page 141.)

A test cross

How can you tell whether a genotype of a purple kernel of corn is *PP* or *Pp*? The best way for many organisms is to run a test cross to find the genotype of an individual. A **test cross** involves mating an individual that has the dominant phenotype but an unknown genotype with another individual that has the recessive phenotype. The individual with the recessive phenotype has a known genotype (homozygous recessive).

For example, if you mated a homozygous purple kernel plant *(PP)* with a yellow kernel plant *(pp,* the homozygous recessive), what would be the color of the offspring? All would be purple. If you mated a heterozygous purple kernel plant *(Pp)* with the same yellow kernel plant, what would be the color of the offspring? Half would be purple and half would be yellow. Thus by looking at the offspring of a test cross you can tell the genotype of the dominant parent (if you have *enough* offspring).

Review Questions 5B-2

1. Two organisms heterozygous for a single trait are crossed. What is the expected genotypic ratio of the offspring? Explain.
2. What is the phenotypic ratio of the cross described in question one? Explain.
3. What can a biologist learn by looking at a Punnett square for a cross?
4. Describe a test cross. What would a test cross be used to determine?
5. What information can a geneticist learn by looking at a pedigree for a cross?

Facet 5B-1: The Key to Genetics—Fruit Flies, pages 128-29

1. What characteristics of the fruit fly make it a useful organism for genetic studies?
2. List three genetic concepts that were discovered or verified by the study of fruit flies.
3. What is a chromosome map?
4. Name a sex-linked characteristic in fruit flies.
5. List two things that we can learn by observing a karyotype of a fruit fly.

Variations of Mendelian Genetics

If the Mendelian concepts studied thus far were the only factors involved in heredity, the prediction of probable phenotypes would be easy. Although genetics is based largely on the concepts illustrated in a monohybrid cross with simple dominant and recessive characteristics, there are many variations. These variations, although simple, make predictions of an organism's phenotype quite difficult. Many human traits, including sex, eye color, height, skin color, blood type, and intelligence, as well as a number of disorders, are determined by these genetic mechanisms.

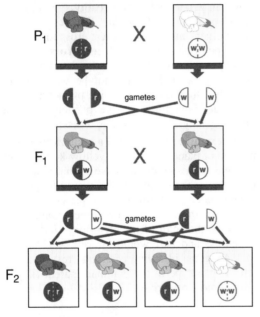

5B-6 *Incomplete dominance in snapdragon color*

Incomplete dominance

Not all genetic traits are dominant or recessive. Many alleles express **incomplete dominance.** Flower color in snapdragons and other common garden flowers demonstrates this condition. When a homozygous red and a homozygous white snapdragon are crossed, all the offspring are pink.

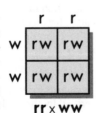

	r	r
w	rw	rw
w	rw	rw

rr × **ww**

ratios:
genotypic 1:0
phenotypic 1:0

In snapdragons neither red nor white is dominant, and in a heterozygous flower both alleles express themselves in the pink color. Crossing 2 pink snapdragons yields 1/4 white, 1/2 pink, and 1/4 red snapdragons.

	r	w
r	rr	rw
w	rw	ww

rw × **rw**

ratios:
genotypic 1:2:1
phenotypic 1:2:1

Note that in the Punnett square 2 different letters represent the alleles. Using capital and lowercase letters might make it appear that the alleles are dominant and recessive. It has become conventional to use different letters when crossing incompletely dominant alleles.

Many human traits appear to be the result of incomplete dominance. People who suffer from *brachydactyly* (BRAK ih DAK tuh lee) lack a bone in each finger and toe and therefore have abnormally short fingers and toes. A person with brachydactyly is heterozygous (that is, he has 1 abnormal gene and 1 normal gene); people with normal fingers and toes are homozygous for the normal gene; and people that are homozygous for the brachydactyly gene are severely crippled, with a complete lack of fingers and toes.

Another human trait which appears to be incompletely dominant is *sickle cell anemia*. Most people in the United States are homozygous for the production of normal hemoglobin. Those people who are heterozygous for sickle cell anemia produce normal and abnormal hemoglobin. Red blood cells which contain abnormal hemoglobin can become sickle-shaped rather than round and disc-shaped. The blood of heterozygous people contains both round and sickle-shaped cells. Their blood cannot carry as much oxygen as normal blood can.

When people carry on strenuous activities or are in high elevations, they undergo oxygen stress. If a person heterozygous for sickle cell anemia is under oxygen stress, some of his red blood cells will become sickle-shaped. In this unusual shape the blood cells may not be able to carry all the oxygen that the body tissues need. About 1 in 12 black Americans is heterozygous for the abnormal hemoglobin and has what is

5B-7 *Blood being tested for sickle cell anemia. Normal blood (left) and sickle-cell blood (right).*

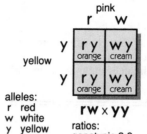

pink

	r	w
y	ry orange	wy cream
y	ry orange	wy cream

yellow

alleles:
r red
w white
y yellow

rw × yy

ratios:
genotypic 2:2
phenotypic 2:2

called the *sickle cell trait*. These people can carry on nearly normal life-styles if they eat properly and get sufficient rest.

About 3 black children per 1,000 born in America are homozygous for abnormal hemoglobin. All their cells are sickle-shaped. This abnormal blood results in aching bones and clogged blood vessels in the spleen and lungs. Although blood transfusions can prolong their lives, these people usually die as children.

Multiple alleles

The traits we have discussed thus far have had 2 contrasting alleles. In peas there is the allele for the tall trait and the allele for the short trait. In sickle-cell anemia there is the allele for normal hemoglobin and the allele for abnormal hemoglobin. The place on a chromosome where a particular gene is located is the gene's **locus*** (pl., loci). The alleles for the traits of a monohybrid cross appear at the same loci on the homologous chromosomes. Since chromosomes in peas and humans and all diploid organisms occur in pairs, there are two of most of their alleles. One of these 2 will be at each locus.

Occasionally, however, there may be **multiple alleles**—that is, 1 of several alleles can be at a given locus. A diploid organism, of course, will have only 2 of the possible alleles—1 on each of the homologues. If there are, then, incompletely dominant alleles for yellow, red, and white flowers, all colors possible at the same loci, new colors

(oranges and creams) will be possible.

A simple multiple allele condition in humans is the A and B blood types. There is 1 allele for the factor causing blood type A and 1 allele for the factor causing blood type B, both of which are dominant. There is a recessive allele for no factor. In diagramming this multiple allele cross, it is traditional to use the capital letter I to represent the chromosome and a superscript to represent the dominant alleles. I^A and I^B are then dominant alleles. The recessive allele, neither A nor B but recessive to both, is represented by the letter i.

A person with blood type A could be homozygous ($I^A I^A$) or heterozygous ($I^A i$); and someone with type B could be $I^B I^B$ or $I^B i$. A person can be heterozygous for *both* dominant alleles ($I^A I^B$) and

	I^A	i
I^B	$I^A I^B$	$I^B i$
i	$I^A i$	ii

$I^A i \times I^B i$

have blood type AB. Someone homozygous for the recessive trait *(ii)* has type O.

Let us use this information to solve a hypothetical problem. Both Mrs. Pearson and Mrs. Brown had baby girls the same day in the same hospital. The Pearsons named their daughter Sally, and the Browns named their daughter Barbara. At home Mrs. Pearson began to feel that Sally was not her daughter. Perhaps there had been some mix-up in the hospital nursery.

Blood tests were made. Mr. Pearson was type B, Mrs. Pearson type A. Mr. Brown was type A, Mrs. Brown type A. Sally was type O, and Barbara was type B. Had a mix-up occurred? Draw Punnett squares to illustrate the genotypes of these people. The answer is diagrammed and explained on page 141.

Some other human blood types and characteristics are believed to be determined by multiple alleles. Coat color and patterns in many mammals are determined by multiple alleles.

locus: (L. LOCUS, place)

Review Questions 5B-3
1. Compare simple dominance with incomplete dominance. List several characteristics that exhibit incomplete dominance.
2. Describe the condition of multiple alleles. What human characteristics are controlled by multiple alleles?

Dihybrid crosses

A **dihybrid* cross** deals with 2 sets of characteristics at the same time. Study figure 5B-8, which is the crossing of a homozygous green, inflated-pod pea plant *(GGII)* with a homozygous yellow, constricted-pod pea plant *(ggii)*.

Since we are now dealing with 2 characteristics, we must consider 4 alleles, 2 for each characteristic. When gametes are made, however, the alleles segregate, and only 1 allele for each characteristic will be in each gamete. Since chromosome pairs separate, there will normally not be a gamete containing 2 alleles of 1 gene and none of the other. The forming of the F_1 by the uniting of the gametes results in individuals that have green, inflated pods. They are, however, heterozygous for both traits.

The formation of gametes in the F_1 results in four different possibilities: *GI, Gi, gI,* and *gi.* (Under normal circumstances a *Gg* gamete or an *Ii* gamete would not occur because segregation of chromosomes in gamete formation separates the alleles, making the gametes haploid.) The procedure for finding the possible gamete combinations for the 2 traits is much the same as for finding the possible combinations in a monohybrid cross: list the possible gametes from the male on the side of, and the possible gametes from the female on the top of, a Punnett square. Since there are 4 possible gametes from each parent, the Punnett

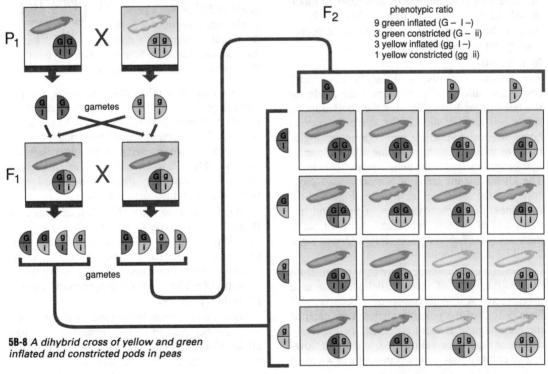

F₂
phenotypic ratio
9 green inflated (G – I –)
3 green constricted (G – ii)
3 yellow inflated (gg I –)
1 yellow constricted (gg ii)

5B-8 *A dihybrid cross of yellow and green inflated and constricted pods in peas*

dihybrid: di- (two) + -hybrid (offspring of different parents)

square for this cross must have 16 blocks. The phenotypic ratio of individuals within the Punnett square is 9 green inflated; 3 green constricted; 3 yellow inflated; and 1 yellow constricted.

Assume that a plant breeder is interested in obtaining a homozygous strain of green constricted peas. In the F_2 Punnett square there are 3 boxes that contain individuals of this phenotype. You will notice, however, that there are, for this phenotype, 2 different genotypes: *GGii* and *Ggii* (1 homozygous and 1 heterozygous for green). How can he tell the difference between them? He cannot do so simply by looking at the peas. One way he *can* find out is to test cross the peas in question. Draw a Punnett square for the 2 possible test crosses to see what you would expect from each of the 2 genotypes. The answer is on page 141.

5B-9 *The G/g alleles are on one chromosome, and the I/i on another (right); thus, they segregate independently of each other. The G/g and the W/w alleles are on the same chromosome (left) and thus do not segregate independently.*

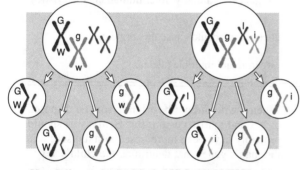

Mendel's concept of independent assortment
Mendel himself used dihybrid crosses, and the results of those crosses led him to formulate his **concept of independent assortment:** the segregation (separation) of 1 set of alleles during gamete formation is not affected by the presence or segregation of another set of alleles. When Mendel was observing 2 sets of characteristics in the same cross, he noted not only that the ratios he was expecting did result but also that these characteristics randomly mixed with the other characteristics. For example, the separating of the green-yellow alleles did not affect the separating of the inflated-constricted alleles. Green color will

not always accompany constricted pods or inflated pods. The traits mix and match freely.

There is a logical exception to this concept, though Mendel did not encounter it in his work with garden peas. If the genes for 2 traits are on the same chromosome, they will not segregate independently as in a typical dihybrid cross (see figure 5B-9). All 7 characteristics Mendel observed were on different chromosomes and were, therefore, segregated independently. The pea has only 7 pairs of chromosomes, though. If Mendel had observed an eighth pair of contrasting characteristics, the "factors" would not have segregated independently, and he might have become confused.

Multiple gene interaction
A single characteristic is not always caused by a single gene. Sometimes 2 or more genes working together result in a single trait, a process called **multiple gene interaction.** One simple example of this is the combs of chickens.

A rose comb is caused by having a dominant gene at a locus and 2 recessive genes at another locus (*RRpp, Rrpp*). A pea comb is caused by exactly the opposite (*rrPP* or *rrPp*). A walnut comb results from having at least a dominant allele in each pair (*RRPP, RRPp, RrPP,* or *RrPp*).

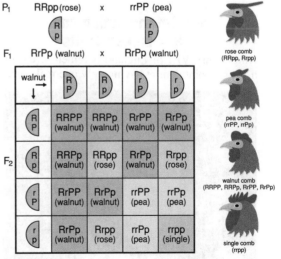

5B-10 *Multiple gene interaction in the combs of chickens*

And a single comb is the result of having homozygous recessive alleles at both loci *(rrpp)*. Because there are 2 sets of genes involved in determining combs in chickens, they must be dealt with as dihybrid crosses. The 9:3:3:1 ratio is the same, but there are not 2 characteristics—just 1; and that one is the type of comb. There are, however, 4 types of combs.

Most human traits have some degree of multiple gene interaction. It seems, for example, that 5 or 6 gene pairs at different loci determine human skin color. The Punnett square for such a large number of gene possibilities requires over 100 different blocks and has dozens of different genotypes and phenotypes. Some of the gene pairs seem to be incompletely dominant, and some work as *inhibitors* (genes which prevent the expression of other genes). It is also possible that 2 or more of these genes are on the same chromosome and thus further confuse matters.

Humans produce very few offspring, and relatively poor records have been kept of the exact

5B-11 *At one time the chromosome was thought to be a nonchangeable unit. Today, scientists routinely manipulate chromosomes and genes.*

shade of skin color for more than a few generations. Knowing a person's genotype and predicting his child's phenotype for skin color are almost impossible.

Hair color and eye color are similar but probably involve few gene pairs. Multiple gene action determines, in part, one's height, body build, intelligence, and many other human characteristics.

Review Questions 5B-4
1. Describe the concept of independent assortment. What condition could cause this principle not to work?
2. Describe multiple gene interaction and distinguish between it and multiple alleles.

Sex Determination and Sex-Linked Traits

King Henry VIII of England is remembered for his disappointment at having only one male heir.

5B-12 *Henry VIII of England*

When a wife did not bear him a son, he disposed of her and married again. But Henry VIII should probably have been more upset with himself: it is the man's genes that determine the child's sex.

Sex chromosomes and autosomes
Karyotypes reveal that normal people have 22 pairs of **autosomes** and 1 pair of **sex chromosomes**. The autosomes are non-sex-determining chromosomes and are traditionally numbered. The sex chromosomes are not numbered but in humans are designated *X* and *Y*. In humans the *Y* chromosome is considerably smaller than the *X* chromosome. A person with 1 *X* and 1 *Y* chromosome is male; a person with 2 *X* chromosomes is female.

During meiosis in females, the 2 *X* chromosomes pair; in the male the *X* and the *Y* chromosomes pair. Crosses of *X* and *Y* chromosomes can therefore be determined on a Punnett square. Note that only the father can give a Y chromosome to his offspring. Since it takes a Y chromosome to form a male offspring, the father thus determines the sex of the child.

female

	X	X
X	XX	XX
Y	XY	XY

male

XX × XY

According to the Punnett square there is a 50/50 chance of each child being a boy. Statistics show, however, that there are actually more boys born. Recent evidence shows that a Y sperm and an X sperm are probably slightly different in their reaction to various chemicals. The chemical make-up of the fluids in a female's reproductive structures varies amongst women and changes regularly in each woman. These differences could account for the slight difference between the expected ratio and the actual ratio of girls to boys. Henry VIII might have been able to blame his lack of many sons on the chemical make-up of 1 wife, or maybe 2; but to have had 6 wives and only 1 surviving son was probably not the fault of all the queens.

Sex-linked traits

The alleles found on autosomes are in pairs. Since autosomes are in pairs, the gene found at a particular locus on one will have a companion gene at the same locus on the homologue. At that locus there may be the exact same gene (homozygous condition) or a variation of that gene (heterozygous condition). But on sex chromosomes conditions may vary. In humans, for example, the X chromosome is much larger than the Y chromosome and thus can contain many more genes.

About 5% of the white males in northern Europe have a reduced amount of a chemical in the retina of their eyes that causes them to be *red-green colorblind*. To them most greens appear tan, olive greens appear brown, and most reds appear reddish brown. The condition is a recessive characteristic which is found on the X chromosome but does not have a companion allele on the Y chromosome.

In order to diagram these crosses and keep straight the sex of the individuals, we will use the X and Y to indicate the chromosome and add superscripts to indicate the genes. Thus X^G is for a female sex chromosome that has the gene for normal vision; X^g is for a female sex chromosome that has the gene for red-green colorblindness; and Y is for the male chromosome. Since the male chromosome does not have a gene for this trait, it does not have a G or a g on it.

Traits which have their genes on the X chromosome and not on the Y chromosome are called **sex-linked traits** because they are linked to the sex of the individual. For example, on a Punnett square, cross a female who lacks the recessive trait with a male who is red-green colorblind. Note the sex of the offspring.

5B-13 *The left picture is what a person with normal vision would see. The right picture has been adjusted to simulate what a red-green colorblind person would see.*

FACETS OF BIOLOGY

5B-2

The Royal Disease–Hemophilia

Hemophilia (HEE muh FIL ee uh) is sometimes called "bleeder's disease." People who have this genetic disorder lack a blood chemical that is essential for blood clotting. Even a small cut, therefore, can result in severe bleeding or death. Bumps, which for most people result in bruises, can cause internal bleeding, swelling, and possibly death for hemophiliacs. In times past, hemophiliacs usually died very young. Today, medication can supply the missing blood chemical.

Hemophilia has been found to be a sex-linked recessive trait. Although there are very old records of people who are believed to have been hemophiliacs, the best

known historical record of the disease involves the royal house of Great Britain. Hemophilia has thus been called "the royal disease." Queen Victoria (reign 1837-1901) was a carrier of this sex-linked trait.

The pedigree on the next page shows only some of Queen Victoria's offspring. Her son Leopold was a hemophiliac. At a time when most hemophiliacs died as infants or young children, he was exceptionally protected and lived to maturity. Although his brothers joined and commanded British military regiments, Leopold was not even permitted to wear a uniform. A record of Leopold's life is one of "falling ill," as his mother

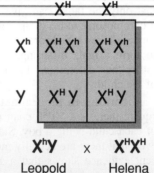

	X^H	X^H
X^h	$X^H X^h$	$X^H X^h$
Y	$X^H Y$	$X^H Y$

$X^h Y$ x $X^H X^H$
Leopold   Helena

put it, and spending long days in bed recovering.

After thwarting most of his attempts to be married, the Queen relented and arranged for Leopold's marriage to the German princess Helena of Waldeck. After a year Alice was born. A Punnett square for Leopold and Helena (see above) shows that their daughters could not be hemophiliacs but would be carriers. This fact is also demonstrated by Alice's offspring.

The second child of Leopold and Helena was a normal son, Charles Edward. Since Leopold must give the Y chromosome to any son, he could not give the gene for hemophilia to any of them. Leopold, however, did not know this and also did not know whether his second child was a hemophiliac or not. At age 31, before his son was born, Leopold hurt his knee and died of internal bleeding within a few days.

Queen Victoria was quoted as saying that hemophilia "was not in our family," and she was correct: no one on her side of the family expressed the recessive characteristic. She supposed that her husband, Albert, introduced

The British royal family (about 1860) with carriers indicated. Left to right: Alfred, Prince Albert, Helena, Arthur (in kilt), Alice, Beatrice (infant), Queen Victoria (seated), Princess Victoria, Louise, Leopold (facing camera) and Edward.

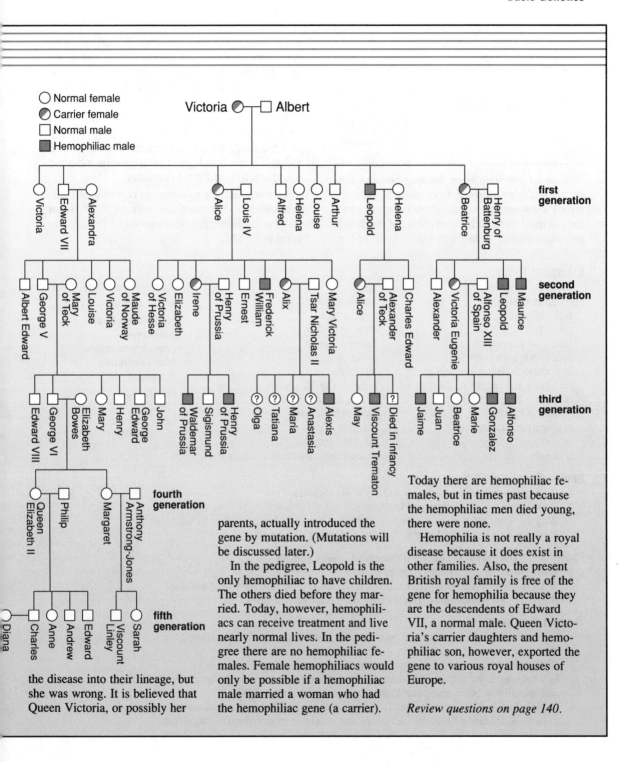

Today there are hemophiliac females, but in times past because the hemophiliac men died young, there were none.

Hemophilia is not really a royal disease because it does exist in other families. Also, the present British royal family is free of the gene for hemophilia because they are the descendents of Edward VII, a normal male. Queen Victoria's carrier daughters and hemophiliac son, however, exported the gene to various royal houses of Europe.

parents, actually introduced the gene by mutation. (Mutations will be discussed later.)

In the pedigree, Leopold is the only hemophiliac to have children. The others died before they married. Today, however, hemophiliacs can receive treatment and live nearly normal lives. In the pedigree there are no hemophiliac females. Female hemophiliacs would only be possible if a hemophiliac male married a woman who had the hemophiliac gene (a carrier).

the disease into their lineage, but she was wrong. It is believed that Queen Victoria, or possibly her

Review questions on page 140.

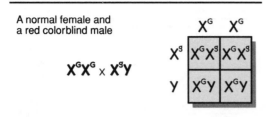

A normal female and
a red colorblind male

$$X^G X^G \times X^g Y$$

None of the sons have the trait because they get their X chromosome from their mother and their Y chromosome (which does not carry genes for this trait) from their father. None of the daughters are red-green colorblind either, because they are heterozygous for a recessive trait ($X^G X^g$). The daughters, however, are **carriers** of the red-green colorblindness trait. A carrier for a sex-linked trait is an individual that does not have the characteristic but does carry the gene for the trait.

Is it possible for a man to pass sex-linked traits on to his son? No. A man will always give the Y chromosome, which lacks genes for sex-linked traits. If a boy is red-green colorblind he inherited the characteristic from his mother.

Is it possible for a woman to be red-green colorblind? Yes. She must, however, be $X^g X^g$. What will be the genotypes of her parents? The answer is on page 141.

Biological Terms

Mendelian genetics	allele	multiple gene interaction
Mendelian Genetics	homozygous	*Sex Determination and*
self-pollinate	heterozygous	*Sex-linked Traits*
cross-pollinate	monohybrid cross	autosomes
first filial generation	Punnett square	sex chromosomes
second filial generation	pedigree	sex-linked traits
unit characteristics, concept of	test cross	carriers
dominant and recessive, concept of	*Variations of Mendelian Genetics*	*Facets*
dominant trait	incomplete dominance	fruit fly
recessive trait	locus (plural, loci)	gene linkage
segregation, concept of	multiple alleles	hemophilia
phenotype	dihybrid cross	
genotype	independent assortment, concept of	

Review Questions 5B-5

1. Distinguish between autosomes and sex chromosomes.
2. Explain how sex is determined in humans.
3. Why are sex-linked traits passed from father to daughter but not father to son? Can a mother give a sex-linked trait to her son and to her daughter?

Facet 5B-2: The Royal Disease–Hemophilia, pages 138-39

1. What are the characteristics of hemophilia?
2. What is a sex-linked characteristic, and how can you be sure hemophilia is one?
3. Why were no hemophiliac females born until relatively recently?

Thought Questions

1. Why are the garden pea and the fruit fly good organisms on which to study genetics? Why is the human a poor organism on which to study genetics?
2. Distinguish between a dihybrid cross and a cross involving multiple alleles.
3. In what way is incomplete dominance an exception to the concept of dominance? Could multiple alleles be an exception to the concept of dominance? Why?
4. Explain how multiple gene interaction may have confused early researchers who expected traits to be inherited by simple dominant and recessive monohybrid mechanisms.

Answers to Basic Genetic Problems

Free or Attached Earlobe, pages 128-29

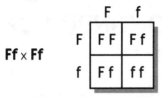

$Ff \times Ff$

	F	f
F	FF	Ff
f	Ff	ff

Genotypes of Guinea Pigs, page 130

1 Bb	5 B–	9 Bb	13 bb
2 Bb	6 B–	10 bb	14 bb
3 bb	7 B–	11 bb	15 bb
4 Bb	8 bb	12 Bb	16 Bb

Corn Kernel Color, page 131

	P	p
p	Pp	pp
p	Pp	pp

ratios:
genotypic 2Pp:2pp
phenotypic 2 purple:2 yellow

$Pp \times pp$

Multiple Alleles Blood Typing, page 133

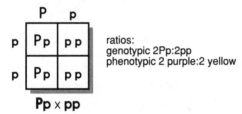

The Pearsons   The Browns
$I^A i \times I^B i$ $I^A i \times I^A i$

Since Sally is blood type O, she could be the Pearsons' child. If both Pearson parents were heterozygous (Mr. Pearson $I^B i$ and Mrs. Pearson $I^A i$), it is quite possible for them to have a homozygous recessive (ii) child who would have blood type O. (See Pearsons' Punnett square above.)

Barbara (type B), however, could not be the Browns' child. Neither Mr. Brown nor Mrs. Brown has the *B* allele; therefore, they could not give it to their daughter. The Browns' children must be either blood type A or blood type O. (See Browns' Punnett square above.) Since the

Pearsons could have a child with blood type B, Barbara must be their daughter, and Sally the Browns' daughter.

How can we be sure that the parents' genotypes are the ones used above? Their phenotypes and their daughters' phenotypes can be used to show that there are no other possible genotypes for any of the parents, except Mr. Pearson. He could be heterozygous B $(I^B i)$ or homozygous B $(I^B I^B)$ and still be Barbara's father.

Dihybrid Cross of Peas, page 134

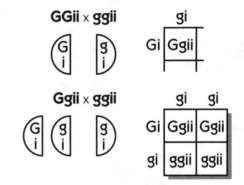

$GGii \times ggii$

	gi
Gi	Ggii

$Ggii \times ggii$

	gi	gi
Gi	Ggii	Ggii
gi	ggii	ggii

Recall that a test cross mates an unknown genotype with a known genotype (the homozygous recessive) which in this case is *ggii*. The test cross of a pea that is homozygous for green and constricted pods *(GGii × ggii)* will produce all green-constricted individuals in the F_1. If this happens, the farmer will know that his parent pea is homozygous for those traits. If a heterozygous green pea is test crossed *(Ggii × ggii)*, 1/2 the offspring will be yellow constricted. If this happens, the farmer knows that his parent pea was heterozygous for pod color.

Red-green Colorblind Female, page 140

A red-green colorblind girl $(X^g X^g)$ can be born to a red-green colorblind man $(X^g Y)$ and a carrier woman $(X^G X^g)$. The father must be red-green colorblind, because if he has normal vision he can give only normal genes for this trait to his daughter. If she gets a normal gene, she will not be red-green colorblind. The mother must be a carrier $(X^G X^g)$ in order to be able to give the recessive trait to her daughter.

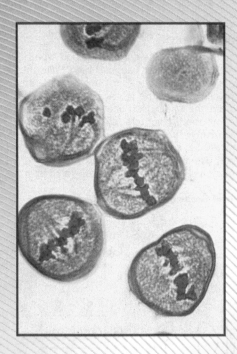

ADVANCED GENETICS
THE CONTINUITY OF LIFE
PART II

SIX

6A– Chromosome and Gene Changes

The inheritance mechanisms discussed thus far could be considered normal. In most cellular divisions, gamete formations, and gamete combinations (fertilizations), the principles of Mendelian genetics hold true. There are, however, many irregularities that can occur. Some of these are merely a reshuffling of genes and happen quite regularly in most organisms without any noticeable effects. Other irregularities are **lethal**, killing the organism or causing abnormal (weak or deformed) organisms.

There are 2 basic types of genetic changes:

❑ **Chromosomal changes** which involve either the *number of chromosomes* or the *arrangement of genes on a chromosome*, and

❑ **Gene mutations*** (point of mutations) which change the sequence of bases in a gene.

---

mutation: (L. MUTARE, to change)

Changes Affecting the Numbers of Chromosomes

The **genome** (JEE NOME) of an organism is 1 single complete set of its chromosomes. A normal haploid gamete contains a complete genome. A diploid organism has cells with 2 complete genomes. Most organisms with which you are familiar are diploid in their adult stage. Diploid organisms must carry on meiosis in order to form haploid gametes. At fertilization, the haploid gametes combine to produce a diploid zygote.

There are, however, some organisms that are haploid even as adults, forming gametes without going through meiosis. Mosses, algae, and many fungi, for example, are haploid. Their diploid zygote, however, usually undergoes meiotic divisions before the organism begins to grow.

In the insect world there are other naturally occurring haploid organisms. The queen and worker bees are diploid, but the drones (males) are haploid, developing from unfertilized eggs. Scientists call the development of an unfertilized egg **parthenogenesis*** (PAR thuh noh JEN ih sis).

Euploidy

Euploidy (YOO PLOY dee) involves the addition or loss of an entire genome. For example, some diploid organisms can be made to produce haploid offspring by artificial parthenogenesis. Unfertilized eggs from many amphibians (frogs and salamanders) can be treated in the laboratory and forced to develop. The resulting haploid organism is smaller and weaker than the diploid organism as well as sterile. Thus far the turkey is the largest animal that has been induced to develop by parthenogenesis. Haploid turkeys are smaller than normal and do not have quite enough feathers.

Any cell or organism that has 3 or more genomes is a **polyploid.** Polyploids are of 2 basic types: those that have multiples of the same genome and those that have multiples of different genomes.

Triploids

If a diploid gamete is fertilized by a haploid gamete, the resulting zygote is **triploid** (3n), having 3 genomes. During mitosis all the chromosomes replicate and divide normally. When a triploid organism enters meiosis, however, and the chro-

Various Chromosome Number Changes			6A-1
euploidy (complete genomes)	**haploid (n)** a single genome	X X X	gametes, moss, algae, fungi, drones
	diploid (2n) multiple of same genome	XX XX XX	most plants and animals, man
	triploid (3n) multiple of same genome	XXX XXX XXX	seedless watermelons, bananas, some plants
	tetraploid (4n) multiple of same genome	XXXX XXXX XXXX	Irish potato, alfalfa, some rare plants
	tetraploid (2n + 2n) multiple of different genomes	XX XX XX XX xx xx	corn, wheat
aneuploidy (incomplete genomes)	**monosomy (2n – 1)**	XX X XX	various types of plants, Turner's syndrome in humans
	trisomy (2n + 1)	XX XXX XX	various types of plants, mongolism and Klinefelter's syndrome in humans

parthenogenesis: partheno- (Gk. PARTHENON, virgin) + -genesis (birth)

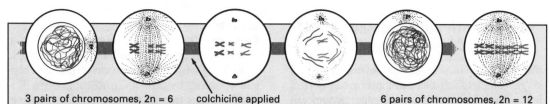

3 pairs of chromosomes, 2n = 6   colchicine applied   6 pairs of chromosomes, 2n = 12

The chromosome number is doubled by prohibiting the segregation of chromosomes during cell division.

Forming Polyploids

Some polyploid organisms exist naturally and some can be induced artificially. To induce polyploids in the laboratory, scientists often use **colchicine** (KOHL chih SEEN), a poisonous drug extracted from the autumn crocus plant. Colchicine dissolves the spindle fibers of dividing cells.

Without spindle fibers the chromosomes do not divide and migrate into the daughter cells.

Since the chromosomes have not separated, the cells will have doubled their chromosome number when the drug wears off. Colchicine, then, applied to cells entering meiosis, causes the production of *diploid gametes.*

mosomes line up, the third homologue prevents successful replication and unfertile (or sterile) gametes are produced.

Living triploids do not occur in the animal kingdom (nor in humans), but they occasionally appear in other kingdoms. Triploid plants are usually taller and stronger, have more and larger leaves, and produce larger fruits than their diploid counterparts. Some triploids are therefore cultivated as ornamental plants.

Triploid grapes, oranges, and other fruits are common on today's market shelves. Because they lack seeds, triploids must be reproduced asexually. A triploid seedless watermelon can be produced with the use of colchicine. Since watermelon vines and other annual plants live only 1 year, however, obtaining seedless fruits from annual plants is expensive.

6A-2
Triploid grapes are larger than their diploid counterparts.

Tetraploid

Tetraploid (TET ruh PLOYD) organisms (having 4 sets of chromosomes) are common in plants but rare in animals. Some cells of the human liver are tetraploid. For some reason, and by an unknown mechanism, some human liver cells completely duplicate their chromosomes without dividing. These cells, then, have 4 genomes (abbreviated 4n). Since liver cells do not form gametes, this unusual chromosome number does not affect the offspring. Other than in liver cells, tetraploidy is unknown in humans.

6A-3

The white potato: 4n = 48.

The white or Irish potato is a tetraploid. The genome of a potato has 12 chromosomes (n = 12), and the diploid state is 24 chromosomes (2n = 24). The cells of an Irish potato, however, have 48 chromosomes (4n = 48). The 4 homologues lining up together result in problems during meiosis, and few fertile gametes are formed. Instead, farmers use the eyes of the potato to reproduce this crop asexually.

Man's Use of Polyploids

Man has often looked at the plants and animals he grows for food and wished that one organism could have the desirable traits of two. The Russian plant geneticist, Karpechenko, is remembered for his desire to have a plant that produced the large edible leaves of a cabbage and the large edible root of a radish. In 1927 he crossed a radish (2n = 18, genus *Raphanus*) with a cabbage (2n = 18, genus *Brassica*) and eagerly awaited the results. He even invented the word *Raphanobrassica* as the scientific name for this new plant.

Some seeds were formed, but the plants that grew were sterile. Since the chromosomes were from 2 different genomes, the 9 radish chromosomes did not pair with the 9 cabbage chromosomes during meiosis. This plant had the diploid chromosome number (2n = 18), but its genetic make-up was really 2 haploid genomes (n + n = 18).

In a few plants, however, the chromosomes doubled, forming a tetraploid (2n + 2n = 36). These plants were fertile, each of the chromosomes having a partner during meiosis and producing seeds that grew new plants. *Raphanobrassica* was hailed as a new manmade species. Although it cannot grow in the wild, it can be cultivated. Today you can buy *Raphanobrassica* seeds, but the plant is not grown for food. To Karpechenko's dismay, it has radish leaves and cabbage roots.

Most of man's attempts to cross organisms from different genetic backgrounds have met with a similar lack of success. Occasionally some crosses between similar species do produce valuable offspring. A cross between a grapefruit and a tangerine results in tangelos. Once a plant with desirable traits is obtained, asexual reproduction is used to keep the organism's line alive.

Crossing a grapefruit and a tangerine (left) forms a tangelo (right).

Many of our most valuable crops are polyploids: corn, wheat, cotton, grapes, alfalfa, bananas, potatoes. Humans had nothing to do with developing these polyploids: They are believed to have happened spontaneously. These plants, however, would also have spontaneously ended were it not for man's cultivation of them. Many polyploids, like grapes and bananas, are either sterile or produce seeds that carry inferior characteristics. Although wild counterparts of these plants exist in nature, the polyploid strains require man's cultivation. Even many fertile polyploids, like corn, wheat, and cotton would become extinct within a few years if man did not cultivate them.

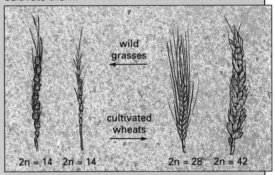

wild grasses

cultivated wheats

2n = 14   2n = 14   2n = 28   2n = 42

The wild grasses are believed to be ancestors of the cultivated wheats.

Man has been greatly involved with the genetics of these cultivatable plant polyploids since they were formed. These plants have been crossed and recrossed, forming many different strains. It appears that their extra chromosomes have permitted a greater flexibility among the expression of their genes. Consequently, many polyploid crops can grow in different areas and produce variations of their products. Consider all the different kinds of corn, wheat, and potatoes.

Some Christians have speculated that God permits these genetic conditions for the benefit of man but does not permit similar genetic variations on a widespread basis. Although various polyploids have apparently formed naturally, polyploidy does not happen often. Man has not actually observed the forming of polyploids except when drugs (such as colchicine) or other experimental techniques are used. Most polyploids induced by man are like *Raphanobrassica*, of little value when compared with the ones that are believed to have happened naturally.

The Mule

The mule is a well-known exception to many of the genetic "rules." A mule is a cross between a female horse and a male donkey. The horse has 64 chromosomes per body cell nucleus, and the donkey has 62. The union of a horse gamete (n = 32) and a donkey gamete (n = 31) results in a mule with 63 chromosomes (n + n = 63). Because the horse chromosomes and the donkey chromosomes are different, they fail to pair properly during meiosis. At the same time, the mule's uneven chromosome number forces 1 chromosome to be without a pairing partner. This presumably causes sterility.

Someone has rightly said that a mule is an animal with an ignoble past and a hopeless future; however, 1 in 10,000 female mules can conceive and bear young. It seems that for some reason the gametes she forms have either all the horse or all the donkey chromosomes. Depending upon the kind of male being bred, the offspring of a female mule are usually horses or

The mule is a cross between a horse and a donkey, but it is a genetic dead end.

donkeys, rarely mules. No fertile male mules have been known to exist.

The mule, with its unusual characteristics, was the ideal animal to meet many of man's needs before the invention of cars, trucks, and certain types of machinery. Today man breeds very few mules.

American upland cotton is a tetraploid of 2 different genomes. The cells of this cotton plant have 52 chromosomes divided into 2 sizes, 13 large pairs and 13 small pairs. The large are called *A*, and the small are called *D* chromosomes. The large *A* chromosomes resemble the chromosomes of a smaller Asiatic cotton from India. The small *D* chromosomes resemble the chromosomes of a wild American plant.

If the Asiatic cotton plant is crossed with the wild American plant, a hybrid offspring with 26

6A-4 *Cultivated cotton is a complex tetraploid.*

chromosomes (13 *A* and 13 *D*) results, but it is sterile. If the sterile hybrids are treated with colchicine, the chromosome number doubles. These treated plants produce fertile flowers and seeds. The seeds produce plants with 52 (2n + 2n) very similar to upland cotton. This evidence does not prove that upland cotton comes from these other 2 plants, but it does support the theory.

Aneuploids

Aneuploids (AN yoo PLOYDZ), some of which lack or have extra chromosomes, do not have complete genomes. Most aneuploids are believed to be the result of an error during meiosis. For some unknown reason, occasionally a chromosome pair fails to separate during meiosis. This is called **nondisjunction.** Two of the resulting gametes therefore have an extra chromosome (n + 1), and 2 lack a chromosome (n − 1).

If the gamete that has an extra chromosome unites with a normal gamete, the result is a *trisomy* (try SO mee) of 1 of the chromosomes (2n + 1). All the chromosomes are in the diploid state, except 1, which has 3 chromosomes instead of 2.

Aneuploidy in Humans

The genetic make-up of humans (as well as animals) appears to be quite fixed when compared to plants, meaning that many of the chromosome changes which are common in plants do not happen in humans or animals. In humans, however, there are a couple of well-known aneuploid conditions.

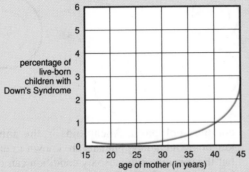

In humans, **Down's syndrome (mongoloidism)** is caused by a trisomy of the twenty-first chromosome. Those with Down's syndrome may be male or female and are characterized by low mentality, shortness, stubby hands and feet, an extra fold of skin on the eyelids (hence the name *mongoloid)*, and often other defects. At one time people believed that having a Down's syndrome child meant there was an oriental in the family's ancestry. This is not true. One out of every 600 people born in the United States has Down's syndrome.

Occasionally someone is born with a trisomic condition of one of the other smaller human chromosomes. In these cases, however, the individual is deformed, and his life expectancy is only a few weeks.

Some Down's syndrome people suffer more mental retardation than others. In the past they were all assumed to have a very low intelligence. Proper training helps them develop to their full potential.

Various aneuploids of the sex chromosomes also occur. Possible conditions are these:

❑ *Turner's syndrome (XO)* Females lack a second sex chromosome resulting in underdevelopment of the female sex glands, shortness, and other deformities.

❑ *Klinefelter's syndrome (XXY)* This male often appears normal but is infertile.

❑ *Trisomy X (XXX)* Various symptoms may develop in these individuals. Many appear normal, but some resemble women with Turner's syndrome, and some are so-called "super females," having a tendency toward male characteristics. Many of these individuals are sterile.

Aneuploids of other human chromosomes have been found in naturally aborted fetuses. Aneuploid conditions of most human chromosomes are therefore believed to be lethal before birth. Only the sex chromosomes (which are believed to carry relatively few genes) and a couple of the autosomes can be trisomic or monosomic and not kill the individual. Almost all human aneuploids that survive birth are sterile, or they die before they reach maturity. Human and animal aneuploids generally do not propagate.

Karyotypes of genetic disorders

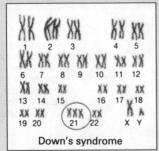

Down's syndrome

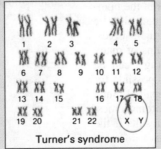

Turner's syndrome

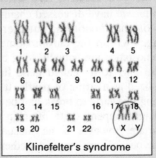

Klinefelter's syndrome

6A-5 *Nondisjunction. Note the gametes and the zygotes made from these gametes have unusual chromosome numbers.*

gametes   fertilization   zygote

If the gamete that lacks a chromosome unites with a normal gamete, the result is *monosomy* (2n − 1). All the chromosomes are in the diploid state except for one, which is single. Other numbers of missing or additional chromosomes do exist but are rare.

Aneuploids are common in the plant kingdom, especially in cultivated crops. Some of the various types of wheat, for example, are aneuploids of a complex polyploid. Aneuploids in the animal kingdom and among humans are known to exist, but the trisomy or monosomy condition can only happen with a few of the chromosomes. It seems that having too few or too many genes is usually lethal in animals and humans.

Review Questions 6A-1

1. Name the 2 major types of genetic changes, and briefly describe each.
2. How has colchicine been used to aid our understanding of polyploid conditions?
3. Why are most tetraploid organisms fertile when triploid organisms are sterile?
4. Distinguish between euploid and aneuploid organisms.
5. Describe how nondisjunction can cause aneuploid organisms.
6. Describe the genetic condition that results in Down's syndrome (mongoloidism).
7. In what ways are polyploid plants advantageous to humans?
8. It has been said that although many polyploid plants appear strong, as a species they are weak. What basis could be used to support this statement?

Changes Within the Chromosome

Thus far we have discussed changes in the numbers of chromosomes, but there can also be changes within the chromosomes themselves. Chromosomes are actually long chains of many genes. This form, called **gene linkage,** can be visualized as a string of pearls. It is possible for a string of pearls to break and be repaired. Such breakage happens quite often in chromosomes. There are, however, some unusual results if the "gene-pearls" are strung together in a different sequence or end up on a completely different strand altogether.

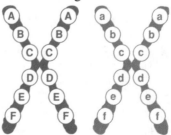

6A-6 *Gene linkage on a homologous pair of chromosomes. All the genes on one homologue are dominant and all on the other are recessive.*

Exchange of genes between homologues

If, during the first metaphase of meiosis when the homologues line up, the 4 sister chromatids break and the pieces join with their own respective ends, nothing noticeable happens. If, however, the sister chromatids break and the pieces join with the ends of the other chromatids, **crossing over** occurs.

Suppose that dominant genes *ABCDEF* are linked in that sequence on one chromosome. When this chromosome has replicated to form sister chromatids, it is illustrated as follows:

$$\frac{ABCDEF}{ABCDEF}$$

A gamete of this individual is shown as follows:

$$ABCDEF$$

A homologue having all the recessive genes would be illustrated like this:

$$\frac{abcdef}{abcdef}$$

In this example, you would always expect an individual who has the dominant characteristic *A* also to have the dominant characteristic *F* because the genes are together on the chromosome. Even a heterozygous individual has the dominant characteristics for *A* and *F*.

heterozygous individual	gametes
$\dfrac{ABCDEF}{ABCDEF}$	$ABCDEF$
	$ABCDEF$
$\dfrac{abcdef}{abcdef}$	$abcdef$
	$abcdef$

If crossing over occurs in a heterozygous individual, it may form a gamete containing both *A* and *f*.

meiosis lineup	crossing over	gametes
$\dfrac{ABCDEF}{ABCDEF}$	$ABCDEF$	$ABCDEF$
	$ABCdef$	$ABCdef$
$\dfrac{abcdef}{abcdef}$	$abcDEF$	$abcDEF$
	$abcdef$	$abcdef$

If this gamete combines with a normal recessive gamete, it will produce an individual who has the

dominant characteristic for *A* but the recessive characteristic for *f*.

Crossing over, although occurring regularly and at a predictable rate for a given set of genes, is not frequent enough to cause the ratios of genes on the same chromosome to be the same as genes that are on different chromosomes. Different rates of crossing over for different sets of genes have enabled geneticists to map genes (determine their sequence) on a chromosome.

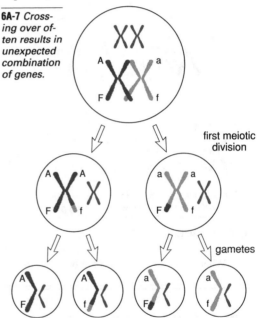

6A-7 *Crossing over often results in unexpected combination of genes.*

Crossing over sometimes happens two or more times within a single chromosome pair. If the chromosomes join together so that there is a complete set of genes in each chromosome, there are no bad effects. This crossing over merely shuffles the genes that are linked on the chromosome and thus permits greater genetic variation.

Exchange of genes between nonhomologues

Occasionally, two nonhomologous chromosomes cross over during meiosis. This crossing over is called a **translocation.*** Some gametes made from cells that experienced translocation will be normal, but some will have extra genes, and some will lack certain genes.

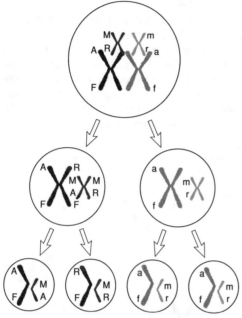

6A-8 *Translocation results in some gametes with extra genes and some gametes with missing genes.*

About 4% of the people suffering from Down's syndrome have a translocation of genes from the twenty-first chromosome onto one of their other chromosomes. This translocation causes the zygote to have 3 sets of the genes on the translocated segment of its twenty-first chromosome. A person with this condition will have Down's syndrome even though he has only one pair of chromosome twenty-one. The 3 sets of *genes* cause the syndrome.

Occasionally a segment of the chromosome is left out after crossing over. This is a *deletion.* For example, for every mongoloid formed by translocation, there should also be gametes formed that have a twenty-first chromosome with *missing* genes. In humans the resulting condition is presumed to be lethal because such individuals have not been found.

Sometimes the deleted segment of a chromosome does not join a chromosome and therefore does not migrate during meiosis. The chromosome piece usually winds up outside the nucleus, where it disintegrates. If this happens, the cell lacks genes. A person with such a lack may suffer very harmful effects. *Cri du chat* (cry of the cat) results from the deletion of part of the fifth chromosome. When a baby has this deformity, its cry sounds like a cat's screeching.

Review Questions 6A-2
1. How could crossing over affect gene linkage?
2. What 2 human conditions are believed to result from translocation?

Gene Action and Gene Mutations

Thus far we have spoken of genes as the basic unit of inheritance. Genes, however, are not unalterable units. They may be turned off (that is, they may become inactive, no longer making their protein) and turned on (that is, they may become active, causing their protein to be made). Genes can also be altered to stop functioning or to stop producing protein.

Gene action

Not all the approximately 100,000 genes you have in every nucleus are functioning in all your cells.

For example, many of the genes for eye color are not functioning in most of your body's cells. *Cell specialization* in the cells of an embryo is caused by turning on some genes and turning off others. By mechanisms we do not completely understand, certain genes that are activated in some cells cause those cells to become nerve tissue; other genes activated in other cells cause those cells to become muscle tissue, and so forth. The fact that cells on your head, and nowhere else, developed into your eyes is one of the mysteries of your body, for it is "fearfully and wonderfully made" (Ps. 139:14).

translocation: trans- (L. TRANS, across) + (LOCARE, to place)

Scientists are working to discover the mechanism for cell specialization in embryos. When successful, they may be able to induce human cells to replace diseased or damaged organs by growing new organs rather than trying to use transplants or artificial devices.

Some factors that control gene action

Some of the genes in your body may function in all your cells. The genes for the manufacture of the enzymes in the citric acid cycle, for example, must be active in all your cells, since all of them are capable of this important cellular process.

Some genes in your cells turn on and off by various mechanisms. A few genes, for example, are affected by the concentration of the proteins they produce. If a cell has an abundant supply of a particular protein, the DNA stops manufacturing the messenger RNA (mRNA) responsible for that protein until the supply reduces.

During the winter the Himalayan rabbit is normally white with black ears, nose, tail, and feet. If, however, the hair on his ears and tail is removed and these body parts are kept in heated mufflers while his winter coat regrows, the fur will regrow white. If an area of the rabbit's back is kept cold while his hair is growing, the hair will be black. In this example, temperature turns on or off the gene for coat color.

6A-9 *An experiment with the Himalayan rabbit demonstrates the effect of temperature on genes.*

Other environmental conditions may cause genes to be turned on or off. The immunities you develop when you are exposed to certain diseases are also the apparent result of turning on and off certain genes. In this case, the factor responsible for turning on the gene is usually either the substance that causes the disease or a product of the disease (see pages 570, 572-76).

Sex-limited characteristics are illustrations of the regulation of genes. The presence or absence of sex hormones turns on or off the genes of sex-limited characteristics. The feathers of the male bird, brightly colored when compared to those of the female of the same species, are a sex-limited characteristic.

6A-10 *The female duck (left) has the genes for the bright colors of the male (right). The expression of these genes, however, is limited by the sex hormones.*

Sex-limited characteristics in humans include growth of body hair, beard growth, breast development, and milk production. Both male and female humans have genes for all these characteristics. The male reproductive hormones stimulate the growth of body hair and beard in young men, while the female hormones stimulate breast development in young women.

Review Questions 6A-3

1. Give an example of the environment's influencing a genetic trait.
2. Since every cell in your body has the same genes, why is every cell in your body not like every other cell?
3. Under normal circumstances the beard genes are not activated in women and the milk-production genes are not activated in men. What mechanism accounts for this?

Gene mutations

The term *mutation* often refers to a **gene mutation** (or *point mutation*): the alteration of an individual gene. A gene is a section of DNA that has the genetic code. The DNA code is used to make messenger RNA (mRNA) that directs the manufacture of an amino acid chain of a protein. The codons of RNA (triplets of nucleotide bases), which code for particular amino acids, can be affected in three basic ways.

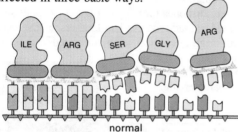

normal

□ *Substitution* A substitution happens when a nucleotide in the DNA sequence is removed and replaced with a different nucleotide or when 2 nucleotides are inverted. If the substitution makes an RNA codon that codes for the same amino acid (for example GCA and GCC both code for alanine), the mutation will not be noticeable. In the substitution illustrated, however, the new codon calls for a different amino acid, but all of the other amino acids in the polypeptide chain of this protein will be the same.

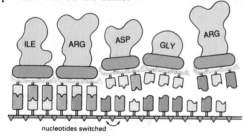

substitution (inversion)

□ *Addition* In addition an extra nucleotide is placed in the mRNA sequence. With a nucleotide addition a new *reading frame* on the RNA is established. In other words, the codons after this point are off. The chance is minute that they will code for a polypeptide chain of amino acids that is at all similar to the original. The exact location

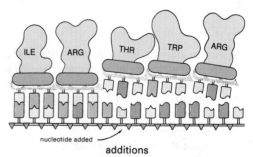

additions

of the additional nucleotide on the mRNA determines if the mutation results in *missense* (the protein made is not able to function) or *nonsense* (no protein is made, generally because one of the new codons is a stop codon) (see page 107).

□ *Deletion* A deletion happens when a nucleotide is removed from the DNA. A deletion has the same results as an addition.

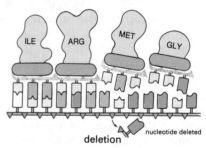

deletion

The above three alterations of genes can have the following effects:

□ *major effects,* because they produce no protein or vastly different protein (which can be lethal or cause genetic diseases), or

□ *minor effects,* because the protein produced is only slightly different or the protein is not important to the functioning of the organism, or

□ *no effect,* because they do not really change the codon.

Generally, only substitution mutations result in minor effects, but it is possible for addition or deletion mutations near the ends of polypeptide chains to cause only minor effects. Some scientists believe these minor mutations may cause some of the different alleles we observe.

Biological effects of mutations

Gene mutations that happen naturally are called *spontaneous mutations.* Mutations can also be induced by *mutagens* (MYOO tuh juhnz), such as various chemicals or radiation. According to some estimates, every human has thousands of mutations in his body. Most of these mutations, however, will not affect a person or his offspring.

A **somatic*** (soh MAT ik) **mutation** is a mutation that occurs in the nongamete cells of the body. A mutation in a somatic cell will usually do one of three things:

❑ *Produce an odd protein.* Some odd proteins either decompose or are given off as waste products. Since most human cells are diploid, most mutations of this sort do not drastically affect the cell: the other allele will still function. This type of mutation may account for certain blemishes or deformities such as moles, and some tumors.

❑ *Have no effect.* The mutation of a gene that was not working in a particular cell has no effect until that gene is turned on. In some human cells certain genes are never turned on. Many substitution gene mutations have no effect because they do not significantly change the codon.

If a blood-forming cell in an adult mutated to the sickle cell gene, would that person suffer from sickle cell anemia? No. Even though the odd protein may be produced by this cell, many other cells are producing normal protein. Most mutations have no effect because they are somatic and in multicellular organisms.

❑ *Kill the cell.* The build-up of an odd protein that is poisonous to the cell or the lack of a needed protein results in the death of the cell. Since there are thousands of every type of cell in the human body, the loss of one cell is not noticed.

Normal Variations

Where did the alleles responsible for all the various human hair colors, heights, lengths of nose, and body sizes come from? We know that all human genes ultimately came from only two persons, Adam and Eve, and that the alleles for the various traits seen in groups of land animals descended from the "two of every kind" or "seven of every clean animal" on Noah's ark. Beyond that we can only speculate at the origin of the naturally occurring variations we see today.

Some traits appear to have been introduced by mutation. Hemophilia, albinism, and other human genetic disorders apparently result from specific gene mutations. All known mechanisms in cellular genetics appear to prevent mutations, or, when they do happen, to eliminate them. The few inherited disorders we can observe appear to be ones that slip through.

Traits that scientists can reasonably trace to mutations are all harmful to the organism that has them. Since a mutation is a random change in a highly specific coded message, harmful effects are expected. Although genetic disorders may be traced to mutations, many scientists believe that alleles for normal variations cannot be the result of mutation.

In the past, evolutionists may have been justified in believing that only mutation could introduce new alleles. Current genetic observations may point to other sources for normal variations.

Much of the DNA in your cells appears not to be used to code for anything. Past estimates indicated that humans used only about 50% of their DNA, but some modern estimates indicate that humans normally use less than 10%. The unused DNA does resemble genes. Could this coded information be used to change specific alleles into other alleles? Is it possible that if different sections of a person's genetic code are used (see exons and introns, page 104), different traits could result? Is it possible that humans have the genetic information for the "normal" formation of other alleles instead of the ones they are expressing? Some evidence suggests these possibilities, but we really do not know.

Observations indicate that there are both a great variety and specific limits in normal human genetic variations. For example, there are dozens of shades of the various hair colors but there are also limits within which these hair colors can occur.

In order for evolution to be true, the range of genetic variability must be virtually limitless. Evolution demands a mechanism that could, if given enough time, take any gene and change it into virtually any other gene. Based on observations of variations and present genetic understanding, this is beyond the scope of normal genetic variability and is statistically impossible (see pages 199-202).

---

somatic: (Gk. SOMA, body)

FACETS OF BIOLOGY

Human Gene Mutations – Treatments and Cures

A **genetic disorder (inherited disorder)** is any undesirable function or shape of an individual's body that is caused by a gene or group of genes. Most humans have at least one genetic disorder, if not several. Some genetic disorders are very mild and are even accepted as normal. Shortness, baldness, larger hands, big ears, and some types of birthmarks are a few of the lesser genetic disorders.

A birthmark is considered to be a lesser genetic disorder.

For most genetic disorders there are, at present, no cures. When an individual has a genetic disorder, every cell in his body has the genetic information for that disorder. For the disorder to be cured, the responsible gene or genes would need to be corrected or replaced in all the cells of the body in which that gene is turned on.

Many genetic disorders, however, can be *treated*. Treatments of genetic disorders relieve only symptoms; they are not cures. For example, if a person inherits hemophilia (see pages 138-39) there is little that can be done to cure

the condition, but today the blood chemicals he cannot make can be supplied to him.

An albino person

Other genetic disorders are apparent at birth. Perhaps you have seen people with pink eyes, pure white hair, and complexions with a chalky appearance. These people have **albinism** – that is, they lack a dark-colored pigment called melanin, which is necessary to make most of the pigments which color various parts of the body. Their eyes and skin appear pink because the red of their blood shows through. An *albino** (al BYE noh) person has 2 recessive, mutant genes for the albino trait. This is

an example of 1 gene controlling several characteristics.

Most albino persons live normal lives, but they must avoid long exposure to sunlight. Lacking melanin, their cells can be harmed by strong light. Some albino persons seek to improve their appearance by coloring their hair, wearing glasses or contact lenses, and wearing make-up.

Mutations which cause human disorders are generally harmful. There are, however, special circumstances under which a harmful mutation can be considered beneficial.

The **sickle cell anemia** trait is believed to be the result of a mutation in a gene for hemoglobin production. The substitution of 1 nucleotide in only 1 codon for 1 of the proteins which go together to make the hemoglobin molecule results in sickle cell anemia. Careful investigations have traced the sickle cell anemia gene to several tribes in the northern part of Africa.

Normal blood cells (left) and sickle-shaped blood cells (right).

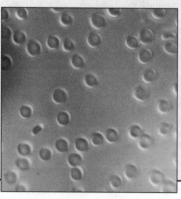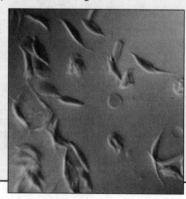

albino: (L. ALBUS, white)

anemia: an- (Gk. AN, without) + -emia (HAIMA, blood)

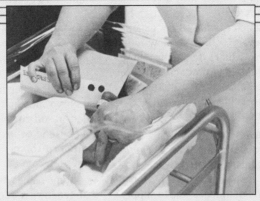

In many hospitals newborn babies have their heels pricked and their blood tested for various disorders, including PKU.

African people with normal hemoglobin generally suffered from malaria, a harmful blood disease caused by a tropical parasite. People with the sickle cell trait, however, appear to be immune to malaria because the parasite cannot live in their blood. People in these tribes who were homozygous for the sickle cell allele died, and those homozygous for normal hemoglobin died of malaria. The advantage of being heterozygous accounts for the sickle cell trait's being found in almost every member of certain tribes. In the U.S., however, the bearers of the trait lack this advantage, since malaria is not a major problem except in tropical areas.

Not all mutations are recessive. An example of a dominant mutation in humans is *achondroplastic dwarfism.* People with this condition have bones that do not develop properly; consequently, their trunk is of normal size, but they have short arms and legs, large misshapen heads, and swayed backs. Their intelligence is unaffected. Although the dwarfs mature physically, their reproductive rate is lower than the reproductive rate of normal people. There is little that medical science can do to help these people.

Some genetic disorders are not apparent at birth. A person with *Huntington's chorea,* for example, usually will not express this dominant gene until he is over thirty years old. A man named Huntington first described the symptoms of this disorder: the slow loss of mental ability, the loss of voluntary control of muscular activity, and occasional spasmodic movements. People with this genetic disorder know they will die after an extended, humiliating period of uncontrolled muscular activity and loss of mind. At present there is little that can be done for people with Huntington's chorea.

Still other genetic disorders have treatments which permit the person to lead an almost normal life. For example, insulin injections can be given to those who suffer from diabetes mellitus (see pages 603-4). A person with hemophilia can be supplied with the missing blood chemicals.

Phenylketonuria (PKU), another genetic disorder, can be controlled by diet. In normal human metabolism the amino acid phenylalanine is converted by an enzyme to tyrosine, another amino acid. If a person lacks the gene for the manufacture of the necessary enzyme, phenylalanine is converted to phenylpyruvic acid. Because the lack of this enzyme affects pigmentation, the person with PKU appears pale. When this and related acids reach a certain concentration level in the blood, they are filtered out in the urine.

However, the high blood concentrations of these acids are toxic to a young child's developing brain. A child with untreated PKU loses mental ability and becomes severely retarded. Most hospitals test newborn babies for PKU. If a child has this disorder, he is put on a special diet which greatly limits his intake of phenylalanine and therefore limits the phenylpyruvic related acids in the blood. Once the child is about 6 years old, he can eat normal food without brain damage because his brain is no longer growing.

Apparently, there are genetic disorders (such as, certain types of diabetes) caused by the turning off of a particular gene. Perhaps scientists will find a way either to prevent the gene from turning off, or turn it back on. Even then, however, such a technique is a treatment, not actually a cure. Because the defective gene still exists in a person, he will pass it on to his offspring.

Review questions on page 156.

A **germ mutation** is a mutation in a cell that is forming gametes (sex cells). Because a germ mutation produces gametes with some genetic change, it will affect every cell in the new individual. Some mutations, which, if somatic, cause either no effect or simply the production of an odd protein, will be lethal as germ mutations. A mutation that kills the cell will, of course, be lethal as a germ mutation.

Elimination of germ mutations

Many germ mutations are eliminated by a *genetic screen*. In haploid organisms a single gene mutation usually results in a total lack of proper protein since there is no additional allele to supply the missing protein. The organism is greatly deformed or it dies, thereby eliminating the mutation. Plant ova and pollen normally grow temporarily in the haploid state. During this period

mutations generally cause deformities; thus, seeds are usually not produced from that gamete.

Animals and humans with major genetic disorders die between zygote formation and birth. In humans a child born with an abnormality is said to have a *birth defect*. If the genetic irregularity is lethal, either the zygote does not form or the embryo dies quickly. Some lethal genetic disorders result in the baby's dying in the mother's womb and *naturally aborting,* or the baby's being *stillborn* (born dead). About half of the natural abortions are the result of chromosome defects.

Some babies die very soon after birth as a result of genetic disorders. It appears that God designed into the genetic mechanism of humans (and most organisms) a genetic screen that eliminates many greatly deformed individuals, preventing major genetic disorders from continuing.

Biological Terms

lethal	colchicine	*Gene Action and Gene Mutations*
chromosomal	tetraploid	sex-limited characteristic
gene mutation	aneuploid	gene mutation
Changes Affecting	nondisjunction	somatic mutation
Chromosome Numbers	Down's syndrome (mongoloidism)	germ mutation
genome	*Changes Within the Chromosome*	*Facet*
parthenogenesis	gene linkage	genetic disorder
euploidy	crossing over	(inherited disorder)
polyploid	translocation	albinism
triploid		sickle cell anemia

Review Questions 6A-4

1. List several natural causes for gene mutations.
2. Gene mutations can affect the code for an amino acid in what three ways?
3. What are three possible results that could be expected if there were a gene mutation in a chromosome of your somatic cells?
4. Why is a germ mutation more significant than a somatic mutation?

Facet 6A-1: Human Gene Mutations—Treatments and Cures, pages 154-55

1. Why is it difficult to cure a human genetic disorder?
2. List several human genetic disorders, and describe the treatments used to overcome the symptoms of the disorders.
3. Some people have said that the mutation that causes sickle cell anemia is a beneficial mutation. What argunemts justify and what arguments are against this statement?
4. List several human genetic disorders for which there are no effective treatments at this time.

6B - Modern Genetics

The atomic bomb dropped on Hiroshima, Japan, in 1945 began the Atomic Age. Since then scientists have learned much about the atom. Most of us are aware of the great power in the atom as well as the threats of nuclear war and of increased radiation (even from peaceful uses). On the horizon, however, is a more powerful and a potentially more dangerous era: the *Genetic Age.*

The Atomic Age promises great benefits but threatens man with major destruction. The Genetic Age also promises great benefits but threatens man with *change,* which may be for better or for worse. Many scholars, scientists, and theologians are concerned about how genetic information will be used. The most important decisions your generation will make may deal with the use of the information obtained in the Genetic Age.

The Gene Pool and Population Genetics

Geneticists often refer to the sum of all the genes that all members of a species of an organism can conceivably possess as the **gene pool** for that organism. Every normal individual has a complete set of genes from the gene pool. That complete set does not have every possible allele of every gene. For example, all the possible genes that Mendel's peas could have had constituted the gene pool for peas, but every pea plant does not have *all* the possible alleles of every gene. A short pea plant (homozygous recessive) does not have the allele for being tall.

The human gene pool has genes for hemophilia in it, but most people do not have this gene. If a person's parents do not have the gene for hemophilia, there is no chance of his having it (unless a mutation occurs). An individual has access to

6B-1 *The dog gene pool. Different dogs are possible because of the large number of alleles in this gene pool. Smaller gene pools exist as "puddles" of this gene pool. Occasionally, "puddles" homozygous for certain genes exist (usually the result of selective breeding), resulting in pure strains of dogs (e.g., collie, dachshund). These purebreds can mate with other members of the gene pool, resulting in hybrids.*

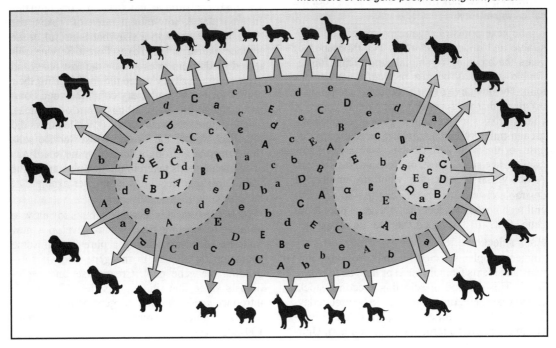

6B-2 *The wild flame azalea (left) has been bred by mass selection and hybridization to obtain various hybrid varieties (right) often seen in southern gardens.*

the gene pool only through his parents, who are two separate accesses to the gene pool. In other words, one parent brings to his children one set of genes, and the other parent brings another set. Some genes in a cross are homozygous, each parent giving the same allele as the other. For some genes, however, the parents give different alleles and thereby produce offspring which are not exactly like themselves. These natural differences between individuals from the same gene pool are called **variations.**

The gene pools of organisms contain both desirable and undesirable traits. For thousands of years the breeding of animals and plants for desirable traits has been a profitable activity for man. The objective of such breeding is to produce offspring that are superior to the parents. Superior characteristics might include greater weight gain, greater milk production, greater resistance to disease, or the ability to survive in an area of low rainfall, late spring frost, or early autumn freezes. Actually, the breeder may want any number of desirable characteristics. He can use any of several techniques to select from the gene pool those genes that will give good traits to the offspring.

Mass selection

Ancient peoples selected the most desirable animals and plants from the herd or field as *breeding stock.* This method of selecting breeding stock, called **mass selection,** continues to be used today. The loblolly pine, for example, is a valuable lumber tree that grows throughout the southern Unit-

ed States. Unfortunately, southern pine beetles often attack forests of the loblolly pine and in a few weeks can kill thousands of trees. Often, only a few trees remain alive after an epidemic. The remaining trees apparently possess something that repels the beetles. Seed that is harvested from those trees is being used in a breeding program to develop a strain of loblolly pine that is resistant to the southern pine beetle.

6B-3 *The pine bark beetle and the destruction these insects can do to loblolly pines*

Let us suppose the obstacle to the tree farmer is, instead of insects, drought. What pine tree seedlings can survive and grow in a dry climate? In an isolated, low-rainfall area of Texas, the "lost pines" grow to a size that is useful in the lumber industry. The Texas Forest Service collected seeds from trees among the lost pines and grew seedlings. They tested the seedlings for their ability to survive under dry conditions and compared the results to seedlings from other areas. The lost pine seedlings survived, while others did not. Each winter the Texas Forest Service sells thousands of "drought-hardy" pine seedlings grown from seeds taken in the lost pine area. The use of lost pine seedlings is another example of mass selection.

Notice that mass selection attempts to cultivate an already existing trait, *not* to develop a new trait. Breeders are seeking a pure line of some characteristic already in the gene pool, *not* expanding the gene pool. Creationists and evolutionists agree that mutation is the only way to introduce *new* genes into the gene pool. Mutation, however, is not necessarily evolution (see pages 199-202, 206).

Hybridization

Hybridization (HYE brid uh ZAY shun) is the crossbreeding of two genetically unrelated individuals. The offspring of such a cross is called a *hybrid.** Hybridization often involves two varieties of the same species. Crossing two strains of corn, crossing two different kinds of apples, crossing two different varieties of chickens, and even the marriage of an Egyptian woman to an Englishman are examples of hybridization of two members of the same species.

The hybrid offspring of animals or plants often have characteristics superior to either parent. This superiority is called **heterosis** (HET uh ROH sis), or *hybrid vigor,* and may involve such things as greater resistance to disease, larger bodies, more milk production, or more crop yield per acre.

Plant breeders have used heterosis to improve crop yield. Corn, a wind-pollinated crop, is usually heterozygous for many traits. Since each corn kernel is fertilized by a different pollen grain, a single ear may have kernels with many different phenotypes. Before careful breeding, 120 bushels per acre (bpa) was an average corn yield. **Inbreeding**–the mating of an organism with itself or with close relatives–can, in time, produce pure strains. **Pure strains** are organisms which are homozygous for various traits. Four different pure strains of corn (labeled *A, B, C,* and *D*) were produced. These pure strains, however, were of low quality. Some of them produced only one small ear per plant, and the ears had very small kernels. The average yield was only about 60 bpa.

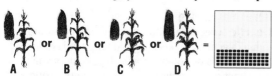

When breeders crossed strain *A* with strain *B*, heterosis produced a crop yield of about 140 bpa. The same was true of the cross of the *C* and *D* strains. But mating the offspring of the *A* + *B*

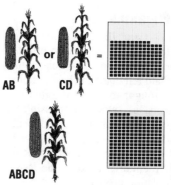

cross with the offspring of the *C* + *D* cross produced a superior corn with a yield of about 200 bpa. This type of hybrid corn is the type most often grown in the United States. Controlled breeding by seed companies supplies hybrid corn seed to farmers. Farmers who try to grow their own corn seed without careful breeding techniques, get poor quality corn, much like the crops before controlled breeding.

In animals, close inbreeding (mating of parents to their own offspring) often results in inferior offspring. Although organisms that are homozygous for good traits are desirable, close inbreeding may also result in organisms that are homozygous for poor traits. Careful inbreeding for generations has produced relatively pure strains of certain dogs, cattle, chickens, horses, and other animals. These domesticated animals possess characteristics man considers desirable. Man's preference for animals with certain traits and his indifference about other traits has determined the lineage of animals such as cows, sheep, and chickens. These animals are now in some respects inferior to the wild stock from which they came, in that many of them are no longer able to live without man's care.

6B-4 *Miniature horses, which stand about a foot tall, are the result of careful breeding.*

Review Questions 6B-1

1. Explain why a single organism cannot have one of every gene from its gene pool.
2. Can a breed be improved after many generations of mass selection? Why or why not?
3. Why does inbreeding often produce inferior-quality organisms?

---

hybrid: (offspring of different parents)

Hybrids between organisms that are not of the same species are discussed on pages 145-46.

Eugenics

The term **eugenics*** (yoo JEN iks), meaning "good genes," is traditionally applied to efforts to improve the human gene pool. This science is by no means new. Plato felt that "the best of both sexes ought to be brought together as often as possible and the worst as seldom as possible" and that inferior offspring ought to be abandoned. As the Roman birth rate fell while conquered peoples multiplied, Caesar offered money to Roman mothers to have children to keep the "superior" Roman population growing.

Probably one of the most wide-spread eugenic endeavors was conducted in the 1930s by Adolph Hitler. The German dictator's systematic killing of millions of Jews resulted from his desire to eliminate what he believed was an "inferior race." At the same time in special camps, scientists of the Third Reich were inbreeding humans of "superior" German stock to form a "super race." What is now known of these experiments (most of the records were destroyed) indicates that the mass selection and inbreeding techniques which these scientists used did not produce a super race. Of course, the experiments lasted only a few years, not enough time for the many generations needed for effective selective breeding.

Consider this opinion:

> I wish very much that the wrong people could be prevented entirely from breeding; and when the evil nature of these people is sufficiently flagrant, this should be done. Criminals should be sterilized and feeble-minded persons forbidden to leave offspring behind them. . . . The emphasis should be laid on getting desirable [sic] people to breed.*

This statement was not made by a Nazi in the 1930s but in 1913 by the American patriot Theodore Roosevelt. Although he was a great leader in other ways, he, with most of the American upper class of the early 1900s, thought that the many immigrants from Europe, Scotland, Ireland, and the Orient were a threat to American society.

As early as 1869, a group of 91 American men and women signed a pledge to participate in "matching those most advanced in health and perfection." By 1900 many such "eugenic farms" had been established to "improve the blood lines" of Americans.

American presidents, respected scientists, well-known educators, and thousands of others expressed their belief in and gave encouragement for "modern scientific eugenic" activities. Remember that Mendel's papers were rediscovered about this time. These people believed that coming up with ideal humans would be about as simple as obtaining a pure strain of round, green peas. It might take longer, they admitted, since there were more traits to deal with and since people reproduce more slowly than pea plants, but this was all the more reason to get started right then.

Additional genetic experiments with animals, however, have shown that most of the practices of eugenic leaders of the early 1900s were contrary to what would eliminate "bad blood" (actually bad *genes*) and encourage "good blood." They also failed to recognize man's environment and spiritual nature as major influences on human behavior and well-being.

The Second World War, with Hitler's atrocities, put a stop (at least temporarily) to most major eugenic activities in the United States. But today, advanced techniques are making eugenics not only a possibility but also a subtle reality in present American life. We shall examine some of the genetic activities which politicians and scientists are using and some they plan to use to improve the human gene pool.

Genetic screening

Genetic screening is the determining of an individual's genetic make-up. In America today, there are hundreds of genetic counseling centers which use genetic screening to be able to supply people with information about either themselves, their relatives, or their future children. Even using the most modern techniques, however, people learn about only a few of their genes.

At present there are three basic genetic screening methods that are widely used:
❑ *Analysis of the pedigree.* By obtaining information about the individuals and their families,

---

eugenics: (Gk. EUGENES, well-born)

Theodore Roosevelt, *The Works of Theodore Roosevelt* (New York: Charles Scribner's Sons, 1926), XII, p. 201.

6B-5 *Tay-Sacs disease, which is found primarily among certain Jewish groups, is caused by a recessive gene. Because of an enzyme deficiency, homozygous individuals go blind and die as children. Carriers have a low level of the enzyme. The amount of the enzyme can be determined by sampling tears or testing blood. The information can be used to predict the likelihood of a Tay-Sacs offspring.*

genetic counselors construct pedigrees. Sometimes people can be tested to determine their genetic make-up regarding a particular condition. If the inheritance pattern of the trait is known, the counselors can then make accurate predictions regarding the probability of individuals having the trait. Many genetic disorders, for example, are simple recessive traits. By constructing pedigrees, a genetic counselor can tell prospective parents

the percentage of their offspring that should have the trait, carry the trait, or be free of the trait.

❑ *Analysis of the unborn.* Today there are several methods of learning about a child before he is born. **Ultrasonic scanning** or *sonography* (sohn NAWG ruh fee), the use of sound to make "shadow pictures" similar to sonar, and **fetoscopes**, a fiber-optic device inserted into the womb, are used to get pictures of the unborn child. The pictures can reveal genetically related deformities. **Amniocentesis** involves removing some of the fluid which surrounds the unborn child. The child's cells in this fluid can be used to produce karyotypes and look for chromosomal defects such as Down's syndrome. The fluids can be chemically analyzed to determine other genetic conditions.

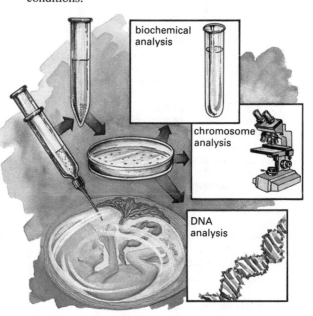

biochemical analysis

chromosome analysis

DNA analysis

6B-7 *Amniocentesis involves removing some of the fluid from around the unborn child to diagnose disorders. The fluid contains cells and chemicals produced by the child. The sex of the child, abnormal chromosomal conditions, and metabolic disorders can be determined before the child is born. Sometimes treatment can begin by changing the mother's diet or even transfusing the unborn child's blood if needed. Amniocentesis is not without risk. The procedure is done only if a physician feels it is necessary.*

6B-6 *In ultrasonic scanning a device rubbed over the woman's stomach releases sound and picks up the echoes that bounce off internal structures. The data is used to produce a sonogram, like the one of the unborn child above. Sonograms can tell if the child is developing properly or has been damaged by injury.*

❑ *Analysis of the newborn.* A baby undergoes a number of tests soon after he is born. Some tests are conducted visually; other tests require blood or urine specimens. The results of these tests give the physician information needed to treat those infants who have certain genetic disorders.

Prospective parents can use the information obtained by genetic screening as they plan their families. By knowing that a child has a genetic disorder, parents and physicians could begin proper treatment at birth, if not before. Some people see this as a good form of eugenics. If those individuals with major genetic deformities did not reproduce, the percentage of genes causing the deformities in the gene pool would decrease. Such knowledge, however, is not without problems, as we shall see in later sections of this chapter.

DNA Probes

The methods of genetic screening may soon be outmoded by more refined techniques. Although not yet readily available for many genes, scientists can use *DNA probes* to determine if a person has a specific gene.

A DNA probe is a small piece of DNA that has known base sequences and can be marked with radioactive substances. When a probe is placed with specially treated DNA from the person being screened, the probe will line up with DNA that has a corresponding sequence of bases. If that sequence does not exist, the probe will not line up with any DNA. Using DNA probes, scientists hope to be able to determine if a cell contains specific genes. This procedure could eliminate much of the uncertainty involved in genetic screening today.

Artificial reproduction

Artificial insemination (in SEM uh NAY shun) is the mechanical injection of sperm into a female's body. It has long been practiced on animals in laboratories and has been used in farming for many years. Artificial insemination is often used in cattle breeding. Cattle sperm can be frozen and stored. Today cattle breeders can have cows produce calves from bulls that have been dead for years.

Human artificial insemination is over 30 years old. Each year thousands of women are artificially inseminated, most because of medical reasons. Few Christians object to artificial insemination between a husband and wife because Biblical principles do not appear to be violated.

Women can also be inseminated with sperm from men who are not their husbands. Human sperm can also be frozen and stored. Women have had children whose **biological father** (the man who supplied the sperm) has been dead for years. Some Christians contend that it is immoral for a woman to be artificially inseminated with the sperm of a donor who is not her husband. Those who condone this form of artificial insemination argue that true purity is not violated by this clinical technique.

Removing an ovum from a female's body is also possible. This ovum can then be fertilized by sperm in a laboratory. If the resulting zygote is implanted in the female's body, it can develop and be born. Scientists can also freeze and store ova. A cow can be forced to produce a large number of ova at one time. All of the ova can then be removed, frozen, and even shipped to other areas. When thawed, they can be fertilized with the sperm from one bull and then placed in different cows to develop. An entire herd can be bred at one time from one set of parents thousands of miles away, or even long dead.

Ova have also been removed from a human female's body, fertilized by human sperm, and then implanted in the woman's body. This process is call **test-tube fertilization** or *in vitro fertilization* and has been used to make childbearing possible for women who lack certain reproductive structures. Few Christians object to the test-tube fertilization of the wife's ovum with her husband's sperm or the implantation of the zygote into the wife's body if physical conditions warrant the use of such techniques.

A person who is the result of test-tube fertilization, however, is not a true "test-tube baby." At this time no human fetus has been nurtured until birth in a test tube, but the techniques for doing so may be forthcoming.

FACETS OF BIOLOGY

6B-1

Genetic Engineering

Genetic engineering is the manipulation of genes by methods other than normal reproduction. There are several methods of genetic engineering that are currently being used and others that are being developed.

Recombinant DNA is currently being used in a technique in genetic engineering. When sections of DNA from two different sources are joined together, the piece of DNA that is formed is called recombinant DNA.

Scientists have found certain enzymes that can snip DNA. These *restriction enzymes* (over 500 different types are known) snip DNA at specific base sequences, leaving several nucleotides unpaired. These unpaired bases often form what scientists call a "sticky end." Another DNA molecule that has been snipped with the same restriction enzyme will have a complementary "sticky end." The 2 complementary "sticky ends" can combine, forming a recombinant DNA molecule.

Using restriction enzymes, scientists can snip genes out of chromosomes and insert them into other chromosomes, even chromosomes of other organisms. Although the process is still in developmental stages, and much of the work is trial and error, genetic engineering using recombinant DNA has yielded some valuable products with promises of more.

An example of the use of recombinant DNA is the manufacture of the protein *insulin,* a chem-

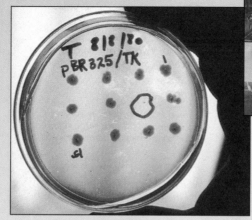

Scientists test the growth of genetically engineered bacteria to see if the gene they wanted is present.

ical essential for the proper use of sugars. Insulin is normally produced in the pancreas, but people who suffer from *diabetes mellitus* either do not make insulin or cannot make adequate insulin and require insulin injections.

In the past, insulin has been obtained from pig pancreases for people who suffer from diabetes mellitus. Pig insulin works well for most diabetic patients. Some people, however, are allergic to animal insulin and have had to be treated with human insulin obtained from donated blood, a very expensive source.

Scientists have taken human cells and used restriction enzymes to snip out the insulin gene. They have then inserted the human insulin gene into a *bacterial plasmid* (a small, circular piece of DNA, similar to a chromosome). The genetic material of the living bacterium now contains a new gene. As the genetically engineered bacterium grows, it produces insulin along with its own proteins. Since

the bacterium has no use for the insulin, it collects within the cell.

Bacteria grow and divide rapidly. Plasmids also replicate and divide as the bacterial cell divides. Thus, cultures of insulin-producing bacteria can be grown. When the bacteria are killed, the insulin can be extracted. Even though bacterial cells are used to produce the insulin, the protein produced is human insulin, since its production was directed by a human gene.

Using recombinant DNA, scientists can now implant genes into genomes of other organisms. Moving genes back and forth between bacteria is relatively easy. Moving genes in plants and animals is more complicated. Recently, scientists found a bacterium which contains a plasmid that enters a plant cell and causes tumors. By snipping out the bad gene and then splicing a good gene into the plasmid, it serves as a *vector* (a gene carrier) for moving the good gene into the genetic make-up of the plant.

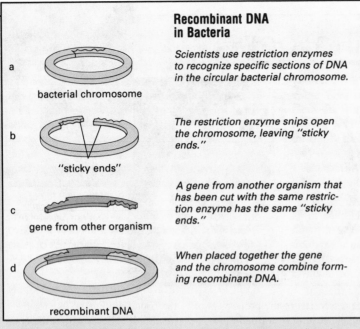

Recombinant DNA in Bacteria

Scientists use restriction enzymes to recognize specific sections of DNA in the circular bacterial chromosome.

a

bacterial chromosome

The restriction enzyme snips open the chromosome, leaving "sticky ends."

b

"sticky ends"

A gene from another organism that has been cut with the same restriction enzyme has the same "sticky ends."

c

gene from other organism

When placed together the gene and the chromosome combine forming recombinant DNA.

d

recombinant DNA

Using this technique, scientists hope to take genes that cause a desirable quality in one plant and implant those genes into another plant. For example, leaves of some plants produce chemicals that make them resistant to certain insects. Perhaps the genes needed to produce this chemical can be put into crop plants that are susceptible to leaf-eating insects.

In 1982 scientists were able to take the growth hormone gene of a rat and introduce it into fertilized mouse eggs. These genetically engineered mice grew and became two to three times larger than normal mice from the same litter. Other attempts with recombinant DNA genetic engineering of animals have met with limited success. There are many genetic mysteries scientists do not yet understand. Many genes appear to work only if they are preceded by specific genes on the chromosome or occur in certain sequences.

Human genetic engineering using recombinant DNA is just beginning. Lesch-Nyhan syndrome is a rare genetic disorder in which people lack a single enzyme. The symptoms include kidney damage, gout, cerebral palsy, uncontrollable gnawing of fingers and lips, and pounding the head. Death comes before the person is 30.

Scientists have taken cells from Lesch-Nyhan children and used viruses as the vectors to introduce the normal gene into those cells. Investigation continues regarding the possibility of using the virus to put the normal gene into humans and hopefully overcome the trait. People with this and similar genetic diseases are often willing to permit scientists to experiment with almost anything that holds promise for them.

Genetic engineers do more than move genes. By taking a protein apart, amino acid by amino acid, scientists can now determine the genetic code necessary to make that protein. Using a specific nucleotide, a gene is made which (when put into the chromosome of a bacterium) makes the protein. Perhaps scientists will someday be able to design proteins and then make genes to produce them.

Many scientific and political groups are concerned about the effects of genetic engineering. Tampering with the genes of an organism could give it unknown and potentially dangerous characteristics. For example, a scientist could accidentally produce an organism capable of causing a harmful disease while experimenting with a harmless organism. Experiments on animals and plants could produce harmful organisms that could alter the balance of life on our planet. Great care must be taken in this type of experimentation.

Scientists believe that they will be able to manipulate human chromosomes and genes within your lifetime. (To a limited degree it is already happening.) Some scientists predict that zygotes with defective genes will be able to have the bad genes removed and good genes introduced into their genetic material. When this ability has been developed, why not design the child to be tall, strong, intelligent and to have other traits that are deemed "desirable"? We may even design him to have some "desirable" nonhuman characteristics, such as the ability to digest cellulose. Such would be the ultimate in genetic engineering. But is this acceptable?

Review questions on page 167.

In some instances of test-tube fertilization, the ovum is supplied by a **biological mother** but the zygote is implanted in another woman who serves as the **surrogate mother.** Some Christians object to biological mothers serving as ovum donors. The arguments regarding ovum donors are about the same as those for sperm donors. Today some women serve as surrogate mothers for other women who cannot or do not wish to become pregnant. Many Christians object to surrogate mothers because the Biblical principles of the family are ignored.

The "Genetic Age": dream or nightmare?

A world populated with people who are strong, healthy, and intelligent does sound like a dream. The medical profession has been working toward this goal for hundreds of years. But now with genetic engineering and artificial reproduction, the prospects of achieving the genetic dream appear near. Much of the technology is already known. If the Lord tarries, decisions will need to be made regarding the use of the technology that scientists hope to perfect in the near future.

In the sixteenth century Sir Thomas More wrote *Utopia** (yoo TOH pee uh), a book that describes an ideal society. We now use the word *utopia* to refer to any ideal society. Many secular scientists believe that mankind will reach utopia through science and that genetic engineering will be a major tool in doing so.

In the early 1900s science fiction writers wrote several *dystopia** (dis TOH pee uh) books such as *Brave New World* by Aldous Huxley and *1984* by George Orwell.* These dystopias illustrate the problems that might arise if mankind possessed great scientific and genetic knowledge. In these books, corrupt man uses this knowledge to form a wicked, oppressive society rather than a perfect world. Interestingly, although the authors wrote their works in the early part of this century, they portrayed technology much as today's authors do. The "super people" in these books turn to science and their world for deliverance from problems. Deep in pride, they turn away from God.

Man's power over animals, plants, and even his physical self, however, cannot make him truly good. Only Christ can save him and give him a new heart. No matter how friendly, strong, intelligent, and disease- and disorder-free man is, his righteousness is nothing but filthy rags unless he has a regenerated, cleansed soul. "For all have sinned, and come short of the glory of God" (Rom. 3:23).

The problems of eugenics

Eugenics may be unable to produce for mankind the improvements it promises. Recall that artificial domestic breeds develop weaknesses that make them dependent on man. Likewise, though scientists may someday successfully breed man for intelligence, strength, or other traits, what traits will be sacrificed? If eugenics is practiced widely, the gene pool will shrink as bad traits are eliminated. In that shrinking, man's resistance to disease and his adaptability to different environments may weaken. Man might become like his domesticated animals: dependent on a controlled environment.

---

utopia: u- (Gk. OU, not or no) + -topia (TOPOS, place)

dystopia: dys- (Gk. DUS-, bad) + -topia (place)

Because of their philosophies and morals, most popular dystopias are not recommended as high school reading.

Since eugenics–like all sciences–cannot make decisions, man will have to make the difficult decisions about which traits will be eliminated. Should sickle cell anemia be eliminated? The trait is disadvantageous in the United States but is of value where malaria abounds. Strength and intelligence are desirable, but should everyone be a muscular genius? Diversity has encouraged human achievement. Many people with undesirable traits, in desiring to compensate for them, have excelled in their fields. Paul's "thorn in the flesh" (II Cor. 12:17) was perhaps one such undesirable trait, but it promoted Paul's spiritual progress.

Christian consideration of eugenics

Some Christians condemn human genetic engineering, artificial reproduction, and the like because they consider these techniques "unnatural." But like X-rays, surgery, and all of modern medicine, these genetic techniques are simply tools in man's hands that God can use. If used within the bounds of Scripture, if used to correct deformities or for morally acceptable therapeutic purposes, these tools would find few opponents. But, just like any other tool, these genetic practices can be misused.

Our government is actively involved in genetic research. Politicians point out that our enemies perform such research and that we can ill afford to fall behind. But one of the problems with eugenics is its potential for governmental abuse, as described in the dystopias. Government is understandably interested in eugenics, for it would assist in governing. But some possible results of government involvement are frightening. Restrictions on childbearing and other domination of the family would contradict God's intent that parents rear families according to His will. Through eugenics, government might also attempt to eliminate "unacceptable" behavior. Most Christians oppose such attempts, since Christianity might be considered unacceptable by a non-Christian government.

Significant problems may possibly result from the experimentation necessary for genetic progress. Many poor-quality individuals are created to develop a good plant or animal strain. Similar-ly, trial and error in human genetic manipulation might produce freaks who would die or live with severe handicaps. Such genetic failures pay for genetic progress by their suffering. Because the Lord values human life, we must be cautious about eugenics. The potential effects of eugenics are great, reaching unborn generations, but Christians cannot condone a eugenic policy that is careless with human life.

One danger of eugenics is that it might lead to the *dehumanization* of man. Man is dehumanized when his essential quality as a living, eternal soul is ignored. Unless eugenics is used carefully, its users may eventually regard man as just another laboratory animal; government may see man as just another "natural resource" to be controlled; and man's spiritual nature may be ignored. Leon Kass stated, "If we come to see ourselves as meat, then meat we shall become."* Since man is created in God's image, he should not be thus degraded.

Dehumanization, though, like government domination and genetic failures, would result from the *abuse*–not merely the use–of eugenics. Those dangers may not arise if genetic research is careful. The reasonable Christian, then, will not

6B-8 *Children are to be trained by parents to love and serve God. Some eugenic practices would hamper this.*

"Making Babies–the New Biology and the 'Old' Morality," *The Public Interest,* Winter, 1972, pp. 53-54.

oppose the correct use of eugenics but will rather oppose its careless or illegitimate use.

In addition to the dangers discussed above, the Christian should temper his approval of eugenics with one other qualification: disagreement with secular scientists who believe that eugenics will solve all man's problems. They think that the problems have physical causes and thus must have physical solutions. The Bible teaches otherwise: man's suffering is the result of God's curse (Gen. 3:17-19). Eugenics will not establish a perfect race, for God's curse on the earth will prevail until Christ returns (Rom. 8:19-21).

As eugenic research expands, we will have to make difficult judgments about its use. In doing so, we must be sure that our position is in accor-dance with Biblical principles and is not merely a personal opinion or prejudice. Although we can-not expect the Bible to deal with specific medical or scientific techniques, the Bible does deal with such principles as the value of human life. (See Chapter 24B.) We cannot violate Biblical princi-ples and consider ourselves obedient to God; however, a conclusion based on feeling and not on the Bible is merely an opinion.

The scientific knowledge gained in the "Ge-netic Age" is just another tool–a very powerful tool–which God seems to be letting man use to-day. Although this tool may effect God's will as any medical or scientific information can, Chris-tians have the responsibility to use this tool in accordance with God's Word.

Biological Terms

The Gene Pool and Population Genetics	pure strain	biological father
gene pool	*Eugenics*	test-tube fertilization
variation	eugenics	(in vitro fertilization)
mass selection	genetic screening	biological mother
hybridization	ultrasonic scanning (sonography)	surrogate mother
heterosis (hybrid vigor)	fetoscope	*Facets*
inbreeding	amniocentesis	genetic engineering
	artificial insemination	recombinant DNA

Review Questions 6B-2

1. List three methods of genetic screening and describe each.
2. List and describe three methods currently used to learn about the unborn.
3. What is meant by a test-tube baby? In what way is this term misleading?
4. Differentiate between a biological mother and a surrogate mother.
5. List (a) several reasons the Genetic Age can be considered a desirable dream and (b) several reasons it can be considered a nightmare.

Facet 6B-1: Genetic Engineering, pages 163-64

1. Name one method of genetic engineering used today.
2. Describe what a restriction enzyme does to DNA.
3. What is meant by recombinant DNA?
4. Give and describe an example of genetic engineering.
5. What are some of the potential uses of recombinant DNA?
6. What are some of the possible drawbacks of using recombinant DNA?

Thought Questions

1. Mutations are generally recessive and inbreeding produces individuals homozygous for traits, but what is a possible explanation for some forms of heterosis?
2. A purebred strain of dogs often has weaknesses (poor traits) in some of the offspring, while crossbreeds produce more and healthier pups. Give an explanation for this.
3. "What is called *artificial reproduction* should more accurately be termed *man-assisted* reproduction." Tell whether you agree or disagree with this statement. Support your opinion.

THE HISTORY OF LIFE

SEVEN

7A-Theories of Evolution

Christians need not wonder about the beginning of life. The beginning of the physical universe is clearly outlined in Genesis 1 and 2. Other Scriptural passages give us additional facts about God's creative act, the history of His physical creation and life, and God's description of what will happen to His creation. Collectively, these passages provide a divinely inspired outline of the history of life. All accurate scientific knowledge, when properly interpreted, fits into this outline. Anything that contradicts this outline is in error.

The first section of this chapter looks at some of what the Word of God says about creation and the history of life. In the next section of this chapter we will consider various interpretations (some acceptable, some unacceptable) of what the Bible says. In the final section we will look at some scientific theories that contradict either the Bible or physical evidence or both.

Evolution conditioning

Some Christians have a serious case of "evolution conditioning." They have heard of the evils of "evolution" for so long that now they cringe and point a finger of condemnation at anyone who even uses the word. The word *evolve,** however, is a good word, meaning "to change, to become more complex."

It is proper, for example, to say that the automobile has evolved. The growing complexity of cars from Henry Ford's models to some of the most recent models is clear. The car, however, did not evolve itself. Rather, human designers and engineers accomplished its evolution. In the same way governments, languages, industry, and most activities in which man engages have evolved.

7A-1 *The evolution of the car*

1896
1908
1928
1932
1935
1965
1990

There is nothing wrong or un-Scriptural about recognizing these progressions as evolutionary.

"Evolution conditioning" affects other Christians when they see pictures of dinosaurs, drawings of strange "prehistoric" plants, or illustrations of half-naked humans with spears chasing odd-looking animals. Many Christians try to ignore them. Other Christians label such pictures "satanic," "atheistic," or "evolutionary."

But, dinosaurs did exist; many plants (very different from the plants of today) are extinct; and even today there are half-naked humans who, armed with spears, chase animals. The evidence to support the past existence of dinosaurs, strange extinct plants, and half-naked, spear-armed men is about as good as the evidence to support the evolution of the car.

The Bible calls Christians the salt of the earth (Matt. 5:13). Salt serves to retard corruption; Christians are to stand against the corruption Satan is spreading and slow down its effects. Two of Satan's best tools for robbing the Christian salt of its savor are to have Christians ignore his activities and to make Christians appear foolish. It is wrong for a Christian to ignore Satan's workings against Christianity. It is also wrong for a Christian to discredit not only himself but also the Lord by making rash, unfounded accusations.

Because Satan has used evolutionary theory effectively against Christians, they should know what they believe concerning this theory. Too many Christians, however, are willing to say, "The Bible is true, and evolution (whatever it is) is false," and leave it at that. The Bible tells us to "be ready always to give . . . a *reason* of the hope that is in [us]" (I Pet. 3:15–emphasis added), not just to *have* "the hope."

Other Christians in a misguided attempt to "be ready" pick up a few ideas, misuse them, and thereby show their ignorance, thus bringing reproach to themselves and their Lord. Christians should know not only what they believe concerning evolution but also what evolution is, before they try to condemn it. We are to "*study* to shew [ourselves] *approved* unto God" (II Tim. 2:15–emphasis added).

---

evolve: e-, ex-, exo- or ef- (L. E-, out) + -volve (VOLVERE, to roll)

The theories of evolution

The **theory of evolution** is a very broad term, encompassing many different concepts. Let us look at some of the major components of evolutionary theory.

❑ **Theory of beginnings** Man's guesses of how the universe, the earth, and even matter and energy came into being are theories of beginnings.

These theories are beyond the scope of this book but are discussed in other books in the Bob Jones University Press science textbook series.

❑ **Theory of biological evolution** (*organic evolution*) Biological evolution deals with the beginning of life (usually by some form of spontaneous generation) and proposes that simple organisms give rise to more complex organisms, which, in turn, produce even more complex offspring. Biological evolution is at the heart of the various other theories of evolution and will be dealt with in the next sections of this chapter.

❑ **Philosophy of evolution** The idea that all things are progressing toward a future perfection is the philosophy of evolution. This theory teaches that things are currently improving. The evolution of man's knowledge and the evolution of human society are given as examples of this type of evolution. There is, however, good reason to doubt that the increase in complexity (the evolution) of technology, governments, and the like is actually an improvement. What is a good definition of "improvement"? For example, the United States Federal Government has evolved (has become bigger and more complex), but many feel it was better when it was not as big and powerful.

When the term **evolutionist** is used in this book, it refers to a person who believes all three of the above. The term **creationist** will refer to those who believe the Bible is the inspired Word of God and that the Genesis account is a literal description of God's creating the physical universe, life, and man.

Review Questions 7A-1

1. Give two wrong attitudes Christians can have toward evolutionary theories.
2. Why should Christians be informed on evolutionary theories and be able to give Bible-based refutations of these theories?
3. List the three major divisions of the theory of evolution and describe each.

The Philosophy of Evolution

The person who carries evolutionary beliefs to their logical conclusion must believe the philosophy of evolution. He might look at how far man has progressed, smile with approving pride, and say, "From chemicals in some prehistoric swamp to a living, thinking, rational being has been a long, slow process. How fortunate things just happened to work out this way. And what about the future? Who knows? Man has come this far; in time he will reach that great perfection toward which he is headed."

When asked about God, an evolutionist may say, "The god-myth was a fine thing that has

The Results of an Evolutionary Philosophy

The implications of evolution lead to these dangerous conclusions:

❏ *Man is not responsible to God.* Since man is a product of evolution, he has no creator, he is not responsible to any god, and there are no absolute rights and wrongs. There can be no moral code except that which man sets up and agrees to follow. *Situation ethics* (do whatever seems best in a given situation) and the *new morality* (do whatever you want to do as long as nobody gets hurt) are acceptable.

❏ *Man no longer needs a saviour.* Since there is no right or wrong, and therefore no sin, there can be no punishment; thus, there is no need for a saviour.

❏ *Man's religion should be scientism.* **Scientism** is the worship of science. Rather than calling on God for help, evolutionists look to science to solve man's problems and advance mankind. Evolutionists see science as a method of man's continuing to evolve.

Though few people would state their beliefs in that way, the philosophy of evolution has infected most of modern man's thinking to the extent that unconsciously many men accept these beliefs. The great future that man supposedly is pushing toward and that is promised by evolutionary philosophy is not taught in the Bible. Despite scientific advancement, morality and spirituality are declining in our society and will continue to decline (II Tim. 3:13) until Christ returns for His thousand-year reign on the earth. But even then, God, not man, will bring peace and abundance.

Now, however, this evolutionist is ready to pronounce, "God is dead. That is, man no longer needs the concept of God. Since humans now realize that evolution is perfecting man, the concept of obedience to a creator-punisher-rewarder is, in fact, getting in the way. People who believe in these god-myths and in the old-fashioned morals demanded by the god-systems are now standing in the way of 'scientific progress.'"

The results of believing evolutionary theory

Few evolutionists will admit to believing the way that the evolutionist just described does. An evolutionary philosophy, however, leads to such beliefs. Most evolutionists believe parts of the biological evolutionary theory and try to ignore the logical ends of the philosophy of evolution.

A matter of viewpoint

Dr. Bob Jones, Sr., often told the story of two men on a high mountain: one looked at the view and marveled at the wonders God had created; the other looked down and commented that he had never before seen the back of a flying buzzard. What you see is, in good measure, colored by how you look at things.

The interpretation of scientific data can be similarly affected by one's expectations. Looking at a reconstructed skeleton of a large reptile in a museum, a teacher who believes in evolution may say to her class, "Note how large these dinosaurs were. They were believed to have lived during the Mesozoic period, between 70 million and 200

7A-2 *The existence of dinosaur skeletons is hard to deny, but their significance is open to interpretation.*

helped us in the past and is still useful for some less intelligent humans. Primitive peoples needed a god-myth to explain their existence and the apparent design and unity of the world around them. Before man had evolved enough to be able to accept the responsibility for what he was, man needed someone else to blame or praise for himself and nature. Some inventive, intelligent men (like Moses, Jesus, Paul, Buddha, and Confucius) invented useful gods and god-systems. The obligation to a creator-controller was used by these leaders to help shape mankind. The concepts of heaven and hell were useful in evolving our society."

million years ago. Dinosaurs probably became extinct 70 million years ago.''

Looking at the same skeleton, a teacher who believes in creation might say to her class, ''Note how large these dinosaurs were. They were believed to have lived prior to Noah's Flood, which many Bible scholars agree occurred about 6,000 years ago. Dinosaurs probably became extinct at the time of the Flood.''

Both teachers are telling what they believe to be the truth about the dinosaur skeleton. They cannot both be right. The different interpretations result from different viewpoints.

Explaining the earth's origin and development by looking at the earth is scientifically impossible. Recall that science is the observation of the physical universe. The origin of the physical universe was not observed by human eyes, nor can men go into a laboratory and create a universe to see how our universe might have originated. The beginning of the world and of life and the past changes in them are actually beyond the scope of science. What a person believes about these things is not the result of scientific facts but of *faith*. One will naturally interpret scientific data according to his faith.

For example, it has been adequately demonstrated that life does not spontaneously generate in today's world. Creationists believe that this is good evidence for the necessity of a Creator. Evolutionists, however, claim that conditions were somehow different when life *did* spontaneously generate. They thus keep looking for the right conditions in their experiments in the laboratory. How one interprets the fact that spontaneous generation does not now happen naturally is a matter of viewpoint. No matter which position a person accepts, he believes it by *faith*. Science cannot help him decide because the beginning of life is beyond the scope of science.

Evolutionary beliefs and the Word of God

For about a hundred years, most scientists and educators have presented the theory of biological evolution as fact–a dishonest, unscientific thing to do. A hundred years ago the scientific facts available could have made an evolutionary inter-

Theistic Evolution

Some people, thinking that a person can believe in parts of the evolutionary theory and the Bible, try to mix the two beliefs. This mixture is called **theistic*** (thee IS tik) **evolution.** A theistic evolutionist tries to interpret Biblical statements in order to support evolution. The Bible teaches that God created by direct act. A person who believes that God directed evolutionary processes is a theistic evolutionist and is in error. When the Bible states one thing and, in an attempt to be scientific, a person believes something else, he is setting up scientific theory as more authoritative than the Word of God.

The Bible is the cornerstone of Christian faith. If the Bible is fallible, if it must be amended to conform to scientific theory or man's beliefs, then Christians are without hope. People who do not believe the Bible is the inerrant Word of God choose what parts they want to believe and ignore those passages they do not want to believe.

If it is permissible to disbelieve the Biblical account of creation, then one might disbelieve other parts as well. He might dismiss God's condemnation of sin and the need of the atonement of Christ's blood because these doctrines do not appeal to him. A person who rejects any portion of the Bible has placed himself above the Bible. The Bible is accurate in *everything,* or it may as well be accurate in nothing.

Christians who try to accept evolutionary theory when the Bible clearly teaches creationism are saying that a section of the Bible is not true. The question of whether the Bible or human speculation is true then becomes a matter of choice, open for debate.

Dr. Bob Jones, Sr., has rightly said, ''Whatever the Bible says is so. Whatever man says may or may not be so.'' This is the *only* consistent Christian position. All scientific facts and the interpretation of those facts, therefore, must fit into the model prescribed by the Word of God. A scientific ''fact'' that does not fit into the model outlined in the Bible is either in error (and therefore not really a fact) or is being misinterpreted.

theistic: the-, theo-, or theis- (Gk. THEOS, god)

pretation *seem* possible. Today, however, many more facts are available, and if these facts are examined thoroughly and honestly, an evolutionary interpretation simply does not fit them.

This is true of all science: accurate observations do not contradict God's Word. All the "proofs" from observations that have been set forth against the Bible are inconclusive for two reasons.

❑ Scientists cannot really *prove;* they can only observe and interpret their observations. (Their interpretations are, of course, affected by their viewpoint.)

❑ Any accurate observation of God's creation could not contradict the revealed Word of God. The Christian's faith can be strengthened by the fact that true science never has contradicted the Bible, and the Christian's faith assures him that it never will.

In many groups it is considered unintellectual to disagree with evolution. Many scientists therefore remain silent about their doubts and dissatisfactions with the theory. Some of them, however, are beginning to say that current evolutionary views are unacceptable and need to be reworked, but they have not yet produced a replacement they consider acceptable. Although

most of them choose to ignore creationism as an alternative, a few are convinced that the Bible's statement of creation is the best and only explanation of man's origin.

The Bible does say certain things about creation. But since the Bible is a spiritual handbook and not a scientific textbook, it does not contain all the details of creation or biological history since creation. Many current scientific observations, therefore, are open to various interpretations. We can be sure, though, that anything that contradicts the Word of God is wrong. You should be tolerant of other Christians who believe theories different from yours unless their theories are un-Scriptural.

In this chapter we will discuss the theories of creation and biological history held by most Christian scholars who believe in the infallibility of the Bible, and then we will briefly discuss many of the beliefs of evolutionists. Complete documentations of all these theories and coverage of all the possible ramifications of the material presented in the next few pages is beyond the scope of a high school survey textbook. For those who are interested in more detailed information on the creationist viewpoints described here, write to Bob Jones University Press.

Biological Terms

evolution, theory of
beginnings, theory of
biological (organic) evolution, theory of

philosophy of evolution
evolutionist
creationist

The Philosophy of Evolution
scientism
theistic evolution

Review Questions 7A-2

1. How would a person who believes in the philosophy of evolution describe God?
2. List three results of believing in the philosophy of evolution.
3. On what basis are the claims of both evolutionists and creationists accepted?
4. Give an example of how a different viewpoint can cause two people to draw different conclusions from the same data.
5. Give several reasons that theistic evolution would appeal to some people.
6. Why is theistic evolution not acceptable to Bible-believing Christians?

Thought Questions

1. Compile a list of the basic beliefs of the theory of evolution. Compile a list of Scripture verses that could be used to show the fallacy of each of these beliefs.
2. Compile a list of modern beliefs, practices, or activities that reflect the philosophy of evolution rather than a Biblical philosophy.
3. Compile a list of Scripture verses that you could use to show a Christian who is a theistic evolutionist the error of his belief.

7B-Biblical Creationism

What does the Bible actually have to say about creation and the history of living things? Some Christians seem to know more about what the Bible does not say on the subject than what it does say. They realize facts such as, "Dinosaurs are not mentioned in the Bible," and "The Bible does not explain where Cain got his wife." Instead of concentrating on what the Bible does not say, let us focus on what the Bible *does* say about creation and history. We can learn much from what the Bible says and from what we are able to observe of the present physical world.

Creation week: long or short days

Review the sequence of events in the creation week as outlined in figure 7B-1, and read the account of the creation as described in Genesis 1 and 2. Some people argue that this sequence of events is scientifically impossible. Noting, for example, that plants were created before the sun, moon, and stars they ask how plants could have lived without the sun. Light, though, was created on the first day but simply had not been organized into the sun, moon, and stars as we know them.

Creation is in itself scientifically unexplainable. Knowing why or how God created things the way He did is not only beyond the scope of science (for it cannot be observed) but also beyond the comprehension of human minds (Job 38-40:5).

Some Christians interpret the seven days in Genesis 1 as seven ages. This interpretation is sometimes called the **long-day theory (day-age theory).** Second Peter 3:8 ("One day is with the Lord as a thousand years, and a thousand years as one day") is often cited as support for the long-day theory. This passage, however, simply teaches that God is eternal and timeless.

Most people who hold to the long-day theory are attempting to put enough time in the Genesis account of creation for evolution to take place. This is an attempt to prove that God *directed or permitted* the evolution of the universe rather than actually created it as He did. If God says He created the world in six days and man refuses to believe it, then man is calling God a liar.

Some Bible-believing Christians believe in the long-day theory. It does not directly contradict Scripture; but a person who believes in the long-day theory for the purpose of appearing more "scientific" is a theistic evolutionist, and his motive is unacceptable.

Other Christians believe that the days in Genesis 1 are 24-hr. periods. This belief is the **short-day theory.** The short-day theory is supported by the phrase "the evening and the morning," repeated often in Genesis, and by the fact that the sequence of events described requires speed. For example, many plants (if they were like today's plants) can live for only a limited period of time without organized day, night, and seasons, and without animals to pollinate them.

The gap theory

According to the **gap theory** there was a long period of time between Genesis 1:1 and 1:2. (Some people place the "gap" even before verse 1.) Gap theorists believe there was a "first creation" which was destroyed, probably (they say) by the fall of Satan described in Isaiah 14:12-17. This period ("first creation" and "gap") may have been thousands, millions, or even billions of years long. The gap theory first appeared in writing about A.D. 400, but it did not become popular until about a century ago when evolutionists began to claim the earth was hundreds of thousands to millions or even billions of years old. The gap theory allowed Christians to accept the evolutionists' "old earth" yet not detract from the creation account in Genesis.

To use the gap theory to harmonize evolutionary theory and the Bible is to misuse it. To say that the first creation is recorded in the fossils, and that the geologic ages evolutionists speak of happened during the first creation is to ignore strong scientific evidence (which will be discussed later in this chapter) and several Biblical implications (see page 176).

The gap theory does not directly contradict Scripture, but it is not the only theory of creation and biological history that fits into the Biblical framework. In reality, the best creationist theories

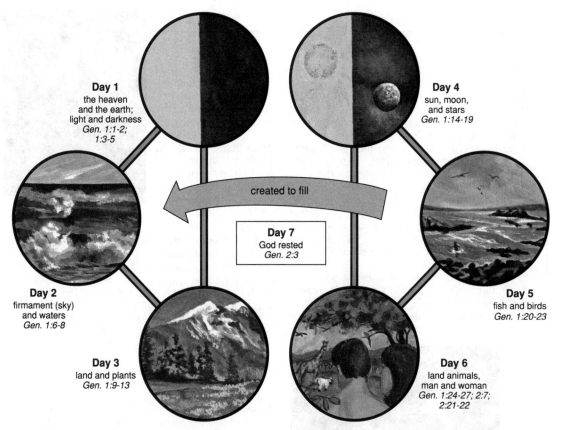

Day 1
the heaven
and the earth;
light and darkness
*Gen. 1:1-2;
1:3-5*

Day 4
sun, moon,
and stars
Gen. 1:14-19

created to fill

Day 7
God rested
Gen. 2:3

Day 2
firmament (sky)
and waters
Gen. 1:6-8

Day 5
fish and birds
Gen. 1:20-23

Day 3
land and plants
Gen. 1:9-13

Day 6
land animals,
man and woman
*Gen. 1:24-27; 2:7;
2:21-22*

7B-1 *The days of creation can be illustrated using the above diagram. The materials created on days 1-3* (left) *correspond to the materials created on days 4-6* (right).

are those that harmonize the literal Biblical account and scientific evidence.

The canopy theory

The Bible tells very little of the **antediluvian*** (AN tih duh LOO vee un) (before the Flood) earth. However, it was similar to the earth in which we now live. There were seas, rivers, and mountains (Gen. 1:10, 2:10, 7:20), as well as animal and plant life, before the Noahic Flood.

The Bible also implies differences. Many Bible scholars agree that there was no rainfall before the Flood, plants being watered by mist which rose from the earth (Gen. 2:5-6). Second Peter 3:6-7 says that "the world that then was, being overflowed with water, perished: but the heavens and the earth, which are now . . . are kept in store." Apparently, "The world that then was"

(before the Flood) differed from "the heavens and the earth which are now" (after the Flood).

One of the major differences mentioned in Scripture and implied by scientific evidence is the existence of a layer of water vapor around the antediluvian earth. Genesis 1:6-8; 7:11; 8:2 and II Peter 3:5-6 attest to this God-created canopy of water above the earth. The water vapor composing this layer would probably have been considerably higher and more abundant than the water vapor now in our clouds.

This canopy of water is believed to have fallen when "the windows of heaven were opened" (Gen. 7:11) at the time of Noah's Flood. The layer of water vapor must have been a transparent layer, not obscuring the sun, moon, and stars but probably affecting the radiation of the sun on the earth.

---

antediluvian: ante- (L. ANTE, before) + -diluvian (flood)

Scripture and the Gap Theory

Biblical Arguments Against the Gap Theory

❑ *The time of Satan's fall* According to many Bible scholars, Isaiah 14:12-15 and Ezekiel 28:12-19 speak of the wicked, earthly kings of Tyre and Babylon and also describe the fall of the ultimate ruler of wickedness, Satan. According to those who believe the gap theory, the fall of Satan described in these passages fits into the gap and explains why the earth was formless and void. Those who do not believe the gap theory believe that the fall of Satan fits better into the period between Genesis 2:25 and 3:1. The clause that "God saw every thing that he had made, and, behold, it was very good" (Gen. 1:31) does not leave much room for Satan and sin on the earth at that time.

❑ *The results of Satan's fall* If the earth had been destroyed by Satan's fall and *became* "without form and void" (Gen. 1:2), there would be no trace left of a previous creation–certainly not the layers of fossils we find today.

❑ *The time of the first sin and death* Romans 5:12 says that "by one man sin entered into the world, and death by sin . . ." This seems to indicate that there was no death until Adam's sin. A "first creation" destroyed, as gap theorists speculate, would apparently contradict this passage.

For their sin Adam and Eve were expelled from Eden.

Biblical Passages Supporting the Gap Theory with Arguments Against Them

❑ *Genesis 1:2* Gap theorists translate the first part of the verse with the word *became* instead of *was:* "And the earth *became* without form and void." Opponents are quick to point out that *was* is the more common meaning of the Hebrew word in sentences like Genesis 1:2.

❑ *Genesis 1:2* The phrase "without form and void" appears in one other Bible passage, Jeremiah 4:23, which speaks of God's judgment. Some gap theorists therefore conclude that Genesis 1:2 also deals with judgment, and they tie the judgment of Satan into Genesis 1. Opponents hold that only the context of Jeremiah 4–not the particular phrase–relates to judgment. "Without form and void" is a neutral phrase.

❑ *Genesis 1:28* Gap theorists observe that the word *replenish* implies refilling or repopulating. Only if the world had been previously filled could man "replenish the earth." Opponents point out, however, that the Hebrew word translated "replenish" can also be translated simply "fill."

❑ *Isaiah 45:18* This passage, a testimony of God's creative power, states that God "created [the earth] not in vain, he formed it to be inhabited." The word translated *in vain* in this passage is the same word used for *without form* in Genesis 1:2, and some gap theorists therefore tie the two passages together. The preceding verse in Isaiah, however, speaks of God's saving Israel. God created the world to be inhabited, not formless, and He accomplished that purpose by filling the earth with creatures. The same power which accomplished this *will* accomplish God's saving Israel. God created the world intending to fill it, just as He called Israel intending to save her.

Michael Overcoming Satan by Giovanni Andrea Sirani, Bob Jones University Collection of Sacred Art.

Satan was cast out of heaven and will be cast into the bottomless pit. The times of these events have been debated by scholars for centuries.

According to this **canopy theory,** antediluvian weather was different from present weather. Because of the thick water vapor layer, a uniformly warm climate with higher humidity existed. This *greenhouse effect* would make conditions over almost all the earth similar to those in the tropics. These conditions would have been ideal for the many large plants and animals (like large dinosaurs and giant insects) that left abundant fossil deposits but are believed to be extinct today. Such organisms would find few, if any, places today with environments suitable for them.

The existence of water above the antediluvian earth is a Biblical fact, but the idea of a water vapor canopy and its effects is theory. Differences between the antediluvian and the *postdiluvian** worlds can be explained by the canopy theory. In harmony with Scripture and many observable features of our current world, many Christians consider it a good theory.

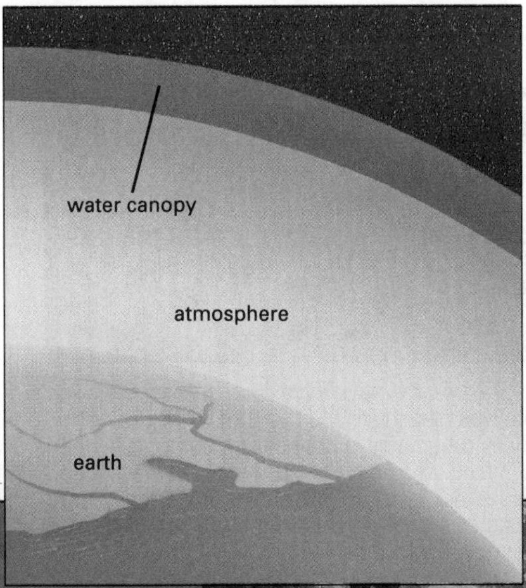

water canopy

atmosphere

earth

7B-2 *The water canopy above the earth* (left) *would have caused a greenhouse effect. Many creationists believe that the antediluvian human civilization and the organisms we now find as fossils coexisted* (below).

postdiluvian: post- (L. POST, after) + -diluvian (flood)

Other Indications of the Canopy Theory

❑ *The sign of the rainbow* The sign God gave to Noah that there would never be another universal Flood was the rainbow (Gen. 9:12-17). If conditions had been the same before the Flood as they are now, rainbows would have been common before the Flood. The canopy, however, could help account for the absence of rainbows before the Flood.

❑ *The length of human life before the Flood* The average human life span before the Flood (based on Genesis) was 912 yr. After Noah the life span quickly dropped to about 400 yr. and continued to decline. Abraham, Isaac, and Jacob lived well over 100 yr., but few men after their time have reached even 100 yr. Many Bible scholars consider this decrease in life span to be a result of sin. A cause for this decrease could

be the loss of the filtering effect of the canopy resulting in direct exposure to solar radiation.

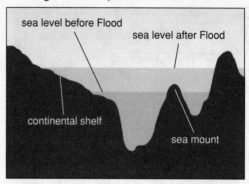
sea level before Flood
sea level after Flood
continental shelf
sea mount

❑ *The continental shelves and seamounts* The shelves of land around the continents, as well as many mountains in the sea, appear to have been dry land at one time. They would have been above sea level before the Flood with the large quantity of water believed to have composed the canopy now on the earth.

Adam	930		Eber	464
Seth	912	THE	Abraham	175
Jared	960	FLOOD	Moses	120
Methuselah	969		PSALM 9:10 –	
Noah	950		70 years	

Review Questions 7B-1

1. List what was created on each day of the creation week.
2. List several reasons for believing in (a) the short-day theory and (b) the long-day theory of creation.
3. List several arguments for and against the gap theory.
4. Describe the canopy theory, and list several reasons it is considered a Scripturally and scientifically acceptable theory.

Fossils and Noah's Flood

A **fossil*** is any direct or indirect evidence of a once-living organism. A dead body or a footprint can therefore be considered a fossil. A dead body usually decomposes quickly; and a footprint, unless made in cement or some similar material, is also temporary. However, the term fossil normally refers to remains of long-dead organisms which have been naturally preserved.

Fossilization

Fossilization (the forming of fossils) is not naturally happening to any appreciable extent today.

When an organism dies now, it is only a matter of time before it decomposes, leaving no trace that it existed. Scientists can only theorize about how the fossils we find so abundantly were made.

Let us look at some of the types of fossils and some considerations of how these fossils were formed.

❑ *Preservation of parts* The most abundant type of fossils is the preserved hard parts of animals (bones, teeth, shells) and plants (stems, seeds). These often lie in vast layers, sometimes hundreds of square miles long and many feet thick. In some

fossil: (L. FOSSILIS, dug-up)

areas even the soft parts have been so well preserved that scientists can determine types of chlorophyll, contents of stomachs, and shapes of muscles. Today when something dies, even its hard parts will usually deteriorate within a few months. In order for its hard parts to fossilize, an organism must have been *quickly* placed under pressure in rock forming sediment. This type of fossil is not formed naturally today.

❏ *Preservation of carbon (coal)* Coal is believed to be a massive collection of mostly plant material which was placed under great pressure. Experiments have shown that under proper conditions plant material can form coal in 20 min. It is estimated that to form a vein of coal 40 ft. thick over 200 ft. of green plant material must be compressed. Although plant material does collect in the bottoms of swamps and bogs, conditions do not now exist for the natural formation of coal in such places. No coal is known to be naturally forming today.

❏ *Preservation of forms (casts or molds)* Casts or molds of organism's bodies are believed to have formed when the organisms were placed in a substance which quickly (before the body could decompose) formed into stone. When the surrounding substance had solidified enough to hold its form and the body of the organism dissolved away, an empty or fluid-filled form was left. This type of fossilization may occur today (though rarely) in tar pits. But no extensive casts or molds are now forming in sedimentary rock.

❏ *Preservation of tracks* Scientists have found extensive areas of preserved animal tracks, usu-ally rock that was once clay or mud. Tracks of large reptiles and various other extinct animals are numerous, and in some cases human footprints can be found in rock. Materials were apparently laid quickly into the tracks to aid their turning to stone before they had a chance to be destroyed. Today footprints made in clay or mud are soon gone.

❏ *Petrification* Usually only the hard parts of an organism are petrified. Petrification seems to happen when water containing dissolved minerals penetrates into the structure. The water then somehow leaves, and the minerals remain, collecting within the spaces of the structure and eventually turning them to stone. Extensive petrification is apparently not happening today. Organisms normally rot underwater.

❏ *Freezing* In Siberia and Alaska large numbers of animals have been found frozen fast. Best known are the mammals that froze so quickly they still had food in their mouths and were in such

7B-3 *Various kinds of fossils*

A petrified tree stump

Preservation of parts

A dinosaur track

good condition that they have been fed to dogs. Today animals are not being permanently frozen in any quantity. The quick freezing of such large animals (many of which are not arctic) suggests some major catastrophe.

Fossils formed by other methods are rare, limited, or unidentifiable.

The deluge and the fossilization

To consider the **deluge*** (DEL yooj) or Noah's Flood (see Gen. 6-9) a local flood is to contradict Scripture. In the box on the right are seven reasons why the deluge must have been a *universal flood* (covering the entire earth). The effects of such a flood are open to considerable speculation. Various theories have come into existence.

7B-4 *Fossil fish. Fossils are frequently found in masses, an indication of a catastrophe.*

The **deluge fossil formation theory** is held by many Christian scholars. Until about a century ago most written material–Christian and non-Christian–indicated that the fossils were formed by the deluge. In the 1800s, however, evolutionists began to suggest that the fossils were a *progressive record* of past times and had taken many thousands, millions, and even billions of years to form. The concept of fossils being formed by various methods over long periods of time was an attempt to support evolutionary theory. Today, however, some research and experimentation is producing support for the deluge fossil formation theory.

An entire earth covered with water, as in the deluge, would contain many strong currents, possibly even stronger than the major currents found in our oceans today. Recall that the purpose of the Flood was to destroy the world. The Flood currents would therefore be strong enough to carry any material on the face of the earth which could be moved.

As the currents slowed down or changed course during the deluge, they would have deposited the materials they carried. This **sedimentation*** (settling out of materials) accounts for the layers of **sedimentary rock** which contain most of the fossils and compose most of the *topography* (tuh

---

Reasons the Deluge Was Universal

1. The purpose of the deluge was to destroy all flesh except that which was in the ark (Genesis 6:13, 17; 7:4, 19-23). This could not have been done if the Flood had been local, since people as well as animals could have migrated outside the area of a local flood.
2. The waters covered the highest mountains to a depth of over 20 ft. (Genesis 7:19, 20; 8:5). Since water seeks its own level, to cover a mountain by this depth requires a universal flood.
3. The duration of the Flood was over a year. Local floods do not last that long.
4. An ark to preserve Noah, his family, and the animals was unnecessary if the Flood were local.
   - The time (over 100 yr.) spent building the ark was wasted if the Flood were local.
   - The raven and the dove would have been able to find places to rest if the Flood had been local.
   - There would have been no need to take most animals into the ark if the Flood had been local.
   - The prescribed size of the ark was unnecessary if the Flood were local.
5. God made a covenant with Noah that there would never again be such a flood. The rainbow symbolizes His promise (Genesis 8:21; 9:11, 15). The covenant has been repeatedly broken if it referred to local flooding.
6. The testimony of Christ (Luke 17:27) is that all were destroyed in the Flood.
7. The testimony of Peter (II Peter 2:5; 3:6) is that the world was destroyed by the Flood.

---

deluge: de- (from) + (L. LAVERE, to wash)

sedimentation: (L. SEDIMENTUM, the act of settling)

Several conclusions about fossilization can be made which support the deluge fossil formation theory and contradict the progressive fossil record that evolutionists imagine.

❏ Abundant fossilization is not taking place today. Sometime in the past, however, fossilization rates must have been vastly different to account for the fossils we find in our present world.

❏ The abundance of fossils and the arrangement of the fossils indicate a major catastrophe.

❏ Fossilization of an organism's parts must be rapid; otherwise, organisms would decompose before fossilization could take place.

❏ Most types of fossils we find today apparently required water movements for depositing them.

❏ Most of the fossils we find today apparently required water for their formation.

Some evolutionists, recognizing the problem of fossilization, suggest that there must have been a series of major catastrophes to account for the fossils we find today. These catastrophes would have to have been separated by long ages, and each one could have formed only a few layers in order for the fossils to verify evolution. The fossils themselves present problems even for *these*

7B-5 *An artist's rendering of Noah's Flood, showing the depositing of layers of organisms.*

PAHG ruh fee), or land features, with which we are familiar. Rock layers are visible where mountains have been cut away by rivers as in the Grand Canyon or by man as in building roads. According to the deluge theory of fossil formation, these rock layers were formed by Noah's Flood.

7B-6 *The erosion of the Badlands in South Dakota is presumed to have taken millions of years. However, the amount of water involved in the Flood could have formed this and similar structures quite rapidly.*

7B-7 *A polystrate fossil runs through several layers of sedimentary rock. Such fossils should have decayed before they formed if the sedimentary layers represent thousands of years as evolutionists claim.*

FACETS OF BIOLOGY

Noah's Ark and the Animals

To many people the story of Noah with the animals on the ark is a delightful children's story which clearly teaches God's punishment for sin and His watch care over His children (and animals). The details and implications of the Biblical account, however, teach us even more about God and His creation.

Based on the Genesis account and a 0.46 m (18 in.) cubit, the ark was over 138 m (450 ft.) long, 23 m (75 ft.) wide, and 14 m (45 ft.) high. It contained 3 internal decks with a total deck area of over 9,500 sq. m. (101,000 sq. ft.), larger than 20 basketball courts.

The ark was probably box-shaped rather than streamlined like a modern boat. Its purpose was simply to float through a severe flood, not to travel anywhere. A completely enclosed structure strengthened by the 3 internal decks, it would have to be turned almost halfway over to capsize. Made completely of wood and covered with pitch (probably a tar-like substance), only major structural damage could have sunk it. Although Noah built a good vessel, the reason for the ark's successful passage through the Flood was that "God remembered Noah, and every living thing, and all the cattle that was with him in the ark" (Gen. 8:1).

Many people have said that the ark could never have contained all the necessary animals. Noah was told to take 7 of every kind of clean and 2 of every kind of un-

Dimensions of the ark. Figures inside the ark are drawn to scale.

13 meters (45 ft.)

22 meters (75 ft.)

137 m (450 f

clean animal. (Probably, there were far more unclean than clean.) Most likely only land animals were on the ark (aquatic animals could have survived in the water). Today there are less than 17,500 species of vertebrate land animals such as mammals, birds, reptiles, and amphibians. Noah's ark, therefore, needed to carry about 35,000 vertebrate land animals.

A sheep is about the average size of the animals taken on the ark. A double-decked railroad stock-car can carry 240 sheep. Only 146 stock-cars would be needed to carry 35,000 ark animals. The only major group of invertebrates to have land-dwelling members includes the insects and a few similar organisms. An additional boxcar or two could contain these. The ark had a total volume of over 530 boxcars, even though only the volume of about 150 was needed to hold its inhabitants.

Noah did not need to catch the animals. The Bible states that God brought the animals to the ark (Gen. 6:20; 7:9, 15). Some people ask if there were dinosaurs or other now-extinct organisms on the ark. The Flood theory of fossil formation assumes dinosaurs were alive in Noah's day. God possibly brought dinosaurs (perhaps young ones) to the ark. There was easily enough room for them.

It is also possible that God, knowing that the after-the-Flood world would not be suitable for large dinosaurs, did not bring them and other now-extinct animals to the ark. Some Christians object to this idea, saying that Noah was to take two "of every living thing of all flesh" (Gen. 6:19) and dinosaurs must have been included. But the next phrase of the verse states "two of every sort." It is possible that the "sort" that included dinosaurs was represented by smaller reptiles, possibly some that we are familiar with today.

Others argue that God would not completely destroy organisms He had created. However, other organisms, for which God's purpose must have been finished, have become extinct since the Flood. God could have destroyed creatures outside the ark in the Flood as easily as He could have destroyed them after the Flood.

Some people see Noah as a harried, understaffed animal keeper with only 7 helpers, running from cage to cage trying to keep things clean and the animals' food and water bowls filled in a rocking, floating zoo. Others wonder how Noah could supply meat for the carnivores without killing some of the animals on board and plants for the vegetarians without a sizable storehouse.

A possible answer is that many of the animals entered into a state of dormancy (hibernation or other quiet states) for the year on the ark. If so, this was the first hibernation that some animals needed. Possessing a canopy, the antediluvian world probably would not have had the major seasonal changes we experience today. Environmental changes are the primary reasons many animals need dormant periods.

Some people object, saying that this would require a miracle from God. But the Flood, the ark, and the animals coming to and entering the ark were all miracles. God finishes the work that He begins. It is not likely that God would have permitted His creatures to harm one another or be overly demanding on Noah and his family. (See *Biblical Kind*, Chapter 8.)

Review questions on page 184.

Finding Noah's Ark

Periodically various Biblical artifacts have supposedly been found, and Noah's ark is one such artifact. There are several remote places in the world today where Noah's ark is supposedly resting.

If a structure which matches Noah's ark is found, it might lend support for the inerrancy of the Bible, but it would do little to increase the faith of Bible-believing Christians. Would finding Noah's ark lead people to Christ? As Abraham told the rich man, "If they hear not Moses and the prophets, neither will they be persuaded, though one rose from the dead" (Luke 16:31).

If Noah's ark is ever found it will be the only physical Biblical artifact we have today. The Jews do not have the Ark of the Covenant, the Tabernacle, or the Temple, all very important to their obedient worship. We do not have any of the original manuscripts of the Scripture.

What would we do with a Biblical artifact if we had it? Hezekiah had to destroy the brazen serpent that Moses lifted up in the wilderness because the children of Israel started worshiping it (II Kings 18:4). Perhaps we do not have Biblical artifacts because we would reverence the objects rather than worshiping God. If Noah's ark is still in existence and is ever found it will probably be used in such a way that most Bible-believing Christians would wish it had not been found.

7B-8 *Some human artifacts*

Gold chain *A 10-inch-long, 8-carat gold chain was found in a lump of coal. Both ends were left embedded in the coal when it broke open, revealing the chain.*

Nampa image *During a well-drilling operation, a carved human figure was discovered 300 feet below the surface.*

Metal jar *A jar 4 1/2 inches high with a 6 1/2-inch base and a 2 1/2-inch mouth was found in solid sedimentary stone. It bears six carved figures, flowers, and a wreath or vine of inlaid silver on a zinc alloy.*

Nail in quartz *A nail, about 6 pennyweight, was found in a quartz formation about the size of a man's fist. The nail was straight and had a perfect head.*

evolutionists. **Human artifacts** (things which man must have made such as gold chains or metal objects) or fossils such as bones and footprints have been found in low fossil layers. If the progressive catastrophes theory held by these evolutionists is correct, man must have evolved very early.

Some Christians adopt a theory similar to that of these evolutionists. Calling Noah's Flood the most recent catastrophe, they put the other catastrophes within the "gap." The human artifacts

then indicate that the before-the-gap creation must have included man. Adam then is not the *first* man but merely the first man of the new (present) creation. Romans 5:12 reveals that it was in Adam's sin that death entered the world. Human artifacts from a time before Adam would contradict this Scripture. Those who believe the deluge fossil formation theory, however, explain fossilized human artifacts by saying that they are from the antediluvian civilization that God destroyed with the Flood.

Review Questions 7B-2

1. List several methods of fossilization.
2. List seven Biblically based reasons why we believe the Flood was universal.
3. Why is the deluge fossil formation theory the most scientifically acceptable theory for fossilization? Is it also a Scripturally acceptable theory?

Facet 7B-1: Noah's Ark and the Animals, pages 182-83

1. List several objections that people have to the Scriptural account of the animals' being on Noah's ark, and give answers to the objections.
2. Compare the size of Noah's ark to the size of some familiar objects.

The Age of the Earth

In the 1600s, James Ussher, an Irish Anglican clergyman, tabulated the dates of various Biblical events by using the ages of people recorded in Scripture and other available historical records. His dates appear in many reference Bibles (including the *Scofield Reference Bible*). In *The An-*

nals of the Old and New Testaments, published in 1658, Archbishop Ussher placed creation at "the entrance of the night preceding the twenty third day of Octob. in the year of the Julian Calendar, 710" (4004 B.C.). Although most people are a bit skeptical about Ussher's exact date and time of day, you can, if you use the Biblical genealogies, arrive at about the year 4000 B.C. (about 6,000 years ago) as the time of creation.

Many Bible scholars, however, agree that Ussher's dates are most likely a bit short. Several Biblical statements show that there are deliberate gaps in some of the genealogies. Compare Gen. 11:12-13 and Luke 3:35-36. These gaps permit dates of creation extending slightly in excess of 6,000 years ago.

7B-9 *Archbishop James Ussher proposed dates for creation based on Biblical events.*

Probably more accurate, and acceptable within the Bible's framework, is that creation was between 8,000 and 10,000 years ago, although some creationists admit that it might be several thousand years older than that. This age of the earth is in keeping with various historical dates recorded by ancient peoples. One such date is given in an ancient translation of the Bible, the Septuagint,

which places Noah's Flood at 3700 B.C. rather than Ussher's 2348 B.C.

Most evolutionists believe that the earth is billions of years old. The evolutionists claim that dates for the beginning of the earth could not have been recorded because man had not yet evolved. They choose to ignore the Word of God, which contradicts their theories on such matters. Evolutionists, therefore, must use other theories to support their hypotheses. These theories fall into two groups:

❑ *The earth must be old because biological evolution must have taken a long time.* Creationists agree that biological evolution would have required a long time *if* it had taken place. But Christians cannot accept this argument for an old earth because the Bible says God directly created living things (see John 1:3).

❑ *The earth must be old because of the physical evidence the earth supplies.* Such evidences fall into three basic categories: dating of fossils, dating by **topography** (the shapes and contours of the earth), and dating by decay or buildup of substances. Dates obtained from the physical earth, however, are circumstantial and often depend upon the assumption that biological evolution took place.

Dating of fossils

A person who counts the number of layers above a fossil and then attributes a certain age to each layer is assuming that fossils were formed progressively. But as we have seen, fossils are probably the record of one major catastrophe, Noah's Flood. Even if they are a record of several major

catastrophes, it would be difficult, if not impossible, to determine which layers belong to which catastrophe and what period of time to assign to each layer.

Evolutionists often use another method to determine the age of the fossil: they consult an evolutionary timetable of when organisms supposedly developed. When consulting such a chart, the evolutionist is assuming not only that biological evolution occurred but also that the fossil record is progressive.

Evolutionists often use *index fossils* to tell the age of other fossils in the same area. An index fossil is the remains of an organism (usually an extinct animal) which supposedly lived at only a certain time in evolutionary history. When an index fossil is found in a layer of rock, evolutionists believe they can consult evolutionary timetables and thereby accurately date that layer as well as the fossil layers above and below it.

If you analyze the above statements, you can see that dating of fossils by the fossils themselves is primarily guesswork. It often winds up with one scientist's quoting another scientist as the authority for their dates. If the other scientists have merely guessed at the date, we still have only a guess, not a scientifically determined age of a fossil. Many scientists, thus, look to other dating methods to determine the age of fossils.

7B-10 *A glacier similar to this one may have covered portions of the earth for a brief period following the Flood.*

Dating by topography

Evolutionists claim that a force of relatively recent origin pushed up on the earth's crust to form mountains. They conclude this because they have found fossils of land vertebrate animals, as well as those of fish and marine animals, at tops of many mountains. These fossils indicate that the mountains were once underwater and were formed after these organisms had evolved.

Evolutionists find it difficult to set a time for both the mountains to have been underwater and the major upheaval that formed vast mountain ranges such as the Himalayas or the Rockies. But Noah's Flood, which covered the mountains, is a sufficient explanation, not only of when the ranges formed but also of what forces formed them. The Flood theory of fossil formation can easily account for fossils on the tops of mountains.

Evolutionists use ice ages—major periods of **glaciation** (GLAY she AY shun)—to explain many of the earth's present features. They say that vast expanses of ice covered entire continents for thousands of years. As the North American ice sheet moved back and forth, it flattened the midwest regions of Canada and the United States, hollowed out the Great Lakes, and deposited larger rocks in the middle of flat prairies.

Setting dates for the ice ages is a major problem. Some Christians attempt to place them in the gap of the gap theory. If they occurred in the gap, though, physical evidence of them would have been destroyed in the deluge, and we would not know that major glaciation periods even existed.

The ice ages as described by most evolutionists probably never happened. Some of the supposed topographic effects of glaciation could easily have been the result of water movements during the Flood. A very brief period of glaciation in certain areas of the world may have taken place immediately after the Flood. Without the protective canopy, the adjusting earth may have had a period of glaciation before it reached the relative stability of today's climate and seasons. This ice which formed after the Flood may have contained some Flood-destroyed organisms, thereby accounting for some of the frozen organisms found in areas of the world today.

7B-11 *Scientists once believed that stalactites and stalagmites like the ones on the left took many millions of years to form. Under the Lincoln Memorial these stalactites and stalagmites formed in fewer than 50 years.*

Cave formation and the forming of stalactites* (stuh LAK TITES) and stalagmites (stuh LAG MITES) in caves, according to many evolutionists, take hundreds of thousands of years. The receding water of the deluge, however, could have caused rapid cave formation. Stalactites and stalagmites can form quickly under the proper conditions. These conditions probably existed immediately after the Flood, as the caves were forming.

Some scientists also believe that many other features of the surface of the earth took millions of years to form. Evolutionists often use rocks (like limestone), deposits of underground salt, and major evidences of erosion (like the Grand Canyon) to date the earth as very old. Because large quantities of similar structures are not being formed in the world today (if they are being formed at all), evolutionists require the old dates to account for these features. But these and many similar geologic phenomena are more easily and more scientifically explained by a major water catastrophe. Most Bible believers claim that that catastrophe was Noah's Flood.

Review Questions 7B-3

1. On what did Ussher base his 4004 B.C. date of creation?
2. On what do evolutionists base their 4.5 billion-year-old earth theory?
3. Describe how scientists use fossils to date fossils and tell why this is an unacceptable method of determining the age of a fossil.
4. What are some of the topographic features which evolutionists attribute to glaciation? How do most Bible-believing Christians account for these features?
5. What topographic features do evolutionists often use to arrive at old dates for the earth?

Dating by decay or buildup

If a person examined the stump of a candle, measured it carefully, and then made the statement that the candle had burned 2 hr. 28 min., you could ask him how he knows. He might say that in the environment in which he found the stump, an 8 in. candle of the same diameter as the first candle would have had to burn 2 hr. 28 min. to reach the final size of the first candle.

All his statements may be accurate and even testable. The several assumptions he is making, however, make his statement pure guesswork, rather than science. He is *assuming* that the candle started at 8 in. long, was the same diameter all the way up, and burned only in the environment in which he found the stump. One or all of these assumptions may not be true. An error in any of them could affect the accuracy of the estimation, perhaps by as much as several hours.

The same principle applies to using the decay or buildup of substances to determine the age of the earth: underlying these methods are many speculative assumptions. Using these methods one can obtain "proof" that the earth was formed billions of years ago, several thousand years ago, yesterday, or even *not yet*. Obviously, dates which say the earth has not yet been formed are wrong, but which of the others should one accept?

Individuals generally accept the dates closest to their personal beliefs. Evolutionists are biased for the old dates and therefore often cite them as accurate. They either ignore the more recent dates or consider them wrong since such dates do not fit into *their* evolutionary timetable.

---

stalactites: (Gk. STALAKTOS, dripping)

Dating Methods That Suggest Relatively Recent Dates for the Age of the Earth

Volcanism Most evolutionists believe that there must have been more abundant volcanic activity in times past. If the current rate of lava production of today's approximately 450 active volcanoes were constant for 4 1/2 billion years, the amount of lava produced would be equivalent to the size of the earth. If at current volcanic activity the earth could not be that old, it certainly could not be that old if volcanic activity had ever been greater.

Water formation Water is being formed (either by volcanic activity or other means) and added to the earth at the rate of about 1 cubic mile per year. If the earth were billions of years old, far too much water would have been produced for there to be any dry land.

Meteoric dust Today about 14 million tons of dust from outer space fall to the earth each year. Estimates indicate that in about 4 billion yr. enough meteoric dust would have fallen to cover the face of the earth a depth of 54 ft. to 100 mi. This dust has characteristic chemicals in it (nickel, cobalt, and other heavy metals) which are relatively rare in the earth's crust. We do not find this amount of meteoric dust (or even the evidence of the proper chemicals) in adequate near-the-surface sources. Even if swept into the ocean by wind and erosion, these chemicals should show buildups somewhere on the ocean floor. Such abundance of these chemicals, however, is not found even there.

Soil formation Evolutionists have stated that soil takes thousands or even millions of years to form. In several areas of the world, however, actual measurements have accounted for several inches of soil being formed in less that 100 yr. This rate of formation indicates that the earth is young.

Human population statistics Considering plagues, wars, famines, and other problems affecting population, 8 people at the time of Noah's Flood would have multiplied to almost 4 billion people today. This figure is about correct. Evolutionists, claiming that man evolved a million years ago, have problems explaining why, using the same mathematical calculations, there are not an astronomical number ($10^{27,000}$) of people on the earth.

Decay of the earth's magnetic field The earth's magnetic field is decaying at a certain rate (based on measurements for the past 100 yr.). At the present rate of decay, if the earth's magnetic field is figured backwards, about 7,000 yr. ago the earth's magnetic field would have been 32 times stronger than it is now, which is the highest limit of possibility. Ten thousand years ago the earth would have been as magnetic as a magnetic star, which is improbable.

Scarcity of helium Many radioactive decay processes form helium. If radioactive decay processes had been going on for billions of years, large quantities of helium should be found in the earth's atmosphere. Helium, however, is relatively rare. Its quantity accounts for an earth with radioactive decay at present rates for only several thousand years.

Creation with apparent age

People often fail to consider that the earth must have been created with **apparent age.** Adam was not an infant on the seventh day of creation. Even though he was just a day old, he had the body of at least a young adult who was able to care for himself. The same was true of the animals. The Garden of Eden had fruit-bearing plants, not just seeds and seedlings.

The earth itself must also have had some apparent age. Although streams, soil, and many other features of the earth take time to form, we find them described as being in God's newly formed creation. If a person had measured the soil depth in Eden the day after creation week and had calculated the age of the garden based on the length of time required for soil production, he undoubtedly would have come up with an age for Eden considerably older than it actually was.

This creation with apparent age throws off some of the buildup and decay clocks that evolutionists use to date the earth. Scientists who measure how rapidly certain chemicals are building up in an ocean, and then compute backwards to a point where none of these chemicals were yet in the ocean, obtain an apparent age but not an actual age, since the newly formed seas already had an amount of these chemicals dissolved in them. If a scientist knew exactly how much of certain chemicals was actually in the sea at creation and knew all the factors (including the Flood) that could affect the further buildup of these chemicals, he could more accurately determine the age of the earth. But this information is not available.

Dates for the age of the earth that are based upon chemicals found in seawater range from just over one hundred years to well over a billion years, depending upon which chemical is measured. It is interesting to note, however, that virtually all the chemicals in the ocean give dates for under a billion years, considerably less than most evolutionists would like.

Most processes of decay or buildup produce relatively young dates for the earth. Moreover, those in this category that can be considered more reliable (those with fewer variables) appear to give younger dates than most others.

Radiometric dating methods

Although highly favored by evolutists because they often give very old dates, radiometric* (RAY dee oh MET rik) dating methods are losing scientific credibility because of faulty assumptions and measurement problems. A **radiometric dating method** measures the decay of a radioactive substance into a nonradioactive substance. Probably the best-known of the radiometric dating methods is the *uranium-lead method.*

Uranium, a radioactive element, decays over a period of time into 15 different subproducts before finally becoming one of the several forms of lead. An atom of uranium-238 (an isotope of uranium with 238 elementary particles in the nucleus) decays to an atom of lead-206 and 8 helium atoms. One gram of pure uranium-238 would take approximately 4.5 billion yr. to become 0.5 g of uranium-238 and the appropriate amounts of lead-206 and helium. In another 4.5 billion yr. it would form 0.25 g of uranium-238, and so on. Uranium-238, therefore, has a **half-life** of 4.5 billion yr. That is, one-half of the existing amount disintegrates in that amount of time.

Other isotopes of uranium have different half-lives and become other isotopes of lead. Most of

the other radiometric dating methods (potassium-argon, rubidium-strontium, and others) are quite similar. At present there is some question regarding the accuracy of past measurements of the half-lives of many substances.

7B-12 *Scientists attempt to date fossils, using radiometric dating methods. This presumes a known starting amount of the radioactive substance in the specimen as well as many other untestable "facts."*

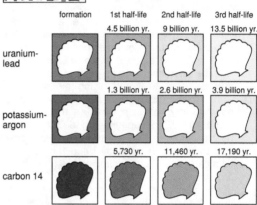

	formation	1st half-life	2nd half-life	3rd half-life
		4.5 billion yr.	9 billion yr.	13.5 billion yr.
uranium-lead				
		1.3 billion yr.	2.6 billion yr.	3.9 billion yr.
potassium-argon				
		5,730 yr.	11,460 yr.	17,190 yr.
carbon 14				

A scientist can measure (with a degree of accuracy) the amount of uranium and the amount of lead in a rock sample. If, however, the scientist then makes a statement regarding the age of that rock based on the ratio of lead to uranium in it, he is assuming several things:

❑ The rock when it was formed contained all uranium and no lead.

❑ The rate of decay has been constant throughout all the time since the rock was formed.

❑ None of the uranium, subproducts, or lead escaped from the rock since it was formed.

In essence, the scientist is assuming the same things as the person who guessed how long the candle had burned. Good evidence indicates, however, that these assumptions are not valid.

Variables in the radiometric dating methods

To assume that there is no lead in newly formed rock is a fallacy. The radiometric dating of rock from recent (less than 200 yr. ago) volcanic activity often yields dates in the millions or billions

---

radiometric radio- (L. RADIARE, to emit beams) + -metric (measure)

The Radiocarbon Dating Method

The **radiocarbon dating method** *or carbon-14 dating method* can be used to date substances that were once alive. Most of the carbon on the earth and in the atmosphere is the nonradioactive isotope carbon-12. In the atmosphere about 6 mi. up, carbon-14 is formed by cosmic radiation bombarding nitrogen. As soon as carbon-14 is formed, it begins to degenerate into nitrogen. The half-life of carbon-14 is *about* 5,730 yr. (Figures vary as much as 200 yr.)

Carbon-14 in the atmosphere combines with oxygen, forms carbon dioxide, and spreads throughout the air. Only a small amount of atmospheric carbon dioxide is made of carbon-14. Carbon dioxide (both of carbon-12 and -14) enters the photosynthetic process of plants and in time is passed to all other living things.

When an organism dies, it stops taking in carbon-14. Scientists can measure the carbon-14 and carbon-12 in a specimen and obtain a ratio. By comparing this ratio to the ratio of carbon-14 and carbon-12 in currently living things, scientists date the specimen, finding the time that its organic elements were last in a living thing.

The radiocarbon dating method can give reliable dates within the framework of several thousand years. Since the ratio of carbon-14 to carbon-12 on the earth is very small, the tiny ratios obtained when measuring the carbon-14 of a supposedly very old organic substance are doubtful.

Scientists realize that if the amount of radiation coming to the earth from outer space was at any time significantly different from the present amount, the dates obtained by radiocarbon dating would be unreliable. Evidence shows that the rate of radiation from the heavens has not always been the same. One can only guess what effects these different rates and the antediluvian canopy which would have filtered out various types of radiation would have.

Before accepting carbon-14 dating, a person must consider its several assumptions:

❏ The method assumes that the amount of carbon-14 forming in the atmosphere is now, and always has been, constant. We know by measurements that the carbon-14 to carbon-12 ratio is increasing. More is being formed than is degenerating. Differences in cosmic radiation (of which there is evidence) could be the reason.

❏ The method assumes that there is an equilibrium of carbon-14: the amount of carbon-14 forming equals the amount decomposing into nitrogen. Assuming present conditions, this equilibrium would take about 30,000 yr. to reach. Present data shows that the carbon-14 ratio is increasing, indicating that the ratio has not yet reached an equilibrium (as those who believe in a young earth are not surprised to learn).

❏ The method assumes that the carbon-14 decay rate is constant. It can be demonstrated that the decay rate is not constant.

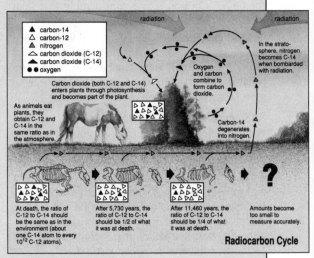

Carbon dioxide (both C-12 and C-14) enters plants through photosynthesis and becomes part of the plant.

As animals eat plants, they obtain C-12 and C-14 in the same ratio as in the atmosphere.

In the stratosphere, nitrogen becomes C-14 when bombarded with radiation.

Oxygen and carbon combine to form carbon dioxide.

Carbon-14 degenerates into nitrogen.

At death, the ratio of C-12 to C-14 should be the same as in the environment (about one C-14 atom to every 10^{12} C-12 atoms).

After 5,730 years, the ratio of C-12 to C-14 should be 1/2 of what it was at death.

After 11,460 years, the ratio of C-12 to C-14 should be 1/4 of what it was at death.

Amounts become too small to measure accurately.

Radiocarbon Cycle

❏ The method assumes that the amount of carbon-12 available to the organisms is constant. The abundance of carbon fossils (coal, oil) indicates that the amount of carbon-12 available has probably not always been the same.

The radiocarbon dating method is probably the most reliable method of dating organic materials of unknown age. But it obtains reliable dates only within certain limits. For relatively short periods of time (up to a few thousand years) the method can accurately tell the age of some specimens. Dates which are very old or are based on specimens which may have been kept in unusual conditions should be "taken with a grain of salt." Radiocarbon dating is not infallible. There are a number of specimens for which the method has given wrong dates. Shells taken from living clams have been dated thousands of years old.

of years old. These old dates occur primarily because of the lead (or other decay products) in the rocks. It is also interesting that, because of the decay products, lava from a single eruption yields many vastly different dates.

Because many of the products and subproducts of radioactive decay easily escape from rocks by exposure to water or even air, the accuracy of dates obtained is even more questionable. Furthermore, when measuring these substances, scientists are measuring minute amounts: the slightest error could change a date by hundreds of thousands or millions of years. For potassium-argon, one of the more popular radiometric dating substances, scientists have demonstrated that its half-life can be altered even by pressure and heat. In order to use this method, one must know all the conditions at which the substance has been kept since it was formed.

In order to account for these variables, scientists try to set the radiometric clock by dates from other sources. For example, when they test a rock found near an *index fossil* (a fossil which has been assigned a date by some other dating method) and the rock yields a certain ratio of the radioactive element to its end product, they often assign the date of the index fossil to that ratio.

Since other rocks in the area have been exposed to similar conditions, they assume that they can date the other rocks by obtaining their ratios and then comparing them to the ratio of the rocks near the index fossil. In other words, they are setting the radiometric clock by the assumed date of the index fossil. The date of the index fossil, as we discussed earlier, is merely an evolutionary guess and contradicts scientific knowledge and the Bible. Setting the radiometric clock by index fossils therefore yields erroneous dates.

Biblical creationism is accepted by faith. A creationist, however, should not feel that science contradicts his faith in God's Word. Rather than being disproved by science, the Scriptural concept of a young earth is actually verified by science.

Biological Terms

long-day theory (day-age theory)
short-day theory
gap theory
antediluvian
canopy theory

Fossils and Noah's Flood
fossil
fossilization

deluge
deluge fossil formation theory
sedimentation
sedimentary rock
human artifact

The Age of the Earth
topography
glaciation

apparent age
radiometric dating method
half-life
radiocarbon dating method
 (carbon-14 dating method)

Review Questions 7B-4

1. List reasons why dating the earth by decay or buildup methods can be unreliable.
2. Describe the radiometric dating methods.
3. What assumptions must one make when using radiometric dating methods?
4. What technique is used to compensate for variables in the radiometric dating methods?
5. List several methods of dating the earth that indicate that the earth is young (around 10,000 yr. old).
6. What assumptions must one make when using the radio-carbon dating method?
7. List several problems that the radiocarbon dating method has which prevent it from obtaining reliable dates.

Thought Questions

1. Discuss why Ussher's date for creation is too short and why dates far more than 10,000 yr. ago are too long.
2. Check five Bible commentaries regarding the gap theory. List which ones agree and which ones disagree with the gap theory. Note carefully the reasons they give. See if you can find flaws in some of the logic used either to support or to discredit the gap theory.

7C-Theories of Biological Evolution

The previous section discussed the fact that there is no history of evolution recorded either by man or by fossils. This lack of evolutionary records does not disturb most evolutionists because they believe they have a model of *how* evolution took place. This model is often illustrated by a **phylogenetic*** (FYE loh juh NET ik) **tree**–a line-up of organisms based on how they are supposedly related in an attempt to show the path that evolution has taken.

It is quite natural to notice similar facial features in different members of one family. But people who look very much alike may be entirely unrelated. One organism may have characteristics similar to another organism's but not be related to it at all.

Evolutionists claim that organisms which are alike in some ways must have had a **common ancestor.** When a limb of a phylogenetic tree branches, a common ancestor is implied. A phylogenetic tree that contains many organisms and is relatively detailed usually has the known organisms (those alive today and those extinct organisms that left fossils) on the ends of the branches. The common ancestors at the forks of the branches are usually *guesses*. Many phylogenetic trees, for example, assume that the birds and the mammals both came from a common reptilelike ancestor. In one line of development, the scales became feathers and the animals became birds. The mammal-bird ancestor may be imaginatively drawn and described, but examples of this common ancestor do not exist among animals alive today or in the fossil record.

The more organisms that are included, the greater will be the difference between the phylogenetic trees proposed by different evolutionists. In other words, there is little agreement among evolutionists about which organisms are the ancestors. Although putting pictures in sequence is easy, when considering the thousands of characteristics of different organisms, it is not always easy to create a logical sequence for them. What characteristic should be used to arrange the organisms? The use of eye development will give one phylogenetic tree, and the use of leg form or another characteristic will give a different phylogenetic tree.

COMMON ANCESTOR?

Creationists have no difficulty with similarities and differences between organisms. God designed each organism for a particular purpose. If four long legs are the right design for movement in one animal, it is likely that four long legs will be the best design for a similar movement in a similar animal. Similarities and differences come from God's design, not from a common ancestor.

---

phylogenetic: phylo- (tribe or race) + -genetic (beginning)

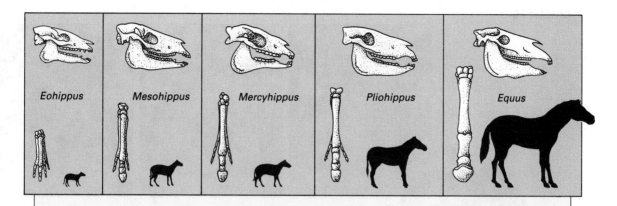

Eohippus   Mesohippus   Mercyhippus   Pliohippus   Equus

The Evolution of the Horse

In order to see some of the problems involved in lining up animals for a phylogenetic tree, let us look at a well-known example often used by evolutionists, the evolution of the horse. The *Eohippus* was an organism about the size of a terrier dog, with four toes on each front foot and three toes on each hind foot. Other extinct animals have been lined up with progressively larger bodies and with foot structures more like that of the horse to form an evolutionary "path."

The evolution seems plausible until one realizes that much of the progression is art work, and much information has been omitted. The fossils of these organisms are not found in sequence in the fossil record. In fact, the fossil record gives evidence that these organisms were alive at the same time. Having the horse and the *Eohippus* alive together at an early date

defeats the evolutionary purpose of the *Eohippus*, though, so that evidence has been ignored.

The supposed evolution of the horse is like a series of piers with the connecting bridges missing. In other words, this line-up of organisms, as with all such line-ups, is without in-between organisms, the **missing links** (common ancestors). According to evolutionary theory, these missing organisms *must* have existed. Research in the fossil record has not revealed any of the missing links in horse evolution. Nor does the fossil record show a clear progression between *any* two different kinds of organisms.

A creationist looking at the fossils of the *Eohippus* or the *Mesohippus* or any others in an evolutionary line-up simply observes that they are interesting animals that must have become extinct during the Flood or shortly thereafter.

The Evolution of Evolutionary Theory

Using the fossil record and phylogenetic trees has not given adequate support to evolutionary beliefs. Evolutionists have thus resorted to trying to figure out how it *could have happened,* rather than showing how it *did happen.* This tactic takes evolution out of the realm of science and puts it into the realm of guesswork.

Lamarck's theory of evolution

In 1801 Jean Baptiste Lamarck, a French biologist, was one of the first to propose a method of biological evolution based on three concepts:
❑ *The theory of need*   In order for an organism to evolve a structure, it must need the structure.
❑ *The theory of use and disuse*   If an organ is used by an organism, the organ will continue to

evolve. If an organism stops using an organ, the organ will degenerate and disappear.
❑ *The theory of inheritance of acquired characteristics*   If an organism acquires a characteristic, it can pass this characteristic on to its offspring.

The most common example of Lamarck's theory is the proposed evolution of the giraffe. Supposedly, the giraffe's ancestors were deerlike animals on the African plain. A long drought forced these early giraffes to stretch their necks to reach higher tree leaves (theory of need). Their necks became longer with stretching (theory of use). Adults with slightly longer necks produced offspring with slightly longer necks (theory of inheritance of acquired characteristics). After many generations, the giraffe's long neck developed.

7C-1 *Jean Baptiste Lamarck and his theory of evolution, illustrated by the giraffe*

In accord with Lamarck's assumptions, however, the story should not have stopped. Most giraffes do not need to stretch their necks for food anymore. In fact, their long necks are actually an obstacle for drinking. If anything, giraffes' necks should now be getting shorter.

Analysis of Lamarck's theory

Most evolutionists today agree that the theory of need is not an actual factor in the evolutionary process. All organisms need structures (most humans could use radar, better hearing, third hands, or eyes in the back of their heads), but the DNA which determines what structures an organism has is not affected by need.

Modern scientists have also disproved the inheritance of acquired characteristics. You inherited genes from your parents, who inherited their genes from their parents, and so on. Although a parent may have developed a certain characteristic in himself, his child will not inherit it. If your father had his arm amputated before you were

Lamarck's Theory and Blind Cave Fish

Evolutionists often explain the blind cave fish, found throughout the world, by the theory of use and disuse. Supposedly some fish were trapped in a cave. After many generations of total darkness, their eyes degenerated.

Scientific evidence indicates that breeding fish in darkness, even for many generations, does not affect their genes. An individual fish may become blind from not using its eyes, just as a person who lies in bed for months may be temporarily or permanently unable to walk. But the children of such a person inherit genes to permit walking. The same is true of a fish that loses its vision: its offspring are unaffected.

How do Christians account for these fish with sightless eyes? Some say the blind cave fish was created that way. Would God create a useless eye? He may have. It is more logical, however, to say that the blind cave fish are merely a pure (homozygous) strain of blind fish.

Blind organisms are known to be hatched or born. Normally these organisms do not survive. Blind fish entering a cave, however, would find themselves in an environment without competition and could survive to set up a breeding population of blind fish. This model for the beginning of blind cave fish is more scientifically acceptable then an explanation based on Lamarck's theories. Because it does not support evolution, evolutionists often overlook this simpler model.

born would you then be born without an arm? No, your father's genetic information is for two arms.

You may inherit the genetic potential to develop a characteristic that your parents developed, but you do not inherit the actual characteristic. For example, even if a boy's father had lifted weights for years and developed a strong, muscular body, the boy does not inherit his father's build. The son may have inherited the genes to *permit* him to develop such muscles, but he will have to exercise to build his body. The same is true of musical and artistic abilities and similar characteristics.

Some people believe, however, that since God removed a rib from Adam to form Eve, all men now have one less rib than women. This belief accords with Lamarck's theory of inheritance of acquired characteristics. God's forming of woman left Adam with one less rib; however, as far as we can tell, it did not affect his genetic make-up and therefore did not affect the rib count of Adam and Eve's children. Today all normal men and women have 24 ribs.

The theory of use and disuse is unacceptable based on modern genetics. Genes can be turned off and on, but under normal circumstances use or disuse does not alter or destroy them for the next generation. Occasionally, however, an evolutionist will cite this theory to explain some characteristic in an organism.

Review Questions 7C-1

1. What is the basic concept used to justify the building of phylogenetic trees? What are some objections to the building of phylogenetic trees?
2. What are some objections to the evolution of the horse proposed by evolutionists?
3. List the three basic tenets of Lamarck's theory of evolution and describe each.
4. List several objections to Lamarck's theory of evolution.

Darwin's theory of evolution

Although Charles Darwin had always been interested in natural phenomena, he failed in his medical studies at the University of Edinburgh. He then reluctantly trained to be a minister in the Church of England. Later Darwin signed up to be an unpaid naturalist on the HMS *Beagle*. The trip, which lasted 5 yr., took Darwin to South America and then to the Galápagos (guh LAH puh gus) Islands off the west coast of Ecuador.

The Galápagos Islands are the result of volcanic activity and have a varied set of habitats. Some of them are very desertlike and even have cactus "forests." Other areas have humid forests.

7C-2 *Charles Darwin made observations in the Galápagos Islands.*

7C-3 *The finches Darwin observed on the Galápagos Islands* (left) *may have been the result of natural selection. But it is no more an example of evolution than are the varieties of pigeons obtained by selective breeding* (right). *No new characteristics have been formed; only "puddles of the gene pool" have been isolated.*

Probably the best-known animal from the area is the giant land tortoise, which can weigh over 500 lb. and live over 100 yr. Darwin recorded riding one of these turtles at "360 yards per hour."

A group of birds Darwin observed reminded him of the finches he had seen in England and other parts of the world. Normally finches are seed-eaters. Some of the finches on the Galápagos Islands did eat seeds, but others fed on the fleshy parts of cacti. One group even used the spine of a cactus held in their beaks to obtain insects from under the surface of the cacti.

Darwin believed that all these various types of finches were descendants of a few finches which had migrated from South America, probably during a storm, and then had evolved to fit the various conditions they found in their new homes. Darwin used these observations to support his **theory of natural selection** and published it in 1859 in his book *The Origin of Species by Means of Natural Selection.*

Long before Darwin began his observations, scientists had recognized variations in organisms. Plant and animal breeders, for example, had practiced controlled breeding to obtain desired strains of existing variations. Literally dozens of varieties of pigeons, for example, have been bred from the wild rock pigeon. **Artificial selection** is man's

choosing individual organisms to breed in order to obtain offspring with certain characteristics. Darwin proposed that the finches he observed, as well as other groups of organisms, had experienced the same type of breeding without man's help. Darwin's theory of **natural selection** is a major tenet of evolutionary theory.

An often-repeated modern example of natural selection involves the peppered moth and a change in its environment. About 100 yr. ago collections of the peppered moth made near London contained about 99% light-colored moths and 1% dark moths. At that time the trees around London were covered with a light-colored lichen. Light-colored moths resting on these trees were difficult to see and were therefore not eaten as

7C-4 *The change in populations of peppered moths in response to the industrial revolution is often cited as a proof of Darwin's theory of evolution. But is it?*

often by birds. Dark-colored moths, on the other hand, were easy prey.

The Industrial Revolution in England, however, so polluted the air that the lichen on the trees near London died, leaving the darker-colored bark exposed. The darker moths were therefore hidden, and the lighter moths were now exposed. In time, collections of the peppered moth began to show larger percentages of dark moths. At one time nearly 99% were dark-colored. Pollution controls in England, however, have permitted the lichen to grow again, and as expected, more recent collections of peppered moths show larger percentages of light-colored moths.

The Effects of Darwin's Theories

Darwin's support of the inheritance of acquired characteristics and improvement through struggle was just what many of the people of his day wanted. In fact, a contemporary of Darwin, Karl Marx, was so in favor of these evolutionary concepts that he wanted to dedicate his communistic work, *Das Kapital,* to Darwin. Darwin's theories are compatible with communism, which teaches that through collective effort man can improve his existence. Because it supported communistic philosophy, Lamarck's concept of the inheritance of acquired characteristics was until recently officially supported by the Russian government.

Darwin's theories have been used to support **environmental determinism,** the concept that the environment determines what an individual is. The concept blames the world around a person for the sin he commits. According to environmental determinism, a drunkard is not a *sinner* because he drinks but a *victim* of his environment; his environment drove him to drink.

The Christian view of man–that man was created perfect but is now a wicked sinner who is responsible for his sin–is by comparison unappealing. The Bible places the blame for sin on the individual. It says that man cannot save himself but is in need of the Saviour.

Darwinian evolution promises great things in the future if man *works* at it. Darwinism is, therefore, contrary to God and His Word in that it blames natural causes for man's present state and hopes in natural causes for man's future. In contrast, the Bible blames man for his condition and presents God as man's only hope.

Analysis of Darwin's theory

The peppered moth illustrates evolution no more than do the different types of cows, sheep, chickens, or corn. The peppered moth gene pool contains (and apparently has, since man first noticed them, contained) the genes to produce dark-colored individuals. Dark moths, however, were naturally "selected against" in an area of England. When an environmental change came, the dark moths were favored by the selection process. Nothing *new* was made. The change of frequency of a characteristic in a population is not biological evolution. A more complex organism has not developed. Biological evolution requires *new* characteristics, not just a regrouping of existing characteristics.

Almost every population of organisms has natural variations. According to Darwin, organisms struggle with one another to find food, shelter, and other necessities of life, because there is always overpopulation. The individuals having the best characteristics for success in the struggle are the ones to survive, reproduce, and pass their characteristics on to the next generation. Darwin called this principle the **survival of the fittest.**

The natural selection of the fittest organisms appears to be quite logical. It has drawbacks, however. First of all, there is not always overpopulation. Some organisms, like predatory birds, have behavior patterns in life cycles which prevent overpopulation. When there is a scarcity of food, these parents permit fewer young to develop so that there will not be overpopulation.

Another drawback to Darwin's "survival of the fittest" is that in nature, it is not always the fittest which reproduce. For example, an animal that can run fast and thereby escape predators may be considered the fittest. If, however, the sets of genes that cause its running ability also cut down on its reproductive ability, the "fittest" may survive, but it may not reproduce.

Consider what would happen if speed were genetically attached to lower intelligence, poor digestion, susceptibility to disease, or other inheritable disorders. Although the organism has particular genes enabling it to survive certain environmental conditions, it may have other undesirable genes. In other words, the *best* all-around organisms are not always the ones to survive, nor are they always the ones to reproduce. Evolutionists, of course, define ''fittest'' as those that survive regardless of their qualifications and thus would not recognize this argument.

Survival of the fittest is not a method of developing new characteristics. It works by simply selecting for or against characteristics that already exist. A *method of variation,* a way to develop new characteristics, is essential to a theory of biological evolution. Another part of Darwin's theory attempted to explain how variations occur. Darwin believed that each organ of the body produces *pangenes,* which travel through the blood to the reproductive organs to be given to the offspring. These pangenes, Darwin thought, are affected by the organ where they originate and therefore result in the inheritance of acquired characteristics. Darwin borrowed this concept from Lamarck but claimed it as his own.

Today scientists consider the inheritance of acquired characteristics by pangenes to be an unacceptable theory. When introduced, however, Darwin's pangenes sounded interesting and scientific. The abundant examples of natural selection he gave in his works were accepted as adequate proof of pangenes. Examples of natural selection, however, have little to do with proving the inheritance of acquired characteristics through pangenes.

Review Questions 7C-2

1. Describe Darwin's theory of natural selection (survival of the fittest). What are some objections to this theory?
2. What mechanism did Darwin propose to supply variations for evolution? What are some objections to this mechanism?
3. Why is Darwinian evolution so compatible with environmental determinism?

Modern Evolutionary Theory

In the early 1900s a Dutch botanist, Hugo deVries, made some observations in his garden. He noticed various sudden changes, which he called *mutations,* in the offspring of an evening primrose, an American plant. In his book *Species and Varieties, Their Origin by Mutation,* deVries suggested that these sudden inheritable characteristics were the means of obtaining variations which could result in evolution. The characteristics which deVries observed, it was later learned, were nothing more than the sorting of characteristics already existing in evening primroses.

The concept that mutation supplies the variations and that natural selection decides which variations will survive and breed is called **Neo-Darwinism** or the **mutation-selection theory** and is accepted by most evolutionists today.

According to the mutation-selection theory, giraffes did not evolve because of a *need* to eat higher tree leaves. Some early short-necked giraffes just happened to have offspring with mutations which caused them to have longer necks. At the same time the long-neck mutations were happening, a drought began. The scarcity of food favored those giraffes with the longer necks, which could reach leaves on higher branches. They thus survived to breed and thereby passed on their long-necked genes, while the short-

7C-5 *Hugo deVries and the evening primrose, in which he first observed his supposed evolution by mutation*

necked giraffes were unfit and therefore died without breeding.

Woe be unto the adolescent giraffe, not considered by the evolutionist: it was too old for mother's milk but not yet tall enough to reach the treetop-eating advantage of its inherited long-necked genes. The natural selection caused by the drought could easily be its premature undoing and eliminate the evolving species.

Mutations and evolution

For evolution to occur, new genes must form and enter the gene pool. A gene mutation is the only known method that could form new genes in nature. Gene mutations, however, are random. Although scientists can increase the rate of mutations, they cannot direct which genes will mutate.

Some scientists estimate that genes mutate once in ten million cell divisions. In a large population (say a billion individuals) the possibility of having a number of mutant genes is rather high. The necessity that these mutations be in the reproductive cells (germ mutations) and that they produce fertile offspring, however, limits the possibility of many mutations affecting the gene pool. The problem of the mutation-selection theory is not that mutations cannot occur. The problem is the accumulation of millions of related "good mutations" in one line of organisms. A "good mutation" is one that leads to the development of a workable new gene—if such a thing is even possible.

The odds of flipping two coins and having both of them land heads up is the product of multiplying the odds of getting heads up with one coin by the odds of getting heads up with the other coin. Assume that, when flipped, a coin lands heads up 1/2 of the time. If you flip two coins at the same time, the odds of getting heads up on both coins is 1/2 times 1/2, or 1/4. In fact, the more times the two coins are flipped, the more likely both coins will show heads 1/4 of the time.

If the odds of a mutation happening are 1 in 10 million cell divisions, the odds of 2 mutations happening to 1 gene are 1 in 100 trillion cell divisions. The question, then, is this: How many mutations are necessary for evolution? To take an existing gene and make it into another gene may

FACETS OF BIOLOGY

7C–1

Anthropology

Anthropology* (AN thruh PAHL uh jee) is the study of the origin and of the physical, social, and cultural history of man. Evolutionists for over 100 yr. have vainly searched for the "missing link" that would tie man to his animal ancestors.

Many times man's history has been "traced" from before the monkey to the present. Rarely do two evolutionists ever agree on this history which is often based not on concrete evidence but on the evolutionist's wishes.

"Human" missing links fall into four categories:

❑ **Human** Bones or complete skeletons that are like humans living today.
❑ **Animal** Bones or complete skeletons that are like extinct or living animals (usually monkeys or apes).
❑ **Insufficient data** Bone fragments so small that valid conclusions cannot be drawn from them. Sometimes a few bone fragments or a tooth are found, and with plaster and imagination, a manlike creature is created. Many supposed "fossil men" should be ignored because there is insufficient data to support their existence.

❑ **Hoax** Bones that have been tampered with. Occasionally a person wanting recognition as the finder of a fossil man or a person playing a joke has created "human fossils."

On pages 200-202 is a line-up of some of the better-known "fossil men." They are arranged from most apelike to those for which there is insufficient data or are hoaxes to those which are assumed to be from extinct tribes or people as human as any person alive today.

Review questions on page 207.

anthropology: anthropo-
(Gk. ANTHROPOS, man) + -logy (the study of)

Rats to Bats—Mutations and Missing Links

For a moment let us ignore the gross statistical improbability of evolution and look at a hypothetical example (but, according to evolutionists, a true example) of evolution. Most evolutionists agree that the bat evolved from the rat (or a ratlike organism). Since rat and bat bodies are quite similar, many rat genes would not need to mutate in order to form a bat. But, of course, a lot of them would. But what about halfway organisms, the ones with becoming-bat mutations, which cause the organism to be neither rat nor bat? We shall call these *missing links* "brats."

Assume that a mutation occurs which causes a rat to have webbed toes. This is the first brat. This web-toed mutation needs to spread through many generations into a population of thousands, or even millions, of brats before another favorable rat-to-bat mutation can be expected. When it does come (probably many years later), it causes web-toed brats to develop front toes twice their usual length, making the second brat. Again, a sizable population must be developed to be ready for the next mutation.

In time, however, we will have brats with large webbed feet suitable neither for running nor for flying. Where do these brats live? How do they move? What do they eat? How do they protect themselves from predators? A large population of these organisms is necessary for the next favorable mutation to have a chance to occur. If evolution is true, these brats must have existed. But how? Natural selection is against the halfway brat's surviving long enough to become the next level of brat. Besides wings, these brats must also be evolving other bat characteristics, some of which (like a radarlike device for flying in the dark) are very complicated.

Evolutionists say that somehow, somewhere, conditions were just right for all the levels of brat to exist at just the right time. When asked what these conditions were, evolutionists respond that they do not know. There are no known conditions (except in tended cages) where such organisms would be favored. But evolutionists claim how fortunate it is that impossible conditions did exist for vast amounts of time somewhere in the past. To prove that these conditions existed, they point out that they were necessary for the bat to develop.

Australopithecus ("southern apes")

This organism supposedly lived 1,750,000-500,000 yr. ago and had a brain size of modern apes and monkeys (435-635 cc).

Lucy

Bones of a 3- to 3.5-foot-tall female organism with an unusual V-shaped jaw and long arms were found in Africa in the mid-1970s. This was probably an ape or monkey that walked on its hind feet. Some evolutionists believe Lucy was not a human ancestor, but rather an extinct organism.

Homo habilis

Known as the "handy man," this relic was found in Africa, but additional evidence is very fragmentary. It is possibly a female or young gorilla. It was called "handy man" because an object thought to have been a tool was found near some skeleton fragments.

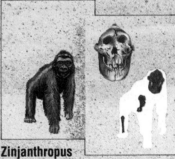

Zinjanthropus

The first one of these was found in Africa in the late 1950s. The skull is exceptionally similar to the skull of a modern great ape. Other later finds are very similar. Evolutionists today admit that this was not a human ancestor but was actually an ape.

200

7C-6 The possibility of an organism's evolving by mutation has been compared to taking all the parts of a skyscraper up one mile, dropping them, and having the building assemble itself on the way down.

require hundreds of gene mutations. Surely the number of mutations necessary to go from one type of organism to another must be in the hundreds of thousands, millions, or billions. Julian Huxley, a famous evolutionist, admitted:

> One with three million noughts [zeros] after it is the measure of the unlikeliness of a horse–the odds against it happening at all. No one would bet on anything so improbable happening; and yet it *has* happened.

Evolutionists, seeing billions of years in the earth's history, have been able to say, "In *that*

length of time *anything* could have happened." Yet evidence has shown that with billions of years, biological evolution could not occur.

Some people have compared the possibility of biological evolution happening to the possibility of a monkey at a typewriter randomly hitting keys and, in time, typing out the complete works of Shakespeare. According to evolutionary thought, if we give the monkey enough time, he just might be able to do it. Recently a man used a computer to determine how long it would take 1 trillion monkeys at 1 trillion typewriters, randomly typing 10 keys per second to type "To be or not to be: that is the question." His answer was that it

Homo erectus ("erect man")
This organism supposedly lived 500,000-300,000 yr. ago with a brain size of 700-1,100 cc (slightly smaller than modern man).

Java man
Bone fragments of a skull top, some teeth, and a thigh bone were found scattered over a 15-20 m stretch of a river bank. Based on what has been found, Java man could be anything.

Peking man
Plaster casts are all that remain of these lost bone fragments. There is disagreement regarding their authenticity. This is a possible hoax; skeletons of modern man and animals were in the same area.

Nebraska man
A tooth found in Nebraska received recognition as a fossil man until another group of scientists found more of the skeleton. The tooth came from an extinct pig.

Gigantopithecus
Teeth purchased through apothecary shops in the Orient were mixed with a great deal of plaster of Paris and lots of imagination and became an 8-ft. man. More teeth were "found," but that is all that exists of this race.

Piltdown man
As a prank, the jawbone of a chimpanzee was filed down, treated with chemicals, and then planted in an area where scientists were going to dig. From 1912-1953 the Piltdown man was an accepted "fossil man."

will take more than a trillion times the evolutionists' estimated age of the universe to get this one Shakespearian line from the monkeys.

The possibility of evolution has also been compared to the possibility of a printed, bound dictionary resulting from an explosion in a print shop. Is such really possible? Yes, but would it ever happen? Even if the calamity happened every minute for 4 1/2 billion years, it is statistically impossible for a dictionary to have formed under such circumstances. The same is true of evolution by mutations.

The harmful nature of mutations

A mutation must alter an existing gene. Since gene mutations are random, happening in any gene, the vast majority of mutations are harmful. They often result in deformity because they change the gene for a needed characteristic. A *random* change in a highly organized system (and life's genetic code is probably the single most highly organized system known) will be a change toward disorder.

You could compare a mutation to randomly selecting one letter in one word on this page and changing it to a letter or puncuation mark that was also randomly selected. The chances of introducing a spelling or grammatical error are very high. Such an error would be considered harmful to the meaning of this page. The more random letter changes you make, the higher the probability of errors. Soon the page would contain many meaningless letter groups, and the meaning of this page would be lost.

Making even one random letter change per second it would take trillions of years before you could expect to have a page with no spelling errors on it, and it would be many times that long before you could expect to have a page that was error-free and made sense.

Those who believe in evolution by mutation are, in essence, contending that books can be rewritten to form other books by random letter replacements. New books are written by authors who carefully select letters to make words that have meaning when put together, not by randomly substituting letters in other books. The genetic material found in living things was designed by God, not by random substitution of nucleotides in the DNA of other living things.

Homo sapiens ("wise man") The genus species of modern man contains several groups which are sometimes referred to as "fossil man."

Rhodesian man

These bone fragments are from a man about 5 ft. 10 in. tall. The apelike skull has some of the characteristics found only in humans. Some scientists believe that the skull does not belong with the other bones. Others suggest this individual had a hormonal disorder which even today causes people to have skulls with similar characteristics.

Neanderthal man

Many complete skeletons show that this group was essentially like modern man. Evolutionists claim that the Neanderthal people lived 75,000-30,000 yr. ago. Some people claim that most Neanderthal characteristics fit the Eskimo and the American Indian.

Cro-Magnon man

Many complete Cro-Magnon skeletons show that these people were essentially like modern man. They had wide cheek bones, deep-set eyes, and a square jaw, but would not be considered unusual if seen in a business suit today. Cro-Magnon men painted in caves, produced clay objects, and possibly worked in metal.

FACETS OF BIOLOGY

7C-2

Arguments That Have Been Used to Support Evolutionary Theory

In times past some evolutionists have used certain "scientific observations" to "prove" evolution. For a long time these arguments held significant sway, especially among nonscientists who were deceived by the words and scientific sound of the arguments. Additional observations and less biased conclusions deflate these impressive arguments.

Ontogeny recapitulates phylogeny

"Ontogeny* (ahn TAHJ uh nee) recapitulates phylogeny (fye LAHJ uh nee)," an impressive-sounding phrase, was at one time called the "biological law." It basically means that the development of an organism, its embryology (ontogeny), replays (recapitulates) its evolutionary ancestry (phylogeny).

In essence the **theory of recapitulation*** (REE kuh PICH uh LAY shun), as it is now called, says that when your zygote was formed, you were going through the single-celled organism stage of evolutionary development again. When the zygote divided a few times, you were recapitulating the colonial organism stage of your evolutionary past. Later you became a fish, a reptile, a mammal, and finally a human, at which point you were born.

When a human zygote is formed, however, it has human genes, not monkey, reptile, fish, or ameba genes. A single human cell is a human cell, not an ameba cell. The only way a single cell can exist is to be like a single cell. This superficial likeness, though, does not mean it is related to other single cells. To become a fully developed human, an embryo must pass through various stages which may physically resemble other things.

Human Tails and Gills

Two structures in human embryos which have been listed in some textbooks as examples of recapitulation are the *human tail* and *gill slits*.

❏ *Human tail* Some of the first structures to develop in the human embryo are the parts of the nervous system. With the end of the spinal cord extending beyond where arm and leg buds are forming, it does appear as if the human embryo has a tail. In time past scientists believed that the tail disappeared, and that this supported the theory of recapitulation. Careful observations, however, reveal that as growth continues, the body catches up to the growth of the spinal cord. This development, not a disappearance of the "tail," changes the embryo's shape.

❏ *Gill slits* Fish and some other aquatic organisms have gill slits, which permit water to pass over the gills so that the organism can exchange oxygen and carbon dioxide between its blood and the water. Several folds develop alongside the human embryo's neck, and for a brief period the embryo appears to have slits between these folds. Actually there are no openings at these points, and there are no respiratory mechanisms (gills) inside them. These structures are not slits but folds and have nothing to do with gills. They are called gill slits only to support the evolutionary theory of recapitulation. In humans the folds grow together to become parts of the upper jaw, the lower jaw, and the upper chest.

6 weeks

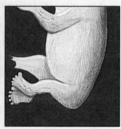
9 weeks

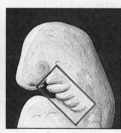
6 weeks

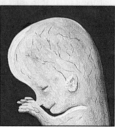
9 weeks

---

ontogeny: onto- (Gk. ONTO, existing or being) + -geny, -gene, or genetic (GENEIA, birth)

recapitulation: re- (L. RE-, back or again) + -capitula- (CAPITULARE, to put under headings)

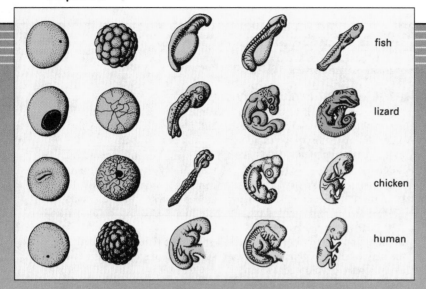

fish

lizard

chicken

human

The resemblance, however, proves nothing.

The theory of recapitulation has fallen from favor because evolutionists have had to admit that it is false. Occasionally, however, comparisons are still made between developing organisms. These comparisons prove only that developing embryos resemble one another; evolutionary relationships are not demonstrated by such comparisons.

Vestigial structures

If evolution by mutation were true, we would expect to find **vestigial*** (veh STIJ ee uhl) **structures** in evolving organisms. A vestigial structure *(vestigial organ)* is one which no longer has a function. These are organs that supposedly were useful to ancestors but are now mutating away.

At one time the list of human vestigial structures had over 180 entries. Gradually scientists dis-

covered that these structures do have functions. Indeed man cannot live without some of these structures once thought vestigial. Man can survive without others but functions best if he has them.

At present there are no structures in the human body that are believed to be vestigial. However, we do not know the function of many structures in plants and animals. It is safe to assume, though, that with further study scientists will discover that there are functions for these supposedly vestigial structures. Because of the intricate design of the creation, man can recognize that God is not a wasteful Creator.

Homologous structures

In science classes students can dissect certain animals to learn about human anatomy. Some animals have many structures in common with humans. Those organs that are similar in structure and func-

Human Structures Once Considered Vestigial

Tonsils The tonsils are part of the body's defense against diseases. Occasionally the tonsils become overly infected (just as any part of the body can) and need to be removed. A good set of tonsils, however, is advantageous.

Coccyx (tail bone) The coccyx, a set of small, fused segments of backbone at the base of the spine, was once thought to be a vestigial tail. This tiny bone serves as a place of attachment for leg and lower back muscles.

Pituitary gland This gland was once thought to be either a degenerating or developing third eye because it is located under the brain, between where the two optic nerves leave the brain and go to the eye. The pituitary gland, how-

ever, produces many hormones that carefully regulate the body's metabolism. Without these hormones, a person would die.

Appendix This organ often becomes infected and must be removed. A person can function normally without it. Scientists now believe that the human appendix does function in digestion and in the body's defense against infection.

Thymus gland A mass of tissue in a child's chest that atrophies (goes away) as the person matures. The thymus gland is now known to produce antibodies and various cells involved with immunity to infectious diseases. Without it a child needs special medical attention to grow to adulthood.

vestigial: (L. VESTIGIUM, footprint)

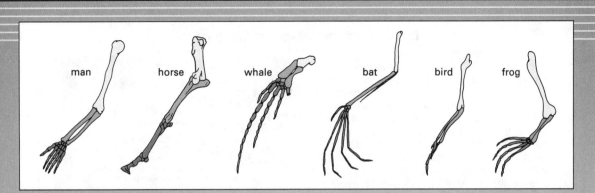

man   horse   whale   bat   bird   frog

The homologous bones in the appendages of man and some animals tells little about how these organisms came into existence.

tion between two different organisms are called **homologous structures.**

Evolutionists assumed that if there were many homologous structures found in two organisms, they must be related by a common ancestor. Since a bird's wing and a whale's flipper have a similar number of bones and muscles which are used in movement, somewhere in their evolutionary past the bird and whale must be related. The observation of bones and muscles may be accurate, but the conclusion is based on bias. Seeing wheels on a car and on a roller skate would not cause one to think they came from the same factory.

The creation shows design. The whale's flipper works as well at moving the whale as the wing does at moving the bird. Some movements these appendages make are similar, some are not. The design is similar in relation to those movements that are similar and different in relation to those movements that are different.

Review questions on page 207.

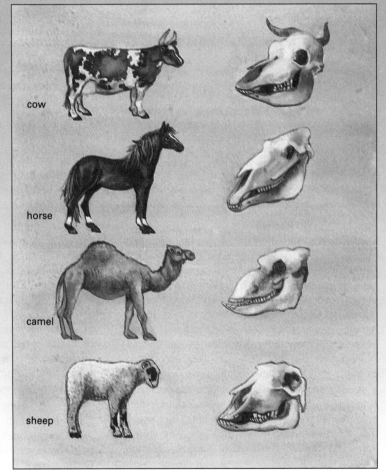

cow

horse

camel

sheep

The teeth of these animals are used for cutting and grinding. Similarity, however, does not imply a common ancestor.

Observed Mutations–Expected Mutations

If evolution were to take place today, it would most likely be in an organism that has had an increased mutation rate and therefore opportunity to evolve by mutations. The fruit fly has been exposed to mutation-inducing chemicals and radiations for many years. Thousands of different mutant fruit flies have been produced. Few of these mutations, *if any*, could even possibly be considered helpful to the fruit fly. Most nonlethal mutations induced in fruit flies produce characteristics like curly wings, deformed eyes, or missing parts, which would quickly be eliminated by selection in nature.

A fruit fly can carry only a certain number of mutations. If evolution were true, organisms would have to be able to carry thousands of mutations which did not benefit the organism. The number of mutations an organism (or sometimes a gene pool) has is often referred to as its **genetic load.** Too much of a genetic load kills the organism. Since mutations are usually recessive to the allele from which they come, a light genetic load is counterbalanced in heterozygous individuals by normal alleles. If, however, the genetic load is too heavy, some homozygous individuals for the mutation develop. For this reason close inbreeding often produces an inferior stock

THE EVOLUTIONARY THEORY OF MUTATIONS HITS A SNAG WITH THIS PENETRATING QUESTION...

of organisms. Such organisms produce few offspring, many of which are deformed.

One might think that since evolutionists believe that mutations are the means whereby evolution takes place, they would encourage them to occur. The exact opposite is true. If a substance is shown to increase the mutation rate, scientists quickly speak against it. For example, many scientists believe that decreasing the ozone layer in our atmosphere would permit more of the sun's mutation-inducing radiation to come to earth. But scientists predict that diminishing the ozone layer would produce not the evolution of man into a super race, but rather thousands of new cases of cancer and other dire consequences.

Punctuated equilibrium

For years non-evolutionists have pointed out that there is no observable example of evolution happening today. Since Darwin's time, evolutionists have been able to answer that evolution is a long, slow process, and man has just not observed closely nor long enough to see evolution. In the hundred years since Darwin's death, scientists have been looking *very* carefully for an example of evolution. But there is no concrete, observable example of it happening today.

As evolutionists have recognized the problem, some have added a new twist to evolutionary theory: **punctuated equilibrium.** This is the belief that there were periods of time when evolution happened rapidly, followed by periods of time when almost no evolution took place.

In other words, there were times when, for unknown reasons, mutations and natural selection

happened rapidly and organisms evolved. Then, for other unknown reasons, mutation rates and natural selection slowed, and evolution virtually ceased. According to these evolutionists, most organisms are in a non-evolutionary phase, which explains why there are no present examples of evolution. Some evolutionists try to explain missing links by saying that they appeared during a period of rapid evolution and quickly died off. Since they were not around long enough to have made fossils, they are truly missing, and we should not be concerned about finding them.

Because punctuated equilibrium seems to explain some of the arguments against evolution, some evolutionists have adopted it. This new twist, however, does not change the basic scientific arguments against evolution. Even when scientists have tried to make evolution happen in a laboratory by increasing the mutation rate (as they assume must have happened during the evolutionary periods), there has been no observable evolution.

Even with punctuated equilibrium, the statistical improbability of evolution is still great. Although mutations may occur rapidly, the possibility of "good mutations" and their coming together are not increased by punctuated equilibrium. Periodically increasing the rate at which evolution is supposed to have happened does not make evolutionary theory any more scientifically acceptable.

Creation shows design

One of the primary characteristics of the creation we observe is its universal design. Everything works together. A delicate balance exists between the organisms and the environments in which they are found. Substances are carefully recycled, and energy is carefully obtained and transferred in systems so efficient that man's best machines are poor copies. A look at the world we know speaks of an all-knowing, all-powerful Creator, not of the continuing disorder necessary for evolution.

When the scientific evidence is examined carefully, the creationist view is more acceptable than an evolutionary view. This is not surprising. The Bible's Author, after all, is the Creator. His record of life's origin would inevitably be correct. Since the world was designed and is sustained by God, what true science observes about the world reveals it as God's creation.

Biological Terms

phylogenetic tree	environmental determinism	punctuated equilibrium
common ancestor	survival of the fittest	*Facets*
missing link	*Modern Evolutionary Theory*	anthropology
The Evolution of Evolutionary Theory	Neo-Darwinism	theory of recapitulation
artificial selection	(mutation-selection theory)	vestigial structure
natural selection, theory of	genetic load	homologous structure

Review Questions 7C-3

1. Describe the basic difference between Darwinism and Neo-Darwinism.
2. List several reasons that gene mutations could not be the means whereby evolution occurs.
3. In what way does the concept of a genetic load support the creationists' views?
4. Describe punctuated equilibrium. Tell why many evolutionists have adopted the theory. Give a creationist's answer to punctuated equilibrium as an evolutionary explanation.

Facet 7C-1: Anthropology, pages 199-202

1. What are the four categories that all supposed human fossils have fallen into?
2. List several fossil finds that fall into each of the four categories of supposed human fossils.

Facet 7C-2: Arguments That Have Been Used to Support Evolutionary Theory, pages 203-5

1. Give two structures often used to support the theory of recapitulation in humans. What are some objections to the use of these structures to support the theory of recapitulation?
2. Name several human structures that were once considered vestigial. Why are they no longer considered vestigial?
3. Briefly describe the evolutionary argument based on homologous structures. Explain why this argument is not valid.

Thought Questions

1. It has been said, "The world was ready for Darwin." Account for the popularity of the theory of evolution after Darwin.
2. Discuss the statement "Evolution by mutations and natural selection is possible, but improbable."
3. Compile a list entitled "Things Evolutionists Must Ignore to Believe Evolution."

• Classification and naming of organisms • The world of microorga
• Insects and their control • Diversity in the animal kingdom • Dinos

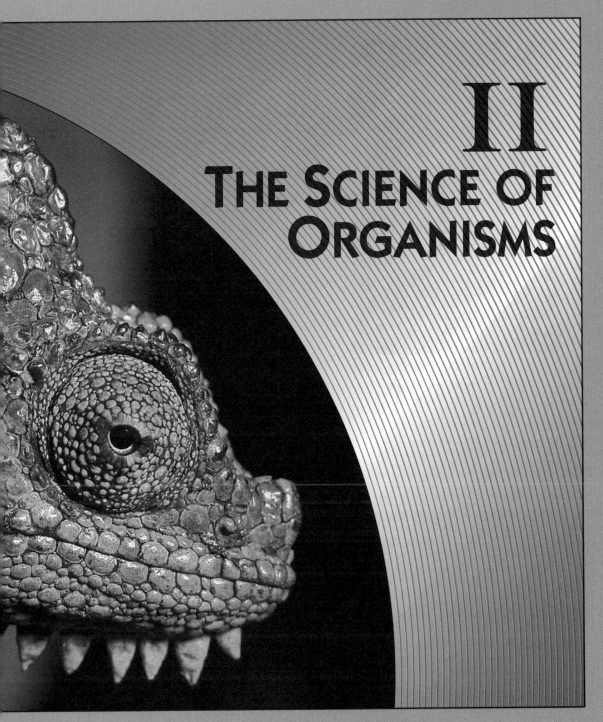

II
THE SCIENCE OF ORGANISMS

...ctious diseases, disorders, and death • Plant anatomy, growth, and reproduction • Animals without backbones
...—and now?

THE CLASSIFICATION OF ORGANISMS

EIGHT

8A-The Necessity of Classifying

People group things together for convenience. All the spices in your mother's kitchen are probably in the same cabinet. At the same time, the pots are in one place, and the dishes are in another. Imagine the confusion you would create if you put spices and cooking utensils into the nearest empty space when you were finished using them.

When you think of musical instruments, you do not only think of them as individual instruments; you also put them into groups, such as woodwinds, strings, percussion, and brass. It is easy to put the violin, viola, cello, and string bass together in the string group. They look alike and are played in essentially the same way. Suppose someone speaks to you about the viola da gamba. When you look puzzled he tells you that the viola da gamba is an antiquated instrument in the string group. You then have a good idea of what type of an instrument it is because you are familiar with other members of the group.

Classifying musical instruments is not easy. The piano, harpsichord, and harp all have strings but are played very differently. Do they belong with the violin? The piano has strings which are struck, not plucked or stroked by a bow. Because of this, some think the piano belongs with the drum, xylophone, triangle, and other percussion instruments. Others think that since the piano has a keyboard, it should be grouped with keyboard instruments. Except for their keyboards, however, the piano and the organ have very little in common. Does the piano actually belong in *all* these groups? Maybe it should be classified by itself.

The same problems apply to **taxonomy*** (tak SAHN uh mee) (or **systematics**), the science of classifying organisms into groups. The taxonomist, however, has over a million different kinds of organisms to group, with 10,000 to 20,000 more being added each year.

Sometimes when a new organism is classified, so little is known about it that it is put in the wrong group. Occasionally, after learning more about a group of organisms, scientists decide to divide the group. At other times they expand the definition of a group to include several groups. The modern system of classification is flexible and useful, although it sometimes appears confusing because of its scope and flexibility.

Today's biological classification system suffers from many of the same problems as classifying the piano. But it does permit similar organisms to be put into groups so that the organisms and information about them can be dealt with conveniently. Were it not for a good classification system, most information about the organisms would be lost in a hodgepodge of facts.

The Classification Hierarchy

The first recorded classification of organisms was attempted by the Greek scientist and philosopher Aristotle. He classified living organisms into one of three plant or three animal groups. Plants were *herbs* if they lacked woody parts; *shrubs* if they had several short, woody stems; or *trees* if they had one large, woody stem. Animals were classified by where they lived: animals living in the water were *fish;* if they could fly, they were *birds;* those that lived on land were *land animals.*

Because Aristotle's six groups were based on appearance, his system is called an **artificial classification system**–one which is based primarily on observable characteristics. In Aristotle's system the lobster and the tuna are both fish, even though the lobster has more physical characteristics in common with insects, which are land animals. Are butterflies land animals or birds? Surely they are more like the flightless insects than they are like robins or hawks.

Whenever physical characteristics are used for classification of the organisms, there will be either useless generalities–"*most* organisms that fly are birds, *most* that swim are fish"–or many exceptions–"birds include all flying organisms *except* butterflies, flies, and bats."

Although Aristotle's artificial classification system left much to be desired, it was used for almost 2,000 yr. The problems in Aristotle's system had long been recognized. In the mid-1700s, when Carolus Linnaeus (lih NEE us), a Swedish

8A-1 *In Aristotle's classification system the Mexican vampire bat (top) and the regal moth (bottom) would be birds since they both fly. The ability to fly is about the only way they are similar.*

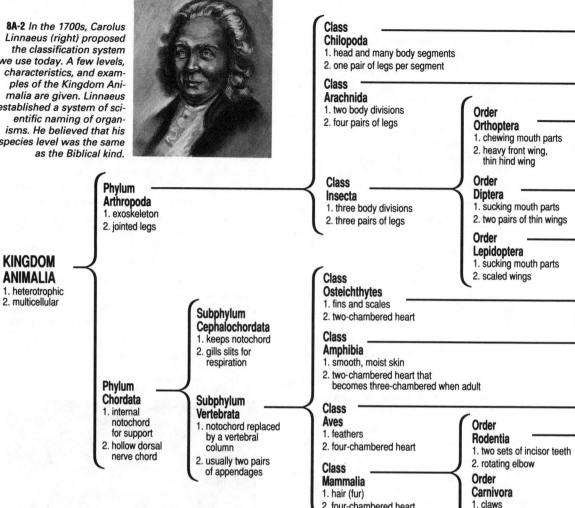

8A-2 *In the 1700s, Carolus Linnaeus (right) proposed the classification system we use today. A few levels, characteristics, and examples of the Kingdom Animalia are given. Linnaeus established a system of scientific naming of organisms. He believed that his species level was the same as the Biblical kind.*

KINGDOM ANIMALIA
1. heterotrophic
2. multicellular

Phylum Arthropoda
1. exoskeleton
2. jointed legs

Class Chilopoda
1. head and many body segments
2. one pair of legs per segment

Class Arachnida
1. two body divisions
2. four pairs of legs

Class Insecta
1. three body divisions
2. three pairs of legs

Order Orthoptera
1. chewing mouth parts
2. heavy front wing, thin hind wing

Order Diptera
1. sucking mouth parts
2. two pairs of thin wings

Order Lepidoptera
1. sucking mouth parts
2. scaled wings

Phylum Chordata
1. internal notochord for support
2. hollow dorsal nerve chord

Subphylum Cephalochordata
1. keeps notochord
2. gills slits for respiration

Subphylum Vertebrata
1. notochord replaced by a vertebral column
2. usually two pairs of appendages

Class Osteichthytes
1. fins and scales
2. two-chambered heart

Class Amphibia
1. smooth, moist skin
2. two-chambered heart that becomes three-chambered when adult

Class Aves
1. feathers
2. four-chambered heart

Class Mammalia
1. hair (fur)
2. four-chambered heart

Order Rodentia
1. two sets of incisor teeth
2. rotating elbow

Order Carnivora
1. claws
2. small incisor teeth, large canine teeth

naturalist, set forth a new classification system in his works *Species Plantarum* and *Systema Naturae,* scholars of the time readily adopted it.

The Linnaean system is also an artificial classification system. Yet because it has more flexibility than previous systems, the Linnaean categories and system of naming organisms are still used today, 200 yr. after their development. Scientists often recommend changes in the system. Some of these changes are accepted by international scientific committees which meet every few years to decide questions of taxonomy.

Today's system of classification

Taxonomists today use a classification hierarchy, an arrangement of graded levels. This system has seven basic levels as follows:

□ **kingdom**
□ **phylum*** (pl., *phyla,* technically called ''division'' in the kingdoms Plantae and Monera)
□ **class**
□ **order**
□ **family**
□ **genus** (pl., *genera*)
□ **species**

---

phylum: (Gk. PHYLON, tribe or race)

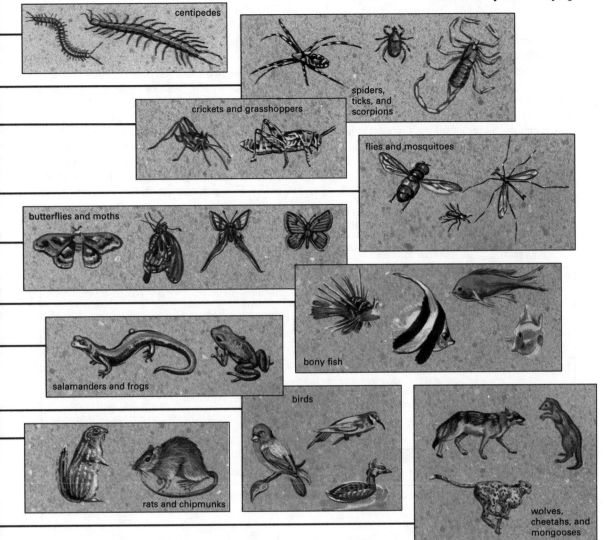

centipedes

spiders, ticks, and scorpions

crickets and grasshoppers

flies and mosquitoes

butterflies and moths

bony fish

salamanders and frogs

birds

rats and chipmunks

wolves, cheetahs, and mongooses

A few of the taxonomic levels in the animal kingdom and a few characteristics for each level are given in chart 8A-2. This table can be used to illustrate the following general rules for using the biological classification hierarchy:

❏ *Each group on one level of the hierarchy may be divided into several groups on the next lower level.* For example, the kingdom Animalia is divided into about twenty phyla (only two are shown in the chart). Each phylum is divided into several classes, the next lowest level; each class is divided into several orders; and so on.

❏ *Each group in the hierarchy has various characteristics that all of the levels under the group possess.* For example, the phylum Arthropoda, according to the chart, contains organisms that have an exoskeleton and jointed legs. Exceptions do exist, however, especially when a classification listing is being simplified. The caption under subphylum Vertebrata reads, ''usually has two pairs of appendages.'' An obvious exception is a snake. Because this is an artificial classification system, terms such as *usually* and *most* appear often.

◻ *Each level of the hierarchy can be divided into smaller units before reaching the next lower level.* For example, in the phylum Chordata there are *subphyla* which are divided into classes. Prefixes such as *sub-* (below), *infra-* (below), and *supra-* (above) are used to name these divisions.

A complete listing of all the taxonomic levels, their characteristics, and all their organisms would be as large as an encyclopedia. A listing of the ones studied in this book and a few others can be found in Appendix B.

The kingdoms

Aristotle's classification system placed his six groups into two main divisions: plants and animals. Linnaeus also used two groups: "kingdom Plantae" and "kingdom Animalia." These two men, however, had no knowledge of microscopic organisms. Nor did they realize the vast difference in some of the groups such as the fungi. They neatly tucked fungi into their systems and, to a great extent, ignored them. Because more types of living things are now known and more

8A-3	The Kingdoms and Their Characteristics				
Kingdom	**Cellular Structure**	**Colonies, Tissues, and Organs**	**Nutrition**	**Reproduction**	**Examples**
Monera	Lack organized nuclei and membrane-bound organelles. Most have cell walls and slime coats.	Often unicellular, but many form simple colonies; no tissues or organs.	Most are heterotrophic, some photosynthetic, or both. Some are chemosynthetic; some carry on only fermentation.	All reproduce asexually.	bacteria, cyanobacteria
Protista	Have organized nuclei and membrane-bound organelles. Many have cell walls.	Unicellular or in colonies (some with specialized structures); no true tissues or organs.	Photosynthetic, heterotrophic, or both.	All reproduce asexually, but many can reproduce sexually by conjugation or gametes.	protozoans, algae (except blue-green)
Fungi	Have organized nuclei and membrane-bound organelles. Many have cell walls.	Unicellular or in colonies (some with specialized structures); no true tissues or organs.	All heterotrophic, digesting food externally and then absorbing the nutrients.	All reproduce asexually, but most forms have sexual reproduction.	mushrooms, molds, yeasts
Plantae	Have organized nuclei and membrane-bound organelles. Have cell walls made of cellulose. Have plastids.	All multicellular with tissues and organs.	Most are photosynthetic with chlorophyll *a*, some are heterotrophic, or both.	All reproduce sexually, but many have asexual forms of reproduction.	trees, ferns, flowers, grains
Animalia	Have organized nuclei and membrane-bound organelles. Lack cell walls and plastids.	All multicellular with tissues and organs.	All are heterotrophic.	All reproduce sexually, but many have asexual forms of reproduction.	worms, sponges, insects, vertebrates

information about organisms is available, it has become necessary to recognize additional groups.

Most scientists agree that two kingdoms are not enough. Yet the international committees responsible for classification have not agreed on the exact number that should be established. The five-kingdom system is increasingly being accepted as the best because its groups are more useful than those of any other system.

It is easy to see the difference between the **kingdom Monera** (moh NEHR uh) and the others. Being *procaryotic,* monerans lack *organized nuclei* and *membrane-bound organelles.* All the other kingdoms have eucaryotic cells. Monerans are all microscopic unicellular or colonial organisms. We have yet to discover thousands of these organisms, and lack much information about how monerans operate.

The algae and protozoans compose the **kingdom Protista*** (proh TIS tuh). Since protists are both autotrophic and heterotrophic, mobile and sessile, unicellular and colonial (sometimes more than one hundred feet long), some scientists place some protists in other kingdoms.

The **kingdom Fungi** (FUN jye) is probably the newest kingdom. Although botanists have long recognized that mushrooms, molds, and other fungi are not really plants, some still try to keep these organisms in the plant kingdom, more for sentimental than biological reasons. Fungi are all heterotrophic. They may be unicellular like the yeasts or colonial like the mushrooms.

Most of the organisms we recognize as plants belong in **kingdom Plantae.** Most plants are autotrophic, but some, like mistletoe, are in part heterotrophic. Plants are usually sessile when adults. The formation of true tissues is found only in the kingdoms Plantae and Animalia. **Kingdom Animalia,** under the five-kingdom system, is not likely to be confused with plants. Animals are all heterotrophic, and most of them have some means of locomotion.

Review Questions 8A-1

1. Give two reasons for having a biological classification system.
2. Why are Artistotle's and Linnaeus's groupings of living things considered artificial classification systems?
3. List from largest to smallest the seven basic levels in the modern classification hierarchy.
4. Describe three general rules for using the modern biological classification system.
5. List the five kingdoms of living things, and give characteristics of each.

Scientific Names

A snake common in the eastern United States is pictured in figure 8A-4. Frequently called the hognosed snake because of its upturned, blunt snout, this nonpoisonous snake rarely bites. When provoked, however, it will spread its neck, open its mouth, and hiss. This imposing bluff has given it a variety of other names, including "common spreading adder," "blowing viper," "spreading viper," and "hissing snake." Still other common names for this snake include "chunkhead," "spread moccasin," and more than sixty others. But it has only one scientific name: *Heterodon platyrhinos.*

8A-4 *Call it what you will, this snake is* Heterodon platyrhinos.

Quite often a common name applies to several different organisms. The name "gopher" may refer to a salamander, a turtle, a frog, one of several snakes, or any of about fifty different types of rodents.

Protista: (L. PROTISTOS, the very first)

FACETS OF BIOLOGY

8A–1

"What is it?" The Identification of Organisms Using Biological Keys

When one sees an organism that he does not recognize, he usually points a finger and asks the question biologists probably hear the most: "What is it?" To most people, being able to identify an organism by name is a worthy goal in itself. When scientists **identify** an organism they find out to which classification groups it belongs including genus, species, and sometimes even variety.

Be careful not to confuse identification with classification. To **classify** an organism a highly trained scientist assigns it to a particular group according to its characteristics. Usually the first person to find and describe the organism classifies and names it.

There are two common methods of identifying organisms. First, you can ask someone. If you can take the organism or a representative piece of it to a qualified person, he can perhaps give you its name.

Another method of identification is to use a **biological key.** A biological key presents to the user a series of questions about the specimen being identified. As the questions are answered, the field of possible organisms narrows more and more until all questions are answered and the organism is identified.

"A Simple Key to the Kingdoms" uses sets of descriptive statements, as do many biological keys. By choosing the statement that describes the organism and then going to the set of statements

indicated in the margin and repeating the process, one can identify the organism.

Follow as "A Simple Key to the Kingdoms" is used to determine in which kingdom the specimen on the right belongs.

❑ **Begin with the first set of statements.** These ask about nuclear membranes and membrane-bound organelles. The picture does not reveal cellular structures. Other characteristics in the first set of statements, however, indicate that large organisms with tissues fall under the second statement. Recognizing a tree as probably being large and having tissues, you de-

An organism to identify

cide that the second statement best describes the organism. In the right-hand margin this choice tells

---

A Simple Key to the Kingdoms

1. Nuclei of cells lack a membrane
   Cells have no membrane-bound organelles
   Organism is unicellular or colonial without tissues.
   Organism is microscopic .... **Monera**
   Nuclei of cells have membranes
   Cells have membrane-bound organelles
   Organism is unicellular, colonial, or having tissues
   Some are microscopic, but others are large **2**

2. Organism is unicellular or colonial **3**
   Organism has true tissues as an adult **5**

3. Organism is autotrophic and either floating or
      sessile .... **Protista**
   Organism is heterotrophic **4**

4. Organism is mobile .... **Protista**
   Organism lacks mobility .... **Fungi**

5. Organism is sessile (occasionally floating) and
      usually photosynthetic .... **Plantae**
   Organism is usually mobile and hetero-
      trophic .... **Animalia**

---

you to go to the statements in number two.

❑ **The statements in number two again ask about tissues.** The second statement is best, and in the margin you are instructed to go to the statements in number five.

❑ **The first statement in number five best describes the organism.** It also indicates in the right-hand margin that the organism being identified is in the kingdom Plantae. There are no additional numbers; you can go no farther using this key.

If you need to identify the phylum, the class, or the genus-species name of an organism, you must use additional keys. Some multi-volumed keys contain all the plants in a region of the United States. Other keys may deal only with pond algae, birds common in the East, or similar limited groups.

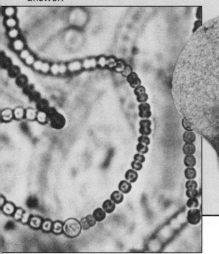

The ball of Nostoc *(right) would be difficult to identify. When seen under a microscope (left), it becomes easier. In what kingdom does* Nostoc *belong? Use the index to check your answer.*

Keys are important to field biologists who must identify exactly what species, and even variety, they have found. Keys also make a hike or camping trip more enjoyable. Using one of the popular *field guides* (which are actually modified keys) to identify plants and animals makes the outdoors more interesting.

Biological keys are not foolproof. If, for example, you scooped up from a pond a ball of *Nostoc* (NAHS TAHK) (see illustration below), it would be almost impossible to identify the kingdom to which this specimen belongs using "A Simple Key to the Kingdoms." By looking at it, you could not tell if it was described by the first or second statements in number one. A high-powered microscope and special stains would be necessary to note the nucleus or membrane-bound organelles. Not being able to see a distinguishing characteristic makes using a key difficult. If a key for the plant kingdom uses only flower color or fruit size as characteristics on which to make one of the choices, and the specimen being identified is not in bloom or has already dropped its fruit, the key is useless.

General keys (such as "A Simple Key to the Kingdoms") often add general statements to the primary statement to help the user if a problem arises. In "A Simple Key to the Kingdoms" the statements in the first set are of this type. Although easily misleading, they are often helpful. Some general keys make false generalizations. To avoid this, the authors of keys often find it necessary to use terms such as "usually," "often," "occasionally," and "some."

Another problem some people have with keys is not knowing what the key is describing. When a person looks at his specimen and decides that "this thingamabob must be what the key is talking about," without knowing, he stands a chance of reaching a wrong answer. One wrong choice will make all subsequent answers wrong.

Not only can the key or the user be inaccurate, but also the specimen can be atypical. If a flower normally having twelve petals is damaged so that it now has only ten, and if the key offers the choice of "twelve petals" or "fewer than twelve petals," then the damaged specimen is misleading. The key and the user of the key may be accurate, but the answer will be wrong. The use of the keys is only as accurate as the key, the user, and the specimen combined.

Review questions on page 219.

8A-5 *No matter what the language, this bird is* Melanerpes erythrocephalus.

The problem of which language to use to name an organism also arises. Is the bird in figure 8A-5 a redheaded woodpecker, *el pájaro carpintero con la cabeza roja, der rotköpfige Holzpicker,* or *le picoteur de bois avec la tête rouge?* If any language is chosen to name an organism, those speaking other languages will have to learn a "foreign term." If all languages are acceptable, then a scientist will have to become a linguist just to be sure he is talking about the same organism his colleagues are discussing.

Binomial nomenclature

To solve these problems, Carolus Linnaeus proposed and used a system of **binomial* nomenclature*** (bye NOH mee uhl ◊ NOH muhn KLAY chur). Binomial means "two-name," and nomenclature means "naming." Our system for naming people is binomial. "Jack Brown" tells us the person belongs to the Brown family and that he is the particular Brown called Jack.

Linnaeus needed to choose a language for his system of naming organisms. Languages that are being used by people as native tongues are constantly changing. English, for example, is changing. New words are added as new things, ideas, or actions are devised. Words also change meaning. For example, the word *charity* today means the giving of money or service. In the 1600s–when the King James Version of the Bible was translated–*charity* simply meant "love."

If Linnaeus had used his own language to name the organisms, his life's work would have become out-of-date as the meanings of the descriptive words he chose changed. Linnaeus therefore used

Latin. No one spoke Latin as a "native tongue," but most scholars knew it and would thus be able to understand the scientific name of the organism. Also, because Latin is a descriptive language, it suited Linnaeus's purpose quite well.

Genus-species names

The scientific name of an organism includes its genus and species names. In other words, the final two categories of the classification hierarchy for an organism are its binomial scientific name, or **genus-species name.** Since the genus-species name of an organism is a foreign term, it is printed in italics. If written or typed, genus-species names are underlined. Only the genus name is capitalized.

Varieties

A species may be a very large group of similar, but different, members. *Canis familiaris,* for example, is the genus-species name of the "familiar canine," the dog. In this particular species, however, there are many different **varieties.** Some of these varieties are purebreds, such as the collie, Irish setter, Chihuahua, Saint Bernard, and dachshund. Others may be crosses, like the pekapoo (a cross between a Pekingese and a poodle); and of course, there are many hybrids in most neighborhoods known as mutts.

As an example, let us look at the genus *Equus* (*equus* means "horse" in Latin). *Equus caballus* is the common horse. This genus and species contains horses ranging in size from the Shetland

---

binomial: bi- (L. BI-, two) + -nom-, nomi-, or nomen- (L. NOMEN, name)

nomenclature: nomen- (name) + (L. CALARE, call)

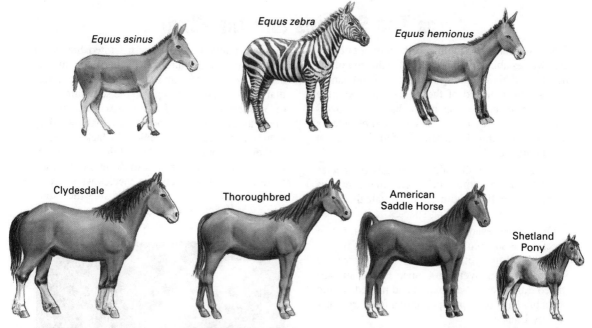

Equus asinus

Equus zebra

Equus hemionus

Clydesdale

Thoroughbred

American
Saddle Horse

Shetland
Pony

Various species within the genus Equus *(top) and varieties within the genus-species* Equus caballus *(bottom). All are drawn to scale.*

pony to the Clydesdale. Other members of the genus are *Equus asinus,* the donkey; *Equus zebra,* the zebra; and *Equus hemionus,* which includes the onager, a wild donkeylike animal native to central Asia.

Genus can be defined as a group of similar organisms. Often the genus name and the common name are the same. For example, *Paramecium caudatum* is the genus-species name of an

organism, but there is a large number of related organisms which share the common name "paramecium." However, when "paramecium" refers to the genus name, the "p" should be capitalized and the word italicized or underlined.

The species name tells which specific organism of a particular genus is being spoken of. Although the concept of a species is very useful, it is almost impossible to define, as the next section discusses.

Biological Terms

taxonomy (systematics)	Fungi, kingdom	genus-species name	classify
The Classification Hierarchy	Plantae, kingdom	varieties	biological key
artificial classification system	Animalia, kingdom	genus	
Monera, kingdom	*Scientific Names*	*Facet*	
Protista, kingdom	binomial nomenclature	identify	

Review Questions 8A-2

1. Give two reasons for having a system of scientific names.
2. What are two reasons for using Latin to name organisms?
3. What is the primary division of a species?

Facet 8A-1: "What is it?" The Identification of Organisms Using Biological Keys, pages 216-17

1. What is the difference between classifying and identifying an organism?
2. Describe a biological key.
3. List several problems that could make using a biological key difficult or inaccurate.

8B-The Species and the Kind

Carolus Linnaeus thought that the number of species was established at creation. By the end of his life, he and his students had described and named almost ten thousand of them. With the possible exception of a few that might have been overlooked or not yet found in some remote places like America and the Orient, he felt that the list was complete.

Today we annually add to the lists of species about the same number of species that Linnaeus found in his entire lifetime. We estimate that there are over one million living species.

One of the reasons that Linnaeus's number of species was so small was that the world of microbiology had not yet been explored. Bacteria, of which there are over 1,500 species and an estimated 3,000 yet to be isolated and named, would probably have been grouped into a few large species by Linnaeus.

The Species

"A group of similar organisms" is probably the only definition of **species** upon which all scientists would agree. This definition, however, is not adequate. All the trees in a forest are "similar" in some ways, but they are not all one species. One problem with defining species is that the term has different meanings in different groups.

For example, a definition that applies to species of trees does not equally apply to species of fish, mammals, protists, or bacteria. Generally speaking, biologists agree that there are two major points of consideration for a definition of species.
❑ Members of a species are structurally similar but do have a degree of variation.
❑ Members of a species can interbreed and produce fertile offspring under natural conditions.
Two significant problems with this concept of species are discussed below.

Problems with the species concept: artificial characteristics

Using physical characteristics to define the limits of a species often causes problems. For example, the tiger salamander, *Ambystoma tigrinum*, lives in some ponds in the western United States. In other ponds immature salamanderlike animals called *axolotls* (AK suh LAH tuhlz) live. A particular type of axolotl was given the scientific name of *Siredon mexicana*. Later it was found that if these axolotls fed on iodine-rich material, they matured into tiger salamanders. A lack of iodine in their environment had caused them not to mature. Their appearance was so different that they were classified as a separate species when really the difference was that the pond in which they grew was deficient in iodine. Scientists no longer use the name *Siredon mexicana*.

8B-1 *The axolotl (top) was given the name* Siredon mexicana *but was later discovered to be an immature tiger salamander (bottom). Now they are both* Ambystoma tigrium. *(This axolotl is an albino.)*

Since an organism's environment can greatly affect its appearance, physical characteristics are only an artificial method of classification, prone to many errors.

Canis familiaris is the genus-species name of the common dog. It includes the toy poodle as well as the Great Dane. Along with variety, though, all dogs have similarities. Dogs interbreed and produce fertile offspring. All dogs have 78 chromosomes. Dogs, then, make a species.

Canis latrans is the coyote. Although coyotes resemble dogs, they are placed in another species of the same genus because they live in particular habitats and have characteristics–coat color, size, and others–which set them apart from most dogs. But coyotes, like dogs have 78 chromosomes. Occasionally, in the wild or in a zoo, a coyote mates with a dog, and a litter of *coydogs* is born. Coydogs are fertile and have characteristics of both parents.

Although the coyote has a certain set of dog characteristics and can interbreed with dogs, it is classified as a separate species because it tends to live by itself in areas where most dogs would not live and because it rarely mates with dogs. Why is the coyote not classified as a particular variety of the dog species, like a terrier or poodle? Maybe it should be. Remember, however, that the classification of organisms was done *by man for convenience*. So far, taxonomists consider it more convenient to ignore the fact that coyotes and dogs are so similar and leave them as two separate species.

Some evolutionists wrongly use the fact that there are varieties designed into creation. By seeing what *has been called* a species mate with another species and produce offspring like both parents, some people conclude that evolution is taking place and that a new species is being formed. If two varieties of dogs were crossed, would the offspring be a new species? No. If a dog and a coyote are crossed, is a new species developing? Some would say yes, because a coydog is a cross between two species and is "new." Remember that *man* classified dogs and coyotes in different species for *convenience*. Remember also that the characteristics of the coydog came from a dog and a coyote. They may be in a new combination, but the characteristics themselves are not new.

Classification by physical appearance or location or any other outward characteristic is artificial. In these cases similarities that cannot be seen but nonetheless exist are often ignored.

Problems with the species concept: interbreeding

The sexual reproduction of a species with other members of the same species has, for quite a while, been considered a method of avoiding artificial classification of organisms on the basis of physical characteristics. If two organisms are capable of sexual reproduction and produce fertile offspring, they should be classified together, no matter what they look like. This idea seems to make sense, but let us examine it closely.

First, there are thousands of organisms (bacteria, and types of protozoans and fungi) that are not known to reproduce sexually at all. Other criteria must be used to classify these organisms.

For a second problem with interbreeding as a criterion for classification, let us look again at *Canis familiaris*. It is physically impossible for a male Saint Bernard to mate with a female Chihuahua. Even if the match were artificially made, at birth the pups would each be about the same size as their mother, which would kill either the mother or the pups long before they were born.

Should this inability to interbreed put the Chihuahuas and Saint Bernards in two separate species? If so, where should the species line be drawn? Chihuahuas can mate with dogs slightly larger than themselves, and these dogs with larger dogs, and finally, several generations and many sizes removed, a Chihuahua offspring may successfully mate with a Saint Bernard. Any line drawn has to be based on *artificial* distinctions.

Another example is *Rana pipiens*, the green, spotted grass frog found in all the eastern United States and in much of Canada. The grass frog that lives in Michigan looks identical to the grass frog that lives in Florida. When these two are mated, however, all the eggs die. Research indicates that one of the unseen differences between the Michigan and the Florida grass frogs involves their rates of development. Michigan grass frogs must develop rapidly because of the shorter summer, whereas Florida grass frogs have longer summers to grow from egg to tadpole to frog.

Scientists now call Michigan frogs and Florida frogs two **ecotypes** (EE koh TYPES). Ecotypes are organisms (usually in the same species) that appear the same but are suited for one environment rather than another and often cannot interbreed.

Michigan grass frogs can mate with Ohio grass frogs, who in turn can mate with Kentucky grass frogs, and so on, all the way down to, and including, Florida grass frogs. This somewhat parallels the Saint Bernard-Chihuahua example. Saint Bernards are a variety of dog well suited for cold climates. The Chihuahua is better suited for much warmer areas. A Saint Bernard in Mexico City or a Chihuahua in a Swiss mountain village would quickly perish were it not carefully tended by man. Thus rarely would a Chihuahua and a Saint Bernard ever be together in the same geographical area. Even if they were, a Chihuahua and a Saint

Bernard would not interbreed because of their sizes.

Though the Florida and Michigan grass frogs have no outward physical differences, the different characteristics are nonetheless there. It is quite probable that there are biochemical characteristics in the Michigan grass frog that, when put with the biochemical characteristics of the Florida grass frog, are lethal. These mismatched characteristics have yet to be discovered.

Evolutionists claim that ecotypes are developing species. Since "species" is a term set up *by man for convenience,* scientists may call Michigan and Florida grass frogs ecotypes or species or anything else that is convenient. Use of certain terms, however, may make it *sound* as if evolution is taking place among grass frogs. It appears that man has discovered a God-designed variation, and some scientists are attempting to use their own terminology to describe that variation in a way that helps to support biological evolution. Language, however, does not prove anything.

God's primary purpose in creating different organisms was to have them perform specific functions in specific ways in specific places, not to make them easily classifiable. Classifying organisms, however, is not wrong just because it is not easy or does not always seem to work. Organisms are classified for convenience of study.

Review Questions 8B-1

1. Give the two commonly accepted parts of the definition of a species.
2. Why are physical characteristics an inadequate basis for grouping members of a species?
3. List two reasons that interbreeding is a difficult basis to use for grouping organisms into species categories.
4. What is an ecotype? What is the difference between an ecotype and a variety?

The Biblical Kind

Scripture does not include a detailed classification system. Occasionally it includes lists of organisms. What God created on which day of the creation week and which organisms were brought into Noah's ark have been suggested as classification systems. These are simply lists, though, and are not meant to be classifications.

The Scriptures state that God created each organism to reproduce "after its kind" (Gen. 1:9-25). It appears that God has established the **Biblical kind** as the natural grouping of organisms and that the ability to reproduce is the criterion established for classification into a Biblical kind.

Carolus Linnaeus, a creationist, thought that he was distinguishing the *kinds* referred to in Genesis as he identified his species. Linnaeus was the first to use the term *species,* which means "kind" in Latin, as a classification unit. But Linnaeus, like modern taxonomists, used various physical characteristics to determine his classifications and therefore had an *artificial* system.

The dog kind

Let us once again consider the species *Canis familiaris.* Linnaeus recognized the possibility of variation and did not put all the varieties of dogs into separate species. The coyote, however, is a separate species according to Linnaeus since it does not naturally interbreed with dogs. Examination, however, shows that the coyote is probably part of the same kind as the dog since dogs and coyotes are capable of interbreeding.

Are there other organisms that should also be placed in the dog kind? What about wolves? It is possible. In order to make a good judgment about which organisms should be placed into the dog kind, extensive breeding experiments would have to be conducted. The failing of a few matings should not significantly affect the conclusions.

Noah's Flood and the Biblical Kind

Many animals and plants which were alive before the Flood are extinct today, it seems. God apparently created a greater variety of organisms than now remains. However, every extinct organism is similar to existing organisms. Dinosaurs were very similar to reptiles that have survived. Trilobites (TRY luh BITES), common fossil forms, are easily classified because they are very similar to organisms alive today. It is possible but not probable that although different groups within a Biblical kind may have become extinct, either naturally or by man's efforts, there are still the same number of kinds existing on the earth.

In any case, the number of animals on the ark could have been far fewer than two of all the land-dwelling and seven of all the clean *species.* God brought *kinds* on the ark. For example, since dogs are unclean, we can assume that there were only two of them on the ark. Possibly several other species similar to the dog are the offspring of the one pair of dogs on the ark.

Trilobites

Remember that Chihuahuas and Saint Bernards do not directly interbreed, but they can "indirectly." The expense, time, and lack of know-how necessary to perform extensive breeding experiments make it probable that we will never know how far the dog kind extends.

Some people claim that Linnaeus unknowingly hurt the cause of creationism. By setting up his species and equating them with Biblical kinds, he implied that his species could not interbreed and that new species would not develop. But species do interbreed (a fact which Linnaeus recognized), and a new set of characteristics can occasionally occur in the offspring of the interbreeding of two species. The hybrid organism may be so different that, according to the currently accepted definition of species, a new species has developed. This type of development has been used to demonstrate biological evolution. The expressing of old genes in new combinations within a Biblical kind, however, is not evolution.

A natural classification system

Today scientists are looking for a more **natural system of classification,** a system based on genetic similarities, not on physical characteristics. Genetic similarities, according to evolutionists, prove common ancestry. In other words, evolutionists are trying to classify organisms according to evolutionary relationships. The experimentation necessary to determine genetic similarities is very costly and time consuming, but occasionally scientists discover a fact that they think helps in establishing the natural classification system. When this new system is all worked out, they expect to have an accurate phylogenetic tree, proving evolution.

At this point we enter speculation, but speculation with Scriptural backing: it would be interesting if scientists distinguished groups of organisms whose members are capable, although possibly indirectly, of interbreeding within the group but not with members of other groups. When this happens, we will *not* have arrived at what the evolutionist was looking for–the path evolution has taken–but we will be closer to realizing what God created–the Biblical kind.

Migration, Adaptation, and the Evolution of Species

It seems logical to assume that following the deluge as the animals moved away from Noah's ark, they formed into loose groups and in time they became distinct groups by natural selection. **Migration,** the moving of organisms from one area to another, can cause a separation of traits to the extent that the groups of organisms could be called two different species. For example, as dogs migrated into semiarid areas, those having long legs, trim bodies, and short hair may have been favored, and the short-legged, heavy-bodied, or long-haired dogs were probably selected against. It appears that in time a population of dogs homozygous for these many traits–the coyotes–developed.

Evolutionists say that this migration and selection is evolution since, according to their definition, a new species has developed. To the contrary, this rearrangement and selection of characteristics is not evolution. A new, more complex organism has not evolved. Rather than new genes being formed, certain genes appear to be eliminated from a small population within a Biblical kind. Such a change is not biological evolution.

To the concept of migration, evolutionists often add adaptation. **Adaptation** is what an organism does when it finds itself in a different environment, either one to which it is not completely suited or one to which it is not accustomed. You would adapt to a cold climate by wearing more clothes or changing your activities.

Assume that dogs migrating into a new area did not find their usual food. These dogs could either continue to migrate, die off, or adapt by eating something else. Suppose mountains or oceans prohibited migration. If there were abundant bird eggs, the dogs might learn to eat them. In other seasons the dogs could possibly adapt by eating insects. Natural selection might favor those dogs that could eat bird eggs and insects most easily. Evolutionists would quickly claim that a new insect-eating dog species had developed and that evolution had taken place.

Such an adaptation to eating eggs and insects, however, did not make any new dog characteristic. Most dogs refuse to eat insects. But if a dog has been forced to eat insects and even prefers them because it has eaten them all its life, evolution has not taken place. An organism can only adapt as far as the organism's genetic makeup will permit. In other words, there are limitations to adaptation. A dog's digestive system, for example, will not permit it to adapt to a diet of grass. An adaptation beyond the natural variations possible in an organism would require mutations. Mutations, however, are random and not based on need.

The eight people on the ark are the ancestors of all people alive today. Yet today everyone does not have the same characteristics nor the same lifestyles. The various races and cultures of people probably developed through migration and adaptations within the limits of variations.

Biological Terms

The Species	*The Biblical Kind*	migration
species	Biblical kind	adaptation
ecotype	natural system of classification	

Review Questions 8B-2

1. What is the primary characteristic which would place an organism into a Biblical kind?
2. List several possible problems with recognizing the Biblical kinds in today's world.
3. How do evolutionists explain biological evolution by migration, selection, and adaptation?
4. Explain how migration, selection, and adaptation might account for various groups of animals coming into existence after the Flood.
5. Why are migrations, selections, and adaptations that establish new groups of organisms not evolution?

Thought Questions

1. Suppose a Christian objects to the modern system of classification, saying that since he does not see a basis for it in Scripture, it is wrong. Prepare an answer for this person.
2. Compare a natural and an artificial system of classification of living things.

THE KINGDOM MONERA AND THE VIRUSES
MICROBIOLOGY PART I

NINE

9A–Bacteria and Similar Organisms

Monera, is in some respects, the largest kingdom. It contains the tiniest known cells; many monerans are visible only with the aid of the higher powers of a light microscope. It is estimated, however, that monerans have a greater combined weight than all the other living things on the earth.

Moneran cells are, on the average, 1,000 times smaller than most human cells. They may be small, but they are numerous. The monerans that live on your skin and in your digestive tract outnumber the cells of your body.

Monerans thrive in places where no other living thing is known to exist. In the atmosphere 6,096 m (20,000 ft.) up, they ride on dust particles. In hot springs at 98° C (208° F) and in melted glacial water, representatives of the kingdom Monera multiply. One gram of common soil contains from 1 to 100 million of them. They exist in every natural water supply, including the water that you drink. Every cubic meter of air contains from 100 to 20,000 of them. Despite the fact that monerans are almost everywhere in astonishing numbers,

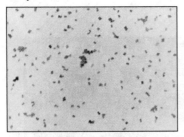  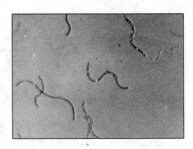

9A-1 *Three different bacteria. Determine the shape and type of each.*

scientists have only recently devised techniques for studying them and have a great deal yet to learn about them.

At one time scientists placed the members of the kingdom Monera in the plant kingdom. Various cellular characteristics, as well as the fact that some of these organisms make their own food by photosynthesis, made this seem logical. However, most biologists are now convinced that monerans should be in a kingdom by themselves. The key characteristic which places organisms in this kingdom is that they are all *procaryotic;* that is, they all lack organized nuclei and membrane-bound organelles. (See Appendix B for a summary of moneran characteristics.)

The Bacteria

When bacteria and similar organisms were first observed it was simple to place them all in one large group. Artificial characteristics were used to place them into subgroups. Today a **microbiologist*** (one who studies microbes) uses various techniques to classify monerans. With the exception of a few groups we will lump all the monerans together and call them bacteria.

When most people think of **bacteria*** (sing., bacterium), they think of germs which cause diseases. Many bacteria are *pathogenic** (disease causing), but most are not. Most bacteria are vitally important to living things, including humans, because of their effects on dead things.

Bacteria (along with fungi) are the primary **decomposer organisms** in soil and water. Decomposer organisms produce enzymes that break down proteins, starches, lipids, and almost every other known organic substance. Without this action by bacteria and fungi, in a few generations all the materials necessary for life would be con-

tained in nondecomposing dead bodies. Think of what our world would be like if dead things were not decomposed, and you will realize that bacteria and fungi are essential to all life.

Bacterial Shapes, Sizes, and Colonies

Generally speaking, bacteria are one of three general shapes.

❑ *Coccus* A spherical bacterium, averaging about 1 μm in diameter, is called a **coccus*** (KAHK us)(pl. cocci). A period (.) could easily have 5,000 cocci bacteria lined up across it.

❑ *Bacillus* A rod-shaped bacterium is called a **bacillus*** (buh SILL us) and averages 1 μm in width and 2-10 μm in length.

❑ *Spirillum* A **spirillum*** (spy RILL um) is a spiral-shaped bacterium that is slightly longer than the bacillus type.

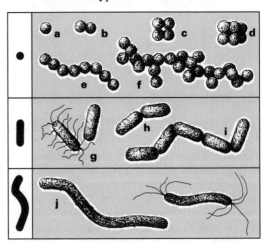

9A-2 *Bacterial shapes and colonies.* **Top,** *coccus* **(a)** *coccus;* **(b)** *diplococcus;* **(c)** *tetrad;* **(d)** *sarcina;* **(e)** *streptococcus; and* **(f)** *staphylococcus.* **Middle,** *bacillus:* **(g)** *bacillus;* **(h)** *diplobacillus; and* **(i)** *streptobacillus.* **Bottom,** *spirillum:* **(j)** *spirillum.*

---

bacteria: (Gk. BAKTRON, rod)

pathogenic: patho- (Gk. PATHOS, emotion or suffering) + -genic (birth)
coccus: (Gk. KOKHOS, berry or pit)

bacillus: (L. BACILLUS, rod)
spirillum: (L. SPIRILLUM, a coil or a twist)

FACETS OF BIOLOGY

9A-1

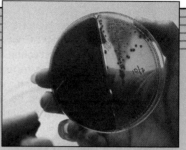

By culturing bacteria on different media, scientists can identify many species.

Uses of Bacteria – Past, Present, and Future

Because bacteria produce only certain chemicals as they break down their nutrients, various bacteria are useful in industry. Bacteria are used when making cheese, yogurt, silage, sauerkraut, and buttermilk. Natural products of bacterial fermentation, such as alcohol, vinegar (acetic acid), and lactic acid, are also useful since they are often the cheapest source for these substances. Other bacteria are useful sources of vitamins (B_{12}, C), amino acids, and most antibiotics.

In the past, most of our uses for bacteria have involved the ability of bacteria to rapidly decompose substances. Today, however, scientists are changing bacteria. Through genetic engineering, bacteria can be made to produce substances that are useless to them, but are useful to humans. Often these bacteria are cultured and then destroyed to obtain the desired substances they produced.

Bacteria are now being used as sources for insulin, human growth hormones, interferons, blood proteins, and other substances. Most of these are produced by human genes that have been placed in bacteria. In the past many of these substances were unavailable except from human sources (donated blood or cadavers). Now a cheap, reliable source for "human" substances is available using genetically engineered bacteria.

Scientists hope to design bacteria that will do profitable things in the environment, not just in the laboratory. Some bacteria, for example, grow on plant leaves and protect them from frost. But these bacteria only grow naturally on certain plants. Scientists are working on ways to get the frost-resis-

tant properties of those bacteria into other bacteria that grow on crop plants. Releasing such genetically engineered organisms in the environment does present some concerns: What will be the effect of this organism on other plants, animals, humans? What will it do when it gets into a stream or lake? Costly and time-consuming research is necessary before anyone can make a wise decision regarding release of genetically engineered organisms into the environment.

Review questions on page 229.

Commercial Uses of Bacteria

Forming cheeses and similar products A starter bacterium added to milk forms lactic acid and causes *curdling* (the separation of milk solids and fluids). The resulting lumps are the *curds* which contain milk proteins, fats, and minerals. The watery substance is *whey*. If most of the whey is drained, the resulting moist curds are *cottage cheese* (and similar types). *Cream cheese* is produced by adding butterfat to curds. Most other cheeses are the result of time, temperature, and the kind of bacteria (or mold) growing in the curd.

Making vinegar Yeasts ferment the sugars in fruit juices into alcohol in an airtight container. Bacteria *(Acetobacter)* then oxidizes the alcohol into acetic acid (vinegar).

Retting flax When the stems of the flax plant are placed in warm water, the soluble materials from the stems form a medium for a bacterium.

The pectin which holds the plant fibers together is fermented by enzymes produced by this bacterium. After about two weeks the stems can be removed and the fibers separated. The fibers can then be processed into linen. This process, used during Bible times, is still used today.

Making sauerkraut In an oxygen-free container a bacterium *(Lactobacillus)* ferments the sugar in shredded cabbage into lactic acid (along with small amounts of alcohol), making sauerkraut.

Tanning leather Certain bacteria are used to remove hair from and to make hides pliable.

Forming silage Silage is a rich food for cattle made of chopped corn stalks, alfalfa, clover, and other plant substances. The plant material is placed in an airtight silo. Soon all the available oxygen is used by plant cells, and an anaerobic bacterium *(Lactobacillus)* then converts the plant sugars into lactic acid, resulting in silage.

Scientific names of bacteria often describe a characteristic of the cells. "Coccus," "bacillus," and "spirillum" are often found in genus-species names. Bacterial cells also form colonies, which are sometimes used in identifying and naming bacteria. Large bacteria can be seen when magnified about 400X. Most bacteria, however, are so tiny that they must be magnified 1,000X.

Structure of a bacterial cell

Bacteria are procaryotic (lacking a true nucleus). The DNA in a bacterium forms a single, circular chromosome. If this circular DNA were stretched out, it would be about 1,000 times as long as the cell itself. Normally this chromosome appears in a non-membrane-bound **nuclear area.**

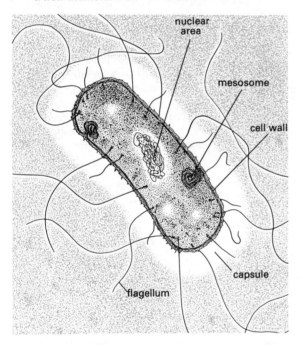

9A-3 *Structure of a typical bacterium*

Although bacteria do not contain membrane-bound organelles, they do contain cellular membranes. **Mesosomes** appear to be twisted indentations of the cell membrane. Mesosomes in different bacterial cells have various enzymes attached to them. Photosynthetic bacteria, for example, usually have some of the enzymes used in bacterial photosynthesis attached to mesosome membranes. Membrane-bound enzymes of cellular respiration are often in the mesosomes.

Ribosomes, the non-membrane-bound organelles associated with protein formation, are abundant in bacterial cytoplasm. Some bacteria contain globules of fats, starches, and proteins.

Bacterial cell walls and capsules

Immediately outside the cell membrane most bacteria have a *cell wall.* Bacterial cell walls lack cellulose and contain several chemicals found only in bacterial cell walls. Bacterial cell walls are rigid, giving each cell its particular shape.

Outside the cell wall bacteria have a **capsule** made of gummy, complex carbohydrates of different types, depending on the bacterial cell. Some capsules are very thin; others may be several times the thickness of the cell. The capsule protects the cell from drying out during temporary dry periods and prevents certain substances from entering the cell. Any substance entering the cell must first pass through the slimy capsule.

The thickness of the bacteria's capsule appears to affect an organism's ability to combat infection by that bacteria. *Streptococcus pneumoniae,* for example, is a bacterium which comes in several strains, some with a thick capsule and some with almost no capsule. When the non-encapsulated strains are injected into laboratory mice, few if any symptoms develop. When an encapsulated strain is injected, the mice develop pneumonia and die. The mouse's body can destroy the non-encapsulated variety but has little effect on the bacteria which have a thick capsule.

Bacterial movement

Many spirilla, bacilli, and a few cocci have *flagella.* A bacterial flagellum is a long threadlike structure usually less than 0.05 μm in diameter but often several times the length of the cell. Bacterial flagella lack the microtubule arrangement of the flagella in eucaryotic cells. Spirilla with flagella usually have clusters of flagella on each end, but bacilli often have flagella scattered over the cell. Most bacteria with flagella are able to direct their movements: they usually proceed either toward or away from some stimulus. Photosynthetic bacteria, for example, swim toward the light source.

Bacterial cells which lack flagella appear to vibrate back and forth as water molecules bump into them. Even bacteria with no known form of movement seem to be able to go toward or away from certain stimuli. All bacteria are small enough to be easily carried along with even the slightest fluid current. It does not take much outside influence to move these small organisms.

Review Questions 9A-1
1. List several characteristics of the kingdom Monera.
2. What is the primary function of bacteria in nature?
3. What are the common cellular shapes and colonies of bacteria?
4. Describe the cellular structures of bacteria.
5. What are two common methods of bacterial movement?

Facet 9A-1: Uses of Bacteria – Past, Present, and Future, page 227
1. What natural properties of bacteria have been used by man in the past?
2. List several ways man has used bacteria in industry.
3. What process now makes bacteria more useful to man?

Bacterial Growth and Reproduction
Under ideal conditions many bacteria are able to grow to full size and divide every 30 min. If these conditions persisted, in about 30 generations (15 hr.) a single bacterial cell would be multiplied to over 1 billion cells. An hour later the initial cell would have become about 4 billion cells. In less than 24 hr. the mass of bacterial cells would weigh over 2,000 tons. In another day there would be billions of tons of bacteria. Within a week the bacteria would weigh more than the earth.

The "clump of bacteria that smothered Chicago," however, is science fiction. Even laboratory cultures of bacteria cannot sustain such a growth rate for long. The bacteria on the outside of a clump may maintain a high metabolism, but those in the center of the mass do not get enough of the materials necessary for growth. Soon the central cells are in a pool of wastes and dead cells. The ideal range of conditions for high metabolism in bacteria is often quite narrow and difficult to maintain for a large quantity of bacteria over an extended period of time.

Reproduction in bacteria
Normally bacteria reproduce by simple cell division. This asexual reproduction does not involve mitosis. After the replication of the bacterial chromosome and the separation of the two daughter chromosomes, an invagination of the plasma membrane forms daughter cells.

Some bacteria can complete cell division in 9 min. Following about 10 min. of growth under ideal conditions, these cells will be full size and ready to divide again. Most bacteria grown in a laboratory can divide about every 30 min., but certain bacteria require 3-4 hr. Some pathogenic bacteria divide only once or twice a day.

During mildly unfavorable conditions, many bacteria decrease activities and wait the return of favorable conditions. This reduced metabolism preserves certain soil bacteria during the higher temperatures of a summer afternoon and the cooler evening temperatures of the spring or fall.

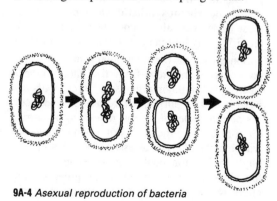

9A-4 *Asexual reproduction of bacteria*

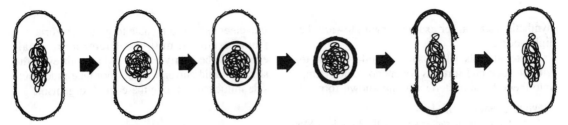

9A-5 *The formation and germination of bacterial endospores*

Some bacillus bacteria and a few other types are capable of forming **endospores*** to survive extended periods of unfavorable conditions. These bacterial endospores differ from the spores of most other organisms in that they are formed within the plasma membrane. Several layers of hard materials form around the nuclear area as an endospore is formed. Within the endospore metabolism is reduced to a low level.

Some endospores can withstand 20 hr. of boiling. Others can withstand freezing, dryness, extreme pressure, and even poisonous gases. When favorable conditions return, the endospore coats (which may be in layers) weaken, bacterial growth resumes, and the cell bursts out of the endospore case. Although the formation of endospores is not a method of reproduction, it is a method of continuing the species of bacteria.

Bacterial nutrition

Of all known groups of living things, bacteria have the widest range of methods for obtaining usable energy and building organic substances. The most complex biosynthesis in bacteria takes place among the *autotrophs*, both the *photosynthetic* and **chemosynthetic** varieties. Some of these bacteria are almost completely independent, requiring only inorganic materials in order to live.

Some bacteria carry on photosynthesis that is considerably different from the photosynthesis carried on by other organisms. *Bacteriochlorophyll* is usually purple, red, or brown. These colors permit bacterial photosynthesis to be carried on in places like the depths of a pond, where the wavelengths of light necessary for green chlorophyll to function could not penetrate. Whereas the photosynthesis carried on by green chlorophyll uses water as a hydrogen source, bacterial photosynthesis usually obtains hydrogen from hydrogen sulfide or other substances. Oxygen, therefore, is usually not a product of photosynthesis involving bacteriochlorophyll.

Although not a large group, the chemosynthetic bacteria perform some important conversions of inorganic materials. Chemosynthesis involves converting inorganic compounds other living things cannot use into usable forms and capturing the escaping energy. Chemosynthetic bacteria use this energy to form materials (usually carbohydrates) for their own use.

The vast majority of known bacteria are *heterotrophic*, obtaining their energy by digesting organic substances. The bacteria we usually think

---

Pasteurization

The preservation of milk presents a special case. If raw milk is heated enough to destroy all bacteria, it loses some of its flavor and food value. Louis Pasteur first devised the process of pasteurization to prevent the souring of wines. It was later used on milk to eliminate the bacteria that caused tuberculosis. Pasteurization is now widely used to control pathogenic and spoilage bacteria in dairy products and fruit juices.

Commercial **pasteurization** of milk involves raising the temperature to either 63° C (145° F) for 30 min. (the holding method) or to 72° C (161° F) for 15 sec. (the flash method) and then quickly cooling the milk. Pasteurization destroys between 90-99% of all bacteria. Pasteurized milk, although it sours much more slowly than raw milk, should still be refrigerated to slow bacterial activity. Sterilized milk, which does not require refrigeration, is now available.

Exposure to the air permits new bacteria to enter processed dairy products, and for this reason processed milk should be kept covered.

---

endospores: endo- (within) + -spores (seed)

FACETS OF BIOLOGY

Controlling Bacteria

Although in some ways man relies heavily on bacterial metabolism and even encourages bacterial growth in some instances, many of man's dealings with bacteria are attempts to control them. Medical science has invested much time and money in attempts to control pathogenic (disease causing) bacteria (see Chapter 9C).

Since bacteria decompose organic material, we should not be surprised that bacteria are among our primary competitors for food. Many foods would remain edible for months were it not for bacterial action fermenting carbohydrates, putrifying proteins, and turning fats rancid. We have two basic ways of controlling bacteria in our food:

□ Destroy the bacteria present and seal the food in a container which will not permit the entrance of other bacteria and

□ Place the foods in an environment that will not permit bacteria to grow or at least not grow rapidly. The bacteria may be present, possibly in a dormant form, but they either will not spoil the food or will spoil it less rapidly.

Some of the more common methods of food preservation are as follows:

□ **Canning** In canning, the food is heated enough to destroy all pathogenic and most other forms of bacteria and then sealed in a can or jar to prevent growth of the residual organisms and the entrance of new ones. Canned foods can keep for extended periods but many foods lose desirable qualities

in the process. Canning is primarily used for fruits, vegetables, meats, and prepared foods.

□ **Preserves or Jellies** Foods that can be placed in a strong sugar concentration can be kept as preserves or jellies. The high concentration of sugar prevents most bacteria from growing. Some aerobic molds can grow on the top of these products so they must be kept tightly covered.

□ **Salt-curing** Some meats can be preserved by placing large quantities of salt on them. The salt causes dehydration of active cells. Most salt-cured meat retains the heavily-salted taste. Salt-cured meats were common before freezing and refrigeration were convenient.

□ **Refrigeration** Foods kept at low temperatures cannot support rapid growth of bacteria or mold. Refrigeration, however, does not stop food spoilage.

□ **Quick-freezing** Those foods that can be frozen and still retain their desirable qualities after thawing can be stored by freezing. Freezing does not kill all the bacteria present, but does greatly retard their growth.

□ **Dehydration** Removing the moisture from a food and then keeping it dry will prevent bacterial and fungal growth. Cereals and other naturally dry foods can be preserved by this method. Many foods cannot be preserved, but can be changed by dehydration (bananas into banana chips, grapes into raisins, fresh apricots into dried apricots).

Chemical Preservatives

The following list shows various chemicals and the foods to which they are added. The Food and Drug Administration (FDA) regards these chemicals as "Generally Regarded as Safe" (GRAS) when used in small amounts.

Sodium or calcium propionate
  Bread, baked goods
Sodium benzoate
  Carbonated beverages, margarine, juices, preserves
Sodium nitrite
  Hams, bacon
Sorbic acid
  Cheese, citrus products, salads
Sulfur dioxide
  Dried friuts and vegetables
Formaldehyde (created within the food during the food-smoking process)
  Meat, fish

Although used for many years, these chemicals are a source of controversy to some people.

□ **Radiation** Placing the food in an airtight plastic container and then exposing it to radiation to kill all living things in the container will prevent food spoilage. In this relatively new process the radiation passes through the food but does not remain in it. Sealed radiation-preserved foods do not require refrigeration until they are opened because there is no living substance inside the container.

□ **Pickling** Acids are used to preserve some foods. Pickles are cucumbers placed in vinegar (2% acetic acid) with other flavorings (like sugar or dill). A few other foods (even meats) can also be pickled.

□ **Chemical preservatives** Added chemicals in some foods retard bacterial or fungal growth.

Review questions on page 236.

of are **parasitic*** (feeding on a living host). Most bacteria, however, are **saprophytic*** (feeding on dead organic matter). Saprophytic bacteria feed by secreting enzymes that digest external substances into soluble forms. These soluble materials then diffuse through the capsule and into the cell. Some of these digestive enzymes are important in the manufacture of cheeses and other useful substances.

Saprophytic bacteria are unable to manufacture all their nutritive materials and, therefore, require certain vitamins or other organic nutrients in their media. Experiments with mutation-inducing radiation or chemicals have produced bacteria whose offspring have reduced abilities to manufacture certain nutrients. The mutant offspring require these nutrient materials in their media. If these mutant bacteria are subjected to the same

Transfer of Genetic Material in Bacteria

The transfer of genetic material from one bacterial cell to another is believed to be a relatively rare occurrence: only a few species of bacteria are known to do it naturally, and only a few have been forced to do it in a laboratory. The transferred genetic material may be a gene, a few genes, or a complete copy of the bacterial chromosome. Since there is no meiosis and no diploid cell or zygote formed, these genetic transfers are not considered true sexual reproductions.

Conjugation* in bacteria is a natural process of genetic transfer. Certain strains of *Escherichia coli,* a common bacterium in the human intestine, possess the *F factor* (F⁺). The F factor (a plasmid) is a gene in a bacterial cell which is not attached to the bacterial chromosome and permits the F⁺ cells to form a *conjugation tube.*

A conjugation tube grows from an F⁺ *E. coli,* and attaches to an *E. coli* which lacks the F factor (an F⁻ cell). Through the hollow conjugation tube a replicated F factor passes from the F⁺ cell F⁻ cell. The F⁻ *E. coli* is now an F⁺ *E. coli.*

In some other bacteria known to carry on conjugation, the entire bacterial chromosome passes through the conjugation tube. The donor bacterium always gives its traits to the receiving bacterium. There is no mutual exchange of characteristics in bacterial conjugation.

In **transformation,** another form of genetic transfer in bacteria, living cells take up the DNA of other bacteria. *Streptococcus pneumoniae* (see page 228) is known to transfer genes by transformation. Scientists can kill cells of the encapsulated *S. pneumoniae* and extract their DNA. If they place this DNA in a culture of non-encapsulated *S. pneumoniae,* these cells produce some non-encapsulated and some encapsulated bacteria. The gene for the capsule was absorbed by the living non-encapsulated cells, transforming them into the encapsulated variety.

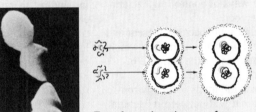

Transformation: the gene for a thick sheath (red) is taken into a living cell from dead cells, causing the living cells to change their genetic make-up. Insert: S. pneumoniae

Today scientists often use bacteria for genetic engineering experiments and also use bacteria with genes planted in them to produce substances (see pages 163-64, 227).

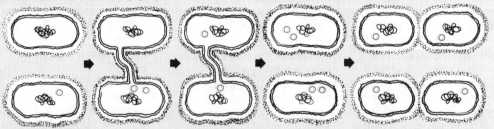

Conjugation: the cytoplasmic DNA (red) passes through the conjugation tube from one cell to the next.

parasitic: para- (Gk. PARA, beside) + -sitic (SITOS, grain or food)

saprophytic: sapro- (Gk. SAPROS, rotten or putrid) + phytic (plant)

conjugation: con- (L. COM-, together) + -jugation (JUGARE, to yoke)

The Cyanobacteria
(The Blue-green Algae)

At one time the *blue-green algae* were considered plants. For a time they had their own phylum in the kingdom Monera (cyanophyta). Today scientists classify them as a group within one of the bacterial phyla and call them the **cyanobacteria***.

The cellular structure of the cyanobacteria is essentially the same as bacteria. Blue-green algae lack flagella, but many of them float in the water, and some (such as *Oscillatoria)* even appear to move by a type of sliding.

Cyanobacteria are often attached by their sheaths to underwater surfaces or to places which are constantly wet. Although most live in bodies of water, some algae live in the soil. Cyanobacteria reproduce by simple cell division. Some species are known to form spores, but none are known to reproduce sexually.

Although a few of the cyanobacteria are unicellular, most of them are colonial, forming **filaments** (long, thin strands of similar cells). In some species these filaments are branched. Some form colonies shaped like discs or globs. Often these colonies share slime coats, and sometimes groups of colonies form large gooey masses visible to the unaided eye.

Usually, within a colony all individual cells are the same. Some cyanobacteria, however, contain a **heterocyst*** (HET ur oh SIST), generally a single cell which may have different functions in different species. Some heterocysts appear to capture nitrogen gas from the environment and make it useful to the algae. Occasionally a heterocyst is a dead cell which permits easy *fragmentation* of the filament. In some species

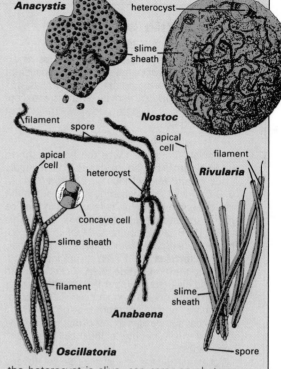

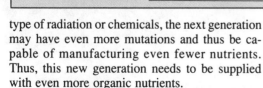

Cyanobacteria growing at the water's edge

the heterocyst is alive, can carry on photosynthesis, and can divide, forming a new filament.

All the cyanobacteria contain chlorophyll *a,* along with accessory pigments. Thus they carry on photosynthesis similar to that of autotrophs in other kingdoms. Many cyanobacteria contain a blue pigment (phycocyanin) and appear bluish green. About half of the cyanobacteria, however, are colorless, gray, green, yellow, orange, pink, purple, brown, violet, or red because of the presence or absence of other pigments.

Certain cyanobacteria, when in abundance, affect the taste or odor of water. Other blue-green algae produce poisons, making the water unfit to drink. When this happens to a farm pond, animals which drink the water may die.

type of radiation or chemicals, the next generation may have even more mutations and thus be capable of manufacturing even fewer nutrients. Thus, this new generation needs to be supplied with even more organic nutrients.

If evolution were true, increasing the mutation rate would produce organisms able to manufacture more and more substances. These organisms would require a smaller variety of nutrient materials. They would be more complex; they would have evolved. Experiments that increase the mutation rate, however, show the opposite. This is a case of change by mutation, but it is degeneration, not evolution.

---

cyanobacteria: cyano- (Gk. KUANOS, blue) + -bacteria (rod)

heterocyst: hetero- (other) + -cyst (KUSTIS, bladder or pouch)

Rickettsias, Spirochetes, and Mycoplasmas

Monera contains several distinct groups of organisms. Three which are significant because of the pathogens they contain are *rickettsias, spirochetes* and *mycoplasmas*. With rare exceptions these are *obligate parasites*—they must have a living host.

The Rickettsias

Dr. Howard T. Ricketts was the first person to describe a small bacterium in the blood of people suffering from Rocky Mountain spotted fever. In 1910 Dr. Ricketts saw a similar organism in the cells of people with typhus fever and in the lice which carry the disease to humans. During his studies Dr. Ricketts contracted typhus and died. This group of organisms was named in his honor.

The **rickettsias** (rih KET sih uz) are *intracellular parasites:* they live inside cells. Rickettsias can grow and divide rapidly, but they are highly specific, growing only in certain cells. They do not form spores and do not reproduce outside living cells. Most substances in the cytoplasm of their host cell easily penetrate their cell walls and membranes.

Rickettsial diseases usually cause fevers, rashes, and blotches under the skin. The blotch-

A strain of typhus fever became known as "trench fever" during World War I because it was passed readily among the soldiers in the close quarters of the trenches (above). The Rocky Mountain spotted fever rickettsia in human cells (right).

es are the result of the rupturing of damaged small blood vessels. Once a person recovers from a rickettsial disease, he is usually immune to its harmful effects even though his cells may still contain the organism. Such a person may host the pathogen without being sick himself.

Typhus fever, caused by a rickettsial organism, is one of the diseases that has claimed the most human lives. Man is the natural host for this dis-

Parasitic bacteria usually need to absorb nutritive substances without digesting them. These bacteria need many nutritive substances in their media. Some bacteria and similar organisms are **obligate parasites;** they require the presence of living tissue in order to grow. Parasitic bacteria lack many of the systems for organic synthesis that the saprophytic or autotrophic bacteria have.

Most evolutionists speculate that bacteria were the first living things. If evolution were true, the simplest organisms would have evolved first. The simplest would be the obligate parasites, the ones with the least complex biological systems. The autotrophic bacteria, those with the most complex biological systems, would have evolved from the simpler parasitic types. Parasites, however, cannot support themselves. Considerable evolution of a previous organism to serve as their host would be essential.

9A-6 *Mutations in bacteria. The bacteria in the upper left can grow on a media without any vitamins. When exposed to radiation it changes.*

Unable to grow on media with no vitamins (a) or on media with only vitamin A (b), it can grow on media containing vitamins A and B (c). What does this tell you about this bacteria's reaction to radiation?

ease, and human body lice and human head lice pass it from one person to the next. The typhus fever rash spreads over the body except for the soles of the feet and palms of the hands. Following a fever which makes the victim sluggish, death may occur within ten days. Drugs can control the disease, but control of the lice which carry the disease is the best preventative.

Rocky Mountain spotted fever was first recognized in the American West, but is more common in the eastern states. It is carried by ticks from small mammals (rodents, rabbits, dogs) to man. About two weeks following the tick bite, the person develops a fever, headache, chills, and rash; the disease is rarely fatal.

The Spirochetes

Most **spirochetes*** (SPY ruh KEETS) are larger than the average bacterium and many are cork-

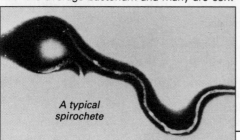

A typical spirochete

screw shaped. Some spirochetes are free-living and normally inhabit the mouths, intestines, and reproductive organs of humans and animals. Some are believed to be nonpathogenic. Some spirochetes are found in sewage and in decomposing plant materials.

Spirochetes lack flagella but have flexible cell walls which permit them to move by contracting their coils. Many are highly specific as to their environment. None are known to form spores. Lyme disease, yaws, infectious jaundice, syphilis, and relapsing fever are a few of the diseases caused by spirochetes.

The Mycoplasmas

Mycoplasmas* (MY koh PLAZ muhz) were discovered about the turn of the century as pathogens in the membranes around the lungs of cattle. Other mycoplasmas have since been found living harmlessly in the human mouth, nasal passages, and urinary tract. Several animal and plant diseases have been attributed to mycoplasmas. Atypical pneumonia, arthritis, and infections of the urinary tract in humans have been associated with mycoplasmas. Mycoplasmas lack a cell wall and thus can assume a variety of shapes. They are highly specific regarding the solute concentrations they can tolerate.

Bacteria and oxygen

Louis Pasteur demonstrated that some bacteria can grow without (and are actually inhibited or destroyed by) free oxygen. Those organisms which grow only without free oxygen are **obligate anaerobes,** and those which grow only with free oxygen are **obligate aerobes.** Many bacteria can grow as either aerobes or anaerobes; they are **facultative anaerobes.**

Many bacteria which grow in the depths of lakes and oceans or the ooze of swamps are anaerobic bacteria. Many of the bacteria used to make cheese, yogurt, sauerkraut, buttermilk, alcohol and other products are anaerobic bacteria. Some anaerobic bacteria are pathogenic, causing diseases such as lockjaw (tetanus), gas gangrene, and food poisoning. Anaerobic bacteria carry on various types of fermentation and form different products, including lactic acid, alcohol, methane, carbon dioxide, hydrogen sulfide (a gas which smells like rotten eggs), acetic acid (vinegar), citric acid, and ammonia. Many bacterial names indicate their fermentation products (*Lactobacillus* makes lactic acid; *Acetobacter* makes acetic acid).

Conditions of bacterial growth

For bacteria to grow and divide, several environmental factors must be within the bacteria's optimal range. These include the following:

❑ *Moisture* Although many are protected by their capsules during temporary dry periods, all bacteria require moisture to grow. Some bacteria grow best submerged in fluids.

❑ *Temperature* Enzyme systems of different bacteria operate at different temperatures. Some bacteria grow near freezing and some at high temperatures, but most bacteria thrive in temperatures from 27° C to 38° C (80° F to 100° F). Human

---

spirochetes: spiro- (L. SPIRA a coil or a twist) + -chetes (Gk. KHAITE, long hair)

mycoplasmas: myco- (Gk. MUKES, fungus) + -plasmas (to mold)

pathogenic bacteria grow best at body temperature 37° C (98.6° F) and have a range of only a few degrees in which they can grow. Most bacteria have a range of about 30° C in which they can grow.

❏ *pH* Although many bacteria can grow in a nearly neutral condition, the pH of the environment is critical to their existence. Raising or lowering the pH can destroy one kind of bacteria but cause ideal conditions for another.

❏ *Nutrition* The food source for heterotrophic bacteria must not only meet the energy needs but must also supply the materials necessary for bacterial biosynthesis. For some heterotrophs, especially the parasites, the proper food source is highly specific. Even though photosynthetic bacteria obtain their energy from light, they often require various substances (inorganic and occasionally organic, such as vitamins) in order to grow. Chemosynthetic bacteria require specific chemicals as their energy source.

Although bacteria live in almost every known environment, what is advantageous for one species may kill another species. Since each species of bacteria requires a specific set of environmental conditions in order to grow and reproduce, bacteria exhibit a high degree of specificity. In other words, they are *highly specific* regarding the environment in which they can grow and multiply.

Biological Terms

microbiologist
bacteria
decomposer organisms
Bacterial Shapes, Sizes and Colonies
coccus, (pl., cocci)
bacillus, (pl., bacilli)
spirillum, (pl., spirilla)
nuclear area
mesosome
capsule

Bacterial Growth and Reproduction
endospore
chemosynthetic
pasteurization
parasitic
saprophytic
conjugation
transformation
cyanobacteria
filaments
heterocyst

rickettsia
spirochete
mycoplasm
obligate parasite
obligate anaerobe
obligate aerobe
facultative anaerobe

Review Questions 9A-2

1. Describe asexual reproduction in bacteria.
2. Describe two methods bacteria use to survive periods of unfavorable conditions.
3. Describe two methods of genetic transfer in bacteria.
4. List several differences between bacterial photosynthesis and photosynthesis in plants.
5. List the two types of autotrophic and the two types of heterotrophic bacteria.
6. List several common characteristics that the cyanobacteria share with other bacteria and several characteristics that separate the cyanobacteria as a distinct group.
7. Describe and compare obligate aerobes, obligate anaerobes, and facultative anaerobes.
8. When culturing a particular bacterium, what conditions must one consider in order to have it survive and grow?
9. Differentiate between an obligate parasite and an intracellular parasite.
10. Describe mycoplasmas, rickettsias, and spirochetes. List several diseases caused by organisms in each of these groups.

Facet 9A-2: Controlling Bacteria, page 231

1. What are the two basic methods of controlling food spoilage-bacteria? List several household or commercial practices and tell how they illustrate these methods.
2. Describe the process of pasteurization. Why must milk be pasteurized if it is not to be consumed immediately.

9B-Viruses

Viruses have plagued mankind for a long time. Some of the earliest recorded diseases and their prescribed remedies were for viral diseases. After the "germ theory of disease" came into prominence during the late 1800s, various protozoans and bacteria were isolated and demonstrated to be the "germs" that caused various diseases. Many diseases, however, defied early attempts to isolate a pathogenic organism.

Both Edward Jenner, who dealt with smallpox, and Louis Pasteur, who dealt with rabies, formulated successful vaccinations for these diseases. They thought they were working with bacteria or similar organisms that had not yet been isolated. But even today we cannot isolate a pathogenic *organism* for these and many similar diseases. The reason is that they are not caused by *organisms;* they are caused by viruses.

The discovery of viruses

In 1892, a Russian biologist, Dimitri Iwanowski, worked with tobacco mosaic, a disease which causes light green patches on tobacco leaves and stunts leaf growth. Iwanowski passed the juice from diseased leaves through an unglazed porcelain filter. Such a filter is so fine that it permits only dissolved substances to pass; not even the smallest bacteria can go through. The resulting fluid, when examined under a microscope, contained no visible particles. Nonetheless, when this juice came in contact with a tobacco leaf, it caused tobacco mosaic disease. Iwanowski assumed that the fluid contained a poison made by a bacterium. A few years later the term *virus,* the Latin word for poison, was assigned to the unknown agent which caused the disease.

In the mid-1930s, Wendell Stanley, working at the Rockefeller Institute, isolated the actual virus. He reduced the juice from about a ton of infected tobacco mosaic leaves to about one spoonful of crystals. These crystals could be kept in a dry,

9B-1 *A normal tobbaco leaf (left) and one infected with TMV (right).*

airtight jar for extended periods of time. They had no metabolism; therefore, they were obviously an inert chemical. But when they were placed in contact with a living tobacco leaf, they caused tobacco mosaic disease. Stanley was awarded the Nobel Prize in chemistry in 1946 for isolating and purifying the **tobacco mosaic virus (TMV).**

There is nothing unusual about a disease caused by a chemical. Various poisons and irritants affect cellular metabolism, resulting in disease and death. A certain amount of cyanide (a chemical poison) given to a laboratory animal will kill it. Careful examination of the animal's body will reveal only the amount of cyanide given to the animal. The animal's body does not make more of the poison.

A virus, however, is very different. A tobacco leaf exposed to a tiny amount of TMV will develop the disease and die. Later if the TMV is extracted from the leaf, much more will be found than was placed on the leaf. TMV apparently "grows and reproduces" when placed on a tobacco leaf. How? Is TMV alive, or is it a "dead chemical?" Does the *leaf* make more TMV? Does TMV alter the genes of the leaf cells? Does TMV supply genes to the cell to have more TMV made? Controlled experiments and careful observations with the electron microscope have supplied many of the answers.

Review Questions 9B-1

1. Give the contributions to the study of viruses made by (a) Dimitri Iwanowski and (b) Wendell Stanley.
2. In what ways is a virus different from a chemical poison?

FACETS OF BIOLOGY

9B–1

Smallpox – A Plague of the Past?

Smallpox plagues have affected man for centuries. But in the late 1700s in Europe smallpox epidemics swept through cities and caused thousands of people to break out in red *pustules* (fluid-filled blisters). Most who contracted the disease died. Any who recovered had permanent scars but were *immune* to (would not again contract) smallpox.

Dr. Edward Jenner, an English physician, noted that people who lived in the country, and especially those who worked around dairy cattle, appeared to be immune to smallpox. He observed that most farmers and dairy workers had previously experienced a mild disease called *cowpox*. This disease caused a small pustule, usually on the hands of those who milked the cows, which healed and left a small scar.

In 1796 during a severe smallpox epidemic, Mrs. Phipps brought her son, James, to Jenner. She feared that James had contracted smallpox and had heard that Jenner was working on a cure. On May 14, 1796, Jenner took matter from a cowpox pustule on the hand of a dairymaid and inoculated James by applying the matter to two shallow cuts he made on the boy's arm. A pustule developed, formed a scab, and then disappeared, leaving only a scar.

Was the boy now immune to smallpox? In June of the same year Jenner again inoculated his patient, this time using matter from a smallpox pustule. For two

anxious weeks Jenner watched James for signs of the disease. None developed. Later in the year, he inoculated him again with material from a smallpox pustule, but James did not develop the disease.

Jenner wrote a paper describing what he called a "vaccination" against smallpox. Today we know that a **vaccination*** is not a cure for a disease but is a method of developing an immunity by exposing a person to either a weakened form of the disease or a similar disease.

At the time of Jenner's work most people did not understand the idea of vaccinations. People organized anti-vaccination campaigns. Cartoons of the time showed people with cow heads, tails, legs, and hoofs growing out of their bodies where they had been vaccinated.

Jenner did not know what caused smallpox or cowpox. About 150 yr. after his vaccination of James Phipps, it was discovered that smallpox and cowpox are caused by similar viruses. When a person develops an immunity to one, he also becomes immune to the other.

About 200 yr. after Jenner's first vaccination, the World Health Organization (an agency of the United Nations) announced that smallpox had been eradicated. Since there is an effective vaccine against smallpox and the only known place the virus can exist is in humans, it is theoretically possible to eliminate the disease. If

everyone were vaccinated against the virus, there would be no place for the virus to exist, and that would be the end of smallpox.

The task of vaccinating over 4.5 billion people proved impossible for even the United Nations. They adopted the idea of vaccinating everyone near an outbreak of smallpox. After a few years there appeared to be no more major outbreaks of smallpox, and in 1980 the World Health Organization certified that smallpox was the first major human disease to be completely eliminated. Routine vaccinations stopped. Today you do not need a smallpox vaccination to attend school or to travel to other countries.

Some scientists doubt that smallpox has been totally eradicated. To say that no one is suffering

Fear of vaccinations inspired cartoons like the one below.

vaccination: (L. VACCINUS, of cows)
From cows because the first vaccine was prepared from the cowpox virus.

Edward Jenner inoculating James Phipps with matter from the cowpox pustule of a dairymaid's hand to develop an immunity in the boy. Jenner first called the procedure a vaccination.

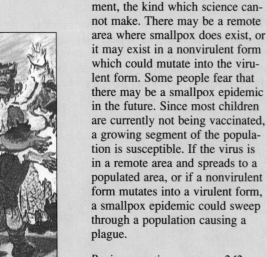

from smallpox is a universal statement, the kind which science cannot make. There may be a remote area where smallpox does exist, or it may exist in a nonvirulent form which could mutate into the virulent form. Some people fear that there may be a smallpox epidemic in the future. Since most children are currently not being vaccinated, a growing segment of the population is susceptible. If the virus is in a remote area and spreads to a populated area, or if a nonvirulent form mutates into a virulent form, a smallpox epidemic could sweep through a population causing a plague.

Review questions on page 242.

Structure and Functions of Viruses

Viruses consist of a molecule of DNA or RNA and a **protein coat.** They have no cell membrane, cytoplasm, or organelles of their own. Essentially viruses are chromosomes. The tobacco mosaic virus consists of a spiral of RNA covered by a protein coat made of repeated subunits.

The TMV RNA contains only about 6,000 bases, enough for a dozen small proteins. When stretched out, the 6,000 bases in a TMV are just over 1.5 µm long. By comparison, the stretched-out DNA in an average bacterium is about 1,000 µm long, which is about the length of the stretched out DNA of the smallest human chromosome. When coiled, however, the TMV is about 300 nm long, while the length of an average bacterium is about 1,000 nm and that of a human red blood cell is 7,500 nm.

Some viruses have several different protein structures in their coats. The **bacteriophage*** (a virus that infects certain bacteria) illustrated in figure 9B-2 is such a virus. These protein structures probably help the virus to enter the bacterial cell. The DNA in the head portion of a bacteriophage contains about 200,000 base pairs. The bacteriophage can produce dozens of different proteins, more than TMV, although the virus particles are about the same size. The more complex structure of the protein coat of the bacteriophage

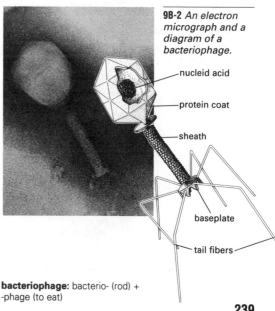

9B-2 *An electron micrograph and a diagram of a bacteriophage.*

nucleid acid

protein coat

sheath

baseplate

tail fibers

bacteriophage: bacterio- (rod) + -phage (to eat)

demands a wider variety of proteins than the simple recurring subunits of the TMV.

The lytic cycle

The ability of a pathogen to affect cells is called **virulence** (VIHR yuh lunce). If the virus does not affect a certain type of cell, the virus is *nonvirulent* for that cell type. TMV, for example, is nonvirulent to human cells. You could eat TMV with little danger. A highly *virulent* virus, however, can enter a cell, produce hundreds of virus particles, and destroy the cell in less than an hour.

Scientists call the activity of a virulent virus the **lytic*** (LIT ik) **cycle.** We will illustrate the lytic cycle of a virulent bacteriophage. The lytic cycle, although slightly different for various viruses, generally follows these steps:

❏ *The virus attaches itself to the cell.* The various coat proteins of some viruses aid in the attachment to the host cell. Some virus particles are engulfed by the cell.

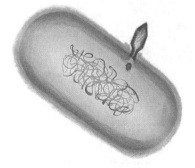

❏ *The DNA (or RNA) of the virus enters the cell.* Often the empty protein coat remains outside the cell. In some viruses the protein coat may enter the cell and then release its nucleic acid.

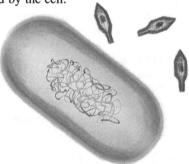

❏ *The DNA (or RNA) begins to transcribe and replicate.* Using the cell's chemical machinery, the virus begins to manufacture mRNA, multiple copies of the viral nucleic acid, and proteins.

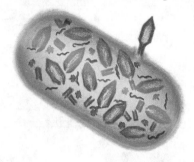

❏ *Virus particles form within the cell.* The virus proteins form coats around the replicated viral DNA (or RNA), producing new viruses.

❏ *The cell bursts, releasing the newly-formed virus particles.* Cellular machinery and supplies used by the virus have not been replaced, and soon the cell dies. By the *lysis* process, the cell ruptures, releasing new virus particles which can then begin the lytic cycle in other cells.

lytic: (noun form is: -lysis) (Gk. LUEIN, to untie or to loosen)

Certain bacteriophages, as well as the viruses causing human polio and influenza, are relatively virulent, forcing the entire cell metabolism to make new viruses. When a virulent virus particle infects a cell, it can sometimes produce hundreds of viruses in as little as 30 min. Each of those new virus particles can infect another cell and multiply into hundreds in each infected cell. It is easy to see how the symptoms of certain viral diseases can be produced very quickly.

Latent viruses

Not all viruses begin to destroy the cell immediately after entering it. A **latent virus,** for example, enters a cell and may remain inactive for long periods of time. In an inactive state some latent bacterial viruses attach to the bacterial chromosome and replicate along with it when the cell divides. In time a good portion of the bacterial population may have the virus. In animal and human cells it appears that many latent viruses reproduce each time the cell divides so that the new cells all have the virus in them.

When a certain stimulus (such as ultraviolet radiation, certain chemicals, or an unknown agent) is applied, the virus becomes virulent, enters the lytic cycle, and destroys the cells. Since the virus may be in a large number of cells before the stimulus is applied, a large area may be affected all at once. The viruses then enter other cells and, unless the stimulus is still present, again become inactive.

The *herpes simplex* virus affects humans. It produces small fluid-filled sacs, commonly called fever blisters or cold sores. These blisters, followed by scabs on the skin, usually form around the lips near the nose. Herpes simplex is believed to be a latent virus; it can exist quietly in the nerve cells for long periods.

In different people the following stimuli may cause the herpes simplex virus to leave the nerve cells and become virulent to skin cells: some foods, skin dryness, sunlight, burns, or injury. In most susceptible people, the body conditions associated with a severe or prolonged cold appear to change the virulence. Some people are immune or can develop an immunity to the virus.

Other kinds of viruses

Viruses can also cause *persistent infections*. In a persistent viral infection the host cell does not go through lysis, but slowly releases virus particles. This type of viral infection may not destroy the cell, but it does hamper the cell's metabolism. Even stress could harm the organism if enough cells contain persistent infection virus.

Some viruses are *transforming viruses*. These viruses transform their host cells by adding new genetic information. They significantly change the cell's metabolism but do not destroy the cell. The transformed cell, however, is not a productive cell in the organism's body.

An example of a transforming virus is one that causes certain warts in humans. The wart virus

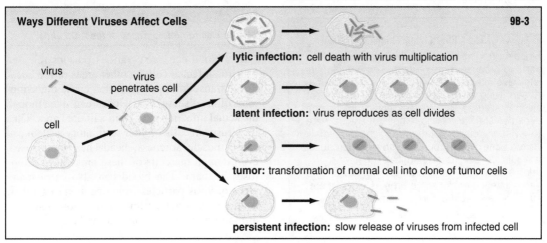

Ways Different Viruses Affect Cells   9B-3

virus

virus penetrates cell

cell

lytic infection: cell death with virus multiplication

latent infection: virus reproduces as cell divides

tumor: transformation of normal cell into clone of tumor cells

persistent infection: slow release of viruses from infected cell

enters the skin cell and transforms it into a wart cell. As the transformed cell grows and divides the wart grows. In time the wart reaches a certain size, and the cells stop growing and dividing. Some tumors are caused by viruses which transform the cells they infect.

Review Questions 9B-2
1. Describe the structure of a virus particle.
2. Describe the lytic cycle.
3. What is the difference between a virulent virus and a latent virus?
4. List and describe two effects, other than the lytic cycle, which some viruses may have on cells.

Facet 9B-1: Smallpox - A Plague of the Past, pages 238-39
1. What is the relationship between smallpox and cowpox?
2. Who was Dr. Jenner and what is he credited with doing?

Viral diseases

Most viruses are highly specific regarding their host cells. It appears that a virus particle in contact with the wrong type of cell either lacks the mechanisms for entering the cell or once in the cell, lacks the mechanisms for affecting its metabolism. This virus would most likely be destroyed by the cell or released as a waste product.

Most viruses are thus limited not only to one type of organism but to one type of cell in that organism. Smallpox, chicken pox, and measles usually affect skin cells. Rabies and polio attack cells in the nervous system. Influenza and the common cold are usually viral infections of the respiratory system. A few viral diseases, however, like rabies and cowpox, can affect similar cells in different organisms.

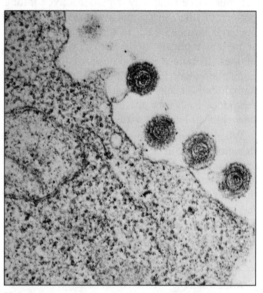

9B-4 An electron micrography of the AIDS virus.

The blood can carry various poisons released by virus-infected cells to other areas of the body. These transported poisons often cause the symptoms of the disease to be widespread, even though the actual infection may be in a limited area. Thus flu viruses in cells of your respiratory system can cause muscle soreness, headaches and nausea, even though the cells of these areas have no viruses in them. The blood can also carry many types of virus particles from one area to another. A viral infection, therefore, is often found in areas of the same tissue throughout the body.

The "First Living Thing"?

Since a virus is a chemical which can use cellular parts to produce more of itself, some evolutionists have claimed that viruses are the step between living and dead organisms. Today most scientists agree that viruses could not be the evolutionists' "first living things." If a virus were to exist in an environment which completely lacked living cells, it could not grow or reproduce. It would just exist until chemicals, heat, or something else destroyed it. Viruses must have come into existence at the same time as cells (at creation) or later at the curse (Gen. 3:19).

Human Viral Diseases

Chicken pox and shingles The same virus causes chicken pox in children and shingles in adults who once had chicken pox. One of the herpes DNA viruses, the chicken pox virus, is very contagious and is probably spread by droplets and physical contact. In the bloodstream it spreads causing a body rash and a mild fever. Adults may develop more serious symptoms from chicken pox. After the chicken pox stage the virus can become latent in nerve cells. Years later the virus may move from nerves to the skin and cause small, often painful sores called shingles. No vaccine is available.

Common cold The common cold is a leading cause of illness. There are many different kinds of viruses that cause the common cold, and each one is different enough to prevent us from developing immunity to the cold. It appears that the common cold is not highly contagious; in one study only about 35% of those directly inoculated with the virus got a cold. Physical conditions (stress, amount of rest, other illnesses, etc.) appear to be significant regarding whether or not a person gets a cold. Direct contact with the infected person or his secretions (such as soiled tissues) appears to be more important in spreading the disease than airborne droplets.

Infectious hepatitis This disease is spread by contaminated food or water. The virus can withstand mild heat, dryness, and chlorination of water. The early symptoms include fever and chills, loss of appetite, headache, muscle pains, jaundice (yellow color of the skin), and abdominal pain and swelling. Once the person recovers, he is immune. The disease causes the liver cells to lose the ability to function, but following recovery (which may take months) the liver can regrow.

Influenza In the U.S. influenza or flu is among the leading causes of illness. The flu is caused by a virus made of a protein coat covering up to 8 pieces of RNA. It is transferred by airborne droplets. The infection begins in the upper respiratory tract and symptoms include soreness and redness of the nose and throat, a dry cough, a fever, muscle soreness, headaches, and nausea. Several major different kinds of flu exist. Each RNA fragment can mutate to form a new strain of flu, and sometimes the RNAs from different kinds appear to combine, forming new strains. These new strains may have different protein coats, the host cells they invade may be changed, or its virulence may be altered. When you recover from a particular flu, you develop a temporary immunity to that strain. But your body must develop an immunity to each new strain.

Measles and rubella Among the "childhood diseases" are measles (rubeola virus) and rubella (German measles). Both are caused by RNA viruses and are highly contagious by droplets and physical contact. Measles symptoms include chills, sneezing, runny nose, and redness of eyes followed by a fever, spots on mucous membranes and a rash. Usually the person recovers and is immune. Complications and secondary infections may occur. Rubella is milder and of shorter duration than measles, but can cause serious problems for the unborn child if a pregnant woman contracts the disease. Vaccination programs begun in the 1960s have greatly reduced the occurrence of these diseases.

Polio The polio virus in the intestines produces mild symptoms that are often confused with other minor illnesses. Occasionally it enters the blood or lymph system with no effects. But sometimes it enters the central nervous system and causes paralysis (poliomyelitis or infantile paralysis). Although many people are infected with the polio virus, being paralyzed by polio is rare. In the mid-1950s a strain of the polio virus was treated so as to be nonvirulent and given to people as a "live"-virus vaccine. Vaccination is now routine for infants.

Rabies Caused by a single stranded RNA virus, rabies attacks the nervous system of many different warm-blooded animals. Often associated with dogs, it is common in other carnivores as well. The virus normally is found in the saliva of an infected animal and enters the next victim as he is bitten. In the body the virus goes to the spinal cord where it multiplies and destroys the nerve cells. Various symptoms develop as the virus spreads toward the brain. In dogs the virus is found in the saliva in about 9 days, but serious symptoms begin to show only after 12 days and are not really noticeable for another day or so. The animal usually dies about 16 days after becoming infected. If a human is exposed to rabies, the only known cure is to develop an immunity using a vaccine.

Once a virus is inside a cell it is virtually impossible to destroy the virus without harming the cell. Since the reproduction rate of virulent viruses is faster than that of the cells they infect, it would seem logical that once a person's cells contracted a virus, the virus would spread until all the cells of that kind were destroyed.

Chemicals called **interferons*** (IN tur FEHR ahnz) are the body's defense against viruses. Interferons are proteins produced by cells that have been attacked by a virus. The interferons released by a virus-invaded cell affect the surrounding cells. These cells are then able to resist viral attack. Since the viruses are not able to spread rapidly once the interferon has been released, the normal body-cleaning processes can often take care of the viruses.

At one time it was hoped that interferons would be a major cure for viral diseases. It was then learned that interferons were only produced in tiny amounts and are highly specific. The interferon produced by a skin cell did not cause nerve cells to resist viruses. Interferons were so specific that those produced by animals were ineffective in humans. Also, since interferons are proteins they are easily digested and cannot be taken as a

9B-5	Other Viral Diseases
In Man	
• AIDS	• Poliomyelitis (polio)
• Chicken pox	• Rabies
• Common cold	• Rubella (German measles, "three day measles")
• Hepatitis, infectious	
• Herpes simplex (fever blisters, cold sores)	• Rubeola (measles)
• Influenza	• Shingles
• Mononucleosis, infectious	• Smallpox
• Mumps	• Warts
	• Yellow fever
In Animals	
• Cowpox	• Hog cholera
• Distemper in dogs	• Rabies
• Foot-and-mouth disease	• Sack brood in bees
• Fowl leukemia	• Sheep pox
In Plants	
• Mosaic diseases in cabbage, cucumbers, potatoes, sugar cane, and tobacco	• "Breaking" diseases as in Rembrandt tulips

pill. Injections did not get enough of the needed interferons to the proper cells. Through genetic engineering bacteria are now used to produce large quantities of specific human interferons. Scientists are once again testing the effectiveness of interferons as an antiviral drug.

Biological Terms

tobacco mosaic virus (TMV)

The Structure and Functions of a Virus
protein coat
bacteriophage
virulence
lytic cycle

latent virus
interferon

Facet
vaccination

Review Questions 9B-3

1. List (a) several viral diseases of man and (b) several viral diseases that both man and certain animals can have.
2. How do interferons help to stop a viral infection?

Thought Questions

1. Often an attack of a viral disease is sudden and extensive. Account for this.
2. Rabies is a viral disease of both man and dogs. Man, however, is not susceptible to viral distemper which affects dogs. Why can certain viral diseases be shared by dogs and man and other viral diseases not be shared?
3. Immunity to cowpox also serves as an immunity to smallpox, but the two are separate diseases. What reasons can you give for one immunity protecting against two diseases?

interferon: inter- (L. INTER, between or among) + -feron (FERIRE, to strike)

9C – Diseases and Disorders

Anyone who has suffered or has seen someone suffer from a serious disease has wondered why there is such a thing and how it originated. Scripture teaches that there was no disease in the original creation. At the end of the creation week "God saw every thing that he had made, and, behold, it was very good" (Gen. 1:31).

Today, however, "the whole creation groaneth and travaileth in pain together" (Rom. 8:22). What happened to destroy the peace and harmony of God's original creation? The answer is found in Genesis 3–man's sin, the fall, and the curse caused a host of degenerative changes in the biological realm including disorders, diseases, aging, and death.

God could have allowed us to live in a disease-free world today in spite of Adam's sin. But He chose to use such afflictions to accomplish His purposes in the lives of men. Many people have come to a saving knowledge of Christ in times of great physical or mental distress because they had nowhere else to turn. In the life of a Christian a disease or disorder can be the tribulation that "worketh patience" (Rom. 5:3). Paul's "thorn in the flesh" may have been a physical disorder which God gave him to keep him humble in the face of abundant blessings (II Cor. 12:7). Physical affliction can force us to come apart from our normal routine of living and commune with God. It can make us helpless that we might learn to trust Him more fully. Finally, it can teach us how to sympathize with and comfort others who are similarly afflicted (II Cor. 1:4).

God does on occasion use disease as a punishment for sin (I Cor. 11:29-30). But we must be careful not to jump to conclusions in specific cases. God calls some of His choicest servants to endure serious illnesses for reasons which, for the present at least, only He understands. Job's affliction was not a result of sin (Job 1:8). On the contrary, it appears that he was selected for special testing because of his uprightness.

The account of a New Testament miracle of healing provides a general principle. In John 9:2 the disciples asked the Lord, "Who did sin, this man, or his parents; that he was born blind?" His answer was, "Neither hath this man sinned, nor his parents: but that the works of God should be made manifest in him." Diseases and disorders are a part of the curse, but they can be tools in God's hands for the working of His will in our lives (Rom. 8:28).

In Bible times God used diseases both to discipline (Num. 16:49; Josh. 22:17; and II Sam. 24:15) and to avenge His people (Exod. 9:1-11; I Sam. 5:6-12). Occasionally, God used fatal diseases to remove evil rulers from office (Jehoram [II Chron. 21:18-19] and Herod [Acts 12:21-23]). He will send pestilences (some of which appear to be infectious diseases) as a sign of the end time (Matt. 24:7; Luke 21:11), and they will reach unprecedented proportions during the tribulation (Rev. 16:2, 10-11).

Infectious Disease

An **infectious disease** is caused by an organism that invades the body. Such organisms, called **pathogens,** are parasites that grow and reproduce within the body of their **host,** injuring it in the process. Bacteria and viruses are the two most important types of pathogens. Others are protozoans, fungi, and some animals such as worms.

Diseases and History

On numerous occasions, diseases have changed the course of history. In the 5th century B.C., typhus fever forced the Persian army of Xerxes to call off its invasion of Greece. Returning Crusaders brought the *bubonic plague (Black Death)* from the Near East to Europe, and in the 1300s, 25% of the population of Europe died from this disease. *Typhus* and *dysentery* played as large a role as the adverse weather and the Russian army in Napoleon's defeat in 1812. Even in the 20th century, disease has determined who would be battlefield victors; again it was typhus fever that became a decisive factor in the Serbian campaign of World War I.

This chapter will deal primarily with the moneran pathogens. Others are discussed in later chapters.

How pathogens cause disease

How can a tiny microbe bring so much distress to a 150-lb. human? During the **incubation period** of the disease, a few microbes multiply into millions of organisms. The incubation period is the time between *contracting* (being exposed to) the disease and the appearance of the first symptoms. Once the pathogens have multiplied sufficiently, they can affect their host in two ways:

❑ *Tissue destruction* Pathogens obtain their nutrition from the host's body, which often amounts to destroying host cells, taking them apart both mechanically and chemically and ingesting their remains for food. For example, *typhoid* bacteria destroy portions of the intestine wall and *tuberculosis* bacteria destroy lung tissue. Viruses divert the cell's metabolic machinery from its own functions and in time destroy the cell.

❑ *Toxin formation* Many bacteria and other microorganisms have the ability to produce poisonous substances called **toxins.** Toxins can cause a malfunctioning of the cells, which in turn produces the symptoms of the disease. In many cases these toxins so disrupt the metabolism of the host's cells that they kill large numbers of cells.

Toxins from pathogenic organisms produce **inflammation*** in surrounding tissues. Inflammation is a condition characterized by increased flow of blood (often causing a reddish appearance), heat, pain, swelling, and occasional loss of function. Some sore throats are an inflammation of the epithelial lining of the throat caused by bacterial toxins. A toxin produced in one area can be carried by the blood to other parts of the body as in *tetanus, diphtheria* and *rheumatic fever*.

Communicable diseases

A disease that can spread from one person to another by either direct or indirect means is called a **communicable disease.** Most of the so-called childhood diseases such as *chicken pox, measles, German measles, mumps,* and *whooping cough* are communicable diseases which are highly contagious. A highly *contagious disease* is one that is easily spread to others.

The contagiousness of a disease often varies with the stage of development of the disease in the patient. Although a person may be suffering the *symptoms* (effects) of a disease, he may be past the *contagious* stage* and therefore incapable of infecting someone else. In many such cases, the pathogen is either no longer alive or no longer reproducing, but the effects of the damage the pathogen did are still evident in the host.

Some communicable diseases are so contagious that health authorities advise placing the patient in isolation. A person with meningitis, tuberculosis, scarlet fever, diptheria, typhoid fever, and certain kinds of dysentery are often isolated from other people. At times people with some communicable diseases were placed in *quarantine*, a strict isolation often enforced by law.

How diseases are spread

One way of distinguishing between types of infections is by examining the various ways path-

---

Kinds of Toxins

There are two basic types of toxins:

❑ **Exotoxins** Toxins that diffuse from the living pathogenic cell into the surrounding tissue are called **exotoxins,*** or **soluble toxins.** Exotoxins are products secreted by the pathogen. The toxins formed by the *tetanus, diphtheria,* and *rheumatic fever* bacteria are examples of exotoxins. Exotoxins cause the symptoms of most infectious diseases.

❑ **Endotoxins** Toxins that remain in the pathogen as part of its structure are **endotoxins.*** Endotoxins become a problem to the host as the pathogen dies and disintegrates. Endotoxins can produce violent reactions in tissues around a dying pathogen if they are present in sufficient quantities. Some diseases caused by endotoxins are *bacterial dysentery, bubonic plague,* and *typhoid fever.*

Toxins that are formed by pathogens before they enter the body are called **preformed toxins.** Preformed toxins are often exotoxins. Some kinds of **food poisoning** are the result of preformed toxins released by bacteria that live on the food before it is eaten.

---

exotoxin: exo- (out) + -toxin (L. TOXICUM, poison)

endotoxin: endo- (within) + toxin (poison)

inflammation: (L. INFLAMMARE, to inflame)

contagious: (L. CONTIGERE, to touch with pollution)

ogens can enter the body. Knowing these ways should help you observe certain simple precautions to safeguard good health.

❏ **Droplet infections** Many diseases are transmitted by pathogens suspended in water droplets that humans cough or sneeze into the air. Airborne infections generally affect the respiratory tract, though some of them affect other parts of the body as well. *Tuberculosis* and *diphtheria* can be transmitted in this manner. The spread of these diseases is curtailed by practicing sanitary precautions. An individual with such a disease can easily contaminate anything he touches; there-

fore, it is wise to avoid direct contact with the person or articles he has touched.

❏ **Contact infections** Some diseases are spread by direct contact with a sore or lesion on the skin or mucous membrane of an infected person. *Scarlet fever, colds, influenza,* and *measles* can be transmitted by touch.

❏ **Contamination infections** Pathogens that enter the body by way of *contaminated food* or *water* often afflict the digestive system. *Cholera, typhoid fever,* and many *dysentery* organisms invade and parasitize the intestines. The intestinal wastes of a person who has one of these diseases

Leprosy

In ancient civilizations leprosy was a dreaded contagious disease. It started with minor white patches of skin and a numbness of the fingers and toes. It caused a progressive disfigurement and so weakened the body that other diseases would infect the person. In time the person died, not always of leprosy, but often of leprosy-related infections.

God told the Hebrews to have lepers live in quarantine "outside the camp" (Lev. 13:46), and if a leper came into a city, the Law required him to cry "unclean" so that others could avoid him (Lev. 13:45).

The disease we call leprosy today *(Mycobacterium leprae)* does not completely correspond to all the descriptions of leprosy given in Leviticus 13 and 14 and similar passages. The disease we call leprosy causes lumpy, discolored patches in the skin that become insensitive to cold, touch, and pain. In advanced cases the patient, if not treated, develops a numbness of the hands, feet, and face. The muscles weaken, and the body becomes disfigured. Because of the numbness, the person can suffer cuts, burns, and even amputation without being aware of it.

In most civilized countries leprosy is rare. Under normal conditions the leprosy bacterium is an obligate parasite of humans and is passed only through direct contact with an infectious leper. Once the disease is diagnosed, it can be treated and stopped before major damage occurs. The person is no longer infectious following treatment. Some lepers, however, continue drug treatments throughout their lives.

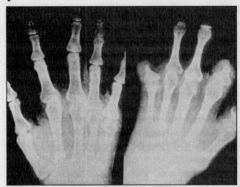

Deformity caused by leprosy. Although there is no known cure for leprosy, it can be controlled.

Today many countries do not require lepers to live in a *leprosarium* (special camp for lepers). Before modern drugs, however, leprosy was dreaded, and quarantine was the only method of controlling its spread.

Most Bible scholars agree that when the Bible describes "leprosy," it is speaking of leprosy, several other skin diseases, some molds, and other fungi of cloth, animals hides, and masonry (walls). The spread of a good number of highly contagious diseases (between which people in Old Testament times had no way to distinguish) was prevented by the laws given in Leviticus. Often in the Bible leprosy represents sin since leprosy comes upon the body, spreads, and severely cripples, just as sin affects our spiritual natures.

are highly infectious. Good sanitary procedures minimize spreading or getting these diseases. The disposal of body wastes prescribed in the Old Testament helped (at least in part) to help maintain sanitary conditions (Deut. 23:12-13). *Tuberculosis* and *undulant fever* can also enter the body through contaminated food.

❏ **Wound infections** Some pathogens enter the body through wounds. Even small cuts can be serious if they are not properly treated. *Staphylococcus* bacteria are among the most common pathogens of wound infections. *Streptococcus* infections are less frequent but more serious, for they are more likely to enter the bloodstream and spread to other parts of the body. Fortunately streptococcus blood poisoning responds readily to antibiotics. *Tetanus* (lockjaw) and *gas gangrene* are serious wound infections.

❏ **Vector-carried infections** Insects or other arthropods that carry pathogens to other host organisms are vectors.* This can be accomplished in two ways: *mechanically,* as with food contamination by pathogens carried on the bodies of flies

9C-2 *The deer tick is the vector for Lyme disease.*

or roaches, or by the *bites* of such organisms as mosquitoes, flies, and ticks, which inject the pathogen into the bloodstream of the host. *Typhus fever, bubonic plague,* and *malaria* are spread by vectors.

❏ **Immune carriers** Diseases are also spread by people (and occasionally animals) who spread pathogens to others without suffering from the disease themselves. Often the carrier has had the disease previously and has developed an immunity to it. Diseases spread in this way include *diphtheria, polio, scarlet fever,* and *typhoid fever.*

Perhaps the most famous immune carrier in medical history was a cook often called "Typhoid Mary." In the early 1900s a number of cases of typhoid fever near Oyster Bay, New York, were found to involve people who had eaten at the place where Mary Mallon worked. Further study led the investigators to the carrier herself. She had no symptoms of the disease but had infected scores of other people. At least 51 cases of typhoid (and 3 typhoid-related deaths) are attributed to her.

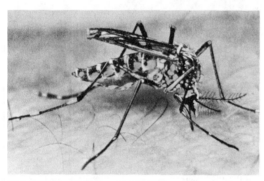
9C-1 *The* Anopheles *mosquito is the vector for the malaria parasite.*

Review Questions 9C-1

1. List several reasons the Lord may have for permitting a person to suffer disease or disorder.
2. Describe the two ways pathogens can affect a host.
3. Compare and contrast exotoxins, endotoxins, and preformed toxins.
4. List and describe six ways a pathogen can enter your body.
5. What causes the disease we call leprosy today? What are the symptoms of leprosy?
6. What are some of the differences between the leprosy described in Leviticus 13 and 14 and the disease we call leprosy today? In the Bible leprosy is often used to represent what spiritual concept? How does this idea parallel the disease?

---

vector: (L. VEHERE, to carry)

Defense Against Infectious Disease

God has wonderfully equipped the human body to resist disease. The majority of us enjoy good health most of the time in spite of the fact that we live in an environment filled with pathogenic organisms. Our body's system of defenses is a solid testimony against evolution. These defenses could not have developed over long periods; the entire population would have been killed off by disease at the beginning. The defenses had to work correctly the first time.

The Lord has also permitted man to develop drugs and medical techniques which can help us overcome pathogens which invade our bodies. The first part of this section will deal with the primary body defenses against infectious diseases: *structural, cellular,* and *chemical.* Then some of the medical techniques used today will be discussed.

Structural defenses

The **structural defenses,** our "first line of defense" against disease, prevent pathogens from entering the body. The *skin* forms an effective barrier against invading organisms. Moreover, the skin secretes certain fatty acids and salts which are believed to inhibit microorganisms.

The *mucous membranes* lining the respiratory, digestive, urinary, and reproductive tracts are composed of closely packed cells that also form a tight wall against invading organisms. The mucus secreted by these membranes traps microorganisms and other incoming materials such as dust and then disposes of them. The mucous membranes of the nose, trachea, and lungs, for example, have cilia which move the mucus with its trapped materials to the throat. The small amount of mucus continuously coming to the throat is normally swallowed. The digestive juices of the stomach are highly acidic and quickly kill most pathogens that are swallowed.

Certain nonpathogenic microorganisms that live in our intestines (the intestinal flora) are beneficial to us. Physicians do not fully understand how this defense works, but they do know that the intestinal flora occupy the areas that pathogens would occupy if they could. When the normal intestinal flora have been destroyed by medications, pathogenic bacteria can become established and cause disease.

Tear glands, in combination with blinking, not only keep the exposed surfaces of the eye moist and dust-free but also ward off certain pathogens. Tears contain *lysozyme,* a powerful enzyme that attacks the cell walls of bacteria.

Cellular defenses

If microorganisms should get past your first line of defense, your second line of defense comes into action. This consists of phagocytic cells, the lymphatic system, and elevated body temperature (fever).

9C-3 *An infection of bacteria causing inflammation, being attacked by white blood cells and being carried to the lymph nodes*

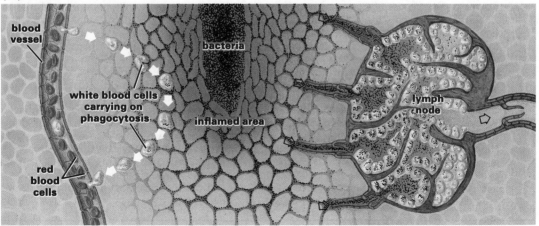

blood vessel

bacteria

white blood cells carrying on phagocytosis

inflamed area

lymph node

red blood cells

Human Infectious Diseases

You may not be familiar with all of the diseases mentioned in this chapter or may have some wrong ideas about them. The following gives some information or tells where in this book you can find information about these diseases. Other conditions are discussed in this book and can be located using the index.

AIDS   See page 571.

African Sleeping Sickness   See page 266.

Botulism is food poisoning caused by a bacterial exotoxin. It is one of the most powerful poisons known. The symptoms generally appear within 12-36 hr. and include fatigue, dizziness, and paralysis of the muscles of the eyes and pharynx. Paralysis spreads to the respiratory system. Botulism is often the result of improperly canned food. If the spores of the botulism bacteria (which can be found in the soil almost everywhere) enter the food and survive canning they can grow anaerobically and produce the toxin.

Bubonic plague is caused by a bacterium which lives in rodents but can be carried to humans by rodent fleas. The symptoms include swelling of the lymph nodes (called *buboes,* which accounts for the name "bubonic plague") and spread through the body. Rodent control is the best prevention. Antibiotics are used in treatment, and the person develops an immunity once he recovers. A virulent form in the Middle Ages caused repeated plagues and killed a quarter of the population of Europe. This form is believed to have caused a breakdown of the blood which turned the person a dark color and accounts for the name "black death."

Colds   See page 243.

Cowpox   See pages 238-39.

Cholera, one of today's most common infectious diseases, is caused by bacteria and is transmitted by contaminated water. The bacteria live in the human intestine and produce toxins which affect the intestinal wall and its permeability. The person loses excessive water, causing extreme dehydration, then shock. Prevention includes treating water and proper disposal of sewage. Vaccines of dead cholera cells are available, but the immunity is of short duration.

Diptheria is caused by a bacterium that generally lives only in the throat where it produces exotoxins. The toxins cause fever, a tired feeling, and can harm the heart muscles, nerves, and fatty tissues. In the throat the bacteria causes soreness and produces a leathery, bluish-white membrane composed of bacteria, dead cells, and blood-clotting fibers. This membrane can cause death by suffocation. Transmission is by droplets. Treatment involves giving antibodies to destroy the toxins and antibiotics to destroy the bacteria. Vaccination by a toxoid is routine, and diptheria, once a major killer of children, is now rare in most of the civilized world.

Dysentery is a condition of abdominal cramps and diarrhea which involves blood in the stool. It may be caused by certain chemicals, bacteria, protozoans, and worms. Bacterial dysentery is caused by several species. Some species cause mild symptoms, but some species cause high fever, chills, convulsions, and frequent bloody stools resulting in dehydration. A spontaneous cure usually happens within a few days. The bacteria invade the body through tainted food, water or unsanitary practices (also see *amoebic dysentery,* page 266).

Flu   See *Influenza,* page 243.

Gas gangrene is caused by bacteria which enter the body through a wound. The bacteria are obligate anaerobes which grow deep in the body and kill tissues. The area often swells and may ooze gaseous and liquid waste products of anaerobic decomposition. The best prevention is to clean dirty wounds thoroughly and to use antibiotics early. Once established, amputation of the infected area is sometimes necessary.

Hepatitis is a general term meaning an infection of the liver (also see *Infectious hepatitis,* page 243).

Impetigo is a bacterial infection of the skin. It causes blisters which release a fluid that dries to form a crust. Transmitted by contact with the fluids from the sore, it is often a problem for infants and small children.

Influenza   See page 243.

Leprosy   See page 247.

Malaria   See pages 265, 267.

Measles   See page 243.

Meningitis is any inflammation of the meninges (the membranes covering the brain and spinal cord). Some viruses and several species of bacteria can cause meningitis. The symptoms include headaches, spasms, stiff neck, and exaggerated reflexes. In severe cases, convulsions and death occur. Most forms of bacterial meningitis enter through the mouth and require close contact to be passed from one person to another. Vaccines are available for some forms.

Polio   See page 243.

Rheumatic fever is a reaction to the toxins produced by several species of bacteria. These bacteria infect the throat and cause a fever. The body produces antibodies in reaction to the bacteria, but these antibodies fail to recognize certain tissues as being part of the body and begin to destroy them. Some of these tissues are in the heart, and the antibodies may cause severe heart damage. The symptoms include a sudden fever and joint pain several days to 6 weeks following a streptococcus infection. Little can be done about the antibodies in the blood, but the bacteria can be treated with antibiotics, thus limiting the antibody production.

Salmonellosis is an intestinal disorder caused by several of the members of a bacteria genus. Technically, salmonellosis is not food poisoning because the organism lives in the intestine where it produces toxins which cause headache, chills, vomiting, diarrhea, and fever between 8-48 hr. after being consumed. The symptoms last a few days and are rarely fatal even without the use of antibiotics.

Scarlet fever is a usually quite mild infection caused by *Streptococcus* bacteria. Within 2-7 days of exposure the person experiences a sore throat (where the bacteria generally begin growing) and fever. A body rash develops and in time the skin peels. The face is flushed (hence the name scarlet fever) with a pale ring around the lips. The person also has a coated, inflamed tongue. Complications, including rheumatic fever, sometimes occur. Former patients have partial immunity. Antibiotics are effective in controlling the disease.

Smallpox   See pages 238-39

Syphilis   See page 644.

Tetanus is also called "lockjaw." The spores of the anaerobic bacteria that cause tetanus are common in topsoil. If they enter a wound they cause damage to the blood supply and then can grow in anaerobic conditions and produce toxins. These toxins affect the central nervous system by causing continual impulses to be sent to the muscles. The muscles contract and remain rigid. The muscles of the jaw are often involved. If not treated the person often dies a painful death as

more and more of his muscles are affected. Antibiotics can kill the bacteria, but the toxin must be treated by antitoxin. Temporary immunity can be achieved by injections of a toxoid.

Tuberculosis (TB) is still a dreaded respiratory infection. It may cause little damage in healthy people, but in others, for reasons not completely understood, the bacteria may cause fatigue, weight loss, and a persistent cough as it forms clumps of damaged lung tissue called tubercules. In advanced cases there is bleeding in the lungs as the bacteria destroy lung tissue and the person coughs up blood. The bacteria are spread by inhaling airborne bacteria which may live in the air for hours. Treatment includes rest and antibiotics. It is difficult to completely wipe out the bacteria, and recurrent attacks are common. A species of tuberculosis bacteria was common in cattle and passed to humans in milk. Pasteurization of milk from healthy cows has virtually eradicated this type of tuberculosis in humans in the U.S. and Europe.

Typhus   See pages 234-35.

Typhoid is caused by a bacterium which enters the body through contaminated food or water. It starts in the digestive tract but later enters the blood. In time, the bacteria invade the organs. A fever and rose-colored spots on the abdominal skin develop. The fever may remain for weeks. In time, the symptoms go away, but the person may still harbor the organism. Often the bacteria live in the liver and gall bladder, causing the person to pass the bacteria in his feces. A vaccine is available and is recommended for those who go to areas where typhoid is common.

Undulant fever is caused by bacteria which normally enter the body through milk or close association with animals. The symptoms include chills, fatigue, headaches, backaches, and fever which normally goes up and down (undulates) within a 24-hr. period.

Whooping cough (pertussis) is caused by bacteria which a person inhales. After an incubation period of about a week the initial symptoms of a sore throat and minor cough develop. A persistent cough develops after 1 or 2 weeks followed by a long forced inspiration (or "whoop") ending in the expulsion of a clear, sticky mucus. This stage may last 4-6 weeks and often leads to other complications.

There are two types of *phagocytic cells*—fixed and free. The fixed cells are found in lymph nodes throughout your body and in certain tissues and organs (such as liver). The free phagocytic cells include certain white blood cells (leucocytes).

When an invasion of microorganisms occurs anywhere in the body, phagocytic white blood cells leave the bloodstream through the walls of tiny blood vessels and travel to the site of the infection. There they isolate the invaders from the rest of the body by forming a barrier around the area. At the same time many white blood cells engulf and digest the pathogens with enzymes. In the process toxins kill many of the white blood cells. The bacteria, white blood cells, and fluids that remain after the conflict form **pus.**

The liquid part of the blood plays an important role in our cellular defensive system. Normally fluid from the blood fills the spaces around all of your body cells. But in an area of infection, extra fluid fills the area, causing much of the swelling seen around an infection. This fluid washes many of the pathogens and other substances from the area. The fluid carrying the foreign substances enters the vessels and nodes of the *lymphatic system.* When in the lymphatic system the fluid is called *lymph.* In the lymph nodes *fixed phagocytic cells* help filter the lymph. The lymph then reenters the bloodstream (see pages 568-69). Enzymes break down the materials that remain in the phagocytic cells of the lymph nodes into soluble, nontoxic substances which are eventually carried away by the blood as wastes.

Although most people think of a **fever** (a raised body temperature) only as a symptom of a disease, a fever is a defense reaction to some infections. Some fevers are local (only at the area of the infection), but in more severe infections fevers may involve the whole body. The higher temperature makes the environment less favorable for many parasitic organisms. Even a small increase can appreciably inhibit the growth of many pathogens. Also, chemical reactions proceed more rapidly at higher temperatures, allowing the body not only to accelerate its defenses but also to use defenses that would not normally be put into operation. However, if the body temperature goes too high or is raised for too long, damage to some body tissues (especially the brain) may result. In such cases a physician often prescribes measures to decrease the body temperature.

Chemical defenses

Our third line of defense against disease is made up of chemicals called **antibodies.*** Antibodies are protein molecules made by the body and carried by the blood, which are able to combat specific pathogens or their toxins. Antibodies are specific, attacking only certain substances. (Antibodies are further discussed in Chapter 21B.)

Medical control of disease

If the body's defenses should not be able to combat the pathogen, or if the physician feels it would be wise to help the body, there are several "chemical warfare" tools available. One of these is **chemotherapy,** the use of chemical agents to treat or prevent disease. Physicians select chemicals that will injure or kill specific pathogens without damaging the host's body. There may be *side effects* (symptoms caused by the chemicals). If side effects are minor, patients must tolerate them during the period of treatment.

Today the most used form of chemotherapy for infectious diseases involves **antibiotics.*** These are chemicals produced by living things which are either *bactericidal* (killing bacteria) or *bacteriostatic* (inhibiting growth of bacteria). To be useful an antibiotic must have little effect on tissues of most humans. The properties of antibiotics were discovered by accident in 1929 by the British bacteriologist Alexander Fleming. Fleming, returning to his laboratory after a short vacation, noticed a blue mold growing on a Petri dish culture that had become full of bacteria. Around the mold there was a clear, circular area where the bacteria had been killed. The mold had produced a toxic substance that had diffused outward, killing the bacteria.

Fleming identified the mold as a species of *Penicillium* and named the substance it produced **penicillin.** Realizing the potential of this substance as a drug, he tested it, found that it was *not* toxic to most laboratory animals, and determined that it was effective against many different

---

antibody: anti- (Gk. ANTI, opposite or against) + -body (Ger. BOT-, container)

antibiotic: anti- (against) + -biotic (pertaining to life)

9C-4 *Although Fleming discovered penicillin in 1929, significant use of the drug did not happen until 1940. Then, under the pressure of World War II, pharmaceutical companies mass-produced it, bringing the price to 1/1000th of its original cost.*

kinds of bacteria. By 1942, scientists had produced a pure penicillin–a yellow powder having a remarkable potency which they used successfully against many bacterial infections.

In 1943 *streptomycin,* an antibiotic produced by the soil organism *Streptomyces griseus,* was discovered. This antibiotic is effective against tuberculosis and several other diseases that do not respond to penicillin. However, it produces various side effects in humans. Because more effective, less toxic medicines are available, streptomycin is rarely used today.

9C-5 *In order to identify bacteria and test their sensitivity to antibiotics, medical laboratories prepare plates such as this one. The right compartments have different media. Which media support growth of the bacteria and what the colonies look like help to identify the bacteria. The paper discs on the left contain different antibiotics. The ring around each disc tells the effectiveness of that antibiotic against the bacteria.*

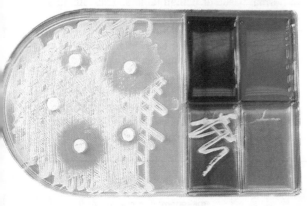

Because antibiotics affect many pathogenic bacteria, some people are tempted to use them without proper medical prescription. But such use can cause long-term or short-term damage to their health. The decisions about whether to use an antibiotic, how much to use, and how long to use it should always be made by a physician.

Since many antibiotics are rapidly removed from the body (usually in the urine), a physician often prescribes a series of doses to be sure the pathogen is completely under control. A pathogen that is only partly "wiped out" can often make a comeback if repeated doses are not taken.

The quest for new antibiotics continues. Some infectious diseases are not yet under control. Then, too, in any population of microorganisms a few may be *naturally resistant* to an antibiotic. Although the nonresistant strains may be killed off by the antibiotic, the naturally resistant ones survive and multiply. As time goes on the resistant organisms form a greater percentage of the total population of that pathogen. This makes it increasingly difficult to treat the disease with the same antibiotic. Since a pathogen resistant to one antibiotic is often affected by another one, scientists are eager to increase the number of antibiotics available.

Occasionally you hear that a pathogen has "developed" a resistance, implying that the pathogen is evolving. This "development" of resistant strains is usually an example of selection from an already-existing gene pool, not the development of new characteristics. Even if a pathogen did become resistant to an antibiotic because of mutation, this is not evolution, but merely a variation of an existing organism.

Review Questions 9C-2

1. What are the body's three lines of defense against disease?
2. List and describe several of the body's structural defenses against disease.
3. Describe the working of the body's cellular defenses against disease.
4. What method can physicians use to help control a pathogen that is in the body?
5. What is the difference between bactericidal and bacteriostatic chemicals?

Disorders

For our study, we will define **disorders** as afflictions which are not caused by a pathogen. Disorders can be grouped into three major types:

❑ **Inherited disorders**   These disorders are either the direct result of an inherited gene (as in hemophilia, PKU, or sickle-cell anemia) or an inherited tendency for a disorder (as may be the case for diabetes mellitus).

❑ **Injuries**   Caused by physical damage to the body, injuries may be temporary (as a bruise or minor cut), or permanent (as the loss of a leg or eye). Burns, broken bones, sprained joints, concussions (impaired activity of the brain caused by a severe jar or shock), and some hearing and vision defects are the results of injuries.

❑ **Organic disorders**   These conditions are not inherited or caused by injury. A *deficiency disease* results from improper nourishment such as the lack of a vitamin or mineral. *Chemical poisoning* and *radiation sickness* result from exposure to environmental factors. Strokes, ulcers, blood clots in the vessels (thrombosis), types of hardening of the arteries, kidney stones, gallstones, and many nervous disorders are caused by unknown or only partially understood factors.

The rest of this chapter includes a discussion on two organic disorders: benign tumors and cancer.

Benign tumors

Occasionally a group of cells stops functioning normally and grows a structure different from the tissue of which it is a part. This abnormal growth of cells is called a **tumor.** If the growth is slow and localized, it is called a **benign*** (bih NINE) tumor. The body often walls off areas of benign tumors, preventing their spread.

Some examples of benign tumors are common (brown) moles and certain birthmarks. The tumor cells often closely resemble those of the tissue from which they originated. Some benign tumors grow to a certain size and stop; others expand slowly, exerting pressure on the surrounding tissues. In some cases the pressure from a benign tumor can seriously impair the functions of an organ. For example, it may obstruct a secretion,

cut off the blood supply to a region, or, as in the case of a brain tumor, cause serious disability or death. Benign tumors of the hormone glands can cause the gland to secrete either too much or too little of its hormones.

The cause of most benign tumors is not known. Surgical removal is a successful and lasting treatment in a vast majority of cases.

Is It Cancer?

Both benign and malignant tumors may occur anywhere in the body. To diagnose which type of tumor is present, a doctor performs a **biopsy.*** In a biopsy a sample of tissue from the tumor is removed and sent to a **pathologist** (puh THAHL uh jist), a specialist in diseased tissues. The specimen is analyzed microscopically to determine if it is benign or malignant.

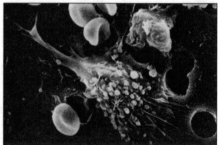

The characteristic spikes of a cancer cell

Cancer

If the growth of a tumor is rapid and chaotic it is called a **malignant* tumor.** A malignant tumor is often called a **cancer.** The nuclei in the cancer cells are larger and often contain more DNA, and cell growth and reproduction are more rapid than in normal tissue or benign tumors. The cells in a malignant tumor often develop a bizarre appearance and may even have an abnormal number of chromosomes. Cells that become cancerous stop their normal functions and become harmful to the body. Cancer cells may separate and travel to other parts of the body, starting new tumors.

Cancer cells are cells of the body that have changed. Cancer researchers point to a two-step process in developing a cancer: *initiation* and then

---

FACETS OF BIOLOGY

9C-1

Aging and Death

In addition to diseases and disorders, humans face the problems of aging and the prospect of death. Scripture indicates that aging and death are both a part of the curse that God pronounced in Genesis 3. *Aging* is the continual degeneration (wearing out) of our bodies. Stooped posture, thinning and graying hair, and wrinkling and drying skin are but some of the outward signs of the deterioration that is taking place throughout the body. Organs gradually wear out; the heart and blood vessels become less elastic; bones become more brittle; joints stiffen; brain cells die and are not replaced; the eyes become less capable of focusing; dental problems make eating difficult; injuries heal more slowly; and the resistance to disease diminishes.

Aging

Much research is being conducted in the field of **gerontology** (JEHR un TAHL uh jee), the science of aging. Researchers have determined that degeneration begins when a person is in his 20s, shortly after his growth has been completed. Scientists still do not agree about the physical causes of aging. One theory holds that it is the cumulative effect of wear and tear, the "battle scars" of the continual fight against disease, injury, and the rigors of life itself.

Aging has also been attributed to waste accumulation in the cells. Wastes are continually being removed from cells, but some types of wastes are not completely removed. Therefore, as cells grow older, the concentration of certain wastes increases, and presumably the function of the cell is being impaired. Although a waste product called *lipofuscin* (LIH poh FUS in) accumulates in older nerve cells, no one has demonstrated that this causes a loss of function.

Another theory is that aging and death are genetically programmed into the body. From the moment the zygote is formed, the individu-al follows a prescribed program through the different stages of life: embryo, infancy, childhood, adolescence, young adulthood, middle age, old age, and death. Thus, aging and death are a natural part of the life cycle, directed by genetic machinery. Some gerontologists believe there are genes that trigger degenerative processes as life progresses. Research has shown that certain human cells have only about 100 generations built into them. After their appointed number of cell divisions they degenerate and eventually die.

There also seem to be complex aging mechanisms through which one part of the body can transmit aging instructions to another part.

Christians view aging as a divinely ordained modification of our physical being that came about after the Fall. We should be willing to accept aging, knowing that ultimately we will receive a glorified body that is incorruptible (unaging) (I Cor. 15:51-57). Unregenerate people, not having this hope,

would like to find some way to block the sequence of aging and thus "beat the system." Perhaps someday man will be able to "push off" the effects of aging, extending useful life. Scientifically, this seems a long way off, but the Bible does not say that man cannot do it.

Death

Someone made a statement once that the surest way to live to a ripe old age is to choose ancestors who lived to ripe old ages. This statement contains a basic element of truth: genes do set limits upon a person's life. But within these limits there is considerable room for individual variation. In addition to having "good genes," one must avoid accidents and diseases and practice good living habits (proper diet, rest, exercise, and a lifestyle conducive to good mental and emotional health).

Yet, barring the Lord's return for His saints, death is inevitable for every person. Most Christians believe that scientists will never find a way to avoid death. Death appears to be a part of the universal degenerative trend and is in keeping with the Scripture, which says "it is appointed unto man once to die" (Heb. 9:27). It appears that only God Himself could change this plan.

What exactly is death? In former times men relied on two main indicators–absence of heartbeat and absence of breathing. But the cells of the body do not die immediately when these functions cease. Victims of drowning and

electrical shock can often be successfully revived if action is taken quickly. Even brain cells, the most fragile type of cells, can live for a couple of minutes after their blood supply is cut off. A person resuscitated within this time would suffer little, if any, permanent damage. If the body temperature is lowered (as may happen when a person drowns in cold water), he may be revived after half an hour or longer without brain damage.

Therefore, a definition of death which is based only on heartbeat and breathing is unsatisfactory. Now scientists usually consider the brain the indicator of the state of the physical organism. A functioning brain produces minute electrical impulses called *brain waves*. An *electroencephalogram** (ih LEK troh en SEF uh luh GRAM) or EEG measures these waves. If there is no electrical activity in the brain, the EEG is "flat." Medical authorities tell us that if there are no brain waves for 24-48 hr., there is no hope for the patient. A person in this condition is **clinically dead.**

Suppose that the heart of a clinically dead person is still beating and that the person is still breathing (without the aid of any supporting equipment). Would it be proper to bury such a person? Even though the brain may be "dead," it would seem strange indeed to bury a body that was still breathing. To avoid such a dilemma, many authorities insist that all three criteria exist before burial. Problems often arise when "life-support" equipment is being used

to maintain the heartbeat or breathing while there is little or no brain activity.

The Christian recognizes death to be the departure of the soul and spirit from the body. For the Christian, to be absent from the body is to be present with the Lord (II Cor. 5:8). Medical instruments cannot measure the non-physical parts of the body to determine when it has degenerated too far to be inhabitable by the soul and spirit. However, we must be careful: God does work miracles!

Most Christians doubt that man will ever be able to conquer physical death through scientific endeavors. Biological problems are numerous, and Scripture tells us that the power of life and death is in the Lord's hands (Matt. 28:18). Although man may not be able to conquer death, there is One who promises us the victory over it. Christ's death on the cross conquered physical death; He rose from the grave having a new, incorruptible (unaging), glorified body.

The just eternal fate of every sinful human being is hell, a place that God prepared for Satan and his hosts. However, Christ also conquered spiritual death so that those who believe on His name would live eternally with Him in their glorified bodies. With these promises in the Word of God, it is easy for the Christian to say, "O death, where is thy sting? O grave, where is thy victory?" (I Cor. 15:55).

Review questions on page 258.

electroencephalogram: electro-
(electricity) + en- (in) + cephalo-
(Gk. KEPHALE, head) + -gram
(GRAMME, letter)

promotion. Initiation is generally accomplished in one of three ways.

❏ **Carcinogenic chemicals** Cancer-causing chemicals are called carcinogens. The best-known carcinogens are in the chemical residue from smoking or use of other tobacco products. A definite link between smoking and lung cancer has been established for many years. Other carcinogenic chemicals include formaldehyde, asbestos, and xylene.

❏ **Radiation** Skin cancer can be caused by excessive exposure to the ultraviolet rays in sunlight. Fortunately, skin cancers (if diagnosed soon enough) are usually mild and often can be removed in a doctor's office. X-rays are also regarded as a cancer hazard. Both skin cancer and leukemia (cancer involving white blood cells) have been linked to X-rays. Highly radioactive substances are considered to be cancer-producing agents. Small amounts of radiation (minor exposure to the sun or medical X-rays) are not believed to be harmful.

❏ **Viruses** In humans some cancers apparently are caused by viruses. It is likely that many cancers are not virus related.

Once the cell is ''potentially cancerous'' it must be affected by environmental factors to convert into a cancerous tumor. These tumors can be promoted by diet, general health, and various other things depending on the kind of cancer and the person's genetic make-up.

Almost any tissue in the body can develop a cancer, but each tissue can get different kinds of cancer, and some tissues can develop several different cancers. What a person does to prevent one form of cancer may have no effect on another form. For example, there are several kinds of skin cancer, and they are not all caused by the same factors.

Who gets what kinds of cancer also depends a great deal on their genetic make-up. Certain cells in some people are naturally resistant to some forms of cancer. These people would rarely get that form of cancer. The next person, however, may have inherited a weaker cell, and he develops that form of cancer even if he is careful to avoid what is believed to initiate or promote that cancer.

It is, of course, wise to avoid those things that are known to induce or promote cancers, but one must also be careful not to be caught up in every ''new fad'' or advertising gimmick designed to cash in on people's natural fear of cancer.

Cancer treatments

The leading method of treatment for cancer is surgical removal of the affected tissues. Many lives have been saved in this way; however, the surgeon is completely successful only if he is able to remove all the cancerous cells. Thus, it is important to diagnose cancer early, while the affected area is still small. If the disorder has spread to the lymph nodes or to vital organs, the chances for survival are reduced. Even if it is impossible to remove all the cancer, surgery may still help relieve pain, restore lost bodily functions, and slow the spread of the disease.

Another treatment for certain cancers is *radiation.* Physicians use X-rays or emissions from radioactive isotopes to destroy cancer cells, and, they hope, to leave most normal cells intact. This method can sometimes completely eradicate localized cancers. In more widespread malignancies radiation therapy may provide relief from pain and prolong the life of the patient, but complete recovery is rare. Radiation, however, can *cause* tumors and other undesirable side effects.

9C-6 *A person being prepared for radiation treatment*

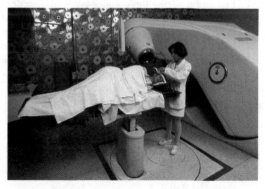

Physicians sometimes treat cancer by *chemotherapy.* In this case the chemical is directed not at an invading pathogen but at cancer cells. Often the chemical chosen interferes with cell division.

Since cancer cells divide more frequently than normal cells, the chemical will affect these cells more than the rest of the body.

Unfortunately, cancer chemotherapy also affects other cells in the body. Normally, the most rapidly growing cells of the body are affected first. This explains anemia (lack of red blood cells), loss of hair, sensitive skin, and general deterioration of the patient's health. When the chemotherapy stops, the symptoms are reversed, and hopefully only the cancer cells have been permanently harmed. Repeated chemotherapy treatments can destroy several forms of cancer. Sometimes chemotherapy is used to kill those cancer cells that were not removed in the surgical procedure, thus increasing the probability that the cancer will not start to grow again.

Future Cancer Treatments

The following two experimental cancer treatments hold exceptional promise:

❑ *Interleukines* are chemicals produced by the body cells that stimulate certain immune system cells to multiply. If some of a cancer patient's white blood cells are grown in interleukine solutions, the cells increase in numbers and activity. When returned to the person's blood stream they attack and kill cancer cells. This procedure is still in the experimental stage.

❑ *Monoclonial antibodies* can be produced in a laboratory. Scientists have developed antibodies that will attach to specific cancer cells without harming the cancer cell. Researchers are trying to attach a substance to the monoclonial antibody that will either hamper or destroy the cancer.

Biological Terms

Infectious Diseases	toxin	*Defense Against*	*Disorder*	cancer
infectious disease	inflammation	*Infectious Disease*	disorder	carcinogenic
pathogen	communicable disease	structural defense	injury	chemical
host	droplet infection	pus	organic disorder	*Facets*
incubation period	contact infection	fever	tumor	gerontology
exotoxin	contamination infection	antibody	benign tumor	clinically dead
endotoxin	wound infection	chemotherapy	biopsy	
pre-formed toxin	vector-carried infection	antibiotic	pathologist	
food poisoning	immune carrier	penicillin	malignant tumor	

Review Questions 9C-3

1. List and describe three major types of disorders. Give examples of each.
2. In what ways can benign tumors cause physical difficulties?
3. What are some of the differences between normal body cells and cancer cells?
4. List and describe three possible causes of cancer.
5. List and describe several present cancer treatments.
6. List two treatments that may be used in the future.
7. Why is it important to detect cancer early?

Facet 9C-1: Aging and Death, pages 255-56

1. List some possible causes of aging.
2. Discuss several criteria that have been used to determine the time of death.

Thought Questions

1. Give examples from Scripture which show how God used diseases or disorders to accomplish His will.
2. Give several reasons man must continually seek new methods of conquering disease. Will man ever conquer all diseases? Why or why not?
3. Does a human soul ever die? What is spiritual death? Support your answers from Scripture.

THE KINGDOM PROTISTA
MICROBIOLOGY PART II

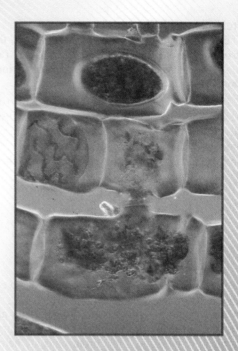

TEN

10A – The Protozoans

Observing drops of pond water with a microscope can be fascinating. An amazing variety of microorganisms whiz past, roll by, float along in microcurrents, or just sit there. Some appear to be globs; others have perfectly geometric shapes. Some are transparent; others are shades of green, yellow, red, blue, and a host of other colors. Some appear tiny while others seem huge. If you take a drop of water from an area just millimeters away from where you took the first drop, you may find completely different organisms.

Although some of the organisms that you observe in pond water may belong to various kingdoms, most of them are in the **kingdom Protista.** Do not get the idea that protists are all small, insignificant organisms. On the contrary, some of them are relatively large; some have played major roles in history being responsible for the defeat of great armies; and currently, many of them play a major role in our environment similar to that of the land plants by manufacturing a good share of the oxygen we breathe.

Protozoans and algae

The kingdom Protista has two subkingdoms, the *Protozoa* (protozoans) and the *Protophyta* (algae). These are convenient groupings of various phyla.

Protozoans are microscopic unicellular (or, occasionally, colonial) organisms which are usually motile. This movement, often quite rapid, prompted Anton van Leeuwenhoek to describe protozoans as "animalcules" and classify them

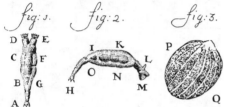

10A-1 *Many of Leeuwenhoek's animalcules were protozoans.*

in the animal kingdom. Most protozoans are aquatic, but many are found in the soil. A large number are parasitic. Most protozoans are heterotrophic, but some are both autotrophic and heterotrophic. Protozoans are divided into four phyla based on their means of locomotion.

Algae* have been called the "grass of many waters." In fact, every natural water supply contains some type of alga. Most are microscopic unicellular or colonial organisms. Algae may appear to be floating mats of green slime or velvety coatings on submerged rocks. Their presence may color water various shades of red, brown, blue, or green. You can find algae growing on soil, rocks, trees, and inside small animals. A few algae form very large colonies–some reach over 30 m (98 ft.). Since algae are generally photosynthetic, at one time taxonomists placed them in kingdom Plantae. Today many scientists recognize five algal phyla in the kingdom Protista. A sixth group, the blue-green algae, is procaryotic and, therefore, placed in the kingdom Monera as cyanobacteria. The eucaryotic algal phyla are discussed in the next section of this chapter.

The protozoans

The term "protozoans" means "first animals." Some early microscopists believed that these "animalcules" gave rise to larger animals, which in turn gave rise to larger animals. This concept is evolutionary and shows an ignorance of the complexity of these tiny organisms. In the space of a single cell, protozoans perform all the functions necessary to maintain their living condition.

Their small size helps protozoans in certain functions. The protozoans, being in a moist environment, merely exchange dissolved gasses between their cytoplasm and their surroundings. Soluble wastes diffuse from protozoan cytoplasm through their membranes into the environment. However, securing and digesting food, response to conditions, movement, and reproduction are not simple tasks. Even though in humans each of these activities requires hundreds of thousands of cells, every protozoan cell can, by some method, accomplish these difficult tasks. Finding out what protozoans do, how they do it, and watching them do it are some of the most interesting activities in introductory biological studies.

Phylum Sarcodina: The Sarcodines

Members of the **phylum Sarcodina** (sar koh DYE nuh) are characterized by their lack of a standard body shape. These single-celled protists are enclosed in a flexible plasma membrane that allows them to constantly change their shape. When dormant, the animal may be nearly spherical. When moving or feeding, it will form numerous extensions of its body that function as "false feet." Some species of sarcodines construct and inhabit shells. Sarcodines live in a variety of habitats, including fresh water, the sea floor, and the human mouth and intestine.

Ameba: a typical sarcodine

Amoeba proteus, the common ameba, looks like little more than a blotch of gray jelly. Usually amebas are not swimmers but are part of the slimy covering of submerged rocks or plants. Here they ingest organic debris and small microorganisms. Like other sarcodines, amebas do not form colonies.

The cytoplasm in the ameba is divided into two types: the clear *ectoplasm** found along the plasma membrane and the *endoplasm,** the cytoplasm in the interior of the animal. A single, disc-shaped

---

algae: (L. ALGA, seaweed)

ectoplasm: ecto- (Gk. ECTOS, outside) + -plasm (to mold)

endoplasm: endo- (within) + -plasm (to mold)

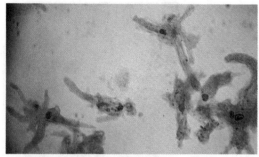

10A-2 Amoeba proteus *stained*

nucleus controls all the metabolic activities of the cell. *Contractile vacuoles* collect and eliminate water, regulating the amount of water in the ameba.

The most outstanding feature of the ameba is its **ameboid movement.** When an ameba moves, its endoplasm streams toward one area of the plasma membrane, causing a bulge to form. This bulge is gradually extended into a long **pseudopod*** (SOO duh POD). The entire cytoplasm of the ameba may flow into a pseudopod and draw the plasma membrane with it, causing the animal to move.

The ameba can respond to a variety of stimuli, generally by a change in the speed or direction of movement. Such actions in response to stimuli are called **taxes** (singular, *taxis*). For example, if a floating ameba touches a solid object, it will move toward and adhere to the object. But the response to touch varies under certain circumstances. If an attached ameba is touched with a glass rod, it will retreat from the stimulus. Amebas will approach an area containing substances diffused from foods and recoil from an area of high saltiness.

Once the ameba has located and selected food (by taxes amebas do show ''food preferences''), it uses pseudopods to engulf it. The food material, such as algae or other protozoans, is thus sealed

into a *food vacuole* within the ameba. Lysosomes in the cytoplasm fuse with the food vacuole and deposit their enzymatic contents into it, and digestion proceeds within the vacuole. The soluble foods then diffuse into the cytoplasm, and the insoluble materials that remain are egested.

10A-3 *Typical structures of an ameba; an ameba engulfing food*

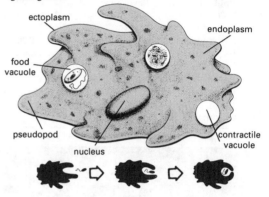

When an ameba reaches a maximum size, it divides into 2 daughter cells (under normal conditions, about every 3 days). The process begins with the replication of the genetic material of the ameba. Mitosis occurs, and the cytoplasm divides, resulting in 2 complete, functional daughter amebas in about 30 min. Amebas are not known to reproduce sexually.

Some ameba species will respond to life-threatening conditions such as dryness or lack of food by becoming a *cyst**, an inactive cell with a tough wall. These dormant organisms become active upon the return of favorable conditions.

10A-4 *An ameba dividing. Beginning to divide (left), about 18 minutes later (middle), and about 20 minutes after the beginning (right).*

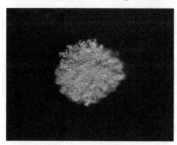 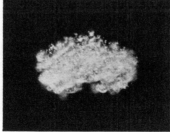 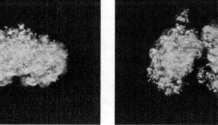

pseudopod or **pseudopodium:**
pseudo- (Gk. PSEUDES, false) + -pod
(PODOS, foot)

cyst: (pouch)

Other Protozoans

In our study of the protozoans one typical or important example has been chosen for each phylum. There are many other examples.

Other Sarcodines

Some sarcodine species live as parasites of other organisms. *Entamoeba coli* live in human intestines and *E. gingivalis* live in human mouths, but neither is pathogenic. *E. histolitica,* however, is a human pathogen (see page 266).

Many sarcodines form *tests* or shells around themselves and then send out their pseudopods through holes in the test. The *foraminiferans* are tested ocean bottom dwellers. Most foraminiferans form tests of calcium carbonate. When they die their shells add to the ooze on the ocean bottom.

An electron micrograph of radiolarian tests

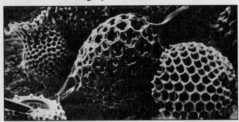

The *radiolarians* form silicon tests and also contribute to the ocean bottom ooze. About a third of the ocean floor is covered with this ooze which may be up to 4,000 m (12,000 ft.) thick. This is impressive when you consider that 1 g (0.035 oz.) may have 50,000 sarcodine tests.

Other Ciliates

The *Stentor* is a giant among protozoans, reaching a size of 2.5 mm (0.1 in.). This trumpet-shaped organism has a ring of cilia about its gullet. The cilia generate a current that draws food into the gullet. A hungry stentor could consume 100 small protozoans per minute.

Vorticella, a ciliate which lives attached by a corkscrew-shaped stalk to a submerged object, has cilia only on the top.

Vorticella

Other Flagellates

The *Volvox* is a small green protozoan with two short flagella. These flagellates join to form large hollow spherical colonies that move in a slow-rolling fashion. The members of the colony are joined by a geometric latticework of cytoplasmic strands. Miniature daughter colonies, formed as a result of asexual reproduction, often float within the adult colony.

Flagellates of the genus *Trichonympha* actually keep many termite species alive. Many termites ingest wood but are unable to digest the cellulose in it. Living in the gut of the termite, these flagellates produce enzymes that digest the cellulose for themselves and for the termite host. The protozoan has a safe place to live, and the termite can "eat" wood; therefore, both thrive. If separated, they both perish.

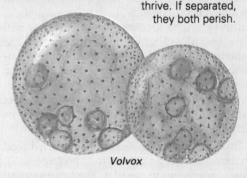

Volvox

Review Questions 10A-1

1. What are the primary characteristics of the kingdom Protista? What characteristics separate protozoans from monerans?
2. Compare and contrast protozoans with algae.
3. Describe the typical movement of a sarcodine.
4. How do amebas obtain food?
5. What is a taxis and what taxes do ameba have?
6. Describe the reproduction of an ameba.

Phylum Ciliophora: The Ciliates

The **ciliates** (SIL ee ihts), members of the **phylum Ciliophora*** (SIL ee AH foh ruh), are among the most intricate and fascinating organisms in the kingdom Protista. These organisms may be up to 3 mm (0.12 in.) long, quite large for a protist, and exist in a variety of shapes.

The characteristic that distinguishes this group is the possession of *cilia*. The cilia of these protozoans beat rhythmically to move either the organism or its food. The arrangement of the cilia varies. Some ciliates are completely covered with cilia; others bear rings or patches of cilia. Most ciliates are free-swimming, but a few can attach to submerged objects.

Paramecium: a typical ciliate

Protozoans of the genus *Paramecium* (PEHR uh MEE see um) are common, free-swimming inhabitants of stagnant lakes and ponds. Paramecia have a distinctive slipper shape maintained by the **pellicle,*** a firm yet flexible covering. The cilia that completely cover the paramecium can beat either forwards or backwards, enabling the organism to turn, rotate, and travel in any direction.

The kidney-shaped **macronucleus*** is the most conspicuous feature of the cytoplasm. The macronucleus appears to be multiple copies of the genetic material of the cell. These copies of genes probably aid the high metabolism typical of most ciliates. The smaller **micronucleus*** functions as the reproductive nucleus.

The body of the paramecium has a funnel-shaped indentation called the **oral groove.** Cilia that line the oral groove sweep food material

through the **mouth pore** into a short, blind pocket called the *gullet*. As food is directed into the gullet, an enlargement forms at the gullet end. This pocket eventually is pinched off, becoming a *food vacuole*. The vacuole is then circulated throughout the cytoplasm, where enzymes from lysosomes digest the food. Any indigestible material is expelled from the paramecium through the anal pore, a tiny opening in the cell.

10A-5 *The path of a food vacuole in a paramecium*

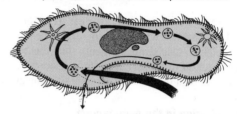

The paramecium has two star-shaped *contractile vacuoles*. The rays of the stars are *canals* that collect excess cell water and empty it into the vacuole at the center. When the vacuole is full, the water is expelled from the cell. The swelling and squeezing of these vacuoles is often seen under the microscope. The concentration of salts in the paramecium's environment determines the rate at which these organelles operate.

Paramecia tend to swim in a forward spiral motion. When the animal collides with an obstacle, it will stop, back up, turn slightly, then move forward again. Paramecia will also avoid temperature extremes and most chemicals in the same way. This *avoiding reaction* is an example of taxis in paramecia. Acidity attracts these protozoans. Because bacteria tend to thrive in acidic

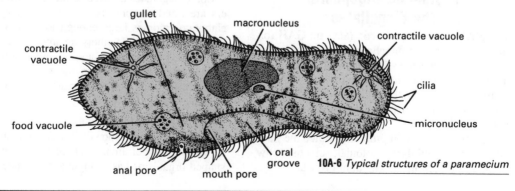

10A-6 *Typical structures of a paramecium*

Ciliophora: Cilia- or Cilio- (L. CILIUM eyelid) + -phora (to bear)
pellicle: (L. PELLIS, skin)

macronucleus: macro- (Gk. MAKROS, large) + -nucleus (central part)
micronucleus: micro- (small) + -nucleus (central part)

environments, this attraction helps paramecia locate bacteria which serve as their food.

10A-7 *A paramecium demonstrating avoidance reaction*

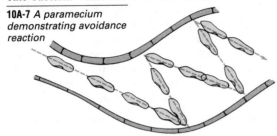

In response to certain stimuli, **trichocysts** (TRIK uh SISTS), which are tiny organelles under the pellicle, discharge filaments into the water. The function of these filaments is uncertain, but they may be a defense mechanism or a means of attachment.

Reproduction in the paramecium

Paramecia reproduce by two methods. The first is *asexual binary fission.* In this process the micronucleus divides by mitosis, and the macronucleus divides amitotically. The paramecium elongates, and a second gullet forms. Finally a furrow forms across the middle of the organism, and it divides into two complete daughter paramecia.

Review Questions 10A-2

1. Describe the typical movement of ciliates.
2. How do paramecia obtain food?
3. What taxes do paramecia have?
4. Describe both sexual and asexual reproduction of paramecia.

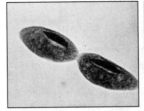 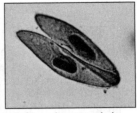

10A-8 *A paramecium in fission (left), and paramecia in conjugations (right)*

Paramecia also reproduce by a type of sexual reproduction called **conjugation.** Two paramecia attach to each other by their oral surfaces. Each animal undergoes a variety of nuclear changes. At one point the cells exchange part of their nuclear material through the cytoplasmic bridge. The cells then separate and undergo more nuclear divisions and changes. Finally, each cell divides to form four paramecia. Conjugation allows a mixing of genetic material that is impossible in asexual reproduction.

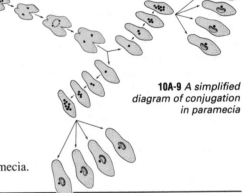

10A-9 *A simplified diagram of conjugation in paramecia*

Phylum Mastigophora: The Flagellates

The **phylum Mastigophora*** (MAS tih GAH foh ruh) consists of the **flagellates,** those protozoans that propel themselves by means of flagella. All mastigophorans are heterotrophic, but some of them have chlorophyll and can produce their own food. Such organisms are both autotrophic and heterotrophic. These ''plant-animals'' were a source of classification problems. Since the flagellates are unicellular or colonial, scientists now place all of them in the kingdom Protista.

Some flagellates are free-swimming while others are fixed to some solid object. Some form elaborate colonies large enough to be seen with the unaided eye while others are among the smallest of the protozoans. They abound in salt and fresh waters, as well as in the soil. Many are parasitic and some are pathogenic in man and animals.

Euglena: a typical flagellate

The genus *Euglena* (yoo GLEE nuh) contains tiny freshwater flagellates. Each of these spindle-shaped organisms has a single anterior flagellum

Mastigophora: masti-
(Gk. MASTIX, whip or lash) + -phora
(to bear)

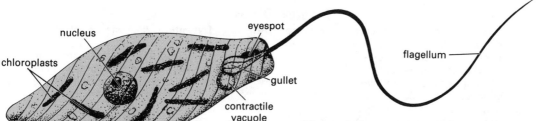

10A-10 *Typical structures of a euglena*

for locomotion. The euglena also has chlorophyll in chloroplasts. Under ideal conditions the euglena survives primarily on the products of photosynthesis. Even under these conditions, however, the euglena is also saprophytic, absorbing dissolved food from the surrounding environment. In low light or darkness, its photosynthetic apparatus shuts down and even degenerates. The euglena can sustain itself on dissolved nutrients.

The body of the euglena is covered with a shape-sustaining *pellicle*. At the anterior end of the animal a small gullet enlarges into a reservoir. Though the reservoir looks much like a mouth, euglenas probably do not ingest food through the gullet and reservoir. Near the reservoir is a tiny, red, light-sensitive *eyespot*. The euglena has a single nucleus containing a large nucleolus. Like most protozoans, the euglena has a *contractile vacuole* which maintains the organism's water balance by expelling excess water from the cytoplasm into the reservoir.

Euglenas usually move by whirling their anterior flagella to pull themselves through the water. They can also move by a modified ameboid movement. The euglena draws its cytoplasm in, making itself almost completely round, and then re-extends itself forward. Employing this **euglenoid movement,** the animal can propel itself with a wormlike motion.

10A-11 *Euglenoid movement*

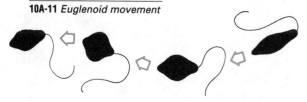

The euglena reproduces by binary fission along the length of its body. Under ideal conditions the euglena will reproduce about once a day. Sexual reproduction in the euglena is unknown.

Phylum Sporozoa: The Sporozoans

The members of the **phylum Sporozoa** (SPOHR uh ZOH uh) are unique among protozoans since, as adults, they do not have pseudopods, cilia, flagella, or any other special structures for locomotion. As the name implies, sporozoans form *spores* at some stage of their life cycle. First, the nucleus of the sporozoan divides several times, and a small amount of cytoplasm gathers around each nucleus. Then the organism breaks apart, and each of the nuclei becomes a spore which may be surrounded by protective coats.

All sporozoans are parasitic, often having complex life cycles involving a number of animal hosts. They feed by absorbing dissolved materials from the host's cells and body fluids. Asexual reproduction may occur by spore formation or by cell division. Many sporozoans also have some means of sexual reproduction.

Plasmodium: a sporozoan

A devastating disease of the tropics is **malaria,** an illness that causes severe discomfort and, frequently, death. Malaria, meaning "bad air," was once believed to be caused by tropical swamp air. Some claim that malaria is the most significant disease of man, directly or indirectly causing more deaths than any other disease and significantly influencing human events.

In the late 1800s the French attempted to dig a canal across Central America that would join the Atlantic Ocean and the Pacific Ocean. The workmen sent to accomplish this task soon fell ill; many died from yellow fever (caused by a virus) or malaria. This epidemic was one crucial reason

Protozoan Diseases

Although most protozoans live harmlessly in the soil or water, there are a good number that live inside other organisms. In some cases the protozoan is beneficial to its host (as in the cellulose-digesting ciliates found in termites). In many cases the protozoans appear harmless. In some cases, however, they are pathogenic.

Most protozoan-caused diseases affect animals. There are, however, several human diseases caused by protozoans. Most of them are rare, but three of them have sometimes changed the course of history and are still health problems today.

Malaria (Sporozoan *Plasmodium*)

Life cycle: The female *Anopheles* mosquito becomes infected by drinking the blood of a human who has malaria. The *Plasmodium* cells mature and develop in the mosquito and migrate to the insect's salivary gland. Before feeding on the blood of another human, the infected mosquito injects saliva into the puncture wound of its new victim and thereby puts the parasite back into the human bloodstream.

One of the mosquitoes common in the U.S. (left) and the *Anopheles* mosquito (right)

In the human, the spindle-shaped *Plasmodium* cells penetrate liver cells where they grow and reproduce in about two weeks. The parasite then enters red blood cells and reproduces. The blood cells burst, releasing cells that may invade other blood cells and repeat this reproductive process. When a mosquito feeds on an infected individual, it ingests the parasite and thus completes the life cycle.

Symptoms and cures: The periodic rupturing of red blood cells releases toxins that are associated with violent fits of chills and fever. The person also suffers anemia (inability of the blood to carry oxygen) and an enlarged spleen. The most successful method of controlling the disease has been to limit human exposure to *Anopheles* mosquitoes. Today a series of drugs can be used to prevent and cure the disease.

Amoebic Dysentery (Sarcodina *Entamoeba histolytica*)

Life cycle: In some areas of the world large portions of the population are *carriers*, (humans with *E. histolytica* in their intestines but not suffering from the disease). *E. histolytica* forms cysts that exit the body in feces. The cysts can live outside the body in moist, warm conditions. The cysts are transferred to humans by contaminated water and houseflies which bring the cysts to food.

Symptoms and cures: In many people *E. histolitica* eats the cells of the intestinal walls causing ulceration. This results in severe diarrhea and can lead to death. In times past the disease was often fatal, but today various drugs can kill the parasite.

African Sleeping Sickness (Mastigophora *Trypanosoma;* different species cause different forms of the disease)

Life cycle: African sleeping sickness is passed from person to person by the blood-sucking tsetse fly which is found only in Africa. The *Trypanosoma* grows and divides in the insect's intestine and then invades the salivary glands. When the fly bites a person the protozoan may enter the blood stream. In the blood stream the parasite reproduces.

Symptoms and cures: After the protozoan has been in the blood it may invade the central nervous system and cause inflammation of the brain resulting in weakness, mental lethargy, and sleepiness which lead to continuous sleep and, possibly, death. Controlling the tsetse fly controls the disease. Drugs can now be given to those suffering from the disease.

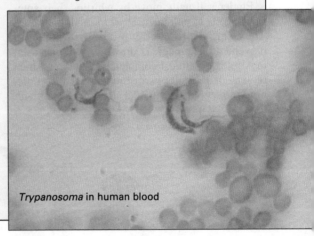

Trypanosoma in human blood

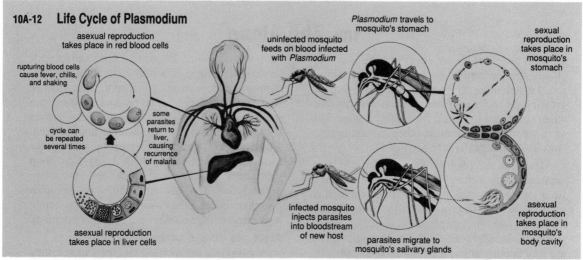

10A-12 **Life Cycle of Plasmodium**

asexual reproduction takes place in red blood cells

rupturing blood cells cause fever, chills, and shaking

cycle can be repeated several times

some parasites return to liver, causing recurrence of malaria

asexual reproduction takes place in liver cells

uninfected mosquito feeds on blood infected with *Plasmodium*

Plasmodium travels to mosquito's stomach

sexual reproduction takes place in mosquito's stomach

infected mosquito injects parasites into bloodstream of new host

parasites migrate to mosquito's salivary glands

asexual reproduction takes place in mosquito's body cavity

why the French project was canceled. The door opened for the United States to build a canal. In 1880, Dr. Charles Laveran discovered the malarial protozoan, a member of the genus *Plasmodium* (plaz MOH dee um). Later research unlocked the complete life cycle of this sporozoan.

Knowing the *Plasmodium* life cycle has helped to control malaria in many areas of the world. When building the Panama Canal, for example, Col. William Gorgas of the United States Army ordered swamps drained and brush cleared in the area where Americans were working. Destroying the mosquito breeding areas eliminated the organisms that transmitted malaria and also yellow fever. This enabled the Americans to finish the canal.

Biological Terms

kingdom Protista	pseudopod	macronucleus	*The Flagellates*
protozoans	taxes (sing., taxis)	micronucleus	phylum Mastigophora
algae	*The Ciliates*	oral groove	flagellate
The Sarcodines	ciliate	mouth pore	euglenoid movement
phylum Sarcodina	phylum Ciliophora	trichocyst	*The Sporozoans*
ameboid movement	pellicle	conjugation	phylum Sporozoa
			malaria

Review Questions 10A-3

1. Describe the typical methods of movement used by euglenas.
2. Describe the methods euglenas use to obtain food (energy).
3. Why was classifying the euglena difficult for many early microbiologists?
4. What taxes do euglenas have?
5. Why is Sporozoa a significant protozoan phylum?
6. Describe the life cycle of the *Plasmodium*.
7. List six protozoans (other than the ameba, the paramecium, the euglena, and the *Plasmodium*) and tell their significance.
8. When visiting certain countries, such as Mexico, people are often warned not to drink the water in smaller towns. Why is this good advice?
9. Why do people in the U.S. not have to worry about catching African sleeping sickness from a person with the disease who visits in their home?

Thought Question

Why is it inaccurate to call a protozoan a simple organism?

10B - The Algae

To most people algae are either the nuisance that clouds the swimming pool water or the slimy green mat floating on the pond. The green threads growing on rocks in a stream seem insignificant when compared to wheat, corn, or fruit trees. But to fish and indirectly most other aquatic organisms as well, algae are the staff of life.

Algae are the photosynthetic organisms that capture the sun's energy in aquatic environments. In any natural water supply there are thousands of tiny floating organisms called **plankton.*** There are two types of plankton:

❑ **zooplankton*** (ZOH uh PLANGK tun), which are tiny floating animals or protozoans; and

❑ **phytoplankton*** (FYE toh PLANGK tun), which are tiny floating photosynthetic organisms, predominantly algae.

Phytoplankton manufacture not only their own food but also the food for zooplankton and many larger organisms. Thus, they are the *primary food-producing organisms* in aquatic environments. Many fish have a specialized feeding apparatus which permits them to strain plankton from the water. Even the largest known living animal, the great blue whale, weighing over 107 metric tons (236,000 lb.), exists by straining the ocean's "plankton soup."

Man has found various uses for algae. In some areas of the world men use sea algae as a natural fertilizer. In recent times algae have been processed to obtain potash, iodine, nitrogen, salt, and other products. Algae are an inexpensive source of certain vitamins and minerals in the feed of domestic livestock.

In various areas of the world people eat algae. The Japanese cultivate algae as a human food crop. In New England a marine alga called sea kale is eaten as a vegetable. Many algal products are used in food processing. *Irish moss,* an alga which grows along the Atlantic coast, supplies a substance used as a thickener in puddings, jellies, and ice cream.

Some people have begun to look to the sea as a future major source of food for humans. The earth has a limited amount of land suitable for farming, and there is a limit to how much food man can produce in any given spot. **Aquaculture** (the farming of ponds, lakes, and the sea) can produce considerably more organic materials than conventional farming of the same area of land. Algae are an important part of aquaculture, as food for fish and for humans. Many algal food substances are edible and wholesome, but many people consider them undesirable. As demands on other food sources increase, however, eating alga bread or alga cookies may become common.

Algae and other organisms

Although algae are an important food source, they benefit other organisms in other ways as well. The algae in the vast expanses of open ocean carry on about 70% of the oxygen-producing photosynthesis that takes place on our planet. Thus, the oxygen-carbon dioxide cycle appears to depend more on algae than on the rooted green plants to which we normally ascribe oxygen production.

Recent studies regarding space flights have reemphasized the life-sustaining importance of algae. In space man must carry his oxygen and food with him. For an extended space flight, the bulk of these two items would be excessive. Some algae, if supplied with ideal conditions, can increase in size a thousandfold in 24 hr. Algae, which could take carbon dioxide from humans and return both oxygen and a food substance, may be the only means of man's survival during lengthy space travel.

Some organisms exist with algae in other profitable relationships. Some protozoans, for example, have algae in their vacuoles. The algae carry on photosynthesis and supply sugars to the protozoans. Some freshwater organisms appear green because of the algae living inside them, supplying them with food.

Although some algae can exist in a wide variety of habitats, some are quite specific as to the type of environment in which they will grow. Scientists use certain algae as **indicator organisms.** For example, if a water sample taken from a lake

plankton: (Gk. PLANKTOS, wandering)

zooplankton: zoo- (Gk. ZOION, animal or living being) + -plankton (wandering)

phytoplankton: phyto- (plant) + -plankton (wandering)

has an abundance of certain species of *Oscillatoria* (a blue-green algae), the scientist suspects that the lake is highly polluted with organic materials. Since *Lemanea annulata* is found only in unpolluted streams, quantities of this red alga is generally a sign of clean, flowing water.

Classification of algae

The classification of algae is open for debate. Because of the great differences–and similarities–in various algae, scientists have not agreed on how many algal phyla exist. Taxonomists often place some organisms normally considered algae in protozoan phyla, and sometimes they move certain protozoans to algal phyla. They have not even settled the placement of the algal phyla into kingdoms.

Many scientists agree that the procaryotic algae, the blue-green algae (cyanobacteria), should be in the kingdom Monera. For convenience, scientists generally place the five eucaryotic algal phyla into the kingdom Protista.

The algae are grouped according to the pigments which they contain, the substances which they store as food, and the materials which comprise their cell walls. Often the pigments in algae greatly affect their colors. Even within a phylum varying amounts of different pigments create wide ranges of colors.

Algal colonies

Many algae are unicellular, and a number form globular masses of cells held together by a common slime coat. Some algae, however, form highly complex colonies. One of the simpler colonies is a **filament,** a slender, chainlike thread of cells. Some algae form *branched filaments;* others form broad plates or sheets of cells. Some algae form special cells called **holdfasts** that anchor them to submerged objects. In large algae the holdfasts may be a group of cells. Algae that grow attached to something are called **sessile*** algae.

An algal colony is called a **thallus.*** A thallus is the body of a plantlike organism which is not differentiated into true leaves, roots, and stems. Often an algal thallus has leaflike, stemlike, and even rootlike structures. But algae do not form tissues or organs. Under a microscope a large algal thallus appears as many intertwined filaments. Each of the algal cells comprising such a colony can live independently in the environment where the thallus grows and (at least theoretically) can become a completely new thallus.

Some algae form **air bladders,** small air-filled spaces that cause the thallus to float. Often a large algal thallus will have a holdfast on one end and air bladders on the other end, causing them to appear to stand upright in the water.

10B-1 *Kelp with air bladders*

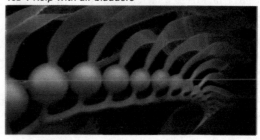

Review Questions 10B-1

1. List several ways in which algae are (a) harmful and (b) beneficial.
2. What characteristics separate algae from (a) the protozoans and (b) the plants?
3. Describe several types of algal colonies.

Reproduction in Algae

When an algal colony cell carries on mitosis, resulting in daughter cells, the colony is enlarged. Most algae can also reproduce asexually by various mitotic means.

❑ *Unicellular reproduction* Unicellular algae, of course, form new organisms by mitotic cell division (see *Chlamydomonas,* page 270 and diatoms, page 272).

❑ *Fragmentation* Most algal colonies can reproduce by **fragmentation:** if the colony is broken by a physical disturbance (currents or fish), each section can grow into a complete colony.

---

thallus: (Gk. THALLEIN, to sprout)   **sessile:** (L. SESSILIS, capable of being a seat)

Chlorophyta, the Green Algae

Chlorophyta* (klor AH fih tuh), the *green algae,* is one of the largest algal phyla. Most green algae are freshwater organisms; however, many terrestrial and a few marine species exist. Usually green algae are unicellular or form simple colonies, but some marine species form extensive thalli. One green algal species that grows off the coast of Mexico produces leaf-like blades that reach 25 cm by 7.5 m (10 in. by 24 ft.). Many green algae produce holdfasts and grow attached to submerged substances, but some unicellular species move by flagella. Many kinds merely float.

Green algae contain chlorophyll *a* and *b* and yellow-orange pigments called *carotenoids** (kuh RAHT uh NOYDZ); therefore, they often appear various shades of yellow green. The chloroplasts in green algae are often unusual. Many cells contain only one large chloroplast of an unusual shape. Such chloroplasts are often used to identify the alga (see *Spirogyra* and *Ulothrix*).

Green algae typically store their food as starch. Large starch granules can often be found around a protein-containing cellular structure, the **pyrenoid** (pye REE NOYD). Pyrenoids probably contain the enzymes necessary for the manufacture of starch from the simple sugars produced by photosynthesis.

Often Chlorophyta is divided into two groups, the unicellular and the filament-forming green algae.

Unicellular Green Algae
Chlamydomonas

Members of this genus are common inhabitants of stagnant freshwater pools. They possess 2 flagella. Asexual reproduction involves the division into 2-8 daughter cells within the cell wall and membrane of the mother cell. As this happens, the parent loses its flagella. Flagella form on the daughter cells just before they are released.

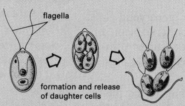

flagella

formation and release of daughter cells

Desmids

Desmids are free-floating algae. Usually they are unicellular, but occasionally cells are joined end to end, forming a filament-like colony. Desmids often are pinched in the middle, forming two symmetrical halves. Often the cell walls have unusual patterns, making desmids some of the most interesting freshwater algae.

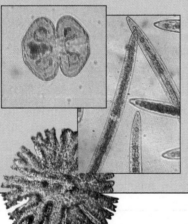

Chlorella

Members of this unicellular aquatic genus are frequently used to study cellular processes like photosynthesis. They often live inside various animals.

Chlorella

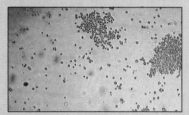

Protococcus

This genus contains terrestrial members, many of which grow as a green film on damp rocks or tree bark. *Protococcus* exists unicellularly but may form clumps of several or many cells.

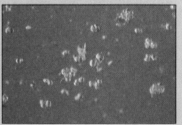

Protococcus

Filament-forming Green Algae
Ulothrix

Ulothrix filaments are usually attached to submerged structures by a holdfast but can be found floating. *Ulothrix* can reproduce asexually by forming from 4-8 zoospores in a single cell (a-d). These zoospores have 4 flagella and

---

Chlorophyta: Chloro- (greenish yellow) + -phyta (plant)

carotenoid: carot- (L. CAROTA, carrot) + -enoid (form or shape)

Ulothrix Reproduction

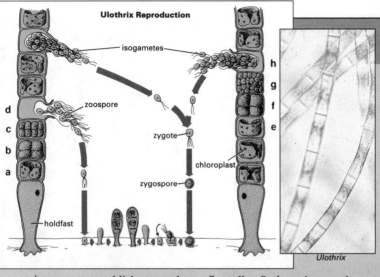

swim away to establish new colonies. Sexually, *Ulothrix* produces from 8-64 isogametes inside a single cell (e-h). Each of these gametes has 2 flagella. When released, they swim, unite, and form a zygote which then becomes a zygospore.

Oedogonium

Oedogonium can reproduce asexually by forming a single, multiflagellate zoospore within a cell.

Sexually, *Oedogonium* produces an egg in a specialized cell called an oogonium. Antheridia produce flagellated sperm which swim to enter the oogonium through an opening in the cell wall and fertilize the ovum. The resulting zygote forms a hard protective wall and can remain inactive for several months of unfavorable conditions. Before the zygote wall ruptures, meiosis takes place and 4 flagellate zoospores are formed (a-c).

Ulothrix

Spirogyra

Named after its unusual spiral-shaped chloroplasts, *Spirogyra* is typical of many filamentous green algae. Usually *Spirogyra,* along with other similar species, is found as floating green mats in ponds or the backwaters of streams. Filaments may reach 0.5 m (20 in.) long. Under proper conditions, *Spirogyra* filaments line up parallel to each other and conjugate (a-e). The cells form a small conjugation tube, and the contents of one cell migrate into the other

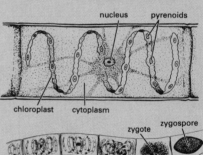

Spirogyra

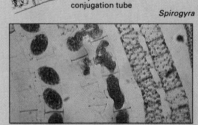

cell. A zygote is formed. A hard, protective wall around the zygote forms a zygospore which is capable of living through unfavorable conditions.

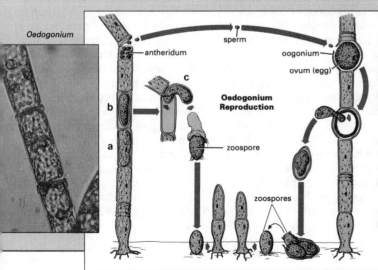

Oedogonium

Oedogonium Reproduction

Chrysophyta, the Yellow-green Algae and the Diatoms

Many algae of the **phylum Chrysophyta*** (krih SAH fuh tuh) are similar to many green algae. The yellow-green algae and diatoms are in a separate phylum because they contain different pigments, store their food as oils, and often have silicon in their cell walls.

Vaucheria

Vaucheria is a filamentous yellow-green algae which is often seen as a thin film on soil, or as mats on the margin of pools and on moist stream banks. The filaments of *Vaucheria* lack dividing cell membranes. They have many nuclei.

Asexually, multinucleate zoospores with many flagella are produced on the ends of clublike filaments. Sexual reproduction in *Vaucheria* is by heterogametes produced in specialized structures on the filament.

Dinobryon

Dinobryon is a flagellate alga which often grows in sessile colonies. Some species of *Dinobryon* cause the water to taste fishy and to have a smooth, slimy feel on the tongue.

Diatoms

Diatoms are a group of organisms in the phylum Chrysophyta. Diatoms, in some respects the most important group of algae, are found in abundance in almost every environment on earth. Among the plankton of the open ocean, diatoms are important in the food chain and are responsible for more oxygen-supplying photosynthesis than any other group of organisms. Usually diatoms are unicellular, but some species exist in chains or in other groupings. Diatoms store their food as oil which often appears as large drops in the cell.

The cell walls of diatoms are in two separate halves, one of which fits inside the other. These walls

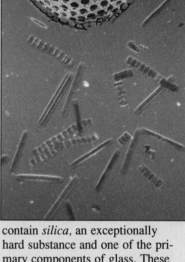

diatoms

contain *silica,* an exceptionally hard substance and one of the primary components of glass. These silica walls remain long after the diatom has died.

Large quantities of diatom shells can be found on the ocean floor. *Diatomaceous earth,* a crumbly substance made of diatom shells, is found in many parts of the world. In California some beds of this substance are 900 m (1,394 ft.) thick. Diatomaceous earth is probably the result of diatoms that were deposited during the Flood. It often serves as a filter in industry and in home aquariums. Since it is a poor conductor of heat, it is used to insulate boilers. The shells of diatoms are often the abrasive agent in silver polish and toothpaste.

Vaucheria

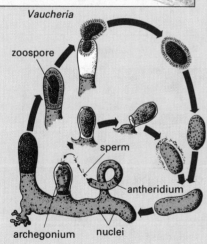

zoospore

sperm

antheridium

archegonium   nuclei

Chrysophyta: Chryso- (Gk. KHRUSOS, gold) + -phyta (plant)

Although highly protective, the hard cell wall of diatoms presents some problems when the cells are reproducing. Since half of the shell goes with each new daughter cell, some cells become increasingly smaller as cell divisions continue. After several divisions some diatoms shed their cell walls, grow, and then produce new shells. Some diatoms reproduce sexually following several asexual cell divisions.

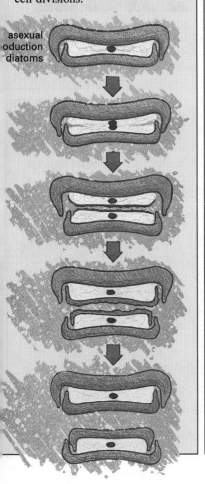

asexual
oduction
diatoms

Phaeophyta, the Brown Algae

Species of the **phylum Phaeophyta*** (fay AH fuh tuh) are all multicellular and almost all marine. The brown algae, found in colder waters, usually grow attached to rocks or to the ocean floor. Larger species live in deeper waters, while smaller species thrive along the coast and are often exposed during low tides. Food is stored as a complex carbohydrate. *Algin*, a gelatinous coating found on many brown algae, serves as a thickener in commercially produced ice cream and other foods.

The thallus of a brown alga is usually composed of a holdfast (often an extensive network of cells), a stemlike structure, and leaflike blades. The stemlike structure usually contains *air bladders*, causing the alga to float near the surface. Brown algae produce sperm and ova in multicellular *antheridia* and *oogonia*.

Fucus

Fucus (often called rockweed) is a common shoreline alga. The thick,

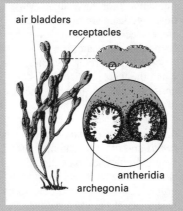

air bladders

receptacles

antheridia

archegonia

30- to 90-cm (1- to 3-ft) leatherlike thallus is not affected by periods of dryness between tides. The swellings at the ends of the thallus are the multicellular reproductive structures.

Kelp

The kelps normally grow attached to rocks in water up to 23 m (75 ft.) deep. Some of these large algae may reach 30 m (100 ft.) long.

Sargassum

Sargassum is a genus similar to the kelp but grows in temperate to tropical areas. One species forms floating mats several hundred meters wide in an area of the North Atlantic called the Sargasso Sea.

Phaeophyta: Phaio- (Gk. PHAIOS, brown) + -phyta (plant)

Rhodophyta, the Red Algae

The algae of **phylum Rhodophyta*** (roh DAH fuh tuh) are almost all marine, multicellular, and red. Most red algae grow in shallow, warmer waters, but sometimes they are found at a depth of over 90 m (300 ft.). Some red algae produce ribbonlike thalli, but many are feathery, and others are slender filaments. Almost all red algae are under 30 cm (1 ft.) long. Red algae are unusual in that they produce nonmotile gametes and spores.

Certain red algae draw calcium from seawater and deposit it as calcium carbonate in the gelatinous coat that surrounds them.

This calcium carbonate is important in building some reefs and islands. Other red algae products are used in foods. Best known of these is *agar,* a gelatinous substance used in growing bacteria.

Chondrus (Irish moss)

Chondrus is the marine red alga which is the source of agar.

red algae

Lemanea

Lemanea is a common freshwater, sessile red alga; its presence indicates clean, flowing water.

Pyrrophyta, the Dinoflagellates

The **phylum Pyrrophyta*** (pye RAH fuh tuh) includes the **dinoflagellates*** (DYE noh FLAJ uh lits). These unicellular algae normally process two flagella of unequal length. One flagellum is normally kept in a groove around the algal cell; the other is used for movement.

The cell walls of the dinoflagellates are made up of multi-sided cellulose plates. Yellowish brown pigments color these algae. Most dinoflagellates are marine, but some species live in fresh water. Some dinoflagellates are bioluminescent (light-producing) and, when the water is disturbed, can emit enough light to cause the sea to glow.

In warm, coastal water certain dinoflagellates (*Gymnodinium brevis* and others) can enter a severe bloom condition called the *red tide.* The abundance of the dinoflagellates during red tides turns vast areas of the sea a reddish

brown. These algae secrete a poison which affects the nervous system of fish. Off Florida's Gulf

Gymnodinium brevis

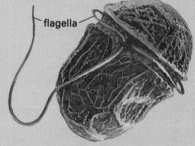

flagella

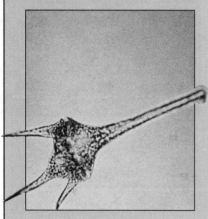

Coast red tides have caused massive fish kills. Smaller quantities of these organisms can pollute shellfish, making them unfit for human consumption.

Review questions on page 276.

Rhodophyta: Rhodo- (Gk. RHODON, rose color) + -phyta (plant)

Pyrrophyta: Pyrro- (Gk. PYRRHOS, fiery) + -phyta (plant)
dinoflagellate: dino- (Gk. DINEIN, to whirl) + -flagellate (small whip)

❏ *Zoospores* Individual cells in some sessile algae can form specialized cells called **zoospores*** (ZOH uh SPORZ), which have flagella and can swim away and establish new colonies (see *Vaucheria,* page 272; *Ulothrix,* pages 270-71; and *Oedogonium,* page 271).

There are three basic forms of sexual reproduction carried on by algae.

❏ *Conjugation* When two cells that are not obviously specialized as gametes unite, **conjugation** has occurred. This permits the nuclear material from one cell to go into the other. *Spirogyra,* a common pond alga, reproduce by conjugation (see page 271).

❏ *Isogametes* Specialized cells which are not obviously different from one another are **isogametes.** Isogametes fuse together, forming a diploid zygote. *Ulothrix,* a freshwater alga, reproduces using isogametes (see pages 270-71).

❏ *Heterogametes* Specialized cells which differ in either size, structure, or both are **heterogametes.** In some algae, like the *Vaucheria* (see page 272), a nonmotile gamete called an *ovum* (egg) is produced in a specialized structure called the **oogonium*** (OH uh GOH nee um). Sperm, which are the motile gametes, are produced in another structure called the **antheridium** (AN thuh RIHD ee um). Also see *Fucus* on page 273.

Some algae can, under different conditions, form different types of gametes.

Following the union of gametes, the zygote of some algae forms a hard, protective covering and is called a **zygospore.*** Many freshwater algae spend periods of unfavorable conditions (winters or dry seasons) in the zygospore stage. Some algae form zygotes that then carry on meiosis and release motile zoospores (usually 4 haploid cells). The zoospores then swim away and establish new colonies.

Algal blooms

In 1729 Captain W. Dampier, sailing off the coast of Peru, wrote:

> [When] our ship [was] about ten leagues off shore, . . . we were suddenly surprised with the change of the colour of the water, which looked as red as blood to as great a distance as we could see . . . . At first we were mighty surprised . . . . We then drew some water up in buckets and poured some in a glass. It continued to look very red, till about a quarter of an hour after it had been in the glass; when all of the red substance floated to the top, and the water underneath was as clear as usual. The red stuff which floated on top was of a slimy substance, with little knobs, and we all concluded it could be nothing but the spawn of fish.*

Captain Dampier and his crew were probably sailing through an algal **bloom.** A *bloom condition* occurs when all factors affecting growth and reproduction for a particular organism are near optimum. The organisms can then multiply rapidly, resulting in great abundance of new life.

Algal blooms are not unusual occurrences. In the summer, ponds and entire lakes often appear green or blue-green because of blooms of certain algae. Some blue-green algae *(Microcystis, Anabaena)* release a poison. When these algae enter bloom conditions in a farm pond, the livestock can be poisoned by drinking the water.

Unpleasant odors and tastes can occur in city water supplies because of an algal bloom. Algae produce oily substances that cause the ''fishy smell'' or ''marsh odor'' associated with certain water supplies. Ill effects of an algal bloom can occur when the algae die. Decomposition and oxygen depletion then foul the water.

Often during a bloom condition, algae color the water with their presence. It is impossible to be sure what caused the red condition described by Captain Dampier. The separating of the water and the ''red stuff'' and the slimy feel of the substance indicate that it was probably an alga.

Some critics of the Bible have suggested that the first plague of Egypt described in Exodus 7 was a natural algal bloom. Verses 20 and 21 state that ''all the waters that were in the river were turned to blood. And the fish that was in the river died; and the river stank, and the Egyptians could not drink of the water of the river.''

At first glance it may appear that an algal bloom caused this phenomenon. Other sections of this passage, however, demonstrate that this mir-

---

*The Distribution of Discolored Water, U.S. Navy Hydrographic Office Pilot Chart No. 1401 (Washington, D.C.: Hydrographic Office, January 1955)

oogonium: oo- (egg) + -gonium (Gk. GONOS, seed)

zoospore: zoo- (animal) + -spore (seed)

zygospore: zygo- (Gk. ZUGON, yoke) + -spore (seed)

acle was not a bloom of microoganisms. The miracle happened "in the sight of Pharaoh, and in the sight of his servants" (v. 20). An algal bloom does not happen instantly; it takes days to build up. Blood was also in all the pools, ponds, and Egyptian vessels (v. 19). Conditions for a bloom in the flowing Nile River would not have caused a simultaneous bloom in the standing water.

Christians must be careful not to attribute miracles to "natural" causes. When the Bible states that God has done a particular thing, we *must* accept His statement. If the water were turned to the *color* of blood, would not God have stated this? The Egyptians, as well as Moses, the human writer of this passage, would have known the difference between blood and alga-polluted, colored water. The repetition of the word "blood" in this passage, as well as in other passages referring to the incident (Ps. 78:44; 105:29), is further evidence that it was blood and not the bloom of some microorganism.

God *can* cause certain "natural" circumstances to work together for His purpose, and He often does so even today. God can also, as is recorded in Scripture, act supernaturally to effect His purpose. These supernatural acts are **miracles.** To try to explain God's miracles by natural circumstances is to deny the power of God.

Biological Terms

plankton	sessile	heterogametes	pyrenoid
zooplankton	thallus (pl., thalli)	oogonium	phylum Chrysophyta
phytoplankton	air bladder	antheridium	phylum Phaeophyta
aquaculture	fragmentation	zygospore	phylum Rhodophyta
indicator organism	zoospore	bloom (bloom condition)	phylum Pyrrophyta
filament	conjugation	miracle	dinoflagellate
holdfast	isogamete	phylum Chlorophyta	

Review Questions 10B-2

1. List three types of asexual reproduction common in algae. List three types of sexual reproduction common in algae.
2. What is the difference between a zygospore and a zoospore?
3. List several characteristics of an algal bloom that help make it an unacceptable explanation for the changing of the water into blood in Exodus 7.

The Algal Phyla, pages 270-74

1. List several characteristics and four examples of the phylum Chlorophyta.
2. Compare and contrast asexual reproduction in *Protococcus* and *Spirogyra*.
3. Compare and contrast sexual reproduction of *Ulothrix, Oedogonium,* and *Spirogyra*.
4. Describe desmids.
5. List several characteristics and two examples of the phylum Chrysophyta.
6. Describe diatoms and list several uses of diatoms.
7. List several characteristics and give an example of the phylum Phaeophyta.
8. List several characteristics and give an example of the phylum Rhodophyta.
9. List several characteristics and give an example of the phylum Pyrrophyta.

Thought Questions

1. "Resolved: Algae are the most significant organisms in the world." Prepare a paragraph for the negative position and a paragraph for the affirmative position. Which do you think is the better position?
2. Read the Scriptural accounts of the ravens feeding Elijah, the unfailing meal and oil, and the raising of the widow's son (I Kings 17). What "natural causes" can you imagine (or find in a Bible commentary) that could be used to explain these three miracles? What Biblical evidence supports the position that these miracles were supernatural acts of God and not the result of natural causes?

THE KINGDOM FUNGI

The Fungi
page 277

Facet:
Edible Fungi–Delicious or Deadly?   (page 280)

ELEVEN

The Fungi

Ergot of rye is a fungus which causes a purplish black swelling in rye grain. In the Middle Ages, the disease caused by eating this infected rye was called ''St. Anthony's fire.'' In 944, an epidemic of St. Anthony's fire killed more than 40,000 people. In August 1722 the men and horses of Peter the Great, poised for an invasion of Turkey, consumed rye brought to them by the local serfs. By the following morning, over a hundred horses were paralyzed; about 20,000 people in the area died; and the invasion was effectively stopped.

In 1951, people in a small village in France ate flour ground from infected rye. More than 200 people were made severely ill from the poison; 30 people went temporarily insane, imagining that demons and snakes were chasing them; 4 people died. Interestingly, ergot of rye was the first source for lysergic acid diethylamide (LSD), a hallucinogenic (causing false perceptions or visions) drug. Drugs derived from ergot cause muscles to contract and blood vessels to constrict and have been used to save lives.

Ergot of rye appears to be both bane and blessing. In some respects many fungi are like that. For example, in the early 1800s potatoes were the major crop in Ireland. In 1845, and for several years following, a parasitic fungus, the *late blight of potato,* destroyed virtually the entire crop. Approximately one million people died of starvation between 1845 and 1847. Within 10 yr. the population dropped from 8 million to 4 million. The Irish, however, learned the benefits of diversifying their livelihoods, and many of the Irish in America today are descendants of those who were forced to emigrate during the potato crop failure.

Destructive fungi

Annually, a five-member American family spends over $600 to control and pay for the damage caused by fungi. With the possible exception of the bacteria, the molds of the kingdom Fungi are man's biggest competitors for food. One estimate indicates that plant diseases cost Americans over $3 billion dollars annually. Fortunately, in America, food production far exceeds need.

Some destructive fungi have caused permanent damage by destroying their host species. One of our most important nut and hardwood lumber trees was the American chestnut; however, the *chestnut blight fungus* has eliminated it from American forests. *Dutch elm disease* is caused by a fungus which is spread by the elm bark beetle. The fungus causes the breakdown of the water conduction tissues, and death of the tree is inevitable. Many towns that once had stately elms lining their streets have been forced, in the space of a few years, to remove them. Although scientists are seeking a solution, no prevention or cure yet exists.

Occasionally natural means of preventing fungi distribution can be used. Starting around 1880, a rust fungus caused the coffee trees of Ceylon (now known as

11A-1 *Chestnut branch growing from the stump of a once large tree*

11A-2 *The Dutch elm disease, carried by a bark beetle, spreads rapidly, killing American elm trees. These stately trees once lined the streets of many American cities, including Washington, D.C. As the trees became infected, they were removed.*

Sri Lanka) to lose their leaves. After losing their leaves a few times, the trees died. Tea, which is not affected by that fungus, is now grown in Sri Lanka, and the coffee industry has moved to Brazil. The coffee trees in Brazil could also be affected by the fungus; therefore, Brazilian coffee growers take special measures to insure that their trees are not exposed to it.

Other fungi have been controlled by other methods. In the late 1870s, a downy mildew of grapes was accidentally introduced into French vineyards. Within a few years the grape crop was suffering. A professor from the University of Bordeaux noticed that vines growing along the roadside in a certain area did not have this fungus. He learned that the vineyard owners placed a mixture of copper sulfate and lime on the vines. The appearance of this mixture discouraged passersby from stealing the grapes. Scientists at the University of Bordeaux refined and marketed the mixture in 1882. It was the first commercial **fungicide*** for plant diseases.

Beneficial fungi

Most people consider edible mushrooms to be the only beneficial fungi. There are, however, many edible fungi. Many cheeses are the result of fungal growth. Natural Swiss and cheddar, for example, are formed by fungal enzymes working on milk products. The fungi that form Limburger and blue cheese are actually eaten as part of the cheese.

---

fungicide: fungi- (L. FUNGUS, fungus) + -cide (to kill)

One of the most important fungi is a group of microscopic organisms called the *yeasts.* Many baked goods are leavened by yeasts. Leavening is a substance which produces bubbles of gas in doughs or batters. These bubbles cause the substance to "rise."

Until the advent of other leavening agents and methods of storing yeast in a dormant state, many families kept a lump of dough containing live yeast. This lump, called the leaven, was mixed with a batch of dough. Since yeast grows and divides rapidly, it would serve as the leavening for the whole new batch. A small lump of the new batch would be set aside to serve as the leaven for the next batch of dough.

In the Bible leavening is compared to sin or false doctrine (Matt. 16:6-12; I Cor. 5:6-8). Just as a little leaven will affect the entire lump of dough, so a little error will corrupt the whole man, or even groups of men. Most Bible scholars agree that, in the Old Testament references to sacrifices, leaven often represents sin permeating all men. For the Passover, various other feasts, and most sacrifices, God demanded unleavened bread, similar to a flat, leathery cracker.

Alexander Fleming, a British physician, discovered another useful function of fungi. In 1929, he noted that a ring of dead bacteria formed around a particular fungus growing on his bacterial cultures. The chemical which killed the bacteria was isolated and named penicillin after the common mold *Penicillium notatum,* which formed it. Penicillin was the first antibiotic. Synthetic penicillin is now many times stronger than the substance Fleming extracted, but some penicillin and other antibiotics are still obtained from fungi.

In their most important and most common function, fungi under natural conditions serve as decomposer organisms. Occurring in the soil and other dark, damp places, these fungi break down complex organic substances into simple, soluble forms that plants can use.

Classification of the Fungi

The **kingdom Fungi** contains colonial and unicellular heterotrophic organisms grouped into several phyla. In this chapter are the three most common phyla: Zygomycota, Ascomycota, and Basidiomycota. Fungi are grouped into various phyla by their colonial structure and their methods of sexual reproduction. Lichens (dual organisms composed of both fungi and algae) are usually grouped by their fungal component and are discussed at the end of this chapter.

At one time scientists classified most fungi in the plant kingdom. With few exceptions fungi have cell walls, are sessile, and produce rootlike anchoring structures. Unlike plants, however, fungi lack true tissues and organs. Even large fungi, like mushrooms, are colonial organisms.

Nutrition and respiration of fungi

The primary characteristic that separates the true fungi from both the plant kingdom and the algae is that fungi lack chlorophyll and therefore are heterotrophic. Some fungi are *saprophytes* (feeding on dead material); others are *parasites* (feeding on living material). There are, however, a few fungi that can be either. *Histoplasmosis,* for example, is a human disease caused by a fungus. In the soil this fungus is a saprophytic mold. However, if a man or animal inhales its spores, this fungus can become a parasite; it no longer appears as a mold but exists as individual cells or clumps of cells which reproduce by budding.

Fungi lack specialized structures for digestion. Many parasitic fungi absorb their food in a predigested form; some obtain nutrition directly from the cytoplasm of the host. Most fungi, however, carry on **external digestion.** External digestion requires the secretion of enzymes which digest the food into a soluble form outside the organism. The soluble foods are then absorbed. The enzymes of external digestion are often the harmful substances of parasitic or poisonous fungi.

Most fungi require oxygen for their metabolism, but a few can grow without an abundant supply of free oxygen. Even the fermentation yeasts, however, grow best with at least some free oxygen. All fungi require abundant moisture for active growth, but many species can withstand periods of dryness. To withstand long dry periods, they form spores.

FACETS OF BIOLOGY

11A–1

Edible Fungi–Delicious or Deadly?

Actually there are many edible fungi. We all eat yeasts in breads, and many eat the blue mold that makes the enzymes that form blue cheese. The morel is highly prized for its delicate flavor. Young puffballs fried in seasoned butter are considered a delicacy.

In Europe, the truffle, a tasty underground fungi, is sought by specially trained dogs or pigs. Dogs, while not as good at finding the fungi, are preferred truffle hunters. You must be alert and always ready to keep the pigs from eating the truffles. Dogs sniff out the fungi, but refuse to eat it.

Bread mold (*Rhizopus*) is not harmful, but most people find it unappetizing. Many of us have eaten bread mold without knowing it. The white hyphae form several days before the obvious dark spores which tell us the bread is moldy.

When you speak of eating fungi, most people think of mushrooms. Today virtually all of the large basidiomycotes which have the "mushroom shape" (and even a few that do not) are commonly called mushrooms. Technically, all mushrooms are edible. The nonedible ones (either because they are tasteless, taste bad, or are poisonous) are toadstools. This, however, is not a good method of classification, since in the same genus are some of the best-tasting mushrooms and some of the most deadly toadstools.

The *Amanita caesarea* (said to be a favorite of Julius Caesar) is, for example, a delicious mushroom while *A. verna* (known as the destroying angel) is one of the most poisonous. This deadly, pure white mushroom causes no symptoms for several hours while the poison enters the tissues. From 6-15 hr. after eating, the person has abdominal pains, vomiting, and diarrhea. Another species, *A. muscaria,* the fly amanita, is fatal in large doses and causes psychological effects in smaller doses. Usually most mushroom collectors avoid all species of *Amanita* to reduce the possibility of getting a poisonous one.

Most people wisely limit their mushroom picking to their grocer's shelves, where they usually find *Quaricus bisporus* (or a similar species) available in any season. They were not collected in a field or forest, but grown in buildings where the temperature and humidity are controlled. Pure cultures of the mushroom fungus are grown in laboratories and are then spread on sterile soil mixed with a rich organic material (horse manure is often used).

After several weeks of growth another layer of soil is spread on the mushroom bed and the mushrooms begin to form. When the buttons emerge, they must be picked quickly because as a mushroom matures it becomes tough and loses its flavor. The bed may be used for a few additional crops of mushrooms, but as the organic material begins to be used up, the whole process must be repeated.

Mushrooms are a true luxury food, but based on their food value, no one should waste time or effort hunting, growing, or buying them. While adding flavor, they add little food value and are not easily digested.

Review questions on page 282.

Amanita
caesarea

Amanita
verna

Cells and colonies of fungi

Most fungi have cell walls composed of *chitin* (KYE tin), a hard but flexible substance. With few exceptions fungi are composed of slender filaments called **hyphae*** (HYE fee). Even large fungi such as mushrooms are merely organized masses of interwoven hyphae.

In some fungal groups the hyphae are *septate;** that is, they are divided into individual cells by cell walls called *septa* (sing., *septum*). These usually have a hole or pore in them, permitting cytoplasm to pass between the cells of the filament. Some fungi have hyphae which lack septa and are

septate hyphae   *nonseptate hyphae*

called *nonseptate.* Nonseptate hyphae are typically multinucleate. Although hyphae are only about 5-10 μm wide, some of them may be almost 1 cm long.

Hyphae serve different functions and are often named accordingly:

❑ **Rhizoids*** (RYE ZOYDZ) are hyphae which are embedded in the material on which the fungus is growing. They serve to support the fungus and digest food.

❑ **Aerial hyphae** are not embedded in the medium. They absorb oxygen, produce spores, and spread the fungus.

❑ **Stolons*** (STOH lunz) are aerial hyphae which produce new filaments.

❑ **Sporophores*** are hyphae branches which produce spores.

❑ **Haustoria*** (haw STOHR ee uh) are hyphae of parasitic fungi which enter the host's cells to obtain nutrition directly from the cytoplasm.

❑ **Mycelia** (mye SEE lee uh) (sing., *mycelium*) are masses of intertwined hyphae. A mycelium may be as simple as a clump of bread mold or as highly organized and specialized as a mushroom.

The Imperfect Fungi

Most of the fungal organisms in the phyla Zygomycota, Ascomycota, and Basidiomycota are sometimes grouped together and called the **true fungi,** or *perfect fungi.* A true fungus is one that has a known form of sexual reproduction and can thus be classified. There are, however, a good number of fungi which are not known to reproduce sexually. These fungi are called the **imperfect fungi,** or *fungi imperfecti.*

The list of imperfect fungi was once quite long, and they were given a separate classification. But as scientists cultured and observed them, they were able to see their sexual reproductive structures and were thus able to classify them. Today scientists generally place the imperfect fungi in the phylum Ascomycota since most of them will probably be in this phylum when they can be classified.

Some imperfect fungi are saprophytes, many are plant parasites. A few, however, are parasites of man. *Ringworm* (a small ring of hyphae under the skin), *athlete's foot* (a fungus causing dry, itchy skin near the toes), and *thrush* (a parasite of the mucous membranes of the mouth, nose, and throat) are common imperfect fungi. Fungal infections deep within the body (usually affecting the brain, kidney, or liver) are much rarer but are considerably more serious; they are difficult to treat and may even lead to death.

Reproduction of fungi

Asexual reproduction is the most common type of reproduction in fungi. All fungi can reproduce asexually by stolons or by fragmentation of the hyphae or mycelia, but the most common method is by spores. In formation of *asexual spores,* the sporophore divides from the rest of the hyphae

11A-3 *Various fungal structures*

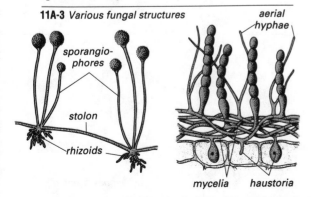

sporangio-
phores

stolon

rhizoids

aerial
hyphae

mycelia   haustoria

---

hyphae: (Gk. HYPHE, web)
septate: (L. SAEPES, hedge)
rhizoid: rhiz-(Gk. RHIZA, root) + -oid (form or shape)

stolon: (L. STOLO, branch or shoot)
sporophore: (sporo- seed) + -phore (to bear)

haustoria: (L. HAUSTOR, a drainer)

by a septum. If the sporophore forms spores within an enclosure, it is a **sporangiophore*** (spuh RAN jee uh FOHR), and the structure in which the spores are formed is a **sporangium*** (spuh RAN jee um). The common bread mold *Rhizopus nigricans* produces sporangiophores and sporangia. The hyphae of bread mold are clear or white. The black appearance of this mold is the result of the colored sporangia and spores.

If the sporophore forms spores by repeated divisions and its spores are not in an enclosure, it is called a **conidiophore*** (kuh NID ee uh FOHR), and the spores are **conidia** (kuh NID ee uh). *Penicillium,* a common fruit mold, produces bluegreen conidia from motile, asexual spores.

Sexual reproduction usually does not involve motile gametes, because a fungus mycelium is haploid and sexual reproduction occurs when hyphae of two different mycelia come into contact. In some fungi, as in the bread mold, the resulting diploid zygote forms a *zygospore.* In other species, such as the mushrooms, a new mycelium is formed which contains separate copies of both nuclei (which often remain side by side). The new mycelium grows and becomes the specialized **fruiting body.** The fruiting body of a fungus produces and disperses spores. In the mushroom, the two haploid nuclei fuse, forming a diploid nucleus which then divides by meiosis just before the sexually produced, haploid spores form.

Review Questions 11A-1

1. List several ways in which fungi are (a) harmful and (b) beneficial.
2. What characteristics separate fungi from (a) the plants and (b) the algae?
3. What is the difference between a septate fungus and a nonseptate fungus?
4. Describe five different type of hyphae, based on their functions.
5. Describe asexual reproduction in the fungi.
6. Describe sexual reproduction in the fungi.

Facet 11A-1: Edible Fungi—Delicious or Deadly? page 280

1. List several fungi people commonly eat.
2. Why is it safe to assume that the mushrooms in grocery stores are not of a poisonous variety that might look similar.

Phylum Zygomycota

Many of the common molds are in the **phylum Zygomycota*** (ZYE goh mye COH tuh). The members of this phylum reproduce sexually by the fusion of hyphae to form a zygote. The zygote often forms a zygospore. Aquatic zygomycotes often produce motile gametes which fuse to form a zygote.

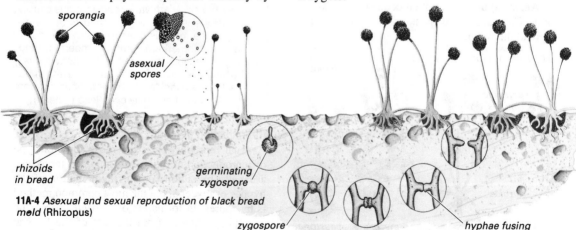

sporangia

asexual spores

rhizoids in bread

germinating zygospore

zygospore

hyphae fusing

11A-4 *Asexual and sexual reproduction of black bread mold* (Rhizopus)

---

sporangiophore: spor- (seed) + -angio- (ANGEION, container) + -phore (carry)

sporangium: spor- (seed) + -angio (container)

conidiophore: conidio- (Gk. KONIS, dust) + -phore (carry)

Zygomycota: zygo- (Gk. ZYGON, yoke) + myco- (Gk. MUKES, fungus)

The genus *Rhizopus* contains a food mold that is everywhere and familiar to us all, the *black bread mold* (*R. nigricans* or *R. stolonifer*). When the airborne spores of this mold land in a favorable environment, they germinate, forming a small *hypha*. This hypha grows into a *mycelium* with *rhizoids*, *stolons*, and finally, *sporangiophores* and *sporangia*. Depending on the species, the spores are either black or shades of brown or green. Although baked goods with this mold look unappetizing, they are harmless if eaten. Some molds, however, produce digestive enzymes or other substances which are toxic to humans.

The *downy mildews* (which are similar to the late blight fungus) are named for the soft, fuzzy hyphae often seen on the affected plant parts.

Downy mildews cause tremendous damage to crops of cabbage, lettuce, cucumbers, spinach, beans, peas, and grapes.

Phylum Ascomycota

The **phylum Ascomycota*** (AS koh mye COH tuh) are the *sac fungi*, for they form 4 or 8 sexually produced spores called **ascospores*** (AS kuh SPORZ) inside a sac called an **ascus.*** Most ascomycetes have septate hyphae.

Molds of the genus *Penicillium* (or *Talaromyces*) are typical asco-

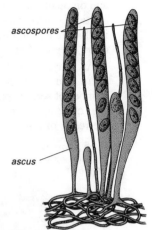

ascospores

ascus

The Yeasts

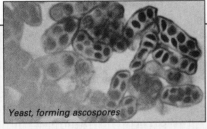

Yeast, forming ascospores

Yeasts are unicellular, predominantly saprophytic fungi found in soil or water. Some yeasts are highly specific (for example, existing only under pine trees), while others live in a wide variety of habitats. A few yeasts are parasites, and a few cause human diseases. The approximately 350 yeast species are in phylum Ascomycota.

Yeasts are typically egg-shaped cells, slightly larger than bacteria. Yeast cells usually have a single vacuole containing stored substances and enzymes. Each cell has a cell wall which becomes thicker and more rigid with age. Some yeasts produce and store large quantities of fat, carbohydrates, or protein and have been grown to supply these materials for human consumption. Yeasts also produce vitamins B and D, especially B_2 (riboflavin). Some people eat yeast or ground yeast products to obtain these vitamins. Yeasts are also grown commercially to produce enzymes used in the manufacture of syrup, cheese, soft-center candies, and medicine.

Yeasts reproduce asexually by **budding.** Near the edge of the cell, the nucleus divides by mitosis. A swelling of the plasma membrane and

the cell wall produces a small pouch, and one of the new nuclei moves into it, forming a *bud*. Attached to the parent cell, the bud continues to grow until it is about the same size. The cell wall and membrane between the two has formed by then, and the cells may separate. Often, however, they remain attached. Additional budding can form random-shaped chains.

During periods of unfavorable conditions, yeast cells can form spores, which can remain dormant for long periods. Active dry yeasts contain the living spores of *baker's yeast* for use in home baking.

Most yeasts grow with oxygen, but many can reduce their metabolic rates and carry on fermentation processes. These fermentation processes account for the leavening action of baker's yeasts and the alcoholic production of *brewer's yeast* (in beer) and *wine yeasts*. Baker's yeasts remain active in only relatively mild alcoholic concentrations (about 4%). They soon die or form spores if favorable aerobic conditions are not restored. In baked goods the heat of baking stops the fermentation process and evaporates the alcohol. Some of the yeasts used in the manufacture of beers and wines can tolerate alcohol concentrations of about 12%. Liquors with a higher alcohol concentration are obtained by distillation (removing water).

Ascomycota: asco- (bag or bladder) + myco- (fungus)

ascospore: asco- or ascus (G. ASKOS, leather bag) + spore (seed)

ascus: (leather bag)

mycetes. These molds form white mycelia which you can easily observe on the rinds of oranges and on other fruits and foodstuffs. Asexual reproduction is accomplished by *conidia*. Other species in this genus produce the flavors of Roquefort (blue cheese), Camembert, and other cheeses.

Ascomycota molds include the genera *Aspergillus* and *Neurospora* (the red bread mold). A number of serious plant diseases such as ergot of rye, chestnut blight, and Dutch elm disease are the result of Ascomycota molds.

11A-5 *Powdery mildew, a parasitic ascomycete, on a leaf*

The *powdery mildews* are named for the cobwebby spores which they form over the leaves of young stems of lilacs, grapes, roses, apples, squash, and other plants. These mildews obtain food from the living plant cells by haustoria. Although powdery mildews usually do not kill the plant, they reduce the size of the plant and the crop, and they often weaken the plant so that it can be easily killed by other factors.

11A-6 *Ascospores are produced inside the spongy-looking top of the edible morel (left) and inside the cup of the cup fungus (right).*

Many ascomycetes, such as the delicately flavored *morel*, form extensive fruiting bodies to release their spores. The *cup fungi* are ascomycetes that form saucer- or bowl-shaped fruiting bodies. Their cups may be 1-10 mm in diameter. Usually saprophytic, the cup fungi grow on the forest floor or on dead wood. Spores are dispersed primarily as falling drops of water splash them out of the cups. Other cup fungi fling their spores into the air.

Phylum Basidiomycota

The **phylum Basidiomycota** (buh SID ee oh mye COH tuh) are called the *club fungi* because they form four sexually produced **basidiospores*** (buh SID ee oh SPORZ) on a club-shaped cell called a **basidium*** (buh SID ee um). This phylum contains the *mushrooms* and similar fungi, *puffballs* and *earthstars*, *shelf fungi* (bracket fungi), *rusts*, and *smuts*.

Mushrooms are usually saprophytic fungi. The well-known but short-lived **cap** and **stipe** (stalk) are only the *fruiting body* of an extensive underground network of hyphae, which may cover several square meters of soil and may be several decades old. When the humidity and temperature are right, the hyphae stop growing and "regroup" stored substances into one or several tiny knobs near the surface of the soil. These knobs are actually twisted networks of hyphae (mycelia) which take on the shape of a compressed miniature mushroom. Once the structures form within their thin covering membranes, the knobs are called the *button stage* of the mushroom.

The **gills** have thousands of *basidia*, each of which produces four *basidiospores*. The basidiospores are shot from the basidium and then fall between the gills onto the soil. If the gills were not lined up properly, the spores would fall on the gills and not be dispersed. Some mushrooms have pores rather than gills under their caps.

Wind and water carry the spores to other areas. A good-sized mushroom may produce billions of spores, but few of them will ever become mushrooms. Even after the short-lived fruiting body has withered, the hyphae may live on to produce other mushrooms in future years.

Puffballs and *earthstars* produce their spores within protective membranes. Mature puffballs release their dust-fine spores as they are disturbed. The outer membrane of the earthstar folds back

basidiospore: basi- or basidio-
(L. BASIS, pedestal) + spore (seed)
basidium: (pedestal)

Rusts and Smuts: Plant Parasites

In the phylum Basidiomycota are several very harmful plant pathogens including the **rusts** and **smuts.** The *rusts* usually have complicated life cycles producing several different kinds of spores and alternating between two different plant hosts.

Wheat rust, for example, causes dark, rust-colored patches on the stems of wheat and other grains. These patches produce red *urediospores* (yoo REE dee uh SPORZ) which can be carried by wind and water to infect other wheat plants generally during the same growing season. At the end of the season, the plant begins to yellow, and the hyphae produce *teliospores* (TEE lee uh SPORZ). Teliospores can live through the winter and then germinate to form *basidia* and *basidiospores.* The basidiospores, however, cannot directly infect wheat. They infect the barberry, and on the underside of the barberry leaves this fungus forms tiny cups in which *aeciospores* (EE see uh SPORZ) are produced. These aeciospores infect wheat and cause the rust-colored spores. The *alternate host* (in this case, the barberry) is essential for a rust to complete its life cycle.

In colonial Massachusetts a law was passed ordering the destruction of all barberry bushes. It was believed that eliminating the barberry would eliminate the wheat rust; indeed, this action did achieve a measure of control. However, a barberry bush can supply aeciospores to infect a wheat field hundreds of miles away. Today wheat rust is controlled by breeding resistant varieties of wheat, as well as by controlling the

Corn smut

number of barberry bushes. Other significant rusts in the United States include the *apple cedar rust* and the *white pine blister rust.*

The *smuts,* like the rusts, produce several different spores in their life cycle, but they usually do not have an alternate host. Smuts infect grains such as wheat, barley, rye, oats, and corn, causing enlargement and filling them with sooty spores. Smuts cause hundreds of millions of dollars worth of damage to crops each year. *Corn smut* survives the winter as spores in the soil. Scientists are seeking to develop smut-resistant varieties of corn.

Wheat rust on barberry (left) and wheat (right)

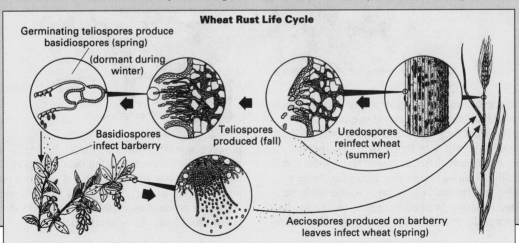

Wheat Rust Life Cycle

Germinating teliospores produce basidiospores (spring)

(dormant during winter)

Basidiospores infect barberry

Teliospores produced (fall)

Uredospores reinfect wheat (summer)

Aeciospores produced on barberry leaves infect wheat (spring)

Lichens

Some of the most unusual organisms are not single, but dual organisms: the **lichens** (LYE kunz). Often found in the harshest environments, the two organisms in a lichen work together to maintain life. Thus many of them can grow in places such as bare sunny rocks and roof shingles, where no known single living thing could survive.

Although most familiar lichens are common on tree bark, fence posts, and brick walls, some of the largest patches of lichen are in the tundra. *Reindeer moss,* an important food source for caribou and reindeer, can be found in mats several centimeters thick and several kilometers wide.

A lichen consists of a fungus and an alga living together. The relationship of two organisms living together is called **symbiosis*** (SIM bye OH sis). In lichen symbiosis the alga captures sunlight and manufactures sugars for itself and the fungus; the fungus supports and protects the alga.

Most lichens can dry out, losing over 30% of their water, and spend many months with an extremely low metabolism. When moisture returns, the lichens quickly absorb water, and full metabolism resumes. Many grow slowly, increasing their radii less than 1 mm per year. Some patches of lichen appear to be over 100 yr. old.

Scientists place the approximately 16,000 lichen species in three categories, based on their appearance.

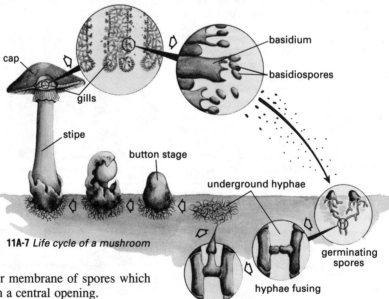

11A-7 *Life cycle of a mushroom*

and reveals an inner membrane of spores which are released through a central opening.

The *shelf fungi* are either saprophytes of dead wood or parasites of living trees. The hyphae in the wood may live for years and produce the shelflike fruiting bodies year after year. Some parasitic species add a new layer to the shelf each year, resulting in shelves almost as big in diameter as the trees on which they grow. Shelf fungi produce spores in pores on the underside of the shelf. When released, they fall out of the pore and are carried away by the wind. Six square centimeters (1 sq. in.) of surface area of some shelf fungi can produce over 200 million spores every twenty-four hours for several months.

symbiosis: sym- (Gk. SUN-, together) + -bios- (life)

□ **Crustose*** (KRUS TOSE) (crustlike) lichens appear as flat smears of dried paint **(a)**.

□ **Foliose*** (FOH lee OSE) (leaflike) lichens look like small, crinkly leaves **(b)**.

□ **Fruticose*** (FROO tih KOSE) (shrubby) lichens have stalks or branches often with conspicuous fruiting bodies on their ends **(c)**.

All the algae in lichens can live independently, but the fungi of lichens are not found by themselves in nature. The fungus produces spores, but when these spores germinate they must quickly contact an alga and parasitize it. This method of lichen reproduction has been demonstrated with great difficulty in the laboratory.

Most lichens reproduce by releasing dustlike pieces of lichen called **soredia** (suh REE dee uh) (sing., *soredium*). A soredium contains both the alga and fungus but not in a protective case. Thus, soredia must be transferred to a place suitable for lichen growth. Birds and crawling animals are responsible for spreading lichen soredia.

Although lichens are able to withstand some of the harshest of natural conditions, they are extremely sensitive to air pollution. Since lichens absorb and concentrate materials from rainwater and air, they stop growing and die if the air contains too much of certain substances. The growth of lichens can indicate air quality. In many industrial cities lichens have died, but farther away from such places lichens grow abundantly.

Biological Terms

The Kingdom Fungi

fungicide	true fungi	yeast	gill
kingdom Fungi	imperfect fungi	budding	crustose
external digestion	sporangiophore	phylum Basidiomycota	foliose
hyphae, (sing., hypha)	sporangium, (pl., sporangia)	basidiospore	fruticose
rhizoid	conidiophore	basidium, (pl., basidia)	soredia,
aerial hyphae	conidia	cap	(sing., soredium)
stolon	fruiting body	stipe	
sporophore	phylum Zygomycota	rust	
haustoria	phylum Ascomycota	smut	
mycelia, (sing., mycelium)	ascospore	lichen	
	ascus	symbiosis	

Review Questions 11A-2

1. Give characteristics and list three examples of each of these phyla: (a) Zygomycota, (b) Ascomycota, and (c) Basidiomycota.
2. Describe the structure of a yeast.
3. What is an imperfect fungus, and why is the list of imperfect fungi growing shorter?
4. List and give the functions of the four types of spores produced by wheat rust.
5. Describe a lichen.
6. List the three basic forms of lichens and describe each.
7. Lichens are often called ''pioneer organisms.'' What characteristics of lichens permit them to serve as pioneer organisms?
8. Describe the structure and the life cycle of a mushroom.

Thought Question

Many fungi grow in a ring shape. Why is this typical of fungi?

---

crustose: (L. CRUSTOSUS, crusted)

foliose: foli- (L. FOLIUM, leaf) + -ose (L. -OSUS, full of)

fruticose: fruti- (L. FRUTEX, shrub or bush) + -ose (full of)

THE PLANT KINGDOM AND PLANT STRUCTURE
BOTANY PART I

TWELVE

12A-Plant Classification

Botany,* the study of plants, may not top your list of interesting subjects. "After all," you may say, "plants are all alike. They are green things that just sit there." If you think this way, you obviously have only a passing acquaintance with these "green things."

First of all, not all green things are plants. Fungi can contain green pigments. Algae, protozoans, and even some bacteria may contain enough chlorophyll to make them green. These tissueless organisms, once classified in various phyla of the plant kingdom, are now usually placed into other kingdoms because the presence of tissues is a plant kingdom characteristic.

Second, not all plants are green. Some have other pigments which mask the green chlorophyll. Although most plants carry on photosynthesis with chlorophyll localized in plastids (autotrophic), there are thousands of *heterotrophic plants*.

Third, we cannot overestimate the value of plants to man. The plant kingdom provides almost all our food. Cereals such as corn, wheat, and

---

botany: botani- (Gk. BOTANE, herb or plant)

rice, along with legumes such as peas, beans, and soybeans, are our primary food sources. We also consume many other fruits and vegetables directly. Even spices, honey, coffee, tea, cocoa, and juices are derived from plants.

Although scientists believe that most photosynthesis-produced oxygen comes from algae, plants contribute a share of this life-supporting gas. Plant products include paper, gum, wax, alcohol, turpentine, cork, lumber, cloth fibers, coal, petroleum, medicines ranging from castor oil to codeine, and cellulose to be made into plastics.

Finally, plants are a source of inestimable beauty. The quiet stateliness of a lush forest and the delicate simplicity of a pale flower are not by-products of God's creation. They are as much a part of His plan as the "useful" aspects of the kingdom Plantae.

Heterotrophic Plants

a Mistletoe is a partially parasitic plant. It contains chlorophyll, and although it gets water and minerals from the host tree, it obtains little food from the tree.
b Dodder, however, has so little chlorophyll that the entire plant appears yellowish orange. Since few of its pigments are capable of photosynthesis, the dodder obtains almost all its food by rootlike structures which penetrate the stems of a host plant.
c Indian pipes, however, are completely saprophytic. Containing no chlorophyll or other pigments, these plants appear a ghostly white. They are believed to absorb food made soluble by certain fungi growing in association with their roots. You may wonder why Indian pipes and similar plants are not classified as fungi. Simply, they contain tissues and produce flowers, fruits, and seeds.

The kingdom Plantae

Botanists have divided the **kingdom Plantae** into nine phyla (often called "divisions"). We will group these phyla into three groups based on the presence or absence of **vascular* tissues** and **seeds.** Vascular tissues are specialized structures that conduct water and dissolved materials in a plant. A seed is a structure that contains a young plant and stored food in protective seed coat.

The Main Groupings of Plant Phyla
❑ **Non-vascular plants** Only one phylum of plants lacks vascular tissues: Bryophyta. In this group are the mosses and similar plants.
❑ **Vascular plants without seeds** Four phyla of plants have vascular tissues but lack seeds. The best known phylum is Pterophyta, the ferns.
❑ **Vascular plants with seeds** This group is usually divided into the following two subgroups:
• Non-flowering plants, the *gymnosperms* (four phyla, the best known is Coniferophyta, the cone bearing plants);
• Flowering plants, the *angiosperms* (one phylum, Anthophyta).

Non-Vascular Plants – The Mosses

Non-vascular plants are in **phylum Bryophyta*** (brye AH fuh tuh) which contains the mosses, liverworts, and a few similar groups. People are prone to call any small green thing a moss, even though it could be grass, fungus, or anything else. Common names for many organisms are misleading. Irish moss is an alga. Reindeer moss is a lichen. Spanish moss is a flowering plant. Club mosses, even though they may look like large true mosses, have vascular tissues and are therefore not bryophytes.

In tropical areas the abundant mosses can give a tree trunk the appearance of being several times its diameter. They are often the dominant vegetation in vast areas of tundra, where they must live for months under ice and snow. Most mosses growing in temperate regions appear as velvety clumps in shaded areas or as delicate green carpets covering rocks or logs near streams, waterfalls, or other sources of moisture.

vascular (L. VASCULUM, vessel)

Bryophyta: bryo- (Gk. BRYON, moss) + -phyta, phyto-, or -phyte (PHYTON, plant)

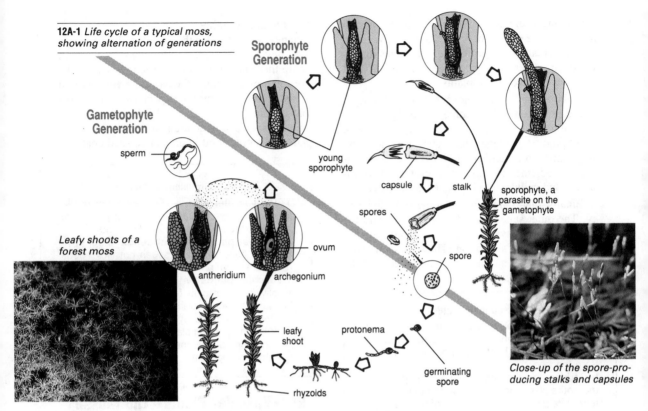

12A-1 *Life cycle of a typical moss, showing alternation of generations*

Sporophyte Generation

Gametophyte Generation

sperm

Leafy shoots of a forest moss

antheridium

archegonium

young sporophyte

capsule   stalk

spores

ovum

leafy shoot

protonema

rhizoids

spore

sporophyte, a parasite on the gametophyte

germinating spore

Close-up of the spore-producing stalks and capsules

In a clump of moss there actually are many densely packed individual plants. The most obvious part of a moss, called the **leafy shoot,** is generally less than 3 cm (1 in.) long and transmits water in small spaces between the cells in much the same way that a paper towel absorbs water. Each of the leaflike structures of a moss is one cell layer thick, except near the center where extra support is needed. Leafy shoots of various mosses may appear vastly different.

On the bottom of each shoot is a tangled mass of rhizoids. **Rhizoids** may appear rootlike, but they lack conducting tissues and therefore are not true roots. Moss rhizoids are usually filaments of cells used for anchorage. Many mosses lack the protective waxy *cuticle* found on most plant leaves. Mosses can therefore absorb water and minerals directly through the leafy shoot, but they can also dry out more readily than most plants. They thrive in moist environments.

Life cycle of a moss

The leafy shoot is only one stage in the life cycle of a moss. There are two different types of leafy shoots: the tip of one has the male reproductive structures; the other has the female structures. Usually these structures are on different plants, but occasionally they are on different branches of the same plant. Since the leafy shoot produces the gametes, this stage in the life cycle is called the **gametophyte*** (guh MEE tuh FITE). The top of a male gametophyte bears saclike **antheridia.** Spiral-shaped sperm are produced inside these sacs. The top of a female gametophyte has one or more vase-shaped **archegonia** (AR kih GOH nee uh). Each archegonium contains an ovum (egg cell) at the bottom of a slender neck. The neck of the archegonium is closed until the ovum is ready to be fertilized.

When water touches the top of the antheridium, the sperm are released. When the water also

---

gametophyte: gameto- (Gk. GAMOS, marriage) + -phyte (plant); [*hence, the plant that produces the next generation of its kind*] touches the top of a female plant, an open archegonium releases a chemical which stimulates the flagellated sperm to swim toward the ovum. Water and clustering of the gametophytes are essential for fertilization of bryophytes, since the sperm must swim from the antheridia to the ovum.

The fertilized ovum (zygote) grows into a stalk with a capsule on the top. Since this structure produces spores in the capsule, it is called the **sporophyte.*** The sporophyte is the result of the union of two gametes and is therefore diploid. The sporophyte begins as a parasite on the gametophyte. Some never contain enough chlorophyll to support themselves and constantly depend upon the leafy shoot.

The capsules and stalks are often brown, red, or orange. When mature, the cap comes off the capsule, and the wind distributes the released spores. When environmental conditions are suitable, the spore begins to grow. First it produces a cellular filament called a **protonema*** (PRO tuh NEE muh). The protonema then forms the leafy shoots and rhizoids of the gametophyte to complete the cycle.

Botanists call the type of life cycle illustrated by the mosses **alternation of generations.** The gametophyte gives rise to the sporophyte generation, and the spores give rise to the next gametophyte. Spores cannot produce sporophyte stalks and capsules, nor can zygotes produce gametophyte leafy shoots. The two generations must alternate. Because the gametophyte generation is the stage more often seen, in bryophytes it is called the **dominant generation.**

Economic importance of bryophytes

The only bryophytes regularly used in large quantities are from the genus *Sphagnum*. These peat or bog mosses grow floating on the quiet waters of a pond. As one layer dies and sinks to the bottom, another begins to grow. The mats fill the pond until it becomes a bog. In time other plants begin to grow in the peat moss, and the area shows no evidence of ever having been a pond.

Thick areas of dried peat moss can be cut with saws and burned as a fuel. Gardeners use sphagnum moss to pack plants for shipment. Mixed with heavy soils, shredded peat moss helps the soil to hold more water and is loose enough to permit plant roots to grow easily.

Although man may not use many bryophytes directly, they are important in the ecology of many areas. In tundras, high mountains, rocky areas, or very shaded spots, where most plants cannot grow, mosses prevent soil erosion and even build soil where none had previously been.

Review Questions 12A-1

1. In what ways are plants valuable to man?
2. List the characteristics of the plant kingdom.
3. What are the three general groupings of plant phyla? What two characteristics are used to put plants into these groups?
4. Describe at least two bryophyte characteristics that limit their size.

Liverworts

Liverworts are common bryophytes with a life cycle similar to that of mosses. The liverwort gametophyte plant is a narrow, flattened, leathery structure called a *thallus* (pl., *thalli)*. The thallus grows along the ground, anchored to the soil by rhizoids growing from the underside.

Marchantia, a common liverwort found near streams and occasionally in greenhouses, has branched, Y-shaped thalli. From the thallus grow short stalks which produce reproductive structures. Antheridia are produced on a flat surface called a *splash platform*. On other stalks archegonia are produced on the undersides of umbrella-shaped structures. Water drops hitting the top of the splash platform splash sperm to the archegonia. The sperm swim to the egg cells in the archegonia. After fertilization of the egg, spore cases develop in sacs under the umbrella-shaped structure.

---

sporophyte: sporo- (seed) + -phyte (plant)

protonema: prot- or proto- (first) + nema (NEMA, thread)

Vascular Plants Without Seeds

All plants other than bryophytes have vascular tissues which conduct water and dissolved minerals through the plant. Thus the vascular plants are not limited to the small size range of mosses. This group of four phyla, however, are unusual in that they do not produce seeds. In their life cycle they produce *spores,* a single cell with a protective coat, which are used to spread the species. The best known representatives of this group are the ferns.

Phylum Pterophyta: the ferns

The **phylum Pterophyta** (tehr AH fih tuh) contains an interesting and diverse group of plants. Most **ferns** are like the typical forest floor fern or the Boston fern, a favorite potted plant. Some, however, are *epiphytes,** plants that grow on other plants but are not parasitic. In the tropics a few remaining *tree fern* species can be found. Their slender trunks, which may reach over 18 m (60 ft.) high, are really an open network of hard stems, not the solid, woody mass normally associated with such tall trees.

Some ferns grow as vines; others grow floating on water. Although they are most prominent in shaded, cooler areas of the tropics, some species grow in almost desert conditions, and others grow next to glaciers. Some ferns are very delicate, among the rarest plants on earth, and quickly perish with the slightest environmental change.

The ferns common to most of North America are typical of the phylum Pterophyta. Each fern leaf, commonly called a **frond,** grows from either a creeping or an underground stem called a *rhizome,* which produces roots. Most fern fronds are long and delicate-looking. Ferns usually grow in clumps, produced by a single rhizome. The rhizome can produce new clumps asexually.

The fern life cycle

Occasionally a person will notice what he thinks are insect eggs or some fungus on the underside of fern fronds. Actually, these are **sori** (SOR EYE) (sing., *sorus*), collections of spore-producing **sporangia.** The sori of various ferns appear different. One characteristic used to name and classify ferns is the location and type of sori. Some ferns have

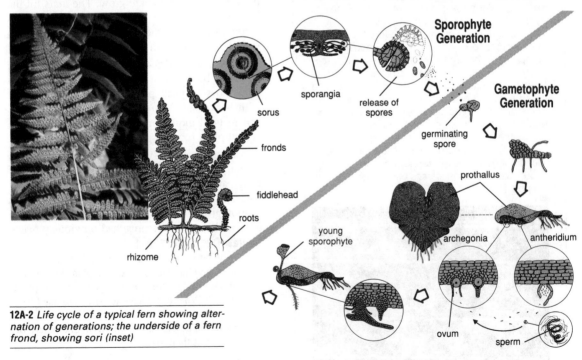

12A-2 *Life cycle of a typical fern showing alternation of generations; the underside of a fern frond, showing sori (inset)*

epiphyte: epi- (Gk. EPI, upon or over) + -phyte (plant)

Minor Seedless Plant Phyla

Sphenophyta: *(horsetails)* Most horsetails grow in wet environments. They have a thick underground stem which continues to grow year after year. From this main stem grow roots and green, erect, annual stems. These stems are ridged, hollow, and segmented by *nodes,* which may produce whorls of branches or of thin, needlelike leaves. Spores form in small, conelike structures at the tops of stems. The stems contain silica deposits. American colonists used the tough, hard nodes to clean pans; hence, the common name, "scouring rushes." Only the genus *Equisetum,* with representatives which grow only about 1 m (3 ft.) high, remains today.

horsetails   ground pine

Lycophyta: *(club mosses)* Club mosses or ground pines look like large moss plants. They usually have a creeping stem which may be un-der the surface of the soil and occasionally sends up erect stems. These erect stems have spore cases collected into conelike structures either at the tip or at the base of each leaf. Most species are evergreens and are less than 30 cm (1 ft.) high, but one tropical species may reach about 60 cm (2 ft.). Fossil club moss trees have been uncovered that measure over 30 m (100 ft.) high and over 1 m (3 ft.) in diameter.

Psilophyta *(whiskferns)* Whiskferns are rare and unusual plants which lack true roots and leaves. A thick stem covered with rhizoids may creep underground or in horizontal cracks in the bark of tropical trees. From this stem may grow smaller green stems which produce small scales instead of leaves.

Together these three phyla contain approximately 1,750 living species, all relatively small plants. The fossil record, however, reveals that before the deluge large members of some of these phyla were widespread, possibly as dominant foliage. Fossil Sphenophyta specimens, for example, were large, unusually shaped trees. Most of our coal and oil deposits are thought to be remains of these and similar plants. To have these large plants in abundance would require extensive areas of special environments that we find only in small, isolated areas today. This fact provides further support for the canopy theory.

fertile fronds, which have spores, and *sterile fronds,* which lack spores. In some ferns the fertile fronds are identical to the sterile fronds except for the presence of the sori. In other ferns the fertile fronds appear different and may not even contain chlorophyll.

When released, the powdery fern spores can be carried by the wind. Under proper conditions fern spores germinate and form a heart-shaped **prothallus*** (proh THAL us) which is one cell layer thick. The underside of the prothallus develops rhizoids (which absorb water and minerals), several *archegonia* (at the notched end of the prothallus), and *antheridia* (near the point of the "heart"). Flagellated sperm are released from the antheridium and swim to the ovum at the bottom of the archegonium. Thus, the prothallus is the gametophyte generation of the fern.

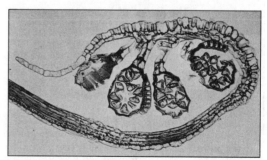

12A-3 *Cross section of a fern frond through a sorus, showing sporangia*

The zygote in the bottom of the archegonium matures and sends the first leaf up and the first root down, beginning the sporophyte generation. The young sporophyte is a parasite on the gametophyte until it is large enough to manufacture

prothallus: pro- (Gk. PRO, before) + -thallus (branch)

its own chlorophyll and begin carrying on photosynthesis. Soon after this, the prothallus dies. In ferns the more prominent generation is the sporophyte.

The first leaf of a fern is often a fan-shaped blade. The second is usually a **fiddlehead,** a coiled young leaf. The fiddlehead has tissue in its coiled end which is able to produce new cells even after the base of the leaf has reached its full size. This permits some ferns to have unusually large leaves. Young fiddleheads of some ferns are edible and can be purchased for use in salads.

Review Questions 12A-2

1. Describe the gametophyte and sporophyte of a typical fern. Is their relationship to each other the same as in the mosses?
2. Where are the sporangia of a fern located?
3. How is the life cycle of a fern similar to the life cycle of a moss? In what ways are they different?
4. In what ways are club mosses, horsetails, and ferns similar in their reproductive processes?
5. Describe the gametophyte and the sporophyte of a typical moss. Explain their relationship to each other.
6. Why is water necessary for the sexual reproduction of bryophytes and ferns?

Vascular Plants With Seeds

The vascular plants that produce seeds are divided into two groups: the **gymnosperms*** (JIM nuh SPURMZ) with three phyla and the **angiosperms*** (AN jee uh SPURMZ) with one phylum. The gymnosperms are non-flowering plants that produce seeds which are not enclosed in an ovary when mature. The pine cone, for example, has seeds that lie on tiny shelves when they are ripe. Angiosperms, which are discussed later, produce flowers and have enclosed seeds like the seeds of an apple or an orange.

The Cedar of Lebanon and Solomon's Temple

One of the best-known plants in the Bible is the cedar of Lebanon, a gymnosperm of the pine family. These trees reach a height of 30 m (120 ft.) and a circumference of 8 m (25 ft.). After the Flood they were the tallest, most massive trees known in the Middle East. As with most cedars, the wood of these trees is durable since it resists rotting and insect infestation. This wood is also delightfully fragrant and exceptionally beautiful.

Solomon built the temple and his own palace of this wood; his palace is sometimes called "the house of the forest of Lebanon" (I Kings 7:2). Scripture states that Solomon made a pact with King Hiram, the ruler of the Lebanon area, to supply the lumber for this project. Solomon was to send 3 shifts of 10,000 men to help Hiram's slaves and lumbermen cut the trees.

Other rulers, as well as Israelite kings, used this lumber for everything from chariots to ships. No reforestation program was practiced, and today the once extensive forests of Lebanon are mere patches of 30-150 trees each. The cedar of Lebanon, however, is not becoming extinct. It is now protected by the government and is easily cultivated wherever proper soil and climatic conditions exist.

gymnosperm: gymno- (Gk. GUMNOS, naked) + -sperm (seed)

angiosperm: angio- (vessel) + -sperm (seed)

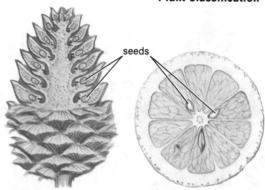

12A-4 *A pine cone has seeds on scales; an orange has seeds enclosed in an ovary.*

Useful Gymnosperms

When we think of useful plants we usually think of those we eat. Except for pine-needle tea (a bitter brew, sometimes causing minor undesirable side-effects), gymnosperms are rarely consumed by humans. Since gymnosperms are all woody trees or shrubs, there are few parts that humans find appetizing.

When many of us think of gymnosperms we think of the over 20 million that are cut each year to supply American homes with Christmas trees. Sometimes the gymnosperms are called evergreens. Although many of them are green throughout the year, many gymnosperms lose their foliage in the fall. And some plants, such as holly, are not gymnosperms but keep their green leaves all year.

The primary economic importance of gymnosperms is in lumber and pulp. America was literally built from the gymnosperm forests that covered extensive areas of the continent. But Americans rashly used almost all the available virgin timber. Over 100 yr. ago nearly every accessible stand of the eastern white pine, a highly prized lumber tree, had been cut. Today most of the lumber and pulp used in America comes from cultivated gymnosperms, specially selected for rapid growth and quality lumber. These trees can be harvested every 20-30 yr.

Gymnosperms range from ornamental varieties which creep along the ground to the giant Founder's Tree, a coastal redwood over 110 m (365 ft.) tall. The bristlecone pine is a species of gymnosperm growing in a dry mountain region of California. By making special drillings, scientists found that one of the bristlecone pines is the oldest living thing. According to the number of its growth rings, it is more than 4,000 yr. old.

bristlecone pine

Phylum Coniferophyta: conebearing plants

Among the gymnosperms the **phylum Coniferophyta** (KAH nih fur AH fih tuh) is the largest. All **conifers** produce seeds in cones. Although not all cones are like the familiar pine cone and not all conifers look like pine trees, the life cycle of a pine tree is typical.

In the spring, pine trees produce two types of cones: *pollen cones* and *seed cones*. **Pollen cones,** usually numerous, small, and short-lived, are found near the tips of the branches. The abundant **pollen** produced by these cones contains the male reproductive gametes. The chance of fertilization would be very small if only a few grains were produced since pine pollen is carried to the seed cones by the wind.

Pollen lands on the open scales of the small, green, upright **seed cone,** usually found on other branches of the same tree. The scales then close tightly, and in many pines the cone begins to point downward. The ova on the scales of the seed cone may not be fertilized until months later, and in some species they may not develop into seeds for several years. When the seeds are mature and environmental conditions are right, the scales of the woody seed cone open and release the seeds.

In the order Coniferales are several distinct families. Although most of the families in this order have cones like the pine tree, some of the cones are very different.

❏ *The pine family* is the largest and most economically important conifer family. The pines have the needles and cones normally associated with

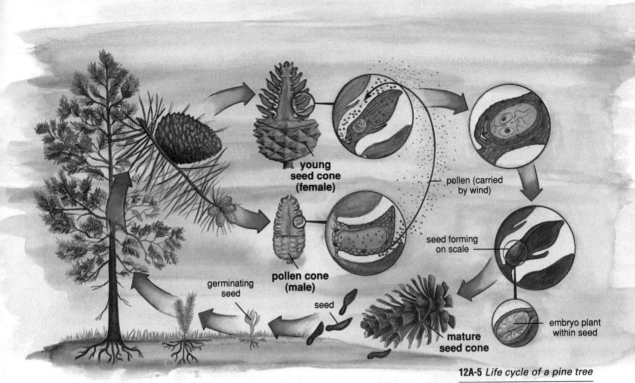

young seed cone (female)

pollen (carried by wind)

pollen cone (male)

seed forming on scale

germinating seed

seed

mature seed cone

embryo plant within seed

12A-5 *Life cycle of a pine tree*

gymnosperms. Pine needles vary in length, roundness, the number in a cluster, and the presence or absence of stripes. These characteristics, along with the type of cone produced, are used to classify the pines, firs, hemlocks, and the other members of this group.

❑ *The yew family,* prized in gardens for its slow growth and waxy green needles, produces fruit that looks like red, open-ended berries.

❑ *The cypress family* includes the *junipers* and the *arborvitae,* both widely cultivated shrubs. Some members of this family bear small, dry

Minor Gymnosperm Phyla

Many of the extinct gymnosperm species were very unlike those alive today. For many years scientists classified with the ferns certain fossil trees with fernlike fiddlehead leaves. When they found seeds attached to the leaves, however, these trees were named *seed ferns* and reclassified as extinct gymnosperms.

The *cycads* comprised a large gymnosperm phylum before the deluge. Only about a hundred species remain in phylum *Cycadophyta.* The cycads look like palm trees, and some of them have fiddleheads. Sometimes called the *sago palms,* these plants bear seeds in conelike structures.

Botanists once thought that all members of the phylum *Ginkophyta* were extinct. In the last century, however, they discovered several large specimens being cultivated in monasteries in

China. Today *ginkgo* trees (also called maidenhair trees) can be found in parks all over the world. The ginkgo sheds its broad, leathery, fan-shaped leaves during late autumn. Ginkgo trees are either male, producing pollen, or female, producing yellowish, cherry-sized, foul-odored fruit.

ginkgo leaves

cycad

12A-6 *A juniper showing scales and cones*

cones, but others have cones that remain fleshy and look like blue-green peas. Most junipers and arborvitae have overlapping evergreen *scales* instead of needles.

❏ *The redwood family* contains some of the largest living things in the world: the giant sequoias. The living organism with the greatest mass is the General Sherman giant sequoia (sih KWOI uh) tree in California. It is 25 m (84 ft.) in circumference and 83 m (273 ft.) tall and has bark about 30 cm (1 ft.) thick. It has been estimated to be about 3,500 yr. old.

Phylum Anthophyta: the flowering plants

Phylum Anthophyta, (an THAH fih tuh) often called angiosperms are the dominant vegetation on the earth today. There is so much diversity among the 250,000 species that they are grouped into nearly 400 different families, based primarily on floral parts. All angiosperms have seeds enclosed in an ovary and flowers. Many angiosperms (or **flowering plants),** however, do not produce colorful blossoms. Corn tassels and the catkins of oak trees are flowers.

An *ovary* of a plant is the structure which encloses the seeds; a mature ovary is a **fruit.** You can easily identify apples, cherries, and tomatoes as fruits. But pods of peas and kernels of corn and wheat are also fruits (see page 335).

Monocots and dicots

Angiosperms are divided into two classes, *Monocotyledoneae** (MAHN uh KAHT uh LEE duh nee) and *Dicotyledoneae** (dye KAHT uh LEE duh nee), commonly called **monocots** and **dicots.** The basic distinction between these two is the number of cotyledons in the seed. A **cotyledon** (KAHT uh LEE dun) has stored food to keep the embryonic plant alive while it is in the seed and to supply the sprout with energy until it can carry on photosynthesis. The peanut, a dicot, easily splits in

12A-7	Comparison of Monocot and Dicot Characteristics	
	Monocot	**Dicot**
Seeds:	One cotyledon One seed leaf	Two cotyledons Two seed leaves
Leaves:	Parallel venation	Netted venation
Roots:	Usually fibrous	Usually a tap root
Stems:	Young stems have scattered vascular bundles and usually become hollow as they mature	Young stems have vascular bundles in a ring and are usually solid
Flowers:	Flower parts usually in threes or sixes	Flower parts usually in fours, fives, or in multiples of these numbers

daylilies

columbines

Monocotyledoneae: Mono- (single) + -cotyledon- (Gk. KUTOLEDON, hollow-shaped cup)

Dicotyledoneae: Di- (two) + -cotyledon (hollow-shaped cup)

half to reveal its two cotyledons. Corn, on the other hand, is a monocot. A corn seed has only one cotyledon and does not split apart. A characteristic that distinguishes between monocots and dicots is the number of leaves the embryonic plant has. Monocots have one; dicots have two.

Leaf venation can often be used for classification of monocots and dicots. Monocots generally have *parallel leaf venation*. The veins in their leaves start at the stem, which may be underground and go to the top of the leaf. The veins are roughly parallel. Dicots generally have *netted leaf venation*. Netted veins continually branch within the leaf blade. Problems may arise in classifying plants by leaves if one is considering a modified leaf, like a cactus needle, or a leaf that is too thick to have visible venation. Of course, some plants that have leaves are not even angiosperms.

Monocots usually have floral parts in threes or sixes. Dicots, like the rose or carnation, usually have floral parts in fours, fives, or multiples of four or five. Classification by floral parts can be misleading, and there are exceptions. Other characteristics used to determine whether a plant is a monocot or a dicot are even less reliable.

Angiosperms are classified into families based upon their reproductive structures. A few of the more important plant families and some common examples of each are listed in Appendix B.

Biological Terms

botany
kingdom Plantae
vascular tissue
seeds
Non-Vascular Plants
  phylum Bryophyta
  leafy shoot
  rhizoid
  gametophyte
  archegonium (pl., archegonia)
  sporophyte
  protonema

alternation of generations
dominant generation
Vascular Plants without Seeds
  phylum Pterophyta
  fern
  frond
  sori
  sporangium (pl., sporangia)
  prothallus
  fiddlehead
Vascular Plants with Seeds
  gymnosperm

angiosperm
phylum Coniferophyta
pollen cone
seed cone
pollen
phylum Anthophyta
flowering plant
fruit
monocot
dicot
cotyledon

Review Questions 12A-3

1. Name and describe the two types of cones produced by conifers. Tell their relationship to each other.
2. How is the life cycle of a pine different from the life cycle of a fern or moss?
3. List several well-known groups of conifers, and describe each.
4. What characteristics do gymnosperms and angiosperms have in common? In what ways are they different?
5. What are the primary characteristics that separate the two classes of the phylum Anthophyta?

Thought Questions

1. If you examine a clump of moss, you will find that only some of the moss has sporophyte stalks and capsules. Why?
2. What is meant by alternation of generations in the plant kingdom, and how do the moss and fern life cycles illustrate alternation of generations?
3. Why would mosses be most abundant in areas such as the tundra and tropical rain forests, where extreme environmental conditions exist?
4. What evidence does the plant kingdom give to support the canopy theory?
5. Seed plants are called the dominant vegetation of the earth today. In what ways are seed plants dominant over other types of plants?

12B·Plant Anatomy

Plant parts can be classified as woody or herbaceous. The trunk and branches of a tree are *woody*. Woody parts generally are strong because their cells have thick walls. In most woody plant parts some tissues remain *undifferentiated* (do not become specialized). Additional plant tissues can form from this undifferentiated tissue in future years. This growth may continue for centuries and produce tall trees with thick trunks.

Herbaceous (hur BAY shus) plant parts, on the other hand, usually live for only one year. Because leaves, flowers, and nonwoody roots and stems lack the thick cell walls of woody structures, they sometimes rely on turgor pressure for support. The herbaceous parts of a plant usually remain green until they die. When dead, many herbaceous plant parts, such as corn stalks, are strong and leave stems which appear woody.

Herbaceous plants lack woody structures; those that have both woody and herbaceous structures are called *woody plants*.

Plant organs and tissues

Plant organs can be divided into two groups: the **vegetative organs** (leaves, roots, and stems) and the sexual **reproductive organs** (flowers, fruits,

and seeds). Technically, leaves, roots, and stems are vegetables. Examples include spinach, carrots, and asparagus. The other parts of a plant are either fruits or seeds. Peas and corn are really seeds; eggplants and tomatoes are really fruits.

Although of great diversity, plant organs are made of the same basic kinds of tissues which can be grouped into three categories.

❑ **Meristematic** (MEHR ih stuh MAT ik) **tissues** Plant cells capable of mitosis are usually found only in meristematic tissues. Meristematic cells are small, thin-walled, and undifferentiated, but can develop into any tissue found in that particular plant. Meristematic tissues are found in the growing areas of plants, such as buds, tips of roots and stems, vascular bundles of some herbaceous plants, and roots and stems of woody plants.

❑ **Vascular tissues** Vascular tissues are *complex tissues;* that is, they are composed of different types of cells. The **xylem*** (ZYE lum), for example, is made of long, thick-walled cells and

◀ sweet Williams
▼ evening primroses

marigolds

Annuals, Biennials, and Perennials

Based on the length of time that they grow, plants can be placed into three groups.

❑ **Annual plants** Most herbaceous plants are annual plants. Annuals sprout, grow, flower, and produce seeds in one growing season. Many showy flower beds contain herbaceous annuals like zinnias, pansies, and marigolds.

❑ **Biennial* plants** Biennials like the foxglove and the sweet William sprout and develop in one growing season but do not flower and produce seeds until the following growing season. After the second year most biennials die.

❑ **Perennial plants** Perennials grow year after year. Woody plants are usually perennials, but some herbaceous plants have thick, underground stems which live many years, even though the above-ground leaves and stems die each year. Tulips, irises, peonies, and gladioli are common examples of *herbaceous perennials*.

---

biennial: bi- (L. BIS, two) + -ennial, (ANNUS, year)
xylem: (Gk. XYLON, wood)

Plant Tissues				
	Names	Function	Structure	Location
Meristematic	Apical meristem	produces new cells for growth in length and formation of leaves and flowers	cone-shaped mass of small, thin-walled cells	at the ends of stems and roots and in buds
	Vascular cambium Lateral meristem	produces new xylem and phloem for growth in diameter	layer of small, thin-walled cells	between the xylem and phloem in woody and some herbaceous stems and roots
	Cork cambium	produces cork cells	layer of small, thin-walled cells	inside cork cells of bark
	Pericycle	produces secondary roots	layer of small, thin-walled cells	inside the vascular cylinder of young roots and stems and inside the cortex layer of the bark and roots
Vascular	Xylem	conducts water and dissolved minerals upward	complex tissues made of • *tracheids:* long cells; dead at maturity; strengthening • *vessels:* long tubes formed by many dead cells lined end to end; conduction • *fibers:* long cells with thick walls; strength • *parenchyma:* shorter cells used for storage	in all vascular bundles of young or herbaceous plants; comprises all woody parts of plants
	Phloem	conducts water and foods downward	complex tissues made of • *sieve tubes:* rows of long, living cells with perforated ends; conduction • *companion cells:* found near sieve tubes; appear to aid them in conduction • *fibers and parenchyma:* same as in xylem	in young or herbaceous parts of plants along with the xylem; comprises part of the bark of woody plants
Structural	Epidermis	protects; covers	one cell layer thick, often with a secreted waxy cuticle; forms guard cells for the stoma which permit exchange of gases; usually lacks chlorophyll and other pigments	on leaves, young roots and stems, and other exposed areas of the plant; comprises the top layer of cells
	Parenchyma	stores food; manufactures food	large cells with thin walls; usually contains plastids; cells of various shapes	in cortex of roots and stems and in fruits
	Palisade mesophyll	manufactures food	cells arranged in neat rows, closely packed; contains many chloroplasts	upper layer of mesophyll of leaf
	Spongy mesophyll	manufactures food	cells loosely arranged with many air spaces; also contains chloroplasts	lower layer of mesophyll of leaf
	Collenchyma	strengthens	thick-walled, long-lived cells	in stems and leaf veins
	Cork	protects; waterproofs	small cells which die and fill with material soon after they are formed	in tree bark and skins of underground structures
	Sclerenchyma	strengthens	cells with thick walls; called *fiber cells* or *stone cells*; dead at maturity	in vascular tissues; common in various hard parts

carries water and dissolved minerals within a plant. When xylem tissue is mature, the cells die, leaving long conducting tubes. The cell walls of another tissue, the **phloem,*** (FLOH EM) are usually slightly thinner than xylem cell walls. Mature phloem is composed of living cells and carries water and dissolved foods (usually sugars). Generally, materials in xylem tubes move upward, and materials in phloem cells move downward. However, in some parts of the plant and at another time of the year, the opposite can be true. For example, during the summer, sugars produced in the leaves are carried in the phloem to the roots. But in the spring tree, phloem may carry water

phloem: (Gk. PHLOOS, bark)

and food upward. The sap rises to help with the formation of leaves and flowers.

❑ **Structural tissues**   The structural tissues include those which produce food, store food, cover, support, and protect the plant. Some of these tissues are thin and delicate while others may remain years after the plant is dead. These tissues will be discussed as the plant organs are covered.

Review Questions 12B-1
1. Differentiate between woody and herbaceous plant parts.
2. Describe and give the functions of the three major categories of plant tissues.
3. Compare and contrast xylem and phloem.

The Leaf

One of the primary functions of a leaf is absorbing energy from the sun. Without this efficient energy-gathering, enough photosynthesis to support the plant would not take place. Ranging in size from a fraction of a centimeter to over 4 m (15 ft.) long, leaves may be thick and heavy or light and delicate. Whereas most leaves are a deep, rich green, some are pale green, yellow, red, pink, or even white. Although modified leaves may help protect the plant, attract and catch insects, store water, or even hold the roots of the plant to a tree trunk, the basic function of typical leaves is photosynthesis.

Structures of a typical leaf

A typical *foliage leaf* has a large, flattened area called the **blade,** which is connected to the stem by a stalk called a **petiole.*** Some leaves, like those of a zinnia, lack a petiole and are called *sessile.* Some leaves have **stipules,** which may be thin tissues that covered the leaf when it was forming, winglike structures attached to the petiole, or leaflike structures at the base of the petiole.

Botanists identify plants by studying the basic shapes of the leaves and leaf parts, including the edges of the leaves called *margins.* Identifying plants by their leaves, however, is not always foolproof. One type of oak may have over twenty different leaf shapes on a single tree.

12B-2 *Leaf margins*

entire   undulate   dentate   serrate

Leaf venation

There are two basic patterns of **leaf venation:** parallel and netted. In **parallel venation** a series of veins originates at the stem and proceeds to the top of the leaf in a roughly parallel fashion. This occurs in monocots like corn, grass, irises, and orchids.

In **netted venation** large veins branch to form a network of smaller veins throughout the leaf. There are two types of netted venation. If the veins branch off one large central vein (the *midrib),* the venation is **pinnate.** Oaks, African violets, and apple trees have simple pinnate leaves. If there are two or more main veins coming from a single point, the venation is **palmate.** Maples, ivy, and geraniums have simple palmate leaves.

If there is only one blade on one petiole, the leaf is a *simple leaf.* If a leaf on a single petiole is divided, the leaf is a *compound leaf.* Each of these blade divisions is called a **leaflet.** If the leaf

12B-1 *A typical foliage leaf*

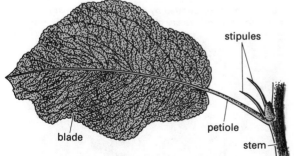

stipules

blade

petiole

stem

petiole: (L. PETIOLUS, fruit stalk)

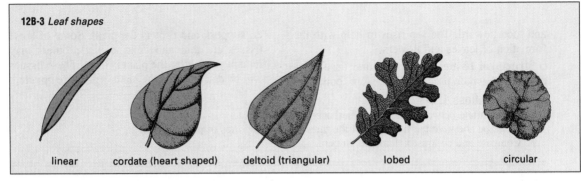

12B-3 *Leaf shapes*

linear   cordate (heart shaped)   deltoid (triangular)   lobed   circular

is basically pinnately veined and the leaflets are arranged down the midrib, the leaf is *pinnately compound*. If the leaf is palmately veined and all the leaflets originate from a single point, the leaf is *palmately compound*. Occasionally there is a *bipinnately compound* leaf, in which the venation is pinnate with the leaflets borne on the secondary veins, not just on the midrib. Some plants even have tripinnately compound leaves. Can you figure out how they look?

Some leaflets are larger than many simple leaves, and a petiole may look like a stem rather than like part of the leaf. One of the easiest ways to tell the difference between a leaf and a leaflet is to look for a stipule. Leaflets usually do not have stipules, but most leaves do. Another distinguishing characteristic is the presence of buds. A bud may be found at the base of a petiole, not at the base of a leaflet. Leaves are found in different planes on a stem, but leaflets are always found on the same plane.

The covering of a leaf

If you were to look at a cross section of a typical leaf under a microscope, you would notice that it appears to have layers of tissue. The top and bottom layers, which are one cell thick, comprise the **epidermis.** The epidermal cells lack chlorophyll and serve as protection.

Often epidermal cells secrete a waxy substance that forms a **cuticle,*** giving the leaf a shiny appearance on one or both surfaces. The epidermal cells of some leaves produce *epidermal hairs.* Epidermal hairs may be extensions of epidermal cells, or they may be composed of several cells. Sometimes these hairs give the leaf a velvety appearance, as in African violets. Some epidermal hairs secrete sticky substances or chemicals with specific odors. If you touch a geranium leaf, you will notice a distinctive scent released by the broken epidermal hairs. Some epidermal hairs are thin and sharp enough to penetrate your skin without your feeling the prick. Stinging nettles, moreover, leave an irritating substance under the skin.

On the underside of most leaves are little openings called **stomata,*** which permit the exchange of gases between the atmosphere and the spaces inside the leaf. Around each stoma are two **guard cells.** These specialized epidermal cells are shaped in opposing crescents. Guard cells contain chlorophyll and manufacture sugars which, in different concentrations, cause the water pressure in the cell to change. When guard cells are turgid, they open the stomata, but when lacking water, they collapse and close the stomata.

Enzymes, temperature, and other factors play important roles in the opening and closing of the stomata. Generally, when water is in abundance and photosynthesis is taking place, the stomata are open. At night, or when the plant lacks water, the stomata are closed to reduce loss of water into the atmosphere.

12B-4 *Stomata surrounded by guard cells; some stomata are open, others are closed.*

cuticle: (L. CUTIS, skin)

stomata: sing. stoma (Gk. STOMA, mouth)

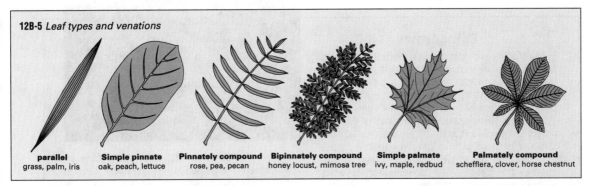

12B-5 *Leaf types and venations*

parallel
grass, palm, iris

Simple pinnate
oak, peach, lettuce

Pinnately compound
rose, pea, pecan

Bipinnately compound
honey locust, mimosa tree

Simple palmate
ivy, maple, redbud

Palmately compound
schefflera, clover, horse chestnut

The stomata of different plants vary in size, number, and location. A lily pad has all its stomata on the upper epidermis; in apple leaves all the stomata are on the lower epidermis. Oat leaves have an almost equal number of stomata on both the upper and lower epidermis. The potato is about average, with 5,100 per sq. cm. on the upper epidermis and 16,100 per sq. cm. on the lower epidermis.

The inside of the leaf

Between the upper and lower epidermis is the mesophyll. These **parenchyma*** (puh RENG kuh muh) tissues are the primary photosynthetic areas of the leaf. The upper layer or layers are called **palisade mesophyll*** (MEZ uh FIL). These mesophyll cells are column-shaped and are lined up side by side. This arrangement permits a large number of cells to be present in a small surface area. These cells have abundant chloroplasts which move in a circle around the central vacuole by cytoplasmic streaming. Each chloroplast gets its turn at the top of the cell where it can absorb the most direct sunlight.

The **spongy mesophyll** is made of irregularly shaped cells with many air spaces between them. These air spaces do not permit this layer to have as many chlorophyll-containing cells as the palisade layer. For this reason the underside of many leaves is not as dark a green as the upper surface. Many vertical leaves, however, have two layers of palisade mesophyll with a layer of spongy mesophyll in the middle.

Plants do not inhale and exhale air as you do, but in a sense plants do breathe. Gas exchange through the stomata and diffusion in the air spaces of the spongy mesophyll supply the carbon dioxide and oxygen exchange necessary for photosynthesis.

The xylem and phloem in the *veins* of the leaf continue though the petiole to the xylem and the

12B-6 *Structures of a typical leaf*

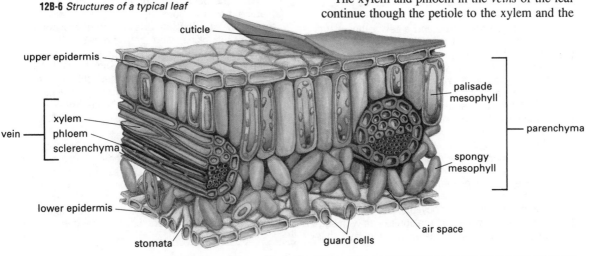

cuticle

upper epidermis

vein — xylem / phloem / sclerenchyma

lower epidermis

stomata

guard cells

air space

spongy mesophyll

palisade mesophyll

parenchyma

---

parenchyma: (Gk. PARENKHUSIS, visceral flesh)

mesophyll: meso-, or mes- (Gk. MESOS, middle) + -phyll, or -phyl-lum (PHYLLON, leaf)

303

Falling Leaves

In the tropics and subtropics where the growing season lasts almost all year, most plants lose their leaves a few at a time and are never completely bare. Most house plants are tropical plants and therefore have leaves all year.

In more temperate regions many woody plants are **deciduous;** they lose their leaves before winter in order to conserve water. A deciduous leaf has a narrow, light green layer at the base of the petiole. This **abscission* layer** is formed even before the leaf is completely developed. Part of this layer is made of cells which begin to die as the days shorten, regardless of the temperature. For this reason deciduous plants that are kept indoors still lose their leaves in the fall. The abscission layer also forms a layer of cork cells that seals the vascular tissues and leaves a *leaf scar* on the stem. Approximately 2 weeks after the separation starts, enough cells have died that a crack has formed. In a breeze, or because of its own weight, the leaf falls.

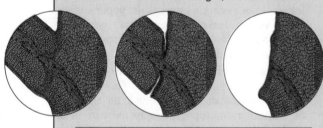

The abscission layer (left) forms layers of cork (center) which separate from the stem (right) leaving a leaf scar.

Most gymnosperms and a few other plants have **persistent foliage.** The leaves do not fall until the following spring when new leaves have formed. Since many persistent leaves retain their chlorophyll all year, the plant has an evergreen appearance.

The beautiful autumn colors seen in North America are evidence of the fact that green leaves have other colored pigments in them. When the abscission layer begins to block the water supply, the leaf can no longer produce chlorophyll. As chlorophyll wears out and is not replaced, other pigments begin revealing magnificent yellows, oranges, reds, and purples.

In many leaves, anthocyanins are formed only in cool temperatures as the sun reacts with sugars that remain after the abscission layer has formed. The brightest leaf colors, therefore, appear when the fall has sunny days with temperatures that dip to about 4° C (40° F). Cloudy, warm fall seasons in some parts of the world do not allow leaf colors to be as brilliant.

Some leaves do not produce these other pigments. When these leaves die, they appear a brownish color as even the most beautifully colored leaves do eventually. This coloring is due to *tannic acid,* the product of the chemical breakdown of plant cell contents. The large concentration of tannic acid found in some leaves is readily dissolved in water to form tea, the most widely consumed beverage in the world. Most other plant leaves also release tannic acid when they are placed in water, but many of them release poisonous or distasteful chemicals as well.

Plant Pigments

Carotenoids are fat-soluble pigments found in the plastids of some plants. *Carotenes* and *xanthophylls,* two types of carotenoids, account for the yellow or orange, as well as some red, colors in certain plants. Carotenoids are responsible for the pale yellow-green areas of leaves that are grown without sufficient light as well as the colors of such plant parts as daffodil flowers, carrots, pumpkins, and corn kernels. When found in conjunction with chlorophyll, some carotenes help capture light necessary for photosynthesis and somehow help protect chlorophyll from intense light. Since carotenoids are the basic substances from which our bodies form vitamin A, a balanced diet contains yellow or red fruits or vegetables.

Anthocyanins* (AN tho SY uh ninz) are red, blue, and violet water-soluble pigments found in the vacuoles of plant cells. Leaves of the scarlet maple and some variegated leaf plants like the coleus have large quantities of anthocyanins, which also color grapes, plums, cherries, geraniums, roses, orchids, beets, and radishes.

abscission: ab- or abs- (L. ABS-, away) + -cission (CAEDERE, to cut)

anthocyanin: antho- (Gk. ANTHOS, flower) + -cyanin-, -cyan-, or -cyano- (KUANOS, blue)

phloem of the stem. The large veins of a leaf contain thick-walled strengthening *sclerenchyma** (skluh RENG kuh muh) tissues around the vascular tissues. As the veins branch and get smaller, the amount of supporting tissue lessens. The smallest veins contain only a single xylem vessel. Xylem is necessary to conduct the water and dissolved minerals from the roots to the cells of the leaf. Every cell in the leaf is only a few cells away from the end of a xylem vessel. The sugars and starches made in the leaf pass by diffusion until they come to a phloem cell. The phloem then carries these leaf products to other areas of the plant for use or storage.

Review Questions 12B-2

1. Differentiate between (a) pinnate and palmate venation; (b) simple and compound leaves; and (c) pinnately compound and bipinnately compound leaves.
2. Describe and give the function of the stomata of a leaf.
3. Draw and label a cross section of a typical dicot leaf.
4. Describe the process whereby leaves change color and fall in the autumn.
5. List and describe plant pigments often found in leaves. What accounts for the brown color of old leaves?

The Root

Most of us think of **roots** as the underground parts of plants. This is only partly true. First of all, not all roots are below ground. The roots of epiphytic orchids, for example, creep along tropical tree branches and obtain water and minerals from the materials that collect in cracks in the bark. The roots of parasitic plants such as mistletoe grow into the tissues of their host. Some aquatic plants have short roots dangling into the water from their floating leaves. Other roots, such as those in the ivy plant, hold the plant onto a rough surface like a brick wall.

Most roots serve to *anchor* the plant, even though they may not be in the soil. They *absorb* water and the dissolved minerals necessary for plant growth. Roots also *transport* these absorbed substances to where they are needed in the plant. Roots also function in *food storage* as with carrots, radishes, and beets.

Root systems

Plant roots differ greatly, depending not only upon the plant itself but also upon the conditions in which the plant is grown.

When the original root that sprouts from the seed, called the *primary root,* continues to grow as the predominant root, the plant has a **taproot system.** Not all taproots are fleshy, as are beets or carrots, but are often long and thin. They produce small, branching *secondary roots.* If the plant lacks a taproot but has many secondary roots, it has a **fibrous root system.**

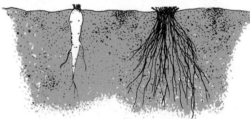

taproot system   fibrous root system

Unless a plant is very slow-growing or lives in very moist soil, its roots will need much more surface area than the leaves. Yet most root systems do not go deeper than 1-2 m (3-6 ft.) into the soil. The roots of some large trees, like the pecan, often are less than 1.5 m (5 ft.) deep but may spread in a circle 30 m (100 ft.) in diameter. An 8-year-old alfalfa plant less than 30 cm (1 ft.) tall may have roots that total 9 m (30 ft.) long. A 4-month-old corn plant may be over 3 m (10 ft.) tall and have more than 150 m (500 ft.) of roots.

Primary growth of a root

If a root of a germinating seed is marked at millimeter intervals and then permitted to grow for 24 hr., the marks closest to the seed will still be

---

sclerenchyma: scler- or sclero-
(Gk. SKLEROS, hard) + -enchyma (that
which fills in)

305

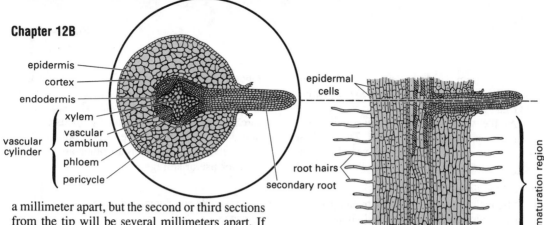

epidermis
cortex
endodermis

vascular cylinder
{
xylem
vascular cambium
phloem
pericycle
}

epidermal cells

root hairs
secondary root

a millimeter apart, but the second or third sections from the tip will be several millimeters apart. If the experiment is continued, the sections that expanded the most during the first 24 hr. will remain about the same length, but the section nearest the tip will continue to get longer. This growth in length is called **primary growth.** Why is primary growth found only in the tip of the root? Examining a longitudinal section of a young root under a microscope will provide the answer.

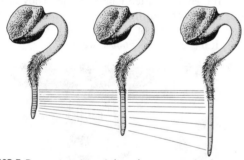

12B-7 *Demonstration of the primary growth of a root*

The tip of the root is covered by the **root cap,** made of dead, thick-walled cells which protect the delicate tissues of the root tip as it pushes through the soil. Just above the root cap is the **meristematic region,** where tiny undifferentiated cells carry on mitosis. The cells formed in the meristematic region begin to grow and establish large vacuoles in the **elongation region,** located just above the meristematic region. As the cells complete elongation, they begin to differentiate and become the tissues of a young root. The area where most differentiation takes place is called the **maturation region.**

The primary growth of a root results from the manufacturing of cells in the meristematic region. The actual lengthening of the root tip, however,

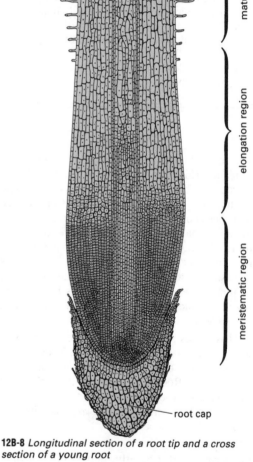

maturation region

elongation region

meristematic region

root cap

12B-8 *Longitudinal section of a root tip and a cross section of a young root*

is because of cell growth in the elongation region. Once the cells have elongated, they will not grow any more in length; hence, in the root marking experiment the marks closest to the seed will not be any farther apart, but the ones in the meristematic and elongation regions will be.

FACETS OF BIOLOGY

12B–1

Modified Plant Parts

Not all plants have only typical leaves, roots, and stems. Many plants have modified structures that permit them to carry on unusual functions or thrive in areas where it would otherwise be impossible to grow.

Leaf modification

Leaves often perform some very interesting functions in addition to, and sometimes in place of, photosynthesis. Spanish moss (which is neither Spanish nor moss but is a member of the pineapple family)

has no roots but drapes gracefully on everything from tree branches to telephone poles by "holding on" with its leaves. The circular scales of the onion are underground storage extensions of the green leaves which carry on photosynthesis above the ground. The

insect-catching apparatus of the Venus's-flytrap and the other insect-eating plants are modified leaves (see pages 321).

Some common leaf modifications are as follows:

❏ **Tendrils** A plant part that wraps itself around something in order to help support the plant

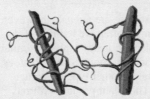

may be called a tendril. Tendrils are often extensions of the midribs of compound leaves, as in the pea. They may be special leaves that lack blades, or outgrowths of the petiole, as in grapes.

❏ **Spines** Technically, a *spine* is a leaf, a *thorn* is a branch, and a *prickle* is an outgrowth of epidermal tissue. The terms are often

used interchangeably since they all refer to hard, sharp, usually nongreen plant protectors. A spine may be a tough petiole, as in the black locust, or a hard, sharp end of a vein, as in holly. Bladeless leaves of a cactus become dead spines which protect the thick photosynthetic stems.

❏ **Succulent leaves** Some plants store water in thick succulent leaves. Often the venation of these leaves is completely hidden. A succulent leaf usually has a tough cuticle and epidermal coating and, as in the aloe, is often edged with protective spines.

succulent leaves   floating leaves

❏ **Aquatic leaves** Plants that live in the water often have leaves with enlarged spongy parenchyma which hold large quantities of air.

Primary tissues of a root

If you were to look at a cross section of a young root made just above the maturation region, you would see the **primary tissues.** Primary tissues are those which are made during primary growth. The outermost tissue, the epidermis, is one cell layer thick; it protects the root and absorbs materials. The epidermis in the maturation region produces cellular extensions called **root hairs.** These hairs penetrate between soil particles to

water sources which would normally be out of reach for the root.

Just inside the epidermis is a layer of large, thin-walled parenchyma cells called the **cortex.***
In young roots the cortex stores materials. Inside the cortex is a single cell layer called the **endodermis.*** The small cells of the endodermis have walls which are bound to each other so that no material may pass between these cells. Substances must pass *through* these cells to enter the vascular

---

cortex: (L. CORTEX, bark or rind)
endodermis: endo- (Gk. ENDON, within) + -dermis (DERMA, skin)

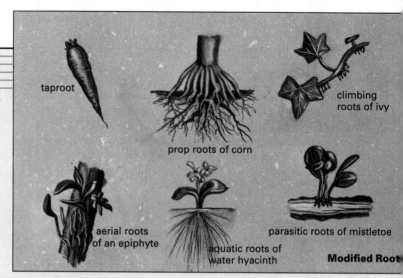

taproot

prop roots of corn

climbing roots of ivy

aerial roots of an epiphyte

aquatic roots of water hyacinth

parasitic roots of mistletoe

Modified Root

This stored air causes the leaves to float and supplies oxygen and carbon dioxide for respiration and photosynthesis.

❑ **Bracts** Some showy flowers lack petals but have brightly colored leaves called bracts. Often there are small flowers in the center of a group of bracts, as in poinsettias and flowering dogwoods.

flowers

bracts

Modified roots

Modified roots can be grouped into five categories:

❑ **Storage roots** Thick and fleshy roots, usually containing starches and oils with pigments and other chemicals, are called storage roots. Taproots are often storage roots. These roots generally have secondary growth of xylem and phloem; and the pericycle, rather than producing cork, produces a thin layer of protective cells. When grown in temperate regions, most of our cultivated root crops such as carrots, beets,

and radishes are annuals; however, they most often are hybrids of perennials with fleshy taproots similar to dandelion roots. Sweet potatoes illustrate another type of storage root. This plant produces fibrous roots which occasionally enlarge into fleshy sections.

❑ **Adventitious roots** Roots that grow from a stem, a petiole, or a leaf are called adventitious roots. They usually help anchor the plant. Adventitious roots that grow from the nodes of corn are called *prop roots*. Many vines have adventitious roots that sprout from the stems. These roots may support the plant by growing into the cracks of a structure and enlarging to fill the cracks. These are called *climbing roots*.

❑ **Aerial roots** Orchids, bromeliads, and other epiphytic plants have aerial roots. These roots not only anchor the plant and absorb water and minerals but also store water for dry periods. Some are green and carry on photosynthesis.

❑ **Aquatic roots** Roots which grow under water are called aquatic roots. They often lack root hairs but many of them have special tubes with the vascular tissues to permit gases to be exchanged in the growing parts of the root.

❑ **Parasitic roots** Roots of parasitic plants grow into the vascular tissues of the host plants and absorb water and dissolved minerals from the xylem. Some parasitic plants also absorb sugars from the phloem.

tissues and pass to the rest of the plant. The endodermal cells insure that only certain materials are permitted into the plant.

The **vascular cylinder** is the central area of the young root. The center of the vascular cylinder in a dicot is the *xylem vessels*. In cross section the xylem in a dicot root often radiates four arms, but may have only two or three arms.

Between the arms of the xylem is the *phloem*. Between the xylem and phloem is the **vascular**

cambium. This meristematic tissue can produce additional xylem and phloem. Between the vascular tissues and the endodermis is the **pericycle*** (PEHR ih SYE kul), which is also a meristematic tissue. If a secondary root is to be formed, it will originate in the pericycle and vascular cambium.

In monocots, pith is surrounded by vascular tissues. The vascular cambium is between the xylem and phloem. The endodermis separates the vascular cylinder from the cortex and epidermis.

pericycle: peri- (Gk. PERI-, around) + -cycle (KUKLOS, circle)

Modified stems

Many common stems have various modifications, but because they are so common, most people do not recognize them as modifications. One easily recognized modification is the **succulent stems** seen in milkweeds and cacti. Succulent stems contain large quantities of water under thick cuticles and usually remain photosynthetic.

A number of different types of modified stems can be found underground. They are involved in producing leaves, keeping herbaceous plants alive over a period of years, and producing new plants.

❑ **Rhizomes*** (RYE ZOHMZ) are thick, fleshy, horizontal underground stems which produce leaves or leaf-bearing branches. Rhizomes of many plants, such as cattails, are edible. Rhizomes are found in many ferns, orchids, peonies, irises, and water lilies.

❑ **Stolons** are more slender than rhizomes, usually are much more branched, and produce secondary roots and aerial branches at nodes. Crabgrass, Kentucky bluegrass, and mints produce stolons.

❑ **Bulbs,** such as are found in onions, are actually collections of underground storage leaves branching from small discs of stems. Roots grow from the bottom of these stems. Other plants producing bulbs include the hyacinth, lily, daffodil, and tulip.

❑ **Tubers,*** such as Irish or white potatoes, are actually storage stems. Tubers produce roots and have ''eyes'' which are the nodes of these underground stems.

❑ **Corms** are thick underground stems that produce aerial leaves. A corm is often covered by several underground leaves. The solid fleshy tissue is a storage area which enlarges each year. Lateral buds form at the nodes of the corm, and additional corms are formed in successive years. Although we often say that gladioli and crocuses sprout from bulbs, they actually come from corms.

Review questions on page 310

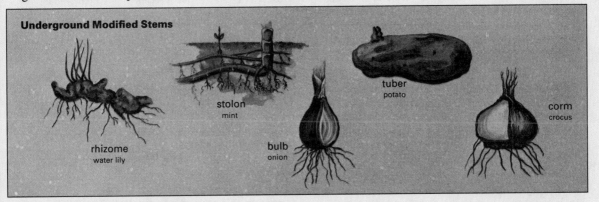

Underground Modified Stems

rhizome
water lily

stolon
mint

bulb
onion

tuber
potato

corm
crocus

Secondary growth of a root

When the primary tissue cells have enlarged as much as they can, growth in diameter stops. Typically, roots of monocot and herbaceous annuals grow no more in diameter; however other roots, especially those of woody plants, do increase in diameter by means of **secondary growth.** Any tissue that is manufactured following primary growth is called a *secondary tissue.* The vascular cambium produces *secondary xylem* around the core of primary xylem. *Secondary phloem* is also produced by the cambium.

Since there is no meristematic tissue to manufacture more cortex and epidermis, enlarging the vascular cylinder by adding secondary xylem and phloem crushes the cortex and epidermis. This destruction would leave the vascular cylinder exposed directly to the soil were it not for the *cork cells* produced by the pericycle. The thick-walled, dead cork cells seal the vascular cylinder so that

---

rhizome: rhizo- (Gk. RHIZA, root)   **tuber:** (L. TUBER, lump or swelling)

it cannot absorb water. Since absorption can now occur only through the epidermis near the tip of the root, the root must continue to grow in length if it is to continue to absorb water. Thus large perennial plants have extensive root systems to overcome this restriction in absorption of water.

Review Questions 12B-3

1. List the four primary functions of a root.
2. Describe the primary growth of a root. Use the names of the primary tissues of a root in your answer. Underline each of the primary tissues.
3. What is the function of root hairs?
4. Describe secondary growth of a root. Use the names of the secondary tissues of a root in your answer. Underline each of the secondary tissues.

Facet 12B-1: Modified Plant Parts, pages 307-9

1. List and describe five leaf modifications.
2. List and describe five common root modifications.
3. List and describe five common modified stems.

excurrent   deliquescent   columnar

The Stem

There are almost as many types of stems as there are types of plants. Above ground stems may be *erect* (as in trees and many flowers), or *climbing* (as in watermelons and cucumbers). Stems may be thin and herbaceous, as in most annuals, or thick and woody. Stems may be subterranean as in the cattail, Irish potato, tulip, and onion.

Most stems perform two major functions: they manufacture, support, and display leaves, and they conduct many of the materials needed for and manufactured by photosynthesis to and from the leaves. Most stems carry on photosynthesis when young; and in a few plants, like the cactus, even mature stems are the primary photosynthetic organs.

Branching Patterns

In stems there are three main branching patterns:

❑ **Excurrent**   In plants such as pines and hollies, the apical bud of the main stem has dominance over the lateral buds. This **apical dominance** is exhibited in varying degrees, depending on the species. Apical dominance results in the **excurrent** branching pattern, usually forming cone-shaped bushes or trees with one main stem.

❑ **Deliquescent**   Most angiosperms (like the apple, oak, maple, and many shrubs) have a **deliquescent** (DEL ih KWEH sehnt) branching pattern. In these plants apical dominance exists when they are young, but later the lateral buds become more active. When these plants are mature, it may be difficult to distinguish the main stem.

❑ **Columnar**   Woody monocots and some dicots have **columnar** growth, which is typified by a crown of leaves atop an unbranched stem. Palm trees and many tropical plants exhibit columnar growth.

Dormant woody stems

If you look at the tip of a woody stem in a cross section, you can see a small meristematic area called the **apical meristem** (or *shoot apex*). Cells formed in this area of active cell division differentiate into leaves, stem tissues, and flowers.

Those woody stems that live through a winter period form **dormant buds** in the fall. The bud at the end of the twig is called the *apical bud*. Buds that form along the twig are called *lateral (axillary) buds*. Lateral buds usually develop only if the apical bud is damaged.

A cross section of a dormant bud reveals **bud scales** protecting tiny leaves and, if the tree is to bloom in early spring, flower parts. These leaves and flowers are formed in the autumn. In the

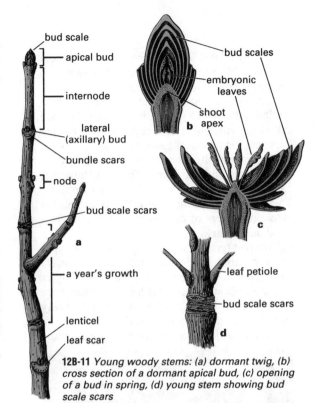

bud scale

apical bud

internode

lateral (axillary) bud

bundle scars

node

bud scale scars

a

a year's growth

lenticel

leaf scar

bud scales

embryonic leaves

shoot apex

b

c

leaf petiole

bud scale scars

d

12B-11 *Young woody stems: (a) dormant twig, (b) cross section of a dormant apical bud, (c) opening of a bud in spring, (d) young stem showing bud scale scars*

spring, water from the root causes these structures to expand to almost full size overnight. When the bud scales fall, they leave rings of *bud scale scars* around the twig. Since dormant buds are formed only in the fall, counting the terminal bud scale scar areas which completely encircle the twig enables you to determine its age.

If you examine a dormant twig of a deciduous plant, you will find the cork-covered **leaf scars.** The tiny dots within the leaf scar, called the *vascular bundle scars*, are where xylem and phloem went from stem to petiole. The shape of the leaf scars and the number and arrangement of the vascular bundle scars are so characteristic of a species that some botanists can identify trees by examining dormant twigs.

The places where leaves are produced on a stem are **nodes,** and the areas between nodes are called *internodes*. By examining the number of nodes and the length of internodes produced in a given year, you can determine how productive the plant was that year.

Structure and growth of woody stems

A cross section of a young stem reveals an exterior coating of *epidermis*. Most young stems have guard cells and stomata which permit the exchange of gases for photosynthesis. Just under the epidermis is a layer of **cork cambium** which will produce cork cells to protect the stem after it has grown too large for the original epidermal cells.

Inside the cork cambium is a layer of cortex, which stores materials and usually is photosynthetic. In older stems the cortex serves for storage but may eventually disappear completely. The phloem, with its strengthening sclerenchyma fibers, is inside the cortex. A thin layer of meristematic cells called the vascular cambium separates the phloem form the xylem. Inside the xylem is the **pith,** the largest area of a young stem. The cells of the pith store and conduct materials. Spokelike **pith rays** extend from the central pith through the xylem and into the phloem areas.

In the first year little secondary growth takes place, but in the next growing seasons secondary growth in woody stems noticeably increases their diameter. Pith continues to be the most central tissue, but its diameter does not increase. *Vascu-*

Kinds of Wood

The central xylem of a mature woody stem is composed of dead cells that have been sealed off with tannins, gums, and other materials. This *heartwood* is often darker. The lighter *sapwood* is used in storage and is able to conduct water and dissolved minerals.

Wood varies in density, hardness, durability, strength, grain, and texture.

❑ *Hardwood* trees are usually angiosperms such as oaks, maples, walnuts, hickories, and cherries. Because of their strength and grain, hardwoods are used primarily for cabinets, furniture, veneers, tool handles, and musical instruments.

❑ *Softwood* usually comes from gymnosperms. Softwoods are easier to work with than hardwoods; but lack the strength, density, and beauty of the hardwoods. Softwoods, including firs, pines, spruces, and cedars, are used for construction, pulp, plywood, and pencils.

lar rays, which permit the horizontal movement of water and dissolved substances, extend from the central pith region to the bark areas.

The vascular cambium produces secondary xylem and phloem cells. If the cell is on the inside of the vascular cambium, it will become xylem; if on the outer surface, it will become phloem. Xylem tissues are called wood. During a growing season the vascular cambium constantly produces new xylem. During the spring when there is abundant water, large xylem vessels are produced. Drier summers cause smaller xylem vessels to be produced. The larger vessels are called *springwood* and are lighter in color than *summerwood.*

When you look at a cross section of a woody stem, you see these layers of springwood and summerwood as **annual rings.** By studying annual rings, scientists can tell not only how old a tree is but also how the weather and other conditions have changed. Some trees produce more than one ring per year; in moist tropics growth rings may be poorly defined and often do not represent a year's growth.

The growth of bark

The vascular cambium produces phloem. Phloem is produced in much smaller quantities than xylem. Secondary phloem in woody stems is usually arranged as a ring of pyramids. Strengthening sclerenchyma is often found between the phloem pyramids. Phloem, its strengthening tissues, and the cortex comprise the **inner bark.**

The *cork cambium* produces flattened, thin-walled cells which fill with a fatty substance called *suberin.* These cork cells then die but are impenetrable to water, gases, and most parasites. Cork is continually produced by the ever-increasing circle of cork cambium. The cork, however, cannot expand along with the cork cambium. Therefore, as secondary growth continues, the outermost layers of cork split, forming the textured **outer bark.**

Different types of trees produce different types of outer barks. The white birch trees of Canada and the northern United States produce thin layers of white cork which peel off the trees. Oaks have thick, rough bark; maple bark is relatively smooth. Experts can determine the family, genus, and even species of a tree merely by examining

12B-10 *Cross sections of a mature woody stem. Can you find the structures that are in the photograph labeled in the drawing? How old is the tree in the photograph?*

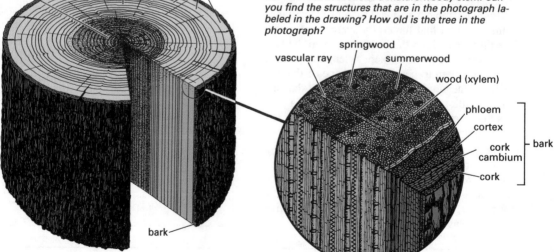

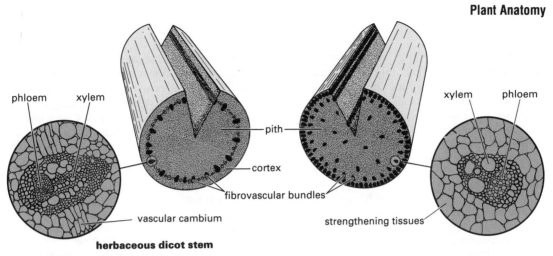

phloem xylem

pith

cortex

fibrovascular bundles

vascular cambium

herbaceous dicot stem

xylem phloem

strengthening tissues

herbaceous monocot stem

12B-11 *Structure of herbaceous stems*

the outer bark. **Lenticels,** tiny openings in the cork layer of a mature woody stem, allow the stem to receive the oxygen necessary for respiration.

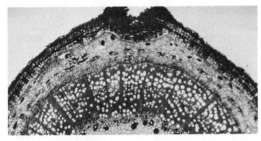

12B-12 *Cross section of a woody twig through a lenticle*

Herbaceous dicot stems

A typical herbaceous dicot such as clover, a marigold, or a daisy does not have a cork cambium and therefore will retain its epidermis throughout its entire life span. Its stem cortex is usually photosynthetic. The vascular tissues do not form continuous concentric circles, as in woody stems, but are arranged in **fibrovascular*** (FYE broh VAS kew lur) **bundles.** These bundles are usually located around the edge of the stem. Inside the fibrovascular bundle ring is the pith, which may contain chlorophyll and be photosynthetic, especially in young stems.

Secondary growth in herbaceous dicot stems is limited. Between the xylem and phloem of the fibrovascular bundles there usually is a layer of meristematic tissue which can produce secondary xylem and phloem. As the fibrovascular bundles grow, however, there can be little increase in the size of the epidermis since there is no meristematic tissue available to add to that made during

Girdling

The functions of the xylem and the phloem in a woody plant can be illustrated by **girdling.** If a strip of bark, including the vascular cambium, is removed from the trunk of a tree, the tree has been girdled. Sometimes gnawing animals or a chain will girdle a tree. Nutrients are still sent up the sapwood of a girdled tree; therefore, the top of the tree will continue to produce leaves and carry on photosynthesis. The trunk above the ring will continue secondary growth.

Below the girdled area, however, the trunk will not grow in diameter. Since the phloem cannot carry sugars produced in the leaves down to the roots, the roots are forced to use stored food to continue growing. As food reserves are depleted, roots will be unable to produce new roots and root hairs. This depletion also prevents water and dissolved minerals from getting to the leaves which will then wither. The tree finally dies because it cannot make its own food.

fibrovascular: fibro- (L. FIBRA, fiber) + -vascular (VASCELLUM, vessel)

primary growth. Some large herbaceous dicots split their epidermis and rely on secondary strengthening tissues around the fibrovascular bundles to protect their stems.

Except at the nodes, monocot stems generally lack meristematic tissue. Secondary growth, even in "woody" monocots, is limited. The slender columnar growth of palm tree trunks is an ex-

ample of this. Herbaceous monocots, like corn and grass, have fibrovascular bundles which, when cut in cross section, usually reveal a "monkey face" of xylem, phloem, and strengthening tissues. These fibrovascular bundles are scattered throughout the pith of the stem. In some monocots, like bamboo, the central pith disappears, leaving a hollow mature stem.

Biological Terms

	epidermis	primary tissue	annual ring
vegetative organ	cuticle	root hair	inner bark
reproductive organ	stomata	cortex	outer bark
meristematic tissue	guard cell	endodermis	lenticel
vascular tissue	parenchyma	vascular cylinder	fibrovascular bundle
xylem	palisade mesophyll	vascular cambium	girdling
annual plant	spongy mesophyll	pericycle	*Facet*
biennial plant	deciduous	secondary growth	tendril
perennial plant	abscission layer	*The Stem*	spine
phloem	persistent foliage	apical dominance	aquatic leaves
structural tissue	carotenoid	excurrent	bract
The Leaf	anthocyanin	deliquescent	storage root
blade	*The Root*	columnar	adventitious root
petiole	root	apical meristem	aerial root
stipule	taproot system	dormant bud	aquatic root
leaf venation	fibrous root system	bud scale	succulent stem
parallel venation	primary growth	leaf scar	parasitic root
netted venation	root cap	node	succulent leaves
pinnate	meristematic region	cork cambium	rhizome
palmate	elongation region	pith	stolon
leaflet	maturation region	pith ray	bulb
			tuber
			corm

Review Questions 12B-4

1. What are the major functions of a stem?
2. Describe a dormant twig. Tell the functions of each structure.
3. Describe secondary growth in a stem.
4. What is the difference between (a) heartwood and sapwood; (b) springwood and summerwood; and (c) hardwood and softwood?
5. Describe the formation of bark.
6. List two differences and two similarities between herbaceous monocot and herbaceous dicot stems.

Thought Questions

1. Why is it essential that every cell in a leaf be near a xylem vessel, while it is not essential that every cell be near a phloem tube?
2. Roots must continue primary growth even though the plant is well anchored. Why?
3. What types of plants have fewer than an average number of root hairs?
4. What can and cannot be determined about a tree by examining its annual rings?
5. Compare and contrast (a) the primary growth of a stem and a root and (b) the secondary growth of a stem and a root.

THE LIFE PROCESSES OF PLANTS
BOTANY PART II

THIRTEEN

13A – Plant Physiology

Although plants require basically the same materials, various plants must have them in different amounts to grow properly. A corn plant requires 135-180 kg (about 300-400 lb.), which is 150-190 liters (L) (40-50 gal.), of water in a growing season, but a healthy desert cactus may not get that much in 10 yr. If the corn were transplanted to the desert and the cactus to the field, one would quickly wither, and the roots of the other would rot. Cypress trees grow best in flooded areas, but a palm tree could not grown there. A forest floor fern, if transplanted into a meadow, would get too much sun and die. A meadow fern transplanted to the forest would also die but for the opposite reason.

Not all the areas of the world were designed to have the same conditions. God designed the plants to have specific sets of requirements. Thus plants *grow* best in certain areas, *survive* in some places, and *do not tolerate* other conditions.

We would think it foolish if someone planted a banana grove in northern Canada. He would be ignoring either the Canadian weather or the requirements of banana plants. A farmer must consider all the environmental conditions of his farm before he plants a crop, or he may experience a crop failure. Even when a person selects a plant for his yard or his room, he should consider the conditions available to the plant.

Plants and Water

Plants contain large amounts of water. If 10 g (0.35 oz.) of grass is dried, it weighs only 3 g (0.1 oz.). Most herbaceous parts of plants are over 80% water. Plants also require large amounts of water. An acre of rapidly growing corn gives off 1,000,000 L (250,000 gal.) of water per day. A single large oak tree may lift 1,000 L (250 gal.) in 24 hours.

Plants use water for several purposes:

❑ *Photosynthesis* For each molecule of glucose made by plants, 6 or more molecules of water must be broken apart.

❑ *Turgor* The abundant presence of water in the cells stiffens the herbaceous parts of plants.

❑ *Hydrolysis* Plants often break apart large molecules by adding water molecules or parts of water molecules.

❑ *Translocation* The materials in a plant can be moved only if they are dissolved in water.

Water in the soil

Most plants cannot absorb the water that falls on or collects on their leaves. The leaves, however, often are arranged so the water falling on them will drop to the soil in the area of the roots of that plant. The root tips then absorb the water.

Soil texture, the size of the particles in the soil, is a major factor in the amount of water that soil can contain. The inorganic components of the soil that affect soil texture are *gravel, sand, silt,* and *clay.* A mixture of sand, silt, and clay is called **loam.** An ideal loam is considered to be 40% sand, 40% silt, and 20% clay. Loams that vary from this ratio are called sandy loams, clay loams, and silt loams, according to their major component.

Topsoil is composed of loam, living organisms, and **humus*** (dead organic matter). Soil is not "dead"; living organisms make up about 10% of the weight of good soil. They break down such things as fallen leaves and dead animals (humus), as well as inorganic substances (loam particles), into absorbable materials that plants can use.

Inorganic and organic components of the soil determine the size and quantity of **pore spaces.** The ability of the soil to contain water and air is determined by the pore spaces. Small soil particles have less space between them; therefore, soils with high concentrations of smaller particles, such as clay, absorb water slowly but remain moist for a long time. Sandy soils, on the other hand, accept water rapidly, but the water quickly passes through, and the soil soon becomes dry.

Some people think that plants will grow well if the roots are kept in water. Like other living tissues, however, the roots of a plant must have oxygen to carry on cellular respiration. Plants cannot use oxygen dissolved in water or oxygen in water molecules; therefore, most plants will die if their roots remain submerged. Those plants that naturally grow underwater have tubes which transport air down from their aerial parts or oxygen from the photosynthetic parts down to the roots. Most plants, however, lack these structures.

Water in the Soil

Runoff: Water which does not enter the soil (unusable to plants)

Gravitational: Water which is pulled through the soil to the water table (unusable to most plants)

Capillary: Water which is held between particles of the soil (absorbed by plants)

Hygroscopic: Film around soil particles after capillary water is gone (unusable to plants)

If water comes more quickly than it can be absorbed by the soil, it either collects in puddles or flows downhill. This is called *runoff water.* The water that goes into the soil may pass through the soil to an impenetrable layer (rock), accumulating to form the *water table.* This is *gravitational water* and is out of reach for most plants. Some plants, however, do send taproots down to the water table. The water in the pore spaces of the soil is called *capillary water* and is the water

---

humus: (L. HUMUS, soil)

which plants absorb. Even when the soil is dry to our touch, there is still a thin film of water around many soil particles. Plants cannot use this *hygroscopic water*.

Water absorption

When there is a good supply of water in the soil, water is taken into the root hairs. The concentration of water molecules is higher outside the cell, and the concentration of solutes is higher inside the cell. This concentration gradient permits the movement of water molecules across the root cell membranes by osmosis. The concentration gradient must be set up by the cell, and the cell *expends energy* to maintain the higher concentration of solutes inside. These absorbed water molecules pass into the cells of the cortex and then to the vascular cylinder.

As more water enters the roots and collects in the vascular cylinder, pressure builds up. This is **root pressure.** This causes a movement of water (and dissolved minerals) up the xylem of the stem. If the stem of a well-watered plant is cut, drops of water will ooze from the vascular tissues as a result of root pressure.

Most of the water a plant uses, however, enters by a second method. When a plant is growing and carrying on photosynthesis, water is drawn away from the roots by the upper parts of the plant, and the cells in the root lose their turgidity. As the water concentration in the root cells lowers, water molecules are drawn into the cells. This process is called **passive absorption** because root cells do not expend energy to make it happen.

Translocation of water

The movement of water and dissolved minerals within a plant is called **translocation.** In small plants it is possible for osmosis and diffusion to move the necessary water and minerals. Indeed, this is the only method possible in bryophytes since they lack vascular tissues. It is also possible to assume that root pressure would be great enough to force water up the vascular tissues of small tracheophytes. Root pressure is rarely more than a fraction of a kilogram per square centimeter. Dozens of kilograms per square centimeter would be necessary to force water up plants that

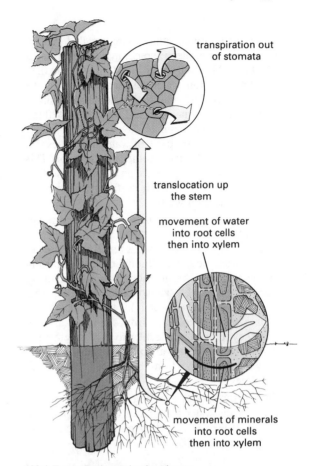

transpiration out of stomata

translocation up the stem

movement of water into root cells then into xylem

movement of minerals into root cells then into xylem

13A-1 *Transpiration-cohesion theory*

are over a meter tall. **Capillarity** (KAP uh LEHR ih tee) is a property of water that, at one time, was considered a possible explanation for translocation. Water rises slightly on the surfaces of its container. Operating according to the same principle by which water is absorbed into a paper towel, water will rise in a thin tube. The thinner the tube, the higher the water will rise. But even tubes as small as xylem vessels cannot produce capillary action to the height of tree leaves.

Although the forces of passive absorption and capillarity help to move water in a plant, most biologists support another theory of translocation. This theory is based on two considerations.

❑ **Transpiration*** Water is constantly evaporating from the leaves of a plant. This release of

---

transpiration: trans- (L. TRANS-, across) + -spiration (SPIRARE, to breathe) water vapor into the atmosphere is called transpiration. For example, a typical maple tree absorbs 361 kg. (800 lb.) of water in a day; but only 0.36 kg (0.8 lb.) of this water are used by the tree; the rest (799 lb.) passes out the stomata. A single mature oak tree may release 1,100 kg. (2,420 lb.) of water on a hot summer day.

❑ **Cohesion** The property of water molecules that causes them to ''stick together'' is cohesion. This is why water forms beads on a smooth surface and why there is enough surface tension for a needle to float on water.

Today most scientists believe that water moves up a plant according to the same principle you use to drink with a straw. As molecules are removed from the top, additional molecules rush in at the bottom. This method of translocation in plants is called the **transpiration-cohesion theory.** The release of water by the leaves which causes water to come up from the roots and the tendency for water molecules to stick together are considered the best available explanations for the movement of water from the soil to all the leaves of a tree.

Turgor pressure and wilting

Most of the water that comes up a stem is given off as water vapor in transpiration. The second

Guttation

Most of the stomata of a leaf are closed at night. In some leaves the stomata at the ends of veins or along the margin of the leaf do not close. When soil moisture, humidity, and temperature are right, these leaves may guttate. In **guttation*** (guh TAY shun), drops of water are forced through the stomata at the margin of the leaf. Guttation is not dew; dew comes from condensation of water vapor in the air. Guttation water originates in the roots and therefore, unlike dew, has dissolved minerals in it.

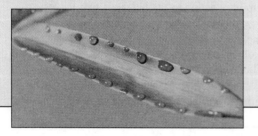

Nastic Movements

Morning glory, morning and afternoon

Prayer plant, day and night

Most of us have noticed that tulips, morning glories, buttercups, or similar flowers open during the day, close in the evening, and reopen the following morning. These are examples of **nastic movements.** Nastic movements in plants are caused by the loss or gain of turgor in certain cells, often at the base of the petal or leaf.

Since nastic movements depend on the presence or absence of water, they are temporary, reversible changes. For example, the sensitive plant folds its leaves by nastic movements in response to touch. A few moments after the leaves have collapsed, they will reopen.

Some nastic movements are based on the direction of light. The leaves of wild lettuce and the disc of the sunflower follow the sun as it crosses the sky. Some nastic movements may appear to be triggered by internal factors when they actually are controlled by some yet unexplained factor within the plant. The prayer plant, a common houseplant, folds its leaves at night (after sunset); however, putting a prayer plant in darkness will not cause it to fold its leaves until its usual time (after sunset). If the plant is placed in an area of constant temperature, humidity, and dim light, it will still open and fold its leaves by its usual schedule, not in response to a man-made environment.

guttation: (L. GUTTA, drop)

major use of water is maintaining turgidity. **Turgor** is the presence of water inside a plant cell in sufficient quantity to give the cell stiffness (see page 80). As long as there is sufficient water available to living cells, they will remain turgid, and the plant will be stiff.

During hot conditions a lack of water in the soil can cause *temporary wilting*. The closing of the stomata stops as much transpiration as possible, but there is still a loss of water into the environment. The loss of water reduces turgor, which causes the herbaceous parts of the plant to droop. Normally temporary wilting is corrected during cooler conditions when transpiration slows down or when the plant is watered.

Occasionally insects, fungi, or other factors damage vascular tissues and cause *permanent wilting*. Permanent wilting can also happen when the available water in the soil is exhausted and not replaced before the tissues die. During transplanting, the root tips can be destroyed, causing permanent wilting.

The Bible refers to the Word of God as the water whereby a Christian grows. If we do not keep ourselves rooted in the Word, our spiritual lives will wilt. In John 4 the woman at the well desired that Christ give her the living water so that she would never thirst again. That living water which keeps our spiritual lives full is available to us all.

Review Questions 13A-1

1. Why will all plants not grow equally well in the same conditions?
2. What are the four main uses of water in plants?
3. A plant that grows best when its roots are in moist soil would thrive best in a loam with a higher percentage of what soil component?
4. List the components of a good topsoil. Tell the significance of each component.
5. What four types of water will be found in or on the soil after a rain? Tell the significance of each in relation to the supply of water to plant roots.
6. Why are root pressure and capillarity inadequate to explain the translocation of water in a stem? Name and explain the method of translocation most botanists agree happens in plants over a few centimeters tall.
7. Compare and contrast temporary and permanent wilting.

Plants and Minerals

For centuries man has known that plants absorb materials from the soil. If a particular type of plant is grown and harvested repeatedly in a field, the yield decreases year by year as the necessary materials are depleted. It was once believed, therefore, that plants ate soil, much as animals eat food. Even today we speak of "plant food."

Except for a few parasitic and saprophytic plants, plants do not "eat food." Plants do *absorb soluble minerals* from the soil and use them to manufacture substances. The sun, however, is the energy source for food manufactured in plants.

Minerals in the soil

The known essential nutrient elements for plants are listed in figure 13A-2. Different plants require different amounts of these elements. Nitrogen may be 1-3% of the dry weight of a plant, potassium from 0.3-6%, and calcium as low as 0.1% or as high as 3.5%. Most minor essential elements and elements found in only a few plants are mere traces of the dry weight of the plant.

Plants are not always able to use an element in its free state. Nitrogen, for example, is a major component of the air. Plants cannot, however, use atmospheric nitrogen. Plant roots absorb nitrogen in the form of nitrates or ammonium ions.

In the American colonial period and the period of westward expansion, farmers did not replenish the minerals removed from the soil by crops. This was partly because most farmers did not know how to care for the land and also because they did not need to. There was still plenty of unfarmed land to use when an area "wore out."

13A-2	Elements Needed by Plants	
Nutrient Elements	**Deficiency Symptoms**	**Some Functions**
Major Essential		
Nitrogen *Nitrates* $(NO_3)^-$ or *Ammonium* $(NH_4)^+$	Light green to yellowish lower leaves; little growth	Amino acids, proteins, nucleic acids, chlorophyll, coenzymes
Phosphorus *Phosphates* $(H_2PO_4)^-$ or $(HPO_4)^{-2}$	Dark green to purplish leaves; stunted growth	Formation of ATP, nucleic acids, formation of some fats, coenzymes
Potassium K^+	Yellowish leaves, turning brown at margin; weak stems	Protein synthesis, cell membranes, nucleic acids
Sulfur *Sulfate* $(SO_4)^{-2}$	Yellowing of young leaves	Some proteins, amino acids, coenzymes
Calcium Ca^{+2} (lime)	Disintegration of young shoots and root tips	Cell walls, aids in regulation of the uptake of other elements
Magnesium Mg^{+2}	Death of leaves from the base of the stem up	Chlorophyll, needed for some enzyme actions
Iron Fe^{+2} or Fe^{+3}	Gradual yellowing of leaves between small veins, then between larger veins	Chlorophyll formation, part of many enzymes
Minor Essential		
Boron Manganese Chlorine Molybdenum Copper Zinc	Stunted growth or poorly formed plant parts, especially flowers and fruits	Primarily serve as activators for enzymes; other functions unknown
Found in Some Plants		
Aluminum Silicon Cobalt Sodium Selenium	Stunted growth or poorly formed plant parts	Various functions in plants specialized for certain environments; other functions unknown

In the Southeast, cotton was the major crop prior to this century. Cotton, however, rapidly depletes the soil of nitrogen. Since fertilizing large areas of the major plantations was almost impossible at the time, farmers planted legumes such as peas, beans, and peanuts. These plants grow well in nitrogen-poor soil. Legumes also produce nodes on their roots which contain *nitrogen-fixing bacteria*. These bacteria take atmospheric nitrogen and add it to the soil as a nitrate, a form of nitrogen that plants can use. Farmers discovered that after a few years of planting legumes, they could again grow cotton successfully. Today *crop rotation* is one method of keeping a mineral complement in the soil.

Today a farmer can have his soil tested to learn what elements it contains. He can also learn what elements are needed by the various plants he wishes to grow. If his soil lacks a particular material, he can add chemical **fertilizers** to the soil. Often the contents of a container of fertilizer are expressed by three numbers, such as 10-10-10. The first number is the percentage of nitrogen; the second, phosphorus; and the third, potassium. Other elements may also be listed. In this way, a farmer adds only the needed minerals to his soil.

A third method of replenishing the minerals in the soil is by adding decomposing organic matter, often called **mulch.** This method builds and maintains the soil naturally. Cultivation often removes the leaves and other materials that would normally become mulch; organic debris can be added after cultivation to replace depleted substances. Adding mulch to cultivated soil also increases the size and number of pore spaces.

Absorption of minerals by roots

Nutrient minerals reach roots in a soluble form. The concentration of solutes is greater in the cell cytoplasm than in the water around the root cells. The cells must expend energy to move these substances in the cells against the concentration gradient. This *active transport* can be demonstrated

FACETS OF BIOLOGY

13A-1

Plants That Catch Insects

There are approximately 450 varieties of **insectivorous*** (IN sek TIV ur us) **plants,** plants that have leaves designed to catch and digest insects. These plants do not obtain energy from the insects they digest; they all contain chlorophyll and produce their own sugars. Most of them, however, live in soils which lack usable nitrogen. Insectivorous plants obtain nitrogen from digested insects. Some of these plants, if grown in soil with ample nitrogen, will not properly form their insect-catching traps.

❑ *Venus's-flytrap* Probably the most familiar insectivorous plant, the 10-15 cm (4-6 in.) Venus's-fly trap, is found in moist soils in the

coastal regions of North and South Carolina. The leaf blade is an effective insect-catching trap. The red color of the trap and the sweet fluids it secretes attract flies and other insects. When the insect disturbs a set of epidermal hairs near the midrib, the two sides of the

Venus's-flytrap

leaf quickly shut and squeeze the victim. Inside the closed trap secreted enzymes digest the insect in a week to ten days. Then the blade reopens, ready to receive another victim. Usually the leaf dies after it has closed for the third time.

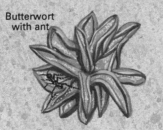
sundew with fly

❑ *Sundew* A small, ground-hugging insectivorous plant with red-tinged leaves is the sundew. Each leaf has about 100 tiny tentacles, each equipped with a drop of sticky, sweet, enzyme-containing material that attracts insects. When an insect touches a tentacle, the others converge on it. Enzymes digest trapped insects.

❑ *Butterwort* On the inside of the narrow, curled leaves of the

Butterwort with ant

butterwort are hairs which secrete a sweet, sticky substance that contains enzymes. When an insect touches these hairs, the leaf curls shut until the insect is digested.

❑ *Pitcher plants* There are many different types of pitcher plants, some of which are tropical epiphytes. A pitcher plant produces hollow leaves which usually have a lip over the top to prevent excess rain water from entering the pitcher. In the bottom of the hollow leaf is a sweet fluid containing digestive enzymes. Most often there are hairs in the neck of the

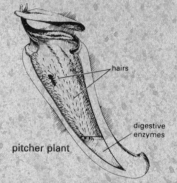
hairs

digestive enzymes

pitcher plant

pitcher plant, all of which point downward. When an insect begins to move toward the sweet fluids it cannot return. In time it falls into the pool of enzymes.

❑ *Bladderwort* A floating plant, the bladderwort has bladders which are insect traps. Each small pouch has several hairs near its opening which, when touched, snap shut over the opening, pushing the aquatic insect inside. Digestive enzymes are then secreted.

Review questions on page 322.

insectivorous: insecti- (L. INSECTUM, segmented) + -vorous(L. VARARE, to devour)

by stopping the supply of oxygen necessary to keep root cells alive. The absorption of minerals stops as the oxygen supply decreases.

If a plant is grown in a soil that has too many soluble materials (such as might happen when an area is overfertilized), there is a higher concentration of ions outside the cell. Now, rather than being moved by active transport, the ions enter in large concentrations, and water molecules leave the cytoplasm to go into the soil. This loss of water causes *plasmolysis* and death of the root epidermal cells. If this cellular destruction is extensive, it will cause the plant to wilt, turn brown, and die. Because of this appearance, plants that have been damaged by overfertilization are said to be "burned" by the fertilizer.

Some soils having high concentrations of salt, even higher than seawater, can still support plants. Plants that grow in these conditions are called *halophytes** (HAL uh FYTES). They have higher concentrations of salts inside their cells than in the soil around them. Salt crystals often form on halophyte leaves as water evaporates from them.

Organic Gardening

Some people feel that *organic gardening,* the adding of mulch only, produces plants which are more beneficial as food than plants which are grown with chemical fertilizers. When deciding which method is best for a particular situation, a grower must consider many factors. One aspect that is *not* important is the source of the substances themselves (minerals and so forth). Plants cannot distinguish between a nitrate from a chemical factory and a nitrate from decomposing leaves because there is no chemical difference between them. The quality of the individual nutrient is not affected by the source from which it comes.

Other factors such as the soil texture, the availability of minor nutrients found in mulch but not often added to chemical fertilizers, *could* make a difference in the decision to use chemical fertilizers or organic matter. Plants grown only using organic mulches and organic fertilizers are not of a better quality than those grown using a good blending of organic gardening and nonorganic fertilizers.

Review Questions 13A-2
1. List three ways of replenishing the mineral content of the soil.
2. Explain how plants absorb minerals from the soil.

Facet 13A - 1: Plants That Catch Insects, page 321
What value does catching insects have for insectivorous plants?

Plant Hormones

In the mid-1920s Fritz W. Went, a Dutch plant physiologist, performed a series of experiments on oat seedling coleoptiles (KOH lee AHP tilz).

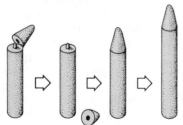

13A-3 *Went's first coleoptile experiment*

When the coleoptile tip which contained the apical meristem was removed, cell elongation stopped. When Went replaced the coleoptile, elongation continued.

If the coleoptile tip was placed on a thin piece of agar and left for a time, the agar, if placed on the coleoptile, would cause elongation to resume. If a piece of untreated agar was put on the seedling tip, no elongation occurred. The untreated agar showed that the elongation was not caused by the weight of the tip but by a substance produced by the coleoptile tip that entered the agar and then passed to the seedling.

halophyte: halo- (Gk. HALS, salt) + -phyte (plant)

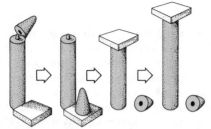

13A-4 *Went's second coleoptile experiment*

In another experiment a section of treated agar was put on only one side of the seedling. Elongation happened on that side only, causing the coleoptile to bend toward the opposite side. The chemical which Dr. Went presumed to cause elongation was later isolated and named *auxin* (AHK sin).

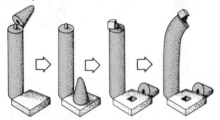

13A-5 *Coleoptile experiment in which the hormone is only placed on one side of the stem*

Auxins
Several auxins have been isolated from plant tissues. Auxins, along with several other plant substances, are called **hormones.** Plant hormones are chemical growth regulators produced in minute amounts by the meristematic regions and usually only affect nearby undifferentiated cells.

Auxins* are commonly found in stems, seeds, leaves, fruits, and in smaller quantities in roots. Auxins move from the top of the shoot toward the base. This movement, however, is not caused by gravity but by an unexplained force. Auxins vary greatly in their effects on different plants and on different areas of the same plants.

The elongation of the coleoptile tips observed by Went was caused by the most common auxin *indoleacetic acid* (IAA). IAA is necessary for the elongation of cells in the maturation region of stems. The rate and amount of elongation varies with the amount of the hormone. If the quantity of IAA in a leaf or a fruit drops below a certain

level, the abscission layer at the base of the petiole forms cork cells, and the fruit or leaf will drop off. Fruit growers spray IAA on their orchards to keep the ripe fruit on the trees so that all the fruits can be harvested at one time.

Auxins can force unfertilized flowers to develop into seedless fruits. Auxins are used commercially to stimulate the formation of roots in woody stem cuttings. Auxins produced by terminal buds serve as inhibitors to lateral buds. Potatoes are sometimes sprayed with auxins to inhibit sprouting of the eyes (lateral buds). The synthetic auxin 2,4-D, when applied in lower concentrations, kills broad-leafed plants like dicots but does not affect narrow-leafed plants like grasses. 2,4-D is used as a lawn weed killer.

Gibberellins and abscissic acid
At the same time Went was doing his work, Japanese scientists were studying ''foolish seedling disease'' in rice. The rice plants grew very quickly but were too spindly to stand. It was discovered that *Gibberella fujikuroi,* a fungus associated with the rice seeds, produced a chemical that, when isolated, caused sprouts to grow rapidly. The chemical was named **gibberellin** (JIB uh REL ihn). At first it was thought that this chemical was foreign to plants, but over twenty different gibberellins have since been isolated from plant tissues.

Gibberellins stimulate both cell division and cell elongation in leaves and stems. When these

13A-6 *The plants on the right were given growth hormones. The plants on the left are growing normally.*

---

auxin: (Gk. AUXEIN, to grow)

plant hormones are applied to dwarfed plants, the plants will grow to their usual height. It could be that, through a mutation, the plant lost the ability to form gibberellins and responds as if the applied hormone were its own. Gibberellins are involved with flower, pollen and fruit formation in some plants and stimulate growth of some seeds.

Abscissic acid appears to stimulate the falling of leaves and fruits. Abscissic acid causes growing leaves to yellow and cork layers at the base of the petiole to begin forming. When applied to growing tips, it forces the formation of dormant buds. According to some scientists, abscissic acid is not a hormone but is an inhibitor to plant growth hormones.

Tropisms: plant growth responses

The growth of a coleoptile with an auxin on only one side is similar to the growth of plants in response to various environmental stimuli. For example, we are familiar with plant stems and leaves growing toward the light. Varying auxin concentrations account for this response. Light appears to cause auxins to migrate to the other side of the stem. The side with the highest concentrations of auxins elongates the most, causing the stem to grow away from the dark, hormone-containing side and toward the lighted, hormone-destroying side. A growth response in plants caused by hormonal action is called a **tropism.***

There are several types of tropisms, named according to the environmental condition which causes them.

❑ **Phototropism,*** a growth response to light, is not the same in all plants or plant parts. Plant

13A-7 *The stem of the bean seedling (right) shows positive phototropism, the root shows negative. The leaves of the African violet (left) have begun to grow toward the light.*

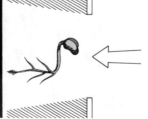

stems respond with growth toward the light, called *positive phototropism.* Auxins, however, inhibit root growth. Since roots grow away from the light, they exhibit *negative phototropism.*

❑ **Geotropism*** is a response to gravity. Normally roots have *positive geotropism* while stems have *negative geotropism.* Gravity seems to affect the root, causing more auxins to be on the lower side. This inhibits growth on this side, causing the root to grow downward.

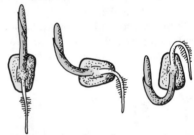

13A-8 *Geotropism of a corn seedling in three different directions. The stem is negative, the root positive.*

❑ **Thigmotropism*** is the response to touch. The elongation of a stem on the side opposite to the side touched is *positive thigmotropism.* The tendrils of grapes and peas, as well as the stems of some vines like the morning glory, exhibit *positive thigmotropism.*

13A-9 *The stems of the morning glory have positive thigmotropism, causing them to twine around whatever they touch.*

❑ **Chemotropism,*** the growth response toward or away from certain chemicals, is in many cases similar to hydrotropism.

*Hydrotropism,** the growth of roots toward water, was once held as an explanation for the full growth of tree roots in water-rich soil while drier areas around the tree remain rootless. There is, however, a much simpler explanation for this

---

tropism: (Gk. TROPOS, turn)
geotropism: geo- (Gk. GE-, earth) + -tropism (turn)

phototropism: photo- (light) + -tropism (turn)
thigmotropism: thigmo- (Gk. THIGMA, touch) + -tropism (turn)

chemotropism: chemo- (chemicals) + -tropism (turn)
hydrotropism: hydro- (water) + -tropism (turn)

growth. When plant roots enter watered areas, they grow in abundance, while roots in less favorable conditions do not grow as well.

In experimental conditions plant roots have all grown at the same rate until some roots reached an area of abundant water. The watered roots grew faster, and the other roots continued in the direction they were growing rather than turning toward the water. Plants cannot sense where water is or grow toward it. Evidences of hydrotropism are usually only evidences of good and bad growing conditions and not really a tropism at all.

Review Questions 13A-3
1. Describe and tell the significance of Went's coleoptile experiment.
2. List four plant hormones. In what ways do these hormones affect plants?
3. How do tropisms affect plants? List several examples of positive and negative tropisms.
4. Explain why many researchers feel there is no hydrotropism in plants.

Plants and Light

Although all plants require light for photosynthesis and other processes, some need more light than others. Plant catalogs often indicate which plants grow best in shady areas and which require full sun. Sun-loving zinnias will be small and produce pale flowers if planted in the shade, and shade-loving impatiens will be scorched if planted in a sunny spot. As most window gardeners know, even the direction of light affects plants. Phototropism will cause geranium leaves to hug the glass if the pot is not faithfully rotated. Until the early 1900s, however, most people were not aware that even the length of time light is available to a plant is important.

Intensity of light
A plant that does not receive adequate light becomes **etiolated** (EE tee uh LATE ed): stem growth is rapid, but both size and number of leaves are greatly reduced. The plant appears to be stretching for light. Since light is necessary for chlorophyll production, etiolated plants are pale green, yellow, or even white. The stem elongates abnormally because auxins are not being destroyed by light.

Some plants, like the dogwood, have two growth patterns, one for full sun and another for shade. Most trees produce different types of leaves in the shade and in the sun, with differing amounts of palisade mesophyll, air spaces, stomata, and chlorophyll to accommodate the different conditions. In some trees, like the maple, *sun leaves* and *shade leaves* can be produced on various parts of the same plant, but the difference between the two types may only be found by careful observation.

Photoperiodism—the length of light periods
A variety of tobacco called Maryland Mammoth grows to be 3-5 m (10-16 ft.) high and produces many leaves, but when grown in Maryland, it does not begin to flower until cold weather sets in. The plants are killed by frost before the seeds form.

In 1906 research was begun to find out why this tobacco flowers so late. If seeds were planted in Maryland greenhouses in the late summer, the plants would flower at the same time as those planted outside, even though they were not nearly as tall as their outdoor counterparts. After more than fifteen years of research, studies were published describing how the length of day and night affects the flowering of many plants, a phenomenon now called **photoperiodism.***

13A-10 *The pea plants on the left were grown in darkness and are etiolated. The plants on the right were grown in normal light.*

---

photoperiodism: photo- (light) + -periodism (Gk. PERIODOS, circuit)

FACETS OF BIOLOGY

13A-2

Dormancy in Plants

Most plants encounter conditions unfavorable for growth at some time during the year. Annuals die during this period, leaving seeds to continue the species. Some herbaceous plants leave roots which sprout the following year. Some woody plants lose their foliage and form dormant buds, which sprout when favorable conditions return. Where the conditions do not get too severe, some plants merely stop growth and wait for better times. For all these plants the period of inactivity is called **dormancy.** Plants have been keyed by the Creator to have their dormant periods terminated by precise conditions so that unusual quirks in the season do not cause early breaking of dormancy, thus destroying the plant.

After a tulip blooms in early spring, it forms a floral bud and by all outward signs is ready to sprout again by mid-summer. The summer sun, however, would scorch and kill the leaves of the plant. The tulip is keyed to enter a period of dormancy after the bud is formed. A period of near freezing temperatures, which destroy

Daffodills are able to withstand cold. A late snow will not harm them, but 90° weather will kill them.

certain chemicals in the bulb, breaks this dormancy. These chemicals prevent the tulip from sprouting in the summer or fall.

Some seeds have chemicals which inhibit sprouting. Only when these chemicals are washed away will the seed sprout. This is important for plants that need a rainy season in order to grow. On

The rockrose is found in Israel. It grows and flowers during a brief rainy season and then becomes dormant. Some believe that this is the lily of the field spoken of in Matthew 6:28.

the other hand, maple tree seeds sprout as soon as they fall from the tree in early spring. It is essential that the maple seedling grow for a full season before winter comes; therefore, maple seeds will sprout even on a block of ice.

Corn seeds and other seeds which are formed in the fall require about 13° C (55° F) to sprout. If a corn seed sprouted as soon as it formed, winter weather

would kill the young plant. A period of dryness and the spring temperatures are necessary to break the dormancy of corn seeds.

Some areas have two growing seasons in a year. These areas usually have dry, hot summers which force plants to grow only in the spring and fall. Some plants are designed to conquer this problem by rapidly growing and producing seeds in the few months of spring or fall alone. Some plants in these

Some plants form seeds in order for their kind to survive unfavorable conditions.

areas have leaves which can become dry, often curling up and becoming brittle; but when moisture returns, the leaves fill with water, and growth resumes. Without these God-designed mechanisms, the plants in these areas would have been killed long ago.

Review questions on page 328.

hours of
sunlight

16

mum
ragweed 15

14

spinach 13

poinsettia 12

11

strawberry 10

9

8

Jan. Feb. Mar. Apr. May Jun. Jul. Aug. Sep. Oct. Nov. Dec.

Miami
Los Angeles
New York
Seattle

ragweed

poinsettias

13A-11 *The length of the daylight period at different times of the year for several U.S. cities has been plotted on this graph. The length of the photoperiod for several plants is indicated on the left. Strawberries (short day plants) are stimulated to flower by 10 hour days and thus bloom in the spring. Spinach blooms only when the photoperiod is about 13 hours (long-day plant). Although mums require a long day to flower, the formation of buds and flowers takes time, and they bloom in the early fall in most areas where they grow outdoors. Since they bloom in the fall, some botantists consider them short-day plants.*

The length of daylight varies greatly, depending on the season as well as the latitude. Knowledge of its photoperiod enables scientists to predict when a plant will flower.

Most plants grown in temperate areas are divided into three groups:

❏ *Short-day plants* flower when the period of light is less than 12 hr.; sometimes less than 10 hr. is required for flowering. Some examples are poinsettias, goldenrods, asters, soybeans, corn, and strawberries.

❏ *Long-day plants* flower when the period of light is more than 12 hr. Some examples are sunflowers, hollyhocks, sweet clover, irises, and radishes.

❏ *Neutral-day plants* flower independently of the photoperiod. These plants usually flower continuously if temperature, moisture, and various other conditions are favorable. Hybrid roses, beans, tomatoes, carnations, snapdragons, peas, marigolds, and zinnias are common neutral-day plants.

As soon as many plants mature, they produce flowers if the photoperiod is right. Some plants will not flower if a photoperiod is off 10 min.

The physiological processes of photoperiodism are based on plant pigments called *phytochromes** (FYE tuh KROHMZ). Two forms of the phytochrome responsible for photoperiodism are found in plants. Light changes one form to the other, and darkness changes it back. Plants flower when the ratio of these two phytochromes is right for that particular variety. In many plants a single exposure to the proper photoperiod induces flowering. In most plants the period of darkness appears to be the critical factor. If the dark period is broken even by a short exposure to dim light, many plants will not flower.

In combination with the photoperiod, plants often flower in response to temperature, available moisture, and other factors. Many spring-flowering woody plants such as fruit trees, azaleas, and dogwoods, along with many flowering bulbs like tulips, crocuses, and hyacinths, form their flower buds one year (often in response to photoperiod changes and to decreased temperatures) and flower the next year following a dormant period, regardless of the photoperiod.

Biological Terms

Plants and Water	topsoil	root pressure	capillarity
soil texture	humus	passive absorption	transpiration
loam	pore spaces	translocation	cohesion

---

phytochrome: phyto- (plant) +
-chrome (color)

transpiration-	*Plants and Minerals*	auxins	phototropism	photoperiodism
cohesion theory	fertilizers	gibberellin	thigmotropism	*Facets*
guttation	mulch	abscissic acid	chemotropism	insectivorous plants
nastic movement	*Plant Hormones*	tropism	*Plants and Light*	dormancy
turgor (adj., turgid)	hormones	geotropism	etiolated	

Review Questions 13A-4

1. List several characteristics of light that are significant for plant growth.
2. Compare and contrast short-day plants, long-day plants, and neutral-day plants.

Facet 13A - 2: Dormancy in Plants, page 326

1. Summarize how a period of dormancy may help certain plants.
2. List several conditions that break dormancy for different plants.

Thought Questions

1. Why is it improper to speak of "plant food"?
2. Some people believe that those fruits and vegetables produced using organic gardening techniques are more beneficial than food grown using other techniques. List arguments for and against this opinion.
3. The plant that thrived in the living-room window all summer slowly turned yellow and lost its leaves when Mom moved it to a window in the back bedroom. Mom said she had been giving it the same amount of water and "plant food." List as many factors as you can that could account for the change in the health of the plant.

13B–Plant Reproduction

One of the characteristics of the plant kingdom is the presence of multicellular sexual reproductive structures. **Sexual reproduction** of flowering plants (phylum Anthophyta) involves the formation of flowers and seeds, the germination of those seeds, and the growth to a mature plant. Although some plants complete this life cycle in the space of a few weeks, others often require many years.

Because there is genetic variation each time there is sexual reproduction, a plant with exactly the desired traits (such as large fruit, certain flower color, or disease resistance) may not be produced by sexual reproduction. For example, a high quality red rose may produce hundreds or thousands of inferior rose plants by sexual reproduction before it has a high quality offspring.

Vegetative reproduction is asexual; therefore, the offspring have the same genetic makeup as the parent plant. Although all plants are capable of sexual reproduction, many ornamental and food plants are reproduced vegetatively since

---

13B-1 Commercially Important Plants

Vegetatively reproduced
almond, apple, banana, blackberry, cherry, chrysanthemum, fig, grape, holly, iris, Irish potato, lily, olive, orange, orchid, peach, pear, pecan, pineapple, poinsettia, rose, strawberry, sweet potato, tulip

Sexually reproduced
barley, bean, broccoli, cabbage, carrot, celery, coconut, corn, cotton, cucumber, lettuce, maple, marigold, melons, oak, pea, peanut, pine, rice, soybean, tomato, turnip, wheat

---

their potential for the various characteristics of species is already known. Also, vegetative reproduction often produces a plant capable of maturing years sooner than a seedling. In other words, in plants such as fruit trees, berry bushes, and many ornamentals, sexual reproduction may be used to develop new varieties and asexual reproduction may be used to "fill the field" with a good variety. But if all plants were reproduced vegetatively, we would not have any new varieties of plants and plant products.

Vegetative Reproduction

Vegetative reproduction of plants can be *natural,* that is, carried on by the plant itself, or it may be *induced.* Induced methods of vegetative reproduction attempt to force the meristematic tissues to grow the missing parts of the plant. Similarly, natural methods of vegetative reproduction sometimes result because a portion of a plant forms the structures to make a complete plant. Often, however, on special stems or leaves the parent plant will form small complete plants called **plantlets** which can grow independently.

Vegetative reproduction by underground parts

If a single sprig of mint is planted in a garden, soon dozens of mint shoots will appear around the original plant. Underground *stolons* like those found in the mint are often responsible for vegetative reproduction. The common cattail, if started from the seed, can in a single year produce almost one hundred shoots from its spreading *rhizomes.* The seeds establish cattail rhizomes in new areas, but vegetative reproduction produces new plants around the parent. Plants like iris, bamboo, lilac, elderberry, grass, and many herbaceous weeds reproduce by rhizomes, stolons, or shoots produced from spreading roots.

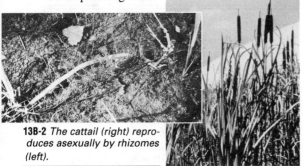

13B-2 *The cattail (right) reproduces asexually by rhizomes (left).*

Corms and bulbs are underground stems that can reproduce vegetatively. Once a corm or bulb matures, tiny corms or bulblets develop from lateral buds at the base of the parent plant. Tulips, hyacinths, and daffodils reproduce this way.

Commercial bananas produce a corm which is sometimes over 30 cm (1 ft.) in diameter. This corm is cut into pieces weighing 1.5 kg (3.3 lb.). Each piece must have a bud on it. If the piece is planted, a new shoot will appear and grow to 9 m (29 ft.) tall, 40 cm (16 in.) in diameter, and produce fruit in 12-16 months. The shoot is herbaceous and will produce fruit only once. The aboveground portions of the plant are cut away after the fruit is harvested. The new corm will then send up more shoots from lateral buds, or it may be dug up, cut, and replanted.

Tubers are underground stems which, unlike most corms and bulbs, often produce abundant lateral buds, each of which may develop into a new plant. The white or Irish potato can be propagated by cutting apart the tuber and planting its "eyes" (lateral buds).

Vegetative reproduction by stems

Runners are usually spindly stems which produce plantlets at their tips. When the plantlets grow too heavy to be supported, the runner bends to the soil where the adventitious roots set in, and a new plant develops. Once the plantlet roots begin to grow, the runner dies. Runners, a common method of natural asexual reproduction, are seen in strawberry plants, spider plants, and eelgrass.

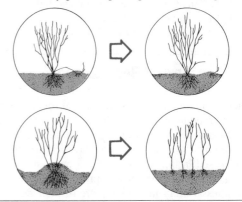

13B-3 *Simple layering (top) and mound layering (bottom) are two methods of layering commonly used to propigate plants asexually.*

Stems are often used in induced vegetative reproduction. A common practice among nurserymen is **layering.** In layering, the stem of a parent plant is usually bent over and buried in moist soil. Often the stem is wounded to reveal meristem and then treated with rooting hormones. In time most plants produce roots from nodes or at the wound. This rooted stem is then cut from the parent plant and replanted. Raspberry and blackberry plants produce spindly stems which often fall over and layer themselves naturally.

A **stem cutting,** or *slip,* is usually a section of a woody stem that is placed in water or in moist sand, soil, or a similar medium. Exposing the meristematic tissues in lateral buds or nodes to moist conditions promotes the growth of roots. Different plants have various requirements for rooting in this manner. Placing some cuttings in water will result in rotting rather than rooting. Many cuttings are best started as the plant enters or is in dormancy; others are best started when the plant is supporting mature foliage. Several plants commonly reproduced by cuttings are hollies, yews, pineapples, cacti, camellias, and roses.

The stems of many vines reproduce asexually. Vine nodes often have adventitious roots for

13B-4 *Kudzu, a Japanese import, is grown in the U.S. to prevent soil erosion and may grow 50 ft. in a summer. The stems become woody and produce roots at nodes. The roots grow, produce buds, and become new plants. Kudzu has escaped cultivation, and threatens native plants.*

climbing. If these roots contact the soil, they can begin to grow and thereby produce new plants.

Under proper conditions almost any leaf can be forced into vegetative propagation. Most leaves, however, wilt and die long before their tissues develop new plants. A couple of notable exceptions are members of the African violet family and succulent-leafed tropical and semitropical plants (often seen as houseplants). A leaf rooting in water or moist soil is called a **leaf cutting.**

Review Questions 13B-1

1. Why are some plants commercially reproduced asexually? What is the value of sexual reproduction of commercial plants which are usually asexually reproduced?
2. Differentiate between natural and induced methods of vegetative reproduction.
3. List several plants that are asexually reproduced by underground roots or stems.
4. Describe the process of layering.

Sexual Reproduction

In the plant kingdom sexual reproduction is carried on in a variety of ways. Sexual reproduction in the phylum Bryophyta differs greatly from the ferns and the gymnosperms. The anthophytes (angiosperms, phylum Anthophyta), which will be discussed in this section, have a basic similarity in their sexual reproductive processes but almost limitless variety in the structure of their flowers, fruits, and seeds. The goal of sexual reproduction, no matter how it is accomplished, is to produce new plants and to recombine genes into different groupings, thereby occasionally producing other varieties.

The flower

Although flowers vary greatly, there are only six basic floral parts. The lower and outermost structures (pedicel, receptacle, sepals and petals) are *accessory flower parts.* The inner two (the anther

and pistil) are the *reproductive parts of a flower.* Usually each flower has only one each of the first two flower parts.

❑ **Pedicel**   The pedicel is the stalk which supports the flower.

❑ **Receptacle**   The enlarged end of the pedicel which bears the remainder of the flower parts is the receptacle.

The other four flower parts are arranged roughly in rings, and flowers often have multiples of each of them.

13B-5 *A tulip cut to show flower parts. Does the tulip have a superior or inferior ovary?*

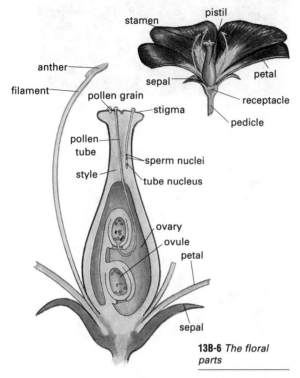

anther
filament
pollen grain
pollen tube
style

stamen
pistil
sepal
petal
receptacle
pedicle
stigma
sperm nuclei
tube nucleus
ovary
ovule
petal
sepal

13B-6 *The floral parts*

Plant ovaries may contain a single ovule, as in peaches or pecans, or they may contain many ovules, like beans, apples, or tomatoes. Some flowers have multiple pistils. The strawberry and magnolia have many individual pistils on a single receptacle. Ovaries of flowers may be *superior,* above the receptacle, or *inferior,* within the receptacle. Occasionally a *floral tube* (fused petals or fused petals and sepals) may cause a superior ovary to appear inferior.

If a flower has sepals, petals, and at least one stamen and one pistil, it is called a *complete flower.* Flowers which lack any of these structures are *incomplete flowers.*

Pollinations

Many complete flowers have showy petals that aid in the transfer of pollen by insects or birds. *Nectar,* a sweet fluid secreted at the base of the petals, is the lure which brings these animals to the flowers. The corolla is often designed as a sort of bull's-eye to guide the pollinators to the nectar.

The anthers and the stigma are usually held in a position so that anything reaching the nectar will have to pass them, thereby aiding pollination. Although some flowers, like the members of the pea family, have their petals wrapped around the stamen and pistil, insuring *self-pollination,* most flowers have mechanisms aiding the probability of *cross-pollination.* Often the stamen and the pistil mature at different times. Some pistils are arranged so that an insect entering the flower will place pollen on the stigma, but as it leaves with pollen from the stamen of this flower, it will not pass the sticky part of the stigma. Some species will not produce seeds if their pistil receives pollen from a stamen of the same flower, or in some cases, from the same plant.

Many flowers, usually incomplete ones, are pollinated by wind. They have no need of showy petals and most often do not have them. Some plants produce male flowers, containing the stamen, and female flowers, containing the pistil. Squash and cucumbers develop from female flowers that contain the pistil. Squash and cucumbers are insect-pollinated plants with separate male and female flowers on the same plant. Many trees,

❏ **Sepals** The outermost ring is composed of the sepals,* collectively called the *calyx** (KAY liks). Sepals are often green and serve to protect the other floral parts as they form in the bud. As in the tulip, however, sepals may be colored and even be indistinguishable from the petal.

❏ **Petals** Petals, often large and brightly colored, are just inside the sepals. Together the petals are called the *corolla** (kuh ROHL uh).

❏ **Stamen** The male reproductive structures, the stamens, comprise the next ring. The stamen is made of the **filament,** or the stalk which bears the **anther.** An anther has four chambers in which **pollen grains** are formed. Pollen grains vary greatly in size and surface structures and contain the male gametes of the plant.

❏ **Pistil** The female reproductive structure, the pistil, is the innermost floral part. The pistil is made of the **stigma,** which when mature has a sticky surface to receive the pollen; the **style,** which supports the stigma; and the **ovary,*** which contains the ovules. If the *ovum* (egg) in the ovule is fertilized, the **ovule** develops into a seed.

---

sepal: sepa- (Gk. SKEPE, covering)
calyx: (Gk. KALUX, cup)
corolla: (L. CORONA, crown)

ovary: ova- or ovi- (egg)

like the oak and pecan, produce *catkins,* which are collections of stamens. Catkin pollen is carried by the wind to inconspicuous female flowers on other parts of the plant. Plants such as spinach, date palms, willows, holly, ashes, and some maples produce male flowers on one plant and female flowers on another.

13B-7 *The oak catkin (a male flower) lacks petals but produces abundant pollen for wind pollination.*

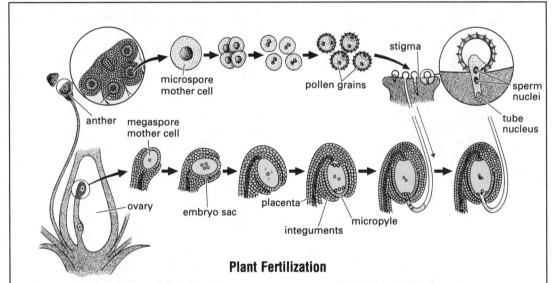

Plant Fertilization

Formation of Gametes

In a young anther chamber are large *microspore mother cells* which carry on meiosis to become *microspores.* Each microspore cell (which is haploid) goes through mitosis but does not divide its cytoplasm. One of the haploid nuclei becomes the *tube nucleus.* The other nucleus is the *generative nucleus.* Later the generative nucleus will divide by mitosis becoming 2 *sperm nuclei.*

Ovules begin as a swelling along the ovary wall, in which a large *megaspore mother cell* goes through meiosis. The *embryo sac* forms around the 4 cells produced by this division. Three of these haploid cells die; the *megaspore* is the cell that remains. Its nucleus divides by mitosis 3 times, resulting in 8 identical haploid nuclei. During this time the embryo sac has been growing and has become covered by *integuments** (in TEHG yoo munts). The integuments attach the ovule to the ovary wall by a stalk called the *placenta.* The **micropyle*** is a small gap between the integuments.

The Union of the Gametes

When a pollen grain lands on the stigma of the right species, chemicals manufactured by the stigma stimulate the growth of the pollen tube. The tube nucleus is near the growing tip of the pollen tube. Immediately behind the tube nucleus are the 2 sperm nuclei. The pollen tube grows down the soft tissues of the style, enters the ovary, and then enters the ovule through the *micropyle.* The tube nucleus then disintegrates.

One sperm nucleus fuses with the *egg cell,* which is 1 of the 8 haploid nuclei in the ovule. Five of the haploid nuclei in the ovule disintegrate. The other 2, found in the center of the ovule, fuse together and then fuse with the second sperm nucleus, forming a triploid nucleus. This triploid nucleus forms the **endosperm,*** which is stored food for the embryonic plant to use while in the seed and when sprouting. Because seed formation requires the fertilization of 2 nuclei inside the embryo sac by 2 sperm nuclei, it is *double fertilization.*

---

integument: in- (in) + -tegu- (L. TEGERE, to cover) + -ment (E. -MENT, action or process)

micropyle: micro-, (small) + -pyle (Gk. PULE, gate)

endosperm: endo- (within) + -sperm (seed)

FACETS OF BIOLOGY

Grafting and Budding

Although not technically a form of vegetative reproduction because no *new* plant is produced, *grafting* and *budding* are used to obtain the large number of genetically identical plants needed for commercial purposes. Many woody plants such as apples, peaches, and roses are reproduced this way.

Grafting is the process wherein a stem, called the **scion** (SYE uhn), is cut off from one plant and placed in contact with the stem of a rooted plant, called the **stock.** Thus the scion begins to grow on

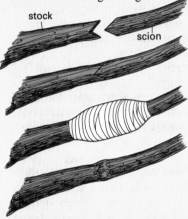

stock

scion

the stock. There are several ways in which a graft can be cut and joined to the stock; each type of plant, however, has a way that works best. The idea is to get the *vascular cambiums* as close together as possible. When these cambiums produce cells, the cells become an undifferentiated mass. After a time, this mass joins the xylem and phloem. When the necessary strengthening and covering tissues are also formed, the graft

has "taken," and the scion will grow on the stock.

Budding is similar to grafting, but rather than using a stem, a bud with a sliver of bark is placed under a slit in the bark of the stock. The top of the stock is cut off, and the grafted bud continues apical growth.

Usually grafting and budding are done while the plants are in dormancy. If the plants were growing, the water demands of the leaves on the scion would not be met while the new cells at the graft were forming. The wounds of the plant must be supported and sealed, usually with elastic tape and a waxlike or plastic substance to prevent the stalk and scion from wiggling loose and drying out. Usually successful grafting or budding will involve members of the same genus or at least the same family. Most often grafting is done with woody plants, but it may be done in some herbaceous plants.

Since the meristematic tissues of the stem produce the fruits, and since there is no exchange of

This Starkrimson Delicious apple tree was grown from a seed. Seeds of this tree will not produce the same variety of apples, however. All other Starkrimson Delicious apple trees are the result of grafting.

genes between the meristematic tissues of the roots and the stems of a graft, the stock usually does not affect the scion, and vice versa. Roots supply water and dissolved minerals. As long as there is an adequate supply of both, the grafted-in portion of the plant will grow and express its genes normally.

When a slow-growing stock is used, the grafted-in portion may not be able to grow as rapidly as it normally would. This can produce dwarf plants. For example, the roots of the slow-growing quince cannot supply enough water for the rapidly growing apple. An apple grafted into quince roots will produce small trees with normal-sized fruits.

Review questions on page 336.

Biblical Grafting

The practice of grafting is centuries old. The Apostle Paul was thoroughly familiar with the principle and procedures of grafting. In Romans 11 he compares Gentile Christians to a grafted wild olive tree branch on the stock of a cultivated olive tree, the house of Israel. The scion is warned not to boast that the original branches were pruned for its sake. The Jews were pruned for the Gentiles' sake, but they were also pruned because of their disbelief. God says that He will prune any rotten branches and will graft in old branches if they repent.

333

13B-8 *Each of the petals of the mum actually has male and female parts. Since they are all on a common receptacle, the mum is a composite flower.*

The sunflower has a large receptacle with hundreds of complete, individual flowers arranged on it. On the outside rim there are sterile flowers which produce large petals but lack most other floral parts. A flower composed of many small flowers is called a *composite flower.* Daisies, chrysanthemums, dandelions, and clover are other composite flowers.

Seeds

Seeds are made of a tiny embryonic plant, stored food, and a seed coat. The seed coat (sometimes called the *testa)* may be smooth and cover the content of the seed tightly, or it may be relatively loose-fitting. Some seeds, such as the milkweed, have fluffy extensions of the seed coat to aid the seed in dispersal. Most seeds reveal a **hilum,** which is the point where the seed was attached to the ovary wall, as well as a small scar indicating the **micropyle.**

The stored food contained in a mature seed may be in several forms. The bean, for example, has an *endosperm,* but it is used up by the embryonic plant as the bean forms. The stored food in a bean is found in its two **cotyledons.** Corn, on the other hand, has a single cotyledon and an endosperm within its seed coat. Remember that anthophytes

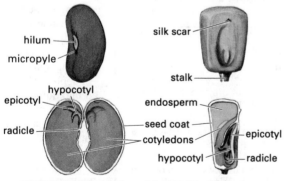

13B-9 *Structures of a bean (dicot, left) and a corn (monocot, right) seed*

are classified into two classes based on the number of cotyledons contained in the seed.

The embryonic plant within the seed has three general areas, based on where the cotyledons attach to it. The part below where the cotyledons attach is the **hypocotyl** (HYE puh KAHT ul), the embryonic stem. The **radicle*** is the end of the hypocotyl which will develop into the primary root of the plant. The end above the point of cotyledon attachment is the **epicotyl** (EP ih KAHT ul) or *plumule.* The epicotyl has one or two tiny, completely formed leaves.

Seed germination

Germination, the beginning of the growth of an embryonic plant within a seed, happens only when three conditions are met:

❑ *Proper moisture*   Many seed coats need moisture to cause them to swell and burst, thereby supplying moisture to the embryonic plant inside. If the embryonic plant were to begin to grow without adequate moisture, it would soon wither and die. Some seeds must be saturated; others require only humid conditions.

❑ *Proper temperature*   Most seeds require a minimum temperature.

❑ *Proper oxygen*   Oxygen is necessary for normal cellular respiration. The embryonic plant also needs oxygen to use the food stored in the endosperm and cotyledons.

Exact amounts of moisture, heat, and oxygen necessary for germination vary considerably among species. Most seeds do not require light for germination. A seed contains enough stored energy for the embryonic plant to get its roots established and to absorb water, as well as to force its first leaves above the soil. At this time the stored food in the seed is usually depleted, and if the plant is not carrying on photosynthesis, it soon dies.

When a seed germinates, the radicle breaks through the seed coat, and the hypocotyl and epicotyl unfold. Once started, the enlargement of a seedling is usually rapid. All the cells necessary to establish the root and first leaves were formed before the seed matured. To enlarge and develop, these cells merely need to be filled with water.

---

radicle: radi- (L. RADIX, root)

Fruits

A **fruit** is a mature ovary with seeds (matured ovules) inside. Auxins formed in the pollen grain cause the ovule to form a seed. These and other hormones cause the ovary to mature into the fruit. Many fruits, however, consist of accessory parts of the flower that mature with the ovary.

Starches, oils, and proteins stored in these structures help the plant continue its species. To do this well, the seeds must be *disseminated* (spread out). If all the seeds of a plant fell around the parent, they would compete with one another and the parent plant for light, minerals, and water.

The fruit of many plants aid seed dissemination. Fleshy fruits are often carried away by animals and man. When the fleshy portion is eaten and the seeds are discarded, dissemination has taken place. Many seeds have heavy protective coats which allow them to pass through the digestive system of an animal undamaged. Some fruits have sticky coatings or hooks which attach to passing animals. Winged fruits like the samara and seeds like those of the dandelion are carried by the wind. The seeds of many plants, like the poppy, are small and are easily carried away from the parent plant by wind or water. Some mature pods and capsules snap open, throwing the seeds away from the parent. Some plants (like the coconut palm) produce fruits that have waterproof walls and can float for long distances.

Simple

Fruits that are produced from a single ovary (even though it may have several divisions) are called simple fruits.

❏ **Dry fruits** Many simple fruits, when mature, are dry.

Pod — bean, milkweed
Capsule — poppy
Samara — maple, elm
Nut — acorn
Grain — corn
Achene — sunflower, dandelion

❏ **Fleshy fruits** Many fruits have thickened fleshy* parts. These fleshy parts may be the ovary, the receptacle, or occasionally other structures.

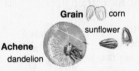

Drupe — olive, peach
Berry — tomato, cranberry
Modified berry — cucumber
orange
cantaloupe

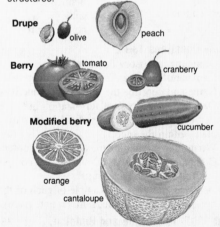

• **Accessory fruits** An accessory* fruit has some floral part (usually the receptacle) which develops along with the ovary.

Pome — apple, pear

Compound

Compound* fruits have several separate ovaries.

❏ **Aggregate fruits** If a compound fruit is made up of several separate ovaries from one flower and if these ovaries fuse, it is called an aggregate fruit.

❏ **Multiple fruits** If a compound fruit is made up of the ovaries of more than one flower, it is a multiple fruit.

Aggregate fruit — raspberry

Multiple fruit — pineapple, fig

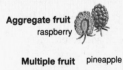

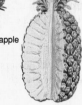

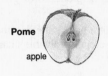

*Many compound fruits can be considered fleshy and accessory fruits.

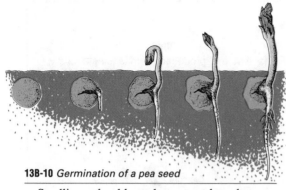

13B-10 *Germination of a pea seed*

Seedlings should not be exposed to dry conditions once germination has begun, for most of them do not have enough stored food to stay alive very long. When the cells have enlarged and the cell walls have become established, the meristematic areas will form strengthening and protecting tissues, and the plant will be able to support itself even during periods of dryness.

Seeds produced in the fall usually must go through a period of dormancy before they can germinate. For some seeds this dormancy may be broken by a period of cold; others require scraping of the seed coat, and some require water to wash away inhibiting chemicals from the seed coat. If kept cool and dry, seeds may remain **viable*** (VYE uh bul) (able to germinate) for many years. The embryonic plants in seeds use stored food to maintain life during dormancy.

If they do not get oxygen, the stored food cannot be used, the embryo will die, and the seeds will become *inviable.* Some seeds, especially those produced in the spring, germinate without periods of dormancy.

Biological Terms

sexual reproduction
vegetative reproduction

Vegetative Reproduction
plantlet
runner
layering
stem cutting
leaf cutting

Sexual Reproduction
pedicel
receptacle
sepal
petal
stamen
filament
anther
pollen grain

pistil
stigma
style
ovary
ovule
micropyle
endosperm
seed
hilum

cotyledon
hypocotyl
radicle
epicotyl (plumule)
germination
fruit
viable

Facet
grafting
scion
stock
budding

Review Questions 13B-2

1. Name the accessory flower parts.
2. Name and describe the male reproductive structures of a flower.
3. Name and describe the female reproductive structures of a flower.
4. Describe the process of fertilization in flowering plants.
5. List and tell the functions of the basic parts of a seed. List the basic parts of the embryonic plant within the seed.
6. What three conditions must be met in order for a seed to germinate?
7. Compare and contrast (a) simple and compound fruits, (b) aggregate and multiple fruits, and (c) fleshy and dry fruits.
8. Describe and give an example of each of the following fruits: drupe, pome, berry, modified berry, pod, capsule, samara, nut, grain, and achene.

Facet 13BF-1: Grafting and Budding, page 333

1. Describe the grafting process. How does this differ from budding?
2. Why is it important to match up the vascular cambiums of the stock and scion?
3. How can dwarf plants be produced by grafting?

Thought Questions

1. Why does the stock of a graft not affect the type of fruit and flowers the scion produces?
2. Why are some commercially valuable plants like fruit trees and Irish potatoes reproduced asexually, while others like corn and wheat are not?

viable: via-, vit-, or vita-
(L. VITA, life)

THE INVERTEBRATES
ZOOLOGY PART I

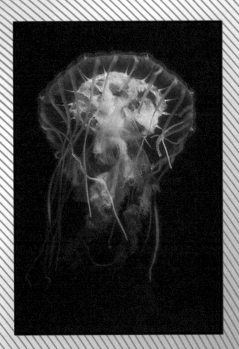

FOURTEEN

14A–Introduction to the Animal Kingdom

The study of the kingdom Animalia is called **zoology*** (ZOH AHL uh jee). Zoology is not limited, however, to scientists in back rooms of a zoo, in a laboratory, or in a forest looking at the fauna. Almost everyone is, to some degree, a zoologist.

Animals have always fascinated mankind. The first recorded human act is Adam's naming the animals. This was a monumental task since scientists now estimate that there are more than 1,025,000 living species of animals, and there are thousands which have become extinct. Even if Adam did not name the animals by species, just recognizing all the different "kinds" would have been a major undertaking.

Animals have served man well. They have been his beasts of burden, his food, his transportation, his sport, and even his companions. Animals, however, have also eaten man's crops, destroyed his homes, killed his domestic animals, and have bitten, stung, attacked, and even killed man himself. Because animals are an important, inescapable part of life, everyone is a zoologist.

---

zoology: zoo- (Gk. ZOON, animals) + -logy (the study of)

Characteristics of the Kingdom Animalia

Animals are so much a part of our daily experience that it seems unnecessary to ask, "What is an animal?" The answer, however, is not simple. **Kingdom Animalia** encompasses a wide assortment of life, from jellyfish to goats and from butterflies to whales. Despite the differences among animals, this group shares certain common characteristics. The basic characteristics of the kingdom Animalia appear in Appendix B. For almost every characteristic, however, some animals prove a glaring exception. Do not let that confuse you. Remember that man's classification system is far from perfect.

Life processes of animals

Organisms in the kingdom Animalia not only share certain common characteristics but also engage in the following processes:

❑ *Movement* To obtain food, most animals engage in some type of locomotion (movement through the environment). Animals that are able to move are called *motile** (MOH tuhl). A few animals are *sessile,* fixed permanently to some object; these animals draw food to themselves by moving their environment.

❑ *Support* Some animals are small and require little or no structure for support, but many animals achieve tremendous sizes and weights. Large animals must have a means of support, or their own weight would crush their internal structures. Some animals, such as sponges, are supported by a network of interlocking needlelike structures. Many animals such as lobsters and insects are supported by an **exoskeleton***, a system of tough plates covering the outside of the animal. Other animals have a more flexible, lighter **endoskeleton***, an internal system of bones or cartilage.

❑ *Protection by body covering* An animal's body may be covered with only a single layer of cells or with such complex structures as feathers, shells, fur, skin, or scales. Even though body coverings differ widely, they all serve to protect the animal from predators. Sharp spines or quills, poisonous or caustic skin secretions, shells, tough hides, or camouflaging coloration can be effective

protection for the animal.

❑ *Nutrition* Animals are heterotrophic; that is, they must find and consume food to supply the building materials and energy necessary for life. Nutrition includes several processes: *ingestion** (in JEHS chun), the intake of food; *digestion,* the breaking down of food into substances the animal can use; and *assimilation,* the animal's absorption of the food for later use as a source of energy or building material. The ways animals obtain food are as varied as their diets, which include almost every living thing.

❑ *Respiration** Some animals have respiration only at the cellular level: each cell of the organism exchanges oxygen and carbon dioxide directly with the environment. Some animals exchange gases through their body coverings. Other animals possess organs and systems which transport the necessary oxygen to their cells; those that obtain oxygen from the air usually have *lungs,* and those that obtain oxygen from water usually have *gills.*

❑ *Circulation* Circulation is the transport of materials throughout the animal. This process helps feed and maintain those specialized tissues which cannot provide for themselves.

❑ *Excretion* Excretion is the elimination of waste materials. Without a means of excretion, the animal's cells would become clogged or poisoned by accumulated waste.

❑ *Response* The ability to perceive and respond to stimuli in the environment is known as irritability. Irritability involves such processes as the reception of stimuli and the conduction of a nerve impulse. Some animals have brains that can sort stimuli and coordinate responses. A few animals possess large brains which add complex reactions such as memory, disposition, and emotion.

❑ *Reproduction* Animal reproduction preserves the life of the species. Budding and regeneration are asexual means of reproduction. Some animals reproduce asexually, but sexual reproduction is found throughout the animal kingdom. An animal's fertilized zygote goes through **embryonic*** (EM bree AHN ik) **stages** as it develops into an independent organism. Some animals have **larval** (not like the adult) **stages** as they mature.

---

motile: (L. MOVERE, to move)
exoskeleton: exo- (outside of) + -skeleton (L. SKELETOS, dried up) [internal support structures]

endoskeleton: endo- (within) + -skeleton (dried up)
ingestion: in- (in) + -gestion (to bear or to carry)

respiration: re- (again) + -spiration (to breathe)
embryonic: em- or en- (in) + -bryonic (L. BRYEIN, to grow)

Animal Classification and Evolution

The different ways animals accomplish the life processes are used as tools in the modern classification system. Classification of organisms in the kingdom Animalia was originally based on appearance. This caused problems. The bat, for example, has the wings, size, and flying habits of a "bird." The bat's fur coat, reproductive process, and bone structure, however, clearly identify it as a flying mammal. Thus, the structures that animals use to accomplish their bodily functions and which help zoologists to classify animals may cause rather than solve problems.

The over twenty phyla in the animal kingdom can be arranged to represent a supposed evolutionary history. If you were to line up a member from each animal phylum, you could, after a few rearrangements, duplicate a model of proposed animal evolution. The fact that this can be done is no accident. Evolutionists have arranged and rearranged the animal groups to make them fit their pattern of evolution. This rearrangement, though, has not altered the simplicity and usefulness of the levels of the classification system. (Nor does this manmade reclassification prove evolution. The changes have added only *apparent* evolutionary significance to the system.)

The use of the present levels of classification is scientifically sound. The system is the most widely used system and it is easily understood. The classification system used in this text is only an organizational tool. Any evolutionary meaning attached to it is artificial.

Review Questions 14A-1
1. List and describe the main characteristics of the kingdom Animalia.
2. List the nine main life processes of animals.

Basic anatomy of animals

Animals have vastly different shapes and structures. This variety, however, can be easily described with several general terms that identify parts of the animal's anatomy.

One feature of an animal's body structure is its symmetry. A *symmetrical* organism can be cut

Common Terms of Animal Anatomy

Cephalic:* concerning the head
Caudal:* concerning the tail
Anterior:* toward the front; forward
Posterior:* toward the rear; further back
Dorsal:* on or near the upper surface; back
Ventral:* on or near the lower surface; front
Lateral:* on or toward the side
Medial:* on or toward the middle
Midline (median): divides into right and left
Transverse:* crosses perpendicular to midline

14A-1 *Some terms of anatomy*

midline (or median) — cephalic — dorsal — ventral — caudal — transverse — lateral — medial — lateral — anterior — posterior

---

cephalic: (brain)
caudal: (L. CAUDA, tail)
anterior: ante- (before)

posterior: (L. POSTERUS, coming after)
dorsal: (L. DORSUM, back)
ventral: (L. VENTRALIS, belly)

lateral: (L. LATERALIS, side)
medial: (L. MEDIALIS, middle)
transverse: trans- (across) + -verse (L. VERTERE, to turn)

into equal halves. Some organisms, however, are *asymmetrical** (AH sih MET rih kuhl) in that their body patterns cannot be divided into equal halves. Asymmetry is characteristic of few adult animals. Different types of **symmetry** are defined by the different ways organisms can be divided into the equal halves. The basic types of symmetry in the animal kingdom include the following:

❑ *Spherical symmetry* A body pattern that can be divided into equal halves by a cut in any direction which passes through the center of the body. A spherically symmetrical animal has no top, bottom, or sides.

❑ *Radial** symmetry* A body pattern that can be divided into equal halves by a cut made through the center of the animal and along its length (not a transverse cut). A radially symmetrical animal has a top and bottom but no right and left sides.

❑ *Bilateral** (bye LAT ur ul) *symmetry* A body pattern that can be divided into equal halves only by a cut which passes longitudinally and divides the animal into right and left sides. Most often

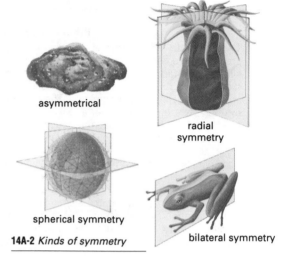

asymmetrical

radial symmetry

spherical symmetry

bilateral symmetry

14A-2 *Kinds of symmetry*

such an animal has a front (head) and a hind (tail) region.

Classifications in the animal kingdom

Although the following division is not always used as a formal classification, the kingdom Animalia is often divided into two groups:

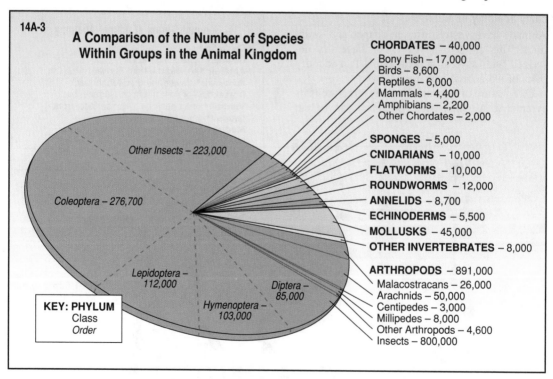

14A-3

A Comparison of the Number of Species Within Groups in the Animal Kingdom

Other Insects – 223,000
Coleoptera – 276,700
Lepidoptera – 112,000
Hymenoptera – 103,000
Diptera – 85,000

KEY: PHYLUM
Class
Order

CHORDATES – 40,000
Bony Fish – 17,000
Birds – 8,600
Reptiles – 6,000
Mammals – 4,400
Amphibians – 2,200
Other Chordates – 2,000

SPONGES – 5,000
CNIDARIANS – 10,000
FLATWORMS – 10,000
ROUNDWORMS – 12,000
ANNELIDS – 8,700
ECHINODERMS – 5,500
MOLLUSKS – 45,000
OTHER INVERTEBRATES – 8,000

ARTHROPODS – 891,000
Malacostracans – 26,000
Arachnids – 50,000
Centipedes – 3,000
Millipedes – 8,000
Other Arthropods – 4,600
Insects – 800,000

---

asymmetrical: a- (without) + -sym- (same) + -metrical (measure)
radial: (L. RADIUS, spoke of a wheel)

bilateral: bi- (twice) + -lateral (side)

□ **Invertebrates*** (in VUR tuh BRAYTZ): those animals without backbones; and

□ **Vertebrates*** (VUR tuh BRAYTZ): those animals with backbones.

Vertebrates include most of the familiar animals: fish, birds, snakes, lions, mice, and elephants. There are, however, not only more kinds of invertebrates but also a much larger total number of invertebrates. At least 95% of the more than 1,025,000 species of animals are invertebrates. Examine figure 14A-3 which shows the relative numbers of species in some of the various phyla and classes of the animal kingdom.

Though they lack backbones, not all invertebrates lack support. The jellyfish and the octopus are soft-bodied. Clams, lobsters, and insects have rigid outer structures to support their boneless bodies.

This chapter presents some common examples of the invertebrate phyla. Chapter 15 surveys the largest invertebrate phylum, the arthropods. Chapters 16 and 17 discuss the various classes of phylum Chordata, the only phylum containing vertebrates.

Biological Terms

zoology	exoskeleton	larval stage	symmetry
Characteristics of the Kingdom Animalia	endoskeleton	*Basic Anatomy*	invertebrate
kingdom Animalia	embryonic stage	*of Animals*	vertebrate

Review Questions 14A-2

1. Describe the types of symmetry common in animals.
2. In a turtle what is (a) the most dorsal structure, (b) the most ventral structure, (c) the most anterior structure, and (d) the most posterior structure?
3. Imagine a fish cut into halves along its midline. List three of its external structures that would be cut.
4. Imagine a transverse cut through the dorsal hump of a camel. (a) Name three structures that would be in the cephalic piece of the camel. (b) Name three structures that would be in the caudal piece of the camel.
5. Which is the larger group in each of these sets: (a) vertebrates or invertebrates, (b) mammals or insects, (c) insects or invertebrates, and (d) sponges or vertebrates?

Thought Question

Why would scientists occasionally want to rearrange the classification of organisms within the kingdom Animalia? Are these reasons justifiable?

14B–Phyla Porifera and Cnidaria

Many people assume that animals are similar to humans. Indeed, in many respects animals are similar to humans. Many animals have systems (such as circulatory system, nervous system, etc.) and organs (such as heart, brain, liver, etc.). Some animals that are quite unlike humans even have systems and organs that function very much like similar structures in humans.

There are some animals, however, that have no organs or systems. These animals are often called the "tissue animals" because the only level of cellular organization they have is that of tissues—a group of cells working together to accomplish a function.

In this chapter we will look at two phyla of "tissue animals": Porifera (the sponges) and Cnidaria (the hydra, jellyfish, coral, and similar organisms). All of these organisms are aquatic. As you study them you should be able to understand why they must live in water.

invertebrate: in- (L. IN-, not) + -vertebrate (L. VERTEBRA, joint)

vertebrate: (joint)

Phylum Porifera – The Sponges

Sponges are unobtrusive organisms found mainly in marine habitats, though there are freshwater species. The adult sponge is sessile. As an organism, the sponge is unresponsive to most environmental changes. Lacking certain animal characteristics, the sponge generated scientific disagreement for many years. Aristotle called it a plant. Others classified it as an animal. Some said it was neither.

Where should sponges be classified? Their cellular structure and their development from zygote to mature organism clearly make them animals. Sponges are in the **phylum Porifera*** (puh RIF uh ruh). Poriferans ("pore bearers") act as living pumps, drawing water into their bodies through tiny **incurrent* pores** and expelling it through a large **excurrent* pore** or **osculum*** (AHS kyuh lum). This pumping of its environment through its body establishes the sponge as an animal.

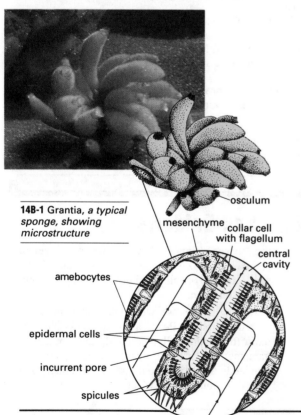

14B-1 Grantia, *a typical sponge, showing microstructure*

osculum

mesenchyme

collar cell with flagellum

central cavity

amebocytes

epidermal cells

incurrent pore

spicules

Structure of sponges

The body of a typical sponge is like a sac with walls composed generally of two cell layers separated by a thin, jellylike layer. The outermost cell layer is the **epidermis,*** which protects the exterior of the sponge's body. The inner layer of cells lines the cavities inside the sponge.

These two layers are separated by a jellylike matrix called the **mesenchyme*** (MES un KYME). Although the mesenchyme itself is noncellular, it contains a variety of structures and cells vital to the existence of a sponge. Amebalike cells called **amebocytes*** move freely within the mesenchyme. They transport food throughout the sponge and carry wastes to the sponge surface where they can be expelled. Amebocytes also operate in digestion.

14B-2 *Cross section of a simple sponge, with one central chamber (left), and cross section of a complex sponge, with a network of canals and chambers (right).*

The sponge is supported by a network of **spicules** found in the mesenchyme. Amebocytes produce these spicules. Spicules may assume a variety of shapes, from needle and multipronged "jack" shapes to hook and barb shapes. These hard, mineral structures, distributed and intertwined throughout the body of the sponge, provide a supporting framework for the animal. The prongs or barbs of the spicules may protrude through the outer cell layer of the sponge to give it a spiny or velvety appearance. Some sponges have spicules composed of calcium carbonate (lime); others, of silica. A third group of sponges is supported by a branching network of tough, proteinlike fibers called *spongin*. Scientists use the composition and shape of the spicules to classify sponges.

Those sponges that have thin-walled, saclike bodies are *simple sponges. Complex sponges* are usually large and have a system of canals and chambers which empty into a central chamber. Some complex sponges grow to be over 2 m (6.5 ft.) in diameter.

Porifera: pora-, pore-, pori-, or poro- (Gk. POROS, opening or passage) + -fer (to bear or to carry)

osculum: (L. OSCULUM, little mouth)

incurrent: in- (into) + -current (L. CURRERE, to run)

excurrent: ex- (out) + -current (to run)

epidermis: epi- (over) + -derm, derma-, or dermi- (skin)

14B-3 *Red cup sponges*

Life process of sponges

The sponge consumes microscopic algae, bacteria, and organic debris. Since the sponge cannot move about to seek this food, it must draw food particles into itself. **Collar cells,** which line the cavities of sponges, have flagella that beat vigorously to generate the water current of the sponge. Thus, water enters through the *incurrent pores* and leaves the *excurrent pore.* The collar cells engulf food particles carried in by the current. The collar cells partially digest the food and transfer it to the amebocytes in the mesenchyme. The amebocytes complete this digestion and then transport the food throughout the sponge.

The Use of Sponges

The sponge has few natural enemies. Its hard, sharp spicules and unpleasant taste and odor generally make it an undesirable mouthful for would-be predators. Animals have used sponges for a variety of purposes. Many animals use the hollow sponge as a ready-made home. Certain crabs stick pieces of sponge to their shells for camouflage. Not all sponges are harmless homes or decoration for animals. One type of sponge, for instance, attaches to mollusk shells and destroys both the shell and the animal.

Throughout history man has used the soft, durable, and remarkably absorbent spongin skeleton of some sponges. These skeletons were used in the past as padding for Greek armor, as Roman paint brushes, and in place of a drinking cup at our Lord's crucifixion (Matt. 27:48).

Today sponges can be durable cleaning tools or, as in the case of the elephant ear sponge, a fine swab for surgical or artistic purposes. The demand for these sponges has made sponge fishing a profitable enterprise.

Diffusion on the cellular level performs excretion and respiration in sponges. Each cell can perform these functions because the sponge's thin-walled structure keeps every cell either in direct contact with or very near the environment.

Reproduction in sponges

In sponges asexual reproduction assumes a variety of forms. In favorable conditions a group of cells from the sponge's body may enlarge and separate from the parent to form a new individual in a process called **budding.** This is the most common type of asexual reproduction in sponges.

During periods of freezing temperatures or drought, many freshwater sponges form **gemmules** (JEM yoolz)—clusters of cells encased in a tough spicule-reinforced coat. When harsh conditions kill the parent sponge, the gemmules survive in a dormant state. When favorable conditions return, the gemmules open, and new sponges form.

The third means of asexual reproduction is **regeneration*** (rih JEN uh RAY shun). A small piece of a sponge can regenerate into a new, complete adult. Commercial sponge growers exploit this remarkable ability. By breaking a living sponge into several pieces and spreading them in beds, they cultivate a large number of sponges in the same area. This type of cultivation makes sponge harvesting much easier and more productive than traditional sponge fishing.

Sexual reproduction in sponges occurs primarily in the spring. Sperm produced by one sponge enters another sponge. A sperm enters a collar cell, and an amebocyte transfers it to an ovum in the mesenchyme. The zygote develops into a flagellated larva, which leaves the parent sponge and swims until it finds a suitable place to attach itself and grow into a new sponge.

Review Questions 14B-1

1. What characteristics of sponges would cause Aristotle to classify them as plants?
2. Briefly tell how a sponge accomplishes each of the nine life processes. Where possible, include structure names.
3. How is a knowledge of the regenerative process of a sponge used commercially?

---

mesenchyme: mes- or meso- (Gk. MESOS, middle) + -en- (in) + -chyme (Gk. KHEIN, to pour)

amebocyte: amebi- or amebo- (Gk. AMOIBE, a change) + -cyte (cell)

regeneration: re- (L. RE-, again) + -generation (GENERARE, to beget)

Phylum Cnidaria

Anyone who has spent time at the ocean is familiar with members of the **phylum Cnidaria*** (nye DAIHR ee uh) (old name: Coelenterata). The jellyfish with its bell shape and painful sting is a common seaside annoyance. Like the jellyfish, all cnidarians are aquatic, and most are marine. Not all cnidarians, however, are flimsy sacs of jelly.

The hydra

The characteristics of the phylum Cnidaria are clearly illustrated by the **hydra,** a small freshwater cnidarian commonly found in quiet lakes or ponds. Hydras are often white, green, or brown. The body of the hydra is basically a hollow tube with a single opening or *mouth.* Long, movable **tentacles,*** which the hydra uses to catch food, surround the mouth. The internal cavity of the animal is the **gastrovascular* cavity** where digestion and food circulation occur.

The hydra's body is composed of two cell layers. The outer layer, the *epidermis,* is mostly protective epithelium. The cells of the **gastrodermis,*** the layer lining the interior of the animal, primarily perform digestion. A jellylike layer called the **mesoglea*** (MEHZ uh GLEE uh) separates the two cell layers.

The cells of both the epidermis and gastroderm have long contractile fibers at their bases. Because these fibers, like muscle cells, can contract, the animal is able to bend its body, move its tentacles, or contract into a tiny ball when disturbed. Although the hydra can move about by a strange somersaulting motion and by various other methods, it usually remains attached by its sticky **basal disc** to some underwater base, like a rock or plant.

The feeding process of hydra

When feeding, the hydra hangs limply from its underwater base and allows its tentacles to dangle in the water. Batteries of stinging cells called **cnidoblasts*** (NYE duh BLASTS) line the tentacles. These stinging cells produce **nematocysts*** (neh MAT uh SISTS), which are capsules containing poisonous barbs, long coiled threads, or a sticky substance. When an unwary worm or other small invertebrate brushes against the tentacles, the

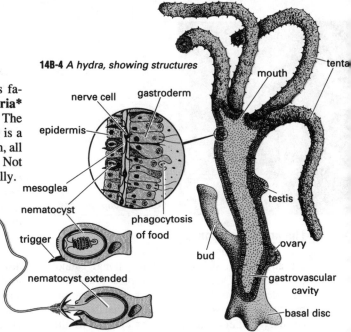

14B-4 *A hydra, showing structures*

nematocysts discharge explosively, piercing the prey with dozens of poisonous harpoons, entangling it in a mesh of threads, and sticking to it.

The hydra's tentacles then draw the paralyzed, helpless prey into its mouth. The food is forced into the gastrovascular cavity where digestive enzymes secreted by gland cells in the gastroderm begin the *extracellular* phase of digestion. The cells of the gastroderm then engulf the partially digested food particles, and digestion is completed in an *intracellular* phase. The hydra egests indigestible matter through its mouth by contracting its body.

The hydra has no special structures for excretion or respiration. The thinness of its body allows all its cells to exchange gases with and excrete waste into the environment either directly or indirectly through the gastrovascular cavity.

The responses and reproduction of hydra

The hydra, unlike the sponge, is capable of dramatic responses to stimuli. The hydra automatically begins drawing in its tentacles and opening its mouth when food touches its tentacles. If you were to touch the hydra with a pin, however, it would contract into a tiny ball. The hydra's **nerve net** makes these different reactions possible. The nerve net is a network of nerve cells and fibers which extend throughout the hydra's body and

---

Cnidaria: Cnid- or Cnide- (Gk. CNIDE, nettle) + -aria (E., related to or pertaining to)

tentacle: (L. TENTARE, to touch)

gastrovascular: gastr-, gastri-, or gastro- (Gk. GASTER, belly) + -vascular (vessel)

gastrodermis: gastro- (belly) + -dermis (skin)

allow it to coordinate its feeding movements for greater efficiency. Once the nerve net receives a stimulus, impulses travel throughout the animal's body; and the entire hydra may respond.

When the seasonal conditions are favorable, hydras reproduce asexually by *budding*. The *bud* starts as a small bump on the side of the adult. It grows tentacles and elongates until it looks like a miniature hydra, then separates from the parent and becomes a new hydra. Hydras can also reproduce by regeneration: if you were to cut a hydra into small pieces, many of these pieces would regenerate into new, complete animals.

The sexual reproduction of hydras occurs usually in the fall or winter. The ova form in *ovaries*, which are small swellings of the animal's body

---

Jellyfish–Polyps and Medusas

Cnidarians assume two basic forms. The hydra illustrates the first form, the **polyp*** (PAHL ip). Polyps are tubular cnidarians with a mouth and tentacles at one end and a basal disc at the other. These cnidarians are usually sessile and reproduce asexually.

In contrast, the **medusa*** (muh DOO suh) form has an expanded bell-shaped body and swims freely. By contracting and relaxing the margin of its body, the medusa glides through the water in a jerky upward motion. As the medusa spurts through the water, it feeds upon the organisms that bump into its *oral* arms,* four long flaps of tissue hanging from its mouth. The medusa typically reproduces sexually.

Although some cnidarians may exist only as a polyp or medusa, many have both polyp and medusa stages in their life cycles. The *Aurelia* (ahw REEL yuh), a common jellyfish, is an example of this two-phase existence. As a free-swimming medusa, the male *Aurelia* produces sperm which are released into the sea. Some of these sperm may enter the gastrovascular cavity of a female, fertilizing the ovum deposited there

The zygote leaves the cavity of the female through the mouth and clings to the oral arms. After a period of development, the zygote becomes a ciliated *larva,* which leaves the female. The larva, called *planula** (PLAN yuh luh), swims away and eventually attaches itself to some underwater base. It then becomes a small polyp about 12 mm (0.5 in.) in length.

The polyp stage of the *Aurelia* can survive for months, store food, and produce new polyps by budding. Under certain seasonal conditions, the polyp changes dramatically: its body develops a number of horizontal constrictions, causing it to look like a stack of saucers. These "saucers" separate, swim free, and eventually develop into large medusas, completing the life cycle.

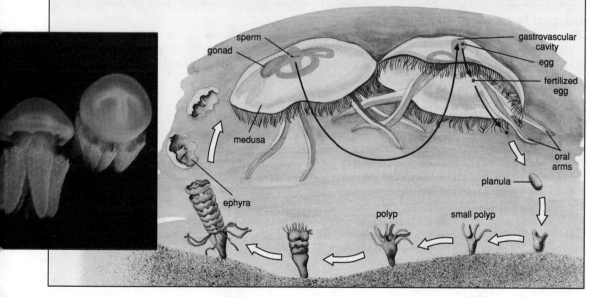

---

mesoglea: meso- (middle) + -glea (Gk. GLOIA, glue)

cnidoblast: cnido- (nettle) + -blast (sprout)

nematocyst: nemato- (thread) + -cyst (pouch)

polyp: poly- (much or many) + -p or -pod (foot)

medusa: (Gk. *mythological woman with snakes growing out of her head*)

oral: (L. OS, mouth)

planula: (L. PLANUS, flat)

wall. Free-swimming sperm form in similar swellings called *testes* (TES teez) (sing., *testis*). Most hydras have only one type of reproductive organ, although occasionally the same animal may have both ovaries and testes. As the ovum ripens, it breaks through the body wall to become exposed to the water. At this time, normally, the ovum is fertilized by a sperm released from the testis of another hydra. While still attached to the parent, the zygote undergoes several divisions to become a mass of cells with a tough protective coat. The mass of cells then separates from the parent and, after a dormant period during the winter months, becomes a new hydra.

Other Cnidarians

Corals like the one above are common and important inhabitants of the sea. The actual coral cnidarian is a minute polyp that lives in a self-made stone skeleton or cup. When not feeding, the polyp can contract into the cup for protection. These fragile animals are important because they frequently cement themselves one upon another and thus form colonies. A colony may consist of thousands of polyps living in a common lime skeleton. These skeletons may grow so large that they form underwater ridges called *reefs,* which may stretch for miles and encircle an island. Corals may even form the foundation for an island.

Sea anemones (uh NEM uh neez), the "flowers" of the sea, live on the sea floor. These large, stout-bodied polyps possess rows of brilliantly colored tentacles which can inflict paralyzing nematocyst stings upon careless fish that get too close.

The Portuguese man-of-war (right) lives on the surface of the water. This highly poisonous animal is a colony of polyps. A large gas-filled polyp acts as the float for the rest of the colony. A variety of special polyps, each with a particular job or function, hang from the float. Some sting and paralyze prey; others feed, consuming the prey; others produce gametes. The entire colony is joined and nourished by a common gastrovascular cavity.

Biological Terms

The Sponges	mesenchyme	regeneration	gastrodermis	nerve net
phylum Porifera	amebocyte	*Phylum Cnidaria*	mesoglea	polyp
incurrent pore	spicule	phylum Cnidaria	basal disc	medusa
excurrent pore	collar cell	hydra	cnidoblast	
osculum	budding	tentacle	nematocyst	
epidermis	gemmule	gastrovascular cavity		

Review Questions 14B-2

1. List the nine life processes of animals and briefly tell how the hydra accomplishes each of these processes. Where possible, include structure names.
2. How do cnidoblasts and nematocysts help in the food-getting and protection of a cnidarian.
3. Compare and contrast the polyp and medusa stages of a typical jellyfish.
4. List and describe several unusual cnidarians.

Thought Questions

1. Compare and contrast the asexual and the sexual reproduction of the hydra and sponge.
2. Compare and contrast the responses of a poriferan and a cnidarian.
3. Poriferans and cnidarians can be called "tissue animals." In what ways is this a good descriptive term for these animals?

14C-The Worms

Worms are soft-bodied, long, and legless organisms, although some have appendages* (uh PEN dih giz). All worms have bilateral symmetry and an anterior, or head, region which is supplied with sense organs. Having a sensitive anterior region, usually with a collection of nerve tissue with which to make decisions is called **cephalization*** (SEF uh lih ZAYE shun). Another characteristic shared by worms is that their bodies develop from three cell layers (as mentioned in the next column). This section will discuss Platyhelminthes, Nematoda, and Annelida, the three most common of the several worm phyla.

Platyhelminthes: The Flatworms

Body shape is the most obvious characteristic that separates the **phylum Platyhelminthes*** (PLAT ih hel MIN theez) from the other worm phyla. Most worms are cylindrical, but the platyhelminth has a thin, flattened body, hence the common name **flatworm.** Flatworms are among the least familiar of animals. Although some flatworms dwell within human bodies, most people have never seen them. Those that are *free-living* shun the daylight to live under rocks or under the leaves of water plants. Most flatworms, however, are *parasitic* and live on or within other animals.

Free-living flatworm: the planarians

The *class Turbellaria,* the free-living flatworms, is illustrated by the **planarians*** (pluh NEHR ee unz). These small flatworms commonly inhabit freshwater lakes and streams and may vary in color from black or brown to white. The body of the planarian is essentially a strip of flat tissues

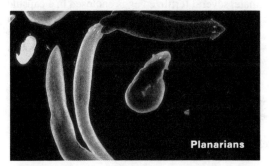

Planarians

about a centimeter long which ends in a triangular point. This point, the planarian's "head," is marked on the dorsal side by an apparently "cross-eyed" pair of *eyespots.* These do not focus on objects but are sensitive to the presence and direction of light.

The planarian's body is composed of three cell layers. The outermost layer (the *epidermis*) not only protects but also provides the animal with a means of locomotion. The innermost layer (the *gastroderm*) lines the digestive tract. The third layer (the **mesoderm***) is between the other layers. Actually, many different organs and systems develop from the cells of the mesoderm.

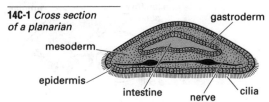

14C-1 *Cross section of a planarian*

Life processes of planarians

The ability to move is important because the planarian must seek and capture its food. Special cells on its ventral surface enable it to move; these cells secrete a layer of slime under the planarian, and ciliated cells propel the planarian over the slime in a smooth, gliding fashion. Contractions of the muscle layers beneath the epidermis contribute to even larger movements.

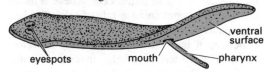

14C-2 *Planarian showing exterior structures*

Planarians usually eat small organisms that they capture. At the center of the animal's ventral surface is an opening, the *mouth,* which releases digestive enzymes. When the food is broken down into small particles, the planarian extends a muscular, tubelike **pharynx*** (FAIHR ingks) through the mouth and sucks up the food particles. The food is then drawn into the branched

---

appendage: ap- or ad- (L. AD-, to or towards) + -pend- (to hang) + -age (E. *suffix meaning* related to)
cephalization: cephal- (head)

Platyhelminthes: platy- (flat) + -helmin- (Gk. HELMIS, parasitic worm)
planarian: plan- or plano- (flat) + -arian (E. *suffix meaning* like)

mesoderm: meso- (middle) + -derma (Gk. DERMA, skin)
pharynx: (Gk. PHARUNX, throat)

intestine where enzymes partially digest the food. Cells lining the intestine then engulf the food and digest it completely. Once digested, the food diffuses throughout the body. Any indigestible material remaining in the intestine is egested through the pharynx.

14C-3 *Structures of the planarian*

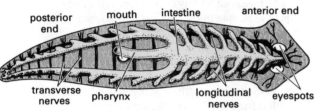

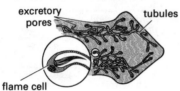

The thin body and extensive digestive tract of the planarian keep most of the animal's cells near food and the environment. Diffusion on the cellular level can thus accomplish respiration and circulation efficiently.

The cells excrete wastes mostly by diffusion, but this excretion is also assisted by a system of tubules that extends throughout the planarian's mesoderm ending in **flame cells**. These cells are hollow bulbs containing a tuft of cilia that beat vigorously to maintain a current in the tubules, which open into the environment by *excretory pores*. This system also helps maintain the animal's water balance by excreting excess water.

The planarian's feeding activities require an elaborate nervous system. The most obvious portion of the system is a mass of nerve tissue called

the "brain" located at the animal's head. Many nerves branch directly from this mass to the sensory structures such as the eyespots and sense organs for taste, smell, and touch in the anterior portion of the animal. Two *longitudinal* (LAHN jih TOOD uh nul) *nerves* extend from the brain down the length of the animal. A number of *transverse nerves* unite the longitudinal nerves, enabling the planarian to coordinate its responses.

Reproductive processes of planarians

Planarians can reproduce both sexually and asexually. To reproduce asexually, the planarian simply pulls itself apart in the middle. Each half of the animal regenerates into a complete adult. Regeneration will produce complete adults even when the animal is cut into many small pieces.

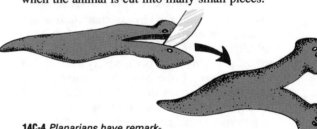

14C-4 *Planarians have remarkable powers of regeneration. If cut, almost any size piece can regenerate into a new planarian. In time, this planarian will pull itself apart, becoming two animals.*

The planarian possesses an elaborate system of organs for sexual reproduction. Every planarian is **hermaphroditic*** (hur MAF ruh DIT ik), meaning it has both male and female reproductive organs. Even though it possesses both reproductive systems, a planarian mates only by cross-fertilization with another individual. After planarians mate, several fertilized eggs enclosed in a capsule are released from the planarian; these eggs then attach to a rock or plant in the water. In less than a month, small planarians hatch and emerge from the capsule.

Review Questions 14C-1

1. What characteristics do worms from the various worm phyla have in common?
2. Name the three cell layers in worms. In relation to each other, where are these three cell layers? Are worms only three cells thick? Explain.
3. List the nine life processes of animals and briefly tell how a planarian accomplishes each of them. Where possible, include structure names.

---

hermaphroditic: (Gk. mythological male Hermaphroditus became united in one body with a female). *Hence, an organism with organs of both sexes.*

Parasitic flatworms

A **parasite** is an organism that fastens itself to a *host* (another organism), depends upon the host (usually for nourishment), and often harms the host. Parasitic flatworms differ from free-living flatworms which have a variety of sense organs and an efficient means of locomotion to find and capture food. Because the parasitic adult is fed by a host, these systems are less important to it. Instead, it needs protection against the host's digestive juices and an effective means of remaining attached to its source of food. The parasitic flatworm has only those characteristics that meet specific needs and does not have those which are unnecessary to it.

Characteristics of parasitic flatworms include the following:

❏ few sense organs as adults,
❏ no external cilia in adults,
❏ a thick **tegument*** (TEG yuh munt) (a protective body covering), and
❏ **suckers** or hooks or both for attachment to a host.

Scientists divide the parasitic flatworms into two major groups: the flukes and the tapeworms.

The flukes

The *sheep liver fluke* is a typical member of this group. As an adult, this flatworm inhabits the liver of a sheep or other grazing animal, causing a disease known as "liver rot." The anatomy of these leaf-shaped parasites is quite similar to that of free-living planarians. The adult feeds upon the host's tissues and fluids by drawing them into its anterior *mouth* using a muscular *pharynx*.

The sheep liver fluke reproduces sexually in a life cycle typical of flukes. The adult produces eggs, which pass through the sheep's bile ducts into its intestine; the eggs are then egested in waste material called *feces*** (FEE seez). The eggs hatch in a body of water, releasing ciliated larvas which enter a particular species of snail; the snail becomes an *intermediate host* (an animal that temporarily harbors the immature form of a parasite).

Within the snail, the immature fluke undergoes a series of changes while reproducing asexually. Eventually the young flukes leave the snail as tailed larvas, attach to vegetation, and become *cysts*. If a sheep eats these cysts, its stomach will digest the cyst wall, releasing an immature fluke. When developed, the fluke will migrate to the sheep's liver and start the cycle over again.

The tapeworms

Tapeworms, in the class Cestoda, are also parasitic flatworms but bear little resemblance to the flukes. The pork tapeworm is a human parasite that, as an adult, makes its home within human intestines. This tapeworm has a ribbonlike body, as long as 6 m (20 ft.) or more, that ends in a small, bulb-shaped "head," the **scolex*** (SKO leks). Suckers and hooks on the scolex attach the worm to the intestinal lining of its host.

14C-5 *Life cycle of the sheep liver fluke*

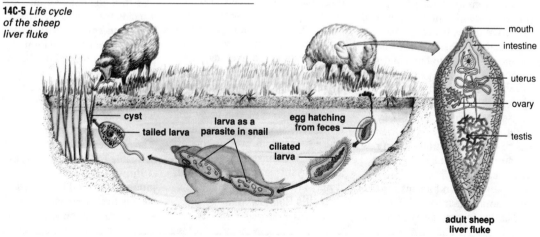

cyst
tailed larva
larva as a parasite in snail
egg hatching from feces
ciliated larva

mouth
intestine
uterus
ovary
testis

adult sheep liver fluke

---

tegument: (to cover)   **feces:** (L. FAEX, dregs)   **scolex:** (Gk. SKOLEX, worm)

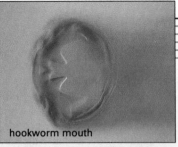
hookworm mouth

FACETS OF BIOLOGY

Parasitic Worms in Humans

In each of the three worm phyla there are worms that are human parasites. Some are more of a nuisance than a major threat, but others have changed the course of history and could become major problems for anyone who does not take proper precautions.

Parasitic Flatworms

❑ **Human Blood Fluke** The human blood fluke lives as an adult in human blood vessels and produces eggs, each possessing a spine. (This spine helps the eggs to penetrate the intestine or urinary bladder.) The eggs are expelled from the host with the wastes. After a period of development within a snail, the young flukes become swimming larvas which invade a human by penetrating his skin. This fluke's life cycle lacks a cyst stage.

❑ **Human Liver Fluke** The human liver fluke adds an additional intermediate host to the life cycle. The eggs from an adult fluke are egested from the host. After a period of development within a snail, the larval flukes penetrate the body and muscles of a fish (the second intermediate host) and form cysts. When a person eats improperly cooked fish that has cysts in it, the flukes leave the cysts and complete their life cycle in the human host. In the Orient, where fish is sometimes eaten raw, the human liver fluke is a major health problem.

❑ **Tapeworms** In humans the beef tapeworm (which has a life cycle similar to the pork tapeworm dis-

cussed in the text) is most common. There are other tapeworms people can get by eating poorly cooked game such as bear, deer and raccoons. Of the human tapeworms, the largest is the fish tapeworm. This worm exists in a larval form within a microscopic invertebrate and encysts in the muscle of fish. When a person eats infected fish that is raw or poorly cooked, the tapeworm is released into the person's intestinal tract, where it matures. This tapeworm may grow up to 18 m (59 ft.) long and dwell in its host for many years.

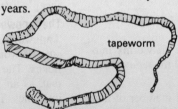
tapeworm

❑ **Hydatid worm** The hydatid (HYE duh tid) worm lives as a small, harmless adult tapeworm in dogs and wolves. Man can serve as the tapeworm's intermediate host. When a human ingests the tapeworm eggs, the larvas hatch and migrate to the liver and other organs, sometimes becoming huge hydatid cysts. These cysts, which may contain millions of young tapeworm scolexes, can grow larger than the size of an orange and cause tremendous pressure upon the organs around them. Unless such a cyst is surgically removed, it may kill its human host.

Parasitic Roundworms

❑ **Ascaris** (See pages 353-54.)

❑ **Hookworm** The hookworm is a tiny parasitic worm common in the southern United States. Hookworm eggs, which are egested with human feces, hatch into larval worms that grow and develop in the soil. Upon reaching the proper size and maturity, the larva invades a human by penetrating the skin. The tiny worm travels through the host's body and by way of the bloodstream is carried to the lungs. It then migrates to the throat, and after being swallowed moves to the intestines.

The adult hookworm within the intestines uses its cutting mouthparts to grasp a piece of the intestinal lining. While so attached, the hookworm feeds upon the blood and tissue fluids flowing from the wound it has made. The worm will also mate and produce eggs. In severe infestations the blood loss from the hookworms' feeding wounds may cause weakness and loss of energy in infected adults and may cause retardation of physical and mental development in infected children. Infection prevention measures include proper disposal of human waste and the wearing of shoes to avoid skin contact with contaminated soil. Various medical treatments are available for infected persons.

❑ **Pinworms** Pinworms commonly afflict children. These small worms live in the large intestine and migrate to the anus to lay

leech

their eggs during the night. This causes irritation and invites scratching, but scratching contaminates hands, bed linens, and even the air with eggs. If a human ingests the eggs, reinfection occurs. The best prevention of pinworm infection is cleanliness. Drugs are available to cure pinworm infection.

❑ **Trichina worm** The trichina (trih KYE nuh) worm is a parasite passed from one meat-eating host to another. If an animal eats meat containing encysted trichina worms, those cysts open in the animal's digestive tract, and the freed worms grow, reproduce, and burrow into the animal's intestinal

walls. There the female trichina worms produce living larvas that migrate to the muscles of the host. Once inside the animal's muscles, the larvas form cysts. If this infected animal is eaten, the process will repeat itself.

Pigs often ingest trichina worms by eating infected rats or food

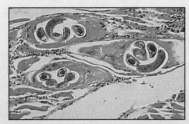
Trichina worms encysted in muscle tissue

scraps containing meat with cysts in it. Humans, in turn, may contract *trichinosis* (TRIH kuh NOH sis) or trichina worm infection by eating insufficiently cooked pork that contains the encysted trichina worm. The extent and effects of trichinosis make the disease an important health consideration. Some studies indicate that nearly 20 out of 100 people in the United States will have trichinosis during their lifetimes. Mild cases of the disease cause little discomfort. Serious trichina worm infection, however, can cause extreme muscle pain, fever, body swelling, and even death.

Parasitic Segmented Worms

❑ **Leeches** The common inch-long *freshwater leech* found in the United States feeds upon the blood of vertebrates. With powerful

suckers, the leech attaches to its temporary host. Once attached, it punctures the skin of the host with its jaws, fills the wound with a chemical that prevents clotting, and sucks blood from the host. In one feeding the leech will consume three to four times its own body weight in blood. This single feeding will sustain the leech for months.

For centuries doctors exploited the *medical leech's* appetite for blood. It was once believed that

Wood cut showing medical leeches and a woman being bled

"bleeding" a person could cure many illnesses; applying a four-inch leech to a sick person became a common medical practice. Although this practice has been discredited, doctors have learned much from leeches. For example, the chemical the leeches use to prevent blood clotting has been used to prevent blood clotting during surgery.

Review questions are on page 353.

Jewish Dietary Laws and Trichinosis

Some people have suggested that the Jewish dietary law forbidding the eating of pork (Lev. 11:7) was to prevent diseases like trichinosis. The law is logical because the trichina worm is an abundant, dangerous parasite, and the Israelites' cooking facilities were not ideal.

The health advantages of the ban on pork are undeniable since even today there are no completely effective drugs for treatment of trichinosis.

We do not know if health was God's reason for issuing the law. God did not ban all foods that may have been harmful, and the Israelites could have had a safe source of energy and protein in their diets if God had permitted them to eat only well-cooked pork. Many of the dietary laws appear to be simply a test of obedience for Israel.

14C-6 *A tapeworm showing scolex (upper left), immature proglottids (upper right), and mature proglottids (bottom)*

A short distance from the head, the body of the tapeworm is divided into segments called **proglottids** (pro GLAH tidz). These segments originate by budding just below the scolex, and they grow larger as they grow older. The small, immature proglottids are immediately beneath the scolex, and the mature, larger ones are near the posterior end of the worm.

The pork tapeworm has no mouth or digestive organs. It can absorb and use only food that the host's body has already digested. For this reason, the adult tapeworm lives in the small intestine. Here the host has completed most of the digestive chores, and the parasite can simply absorb the predigested food. The tapeworm's tegument protects it from the harsh digestive juices in the intestine while allowing the digested food to pass unobstructed into the worm's body.

Most of the tapeworm's metabolism is dedicated to reproduction. Containing a complete set of male and female reproductive organs, each proglottid produces, fertilizes, and stores eggs. When mature, the proglottid (which now contains thousands of eggs) breaks off and is egested in the host's feces.

If a pig (the pork tapeworm's intermediate host) eats the proglottid, the eggs are released and hatch in the intestine. The microscopic larvas burrow through the pig's intestinal lining to blood vessels and are carried through the bloodstream to muscle tissues throughout the animal. Within the pig's muscles these larvas form cysts or *bladderworms*. Each bladderworm contains a completely formed tapeworm scolex. If a person eats muscle tissue of an infected pig that has not been cooked enough to kill the cyst, the scolex emerges, attaches to the human's intestinal wall, and begins to produce proglottids.

Though tapeworms deprive the host of some of his food and do release their toxic wastes for the host to absorb, these parasites usually pose little physical danger to the host. Serious danger arises if the worm becomes so long and tangled that it clogs the intestine or if a human accidentally consumes some of its proglottids. In the second case,

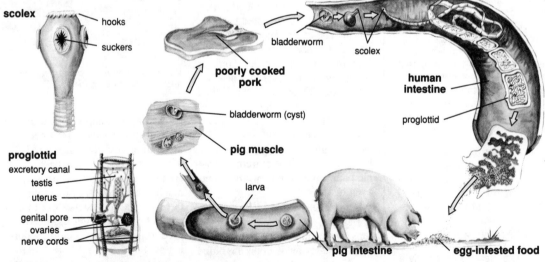

14C-7 *Life cycle and structures of the pork tapeworm*

the human can become the intermediate host, with the worms forming cysts in his muscles, eyes, brain, or other organs. Man can easily avoid tapeworm infection by thoroughly cooking meats which may contain the bladderworms and by practicing sanitary precautions.

Review Questions 14C-2

1. What are the four primary structural differences between a free-living flatworm and a parasitic flatworm?
2. Describe the life cycle of the sheep liver fluke. Why would removing snails from an area help to control these parasites?
3. Describe an adult tapeworm.
4. Outline the life cycle of the pork tapeworm.

Facet 14C-1: Parasitic Worms in Humans, pages 350-51

1. Describe the three flatworms other than the pork tapeworm that infect humans.
2. Describe the life history of the hookworm.
3. Describe the life history of the trichina worm.
4. Describe a leech.

Nematoda: The Roundworms

Members of the **phylum Nematoda*** (NEM uh TOH duh), the roundworms, are tiny, cylindrical worms usually less than 2.5 cm (1 in.) long. But what the **roundworms** lack in size, they more than make up for in sheer numbers. Although often not visible, these tiny animals inhabit virtually every environment and every living thing. Roundworms may be found in a shovel full of dirt, an oak tree, or a human.

Not only do these worms exist in great numbers, they also live in places where other animals would not. Roundworms thrive in the frozen arctic tundra, the heat of hot springs, the heights of mountaintops, and the pressurized depths of the ocean floor. To survive in these environments, roundworms endure extreme environmental conditions. For example, the *vinegar eel,* a roundworm found in vinegar, thrives in an acidic environment that would kill most other forms of life. Other roundworms can survive in areas of drought or famine. The range and durability of these animals is virtually unmatched elsewhere in the kingdom Animalia.

The roundworms are characterized not only by the enormous range of their living environment but also by the unique *specificity* of some environments in which they live. Certain worms live only in particular places. This characteristic "choosiness" is exemplified by many parasitic roundworms, which are highly selective even about where they live in a chosen host. A parasitic roundworm living in one part of a certain animal may not survive in another part of the same animal, or even in the same part of another animal. For this reason we need not fear most parasitic roundworms, for many simply have no taste for man.

A typical roundworm: *Ascaris*

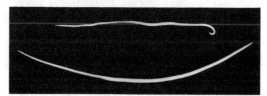

14C-8 *The Ascaris male has the hook; female is larger.*

Ascaris (AS kuh ris), an intestinal roundworm, is a good general representative of the phylum Nematoda. *Ascaris* is one of the larger parasitic roundworms, reaching 30 cm (12 in.) in length. It has an elongated, cylindrical body that tapers to a point at both ends. The body's structure is basically a tube within a tube. The outer tube consists of the *epidermis* and a thick, noncellular *cuticle* secreted by the epidermis. The cuticle contains fibers that give the roundworm support and protection from the host's digestive enzymes.

Nematoda: nemat- (thread) + -oda or -ode (Gk. ODES, of the nature of)

Within the outer tube is another tube, the *digestive canal,* that extends the length of the worm and has an anterior and a posterior opening. The posterior opening, the **anus,** permits the egestion of indigestible materials without interrupting food intake at the mouth. *Ascaris* is supported primarily by the organs and fluid that fill the space between the two tubes.

In contrast to the smooth, gliding movement of the flatworm, *Ascaris* moves by a frantic, thrashing motion. *Ascaris* possesses only longitudinal muscles which are arranged in four bands along the animal's length. Muscle contraction in only one direction and the stiffness of its cuticle determine this roundworm's type of movement.

Ascaris feeds upon the digested food matter found in its host's intestine. The animal sucks food into its digestive tube through a long, nonmuscular *intestine.* The intestine absorbs digested materials and eliminates unuseable substances through the anus.

Having no organs or systems, this roundworm accomplishes respiration and circulation on the cellular level, aided by the fluid that fills the space between the worm's digestive tube and outer body wall. Digested food from the intestine and respiratory gases from the epidermis diffuse into this fluid, which is kept circulating by the worm's movements. Two *lateral excretory canals* running the length of the animal excrete its wastes: these canals empty through a single *excretory pore* just below the mouth.

The nervous system of *Ascaris* consists of a ring of nervous tissue around the pharynx and two long nerve cords extending from the ring down the animal's dorsal and ventral sides. The roundworm's sensory apparatus is concentrated around the mouth. Roundworms may also have chemical receptors along their sides.

Reproductive processes in *Ascaris*

Ascaris, like most roundworms, reproduces only sexually, not being hermaphroditic. The female *Ascaris* is larger than the male. The primary male reproductive organ is a single, long, coiled tubule, the *testis.* The female possesses a pair of coiled tubules called the *ovaries.*

After mating, the female *Ascaris* within the human host's intestine begins producing eggs at a rate of up to 200,000 eggs per day. The eggs are egested daily with the host's feces. If a human swallows these eggs, they hatch into tiny larvas that burrow through the intestinal wall. The blood carries these young, extremely small roundworms to the lungs. They penetrate the lungs and migrate up the air passage to the throat, where they are swallowed. Once back in the digestive tract, the worms mature and settle in the intestines, mate, and begin producing more eggs.

The adult intestinal roundworm usually poses little threat to an otherwise healthy host. But when the *Ascaris* population in a host gets too large, they may completely clog the intestine or migrate to other organs such as the liver, where they can cause serious damage.

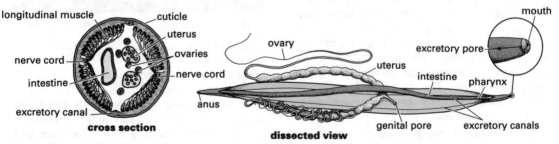

cross section

dissected view

Review Questions 14C-3

1. Give a general description of the organisms in the phylum Nematoda.
2. List the nine life processes of animals and briefly tell how *Ascaris* accomplishes each of these processes. Where possible, include structure names.

Annelida: The Segmented Worms

"Little rings," a literal translation of **Annelida,** reveals the most outstanding characteristic of this phylum: the bodies of annelids are divided into similar rings or segments. This *segmentation* is not limited to external appearance but extends into the internal organs and systems of the worm. Internally, each segment of an annelid's body is separated by a thin membrane, the **septum** (pl., *septa).* Most annelids inhabit salt water, but freshwater and terrestrial species are not uncommon.

The earthworm

Often seen on sidewalks after a long rain, these red-brown inhabitants of almost every moist soil in the world are the most familiar of the annelids. Obvious features of the earthworm include its segments and the **clitellum*** (klye TEL um), a barrel-shaped swelling usually covering segments 32 through 37; segments are numbered from the anterior to the posterior end. The clitellum is used in reproduction and helps to identify the worm's anterior end. From outward appearances, the earthworm has no distinct head, although its anterior end is more pointed and is usually darker. A small mouth beneath a liplike *prostomium** (proh STOH mee um) is at the anterior tip of the earthworm. The *anus* is at the posterior tip.

Along the worm's ventral and lateral surfaces are **setae*** (SEE TEE), tiny bristles, four pairs to each segment, which can be retracted into the worm's body. The earthworm moves by means of its setae and two muscle layers—one a *circular layer* that makes the worm longer and thinner when contracted and the other a *longitudinal layer* that contracts to make the worm shorter and thicker. To move forward, the worm contracts the circular muscles, lengthening the anterior portion of its body. Next the setae anchor the anterior end while the longitudinal muscle layer contracts, drawing the posterior end forward. The setae then anchor the posterior end of the worm as it re-extends its anterior end. When on the surface or tunneling through loose earth, the earthworm uses this method to push itself along. If the soil is firmer, the worm will tunnel by literally eating its way through it.

Nutrition of the earthworm

The earthworm feeds upon vegetation, refuse, and decayed animal matter in the soil. It draws soil containing these substances into its mouth with its muscular, sucking *pharynx.* The food-laden soil is passed down the **esophagus*** (ih SAHF uh gus) to the **crop,** where it is stored temporarily, then passed to the **gizzard.** The gizzard's muscular contractions grind food against the ingested soil and break the food up into small pieces.

The actual process of digestion occurs in the *intestine,* where the food is broken down by digestive enzymes. Earthworms, like most other annelids, have a straight tubular digestive tract. The indigestible materials that the worm has consumed are passed down the intestine and expelled through the anus. These solid wastes are called *casts.* The digested food is absorbed by the blood

---

clitellum: (L. CLITELLAE, packsaddle or saddlebag)

prostomium: pro- (before) + stomium (Gk. STOMA, mouth)

setae: (L. SETAE, bristles)

esophagus: (Gk. OISOPHAGOS, gullet)

circulating through the walls of the intestinal tract and transported to all parts of the worm.

Earthworm circulation, respiration, and excretion

The earthworm's size and complexity demand that it have some means of transporting vital substances such as food and oxygen to all the cells of its body. This need is met by a **closed circulatory system.** The system involves a series of vessels containing *blood.* The blood absorbs nutrients and oxygen from the digestive and respiratory structures and then discharges these substances into the tissues of the body. The circulatory system is closed; that is, the blood remains in the blood vessels throughout the entire cycle.

The major vessels of this system are the *dorsal blood vessel,* which pumps the blood toward the anterior end of the animal, and the *ventral blood vessel,* which carries blood toward the posterior end. Many small vessels connect these major vessels to the body wall, the internal organs, and to each other. In the region of the esophagus, the two major vessels are joined by five pairs of thickly muscled vessels called *aortic* (ay OR tik) *arches.* These arches help to regulate blood pressure.

Respiration is closely linked to circulation. The earthworm's thin epidermis is the site for the exchange of gases. Tiny vessels bring the blood close to the body surface. Here carbon dioxide diffuses out of the blood, and oxygen is absorbed into the blood. The blood then carries the oxygen to all the animal's tissues. The epidermis is covered with a thin, protective *cuticle* which must be kept moist to permit the passage of oxygen through it.

During heavy rains, the earthworm is in danger of suffocating. Though the worm can obtain dissolved oxygen from water, the rainwater that filters through the soil filling its burrow has lost most of its oxygen. To escape suffocation, the earthworm often surfaces during a rain and then faces the dangers of hungry birds and man's feet.

To excrete metabolic wastes, the worm has a pair of tubelike **nephridia*** (neh FRID ee uh) in each body segment except the first three and the last. These organs filter wastes from the blood and expel them through small openings on the animal's side.

Earthworm nervous and reproductive systems

The major structure of the earthworm's nervous system is its "brain," which is actually a pair of **ganglia** (GANG glee uh) (sing., **ganglion),** a mass of nervous tissue. These ganglia above the pharynx are joined by two nerves to another ganglion below the pharynx. A double *ventral nerve cord* extends from the large ganglion to the end of the worm. Along this cord are smaller ganglia, one for each segment of the earthworm. Nerves leading to the muscles and sensory structures of each segment branch from these ganglia.

Earthworms are sensitive to light, touch, and certain chemicals. Their sensory cells are not grouped into large sense organs but are distributed over the animal's entire body. The anterior and posterior ends of the worm have high concentrations of sensory cells.

14C-10 *Structures in an earthworm*

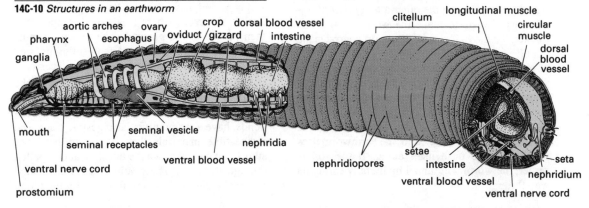

nephridia: nephr- or nephro- (Gk. NEPHROS, kidney)

Other Segmented Worms

Not all segmented worms live timidly in holes in the ground, feeding upon soil, as the earthworm does. Segmented worms live in a variety of habitats and feed in many unique ways. Some are parasites that feed only every few months; others are voracious predators; still others passively nibble on whatever passes their way.

The *clam worm,* which frequents the seashore at low tide, is a commonly studied annelid that preys upon small animals and other worms. Unlike the earthworm, the clam worm has a definite head with sense organs and two rows of fleshy appendages along its body. To catch its prey, the worm extends its pharynx and retracts it back into its mouth, drawing the prey with it.

The *feather worm* constructs a sturdy tube to live in and feeds by sliding its head out of the tube. The worm's head has several rings of long tentacles covered with a mucus to entrap food particles. When food clings to the tentacles, cilia direct it to the animal's mouth. The spray of feeding tentacles at the end of the body tube gives the animal its feather-duster appearance. When threatened, it quickly pulls its elaborate feeding apparatus into the safety of the tube.

The normal mode of earthworm reproduction is sexual, although certain species of earthworms, when cut in two, can produce complete adults by regeneration. Not all segmented worms, however, have the ability to regenerate.

The earthworm is *hermaphroditic* with male and female sex organs located in separate segments. The earthworm's male organs are two pairs of *testes* located in segments 10 and 11. Sperm from its own testes are stored in *seminal* vesicles* until mating; seminal receptacles in segments 9 and 10 store sperm received from its mating partner. The worm's female organs are a pair of *ovaries* in segment 13. The eggs discharged by the ovaries are collected in the tubular *oviducts* in preparation for mating.

In sexual reproduction two worms must exchange sperm. While pointing in opposite directions, the worms join the ventral surfaces of their anterior ends. A *slime tube* secreted by both worms holds them together. The sperm released from the seminal vesicles leave the worm through the *sperm ducts* on segment 15, travel along a groove on the worm's body, and enter the seminal receptacles of the other worm. After exchanging sperm, they separate.

A few days later a *cocoon* forms around the clitellum of each worm. The worm then backs out of the cocoon. As the cocoon passes over the openings of the oviducts, eggs are released. Then the seminal receptacles release the sperm obtained from the other worm. After the worm has pulled out of the cocoon, the ends of the cocoon seal, and fertilization occurs. In 2-3 weeks a young earthworm emerges from the cocoon.

Some earthworms live to be several years old. To survive the freezing winter, they burrow beneath the level at which the soil freezes and congregate in large masses. Their combined metabolism generates the warmth necessary to keep them alive during dormancy.

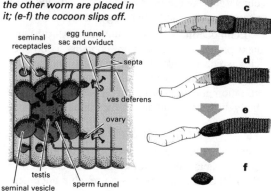

14C-11 *Dorsal view of earthworm's reproductive structures (below) and the reproductive process (right): (a) exchange of sperm in slime tube; (b) cocoon formed around clitellum; (c) worm backs out of slime tube and cocoon; (d) cocoon passes the reproductive organs, and ova of this worm and sperm from the other worm are placed in it; (e-f) the cocoon slips off.*

seminal receptacles

egg funnel, sac and oviduct

septa

vas deferens

ovary

testis

seminal vesicle

sperm funnel

seminal: semin- or semen-
(L. SEMEN, seed)

Biological Terms

cephalization	flame cell	*Nematoda:*	clitellum
Platyhelminthes:	hermaphroditic	*(The Roundworms)*	setae (sing., seta)
(The Flatworms)	parasite	phylum Nematoda	esophagus
phylum Platyhelminthes	tegument	roundworm	crop
flatworm	sucker	anus	gizzard
planarian	fluke	*Annelida:*	closed circulatory system
mesoderm	tapeworm	*(The Segmented Worms)*	nephridia
pharynx	scolex	Annelida	ganglion (pl., ganglia)
intestine	proglottid	septum (pl., septa)	

Review Questions 14C-4

1. Describe segmentation.
2. List the nine life processes of animals and briefly tell how an earthworm accomplishes each. Where possible, include structure names.
3. Describe two annelids other than the earthworm.

Thought Questions

1. Most evolutionists claim that parasitic flatworms evolved *after* their vertebrate hosts. Explain why this would be devolution and not evolution.
2. What are the problems with the view that man would be healthier if he practiced Jewish dietary law?
3. In the animals hydra, sponge, planarian, tapeworm, *Ascaris,* and earthworm, compare the following: a) nervous systems and responses; b) circulation; c) asexual reproduction; and d) sexual reproduction.

14D-Other Invertebrates

Based on numbers, the largest animal phylum is Arthropoda with 891,000 species of insects, crabs, lobsters, and spiders. The next largest phylum, *Mollusca* (muh LUS kuh), has 45,000 species of snails, slugs, clams, and octopuses. Mollusks may seem like strange, secretive animals with no direct relation to humans, but they are our largest source of invertebrate food, and their sheer numbers make them significant.

Echinodermata (ih KYE nuh dur MAH tuh), the next phylum in this section, contains 5,500 species which include starfish, seafans, and sea urchins. The members of this small phylum are common inhabitants of the seashore, and their body structure is unique in the animal kingdom.

Phylum Mollusca

Centuries ago, mariners lived in fear of enormous sea monsters with snakelike arms that could crush the hull of a ship. There is no reliable documentation of ships being mangled by such creatures, but, on the other hand, these tentacled monsters were no myth. These were very large mollusks commonly called "monsters" and "devilfish," in contrast to other mollusks which are small, quiet animals. The **phylum Mollusca*** includes octopuses, oysters, snails, slugs, squids, and clams.

Apparently an extremely varied group, mollusks share most of the following characteristics:
❑ **Mantle:** a sheath of tissue that encloses the vital organs of the mollusk, secretes its shell, and forms its respiratory apparatus;
❑ **Shell:** the tough, multilayered structure secreted by the mantle as a means of protection or body support;
❑ **Visceral*** (VIS ur ul) **hump:** the part of the mollusk's body that contains its heart, digestive, and excretory organs, often covered by the mantle;

Mollusca: (L. MOLLIS, soft) **visceral:** (L. VISCUS, body organ)

❏ **Foot:** a fleshy, muscular organ that is used for locomotion and assumes a variety of forms, depending on the animal;

❏ **Radula*** (RAHJ oo luh): a small organ covered with many tiny teeth that scrapes up food particles and draws them into the mollusk's mouth.

Phylum Mollusca is divided into six classes based on the shape and type of shell and the kind of foot. The three classes presented in this section are Bivalva (the *two-shelled* mollusks), Gastropoda (the *stomach-footed* mollusks), and Cephalopoda (the *head-footed* mollusks).

Class Bivalva: two-shelled mollusks

The **class Bivalva** comprises over 7,000 species, including clams, oysters, mussels, and scallops. The clam, a typical animal of this class, has a soft, flattened, oval-shaped body encased in a two-piece shell. Each half of the clam's shell is called a **valve,** hence the class name Bivalva, meaning "two-shelled."

The valves are secreted by the mantle and are composed of the following three layers: the thin, protective *horny outer layer;* the center, thick *prismatic layer;* and the innermost, smooth *pearly layer*. The two-piece shell, which enlarges as the animal grows, protects it not only from exterior attack by predators but also from interior irritation. If a grain of sand or a parasite slips between the valves and is caught between the mantle and the shell, the mantle will cover the foreign object with a secreted material identical to that in the pearly layer. The result is a pearl.

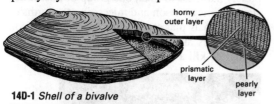

14D-1 *Shell of a bivalve*

The *foot* is the clam's organ for locomotion and burrowing. The animal extends the foot between its valves into the sand. The end of the foot is enlarged into a hatchet-shaped anchor. Then the clam contracts its foot muscles, and the shell is dragged toward the foot deeper into the sand.

14D-2 *Clams*

Life processes of the clam

Clams are called *filter feeders* because they feed on the organic materials they strain from the water. The clam circulates water over its body through two tubes or **siphons.** The **incurrent siphon** brings water into the animal; the **excurrent siphon** carries water out of the animal. Bivalves lack a radula. As food particles in the water enter the clam, they are trapped in stringy, sticky *mucus*

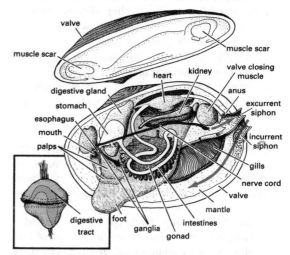

14D-3 *Structures of a clam and a trochophore (inset)*

secreted by the gills and by the *palps,* a pair of lobelike organs which surround the clam's mouth. Cilia on these structures move the mucus and food into the animal's mouth. The food passes through the stomach and is digested in the *digestive gland*. Indigestible materials pass into a looped intestine and are expelled through the *anus* near the excurrent siphon.

Respiration is accomplished with two pairs of **gills.** The gills are thin-walled structures richly supplied with blood vessels. Cilia on the gill surfaces sweep water containing food and oxygen into the animal. The water flows through the gills

radula: (L. RADERE, to scrape)

14D-4 *A scallop, which is a bivalve, has tiny eyes on individual stalks.*

where oxygen and carbon dioxide are exchanged within the bloodstream. An open circulatory system consisting of colorless blood, a pumping heart, and a few blood vessels distributes oxygen and digested food. A *kidney* filters wastes from the blood.

The clam's nervous system consists of three major *ganglia* joined by nerves and various sense organs, such as balance receptors in the foot, sensors around the incurrent siphon to detect various substances in the water, and light and touch receptors around the mantle's edge.

The life cycle of the clam involves sexual reproduction and larval stages. Many mollusks have a ciliated larval form called the **trochophore** (TRAHK uh FOHR) in their life cycles. The trochophore larva is a key characteristic used to identify members of the phylum Mollusca.

Class Gastropoda: the stomach-footed mollusks

The **class Gastropoda** (gas TRAHP uh duh) includes the snails, slugs, and nudibranches. These animals can be found on the land and in fresh or salt water. The snail best illustrates the class's major characteristics. Its *foot* is located immediately below the *visceral hump,* the portion of the mollusk's body containing the stomach. The snail is therefore "stomach-footed." The snail moves by laying down a thin layer of slime on which it glides by rhythmical contractions of its muscular foot. This activity enables the snail to achieve speeds of about 3 m (10 ft.) per hour.

The snail is a *univalve,* meaning it has a single shell that serves as its protective home. When the environment or predators threaten, the head and foot of the snail can contract into its shell that, in many snails, is then closed with a special "door."

The snail grazes upon plant material, using its tonguelike *radula* to grate and ingest it. The food is broken down in a coiled digestive tract, and indigestible material is expelled at the *anus* above

the mouth. The strange position of the anus is the result of *torsion,* the twisted asymmetrical body arrangement unique to gastropods, produced by uneven growth in certain of the snail's muscles.

The **mantle cavity,** the space between the mantle lining, the shell, and the animal's soft body, is thickly supplied with blood vessels, and functions as a lung in respiration. A series of *ganglia* around the head region constitutes this mollusk's "brain." The snail's sense organs include a pair of eyes set at the ends of two bobbing, telescoping *tentacles.* Other receptors for smell, touch, and some chemicals are located in the head and foot.

14D-5 *Structures of a snail*

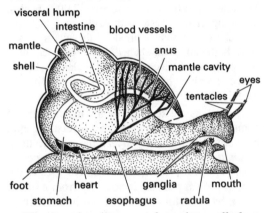

The size of snails ranges from the small plant-eating but destructive *garden snail* to the giant *Australian trumpet,* a sea snail with a shell almost 0.6 m (2 ft.) long. Although most snails are completely harmless to man, one group of Pacific sea snails forms a poison and injects it into worms or small animals that serve as its food. This poison immobilizes and kills the prey and is powerful enough to kill a human.

14D-6 *Gélapagos conch*

Other Gastropods: Slugs and Nudibranches

Not all gastropods are exactly like the snail. The slugs and nudibranches, for example, lack an obvious shell. The *slug* is a terrestrial gastropod and harmful garden pest that looks like a homeless snail. Like the snail, the slug glides on a slime trail. The protective quality of this slime is demonstrated by the slug's ability to crawl over the edge of a razor blade unharmed.

The *nudibranch* (NOO duh BRAHNK), the marine equivalent to the slug, is one of the most beautiful and graceful of the sea creatures. The edges of its shell-less body may be delicately laced or covered with brightly colored tentacles. Some nudibranches that eat sea anemones incorporate the cnidarian's colors and nematocysts into their own bodies. Using gentle wavelike undulations of its body, the nudibranch swims gracefully.

Class Cephalopoda: the head-footed mollusks

Class Cephalopoda (SEF uh LAHP uh duh) includes the "sea monsters" such as the squid and octopus, as well as the less fearsome nautilus and cuttlefish. The foot of the *cephalopod* extends from the animal's head region (thus its descriptive name). The foot is usually divided into a number of sucker-bearing arms which are used to catch food (not to dismantle ships or strangle divers).

The cephalopods live active lives in the open sea. They possess special defense mechanisms, enabling them to survive in this dangerous environment. For example, most cephalopods have pigment cells that enable them to change colors to blend with the environment. Also, when threatened by predators, most cephalopods can squirt a dense black, inky fluid into the water to confuse their attackers.

The *squid* is a torpedo-shaped cephalopod with a rodlike internal shell that gives it shape and support. The large eyes of this mollusk are much like mammalian eyes and are capable of very accurate vision. The giant squid is the largest known invertebrate, reaching over 15 m (49 ft.) in length.

The *octopus** is a familiar mollusk "monster." This cephalopod has eight heavily suckered arms, which it can use to drag itself along the sea floor. When it needs to move rapidly, the octopus can "jet" backwards through the water like a squid by forcing water out of its siphon. Unlike the fictional man-killer of adventure stories, the octopus is extremely timid and usually avoids man.

The *nautilus** lives in a large, external shell. This shell is a series of chambers, each of which the mollusk once occupied but outgrew. The animal simply adds a larger chamber to its shell when it needs more living space.

14D-7 *An octopus*

Review Questions 14D-1

1. What characteristics do all mollusks share that separate this phylum from other phyla in the kingdom Animalia?
2. Describe the valve of a clam.
3. List the nine life processes of animals and briefly tell how a clam accomplishes each.
4. Describe the locomotion of bivalves.
5. How do gastropods differ from bivalves?
6. How do cephalopods differ from (a) bivalves and (b) gastropods?

---

octopus: octo- (Gk. OKTO, eight) + -pus (foot)

nautilus: (Gk. NAUTILOS, sailor)

Phylum Echinodermata

The **phylum Echinodermata** includes marine animals ranging from the prickly sea urchin to the most familiar echinoderm, the starfish. This radially symmetrical animal has five or more arms tapering gradually from a *central disc*. Its shape and support are maintained by a system of small, hard plates joined by connective tissue beneath the epidermis. These plates have spines which give the starfish its characteristic rough, spiny appearance.

Life processes in starfish

The starfish shares with all the echinoderms a unique **water-vascular system**—a series of canals and tubules for locomotion and food capture. The most obvious parts of the system are the hundreds of **tube feet** in the deep grooves along the lower surface of the echinoderm's **rays** (arms). These hollow feet are joined by a water canal that extends along the starfish ray to the *ring canal* within the central disc. The water-vascular system opens at the *sieve plate* on the dorsal surface of the animal. This system is used to vary the water pressure in the tube feet. Thus, the foot can, by suction, grip an object or release it. The animal can then slide along the ocean bottom or cling securely to rocks.

Some starfish also use their tube feet to pry open the shells of their favorite food—clams and oysters. By applying steady pressure with these feet upon the mollusk's shell and by working the tube feet in shifts, the starfish can fatigue the mollusk's muscles and open its shell. Once it has opened the shell, the starfish protrudes its stomach through its mouth (located in the center of its lower surface) and into the shell of the prey. The everted* stomach secretes enzymes to reduce the soft parts of the clam or oyster to a soupy broth and then absorbs this material and transports it to highly branched *digestive glands* for digestion to be completed.

Respiration and excretion in the starfish occur between the *coelom** (SEE lum), the body cavity, and the environment. The fluids of this internal cavity are brought close to the environment through a number of small, fingerlike projections on the surface of the animal called *skin gills*. Gases easily exchange through these thin-walled extensions of the coelom.

The skin gills are also important excretory organs because many wastes diffuse out of the body directly through them. Also, cells called *amebocytes* move through the fluid of the coelom and gather other waste materials. Once laden with this metabolic waste, the cells penetrate the walls of the gills and escape into the environment, taking the wastes with them.

In starfish, like most echinoderms, the sexes are separate and fertilization is external. To reproduce sexually, they expel eggs and sperm into the water, where these gametes unite. After fertilization, the zygote develops into a ciliated, bilaterally symmetrical larva. The larva eventually settles to the sea floor and becomes a radially symmetrical adult.

Starfish, like all echinoderms, have remarkable powers of regeneration. If a starfish is dismem-

14D-8 *Structures of a starfish*

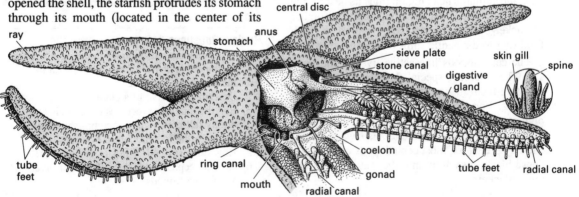

---

everted: e- (out) + -verted (to turn)   **coelom:** (Gk. KOILOMA, cavity)

bered, a single ray can grow into a complete adult if it has even a small portion of the central disc attached to it.

Though the slow-moving starfish may appear to be a relatively harmless creature, it often is not. One starfish can eat a dozen clams and oysters a day. Indeed, a few starfish can practically destroy a commercial shellfish bed in a short time. Starfish can also severely damage other forms of sea life. The *crown of thorns starfish,* a spiny, poisonous echinoderm, has done tremendous damage to many coral reefs by eating large quantities of the young coral polyps. Biologists have not been too successful in controlling these animals.

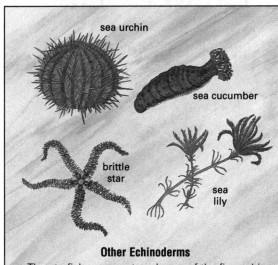

sea urchin

sea cucumber

brittle star

sea lily

Other Echinoderms

The starfish represents only one of the five echinoderm classes. The other classes are represented by these four organisms:

❑ The *sea urchin* has been called the "porcupine of the sea." This globular animal has long, pointed spines and equally long tube feet in rows over its body. Sea urchins are scavengers, eating almost any organic material. Their spiny body protects them from most predators but not from the damsel fish. This fish patiently bites off the urchin's spines and then eats the helpless animal.

❑ The *sea cucumber* is a slow-moving, sac-shaped echinoderm that feeds upon the organic materials it traps in its sticky, feathery tentacles. Its only defense from predators is self-mutilation: when attacked, this echinoderm will jettison some of its internal organs. This meal often appeases the attacker, while the sea cucumber retreats and regenerates a new set of organs.

❑ The *brittle star* resembles the starfish but has thin, tentaclelike arms. The star moves by the snakelike action of its arms. This echinoderm is called "brittle" because it readily discards its arms when attacked or disturbed.

❑ The *sea lily,* a plantlike echinoderm, spends its adult life fixed to the ocean floor by a long stalk. This sessile animal feeds on the minute food particles that its ciliated arms direct to its mouth.

Biological Terms

Phylum Mollusca	foot	incurrent siphon	mantle cavity	tube feet
phylum Mollusca	radula	excurrent siphon	class Cephalopoda	ray
mantle	class Bivalva	gill	*Phylum Echinodermata*	
shell	valve	trochophore	phylum Echinodermata	
visceral hump	siphon	class Gastropoda	water-vascular system	

Review Questions 14D-2

1. Describe the water-vascular system. How does it help the starfish obtain food?
2. What characteristics distinguish echinoderms from other invertebrates?
3. List three examples of the phylum Echinodermata other than the starfish.
4. List the nine life processes of animals, and briefly tell how a starfish accomplishes each. Where possible, include structure names.

Thought Questions

1. Trace a particle of food through the digestive system of (a) a planarian, (b) an *Ascaris,* (c) an earthworm, (d) a clam, and (e) a starfish.
2. Describe how cellular waste would be excreted by (a) a planarian, (b) an earthworm, (c) a clam, and (d) a starfish.

THE ARTHROPODS
ZOOLOGY PART II

FIFTEEN

15A–Introduction to Arthropods

The **phylum Arthropoda*** (ar THRAH poh duh), which includes lobsters, spiders, scorpions, millipedes, and insects, encompasses over 891,000 species. Arthropods live virtually everywhere. We cannot ignore their influence upon man and the environment. They can destroy crops, compete with other animals for food, and transmit deadly diseases. They also produce such valuable things as wax, honey, drugs, and silk. Moreover, they help maintain plants and crops by assisting cross-fertilization, and some even help to control the numbers of harmful arthropods.

Characteristics of arthropods
Despite the diversity in this phylum, arthropods possess many common characteristics.

• *The exoskeleton* The most obvious characteristic of an arthropod is its **exoskeleton.** The exoskeleton is a nonliving body covering–a ''suit of armor''–secreted by the epidermis. **Chitin,**

Arthropoda: Arthro-
(Gk. ARTHRON, joint) + -pod or -ped
(foot)

(KYTE in) a chemical component of the exoskeleton, gives the body covering toughness and flexibility. On the other hand, mineral salts in the exoskeleton protect the animal from harsh chemicals in its environment and from the attacks of predators. The exoskeleton also supports the arthropod's body. Unlike a human's internal skeleton, an arthropod skeleton is worn externally.

This system limits the arthropods. The weight of this armored body covering limits to some extent the size of the animal. As long as the arthropod is small, it has sufficient muscle power to move the exoskeleton easily, but if it were to get very large, the total weight of an exoskeleton necessary to support it on land would make it difficult for the animal to move. Most large arthropods, such as the Japanese crab, which can have a span of 4 m (13 ft.) between its claws, are aquatic. No known living insect has a measurement greater than 28 cm (11 in.).

15A-1 *Cross section of an arthropod molting*

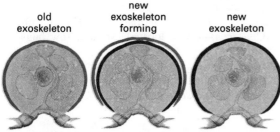

old exoskeleton   new exoskeleton forming   new exoskeleton

The exoskeleton also poses an obstacle to body growth. Because it is nonliving and cannot grow, the arthropod must periodically **molt** (shed the covering) in order to grow. To molt, the arthropod produces enzymes that eat away at the inside of the old exoskeleton while a new exoskeleton is produced beneath it. Some arthropods then take in water and air to swell and rupture the old shell; others merely wiggle out. Once free of its old exoskeleton, an arthropod may go into seclusion until its new, expanded exoskeleton hardens.

• *Jointed appendages* The term *arthropoda* means ''joint-footed'' and describes the appendages of this animal group. Although arthropods, vertebrates, and man all have jointed limbs, the structure of arthropod limbs is unique. The joints

of a man's arm or leg lie between internal bones that are covered with muscles. The muscles of the arthropod, however, move the limbs from within its exoskeleton.

Appendages on arthropods come in a variety of forms and functions. The delicate limbs of the spider and the powerful jumping legs of the grasshopper are used for locomotion. The ''fangs'' of the centipede enable it to capture its food. Appendages may also be a means of defense: crabs and lobsters bear formidable claws for that purpose. Some jointed appendages (like antennas) are for sensory reception, some for chewing food, and others for sexual reproduction.

• *Body segmentation* The body of the typical arthropod is divided into three major segments: the **head,** the **thorax** (these two are often united into a **cephalothorax*** [SEF uh luh THOHR aks]), and the **abdomen.** Further segmentation may occur within these major divisions. Certain members of this phylum have body segments designed for specific functions. The scorpion, for example, has abdominal segments that form a ''tail'' which arches over its back. The abdominal segment at the end of the tail is a poisonous stinger that the animal uses to protect itself and to immobilize its prey.

• *An open circulatory system with a dorsal heart* The circulatory system of the arthropod does not limit its blood to blood vessels. Instead, the *dorsal heart* pumps blood through short vessels that empty into cavities within its body and bathe its organs. The **open circulatory system** is not as efficient as the closed circulatory system because it depends in part on gravity for its operation.

15A-2 *Cross section of an arthropod*

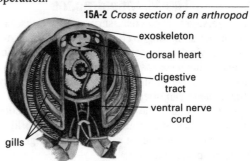

exoskeleton

dorsal heart

digestive tract

ventral nerve cord

gills

---

cephalothorax: cephalo- (head) + -thorax (Gk. THORAX, breastplate)

• *A ventral nervous system* The arthropod nervous system consists of a ''brain'' (a pair of *ganglia*) centered over the esophagus and joined by two major nerves to a ganglion below the esophagus, and a *ventral nerve cord.* The ventral position of the nervous system places the vital nervous pathways of the arthropod in a place of maximum safety: the ventral nerve cord is protected not only by the hard exoskeleton but also by the bulk of the body of the animal. This ventral position also places the nervous system near the appendages, the structures most often requiring nervous commands and coordination.

The nervous system receives sensory information through a variety of organs. **Antennas,** appendages in the head region, provide taste, smell, and touch sensation to most arthropods. Many arthropods bear sensory bristles scattered over their bodies.

Virtually all arthropods have some type of eyes. **Compound eyes** (in most insects and malacostrans) contain thousands of individual lenses. These lenses are each set at a slightly different angle, giving the arthropod a mosaic image of the world. Some compound arthropod eyes see size, shape, and movement, and a few sense color. **Simple eyes,** like those of the spider, contain only one lens and present a very limited view. The image seen through some simple eyes would be

15A-3 *Simulation of what scientists believe a compound eye would see (left)*

much like the view you would see looking through a straw. Some simple eyes produce a poor image, and some respond only to the presence or absence of light. Some arthropods seem to be able to sense ultraviolet light with their eyes.

Classification of arthropods

Within the framework of the characteristics of the phylum Arthropoda are five major classes. The primary characteristics that separate the groups are body divisions, number and kinds of appendages, and means of respiration.

❑ *Class Malacostraca* (mal uh KAHS tru kuh) (Crustacea) – crabs, lobsters, shrimp, sow bugs, barnacles

❑ *Class Arachnida* – spiders and scorpions

❑ *Class Diplopoda* – millipeds

❑ *Class Chilopoda* – centipeds

❑ *Class Insecta* – insects

Review Questions 15A-1

1. List the major characteristics that distinguish Arthropoda from the other phyla in kingdom Animalia.
2. List some advantages and disadvantages of an exoskeleton.

The Malacostracans

Lobsters, crabs, crayfish, shrimp, sow bugs, and barnacles all belong to **class Malacostraca** (Crustacea). Most malacostracans are free-living and aquatic; however, parasitic and terrestrial species exist. Because of its large size and availability, the malacostran often used for classroom study is the *crayfish,* or ''crawdad.'' The crayfish is common in lakes and streams around the world. It resembles the lobster, a sea dweller, though most lobster species are larger.

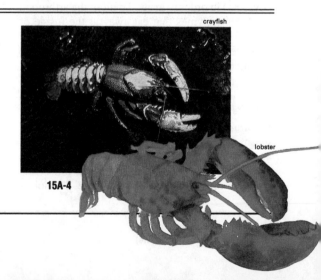

15A-4

Like all arthropods, the crayfish is covered with a tough exoskeleton composed of *chitin*. The exoskeleton is thick and immovable over most of the animal's body but thin and flexible at the joints. The body of the crayfish is divided into two major sections: the *cephalothorax,* which is covered by the *carapace* (KEHR uh PACE), a single exoskeletal plate; and the abdomen, which is composed of six segments, each covered by a set of plates.

Life processes of crayfish

Crayfish are scavengers, eating virtually any edible material. To feed, the mouthparts of the crayfish first reduce the food to swallowable size. The food passes through the *mouth* and a short *esophagus* into the anterior portion of the *stomach.* There it is ground into fine particles by the muscular action and *chitinous teeth* of the *gastric mill.*

In the posterior portion of the stomach the food is sorted: fine particles are directed to *digestive glands* where digestion is completed, and coarse particles are moved to the *intestine.* These coarse particles, along with indigestible residue from the digestive glands, are passed through the intestine and eliminated through the *anus,* which is in the last abdominal segment.

The respiratory apparatus of the crayfish consists of two sets of feathery *gills* found in two lateral *gill chambers* along the thorax region. These gills are covered by the lateral portions of

the carapace, leaving openings only along the animal's ventral surface. Some gills are attached to various appendages. Appendage movement and the second maxillae help to keep oxygenated water flowing over the gills. Blood traveling through the thin-walled gills releases carbon dioxide and absorbs oxygen. Many malacostracans can store water in their gill chambers in order to walk on land. In other words, on land they can "hold their water" like you "hold your breath" in the water.

The crayfish has an *open circulatory system.* Blood collects within the *pericardial** (PEHR ih KAR dee ul) *sinus,* the cavity surrounding the heart. The blood enters the dorsal heart through tiny openings. As the heart contracts, valves close the openings, preventing the blood from passing back to the sinus.

The blood is forced through a series of arteries that empty into spaces within the body cavity. Once the blood has drained through these spaces and bathed the organs, it collects in the large, ventral, *sternal* sinus.* The blood then passes through the gills, becomes oxygenated, and returns to the pericardial sinus by efferent* channels. As the blood circulates, waste materials are filtered out by the **green glands,** structures near the base of the antennas. The fluid waste is then excreted through a pore just anterior to the mouth.

15A-5 *Internal structures of a crayfish*

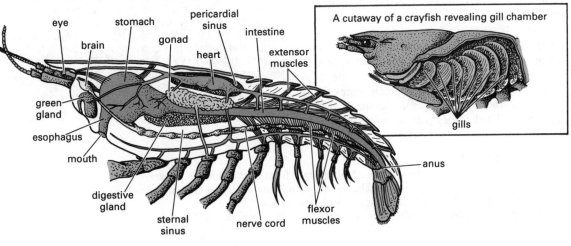

A cutaway of a crayfish revealing gill chamber

pericardial: peri- (Gk. PERI-, around) + -cardia- (KARDIA, heart)
sternal: stern- or sterno- (Gk. STERNON, breast or breastbone)

efferent: e-, ef-, or ex- (away from) + -fer or -ferent (to carry)

367

The ventral nervous system receives information about the environment from a number of sensory sources. The most obvious sensory organs of the crayfish are its compound eyes (which sit atop a pair of movable stalks), antennas, and **antennules.** Tiny bristles for touch are found on many of the appendages.

At the base of each antennule is a **statocyst*** (STAT uh SIST), the organ of balance. The statocysts, sacs lined with tiny sensory hairs, contain several grains of sand. As the animal's body tilts, the grains shift within the statocysts, stimulating particular sensory hairs. The impulses from the organs travel to the brain, and the crayfish then rights itself. When the crayfish molts, it loses the grains in its statocysts and must find replacements. Experimentally, scientists have given crayfish iron filings instead of sand. After the filings were within the statocysts, the scientists placed a magnet above the animal's back, causing the filings to rise to the top of the statocysts. The crayfish flipped on its back, remaining upside down as long as the magnet was in place.

Crayfish regeneration and reproduction

Though the crayfish cannot reproduce asexually, it is capable of regeneration. In arthropods, regeneration is a method of repair. When battling with predators, the crayfish may lose or deliberately discard a limb. This can be done without excessive blood loss thanks to a sealing double membrane in each limb. After the loss of a limb, the animal will gradually grow a new appendage to replace it.

Crayfish usually mate in the fall. During this season, the male transfers its sperm to special receptacles in the body of the female, using its reproductive swimmerets. The female stores the sperm until she lays her eggs in the spring. The eggs are fertilized as they pass out of the oviduct in slimy bunches. When the egg clusters are attached to the swimmerets to develop, the female is "in berry." Within 5-6 weeks the eggs hatch, releasing young that are miniature replicas of the adult. These young crayfish continue to cling to the mother for several weeks.

As the young crayfish grows, it seems trapped within its exoskeleton. The crayfish then begins molting. During its first year the crayfish will molt seven times. The animal molts about twice a year for the rest of its life (3-8 yr.).

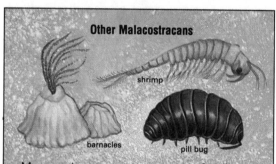

Other Malacostracans

shrimp

barnacles

pill bug

Many malacostracans are not as familiar as crabs, lobsters, and crayfish. Many children have played with the *pill bug,* or "roly-poly," the tiny animal that rolls into a ball when disturbed. The pill bug is a terrestrial malacostracan that keeps its gills moist by living in moist soil under rocks or logs.

The *barnacles* that encrust wharves and ship bottoms are another unusual type of malacostracan. Once thought to be mollusks, these sessile animals live in shell-like exoskeletons containing calcium and feed by sweeping food into their "shells" with jointed appendages. These animals will attach to virtually any underwater object, including live lobsters and whales' teeth. Their accumulation on ship hulls can become so great that the vessel must be dry-docked to remove them.

Review Questions 15A-2

1. What characteristics distinguish class Malacostraca from other arthropod classes?
2. List the nine life processes of animals, and briefly tell how a crayfish accomplishes each of these processes. Where possible, include structure names.
3. List three malacostracans other than the crayfish, and tell how they differ.

---

statocyst: stato- (standing) + -cyst (bladder or pouch)

The Arachnids

The **class Arachnida*** (uh RAK nih duh) encompasses animals such as spiders, scorpions, ticks, and mites. The arachnids are one of the most universally feared animal groups. Although some arachnids have painful stings and many transmit disease, most are completely harmless to man. Man's fear probably stems from an almost superstitious aversion to animals that live in dark places, attack with lightning speed, or feed by drinking the "blood" of their victims. Most arachnids, however, actually benefit man because they help control many harmful insects.

Many arachnids with their small, compact bodies and long, delicate limbs are often mistaken for insects. The arachnids, however, have several characteristics that distinguish them from the insects and other classes of this phylum:

- ❏ Four pairs of walking legs;
- ❏ Body divided into two major segments: cephalothorax and abdomen;
- ❏ No antennas or mandibles;
- ❏ Respiration by book lungs; and
- ❏ Usually four pairs of simple eyes.

Spiders

The spiders are the largest, most familiar group within the class Arachnida. They are cunning hunters and skillful architects. Spiders are also efficient predators, attacking and eating insects, small malacostracans, and even birds and fish.

In contrast to other arthropods, the spiders have no antennas. The spider does possess six pairs of appendages:
- ❏ One pair of **chelicerae** (kih LIS uh REE) armed with poisonous fangs used to paralyze prey;
- ❏ One pair of **pedipalps*** (PED uh PALPS) used for sensory reception and, in the male, for the transfer of sperm; and
- ❏ Four pairs of **walking legs** used for locomotion.

Although the means of capturing food vary, the method spiders use to eat the food does not. When the prey has been immobilized by a bite from the chelicerae, the spider injects digestive juices into the victim. The spider later sucks up the partially digested tissues of the prey, using a muscular stomach and pharynx. This food is then transported to the digestive gland in the abdomen of the spider where it is stored for future use. A few wolf spiders and tarantulas can consume the body of their victims as well as the fluids.

15A-6 *Internal structures of a spider*

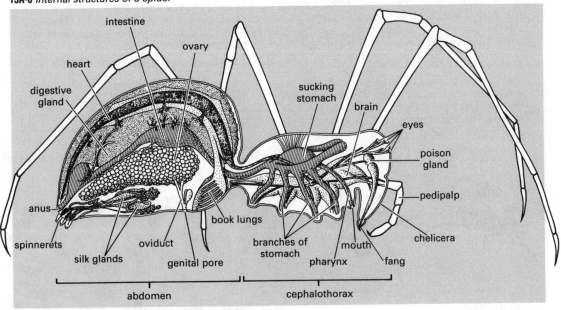

Arachnida: (Gk. ARAKHNE, spider)

pedipalps: ped- or pedi- (foot) + -palps (L. PALPUS, a touching)

Only arachnids have and use *book lungs* for respiration. Air enters the spider through a slit in the abdomen and flows between the pagelike folds of the book lung where oxygen and carbon dioxide are exchanged. Some spiders have **tracheae** (TRAY kee EE), minute tubules that transport oxygen directly to tissues.

The sexes are separate among spiders, with the female often larger than the male. The male places his sperm in a tiny web sac which he stores in special cavities of his pedipalps. The male will then transfer the sperm sac to the seminal receptacles on the ventral surface of the female's abdomen. This action is usually preceded by some courtship ritual such as the male's offering the female a gift of food.

In a few species the female will eat the male after mating. As the female lays her eggs, they are fertilized by the stored sperm. The eggs are usually placed within a silk cocoon which she attaches either to her body or to a web. When the young spiders hatch, they remain in the cocoon for several weeks.

Other Arachnids

The *scorpion,* an arachnid found in tropical countries and throughout much of the United States, has a long, segmented body bearing two outstanding features: a pair of pedipalps that are large pincers used to capture food and a segmented abdomen with a poisonous stinger in its last segment. The scorpion keeps its tail-like weapon coiled, ready to strike and immobilize an attacker or its prey. Like spiders, scorpions are feared by most of us although only a few species found in the United States can cause man any significant harm. Large scorpions can inflict very painful stings, and a few tropical varieties have killed men.

Dangerous Spiders

Most spiders produce a poisonous venom, but this venom is rarely harmful to man. Although some spiders in various parts of the world can inflict bites harmful to humans, in the United States only two spiders have dangerous bites.

❑ *The black widow* The female black widow has a shiny black body with a berry-shaped abdomen bearing the characteristic red "hourglass" marking on its underside. The male spider is small and harmless. The female's name "widow" implies that she eats the male after mating; however, this does not often occur. The black widow usually constructs its irregular web in dark, secluded places such as in cellars or under objects. The poison of the spider is a *neurotoxin,* affecting the nervous system and causing such symptoms as intense pain, muscle spasms, and vomiting. The bite is serious but rarely fatal.

❑ *The brown recluse* A small brown spider with a dark, violin-shaped marking on its cephalothorax, the brown recluse produces a poison that kills tissue around the bite. The bite of the brown recluse may be fatal. This spider is native to Missouri and Arkansas but is also found in other eastern states.

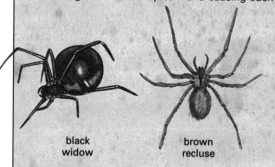

black
widow

brown
recluse

Tarantulas

The tarantula is a large, hairy spider of the American Southwest. Although this spider looks extremely frightening, it is actually good-natured and rarely bites. Its bite is no more dangerous to most people than the wasp's sting.

FACETS OF BIOLOGY

Spider Webs

In making a list of small wise things, Solomon, the wisest man who ever lived, ends his list with spiders: she "taketh hold with her hands, and is in king's palaces" (Prov. 30:24, 28). Spiders and their webs are found virtually everywhere, and anyone who has watched a spider spin her web has marveled at the wisdom of this eight-legged architect. Especially marvelous is the skill of these tiny creatures when you realize that they are virtually blind and have never been able to study any web before they go about building their own. The know-how to build the type of web characteristic of its species is inborn.

Those spiders that produce *silk* use it to make their webs for capturing food. Silk-producing spiders possess two or three pairs of **spinnerets,** small projections at the posterior of the abdomen. Silk glands produce a protein secretion that is forced through the spinnerets and that hardens into silk upon contact with the air. Though the silk may seem flimsy, it actually can stand more stress than a steel thread of equal size.

The primary purpose of the silk is to capture food. Usually the spider uses its silk to build a food-catching web. The web is made of two types of silk: a tough, non-sticky fiber that gives the web strength and structure, and a sticky, elastic fiber that snags and entangles the prey. After weaving its web, the spider usually waits patiently at the corner of its trap.

When an insect blunders into the web, the spider senses the vibrations and uses that information to determine the size and location of the captured prey. The spider approaches its victim, paralyzes it with a poisonous bite, and wraps the helpless prey in more silk.

Different species of spiders manufacture different webs, but most fit into one of four design categories.

❑ *Irregular webs* The tangles of silk in the corners of the cellar are cobwebs or *irregular webs* and have strands radiating in many directions.

❑ *Sheet webs* The *sheet web* as its name states, is a single plane of silk. The spider usually hangs on one side of the sheet. When an insect becomes trapped in the web, the spider bites it and pulls it through the web. The spider uses this sticky net not only as a tool for capturing prey but also as a defensive shield from predators.

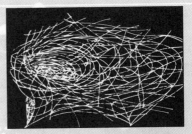

❑ *Funnel webs* The *funnel web* is a sheet web that forms a funnel at one end. The spider hides and then eats its prey in the small end of the funnel.

❑ *Orb webs* The *orb web* is a masterpiece of geometric beauty. It consists of a continuous spiral of sticky webbing woven into a spoked "wheel" of nonsticky fibers. The construction of such a

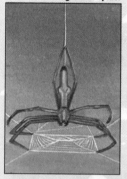

ogre-face spider

water spider

trapdoor spider

web is an engineering marvel in itself, for the orb web may extend over large spaces and yet be supported by only a few threads.

Some spiders capture their prey by using their silk in unique ways. The *ogre-face spider* of the southwestern United States weaves a tiny elastic web and holds it in its front four legs. When a potential victim draws near, the spider leaps at it and throws the web around it. The *lasso spider* twirls a single thread of silk with a sticky drop at its end and throws it at its prey.

Spiders may also use their silk to manufacture a home. The *European water spider* makes a "diving bell" web under water. By making periodic trips to the surface and bringing the air bubbles that cling to its body into the bell, the spider maintains the oxygen in its submarine home.

The *trapdoor spider* lines a burrow with silk and covers it with a camouflaged silk trapdoor. Using tiny web handles, the spider holds the trapdoor ajar to see outside. When an insect happens by, the spider springs from its hidden home, seizes the prey, and drags it back into the burrow.

The silk of the spider may also be used for reproductive purposes. Spiders usually lay their eggs in silken cocoons. The young spiders of certain species will leave the area where they hatch by *ballooning*, using long loops of silk that catch the wind and send them floating through the air.

Review questions on next page.

Legs and More Legs: Centipedes and Millipedes

The centipedes and millipedes share the same outstanding characteristic: a large number of jointed legs. Both groups are similar to insects in internal anatomy. Occasionally these arthropods have been mistaken for the larval forms of insects. Although the common names "centipede" and "millipede" are often used interchangeably, these names identify two distinct classes of animals.

Centipedes

The *centipede**, a member of **class Chilopoda*** (kye LAHP uh duh), is a carnivore having a flattened body divided into a number of similar segments. Its head bears a pair of antennas and several pairs of mouthparts. Each body segment bears one pair of limbs, but the total does not come near the hundred legs that the name "centipede" implies.

The centipede moves with amazing speed and agility, considering the problem of coordinating all its appendages. The limbs on the first body segment are poisonous claws used to immobilize and capture the insects and small animals the centipede eats. The common house centipede is a small member of the class, reaching only about 4 cm (1.6 in.) in length. Some tropical centipedes may be 30 cm (12 in.) long and capable of subduing worms and even snakes. The bite of most centipedes, though occasionally painful, is rarely fatal to humans.

Millipedes

Millipedes* do not really have the thousand legs suggested by their name. They belong to the **class Diplopoda*** (dip LAH puh duh), which literally means "double feet." The millipede does indeed have "double feet" in that it has two pairs of feet per body segment. Most of these dark-colored animals vary in size, most being about 5 cm (2 in.) long. Unlike that of the centipede, the segmented body of the millipede is rounded and cylindrical. The millipede moves slowly by the graceful wavelike motion of its legs and feeds mostly on vegetation and organic debris. It has no poisonous claws, and when disturbed, it often curls up into a ball.

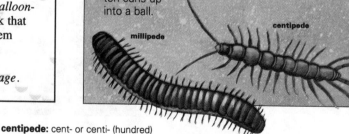

millipede

centipede

Chilopoda: Chilo- (Gk. KHEILOS, lip) + -poda (foot)

centipede: cent- or centi- (hundred) + -pede (foot)

Diplopoda: Diplo- (Gk. DIPLOOS, double) + -poda (foot)

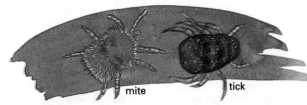

mite   tick

Mites and ticks have bodies fused into unsegmented ovoid shapes. Both these groups can cause varying amounts of damage to man and animals. *Ticks,* blood-sucking parasites of vertebrates, transmit diseases such as Rocky Mountain spotted fever and Lyme disease. *Mites* are much smaller than ticks but can also cause considerable discomfort. Mites can cause mange, a skin disease of animals. *Chiggers,* or red bugs, are mites which, in their larval stage, may infest the skin of man, causing itching and redness.

Biological Terms

phylum Arthropoda	cephalothorax	*The Malacostracans*	*The Arachnids*	class Chilopoda
exoskeleton	abdomen	class Malacostraca	class Arachnida	class Diplopoda
chitin	open circulatory system	green gland	chelicera	*Facet*
molt	antenna	antennule	pedipalp	spinneret
head	compound eye	statocyst	walking leg	
thorax	simple eye		tracheae	

Review Questions 15A-3

1. List several characteristics which distinguish the class Arachnida from the other classes in phylum Arthropoda.
2. List the spider's six pairs of appendages and tell the functions of each.
3. Describe (a) the food-ingesting process, (b) the respiration, and (c) the reproductive process of spiders.
4. List and briefly describe two arachnids other than spiders.
5. What characteristics distinguish class Chilopoda and class Diplopoda from the other arthropod classes?
6. Briefly describe and distinguish between the centipedes and the millipedes.

Facet 15A–Spider Webs, pages 371-72

1. List the two basic types of silk that spiders use to produce a web. What is the primary purpose of spider silk?
2. List and describe the four basic types of spider webs.

15B - Class Insecta

Class Insecta* encompasses over 800,000 species, nearly 75% of all the animal species. Not all of them are as familiar as the grasshoppers, flies, bees, and butterflies. Many of God's most unusual creatures belong to this diverse yet surprisingly homogeneous group.

Certain characteristics of insects help explain why they can be so abundant. One of the most important is that most insects can fly. This ability enables them to escape from danger, find a mate, look for food, and search for a suitable environment. Insects also have tremendous reproductive capabilities; certain species can produce thousands of eggs in a single day. Finally, insects vary so much that they rarely compete with one another for food or living space. Some insects eat leaves or fruit; others suck plant juices, drink human blood, or prey upon animals.

The sheer numbers of insects make them a major influence in nature and an important part of man's life. Some insects produce honey, silk, and wax and perform beneficial services. Others destroy crops, transmit deadly diseases, and are just plain pests.

millipede: milli- (thousand) + -pede (foot)

Insecta: (L. INSECTUM, segmented)

Characteristics of Insects

The members of the class Insecta share several characteristics that distinguish them from the other arthropods:

❑ Three pairs of walking legs;

❑ Wings usually present;

❑ Body divided into three segments: head, thorax, abdomen; and

❑ One pair of sensory antennas.

Legs of insects

Insects have three pairs of jointed legs located along the thorax. The structure of the limb varies with the type of movement the insect performs. The legs of the fly have tiny claws and sticky pads, enabling it to climb smooth surfaces. The jumps of the grasshopper are made possible by heavily muscled hind legs. The closely set bristles on the long legs of the water strider allow the animal to skitter across the surface film of water.

The legs of some insects were designed for functions other than locomotion. For example, the front limbs of the praying mantis are powerful ''claws'' for seizing prey. The fuzzy legs of the bee have special combs and hairs that are used to groom its body and carry pollen. Some insects use their legs to make sounds to attract a mate.

Wings of insects

Although most insects have two pairs of wings, some species have one pair, and wingless species do exist. Insects are the only invertebrates that can fly. Their flying styles and speeds vary. The butterfly flaps its wings 5-6 beats per second. The bee, on the other hand, whips the air with up to 200 beats per second. Flight speeds vary for the fly, which averages 8 kmph (5 mph), to the dragonfly, which cruises at 40 kmph (25 mph).

Insect wings, like their legs, differ in structure and function.

❑ *Membranous wings*   Membranous wings are thin, transparent, and crisscrossed with supporting *veins*. These are the flying wings of most insects.

❑ *Scale-covered wings*   The flight wings of butterflies and moths are covered with delicate, beautifully colored scales which rub off easily.

Two other wing types are protective.

❑ *Leather-like wings*   The grasshopper has its membranous wings covered by a front pair of leather-like wings. When the insect is not in flight, these wings protect the flying wings.

❑ *Horny wings*   The front wings of beetles, like the ladybug, are horny wings–thick shields that cover not only the membranous wings but also most of the dorsal surface of the insect.

Mouthparts of insects

The mouthparts of an insect suit its particular food. The typical insect mouthparts are for *chewing*. They consist of the upper lip or *labrum** (LAY brum), a pair of chewing *mandibles,* a pair of feeding appendages called *maxillae,* and a lower lip or *labium** (LAY bee um) bearing another small pair of appendages called *labial palps*. Insects such as grasshoppers and beetles use these mouthparts to consume plant material, often with disastrous effects on crops.

Insects like the mosquito have mouthparts designed for *piercing* the surface of a plant or animal and feeding on its juices. Moths and butterflies have a third type of feeding apparatus,

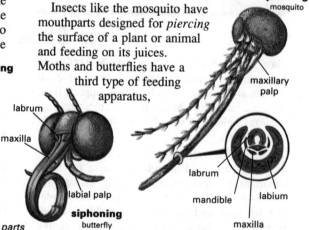

chewing
grasshopper

labrum

mandible

maxilla

maxillary palp

labial palp

sponging
fly

maxillary palp

labium

labrum

maxilla

labial palp

siphoning
butterfly

piercing
mosquito

maxillary palp

labrum

mandible

labium

maxilla

15B-1 *Various types of insect mouth parts*

labrum: (L. LABRUM, lip)
labium: (L. LABIUM, lip)

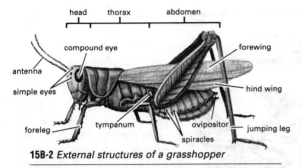

15B-2 *External structures of a grasshopper*

a long flexible *siphoning* tube for drawing nectar from flowers. When not in use, the tube is coiled under the head. Mouthparts designed for *sponging* or lapping up liquid food consist of an elongated labium with two enlarged lobes at its tip. Grooves along the lower surface of these lobes soak up liquid food. The common housefly has sponging mouthparts.

Nutrition of insects

Beyond the differences in mouthparts, the digestive system is virtually the same for all insects and is divided into three main parts:

❑ *Foregut* Food enters the foregut through the mouth, which is supplied with the secretions from **salivary glands.** The food passes through a short *esophagus* to the *crop,* a thin-walled sac in the thorax used primarily for storage. The food continues to the *gizzard,* a muscular organ lined with *chitinous plates,* that thoroughly grinds the food.

❑ *Midgut* The gizzard opens by a valve into the midgut, or stomach, located in the abdomen. Pouchlike organs called **gastric ceca** (SEE kuh)

surround the stomach, supplying it with digestive juices. The midgut is the major site of digestion and absorption since tough chitin plates line the rest of the digestive tract. This lining is shed at each molt.

❑ *Hindgut* Any solid residue in the midgut after digestion passes through the hindgut, or *intestine,* and out of the body through the *rectum* and *anus.*

Respiration, circulation, and excretion of insects

The respiratory system of insects is an elaborate system of tubules called **tracheae** which branch throughout the animal. This system is so complete that oxygen is transported through the animal without using the circulatory system. These tubules open to the outside through a series of **spiracles,*** small pores that run along each side of the animal. The insect "breathes" as abdominal contractions pump air in and out of its trachea.

The primary circulatory organ of the insect is a *tubular heart* above the digestive tract. Blood is pumped through the heart toward the head and pours through the thorax and back over the abdominal organs. This *open circulatory system* is involved only in the transport of nourishment and the collection of waste. As the blood washes over the organs, it passes over a ring of thin tubules encircling the juncture of the stomach and intestine. These **Malpighian** (mal PIG ee uhn) **tubules** extract nitrogenous wastes from the blood and pour them into the intestine for elimination. In the rectum, most of the water in the waste is reabsorbed in special glands.

15B-3 *Internal structures of a grasshopper*

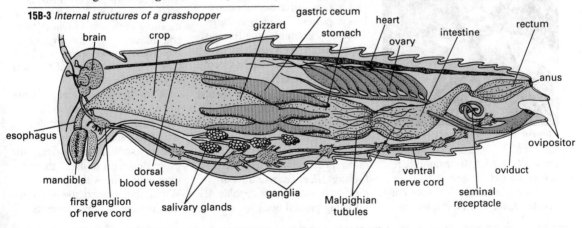

---

spiracle: (L. SPIRARE, to breathe)

FACETS OF BIOLOGY

Insect Survival

Not only are there more species of insects than any other type of animal, but usually there are more individuals in an insect species than in other species in the kingdom Animalia. Insects survive so abundantly because they are equipped with a large number of varied defenses. These defenses may serve to keep the individual insect or the entire species alive. Some of the common insect defenses are discussed here.

Physical appearance as defense

The first line of insect defense is the insect itself. The body color and shape are often simple but effective camouflage, making some insects almost invisible to would-be predators. When they rest open-winged on the bark of a tree, some mottled-colored moths are virtually invisible. Some insects blend into the scenery by resembling objects like leaves, twigs, flower petals, and even thorns. The body of

The Australian leaf insect resembles dead leaves.

the *walking stick,* for example, resembles a twig.

Many insects have brilliant colors that make them conspicuous.

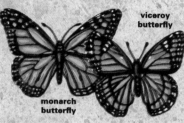

viceroy butterfly

monarch butterfly

In many cases this is warning coloration, informing potential predators that the insect tastes bad or can defend itself. The *monarch butterfly,* for example, tastes bad to birds and causes them to vomit. A bird which has had an unpleasant experience with a monarch will remember the distinctive appearance of the insect and not try to eat another one. Predators also learn that the vivid color patterns of bees and hornets mark insects that can deliver a painful sting.

Other insects "outwit" their predators by resembling insects that predators avoid. The *hornet moth* with its furry yellow and black body and thin, transparent wings looks like a hornet. An organism that has been stung by a real hornet will avoid this harmless imposter. The *viceroy butterfly* closely resembles the foul-tasting monarch. As a result most predators avoid the edible viceroy.

Weapons of insects

Some insects depend upon special weapons to repel attackers. The most familiar weapons are the poisonous stingers of bees and wasps and the piercing mouthparts of mosquitoes. Some insects, like *bedbugs, lice, fleas,* and *tsetse flies,* have mouthparts capable of inflicting painful bites.

The insect world has its share of "skunks": insects that secrete foul odors to repel their enemies. The *bombardier beetle* has a chemical laboratory in its body which can produce an explosive chemical mixture. When threatened by a predator, the beetle directs its abdominal duct at the enemy, mixes the chemicals of its weapon, and blasts the attacker with an explosive burst of irritating gas. Rapid repeat firings of this weapon discourage most predators.

The firebug (one of the stink bugs) releases odors when disturbed.

Social defenses of insects

The timeworn phrase "there is safety in numbers" assumes great meaning in the insect world. Several insect species, mostly within the orders Hymenoptera and Isoptera, insure their survival by forming large colonies.

A striking example of the benefits of an insect society is the termite colony. A single termite is wingless, blind, and has an exoskeleton so thin that it offers little protection. Left to itself, the termite would die within hours. Within the organization of the termite colony, however, termites

mud dauber wasp with larva

thrive. A major task of the colony is to build shelter. In some species the home of the colony may be a rotten log. Others manufacture mounds of a stonelike material which may reach 6 m (20 ft.) in height. Within this home the members of the colony maintain an environment suitable for their survival.

Reproductive defenses of insects

Many insects produce enormous numbers of young. In its lifetime the common housefly will produce 1,000 eggs. A queen termite can produce 8,000 to 10,000 eggs a day or 500 million during her entire life.

Even if disease or predators claim many of these young, the sheer number of eggs guarantees that some young will survive, mature, and reproduce. Many insects improve the survival chances of their young by providing special care to the eggs. The *mud dauber wasp*, for example, builds a set of clay tubes for its young. The nest, therefore, is divided into separate cells in which the eggs are placed. Each cell also contains a spider paralyzed by the female wasp to be food for the larvas. With a protective home and food supply, the wasp eggs and larvas have a good chance of survival.

Insect behavior as a defense

Insects' behavior can also serve them in times of danger. The most common response to danger is escape. The ability to fly is a great asset because many predators cannot follow the insect into the air. Some insects will "play dead" when faced with danger. This usually involves folding the legs tightly under the body and remaining motionless until the threat passes. If attacked or provoked, some insects will turn and fight back. For example, when even a large animal breaks into a wasp nest, the wasps will not flee but will sting the attacker.

It is easy for us to think of the actions of an insect in human terms. Since the queen bee is mother of the hive and is constantly attended by the workers, some people think of her as a ruler. Actually, the bees perform their functions because of their inherited behaviors. There is no loyalty or duty involved. They do what God designed them to do.

A swarm of hornets charging a person who disturbed their nest may appear to be a well-organized attack. Actually, each charging individual is responding to the same stimuli. Since they all have the same genetic makeup (a common parent), they all respond in unison.

The know-how to build a termite colony, the industriousness to store large quantities of food for the winter, or immediate reactions such as flying away from danger or catching prey are all inherited reactions in insects. Insects do not learn or figure out how to do these things. These *instinctive behaviors* had to work the first time, or else the insects would not have survived. Insect behavior is a good testimony to God's careful design.

The apparent "wisdom" of an "industrious" bee and the "foolishness" of a "lazy" grasshopper are nothing more than man's applying his own standards and attributes to insects, an activity we should be careful to avoid. God designed the bee to build hives and store food for the winter. God also designed the grasshopper to lay eggs to survive the winter since the cold kills the adults. The grasshopper is not foolish for not doing as the bee. They were not made alike.

God, however, does admonish us to learn from what He created. In Proverbs 6:6 we are told to "Go to the ant, thou sluggard; consider her ways, and be wise."

Review questions on page 380.

Some termite mounds are 6 m (20 ft.) tall.

Irritability of insects

In keeping with the arthropod pattern, the insect's nervous system consists of an *anterior "brain"* connected to an *anterior ganglion* and a *ventral nerve cord*. The system receives information from a variety of sense organs. The sense of smell is usually centered in the antennas. Taste receptors are abundant on the mouthparts. Numerous tactile hairs on the antennas, limbs, and body make the sensation of touch possible. The compound eyes are often so large that they bulge, dominating the head and giving the animal tremendous visual range. Many insects also have several simple eyes which respond only to the presence of light.

Several insect species possess organs for hearing, often in unexpected places. The grasshopper hears with its **tympanum*** (TIM puh num), a membrane-covered chamber in the first abdominal segment. The katydid listens with an organ in its foreleg. Hearing is important to these insects, not for escaping their enemies or finding food, but for finding mates.

Reproduction of insects

In insects the sexes are separate. The female stores the sperm in a seminal receptacle. As the female lays the eggs, they are fertilized. The **ovi-**

15B-4 *A grasshopper on a leaf*

positor* (OH vuh PAHZ uh tur), a pointed extension of the abdomen, is the organ which deposits the eggs.

The exact structure of the ovipositor varies. The grasshopper uses its short, stout ovipositor to dig a burrow for its eggs. The ichneumon wasp,

with a slender ovipositor reaching 15 cm (6 in.) in length, inserts this probe deep into the bark of a tree to place its eggs in wood-burrowing beetle larvas. The wasp larvas will feed upon the beetle larvas. Some female insects cover their eggs with a protective secretion. The praying mantis lays its eggs in a gummy mass that hardens into a protective case. Other insects "shellac" their eggs to leaves or bark to hold them in place and waterproof them.

Insect metamorphosis

During its development from egg to adult, an insect may assume a variety of forms that differ vastly in appearance, structure, diet, and habitat. This series of developmental changes is **metamorphosis*** (MET uh MOHR fuh sis). For many insects these changes permit their various stages to accomplish different functions. For example, some insects eat only during their immature forms and become adults only to reproduce and die in a few hours.

Although some insects have no metamorphosis, for most insects the process of metamorphosis takes one of two major routes.

❑ **Incomplete metamorphosis**–the line of development followed by such land insects as grasshoppers, cicadas, and true bugs–is a process involving three basic stages: *egg, nymph,* and *adult*. The **nymph,** which hatches from the egg, is like a miniature, oddly proportioned adult. The nymph lacks wings and external reproductive structures. As the nymph grows and molts, it becomes more like the adult. When it finally develops wings and

15B-5 *A molting cockroach. Judging by the empty exoskeleton, what type of metamorphosis does it have?*

---

tympanum: (Gk. TUMPANON, drum) **ovipositor:** ov-, ova, or ovi- (egg) + -positor (POSITOR, a placer) **metamorphosis:** meta- (Gk. META-, involving change) + morph- or morpho- (MORPHE, form)

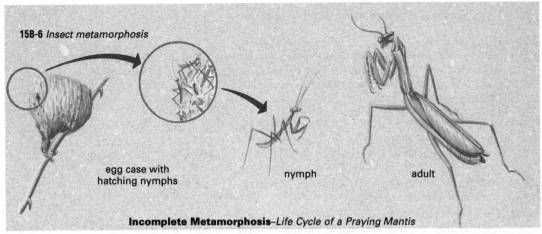

15B-6 *Insect metamorphosis*

egg case with
hatching nymphs

nymph

adult

Incomplete Metamorphosis–*Life Cycle of a Praying Mantis*

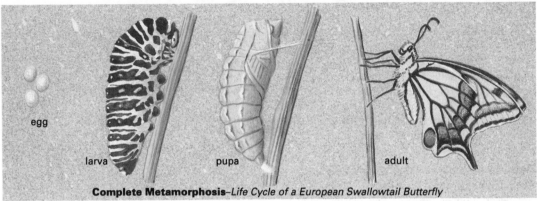

egg

larva

pupa

adult

Complete Metamorphosis–*Life Cycle of a European Swallowtail Butterfly*

mature reproductive structures, the insect is an adult. The diet and habitat of the nymph are identical to those of the adult.

In incomplete metamorphosis, if the immature stage of the insect lives in water, it is called a **naiad** (NAYE uhd). Dragonflies and mayflies have naiads. The naiad differs significantly from the adult since it is wingless and has gills. After a period of growth and several moltings, the naiad climbs out of the water and molts once again to become a flying, reproductive adult.

❑ **Complete metamorphosis,** the spectacular process of development used by almost 90% of the insects, involves four stages: *egg, larva, pupa,* and *adult.* The egg hatches into the **larva,** a segmented wormlike stage. Most Bible scholars agree that the term *worm* in such passages as the description of hell "where their worm dieth not" (Mark 9:43-48) and Jonah's worm (Jon. 4:7) re-

fers to the larvas of insects. The larvas of various insects have common names: *maggots* for flies, *grubs* for beetles, *wigglers* for mosquitos, and *caterpillars* for moths and butterflies. The most important activity of any larva is to feed.

After a period of eating and molting, the larva enters the *pupal stage.* In some insects the pupa is as active as the larva, but in many insects the pupa is a resting stage. During this stage the **pupa** forms a case about itself or weaves a silken *cocoon.* Though outwardly quiet, the pupal stage is a period of considerable activity. Within the protective case the body structures and organs of the larva are dismantled and completely reshaped. Eventually the pupa case opens, releasing a fully grown, fully developed adult insect. The process of complete metamorphosis is controlled by *hormones,* chemicals secreted into the blood by glands.

Review Questions 15B-1

1. What characteristics separate the class Insecta from other classes of the phylum Arthropoda?
2. List three different types of (a) insect legs, (b) insect wings, and (c) insect mouthparts.
3. List the three major parts of the insect's digestive system. List the structures within each part and give their functions.
4. Describe the respiration of insects.
5. Describe (a) the sense of touch in insects, (b) the sense of sight in insects, and (c) the sense of hearing in insects.
6. List the steps in incomplete metamorphosis and give several examples of insects that have incomplete metamorphosis. Do the same for complete metamorphosis.
7. List the common names of several familiar insect larvas.
8. What controls the molting process?

Facet 15B - 1: Insect Survival, pages 376-77

1. List and describe five factors which help insects to survive and thrive in our world.
2. How is insect behavior different from human behavior?

Major Orders of Insects

Taxonomists divide the class Insecta into approximately 26 orders. Fifteen of the most common orders and some of the characteristics used to classify them are given in Chart 15B-8. A few of these common insect orders are discussed in the following sections.

Order Hymenoptera–bees, wasps, ants

Hymenoptera* means "membrane-winged," an apt description of the bees and wasps found in this order. Many members of this order are social insects; they live in large groups and have *castes* (classes) which perform different functions for the group. In a bee colony, for example, there are one *queen*, several *drones* (males), and a large number of *workers*. The queen and drones serve primarily in reproducing while the workers build and maintain the hive and make honey.

Although many insects can inflict painful bites, only hymenopterans can sting. The ovipositor of the workers in some social hymenoptera groups is not used to lay eggs but to inject venom. When a disturbed bee injects its stinger into its victim, it then rips off its last abdominal segment which continues to pump more venom. Soon after the bee stings, it dies. Hymenopteran stings cause soreness and pain. A person who is allergic to the venom may die within several minutes without proper medical attention.

Killer Bees

The highly publicized "killer bees" are the result of a cross of aggressive African bees with gentler European honeybees. These experiments in crossbreeding were conducted in Brazil in the 1950s. A number of the offspring escaped the experimental area and have migrated through much of South and Central America. Their stings are not particularly more painful or harmful than those of the relatively docile North American honeybees, but the "killer bees" are much more easily aroused and are relentless in their pursuit of any disturbance.

Many livestock as well as human deaths have been attributed to these bees which are now invading Central America and are expected to reach the United States in the 1990s. Scientists hope that as these bees mate with more gentle bees cultivated in the United States, they will become less aggressive.

15B-7 *Castes of bees*

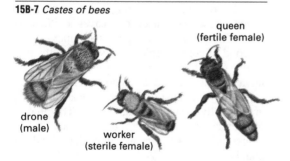

queen
(fertile female)

drone
(male)

worker
(sterile female)

Hymenoptera: Hymen- or Hymeno- (Gk. HUMEN, membrane) + -ptera (PTERON, wing)

15B-8	Major Orders of Insects			
Orders Grouped by Metamorphosis	**Type of Wings**	**Mouthparts in Adults**	**Economic Impact**	**Examples**
No metamorphosis				
Thysanura (tassel tail)	None	Chewing	Feed destructively on starch in book covers and clothing	Silverfish, firebrats
Anoplura (unarmed tail)	None	Piercing and sucking	Parasites; infest hair and skin of man and mammals, transmit diseases such as typhus fever	Sucking lice
Incomplete metamorphosis, land				
Orthoptera (straight wing)	1 pair, membranous 1 pair, leatherlike	Chewing	Cause extensive crop damage	Grasshoppers, crickets, cockroaches, praying mantises
Isoptera (equal wing)	2 pairs, membranous	Chewing	Feed on wood, destroying trees and wooden structures	Termites
Hemiptera (half wing)	1 pair (anterior half, leatherlike; posterior half, membranous)	Piercing and sucking	Damage plants, annoy man	True bugs (bedbugs, stinkbugs, water bugs, water striders, chinch bugs)
Homoptera (same wing)	2 pairs, membranous	Piercing and sucking	Destroy plants and crops	Cicadas, aphids, leafhoppers, scale insects
Dermaptera (skin wing)	1 pair, leatherlike	Chewing	Destroy plants and crops	Earwigs
Incomplete metamorphosis, water				
Odonata (toothed)	2 pairs, membranous	Chewing	Destroy harmful insects	Dragonflies, damselflies
Ephemeroptera (lasting only a day)	2 pairs, membranous	Do not feed	Naiads serve as food for freshwater fish	Mayflies
Complete metamorphosis				
Coleoptera (sheath wing)	1 pair, horny 1 pair, membranous	Chewing	Destroy crops, annoy man, destroy harmful insects	Beetles, weevils
Lepidoptera (scale wing)	2 pairs, scaly	Siphoning	Damage crops and clothing, produce silk, pollinate flowers	Butterflies, moths
Hymenoptera (membranous wing)	2 pairs, membranous	Chewing or siphoning	Pollinate flowers, make honey, annoy man, parasitize pests	Bees, ants, wasps
Diptera (two wings)	1 pair, membranous 1 pair, balancers	Piercing or sponging	Annoy man, transmit diseases such as typhoid fever, malaria	Flies, mosquitoes, gnats
Siphonaptera (siphon without wings)	None	Sucking	Annoy man, transmit diseases such as bubonic plague	Fleas
Neuroptera (nerve wing)	2 pairs, membranous	Chewing	Destroy harmful insects	Dobsonflies, ant lions, lacewings

Hymenoptera also includes the ants. In most ant species, however, the male and female reproductive castes are the only ones that have wings. Since males usually die after their mating flight, and the queen usually loses her wings after mating, and workers never have wings, most ants we see do not have wings. Ants lack stingers, but some species can inflict painful bites.

Most ants live in a caste society with divisions of labor and make their living in many fascinating ways. The *leaf-cutter ants* make expeditions from their underground home to cut and gather bits of foliage for the colony. In special underground chambers ants chew the leaves, mixing them with salivary secretions to produce a suitable material on which to grow fungus. These ants then use the cultivated fungus as food.

African or South American *army ants* have no permanent homes. During their hunting raids, a temporary shelter is built for the queen and the young by using the bodies of the ants themselves.

A South American species of fire ant was introduced to the United States and is now in most of the southern states. They pinch the skin with enlarged mandibles and then bend their abdomens under to inject their venom. The sting is more painful than a mosquito bite, but less painful than a bee sting.

15B-9 *A leaf-cutter ant (right), an army ant (left), and a a fire ant (bottom)*

Order Lepidoptera – butterflies and moths

At one stage in the life of a **Lepidopteran*** (LEP ih DAHP tur un), it is a vividly colored worm, often bristling with spines. At another stage it is a graceful insect bearing large powdery wings.

15B-10

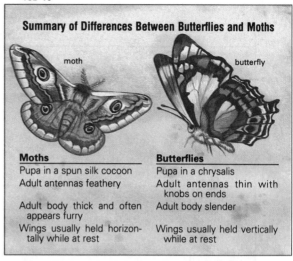

Summary of Differences Between Butterflies and Moths

moth   butterfly

Moths	Butterflies
Pupa in a spun silk cocoon	Pupa in a chrysalis
Adult antennas feathery	Adult antennas thin with knobs on ends
Adult body thick and often appears furry	Adult body slender
Wings usually held horizontally while at rest	Wings usually held vertically while at rest

The complete metamorphosis from caterpillar to butterfly or moth is one of the most noticeable characteristics of this order.

The *monarch butterfly* lays delicately sculptured eggs which hatch, releasing *caterpillars*. The monarch caterpillar has sixteen legs and, after several molts, bears brilliant zebra-patterned coloration. The caterpillar has chewing mouthparts designed for its vegetarian diet. During its brief existence, the caterpillar does little more than feed, grow, and molt. When signaled by hormonal changes, the caterpillar attaches itself to a leaf and enters the *pupal stage*. Within a protective case called a *chrysalis* (KRIS uh lis), the insect makes its most dramatic change. After 2-3 weeks, the adult monarch butterfly emerges. The mouthparts of the insect are now a coiled tube for sucking nectar from flowers. The adult has the characteristic six legs.

Although the main activity of the adult is to reproduce (in fact, some lepidopteran adults do not eat but live only long enough to reproduce), many monarch butterflies migrate. The adult monarchs alive in the fall will migrate from most of the U.S. and Canada to special areas of Mexico and Florida where they will land on certain trees and "rest" through the winter. In the spring they migrate back through North America.

The beautiful butterflies and moths, however, are not always liked by farmers. The larvas of

Lepidoptera: Lepid- or Lepido- (Gk. LEPIS, scale) + -ptera (wing)

FACETS OF BIOLOGY

15B-2

Control of Insects

In the book of Exodus we read how God dealt with the Pharaoh of Egypt to force him to release the captive Israelites. God sent ten plagues upon Egypt; three of which involved insects. Lice were miraculously made from the dust and sent to annoy the Egyptians. When Pharaoh hardened his heart, God sent the next plague: swarms of flies. But again Pharaoh refused to release the Israelites. A later plague involved locusts (probably a type of grasshopper) which ate every plant in Egypt.

These miracles took place approximately 3,500 years ago in a distant land and therefore seem old and remote to us. Occasionally, however, plagues of grass-hoppers invade vast areas of farmland in the United States and destroy millions of dollars in food. Even with all our "advanced" knowledge, people involved in these modern disasters are about as helpless as Pharaoh's servants in the Old Testament. Although the idea of insects taking over the world is only science fiction, insects do pose a major threat to our way of life.

Some insect activities are essential to life on earth as we know it. Many plants are pollinated only by insects. From honeybees, man obtains 110 million kg (240 million lb.) of honey and 2 million kg (4.4 million lb.) of wax annually; from silkworms, over 30 million kg (66 million lb.) of silk per year; and from other insects, valuable drugs and dyes. However, insects also

Spraying insecticide on a crop

Problems with Insecticides

Insecticides have several drawbacks. Often the quantity of insecticide necessary to kill a harmful insect also kills beneficial insects and other organisms. Some insecticides are very stable; that is, they do not easily break down into smaller compounds in natural conditions. If a stable insecticide is applied repeatedly in an area, the concentration may build up. Although the quantities applied may not be dangerous to organisms other than insects, the buildup may become dangerous to other organisms and man.

In the past DDT (dichloro-diphenyl-trichloroethane) was one of the most useful insecticides. A contact poison, DDT paralyzes the nervous system of the insect. Roaches, mosquitoes, and bedbugs, as well as general farm and garden pests, are quickly killed by it. DDT, however, is a stable chemical and has been found in an area more than 20 yr. after its application. DDT, when eaten by animals, accumulates in body fat. In areas of heavy DDT application, it has been found in cow's milk, fish, and birds. Although the long-range effects of DDT on humans and many animals are unknown, some birds, when they have large amounts of DDT in their bodies, lay eggs with thin shells which break prematurely. The federal government has banned the widespread use of DDT.

Occasionally we hear of insects that have "developed" a resistance to an insecticide. Evolutionists would say that these insects which are resistant to the insecticide have evolved because of their being exposed to the insecticide. Actually, by killing those insects which are most sensitive to the insecticide, only those with the strongest resistance to the insecticide are left. The insects which have the resistance were already in the population; otherwise they would have been killed by the insecticide.

Although it *may* be possible for insects to have a mutation which causes a variation capable of tolerating certain insecticides, this is not evolution. There would be no new insect, just a variation of an existing insect.

eat our grain, fruit, and vegetables; injure and destroy ornamental trees and shrubs; destroy wood and buildings; damage fabrics; carry disease; and parasitize plants, animals, and man. In the U. S. alone the losses from insects and the amount spent to control harmful insects total over $7.5 billion annually.

The gypsy moth was introduced into America. The larva (top) consumes leaves. In large groups they can strip land bare. Damage has spread over large areas of the northwestern U.S. Scientists have tried various types of control, but with limited success.

Scientists attempt to control harmful pests while preserving beneficial insects. Many methods of control have been attempted with varying amounts of success.

Quarantine

Within the U. S. Department of Agriculture is the Bureau of Entomology and Plant Quarantine. This bureau oversees the entry of plant materials and insects into the U. S. Widespread damage has been caused by more than 75 harmful insect species that have been introduced into the United States.

The *gypsy moth,* the *Japanese beetle,* the *cotton boll weevil*, and the *European corn borer* are not native to North America, but they are among the most serious insect threats in the U. S. In regard to most plant and animal material, therefore, the U. S. is now under **quarantine.** Materials are carefully inspected before they are permitted into the country to be sure that an unwanted organism is not entering also.

Insecticides

Chemicals that man uses to poison insects are **insecticides.*** Usually insecticides affect insects in one of two ways:

❑ *Stomach poisons* are applied to the leaves of plants which are being attacked by a foliage-eating insect. When the insecticide is eaten in sufficient quantity, the insect dies. Some insecticides are *systemic,* meaning they enter the plant and remain inside the plant tissues. When an insect sucks the plant juices or eats part of the plant, it consumes the poison. Systemic insecticides are often used on ornamental plants or plants being grown for wood or fibers.

❑ *Contact poisons* are applied near insects that either suck plant juices or for some other reason would not eat a stomach poison. Contact poisons can either affect the tracheas of the insect and cause suffocation or dissolve into the blood of the insect, usually poisoning the nervous system.

The initial results of using insecticides are often encouraging. Through careful work scientists

have been able to synthesize chemicals which will kill insects but not harm the plants on which they are placed. This is very important for farmers. Often when large numbers of insects attack a crop, using insecticides is the only way of quickly controlling them.

Environmental changes

Often, by knowing the life history of an insect, man can prevent its development. Knowing that flies breed in garbage and wastes, man can prevent large quantities of flies by properly disposing of wastes. The egg, larval, and pupal stages of the mosquito are aquatic. If a pond or swamp where mosquitoes breed is periodically drained, the mosquito population can be controlled.

The cotton boll weevil taught Alabama farmers crop rotation.

The people of Enterprise, Alabama, erected a monument to the cotton boll weevil. For many years this weevil ruined cotton crops. When the farmers were almost ruined financially, they planted other crops. The boll weevil could not live in these crops, and its numbers were reduced. The farmers could then return to planting cotton for a few years until the boll

---

insecticide: insecti- (insect) + -cide (to kill)

weevil population became too large. These farmers were forced to practice *crop rotation.* Crop rotation changes the insects' environment and thereby helps to control their population. Crop rotation also helps to control plant diseases, depletion of soil minerals, and several other problems.

Biological controls

Biological control of insects involves using one of several techniques to destroy an insect but not harm the rest of the environment. One popular method is the use of *natural predators* and *parasites.* Today many gardeners encourage frogs, toads, snakes, spiders, birds, and predatory insects to live near their gardens. The ladybug is a favorite among farmers for its tremendous appetite for destructive aphids and scale insects. Some seed companies sell ladybug and praying mantis eggs to be placed in gardens.

Today large Mexican toads with large appetites for insects are being imported to certain areas of the United States. Great care must be taken when importing a natural

predator. Although the predator may help control unwanted insects, it may also attack beneficial insects or other organisms and become a pest itself. The gypsy moth is an imported menace to trees. If the parasites of the gypsy moth, which keep its numbers in control in its natural habitat, were introduced to America, they would attack not only the gypsy moth but also beneficial native insects.

The Japanese beetle (right), an introduced pest, is lured to the colorful trap (left) with pheromones and flower scent. When in the trap it cannot escape and dies without the use of poisons.

One of the most promising insect control methods involves *pheromones.* Pheromones are chemicals that insects secrete to attract a mate. The female gypsy moth, for example, produces a pheromone that attracts males from great distances. By using that same chemical substance as a lure, the male moths can be drawn into a trap. The advantage of using pheromones is that they are extremely specific, attracting only the target insect.

Another biological control of insects involves either capturing or growing males of the species and

then bombarding them with radiation to make them sterile. The sterilized males are then released and mate with females. The eggs of those females will not be fertilized. If this genetic sabotage is continued, the unwanted insect's population will decrease. Scientists have used this technique effectively against the *screwworm fly,* a menace to livestock.

screwworm fly

Bacteria and viruses are potential weapons against insects. One such bacterium produces a substance toxic to the larvas of butterflies and moths. This microscopic killer is very specific, causing no harm to vertebrates, other insects, or even the parasites within the body of the caterpillar.

Biological control techniques are not the perfect answer to insect control. Natural predators, which are safe to the environment, are often difficult to find and use effectively. The development and safe use of manmade biological weapons are time-consuming, difficult, and expensive. Many are still in the experimental stages and not ready for general use. Nevertheless, biological control techniques show the greatest promise in combating unwanted insects without the harmful side effects of chemical insecticides.

Review questions on page 387.

praying mantis hatchlings

certain lepidopteran species–armyworms and cut-worms, for example – cause tremendous damage to crops. Some moth larvas also damage stored goods and clothing.

Order Coleoptera–beetles

Beetles are the largest order of insects, including 250,000 different species. With their compact bodies covered by heavy armor, most beetles look like miniature war machines. Some bear large chitinous horns or mandibles enlarged into fear-some-looking pincers. The exoskeleton of these insects is remarkably strong; in some instances it can sustain over 1,500 times its own weight.

The most obvious parts of a beetle's body are the *horny wings,* a pair of thick, often colorful protective sheaths that cover most of the body. These armor wings give the order its name: **Coleoptera*** (KOH lee AHP tur uh) means "sheath wing." Carefully folded under the horny wings is a pair of small, thin *membranous wings* used for flying.

The appetite of beetles makes them both a curse and blessing to man. Armed with chewing mouth-parts, beetles can destroy a variety of crops and plants. The *Japanese beetle* plagues gardeners in the United States. The *rice weevil* makes its home where man stores his food, destroying products such as wheat, barley, oats, corn, rye, and rice. The familiar red and black *ladybug,* however, feeds almost exclusively upon aphids and scale insects, animals which ravage crops. A single ladybug can eat 90 adult scale insects and 3,000 of their larvas in its own larval lifetime.

Order Diptera–flies, mosquitoes, and gnats

Insects of the **order Diptera*** (DIP tur uh) have caused man much pain and discomfort. Although most insects eat plant parts, many dipterans use man or other mammals as their targets.

The mosquito, an annoying and potentially dangerous member of this order, lights so softly that the victim is usually not aware of its presence. The mosquito's mandibles and maxillas taper into a set of four slender needles which easily pierce the skin. Its needlelike mouthparts then fill the wound with a chemical to prevent blood clotting. Finally, a slender food tube sucks up the blood. When the meal is over, the victim is left with only a little blood loss but a painful, itchy swelling caused by the anticlotting chemical. A mosquito can be more than a pest since it may harbor yel-low-fever virus, malarial organisms, and the lar-vas of parasitic worms.

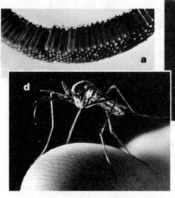

15B-11 *Life cycle of the mosquito: The eggs form a small floating raft (a) and hatch into larvas (b) which swim about feeding, but must return to the surface to breathe. The pupa stage (c) is also aquatic, feeds actively, and must breathe at the surface. The adult female (d) must have a blood meal before she can lay her eggs.*

The common *housefly,* another dipteran, is potentially dangerous because of what it can carry. The housefly may transport 33 million microorganisms in its intestinal tract and 500 million on its body. When the fly lights on human food, some of the microorganisms from its body may be left. When a fly feeds, it expels digestive fluids onto its food and then laps the fluids and digested food. In the process many microorganisms from the animal's intestinal tract, some of which may be pathogenic, remain.

Coleoptera: Coleo- (Gk. KOLEON, sheath) + -ptera (wing)
Diptera: Di- (two) + -ptera (wing)

15B-12 *A desert grasshopper*

Order Orthoptera – grasshoppers, cockroaches

Although not one of the largest insect orders, the **order Orthoptera*** contains many significant and well-known species. Incomplete metamorphosis, chewing mouthparts, and one pair of membranous wings covered by a pair of leathery ones set this group apart.

Of the many grasshopper species only a few are economic pests. The migratory species, called *locusts,* that live in grasslands are usually the most harmful. Although all grasshoppers have

hind legs they can use for jumping, not all of them are good flyers. Some, however, have larger wings and can fly for long distances. The *cricket,* another orthopteran known for its jumping ability, can rub its legs together to chirp. Only male crickets chirp, and they do so to attract females and ward off other males.

Few insects are more despised than the *cockroach.* Of the over 2,000 species of *roaches* only a few have invaded human dwellings. Known for their long, slender antennas and shiny black or brown, leathery body-covering wings, these insects prefer dark, warm, humid environments.

German cockroach

American cockroach

Biological Terms

class Insecta	tympanum	complete metamorphosis	Coleoptera
Characteristics of Insects	ovipositor	larva	Diptera
gastric ceca	metamorphosis	pupa	Orthoptera
trachea	incomplete metamorphosis	*Major Orders of Insects*	*Facets*
spiracles	nymph	Hymenoptera	quarantine
Malpighian tubules	naiad	Lepidoptera	insecticide

Review Questions 15B-2

1. List the characteristics and give several examples of these insect orders:
   (a) Coleoptera, (b) Lepidoptera, (c) Hymenoptera, (d) Diptera, (e) Orthoptera.
2. What are the three castes seen in the social insects? What are their functions within the insect colony?
3. What characteristics separate the insects into various orders?

Facet 15B-2: Control of Insects, page 385

1. List and describe four methods man uses to control insects.
2. Describe the two main types of insecticides.
3. Give three methods of biological control of insects.
4. Will the continued use of DDT bring about the evolution of immune insect populations? Why or why not?
5. What value are the pheromones to (a) insects and (b) farmers?

Thought Questions

1. Is it possible for a small butterfly to grow and become a larger butterfly? Explain.
2. Why is DDT considered an undesirable insecticide? Some have noted that not using DDT has resulted in an increase in certain types of insects. Should this justify the resumed, uncontrolled use of DDT? Should it justify controlled use of DDT? Explain.

Orthoptera: Ortho- (Gk. ORTHOS, correct) + -ptera (wing)

THE ECTOTHERMIC VERTEBRATES
ZOOLOGY PART III

SIXTEEN

16A- **Phylum Chordata**

The shark swimming soundlessly in the sea, the monkey chattering from a treetop, the frog perched upon a lily pad, the hawk soaring on currents of air, the snake slithering in the grass, the cheetah running over 96 kmph (60 mph), the small, wormlike amphioxus gliding slowly near the shore–all are members of the **phylum Chordata*** (kohr DAH tuh). Three characteristics place these animals in this phylum.

❑ *Dorsal notochord* The **notochord*** (NOH tuh KORD) is a rod of tough, flexible tissue run-

ning the length of the animal's body and serving as its primary support. For some chordates the notochord remains throughout the animal's life. But in most chordates, before birth or hatching, the notochord is replaced by **vertebrae** (VUR tuh bray). Vertebrae, which serve as the primary support for the animal, are either a tough, flexible material or bone. Together all the vertebrae are called the **vertebral column,** or backbone.

❑ *Dorsal tubular nerve cord* The **nerve cord** is dorsal to the notochord or vertebral column. It

---

Chordata: (L. CHORDA, cord)

notochord: noto- (Gk. NOTOS, back) + -chord (cord).

and the *brain*–connected at the anterior end of the cord–compose the main part of the animal's nervous system. In many species the vertebrae encase the nerve cord to protect it.

❏ *Pharyngeal pouches* During embryonic development, all chordates have folds of skin along the neck (pharyngeal region) called **pharyngeal*** (fuh RIN jee uhl) **pouches.** In most aquatic chordates, openings develop at these pouches. These openings permit water to flow over the gills, which develop inside the pouches. In nonaquatic chordates the pouches never open and are never associated with lungs or respiration. The phayrngeal pouches of terrestrial animals (as well as man) develop into various structures of the lower face, neck, and upper chest.

At one time evolutionists cited *gill slits* (openings by the pharyngeal pouches) as a characteristic of all chordates and used their presence to support the theory of recapitulation (see pages 203-4). Since later research revealed that only aquatic chordates develop these openings, gill slits can no longer be used to support that theory.

Classification Within Chordata

Phylum Chordata is divided into three subphyla.
❏ *Subphylum Cephalochordata** (SEF uh luh kohr DAH tuh) retain their notochords throughout their entire lives.
❏ *Subphylum Urochordata** (YOOR uh kohr DAH tuh) have notochords at larval stage.
❏ *Subphylum Vertebrata* (vurt uh BRAHT uh) develop vertebral columns, usually before they are born or hatched.

The organisms in the first two subphyla are aquatic, relatively small, few in number, and of little economic importance.

A typical notochord-retaining organism is the *amphioxus,* or lancelet, a slender marine animal about 5 cm (2 in.) long. It exists in tropical and temperate coastal waters. The amphioxus feeds by filtering plankton from the water.

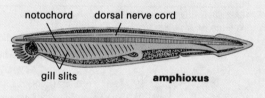

---

is well below freezing. In contrast, the brotulid fish thrives under nearly 8 km (5 mi.) of ocean water, a depth where light never penetrates. Environments hostile to most forms of life will support certain chordates. The polar bear, a large carnivore, dwells on the apparently lifeless ice floes of the Arctic Circle. Equally forbidding, the deserts support a variety of vertebrates, including snakes and lizards.

Vertebrate support and movement

The exoskeletons of the arthropods and other invertebrates greatly restrict their growth and movements. Vertebrates, however, are characteristically supported by an internal skeleton, or **endoskeleton.** The structures of the endoskeleton often surround, protect, and support delicate organs such as the brain, heart, and lungs. Movements are accomplished by muscles which cover the bones. This structural difference permits greater freedom of movement than the exoskeleton armor of the insects, crabs, and other invertebrates. Providing the same amount of support, the endoskeleton is considerably lighter than an exoskeleton. Therefore, a vertebrate moves more freely

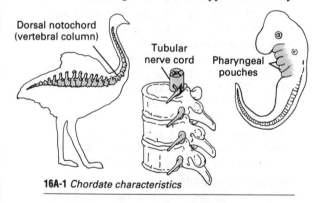

16A-1 *Chordate characteristics*

The Vertebrates

Within phylum Chordata the **subphylum Vertebrata** contains the *vertebrates* (animals with backbones) and is unmatched in its variety. It includes fish, amphibians, reptiles, birds, and mammals. Vertebrates live in virtually every habitat from the ocean floor to the upper fringes of the atmosphere. The bar-headed goose has been sighted flying over the Himalayas at a height of 9.1 km (5.6 mi.). At that altitude the temperature

---

pharyngeal: (Gk. PHARUNX, throat)

Cephalochordata: cephalo- (head) + -chordata (cord)

Urochordata: Uro- (Gk. OURA, tail) + -chordata (cord)

and can also be much larger than an invertebrate with an exoskeleton.

The skeleton of the vertebrate has the following two major divisions:

❑ **Axial* skeleton** The axial skeleton consists of the vertebral column, the skull, and the ribs.

❑ **Appendicular skeleton** Most vertebrates have two *girdles* suspended from the axial skeleton for the attachment of limbs. The **pectoral** (PEK tuhr uhl) **girdle** is in the anterior region, and the **pelvic girdle** is in the posterior. Attached to each girdle are the bones of the limbs, which may be in the form of fins, flippers, legs, or wings. The girdles and limb bones form the appendicular skeleton.

16A-2 *Divisions of the vertebrate skeleton, using a cat skeleton as an example*

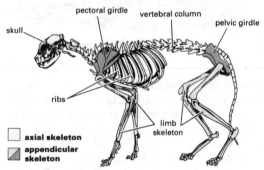

- axial skeleton
- appendicular skeleton

Vertebrate circulation and excretion

Vertebrates have a *closed circulatory system* consisting of a heart of 2, 3, or 4 chambers which is ventral to the vertebral column and blood vessels. There are three basic types of blood vessels in vertebrates.

❑ *Arteries* carry blood away from the heart to body tissues.

❑ *Capillaries** (KAP uh LAIR eez) are branches of the arteries. They are tiny, thin-walled vessels that pass through the body tissues. They supply the tissues with nutrients and oxygen and take wastes and carbon dioxide away from the same tissues.

❑ *Veins* begin as capillaries which carry blood from body tissues back to the heart. Normally, red blood cells do not leave the blood vessels.

All vertebrates have red blood because certain of their blood cells contain **hemoglobin*** (HEE muh GLOH bin), a red, oxygen-carrying pigment. In most vertebrates the blood passes through a pair of kidneys where wastes are filtered out.

Vertebrate nutrition

Although there is a great deal of similarity between members of the subphylum Vertebrata, there is also considerable variety. The feeding methods and foods of vertebrates are as varied as the animals themselves. These feeding techniques, however, fit into three categories:

❑ **Carnivorous*** (kahr NIHV uhr us) animals feed upon other animals. Sharks, lions, and eagles, for example, capture and tear their prey with sharp teeth or claws. Frogs and chameleons snag their insect victims with rapid-fire sticky tongues.

❑ **Herbivorous*** (huhr BIHV uhr us) animals eat plants. Grazing animals such as cows and horses are familiar herbivores. A plant diet presents some problems. The cellulose walls that encase plant cells are difficult to digest. To break up these walls, most herbivores use grinding teeth to thoroughly chew the plants. Bacteria in the digestive tract often supply the enzymes necessary for breaking down plant materials.

❑ **Omnivorous*** (ahm NIHV uhr us) animals, such as pigs, bears, and rats, eat both plants and animals. These animals often have varied teeth, some designed to tear meat, others to chew plants.

In vertebrates the *alimentary canal* (food tube) is composed of an esophagus, stomach, and intestines (with a liver and a pancreas). The digestive system is ventral to the vertebral column.

Review Questions 16A-1

1. List and describe three characteristics of organisms in phylum Chordata.
2. Describe the amphioxus and tell why it is in the same phylum as the vertebrates.
3. What are the two major divisions of the vertebrate endoskeleton? What are the major groups of bones in each of these divisions?
4. List distinguishing features of the three major types of blood vessels.
5. Why is the blood of vertebrates red?
6. Based on feeding methods, what are the three major groups of vertebrates?

---

axial: (L. AXIS, hub)
capillary: (L. CAPILLUS, hair)

hemoglobin: hemo- (blood) + -globin (L. GLOBUS, globe)
carnivorous: carni- (L. CARN-, flesh) + -vorous (VORARE, to devour)

herbivorous: herbi- (L. HERBA, herb) + -vorous (to devour)
omnivorous: omni- (L. OMNIS, all) + -vorous (to devour)

Vertebrate reproduction

In most vertebrates the sexes are separate. The males have paired *testes* which produce sperm, and the females have paired *ovaries* which produce eggs. There are two basic methods by which the sperm come in contact with the eggs.

❏ In *external fertilization* the female lays eggs, and the male fertilizes the eggs by releasing sperm onto them. External fertilization takes place in water, and there cannot be a shell on the egg.

❏ In *internal fertilization* the male places the sperm inside the female's body, where the eggs are fertilized. Certain aquatic animals and most land animals breed by internal fertilization. Internal fertilization permits a shell to be placed on the egg as it is formed. Eggs usually have some form of protective coat (shell) which permits them to be laid and to develop outside the mother's body.

Although exceptions exist, there are three basic methods of development for the young vertebrates:

❏ **Oviparous*** (oh VIHP uhr us) organisms, such as birds, produce offspring from eggs hatched outside the body.

❏ **Viviparous*** (vye VIHP uhr us) organisms produce live offspring that have been nurtured to birth through some type of placenta. The placenta, an attachment between the mother and the fetus, supplies nutrients to the offspring. Most mammals are viviparous.

❏ **Ovoviviparous*** (OH voh vye VIHP uhr us) organisms produce live offspring which were not nurtured through a placenta. The fertilized eggs, often with a shell, remain in the mother's body and hatch there; and then the young emerge. The common guppy is a good example.

Vertebrate nervous system

The nervous system of vertebrates contains the *brain, spinal cord, cranial nerves* (which branch from the brain), *spinal nerves* (which branch from the spinal cord), and *sense organs* (such as eyes, ears, and taste buds).

16A-3 *Typical vertebrate nervous system*

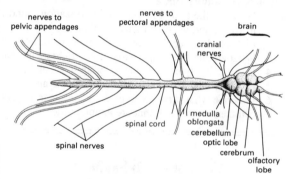

The primary functions of the five major lobes (divisions) of the typical vertebratal brain are listed below from anterior to posterior.

❏ The **olfactory* lobes** receive impulses from the smell receptors of the nostrils.

❏ The **cerebrum*** controls voluntary muscle activity.

❏ The **optic* lobes** receive impulses from the eyes.

❏ The **cerebellum*** coordinates muscle activity and some involuntary activities.

❏ The **medulla oblongata** (muh DOOL uh ◊ AHB long GAH tuh) transports impulses to and from the spinal cord, including some reflexes.

In most vertebrates the larger the portion of the brain given to a certain function, the more skilled the animal is at performing that function.

Supposed Evolution of Vertebrate Reproduction

Some evolutionists try to trace evolution through the means of reproduction. Supposedly, oviparous reproduction developed first, followed by ovoviviparous and then viviparous reproduction. When examined superficially, this may appear to follow an evolutionary path. Fish and amphibians reproduce oviparously with external fertilization; reptiles and birds are oviparous with internal fertilization; and mammals are viviparous with internal fertilization.

However, when examined carefully, the theory breaks down. Sharks, which supposedly developed early in vertebrate history, reproduce with internal fertilization both ovoviviparously and viviparously. Though fish and reptiles are predominantly oviparous, some, like the mosquito fish and the queen snake, reproduce ovoviviparously. Mammals are predominantly viviparous, but the duckbilled platypus, a mammal found in Australia, is oviparous.

---

oviparous: ovi- (egg) + -parous (L. PARERE, to give birth to)

viviparous: vivi- (L. VIVUS, alive) + -parous (to give birth to)

ovoviviparous: ovo- (egg) + -vivi- (alive) + -parous (to give birth to)

olfactory: (L. OLFACERE, to smell)

cerebrum: (L. CEREBRUM, brain)

optic: (Gk. OPTOS, visible)

cerebellum: (L. CEREBELLUM, small brain)

Vertebrate classifications

Traditionally, vertebrates have been put into two groups: cold-blooded and warm-blooded. Although not part of the modern classification system, the groupings are still useful. An animal is *ectothermic** (EK tuh THUR mik), cold-blooded, if it does not have the ability to generate its own body heat and thus maintain a body temperature above that of its surroundings. Ectothermic animals depend upon heat from sources outside themselves to stay alive. These animals are usually sluggish when cold and active when warm. To warm themselves, ectothermic animals such as lizards and snakes often lie in the morning sun. If they get too warm, they seek cooler, shaded places.

*Endothermic** (EN doh THUR mik), warm-blooded, animals generate their own body heat and often have elaborate mechanisms for maintaining body temperature within a narrow range. Endothermic animals can be active regardless of the external temperature, but most often they adjust their activity to permit their bodies to generate more heat or lose excess heat. Birds, mammals, and humans are endothermic organisms.

The subphylum Vertebrata has 7 classes–5 are ectothermic and are discussed in this chapter. This includes 3 classes of fish and fishlike animals, 1 class of amphibians (frogs and salamanders), and 1 class of reptiles (lizards, snakes, and turtles). The 2 endothermic classes (birds and mammals) are discussed in the next chapter.

Review Questions 16A-2

1. What are the two basic types of fertilization found in vertebrates? Which requires mating in water, and which may be accomplished in water or on land?
2. List and describe the three basic methods of development of vertebrate embryos.
3. What are the five major parts of a vertebrate nervous system?
4. List the five typical vertebrate brain lobes and tell the primary function of each.
5. List fourteen characteristics shared by the animals in subphylum Vertebrata.
6. Describe what it means to be ectothermic and endothermic. List five organisms that are ectothermic and five that are endothermic.

Vertebrate Behavior

The way an animal responds to its environment is its **behavior.** Although it can be said that the responses of a worm or a hydra are behaviors, the most noticeable and interesting animal behaviors are found in the vertebrates. Most scientists agree that different vertebrates have various levels of three types of behavior: inborn, conditioned, and intelligent.

Inborn behavior

Inborn behavior *(innate behavior)* is that behavior which the organism has from birth and does not need to develop. It predominates in the activities of many animals. Inborn behavior can be divided into two groups:

❏ **Reflex** behavior is automatic, involuntary response to a stimulus. Blinking an eye when it is touched and recoiling from pain are reflexes.

16A-4 *A reflex controls the size of the openings of a cat's eyes in different light intensities.*

Many normal body functions are reflexes. Breathing, for the most part, is a reflex and continues even during sleep. The same is true of digestion and the beating of the heart.

---

ectothermic: ecto- (outside) + -thermic (Gk. THERME, heat)

endothermic: endo- (Gk. ENDON, inside) + -thermic (heat)

❏ **Instinct** behavior is a fascinating and little-understood form of behavior. Instincts are elaborate behaviors, apparently the result of a stimulus or series of stimuli. For example, the mating of salmon often involves migrating hundreds of miles inland. From the ocean the salmon swims upstream to its birthplace. The female then digs a shallow "nest." At last the salmon spawns. This complex mating cycle is an unlearned instinct apparently stimulated by temperature, length of days, available foods, and even odors in the water.

16A-5 *Caring for young, like this mother red wolf returning her pup to the den, is an instinct.*

Often an animal's instincts are highly specific. Birds raised in captivity that have never seen the mating ritual of their species can perform those rituals perfectly. Some instincts, such as *self-preservation* (often called the "flight or fight" instinct), are found in almost all animals. Most animals, for example, will instinctively flee from a large adversary. If cornered or trapped, however, they will turn and lash at the intruder, even if they stand little chance of winning the fight.

Conditioned behavior

Conditioned behavior *(learned behavior)* is response learned by experience. Many vertebrates are capable of this second type of behavior. The antics of a trained circus elephant are behaviors the animal would not perform instinctively. They are behaviors carefully encouraged through a system of rewards and punishments. The process is familiar to anyone who has attempted to train the family dog to sit up or roll over. Even fish and pet turtles can be trained to come to certain areas for feeding.

Not all learned behaviors, however, are induced by man. After being sprayed by a skunk, most animals learn to leave the black animal with the white stripes alone. A raccoon that finally opens the garbage can after many unsuccessful tries soon "learns" the best method and therefore cuts down on his unsuccessful tries.

Intelligent behavior

Some vertebrates are capable of the third type of behavior: *intelligent behavior*. **Intelligence** can be expressed as the ability to use knowledge to manipulate the environment or the ability to communicate. Such behavior is seen in some birds and most mammals.

A chimpanzee, for example, is intelligent enough to stack objects in order to obtain food suspended out of reach. In the wild, animals may use sticks, stones, and even grass as tools. Many animals communicate with each other. Some of this communication is instinctive, but the communication of some animals (apes, whales, and porpoises) appears to be learned. Some apes and other mammals have even been trained in the use of specialized languages (sign language or a language of symbols) and have even taught some of the language to other members of their species. This indicates a level of intelligence above what most scientists expected of animals.

Biological Terms

phylum Chordata	*The Vertebrates*	capillaries	ovoviviparous	*Vertebrate Behavior*
notochord	subphylum Vertebrata	vein	olfactory lobe	behavior
vertebrae	endoskeleton	hemoglobin	cerebrum	inborn behavior
vertebral column	axial skeleton	carnivorous	optic lobe	reflex
nerve cord	appendicular skeleton	herbivorous	cerebellum	instinct
pharyngeal pouches	pectoral girdle	omnivorous	medulla oblongata	conditioned behavior
	pelvic girdle	oviparous	ectothermic	intelligence
	arteries	viviparous	endothermic	

Review Questions 16A-3

1. Outline and define the basic types of animal behavior.
2. Give examples of each of the types of animal behavior.

Thought Questions

1. It appears that animals with more intelligence have fewer instincts. Why would this be logical?
2. Which method of embryonic development found in vertebrates would you consider the most efficient? Why? Can efficiency of embryonic development be used to support evolution? Explain.

16B–Class Osteichthyes: The Fish

For 200 years after Christ's ascension the symbol of Christianity was the fish. The Greek word for *fish,* IXΘYE, was used as an acrostic: each letter stood for a word in the Greek phrase "Jesus Christ God's Son Saviour." In the catacombs beneath Rome, where Christians hid during the Roman persecution, fish are carved on the walls and grave markers. Only when crucifixion became illegal in the Roman Empire did the cross replace the fish as the symbol of Christianity.

Fish have been a main food source for people since early times. It was one of the meats acceptable for eating by the children of Israel (Deut. 14:9-10). Christ fed the multitudes with fish.

Christ told Peter to catch a fish in order to pay the Roman tax (Matt. 17:24-27). Christ told His disciples to follow Him and become "fishers of men" (Mark 1:17). An interesting Scriptural reference is Jonah's three-day "submarine" voyage in the belly of a great fish (Jonah 1:17).*

Classification of fish

Normally there are three classes in subphylum Vertebrata that are considered fish. The two which have cartilage skeletons throughout their entire lives are *Agnatha* (AG nuh thuh) (the lamprey) and *Chondrichthyes* (kahn DRIK thih eez) (the sharks and rays). These two classes are discussed on pages 395 and 398-99. By far the vast majority of fish have some bony parts in their skeletons and belong to the class *Osteichthyes* (AHS tee IK thih eez).

Class Osteichthyes

Normally when you think of fish, members of the vertebrate **class Osteichthyes*** come to mind. Some members of the class, such as the sea horse, are unusual in their appearance; and some non-bony fish, such as the shark, may appear similar to the bony fish. There are major differences which separate the true bony fish from other classes.

Most fish have the typical flattened, spindle-shaped body, ideally designed for movement in the water. Some fish, however, are flattened top to bottom. Some are round like a pencil; others resemble boxes, pyramids, balls, or just about any

---

*In Matthew 12:40, however, Jonah is said to have been swallowed by a whale. *Great fish* and *whale* are virtually interchangeable in ancient languages, and which one it was is insignificant to the story and to Christ's teaching.

Osteichthyes: Os- or Osteo- (Gk. OSTEON, bone) + -ichthyes (Gk. IKHTHUS, fish)

FACETS OF BIOLOGY

16B-1

Jawless Fish—Class Agnatha

lamprey

lamprey mouth

The lamprey and hagfish are in the *class Agnatha.* These animals are identified by a lack of scales, an eellike shape, unpaired fins, a skeleton of cartilage, and a jawless, sucking mouth. Although this class has few species, its members have caused tremendous damage in certain areas.

The adult sea lamprey may reach 60 cm (24 in.) in length. It has two single dorsal fins and a tail fin. Its two eyes are separated by a single nostril. The nostril leads to a sac supplied with olfactory nerves. Seven oval gill slits appear on each side of the head of the organism. These openings lead to a chamber containing gills.

The most conspicuous feature of this animal is its circular, funnel-shaped mouth lined with rows of teeth. The mouth is used to cling to the body of a fish. Once attached, the lamprey wounds the victim and sucks its blood and body fluids. Sometimes the fish

hosts survive the attacks, but often they do not.

Lampreys spawn in freshwater streams. The male and female lampreys dig a shallow depression in the stream bottom into which the female deposits 25,000 to 100,000 eggs. The eggs are fertilized externally. In about two weeks the eggs hatch, releasing tiny, wormlike larvas. The larvas float downstream until they reach an area with a quiet, muddy bottom. The larvas burrow into the mud and remain there, feeding on organic debris, for three to seven years. After this period of growth, the larvas change into adults, swim downstream to the ocean, and begin their lives as parasites.

Niagara Falls once kept marine lampreys from traveling from

Lake Ontario into the upper Great Lakes. In 1829, however, the Welland Canal was built around Niagara Falls so that ships could pass between Lake Ontario and Lake Erie. In 1921 a lamprey was caught in Lake Erie, marking the beginning of disaster. Lampreys attacked the rich trout populations of the upper Great Lakes. The prosperous fishing industry on the lakes suffered catastrophic losses. Annual catches of lake trout in Lake Erie shrank from 15 million to 1/2 million pounds.

Various methods have been developed to eradicate this devastating parasite. Electric nets have been used to catch adult lampreys as they migrate upstream to mate; however, the nets are a hazard to people as well as the other migrating fish from the many streams feeding the Great Lakes.

A chemical poison that destroys the mud-dwelling larvas of the parasite (but does not "permanently" harm other organisms) has been used extensively in recent years. Devices on the locks of the canal now prevent additional lampreys from entering Lake Erie.

Although these measures have not been entirely successful, the lamprey population is decreasing, and the edible fish are making a comeback. The fishing industry of the Great Lakes may reach its original level someday, but the cost of "progress" has been high.

Review questions on page 399.

Agnatha: A- (Gk. A-, without) + (GNATHOS, jaw)

16B-1 *Evolutionists dated coelacanth fossils as 400 million years old and presumed the fish was extinct. In 1938 a strange, metallic blue 6 ft. long fish was caught in the Indian Ocean. Biologists were astonished at the "living fossil." Other living coelacanths have also been caught. The fleshy lobes supporting some coelacanth's fins were thought to help the fish crawl across muddy areas. The coelacanth, however, is a deep-sea fish.*

Many fish are uniquely designed to live in a very specific place. The four-eyed fish is designed to live along the water surface. Its eyes are divided, enabling the animal to poke the top of its eye out of the water and watch what goes on above and below the water. The flounder dwells on the sea bottom. In the adult stage both of its eyes are on one side of its flat body so that it can lie on its side in the mud while both eyes watch the water above for food or predators.

Support and movement of fish

Members of the class Osteichthyes have bony skeletons. *Bone* is basically a special type of cartilage hardened by mineral deposits. It is considerably harder and offers much more support than cartilage. The bony fish, however, usually have only a vertebral column and skull of bone. The

other shape imaginable. In length, most fish are less than 1 m (3 ft.). The Philippine goby is only 10 mm (0.4 in.) long, while certain river sturgeons are over 4 m (13 ft.) long and weigh over 900 kg (2,000 lb.).

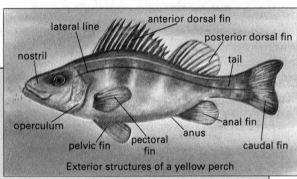

Exterior structures of a yellow perch

The Fins of a Fish

The fins, which project from the fish's body, are supported by either bone or cartilage. Fish generally have two sets of **paired fins:**
❑ The *pectoral fins* are close to the head on either side of the body.
❑ The *pelvic fins* are below and slightly behind the pectoral fins.

The **unpaired fins** of fish are often greatly modified for special functions:
❑ The *anterior dorsal fin,* on the back of the fish, is often supported by sharp spines, forming a convenient weapon against predators and careless fishermen.
❑ The *posterior dorsal fin,* behind the anterior dorsal fin, is generally smaller and softer than the anterior fin. Both dorsal fins are stabilizers, keeping the fish upright while swimming.
❑ The *anal fin* is on the ventral surface of the fish behind the anal opening.
❑ The *caudal* fin,* at the extreme posterior end of the fish, is the tail fin, used to propel the animal through the water.

The fins of a fish are most often used for guidance or slow swimming movements. In some fish, however, the fins may serve a number of

unusual functions. The *sea robin,* for example, uses its pectoral fins to "walk" along the sea bottom. The *walking catfish* can, by holding water on its gills, jump along on land for long distances if the pond it is in begins to dry up. Poison on its sharp fins protects it from predators. The pectoral fins of the *flying fish* serve as gliding wings that enable some species to leap out of the water and glide at speeds of 55 kilometers per hour (34 mph) and distances of 46 m (150 ft.).

caudal: (tail)

ribs and the pectoral and pelvic girdles (if present) are often of cartilage, but some fish have both cartilage and bone in these structures.

A fish moves through the water primarily by the whipping motion of its body. The power behind this action lies in the wavy, muscular bands found in the fish's trunk and tail. The effective use of these muscles, combined with the friction-reducing shape and smooth body coating, helps the fish move with a minimum of wasted effort.

Because fish are heavier than water, they face the problem of staying afloat. Many bony fish have an **air bladder,** a thin-walled sac in the body cavity which enables the fish to control its depth and to maintain that depth without swimming. Gases diffuse into and out of the air bladder through the bloodstream or by contact with the digestive system. By increasing the gas volume, the fish will rise in the water; by decreasing it, the fish will sink. Bottom-dwelling fish such as the flounder and sculpin have no air bladder.

Body covering of fish

The body covering of most fish consists of overlapping **scales.** The number of scales a fish has usually does not change; as the fish grows, its scales merely grow in proportion. Thus, one can estimate the age of some fish by counting their *scale rings.* Usually, any fish that grow in waters that remain the same temperature throughout the year do not develop scale rings. Since scale rings obscure the colors of the skin, these fish are often more colorful. Not all fish possess typical scales. Some, like certain catfish, are scaleless. Other catfish are covered with bony plates. The sturgeon has rows of large enamel-like plates.

16B-2 *Fish scale*

Special glands beneath the scales secrete a slimy **mucus** that covers the exterior of the fish. The mucus coats the scales with a nearly waterproof covering, protects the fish from parasites, and lubricates the fish for smoother movement through the water. Studies have shown that the slimy covering reduces water friction by 66%.

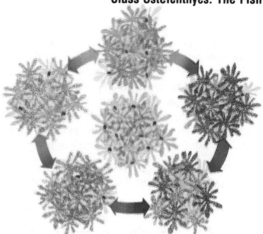

16B-3 *The operation of chromatophores explains the ability of certain fish (and other animals) to change color.*

Fish exist in a variety of colors. Those that live among colorful coral reefs are generally brilliant red, yellow, blue, and purple. Fish in other environments are subdued browns and greens. Blue and green colors are the result of light interference in the scales of fish. **Chromatophores*** (kroh MAT uh FORZ) are branched cells responsible for producing some of the pigments that color fish. In some fish all the chromatophores produce the same color pigment. In other fish, however, there are different colored chromatophores which, when viewed together, produce a color.

Some fish have the ability to alter their color and color patterns by rearranging the pigment in various chromatophores. When stimulated by certain nerves, the pigment is either concentrated in the center of the cell or dispersed throughout it. When dispersed, that color is apparent on the body of the fish.

Fish will often change color in response to temperature, diet, states of excitement (chase some aquarium fish with a net and note their color changes), and physical condition. Normally the fish's colors are brightest during the mating season. The flounder is probably the champion "chameleon" of the fish world. In minutes it can change its pigmentation from dark to light and from solid to spotted. It has colors ranging from yellow to black to green to red, which it uses to match the color of its background.

---

chromatophore: chroma- or chromato- (color) + -phore (to bear)

Many fish possess a form of camouflage known as **countershading.** The upper half of the fish is dark colored so that, when viewed from above, it blends with the bottom of the body of water. The lower part of the fish is light colored, which makes it blend with the brightly lit water surface when viewed from below. Countershading helps to protect fish from predators above and below it.

16B-4 *Countershading is common in many aquatic animals, as seen on the great white shark here viewed from below.*

FACETS OF BIOLOGY

16B-2

Cartilaginous Fish–Class Chondrichthyes

Some of the most feared animals in the ocean belong to the *class Chondrichthyes,** a class including sharks, rays, and skates. The term *Chondrichthyes* reveals one of their major characteristics, an elaborate skeleton composed of strong yet flexible cartilage.

Tales of the crushing jaws of the shark and the deadly sting of the stingray have given this group of animals a sinister reputation. Yet not all cartilaginous fish are fearsome. Even most sharks are timid and harmless. For example, the *whale shark* is one of the largest sharks, but it feeds only on microscopic plankton. Worldwide, sharks cause fewer than fifty deaths each year, considerably fewer than the yearly victims of murder or automobile accidents.

Sharks

Sharks are easily recognized by their sleek torpedo shape, which enables them to glide through the water with a minimum of friction. Their skin appears smooth, but close examination reveals that it is actually covered by many tiny scales, making it as rough as sand-

paper. The shark has the same basic fins as the Osteichthyes. In the sharks, however, the dorsal part of the caudal fin is always larger than the ventral part, which is not true of bony fish.

Behind and below the anterior point, or *rostrum,* of the shark is the mouth. The mouth has rows of razor-sharp, triangular teeth. These teeth can be straightened for biting or tearing and folded into the mouth when not in use. If a tooth is lost, another moves forward to replace it.

While some feed on large fish and animals and others on microscopic plankton, all sharks are carnivorous. Sharks will generally seize their prey with their powerful jaws and sharp teeth. Sharks usually swallow their food whole,

passing it to the stomach for storage. Sharks have been known to store undigested whole dolphins for as long as a month. Digestion occurs in a short intestine.

Sharks obtain their oxygen by passing water over their gills. These gills are exposed to the environment by a series of gill slits on each side of the shark's body. When motionless, a shark can be observed pumping water through its gills. The circulatory system is similar to that of bony fish.

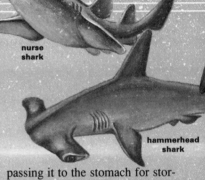

nurse shark

hammerhead shark

External structures of a shark

caudal fin

posterior dorsal fin

anterior dorsal fin

nostril

pelvic fin

pectoral fin

gill slits

Review Questions 16B-1

1. List several characteristics of the class Osteichthyes that separate its members from other vertebrate classes.
2. List and describe the six major types of fins found on a typical fish.
3. Describe several unusual fish fins and their uses.
4. How do fish maintain their depth in the water?
5. Describe the body surface of a fish.
6. How do chromatophores cause color changes in fish?
7. What are the advantages of countershading?

Facet 16B-1: Jawless Fish—Class Agnatha, page 395

Give an example of class Agnatha and list five characteristics of the class.

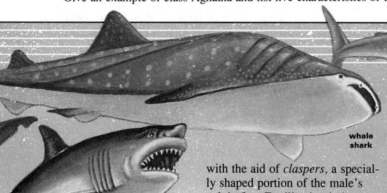

mako shark

whale shark

great white shark

An elaborate set of sensory structures assists the shark in its search for prey. The shark's two large eyes function efficiently only at close range. Paired nostrils on the ventral side of its head lead to olfactory pouches. These organs of smell enable the shark to detect extremely small amounts of blood in the water. Prey, however, cannot be detected at great distances. The *lateral line*, a sensory canal, runs the length of the shark's body. The cells in this canal respond to minute water vibrations caused by distant moving objects. Many sharks investigate any unusual vibrations as a potential food source.

In sharks the sperm are transmitted from the male to the female with the aid of *claspers*, a specially shaped portion of the male's pelvic fins. Fertilization is *internal*. Oviparous sharks release the fertilized eggs in a capsule which is then attached to a submerged object. Some sharks are viviparous, a rarity outside the class mammalia, and some are ovoviviparous.

About twelve species of sharks are dangerous to man. The largest and most notorious man-eater is the *great white shark*. This shark may reach a length of over 6 m (20 ft.), and some divers have reported seeing them 12 m (40 ft.) long. The appetite of these monsters is phenomenal. One captured great white shark had an intact horse in its stomach. Other known man-eaters are the *hammerhead shark*, the *mako shark*, and the *tiger shark*.

Rays and skates

Rays and skates are flat and thin, not spindle shaped like sharks.

The pectoral fins of the ray form flat wings that propel the fish through the water. In motion these animals look like underwater birds.

Though graceful and beautiful, some rays can be quite dangerous. The *stingray* has one or more sharp spines along its tail that can inflict painful, slow-healing wounds. The *electric ray* has a pair of muscular organs which can generate a powerful electric jolt to stun prey or discourage attackers. One of the largest rays, the *manta ray* or "devilfish," sometimes measures over 6 m (20 ft.) across. Despite its fearsome size, the manta ray eats plankton—not people.

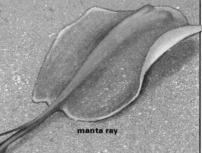

manta ray

Review questions on page 404.

Chondrichthyes: Chondr- or Chondro- (Gk. KHONDROS, cartilage) + -ichthyes (fish)

Digestion in fish

Fish feed on a variety of foods ranging from plankton, worms, insects, and plants to other fish and even mammals. Food is ingested through the mouth, which often contains teeth for biting or holding the prey. The mouth and teeth vary according to the diet of the animal. Predatory fish such as the barracuda have large, anteriorly located mouths armed with sharp teeth. The kissing gourami has large lips and a sucking mouth for scraping food from submerged objects. The parrot fish uses its tough, beaklike mouth to break chunks of coral reef and dislodge the tiny animals that it eats.

Food passes whole through a flexible throat or *pharynx* and a short *esophagus* into the saclike *stomach* for storage. Digestion occurs in a short *intestine*, which extends from the bottom of the stomach. Short tubes called *pyloric ceca,* located at the junction of the stomach and intestine, are thought to be absorptive or secretory in function. A large *liver* is found near the stomach.

Fish use various methods to capture or obtain their food. The razor-toothed piranhas of South America travel in schools, and some species viciously attack animals. It is a known fact that one such species reduced a 45 kg (100 lb.) mammal to bone in less than a minute.

For some fish, brute strength gives way to stealth. The goosefish waits motionless on the sea floor, camouflaged by its speckled coloration. A portion of its dorsal fin forms a spine topped with a fleshy "worm" which it wiggles as bait. When the prey comes close, the goosefish opens its huge mouth, creating a powerful suction that pulls the prey inside. The archer fish accurately "shoots down" insects up to 1.2 m (4 ft.) away by firing a spurt of water out of its mouth to knock the insect into the water. The fish then quickly eats the water-bound victim.

Respiration in fish

Almost every fish has an *operculum** (oh PUR kyuh lum) (pl., opercula), a conspicuous plate behind the eye on each side of the head. The opercula pulsate regularly. Beneath each operculum is a series of *gills,* the major organs of respiration. The gill consists of two rows of thin *gill filaments* on a band of cartilage called the *gill arch.* Close examination of the gill filaments reveals that they are stacks of thin plates covered by a thin epithelium and richly supplied with blood vessels. The *gill rakers,* a number of cartilage projections on the inner margin of the gill arch, prevent food and debris from passing over and clogging the gills.

The fish obtains oxygen for cellular respiration by utilizing the oxygen dissolved in water (not the oxygen of the water molecule). In respiration the fish closes the opercula and expands the gill arches laterally, drawing water into its mouth. The fish then closes its mouth, contracts the gill arches, and opens its opercula, forcing the water over the gills.

As the water passes over the gills, oxygen diffuses into the numerous tiny blood vessels in the

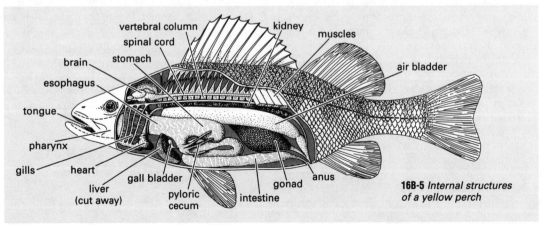

vertebral column
spinal cord
stomach
brain
esophagus
tongue
pharynx
gills
heart
liver
(cut away)
gall bladder
pyloric
cecum
intestine
gonad
anus
kidney
muscles
air bladder

16B-5 *Internal structures of a yellow perch*

operculum: (L. OPERCULUM, cover)

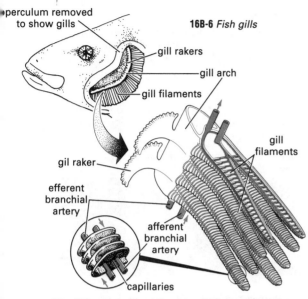

perculum removed
to show gills

16B-6 *Fish gills*

gill rakers

gill arch

gill filaments

gill filaments

gil raker

efferent branchial artery

afferent branchial artery

capillaries

gills. Waste carbon dioxide diffuses out of the blood and into the water. This gas exchange process is so efficient in some fish that 85% of the oxygen dissolved in the water is absorbed in one pass over the gills.

Circulatory and nervous systems in fish

The circulation of blood enables oxygen and nutrients to reach every cell of the fish. The moving force behind circulation is a *two-chambered heart,* located behind and below the gills. The **atrium** (AY tree um) (pl., atria) is the chamber in the heart designed to receive the blood from the body tissues. The atrium empties the blood into the **ventricle** (VEN trih kul), a muscular chamber designed to pump the blood forward through the arteries.

The major organs of the fish's nervous system are the brain and spinal cord. Ten pairs of cranial nerves branch from the brain; and many pairs of spinal nerves, from the spinal cord. The brain contains the major *lobes* (divisions) that are typical of most vertebrates. Judging by its large optic lobes and large eyes, fish should be able to see well. Their sight, however, is limited; this is due in part to the diminished light under water.

cerebrum   optic lobes

olfactory lobes

cerebellum

spinal cord

olfactory sacs   **The brain of a fish**

medulla oblongata

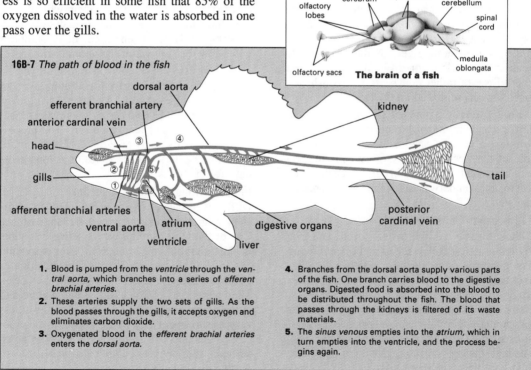

16B-7 *The path of blood in the fish*

dorsal aorta

efferent branchial artery

anterior cardinal vein

head

gills

afferent branchial arteries

ventral aorta   atrium

ventricle

liver

digestive organs

kidney

tail

posterior cardinal vein

1. Blood is pumped from the *ventricle* through the *ventral aorta,* which branches into a series of *afferent brachial arteries.*

2. These arteries supply the two sets of gills. As the blood passes through the gills, it accepts oxygen and eliminates carbon dioxide.

3. Oxygenated blood in the *efferent brachial arteries* enters the *dorsal aorta.*

4. Branches from the dorsal aorta supply various parts of the fish. One branch carries blood to the digestive organs. Digested food is absorbed into the blood to be distributed throughout the fish. The blood that passes through the kidneys is filtered of its waste materials.

5. The *sinus venous* empties into the *atrium,* which in turn empties into the ventricle, and the process begins again.

Salt-water and Freshwater Fish

Most fish dwell in either salt water or freshwater; both environments pose special problems for the fish. In freshwater, the concentration of salt in the water is much lower than that of the fish's body fluids. By diffusion water enters the fish while salt escapes from it.

Though the scales and slime coat are waterproof, water gain and salt loss do occur through the gills of freshwater fish. To counteract this flow and maintain body-fluid balance, the kidney of a freshwater fish excretes excess water with wastes while special salt-absorbing cells in the gills actively transport salt from the water into the fish's blood.

Ocean water has a salt concentration higher than the body fluid of the fish, causing the fish to gain excess salt and lose body water. To maintain water balance, the marine fish drinks sea water, which also brings excess salt into the fish. Excess salt is passed from the fish by salt-secretory cells in the gills, is left in the intestine to be ejected with solid wastes, or is excreted by the kidney.

Some fish such as the salmon, sculpin, eel, and steelhead trout travel regularly from salt water to freshwater. These fish have highly adaptable fluid regulation devices.

salmon before breeding (left, salt water) and after breeding (right, freshwater)

The sense of smell is one of the fish's keenest senses. Although we speak of tasting water, fish actually smell the water that enters the **olfactory sacs** (small pouches behind the nostrils on the fish's snout). Fish can detect incredibly minute amounts of substances dissolved in water. Some experts believe that certain migratory fish are guided to their home rivers by the precise combination of smells produced by the plants in that river. Taste (a rather dull sense in the fish) and touch are accomplished on the tongue.

Fish have no external ears; however, they can detect sound vibrations through their skulls. Bony fish have a sensory canal or **lateral line** on each side of their bodies. The sensory cells in these canals respond to changes in current, enabling the fish to detect underwater movements and pressure changes.

Reproduction in fish

Although some fish are ovoviviparous and even viviparous, most follow the same basic reproductive plan: the eggs are laid and then fertilized externally. The female fish has paired *ovaries,* which in some species can produce hundreds of thousands of eggs. The male sex organs, the *testes,* produce sperm. When environmental conditions are right, the female **spawns** (lays the eggs). The male then covers the eggs with **milt** (a milky fluid containing the sperm).

Proper conditions for *spawning* often include slight changes in temperature, types and amount of food, pH of water, and other factors. Any home aquarist who has tried to raise them will attest to the "finickiness" of some fish. God designed fish to spawn only when environmental conditions will allow the survival of the young fish.

The fertilized eggs develop into embryos. In the egg the embryo usually forms atop a ball of food material called **yolk.** As the embryo grows, the yolk shrinks. Eventually a tiny larval fish will escape the egg and fend for itself. The process from egg to larva may take only a few hours for some tropical freshwater species or as long as 90 days for the brook trout.

Unusual forms of fish reproduction

Different species of fish practice involved courtship, migration, and even nest-building rituals. One of the most familiar reproductive behaviors is the migration of *salmon* to their spawning grounds. The salmon hatched in freshwater streams migrate to the open waters of the ocean. They remain at sea for years. When mature and at the proper season, these fish will return to the very stream where they were hatched. In the process, the salmon will leap waterfalls, battle fierce currents, and navigate complicated waterways to reach their spawning grounds.

16B-8 *The male stickleback guarding its nest*

Many female fish scatter their eggs in the spawning area as the male darts behind, fertilizing as many as possible. This completes the mating instincts of both parents, and they turn and eat as many eggs as they can find. Other fish lay eggs in the open or in shallow depressions in the sand and then leave them to whatever predator cares to find and eat them.

The male *stickleback,* however, constructs an elaborate nest of aquatic vegetation, using a sticky body secretion to glue the nest together. The male then entices the female into the nest to spawn. Once she has laid the eggs, the female leaves. The male fertilizes the eggs and then guards them till they hatch. Even after they hatch, the male stickleback remains a dedicated parent.

The stickleback is not the only example of a fish's supplying parental care. With the freshwater *angelfish,* a common aquarium fish, both parents take care of the eggs. Once the rows of sticky eggs have been laid and fertilized, the parents take turns protecting the eggs from predators and fanning bacteria and fungus from the eggs with their fins. Normally, the parents destroy only those eggs that are unfertilized or begin to develop abnormally.

In many fish species the male provides all the care for the young. The male *sea catfish* keeps the fertilized eggs in its mouth until they hatch. The female *sea horse* lays eggs in a special brood pouch on the male where the eggs will hatch.

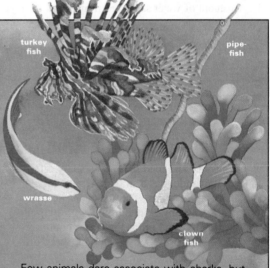

Unique Fish

To survive in the highly predatory aquatic world, many fish use unusual behaviors or defense mechanisms. Camouflage is a common method of self-defense. The long, slender body of the *pipefish* looks like a strand of the seaweed in which it hides.

Some fish bear frightening weapons. The dazzling coloration of the tropical *turkey fish (lion fish)* makes it a conspicuous target, but its long, elegant fins have extremely poisonous spines.

Fish differ in their relationships and interactions with other animals. Some travel with other members of their species in huge groups called *schools.* Others are loners, confronting other fish only when about to eat, be eaten, or to mate.

Several fish have beneficial partnerships with other animals. For example, certain *clown fish* have found a partner in the sea anemone. When most fish swim within range of the anemone's tentacles, they are immediately paralyzed by the tentacles' nematocysts or stinging cells. The clown fish, however, can swim among the tentacles without being harmed. Thus, whenever a predator is near, the clown fish can enter a refuge where few enemies can follow.

Few animals dare associate with sharks, but the *remora* does so with benefit to both animals. The remora, a relatively small fish with a sucker organ on the top of its head, attaches to the body of the shark and eats the parasites it finds on its host. The shark thus obtains a cleaning service; the remora, free meals.

The *wrasse* also performs a cleaning service; however, it sets up "shop" to which other fish come for cleaning. Wrasses flit about the head and gills of groupers, snappers, and eels, picking parasites off their "customers."

Biological Terms

Class Osteichthyes	air bladder	countershading	atrium	spawn
class Osteichthyes	scales	*Digestion in Fish*	ventricle	milt
paired fins	mucus	operculum	olfactory sac	yolk
unpaired fins	chromatophores	gills	lateral line	

Review Questions 16B-2

1. Describe the digestive system of a fish.
2. List several methods specific fish have for obtaining food.
3. From what source and by what means do fish obtain oxygen for respiration?
4. What methods do fish use to maintain the water and salt balance between their body fluids and their environment?
5. Describe the heart of a fish.
6. Describe the senses of sight, smell, taste, hearing, and touch in fish.
7. Describe the reproductive process used by most fish.

Facet 16B-2: Cartilaginous Fish-Class Chondrichthyes, pages 398-99

1. List several characteristics of class Chondrichthyes that separate it from class Agnatha and class Osteichthyes.
2. List and describe two members of the class Chondrichthyes.

Thought Questions

1. A fish out of water soon dies from a lack of oxygen even though it is in an environment which has more oxygen than its normal environment. Explain why.
2. Why is it important for fish to mate only when certain environmental conditions are met? In what way is this timed mating anti-evolutionary?

16C-Class Amphibia: The Amphibians

The salamander and toad seem drastically different. The salamander has a smooth, almost tubular body with fragile limbs. The toad, on the other hand, is a fat, lumpy-skinned blob with bulging eyes, a wide grin, and limbs that seem comically disproportionate to its body. Although very different, these two animals are members of the **class Amphibia*** (am FIB ee uh) and share many characteristics.

Metamorphosis in amphibians

The term **amphibian,** meaning ''double life,'' aptly describes the remarkable dual existence of most members of this vertebrate class. Their life cycle begins in the water. The female amphibian lays its jellylike eggs in the water. Toads lay strings of eggs; frogs produce egg masses. Usually many eggs are produced, but the number var-

ies dramatically. A small Cuban frog produces only a single egg. A land salamander may produce 30; a large toad, 30,000. In most amphibians fertilization is external: the male fertilizes the eggs by discharging *milt* over the eggs. Usually after a period of development, an aquatic *larva* escapes the egg.

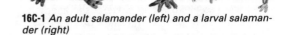

16C-1 *An adult salamander (left) and a larval salamander (right)*

The larval salamander resembles the adult but bears feathery external gills about its head. The larval frog is the familiar **tadpole** with its oval

---

Amphibia: Amphi- (Gk. AMPHI, on both sides) + -bia (life)

16C-2 *An adult frog (left) and a tadpole (right)*

body tapering to a slender tail. The gills of the tadpole are covered by a flap of skin. The tadpole undergoes major physical changes to become an adult: the gills degenerate, the characteristic frog limbs appear, the eyes grow and bulge, the mouth widens, and the tail is absorbed. The resulting land-dwelling, air-breathing adult bears little resemblance to the tadpole.

The basic scheme of amphibian metamorphosis has a number of variations. The *mud puppy,* a common salamander, remains an aquatic, gill-breathing form throughout life. Certain salamanders will remain aquatic forms as long as they have water to live in. When their watery homes dry up, certain internal mechanisms are triggered, and these larvas change into air-breathing adults.

The physical changes that occur in metamorphosis may be quite dramatic. Scientists first observed the *paradoxical frog* of Trinidad in the form of a tadpole 36 cm (14 in.) long. They sought in vain for the adult frog which they assumed must be huge. After painstaking research, they discovered that the paradoxical frog tadpole "grows" into an adult only 4 cm (1.6 in.) long.

Skin of amphibians

Amphibians are covered with a smooth, scaleless skin that is richly supplied with blood vessels and moistened by secretions from glands of the skin. This skin is more than a body covering. Some amphibians secrete poisonous substances over their skins to discourage potential predators.

16C-3 *The skin secretion of the poison arrow frog is used to poison the tips of arrows used by certain American natives.*

These poisons may only taste bad, or they may be strong enough to burn the animal that touches the amphibian. The Central and South American *poison arrow frog,* with its orange body and blue feet, secretes a poison so potent that it is used to tip the arrows of local natives.

The skin can also function as a respiratory organ. The tiny blood vessels in the thin, moist skin bring the blood into close contact with the environment where the exchange of oxygen and carbon dioxide can occur.

Chromatophores color the skin of amphibians. These cells may provide camouflage coloration for some, but many amphibians are brilliant shades of red, yellow, gold, and blue. In most cases these are warning colorations; the bright color labels the animal as dangerous or inedible.

Respiration in amphibians

Amphibians may use one or more of four mechanisms to obtain the oxygen they need. The first method, used by every amphibian during some phase of its life, is respiration by *gills.* Since most amphibians spend the early part of their lives as aquatic animals, the necessity of such an apparatus is obvious. The gills degenerate when the amphibian begins its terrestrial existence.

Many amphibians have **lungs,** internal organs for the exchange of gases between the atmosphere and blood. One such amphibian is the adult frog. The frog does not depend only upon lungs to obtain oxygen. In fact, most amphibians can spend long periods without refilling their lungs.

The lining of an amphibian's mouth and throat is abundantly supplied with blood vessels and may serve as a third means of respiration. Finally, the most unusual amphibian respiratory organ is its skin. The skin accounts for 90-95% of the respiration of certain lungless salamanders. Frogs depend upon their skin for respiration while under water for long periods of time.

Circulation in amphibians

The major differences between the circulatory system of amphibians and that of fish are the amphibian's three-chambered heart and an additional "loop" in the circulatory cycle. The upper part of the amphibian's heart consists of two *atria*

American Frogs and Toads

The terms *toad* and *frog* are often used interchangeably, but both represent specific amphibian groups. Most anurans fit into one of three groups: frogs, toads, or tree frogs.

The most common true *frogs* in America are in the genus *Rana*. They generally have a smooth, shiny skin that dries easily. For that reason, frogs usually stay near the water. Common American frogs include the *leopard frog (R. pipiens)*, a spotted frog, and the *green frog (R. clamitans)*. The largest American frog is the *bullfrog (R. catesbeiana)*, a common inhabitant of the east coast, reaching a length of 23 cm (9 in.). This amphibian has a deep voice, and its hind legs often appear on the dinner table as an entree.

Many *toads* belong to the genus *Bufo*. Unlike the frog, the toad has a dry, rough, warty skin. Despite superstitions to the contrary, this warty skin does not produce warts on humans. The toad is strictly a land dweller, entering the water only to mate. Often you may find these amphibians in the leaves and moist soil of the forest floor far from a body of water. *B. terrestris* is a common toad of the eastern United States.

Tree frogs (genus *Hyla* and others) are generally smaller than frogs or toads. These frogs have enlarged, sticky discs at the ends of their toes that enable them to cling to tree branches. The *spring peeper (H. crucifer)* is a tiny tree frog whose peeping call is a familiar sound on spring evenings.

a. American toad *(Bufo)*
b. Spring peeper *(Hyla)*
c. Bull frog *(Rana)*

which receive blood from different parts of the body. The atria empty into a single muscular *ventricle*, the chamber which pumps the blood to the organs and tissues of the animal.

The added loop is a connection between the heart and the respiratory apparatus. Oxygenated blood enters the left atrium. The right atrium collects deoxygenated blood from the body. Both atria empty simultaneously into the ventricle, where the oxygenated and deoxygenated blood partially mix.

The ventricle then pumps the blood through a single large artery. A portion of that blood goes by one branch of this artery to the lungs and skin. This blood is oxygenated and returned to the heart, completing the respiratory loop. The remaining blood goes by other branches to the body, supplying the tissues with oxygen.

Amphibians are *ectothermic*; their body temperatures and levels of activity vary with the surrounding temperature. In winter, when the temperature drops, the amphibian's body processes slow down. During this time the amphibian will usually burrow into the mud of a stream or lake to wait out the cold weather in a "lifeless" state called **hibernation.*** The animal becomes inert; its heartbeat and circulation almost cease.

In this slowed state of metabolism the animal needs little food. Stored food is slowly used to meet the animal's nutritional needs. The small amounts of oxygen needed usually diffuse through the skin. When warm weather returns, the amphibian "awakes" and resumes its normal activities.

Extreme summer heat can also create problems for cold-blooded animals. With no mechanisms to keep cool, some amphibians must escape the heat by staying at the bottom of a pond, burrowing into the mud, or hiding in a cool place. This period of inactivity is **estivation*** (ES tuh VAY shun). When the temperatures are suitable again, the animal becomes active.

Classification of amphibians

The class Amphibia is divided into three orders on the basis of body shape and type of limbs.

❏ *Order Apoda** (AP uh duh) This order contains

hibernation: hibern- (L. HIBERNUS, winter)

estivation: estiv- (L. AESTAS, summer)

Apoda: A- (without) + -poda (foot)

a small group of strange, wormlike animals called caecilians. These amphibians lack limbs and limb girdles. Most species are subterranean and are totally blind as adults. They burrow to find the worms and invertebrates that are their food.

❑ *Order Caudata** (kaw DAH tuh) Salamanders are often mistaken for lizards. These animals do resemble the reptile; however, their structures and life cycles clearly label them as amphibians. Salamanders are distinguished from other amphibians by the presence of a definite head, trunk, and tail. Most salamanders have two pairs of small, identical limbs along the trunk.

❑ *Order Anura** (uh NOO ruh) The frogs and toads have wide heads that fuse with short, pudgy bodies. Their large eyes bulge on the top of their heads. They have wide mouths that appear to be locked into permanent smirks. The major characteristics that distinguish frogs and toads from other amphibians are their lack of tails and their uniquely designed limbs. The front legs are small and function primarily as props for the sitting frog and shock absorbers for landings from jumps. The hind legs are larger and heavily muscled. These limbs are designed for jumping on land and swimming in the water. The toes of the hind legs are webbed for swimming.

Salamanders

Another group of amphibians found in the United States is the salamanders. Most salamanders in the United States are small, rarely more than 15-25 cm (6-10 in.) long, and are also subdued in color. Of course, several notable exceptions exist. Some species are brilliant oranges, reds, and yellows. The *tiger salamander* receives its name from the bright yellow stripes and blotches that mark its skin.

The American *newt* is a common inhabitant of the eastern United States. After an aquatic larval stage, this salamander spends a part of its life on land before returning to the water to become an aquatic adult.

Larger American salamanders include the *hellbender*, a stream dweller of the eastern United States, and the *mud puppy*, an inhabitant of muddy stream bottoms in the Midwest. Both may reach 60 cm (24 in.) in length.

16C-4 *The tiger salamander (top) and the hellbender salamander (bottom)*

Review Questions 16C-1

1. List several characteristics of the class Amphibia that separate its members from other vertebrate classes.
2. Identify at least three functions of an amphibian's skin.
3. List four structures which amphibians use for respiration. Tell which are normally used during each stage of life.
4. What are the major differences between the circulatory system of a larval amphibian and that of an adult amphibian?
5. What are the primary differences between hibernation and estivation?
6. What characteristics set salamanders apart from other amphibians?
7. What characteristics set the anurans (frogs and toads) apart from other amphibians?
8. What are the three main groups of frogs? What characteristics separate them?

Anatomy of the Frog

The frog is a common laboratory animal. Frogs are inexpensive and easy to obtain, but more importantly, their anatomy and physiology partially resemble those of mammals and man.

External structures of the frog

The most conspicuous feature of the frog's head is its large, bulging *eyes*. A colored **iris** surrounds the dark **pupil**, the opening for light. The iris can enlarge or reduce the size of the pupil in response

Caudata: (tail)

Anura: an- (without) + -ura (tail)

to varying amounts of light. At the bottom of the eye is the transparent, folded **nictitating*** (NIK tuh TATE ing) **membrane.** This "third eyelid" moves across the frog's eye, keeping it moist and protected.

The two small *nostrils* on the frog's snout open into its mouth. These structures allow the animal to breathe with just the top of its head above the water. A circular membranous structure situated behind each eye is the **tympanic*** (tim PAN ik) **membrane.** This membrane serves as an eardrum, transmitting sound vibrations to the ear cavity underneath.

Mouth of the frog

The frog's large mouth is designed to capture the insects the animal eats. A large sticky tongue is attached at the front of the floor of the mouth. When an insect comes within range, the frog flips out its tongue, snagging the prey. The frog then flips the tongue and insect back into the mouth. Frogs "blink" when they swallow. This is not because the food tastes bad; the eyes are actually being pressed toward the mouth cavity to help crush the food and force it down the gullet.

The inside of the mouth of the frog contains several openings. At the front of the roof of the mouth are the *internal nostril* openings. The openings of the **Eustachian** (yoo STAY shun) **tubes** uniting the ear cavity with the mouth are at the back corners of the mouth. The passage to the digestive tract is the **gullet** at the extreme back of the mouth.

Immediately in front of the gullet is a small swelling parted by a slender opening. This is the **glottis*** leading to the lungs. Male frogs have a pair of openings in the back of the lower jaw

leading to the **vocal sacs** in the floor of the mouth. The frog passes air through these openings into the sacs when it "croaks," increasing the volume of the sound.

The frog possesses two sets of inconspicuous teeth: a ridge of tiny *maxillary** (MAK suh LEHR ee) teeth in the upper jaw and two sets of *vomerine* (VOH muh rine) teeth between the internal nostril openings in the roof of the mouth. These sets of teeth assist the frog in grasping its prey, not in chewing. The lower jaw bears no teeth.

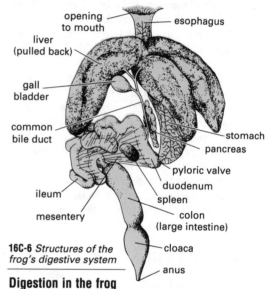

16C-6 *Structures of the frog's digestive system*

Digestion in the frog

The frog is a carnivore, ingesting insects, spiders, slugs, worms, or any other moving object it can fit into its mouth. Some larger frogs have been known to eat rats. The food, once ingested, passes through a short *esophagus* to the *stomach,* an enlarged portion of the digestive tract which serves as a storage sac and site of preliminary digestion. The stomach narrows at the region called the *pylorus** (PYE LOR us), where the muscular *pyloric valve* controls the further passage of the food.

The stomach joins the *small intestine,* a thin tube consisting of the enlarged *duodenum* (DOO uh DEE num) joined to the stomach and the coiled *ileum* (IL ee um). The small intestine empties into the short, stubby *colon* (KOH lun) or *large intestine.* From here all indigestible material is passed

16C-5 *Structures of the frog's head*

nictitating membrane
tympanic membrane
opening of Eustachian tube
glottis
nostril
internal nostril openings
vomerine teeth
maxillary teeth
gullet
opening of vocal sac
tongue

---

nictitating: nicti- (L. NICTARE, to wink)

tympanic: (Gk. TUMPANON, a drum)

glottis: (Gk. GLOTTA, tongue)

maxillary: (L. MAXILLA, upper jaw)

through the short, tubular *cloaca** (kloh AY kuh) and expelled from the body.

Two glands outside the digestive tract contribute to the digestive process. The *liver* is the large, maroon, three-lobed organ that dominates the body cavity. It produces *bile,* a substance that assists digestion. The bile collects in the small, saclike *gall bladder* and flows to the upper portion of the small intestine through the *common bile duct.* The liver also performs a variety of other functions, including the storage of digested food.

The *pancreas,* another digestive gland, is a small strip of tissue near the stomach. Pancreatic secretions also pass into the small intestine through the common bile duct. All the digestive organs are enclosed in transparent membranes called **mesenteries** (MES un TEHR eez), which bind the organs to the dorsal body wall. Blood vessels flow through the mesenteries to the internal organs.

Respiration in the frog

The frog obtains oxygen by using its skin, mouth lining, and lungs. When its oxygen requirements are low (for example, during hibernation), the frog can obtain all the oxygen it needs through its skin. The frog may also use its capillary-rich mouth lining to supplement its respiration. When active, however, its increased oxygen needs must be supplied by its pair of small lungs.

The lungs join to a single tube called the **trachea,** which opens into the mouth cavity through the slitlike *glottis.* The frog lacks the ribs and muscles needed to inhale and exhale as humans do. To breathe, the frog draws air into the mouth through the nostrils by lowering the floor of its mouth. Then with nostrils closed and glottis open, the frog swallows the air, forcing it into the lungs. Contraction of the body wall expels the air.

Circulation in the frog

Blood circulating through capillaries in the lungs becomes oxygenated and flows through the *pulmonary vein* to the left atrium of the heart. At the same time, deoxygenated blood from the body organs and muscles flows through three large veins called the *venae cavae* to a thin sac at the back of the heart, the *sinus venosus,* which empties into the right atrium. Once filled, both atria contract simultaneously, emptying their contents into the muscular ventricle.

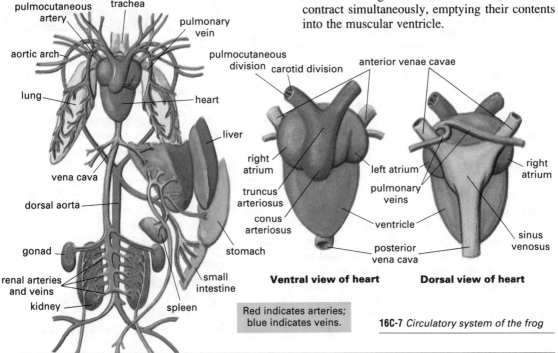

Red indicates arteries; blue indicates veins.

16C-7 *Circulatory system of the frog*

---

pylorus: pyl- (Gk. PULE, a gate) + -orus (OUROS, watcher)

cloaca: (L. CLOACA, canal)

mesentery: mes- or meso- (Gk. MESO-, middle) + -entery (ENTERON, intestines)

Frog and Toad Reproduction

During the mating season the male frog croaks to attract a mate. The female will respond to the call when her eggs are ripe. In the water the male clasps the female from behind, a process called **amplexus,*** which stimulates the female to release her eggs. Each egg is coated in a jelly produced by an oviduct. As the eggs are released, the male covers them with sperm.

After fertilization, the parents usually abandon the eggs, making them easy prey for various insect larvas, leeches, and flatworms. Fish, and even adult frogs, feed on tadpoles. As a result, it is typical for only about 5% of the fertilized eggs to survive to adulthood.

The process of egg-laying varies dramatically in certain frog species. During mating, the male Surinam toad presses the fertilized eggs into the spongy tissue on the female's back. The young hatch and develop within the skin of the mother. After several months, the young toads emerge.

With lakes and ponds scarce in Jamaica, a species of tree frog on this island lays its eggs in the pool of water found in the leaves of a native plant. The plant maintains this pool even in the driest seasons, providing an ideal home for the developing tadpoles. Some male frogs carry the eggs and tadpoles in their vocal sacs until the young are fully developed.

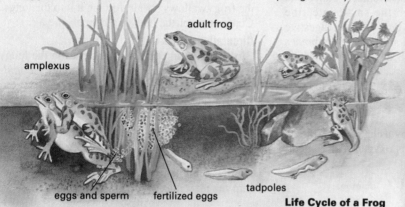

adult frog

amplexus

leopard frog

eggs and sperm   fertilized eggs   tadpoles

Life Cycle of a Frog

The ventricle contracts, forcing oxygenated and deoxygenated blood through a single large vessel, the *conus arteriosus*, which branches into a right and left *truncus arteriosus*. From each truncus arteriosus branches a *carotid* (kuh RAHT id) *arch* (blood to the head), a *pulmocutaneous** (PUHL moh kyoo TAY nee us) *artery* (blood to the lungs and skin), and *aortic arches* which fuse into the single *dorsal aorta* (blood to the body organs and muscles).

Nervous system of the frog

The nervous system of the frog can be divided into two sections. The *central nervous system* consists of the brain and spinal cord encased in the bony skull and spinal column. The amphibian brain has the five basic lobes common to most vertebrates. The lobes of the amphibian cerebrum occupy a much larger part of the brain than do those of the fish. The optic lobes, however, are

proportionally smaller in the amphibian. The amphibian cerebellum is unusually small, being only a thin strip of tissue behind the optic lobes. Since the cerebellum controls muscle coordination, the small size of this brain region may explain why frogs are not very graceful or coordinated.

The second division of the frog's nervous system is the *peripheral** (puh RIF ur ul) *nervous system*. Included in the peripheral nervous system are all the nerves which transmit impulses between the central nervous system and the frog's muscles and sensory organs.

16C-8 *Structures of a frog's brain*

medulla oblongata   cerebellum   cerebrum

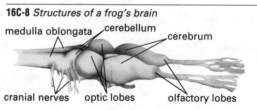

cranial nerves   optic lobes   olfactory lobes

---

amplexus: (L. AMPLECTI, to wind around)

pulmocutaneous: pulmo- (L. PULMO, lung) + -cut- (CUTIS, skin)

peripheral: peri- (Gk. PERI-, around) + -phora or -phera (PHEREIN, to carry)

Excretion and reproduction in the frog

Fixed against the dorsal body wall are a pair of long, red-brown structures, the *kidneys*. Blood passes into these organs through a series of *renal arteries* and out through *renal veins*. The kidneys filter wastes and excess water from the blood, concentrating them in the form of urine. This liquid waste empties by a pair of thin, tubular *ureters* into the cloaca. It may then be excreted from the body or passed through a small passage into the *urinary bladder*, a sac which can store the urine for future disposal.

The female frog has large lobed *ovaries* above the kidneys. The ovaries fill with eggs until, during the breeding season, the thin walls of the ovaries burst, spilling the eggs into the female's body cavity. Abdominal contractions direct the eggs into tubular oviducts to be transported out of the body. Cilia in the oviducts propel the eggs through the long, coiled tubes and into the saclike *uterus** (YOO tur us) where the eggs are stored until they are laid. To lay the eggs, the frog passes the eggs from the uterus into the cloaca from which they are ejected during mating.

The male frog possesses a pair of oval *testes*, found on the ventral side of the kidneys. The sperm produced by these organs travel to the kidneys in thin tubes, the *vasa efferentia*. These tubes empty through the kidneys into the cloaca.

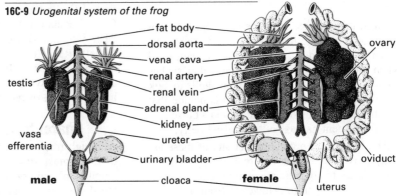

16C-9 *Urogenital system of the frog*

fat body
dorsal aorta
vena cava
renal artery
renal vein
adrenal gland
kidney
ureter
urinary bladder
cloaca

testis
vasa efferentia
male

ovary
oviduct
uterus
female

Biological Terms

class Amphibia	hibernation	*Anatomy of the Frog*	tympanic membrane	vocal sac
amphibian	estivation	iris	Eustachian tube	mesentery
tadpole		pupil	gullet	trachea
lung		nictitating membrane	glottis	amplexus

Review Questions 16C-2

1. Describe the methods frogs use to capture and swallow food.
2. List and tell the function of each of the openings within the mouth of a frog.
3. List the structures a morsel of food passes through from the time it is swallowed by a frog until it is egested.
4. Describe how a frog takes in and releases air.
5. Draw and label a simplified diagram of the blood flow in the frog's circulatory system.
6. List and give the functions of the organs in the frog's excretory system.
7. What are the two major divisions of the nervous system of the frog, and what structures belong in each division?
8. Describe (a) the male reproductive system of a frog, (b) the female reproductive system of a frog, and (c) the mating process of frogs.

Thought Questions

1. Describe the major differences between the circulatory system of a fish and that of a frog.
2. Based on the sizes of the brain lobes, what function would you expect to be most acute in the amphibians? Is this accurate? Do the other lobe sizes, when compared to the sizes of the same lobes of the fish brain, adequately explain the behavioral differences between frogs and fish? Explain.

uterus: (L. UTERUS, womb)

16D–Class Reptilia: The Reptiles

In Genesis 3 the serpent, or snake, is controlled by Satan, and by speaking to Eve beguiled her into eating the forbidden fruit. Then in verses 14-15 the Lord speaks to the serpent: "Because thou hast done this, thou art cursed above all cattle, and above every beast of the field; upon thy belly shalt thou go, and dust shalt thou eat all the days of thy life: and I will put enmity between thee and the woman, and between thy seed and her seed; it shall bruise thy head, and thou shalt bruise his heel."

From this passage some people conclude that this reptile was the most beautiful of the beasts. Since the Bible does not say Eve was surprised when the snake spoke, a few claim that snakes (and possibly other animals) were able to talk before the fall of man. Some also conclude that the snake had limbs since part of God's curse was that the serpent had to go "upon [its] belly."

The Bible does not contradict any of these assumptions, but it does not really support them either. True, today there are many snakes that can be considered beautiful. However, beautiful is not necessarily the same as subtle. A snake's slithering motions, its stalking of prey, or other characteristics may be considered subtle.

Some Bible scholars think that Satan took control of the snake's body or at least directed the snake's actions while it tempted Eve. Even though the Bible does not record Eve's surprise, there is no real proof that animals were able to talk before the fall. Satan may have overcome her suspicion of a talking animal. (Numbers 22 does not record that Balaam was surprised when the ass spoke either.) It may also be possible that Eve was spoken to by a form of telepathy (communication from mind to mind). It is even possible that many or all animals communicated by telepathy before the fall, but a strict interpretation of the Bible does not *demand* such.

The idea that the snake once had limbs may appear logical in that the first part of the curse condemns it to slithering. The removal of the snake's legs (or wings), however, is only *implied;* the snake may have never had appendages.

Again, we must remember that the Bible is a spiritual handbook and is not given to reveal all knowledge, but what the Bible does say is scientifically accurate. More significant is the second part of the curse. According to most Bible scholars, this curse speaks not so much of man's fear of snakes (which is not inborn but learned by humans) but of the relationship between Christ–the offspring of the woman's seed–and Satan. Here, at the time of the fall of man, is the first of God's promises of a coming Saviour, the One who shall truly bruise the head of Satan by destroying him (Heb. 2:14) and condemning him to hell (Rev. 20:1-3, 10). The snake makes an interesting topic for Bible study since it regularly appears as a symbol of Satan and is often tied into the theme of redemption.

Characteristics of Reptiles

Although many amphibians are terrestrial, most of them must stay in moist environments. The amphibian's thin skin must be periodically moistened, and amphibian eggs must be deposited in a wet area to develop. The reptiles, however, have a special protective skin, possess lungs from birth, and lay eggs encased in shells. These features make many reptiles well suited for life on land. All reptiles must breathe air; therefore, even marine reptiles, such as certain turtles and sea snakes, can drown.

One characteristic most reptiles share with amphibians is the three-chambered heart. Three-chambered reptile hearts have a partially divided ventricle which helps to keep oxygenated and deoxygenated blood from mixing. Some reptiles (the crocodilians) have a four-chambered heart similar to that of mammals and birds. Reptiles, if they have limbs, have claws on their toes, a characteristic not shared by the amphibians.

Skin of reptiles

Snakes and lizards are often called "slimy," an inaccurate description. If you hold a reptile, you can feel that its skin is cool, dry, and leathery. The scales, which give the reptile's body this texture, are part of a thick skin with few glands.

FACETS OF BIOLOGY

16D–1

Dinosaurs

The term **dinosaur*** was coined by Sir Richard Owen in 1842, about the time of the first fossil finds of large reptiles. Although we normally think of dinosaurs as large beasts, most dinosaurs were about the size of horses. Normally, however, the term is used to describe the larger of the presumably extinct reptiles.

Biblical and scientific evidence tend to support the idea that men and dinosaurs existed at the same time. Two references to animals believed to be reptiles are found in the final chapters of Job. God, calling Job's attention to His mighty works of creation, describes "behemoth," a large, powerful, swamp-dwelling vegetarian whose bones were like bars of iron and whose tail resembled a cedar tree (Job 40:15-24). The description fits the *Apatosaurus* or *Brachiosaurus* (both formerly called brontosaurus*) far better than the hippopotamus or elephant, as proposed by some scholars. Elephant and hippopotamus tails are very *unlike* cedar trees. In verse 19 "behemoth" is called "the chief

of the ways of God," implying that it was the greatest animal God ever made. An elephant, hippopotamus, or similar creature simply does not fit that description.

Another mighty creature in Job 41, the "leviathan," fits the description of a marine reptile such as the *Plesiosaurus* or *Mosasaurus*, but not the crocodile some scholars suggest.

Not all Bible scholars agree on the time that Job lived since there is little within the Bible to pinpoint a date. In any case it would be illogical for God to ask Job to think of something with which he was not familiar. Although Job may never have seen these animals, it is safe to assume he was at least familiar with oral traditions about them. This is a good indication that man was alive at the same time as dinosaurs.

Some people believe that dinosaurs were alive after the Flood. Relatively accurate representations of dinosaurs appear in ancient rock carvings and paintings. On the wall of Rattlesnake Canyon in Colorado is an etching of a reptile that appears to be either an *Allosaurus* or a *Tyrannosaurus.** The characteristic upright posture, long neck, and long tail are evident. On the same wall pictures of goats, horses, and men are also carved.

Paintings of the *Apatosaurus* can be seen on the walls of a cave near Salisbury, Zimbabwe. The

Unearthing animal fossils

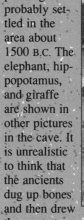

St. Bartholomew with a dragon and a sword, painting by Jean Bellegambe (circa 1470-1533)

bushmen who made these paintings probably settled in the area about 1500 B.C. The elephant, hippopotamus, and giraffe are shown in other pictures in the cave. It is unrealistic to think that the ancients dug up bones and then drew these creatures. They may have been depicting animals they had actually seen.

The recurring "dragon" theme in folklore helps support the idea of the dinosaur's coexistence with man. The Chinese dragon symbolism is well known, as are the Egyptian and Irish dragon mythologies. *Beowulf* is typical of many ancient stories in which a man slays a dreadful monster. Saint Michael and Saint George are often depicted in connection with dragons. These and other examples lead us to suspect that our ancestors may indeed have witnessed such creatures and then passed down the descriptions.

Most people assume that dinosaurs are extinct. True, these large reptiles are not in zoos or regular

---

dinosaur: dino- (Gk. DEINES, fearful or monstrous) + -saur (L. SAURUS, lizard)
brontosaurus: bronto- (Gk. BRONTE, thunder) + -saur (lizard)

tyrannosaurus: tyranno- (Gk. TURANNOS, tyrant) + -saur (lizard)

sights on wild animal safaris. Many people believe that changing conditions (an evolutionist would say because of gradual changes such as glaciation; a creationist would say because of either the gap or changes after the Flood) drastically reduced the areas in which dinosaurs could live, and the dinosaurs simply died out.

Evolutionists claim that dinosaurs died out millions of years ago and assume their extinction. Creationists place the change as recently as 4,000 yr. ago and should not be surprised if extinction is not complete. In fact, there is some evidence that what we call dinosaurs may not have entirely disappeared.

The puzzle of the "Loch Ness Monster" in Scotland has been extensively studied. Scientists have searched the deep lake in a submarine. The "monster" has been found on sonar and photographed numerous times. Many people are still not convinced, since photographs can be faked. From the photographs and descriptions, however, the creature appears to be like a *Plesiosaurus.*

Less familiar "monsters" have also been sighted. The relatively small size of Loch Ness (about 360 sq. mi.) makes investigations there easy compared to those at sea. In 1883, for example, the captain of the HMS *Fly* made an interesting sighting in the Gulf of California. He saw a large marine creature having the general form of an alligator but with a much longer neck and with flippers instead of legs. This description,

In 1977 fishermen off the coast of New Zealand found what appeared to be the badly decayed remains of a young, supposedly extinct Plesiosaurus *about 30 ft. long. It was thrown overboard before it could be properly identified.*

also, is similar to the *Plesiosaurus.* Finding this creature would be difficult, but it is impossible to prove that it does not exist.

In some areas of the world, natives tell stories of dinosaurlike animals. In Africa, some stories describe a land monster, the *Mokeli,* as a water elephant with a head on the end of its trunk, a possible description of an *Apatosaurus*-like creature. In Zambia some natives tell of a meat-eating, long-necked *Chipekwe,* which attacks rhinoceros, elephants, and hippopotamuses. They describe it as having a single horn and other features similar to a *Ceratosaurus.*

These stories may be fanciful since investigation has not produced any scientific evidence of such animals. Perhaps, however, scientists have not looked hard enough for something most of them do not believe exists.

Review questions on page 416.

Apatosaurus (brontosaurus)

Tyrannosaurus

Plesiosaurus

Mosasaurus

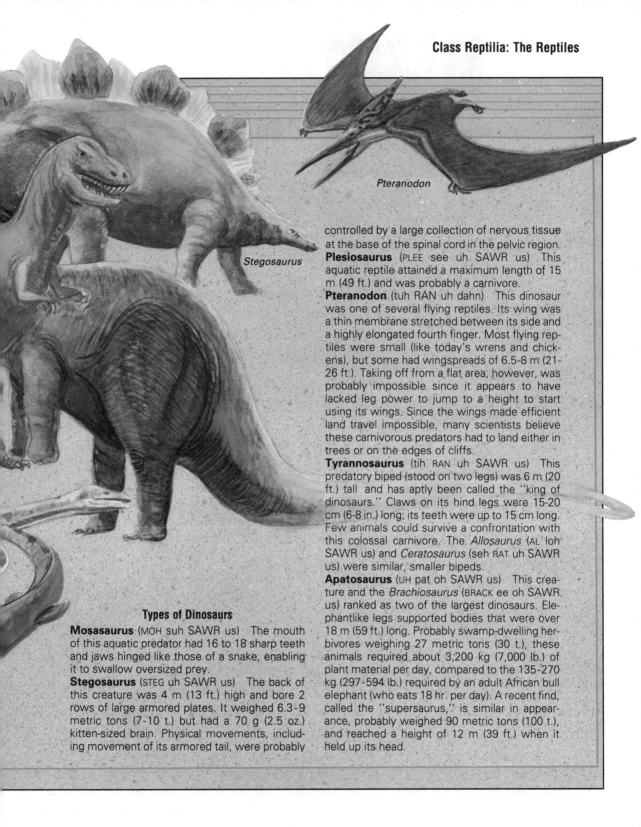

Pteranodon

Stegosaurus

controlled by a large collection of nervous tissue at the base of the spinal cord in the pelvic region.

Plesiosaurus (PLEE see uh SAWR us) This aquatic reptile attained a maximum length of 15 m (49 ft.) and was probably a carnivore.

Pteranodon (tuh RAN uh dahn) This dinosaur was one of several flying reptiles. Its wing was a thin membrane stretched between its side and a highly elongated fourth finger. Most flying reptiles were small (like today's wrens and chickens), but some had wingspreads of 6.5-8 m (21-26 ft.). Taking off from a flat area, however, was probably impossible since it appears to have lacked leg power to jump to a height to start using its wings. Since the wings made efficient land travel impossible, many scientists believe these carnivorous predators had to land either in trees or on the edges of cliffs.

Tyrannosaurus (tih RAN uh SAWR us) This predatory biped (stood on two legs) was 6 m (20 ft.) tall and has aptly been called the "king of dinosaurs." Claws on its hind legs were 15-20 cm (6-8 in.) long; its teeth were up to 15 cm long. Few animals could survive a confrontation with this colossal carnivore. The *Allosaurus* (AL loh SAWR us) and *Ceratosaurus* (seh RAT uh SAWR us) were similar, smaller bipeds.

Apatosaurus (UH pat oh SAWR us) This creature and the *Brachiosaurus* (BRACK ee oh SAWR us) ranked as two of the largest dinosaurs. Elephantlike legs supported bodies that were over 18 m (59 ft.) long. Probably swamp-dwelling herbivores weighing 27 metric tons (30 t.), these animals required about 3,200 kg (7,000 lb.) of plant material per day, compared to the 135-270 kg (297-594 lb.) required by an adult African bull elephant (who eats 18 hr. per day). A recent find, called the "supersaurus," is similar in appearance, probably weighed 90 metric tons (100 t.), and reached a height of 12 m (39 ft.) when it held up its head.

Types of Dinosaurs

Mosasaurus (MOH suh SAWR us) The mouth of this aquatic predator had 16 to 18 sharp teeth and jaws hinged like those of a snake, enabling it to swallow oversized prey.

Stegosaurus (STEG uh SAWR us) The back of this creature was 4 m (13 ft.) high and bore 2 rows of large armored plates. It weighed 6.3-9 metric tons (7-10 t.) but had a 70 g (2.5 oz.) kitten-sized brain. Physical movements, including movement of its armored tail, were probably

16D-1 *Skin of a chameleon*

Generally, reptilian scales are nonliving and cannot grow with the animal. The reptile must periodically shed its outgrown scales and replace them with a larger set, which the reptile grows before it sheds the old. Unlike amphibian skin, which is thin and moist to permit respiration, reptilian skin and scales are thick and dry to prevent water loss. Since many reptiles live where water is scarce, this water-preserving function is essential to the animal's survival.

The thick skin of a reptile helps it conserve some heat in its body. Reptiles are predominantly *ectothermic*. Many reptiles do ''sun themselves'' to warm their bodies, but too much heat can kill them. Most reptiles therefore hide in cool spots during the hot part of the day. In cool weather most reptiles hide and enter an inactive state similar to hibernation.

Reproduction in reptiles

Reptilian eggs differ from those of water-breeders such as fish and amphibians. In water small eggs covered with a gelatinous material are fertilized and develop without difficulty; on land, such eggs would quickly dry up and die. The reptile must, therefore, have an egg that maintains a suitably moist environment for the developing animal. The **amniotic** (AM nee AHT ik) **egg,** which is produced by all reptiles, meets this condition.

The amniotic egg must be fertilized within the body of the female. Once fertilized, the egg is encased in a protective **shell** and is passed from the female's body. The shell is porous, permitting the exchange of gases between the egg and the environment but preventing excessive water loss. The tiny embryo grows atop a ball of stored food material called the **yolk.**

Four *embryonic membranes* form during development within the amniotic egg. The first membrane, the **amnion** (AM nee ahn), grows around the embryo, protecting it in a fluid-filled sac. The second membrane is the **yolk sac,** which

16D-2 *The amniotic egg*

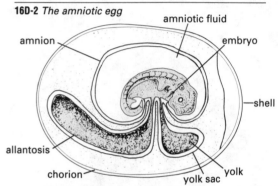

surrounds the yolk. As the yolk is consumed, this sac is slowly drawn into the embryo until it disappears altogether. The **chorion*** (KOHR ee AHN) is a membrane that lines the inner surface of the shell. The fourth membrane, the **allantois** (uh LAN toh iss), is a sac richly supplied with blood vessels from the embryo. Respiration and excretion occur through the vessels of this membrane.

The embryo in an amniotic egg is an independent, self-sustaining unit provided with a protective home, a moist environment, and a built-in food supply.

Review Questions 16D-1

1. Based on Genesis 3, what three characteristics do some people claim the snake had before the curse? Which, if any, of these characteristics are necessary according to Scripture?
2. What characteristics separate the class Reptilia from other vertebrate classes?
3. Describe and list the structures found within an amniotic egg.
4. What type of fertilization is associated with animals that develop from amniotic eggs?

Facet 16D-1: Dinosaurs, pages 413-15

1. List and briefly describe four dinosaurs.
2. Tell why the behemoth described in Job 40:15-24 is not a hippopotamus or an elephant.
3. List evidences to support the belief that man and dinosaurs lived at the same time.

---

chorion: (Gk. KHORION, afterbirth)

Classification of Living Reptiles

The class Reptilia encompasses nearly 6,000 living species. The smallest reptile is a lizard about as thick as a pencil and 5 cm (2 in.) long. Crocodiles have been measured at 7 m (23 ft.). Most, however, are only about 4.5 m (15 ft.) long. The anaconda, a snake of the tropics, may reach 11 m (36 ft.) in length. Most lizards in the United States, however, are under 60 cm (24 in.), and a snake over 1.5 m (5 ft.) long is considered large.

Reptiles are classified in four orders:
- *Squamata*–snakes and lizards
- *Testudinata*–turtles and tortoises
- *Crocodilia*–alligators and crocodiles
- *Rhynchocephalia*–tuatara *(Sphenodon)*

Snakes

When most people see a snake, they flee in terror or attempt to kill it. True, there are some poisonous snakes that are a real danger to humans; however, most snakes are harmless to man, and many actually benefit him. Without snakes' feeding upon rats, mice, and insects that plague man, the uncontrolled populations of vermin could become serious problems.

Snakes lack appendages and, depending upon the snake and the terrain, use one of four locomotion techniques.

- *Serpentine movement,* used by the snake both in crawling and swimming, involves the winding of the snake across the ground in a series of "S" curves. Twigs and stones on the ground aid traction.
- *Concertina movement* involves the snake's drawing itself into a tight "S" shape, then extending itself forward. This is normally used when the snake is between two structures.

Tuatara: One of a Kind

The tuatara (TOO uh TAR uh) is a 50-80 cm (20-32 in.) reptile found only on a few islands near New Zealand. It is unusual in that it has traces of a light sensitive structure on the top of its head. This third eye is nonfunctional and is covered by scales in the adult. It is the only living member of the reptilian order *Rhynchocephalia* (RING koh suh FALE yuh).

- *Rectilinear* (REK tuh LIN ee ur) *movement* involves **scutes,** which are broad scales on the ventral surface of the snake. With wavelike muscular action, the snake forces the scutes along parts of its body forward. As scutes grip the earth, the animal pulls itself forward in a straight line.
- *Sidewinding* is used by snakes in deserts or sandy areas where traction is poor. The snake shuffles sideways through the sand by continually looping its body forward. Except at two or three points, it keeps its body raised above the sand.

Most snakes are good swimmers and climbers. A few can spread their sides to help them glide on air, and some even dig into sand.

Feeding of snakes

Snakes are strictly carnivorous and feed on living prey. A snake's diet includes rodents, insects, lizards, small mammals, eggs, and even other snakes. To locate its prey, the snake uses a variety

16D-3 *Types of snake locomotion*

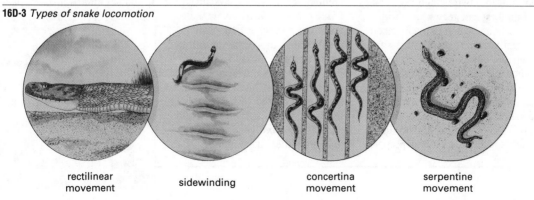

rectilinear movement   sidewinding   concertina movement   serpentine movement

of sense organs. The snake's lidless, staring eyes are not exceptionally sensitive (except in certain tree-dwelling species), but several acute senses compensate for this weak eyesight.

Nostrils lead to the nasal cavities provided with olfactory nerve endings. In the reptile's mouth a pair of sensory pits, called **Jacobson's organs,** aid the sense of smell. As the snake's forked tongue flits out of its mouth, it gathers traces of chemicals and odors and transfers them to the Jacobson's organs. These pits, combined with sensations from the nasal cavities, enable the snakes to detect very slight traces of odors.

One group of snakes, called the pit vipers, has *heat-sensing pits* between the nostrils and the eyes. These pits enable the snake to track and strike accurately at warm-blooded animals, even in total darkness. Snakes have no external ears and are totally deaf to airborne vibrations, but they can detect some vibrations in the ground.

After locating the prey, snakes most often use one of three methods to capture it. The simplest method is to simply swallow the prey alive, a process often used by insect-eating snakes but occasionally seen in snakes that eat animals even larger than they are.

FACETS OF BIOLOGY

16D-2

Poisonous Snakes

It is the reputation of the poisonous snakes that causes people to fear all snakes. In fact, these dangerous snakes form only a small percentage of the total snake population.

The snake's venom (poison) takes one of two forms (although some snakes produce both):

❏ **Neurotoxin*** (NOOR uh TAHK sinz) attacks the nervous system and often quickly paralyzes the prey.

❏ **Hemotoxin*** (HEE muh TAHK sin) is more deadly for large animals and humans. Slower than neurotoxin, it destroys blood vessels and red blood cells.

Short, fixed-fanged snakes

Based on fangs, poisonous snakes are put into two categories. Snakes in the first category have short, fixed fangs which deliver poison (usually neurotoxins) as the snake "chews" on their prey. Three types of poisonous snakes are in the short-fanged category.

❏ **Cobras** inhabit Asian countries. Snakes, mostly cobras, in India kill 75% of all people who die from snake bites. Cobras prepare

Indian cobra

sea snake

to strike by lifting their heads high and spreading their bodies immediately behind the head into the characteristic "hood." The 2-m (6.5-ft.) *Asian cobra,* which bears the well-known "hourglass" marking on its hood, is the most common cobra species. African *black-necked cobras,* as well as some other species, can "spit" their venom; this behavior will not harm humans unless the venom gets into the eyes, where it may cause blindness. The largest poisonous snake, the *king cobra,* may reach 5.5 m (18 ft.) in length and can deliver more venom per bite than any other snake.

❏ **Coral snakes** cause fewer human deaths than any other poisonous snakes in North America. A species of coral snake (*Micrurus fulvius*), the American counterpart of the cobra, inhabits the southern United States as well as tropical areas. Marked with brilliant red, yellow, and black bands, this shy and secretive snake has a potent venom. It has a small head and short fangs that cannot penetrate heavy clothing and for some un-

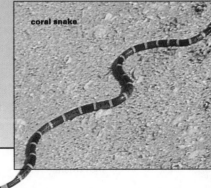

coral snake

Many nonpoisonous snakes kill their prey by **constriction.** When the snake spots its prey, it seizes it in its mouth. The teeth of the snake curve inward and provide a firm grip. The snake then coils its body around the prey and squeezes it to death. The prey is not crushed by the pressure (usually the ribs are not broken), but it is suffocated.

The final method of prey capture is *poisoning*. A few snakes have glands which supply poison to a pair of needlelike **fangs** on its upper jaw. To attack, the snake opens its mouth wide and thrusts its fangs into its victim. The poison flows from

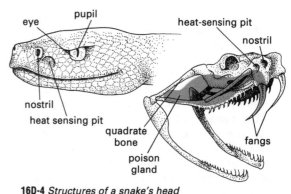

16D-4 *Structures of a snake's head*

Mohave rattlesnake

known reason does not always release venom when striking.

❑ **Sea snakes** are unusual air-breathing reptiles that spend their entire lives at sea. The sea snake has a large lung that enables it to remain submerged for hours on a single breath of air. Usually non-aggressive, these snakes can be extremely dangerous when coming to the surface for their life-supporting breath of air. Scientists have calculated that the venom of these snakes may be from 2-50 times more deadly than that of the king cobra.

Long, retractable-fanged snakes

Snakes in the second category have long fangs which fold into pockets in the snake's mouth when not in use. These snakes usually produce hemotoxin and can be divided into two groups:

❑ **Vipers** are not found in the United States but are common in Africa, Europe, and Asia. The most abundant viper is the common *European viper;* it is the only poisonous snake in Great Britain.

❑ **Pit vipers** possess heat-sensing pits behind their nostrils. These pits permit the snake to sense warm-blooded prey even in the dark. In the United States the only poisonous snakes other than the coral snakes are pit vipers.

The *water moccasin,* a thick-bodied pit viper of southern swamps and lakes, has a distinctive display that it often uses to warn intruders. Before striking, the snake may open its mouth wide, revealing the stark white interior; hence, the animal's common name, *cottonmouth.*

The *copperhead,* a common pit viper of the woodlands of the East Coast, is responsible for most poisonous snakebites in the United States, but its bite is rarely fatal.

The *rattlesnake* is the most widely distributed and most dangerous of the pit vipers in the United States. The rattle at the end of the snake's tail is a series of loose, horny segments. Each time the snake sheds, a new segment may be added to the rattle. The number of rattles, however, does not indicate the age of the snake. Snakes will often shed more than once a year, and old rattles easily break off. When preparing for its lightning strike, the rattlesnake coils, raises its tail, and often shakes its rattles, producing a loud hissing sound.

The most dangerous rattlesnake is the *western diamondback,* found from Texas to eastern California. This snake is responsible for more deaths in the United States than any other snake. The largest rattlesnake, the *eastern diamondback,* which ranges from North Carolina to Florida, attains a length of 2 m (6.5 ft.) and a weight of 11 kg (25 lb.).

Review questions on page 421.

---

neurotoxin: neuro- (Gk. NEURON, nerve) + -toxin (L. TOXICUM, poison)

hemotoxin: hemo- (blood) + -toxin (poison)

the glands, through grooves or tubes in the fangs, and into the prey. Usually the snake will then release the prey and wait for it to die before swallowing it. Poison is also used as a defense when the snake is threatened.

The snake does not tear or chew its food but swallows it whole; however, its food may be four to five times bigger around than the snake itself. The snake's lower jaw fastens to the **quadrate* bone.** This bone acts as a hinge, enabling the snake to open its mouth wide. The lower jaw bones join at the front by an *elastic ligament,* permitting flexibility. When swallowing, the snake can move its lower jaw bones independently; one side of the jaw stretches forward to gain a new grip on the prey while the other pulls back to draw the prey into the snake.

Since the teeth point inward, even an animal that recovers from the constriction or the poison will not be able to wiggle free. The skin of the mouth and neck region are extremely elastic. When the snake is swallowing or digesting large prey, its ribs may even dislocate temporarily.

Lizards

Though both **lizards** and snakes belong to the reptilian order Squamata, lizards differ from snakes in several ways.

❑ Lizards usually have two pairs of limbs; the snakes have none.

❑ Lizards have external ear openings, enabling them to sense airborne sounds to which snakes are deaf.

❑ Most lizards have eyelids and can close their eyes; snakes' eyes are permanently open and covered by a protective membrane.

❑ The lizard's belly is covered with scales similar to those on the rest of its body; the large scutes on the snake's belly assist in crawling.

chameleon

Anole

Lizards

True *chameleons*–tree dwellers of Africa, Madagascar, and India–are able to change color in response to changes in light, temperature, and even excitement level. The chameleon has a number of unique structures that enable it to hunt and thrive in trees. Its toes can grasp branches securely, and its tail can wrap around branches for extra support. Its keen eyes can act in unison or move independently of each other. When the chameleon spots an insect, it "fires" its long tongue and snags the prey with the sticky end. The chameleon's extended tongue may be longer than the chameleon itself. The "chameleon" that most people see in pet shops

is not a true chameleon but an *Anole,* an American lizard that is capable of color change.

The two known poisonous lizards belong to the same genus. The *Gila monster* of the southwestern United States and the *Mexican beaded lizard* have venom glands in their lower jaws. Once these lizards clamp onto their prey, they hang on tightly, release venom into their saliva, and inject it into their victim by their chewing. Fortunately, the chances of being bitten by these slow-moving lizards are slight.

In the fourth century, members of the monitor lizard family were described as "land crocodiles." These reptiles usually live on land, but many of them swim and climb with ease. In 1912 a visitor to the island of Komodo in the East Indies discovered the largest of the lizards, the *Komodo dragon,* which reaches 3 m (10 ft.) long and weighs 135 kg (297 lb.).

Komodo dragon

quadrate: (L. QUADRUS, a square)

Review Questions 16D-2

1. List the four major groups of living reptiles. (Use common names.)
2. Describe the tuatara.
3. What senses do snakes use to locate prey?
4. What are the three methods snakes use to kill their prey?
5. What structures of the snake permit it to swallow large prey whole?
6. What are the four major differences between snakes and lizards?
7. List and describe five lizards.

Facet 16D-2: Poisonous Snakes, pages 418-19

1. Name the two types of venom produced by snakes and tell what part of the human body that each type of venom affects.
2. Name the two groups of poisonous snakes (based on their fangs) and distinguish between them. List several types of snakes in each group.
3. List the types of snakes found in the United States and give specific examples of each type.
4. What is the most widely distributed poisonous snake in the United States?

Turtles and tortoises

The term *turtle* actually refers only to water-dwelling members of order Testudinata* (tes TOOD ih NAH tuh), although it is often used to refer to all within the order. We usually call the land dwellers of this group *tortoises.*

These organisms are covered by a hard shell consisting of a dorsal **carapace** and a ventral **plastron.** From within the shell, the head, thick limbs, and tail protrude. Some species can pull these appendages completely into the shell and close the front opening with a ''trapdoor'' on the plastron, becoming impenetrable fortresses when attacked.

Each limb of most turtles and tortoises is short and thick and has five claws. Some turtles have paddlelike flippers. An upper eyelid, a lower eyelid, and a transparent *nictitating membrane* inside the other lids protect the eyes. The animals lack teeth but have jaws formed into tough *horny beaks* that can cut and tear food. The nostrils are placed high on the snout; thus, the animal can hide underwater and breathe with only a small portion of its head above water. Females usually bury their eggs in a burrow and then abandon the eggs. No parental care is supplied to the young.

Crocodilians

Alligators, crocodiles, caimans, and gavials belong to the order Crocodilia and are among the

Turtles and Tortoises

Though most tortoises are small, weighing up to a few pounds, the giant tortoises of the Galápagos Islands may weigh over 160 kg (352 lb.). In years past, these giants were captured by crews of the passing sailing vessels to be used as meat on long voyages.

The largest turtles are the *leatherback sea turtles,* which may weigh 680 kg (1500 lb.). These reptiles, which spend virtually their entire lives at sea, have lightweight, streamlined shells and large flipperlike limbs for efficient motion in the water. Sea turtles usually come to shore only to lay their eggs. Some, like the *Ridley turtle,* travel great distances to return to the beaches where they were hatched. Once on the beach, these turtles dig a pit in the sand with their hind flippers, deposit the eggs, cover them, and then return to the sea. All the young usually hatch at about the same time. Instinctively the hatchlings dig out and head for the sea. The most hazardous trip that many of these turtles make is from the egg to the sea, since many animals often feast on these young hatchlings.

Ridley sea turtle

Giant Galápagos tortoise

Testudinata: (L. TESTUDINATA, tortoise)

largest living reptiles. Often *crocodiles* and *alligators* are mistaken for one another. Examining each animal's head reveals that the alligator has a blunt, thick snout and teeth that fit within the jaws; the crocodile has a thinner, more pointed snout with some teeth protruding from the jaws when the mouth is closed. Most people, however, do not get close enough to these animals to evaluate their snouts or teeth.

Crocodiles are stealthy carnivores. They glide smoothly just below the surface of the water when

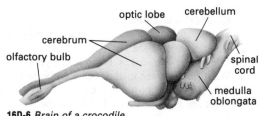

16D-6 *Brain of a crocodile*

they search for prey. The crocodile's eyes and nostrils are on the top of its head; thus, the animal can see and breathe while keeping most of its head underwater. When it comes upon a potential victim, the crocodile seizes it in its powerful jaws and thrashes it about, tearing the victim in its teeth. While it does this, its nostrils can be closed, and valves keep water from flowing into its ears. These reptiles also have a special flap that can cover the windpipe to prevent drowning during underwater feeding.

Crocodiles and alligators are oviparous. American alligators deposit eggs in a mound of decaying vegetation. The heat generated by the rotting vegetation warms the eggs. After 11-14 weeks, the young alligators make audible ''peeps,'' signaling the mother to dig them out. Once they are unearthed, the mother gently carries her young to the water in her mouth.

16D-5 *Heads of a crocodile (left) and an alligator (right)*

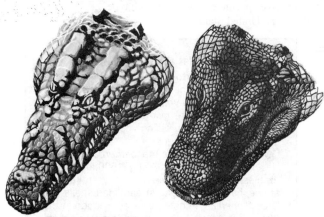

Biological Terms

Characteristics of Reptiles	chorion	constriction	*Facets*	sea snake
amniotic egg	allantois	fang	dinosaur	viper
shell	*Classification of*	quadrate bone	neurotoxin	pit viper
yolk	*Living Reptiles*	lizard	hemotoxin	
amnion	scute	carapace	cobra	
yolk sac	Jacobson's organs	plastron	coral snake	

Review Questions 16D-3

1. List several characteristics of turtles that separate them from other reptiles.
2. List and describe three turtles.
3. What are the observable differences between alligators and crocodiles?

Thought Questions

1. What does ''ectothermic'' mean? How would humans have to change their lifestyles if they were ectothermic? List things ectothermic animals do to compensate for this condition.
2. What characteristics do reptiles have that permit us to call them land animals?
3. Considering the respiratory mechanisms, number of offspring, amount of parental care, and types of reproduction of fish, amphibians, and reptiles, some people observe an ''evolutionary trend'' from water to land. What would be your answer to an evolutionist who used this ''trend'' to support his theory of evolution?

THE ENDOTHERMIC VERTEBRATES
ZOOLOGY PART IV

SEVENTEEN

17A-Class Aves: The Birds

In a Greek legend, Daedalus and his son Icarus sought escape from an island prison. Seeing the birds fly to and from the island, they decided to attempt flying to freedom. Wearing wings made of wax and feathers, they leaped from a cliff and soared over the ocean. The father reached land, but Icarus, enjoying flight, went higher and higher. He flew too near the sun; his wings melted, and he was lost in the sea.

Many men have envied the apparently effortless flight of birds. Leonardo da Vinci's sketch-books contain drawings of winged machines. Many odd, contraptions were designed by would-be fliers; a few got off the ground, but none stayed there. In 1903 the Wright brothers, designed an awkward-looking biplane and took a 12-sec. flight at Kitty Hawk, North Carolina. The legend came to life, and man was flying.

Since then man has learned that flight requires more than just a pair of wings. Anything that flies, be it an airplane or a bird, must meet specific design requirements if it is to get off the ground and stay aloft. Flight requires a structure that is streamlined and lightweight but extremely strong. Airplanes require intricate designs and large quantities of fuel to take off, direct their flight, and land. Birds, however, can fly with considerably more control and proportionally far less energy than the best airplane. The bird's body is a clear illustration of the completeness and perfection of God's design.

Characteristics of Birds

The appearance of many animals is confusing and makes them difficult to classify; sharks may look like bony fish, and some amphibians look like reptiles. Birds, however, are simple to identify since many of their characteristics are obvious to even the untrained eye and are unique to the **class Aves*** (AYE veez).

Feathers of birds

The strong yet virtually weightless feather grows from a tiny structure of the skin called a papilla (puh PIL uh). The feather is comprised of a flat **vane** and shaft. The shaft within the vane area is the **rachis*** (RAY kis), and the shaft from the papilla to the vane is the hollow **quill.**

17A-1 *A flight feather*

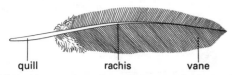

quill   rachis   vane

The vane consists of parallel rows of thin *barbs* that originate in the rachis. Parallel rows of tiny *barbules* extend from each barb. The barbules of one barb firmly interlock with the barbules of another. If adjacent barbs are forced apart, the bird can reattach them by stroking the edge of the vane.

Many birds oil their feathers to keep them from becoming brittle. A gland at the base of the tail produces the oil. In *preening,* the bird applies the oil with its bill. The oil also provides a waterproof shield valuable to swimming birds such as ducks. Without such protection, the feathers of these birds would become soaked, making it difficult for the animal to remain afloat and stay warm.

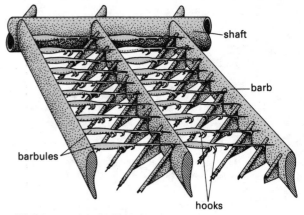

17A-2 *Structures of a feather*

The following are the most common types of feathers:

❑ **Down feathers** have barbules that do not interlock with one another. As a result, the barbs of those feathers do not form an orderly vane but a "feather duster" tuft instead. These feathers are an under layer, providing insulation.

❑ **Contour feathers** are the common vaned feathers. They cover most of the animal's body, giving it its external shape and color. The large **flight feathers,** which extend from the wings and tail, are also contour feathers.

Fully developed feathers are dead like scales or hairs. Periodically, the bird sheds or *molts* old feathers and replaces them. In many birds this process occurs in late summer so that the new feathers are ready for the fall migration.

Unlike the skin shedding of reptiles, the molting of birds is a gradual, highly ordered process. A bird missing many flight feathers on one wing would be crippled; therefore, birds shed these feathers in corresponding pairs (one from one wing and the same one from the other wing). Once one pair of flight feathers has been lost, another pair will molt only when the replacements for the original pair have appeared. Most birds

Aves: (L. AVIS, bird)
rachis: (Gk. RHAKHIS, spine)

can fly normally even while molting. Some birds molt certain feathers just prior to mating and have new, colorful plumage to attract a mate.

Appendages of Birds

Except for some flightless birds, such as the penguin, which uses its wings for swimming, most birds use their wings to propel them through the air. No bird uses its wings to manipulate items; many birds use their long flexible necks as substitutes for arms and hands.

The lower part of the hind limbs of the bird are usually thin and covered with scales, and most birds have three or four clawed toes. The design of the legs and feet suits the needs of the particular bird. The hummingbird, which spends most of its time in flight, has tiny legs; the flightless ostrich, however, has well muscled legs, permitting it to run overland at 65 kilometers per hour (40 mph). God, when speaking of the ostrich's speed, says, "What time she lifteth up herself on high, she scorneth the horse and his rider" (Job 39:18).

Wings of Birds

Based on the kind of flying birds need to do, the design of their wings differs. Most wings fit into one of four design categories.

❑ *Elliptical wings* are short and wide and provide for quick takeoffs and landings, low-speed flight, and maximum maneuverability. The elliptical wings of sparrows and woodpeckers permit them to change direction quickly in their forest habitats.

❑ *High-speed wings* have a thin, long, tapered shape that generates little drag in the air. Terns, swifts, and sandpipers have this wing type and are among the fastest fliers.

❑ *Soaring wings* are long and thin and resemble the wings of a glider. These wings enable water birds such as gulls to expend a minimum of energy in staying aloft. This increased flight efficiency, however, is obtained at the expense of maneuverability.

❑ *High-lift wings* are large and convex and provide a tremendous amount of lift even at low speeds. These wings allow birds of prey such as hawks, owls, and eagles to carry large prey. Many of these birds are skilled at soaring, riding thermal air currents, and changing course with subtle movements of their wing tips.

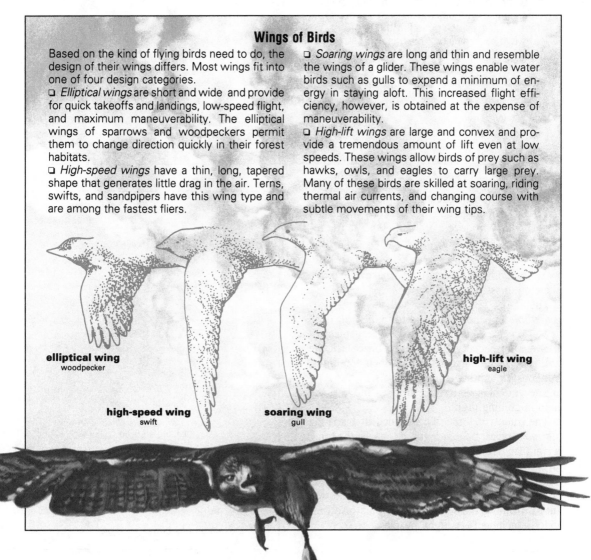

elliptical wing
woodpecker

high-speed wing
swift

soaring wing
gull

high-lift wing
eagle

Common Types of Birds' Feet

❏ *Wading* Wading feet have long, thin, widely spread toes, which distribute the weight of the bird so that it does not easily sink into a muddy bank. The thin toes and legs can move through the water without creating turbulence that would scare away the water animals the bird eats.

❏ *Swimming* Many swimming birds, such as the duck, have webbed feet, which serve as effective paddles.

❏ *Climbing* Birds, such as the woodpecker, spend much of their time clinging on vertical surfaces. Their climbing feet with two front toes and two back toes provide grip and balance.

❏ *Running* Many flightless birds have long, heavily muscled legs for running

❏ *Grasping* The foot of a bird of prey is designed to grasp and kill prey; the toes bear **talons** (long curved claws).

❏ *Perching* The perching feet of most song birds, such as the robin and wren, have three front toes and one back toe. A "locking device" closes the toes as the bird lands on a branch and remains tightly closed until the bird releases it.

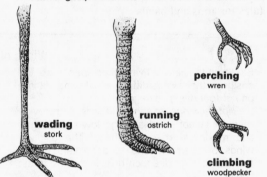

webbed (swimming)
duck

grasping
falcon

wading
stork

running
ostrich

perching
wren

climbing
woodpecker

Skeleton of birds

The most outstanding feature of the bird's skeleton is the numerous air-filled cavities within the bones, which produce extreme lightness. The reduction in weight, however, does not reduce the strength of the bones.

Several other characteristics make the bird's skeleton unusual.

❏ The upper jaw *(maxilla)* and the lower jaw *(mandible)* are elongated and form the *bill.*

❏ Many neck vertebrae grant free movement of the head, especially useful since birds lack the ability to manipulate items with their forelimbs, and most do not have movable eyes.

❏ The vertebrae of the tail are free moving and help in guiding flight.

❏ The trunk vertebrae, the flattened ribs, and the *sternum* (breast bone) are fused to make the trunk a rigid framework.

❏ The large sternum has a ridge called the **keel.** The keel provides attachment for flight muscles.

❏ The *clavicles* (collarbones) are enlarged and fused, forming the "wishbone." This also provides attachment for flight muscles.

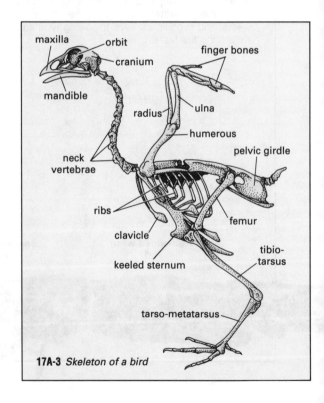

17A-3 *Skeleton of a bird*

Review Questions 17A-1
1. Which characteristics of class Aves separate birds from other classes of vertebrates?
2. Describe a feather. How do birds care for their feathers?
3. Describe the two major types of feathers and tell their functions.
4. List and describe four types of birds' wings and give an example of a bird with each.
5. List and describe four types of birds' feet.
6. List six characteristics of the bird's skeleton.

17A-4 *Types of bird beaks*

Digestion in birds
The high body temperatures and flying activities of birds create an enormous energy demand, which they satisfy by eating large quantities of food. Young birds may eat more than their own weight in a day. Some adults of small species will eat over a quarter of their weight a day. Once they ingest the food, it is quickly digested by an efficient digestive system. For example, berries pass through the thrush's digestive tract in 30 min., and a shrike can digest a mouse in only 3 hr. Rapid digestion is essential because birds cannot afford to carry heavy quantities of food in their stomachs for long periods.

The bird's unique structure for food gathering is its *bill*. The appearance and use of the bill vary with the bird's diet. Birds that spear fish or pluck insects from cracks in tree bark usually have long, slender bills. Short, stout bills are used for cracking and crushing seeds. Predatory birds often have hooked, pointed bills for tearing prey apart. The flamingo and other birds that feed on tiny plants and animals have sieves in their bills for filtering mud from their meal.

Digestion begins as the food, usually swallowed whole, passes down the elastic *esophagus* and enters the **crop.** The crop (an enlargement of the esophagus) stores the food until it can pass into the two-part *stomach.* The first part of the

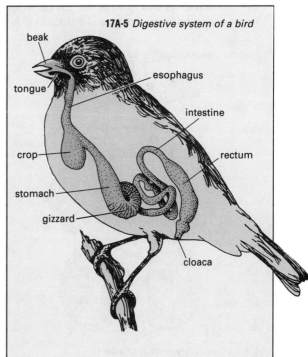

17A-5 *Digestive system of a bird*

stomach produces digestive juices. The second section, the thick-walled **gizzard,** contains particles of sand and small stones swallowed by the bird. Muscular contractions of the gizzard grind the food against the sand and stones and mix the digestive juices.

The food then passes into the intestine, where final digestion and absorption occur. Undigested wastes are passed into the **cloaca** and out of the body. The cloaca in birds provides a common opening for the intestine, kidney ducts, and reproductive organs.

Respiration in birds

The bird's small, inelastic lungs are unable to supply all the oxygen the bird needs to maintain its high metabolism; therefore, a series of *air sacs,* structures unique to birds, aids the lungs. About 25% of the air drawn through nostrils in the bill enters the gas exchange areas of the lungs. About 75% is routed into the air sacs. As the bird exhales, the air in the lungs passes out, and the fresh air in the air sacs passes through the lungs. Thus, oxygen-rich air passes through the gas exchange areas during both inhalation and exhalation. Air

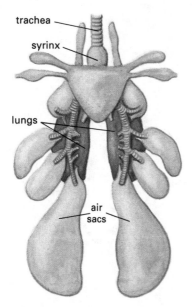

17A-6 *Respiratory system of a bird*

sacs also fill spaces which would be filled by fluids and fat in other animals. Thus, air sacs help to make the bird light.

Respiration not only provides oxygen; it is also the bird's primary means of cooling. High metabolism creates much heat, yet birds lack many cooling devices, such as the sweat glands and large external ears that mammals possess. Feathers minimize heat loss through the skin. The lungs expel this excess heat with expired air.

One of the most familiar features of birds is their song. Bird songs are produced by the **syrinx*** (SIHR ingks), or song box, an enlargement of the *trachea* just above where it divides to enter the lungs. The syrinx, in conjunction with other structures, can produce a variety of sounds. Some species of birds have only a few typical songs. Other birds, however, can imitate sounds as diverse as the songs of other birds, frog croaks, cat meows, laughter, and squealing tires.

The imitation ability, however, is probably best known in the "talking birds" such as the parrot, macaw, and parakeet. When speaking, these birds usually do not use the syrinx as much as they use other structures. Talking birds are mimics with no understanding of anything they say.

Circulation and excretion in birds

The bird's circulatory system has complete separation of the oxygenated and deoxygenated blood, a characteristic also found in mammals. This separation is possible because of a four-chambered heart. The right side of the heart receives deoxygenated blood from the body and pumps it to the lungs. Once the blood is oxygenated in the lungs, it flows into the left side of the heart and then is pumped to the body.

To maintain the high metabolic rate, the comparatively small heart of a bird must beat rapidly. Heartbeats per minute range from 135 to 570, and in some birds, like the chickadee, up to 1,000. It has been said that birds do not die of old age; they "burn themselves out"–not really a scientific description, but nonetheless appropriate.

Metabolic wastes are filtered from the blood by a pair of kidneys that lie along the back of the body cavity. The wastes empty directly from the

---

syrinx: (Gk. SURINX, shepherd's pipe)

kidneys into the cloaca. Birds have no bladder for storing urine and also do not store feces. When wastes arrive at the cloaca, they are eliminated, helping the bird remain light.

17A-7 *The bittern stands in water, casting shadows with its wing. Fish attracted to the shade are eaten by the bittern. This behavior is believed to be an instinct.*

Responses in birds

God's design becomes obvious from a study of the various animals. Reptiles, amphibians, and fish rely heavily on the senses of smell and taste. In contrast, their vision and hearing are weak. Many of these animals live in a watery environment which muffles sound and reduces light, making hearing and vision of little value. Even those reptiles and amphibians living on land have little use for strong eyes; they live in or close to the ground, limiting their field of vision. Thus, God provided the specific senses these animals need for their activities and environment.

A bird's life-style differs vastly from that of fish and reptiles and requires different sensory abilities. A bird in flight must be able to spot obstacles in its path soon enough to avoid them. Locating food from the air requires a keen eye. Hearing is important because birds communicate and seek mates by various sounds. To match these

needs, God has given birds good hearing and the keenest sight in the animal kingdom.

The bird's eyes are large and set deep in the skull. They are usually immovable. In order for the bird to look about, it must move its flexible neck. Bird eyes are usually set on either side of the head, permitting a wide field of vision. Some birds have exceptionally keen sight; the vision of a hawk is eight times more acute than that of man. A hawk can spot a crouching rabbit at a distance of more than 1.5 km (about 1 mi.). An owl can spot prey in light 1/10 to 1/100 the brightness required by man to see.

The ear openings of a bird are often covered with feathers. Ear canals open behind the eyes and lead to a complex sensory mechanism within the skull. Hearing is sensitive in the upper sound range, where most birdcalls are made.

17A-8 *The bird's brain*

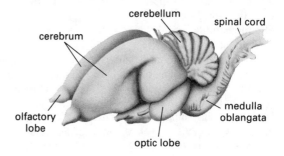

The structure and size of the major areas of the brain indicate the sensory, physical, and mental strengths and weaknesses of the animal. The *olfactory lobes* are small in the avian brain. The *cerebrum,* which probably serves in the bird's many complex instincts, is large. The *optic lobes* behind the lobes of the cerebrum are large. The *cerebellum,* which coordinates the muscular activities, is large.

Review Questions 17A-2

1. Birds lack teeth. Which structures of the bird's digestive system compensate for this?
2. What can be learned by studying birds' bills?
3. Give two functions of the air sacs in a bird's respiratory system.
4. Give a method for conserving heat and a method for eliminating heat in a bird's body.
5. Describe a bird's heart. What advantage does this design have for birds?
6. What are the most acute senses in birds? How does this illustrate design?

FACETS OF BIOLOGY

17A–1

Types of Birds

With the exception of the fish, the class Aves is the largest vertebrate group. Over 35 birds are singled out in the Bible; thus, Aves is the group with the largest number of individuals represented in Scripture. The list of unclean birds in the Jewish dietary laws (Lev. 11:13-19) is the most complete list of any group of animals in the Bible.*

The living members of the class Aves have been organized into 27 orders. For convenience we will categorize birds into general groups according to appearance, activities, and habitats.

Flightless birds

Though all birds have wings, there are many *flightless birds*. The ostrich is the tallest living bird, reaching a height of 2.5 m (8 ft.). It lives in the dry African grassland. Its slender, flexible neck and long, powerful legs are naked, but its body is covered with long, luxuriant feathers, often used to adorn hats. A passage in Job 39 describes the fact that the female will often cover her eggs with

Kiwi: a flightless bird of New Zealand

sand during the day when she goes feeding. Ostriches can kick powerfully and cut off fingers with their bills. Swift runners and fierce fighters, they do not hide their heads in the sand when threatened; however, when surprised, they will often place their heads near the ground, looking carefully at whatever disturbed them.

Penguins are fitted in a "tuxedo" of dense feathers and a layer of fat under their skin which enables them to thrive in the icy waters and on the ice floes of Antarctica. Using paddle-shaped wings, penguins swim gracefully; and, being social birds, they usually travel in large flocks.

Birds of prey

The *birds of prey* are certainly the "kings of birds." The power, grace, and deadly efficiency of these aerial hunters have won them the admiration of mankind. Birds of prey can be placed into three groups: *daytime hunters, carrion feeders,* and *night hunters*.

Eagles, hawks, and falcons are daytime hunters. Their basic method of hunting involves sitting

upon a high perch or floating in the air and scanning the surroundings with keen eyes. When food is sighted, they begin a high-speed dive; razor-sharp talons grip the prey. The force of the dive may stun or instantly kill the victim. The hunter may feed where it is or carry its meal to some inaccessible spot before eating.

The eagle is often mentioned in the Bible. The *imperial eagle,* now scarce in Palestine, and the golden eagle were probably most common during Bible times. In the Bible we find references to eagles as majestic birds (Ezek. 17:3); as builders of solitary, high nests (Jer. 49:16); and as strong, fast fliers (Exod. 19:4; Deut. 28:49; Prov. 23:5; Jer. 4:13; Rev. 12:14).

red-tailed hawk

Daytime birds of prey in North America include the large *golden eagle,* having a wingspan of 2 m (6.5 ft.), and the *red-tailed hawk.*

*This listing also includes the bat, a "fowl" which is classified not as a bird but as a flying mammal.

spotted owl

Vultures generally have a bad reputation, for they feed on *carrion* (dead bodies). The *Griffen vulture* is probably the most common vulture in Palestine and the one most often referred to in the Scripture. Until a few years ago the vulture population in Palestine was quite large, but modern practices of hunting and proper disposal of dead bodies have considerably reduced the vulture population. The turkey vulture, or ''buzzard,'' is a bare-headed scavenger often seen circling the kills of other predators in North America.

condor

As the eagles and hawks dominate the day, the owls rule the night. The owl has special equipment for night hunting: soft flight and body feathers enable the bird to fly and dive upon a rodent or snake without making a sound; large eyes in the front of the head give the animal keen vision and depth perception; amazing night vision and keen ears can detect the slightest movement in the grass. Common owls include the *barn owl*, with its white, heart-shaped face, and the *horned owl*, whose ''horns'' are actually tufts of feathers.

Game birds

Game birds such as the turkey, quail, pheasant, partridge, dove, and chicken frequently appear on the dinner table. Their tender breast meat or ''white meat'' is actually their flight muscles. The white meat lacks the abundant blood supply (with its supply of food and oxygen) that the other muscles have. Thus the flight muscles fatigue quickly. The game birds can only fly in quick bursts and must soon glide to a landing.

A domesticated game bird often mentioned in the Bible is the *dove*. The word ''dove'' is used loosely for all the small members of the family Columbidae, and the word ''pigeon'' is used for all the larger members. ''Turtledove'' refers to members of a particular genus of doves. The writers of Scripture

Domesticated Game Birds

The *turkey*, one of the larger game birds native to America, was described by Benjamin Franklin as ''a bird of courage, [that] would not hesitate to attack a grenadier of the British Guards, who should presume to invade his farmyard with a red coat on.'' Had Franklin had his way, the turkey rather than the bald eagle would have become our national emblem. Although the turkey is a fine bird, it would seem a little unpatriotic to eat our national symbol for Thanksgiving.

The *red jungle fowl* is a ground-dwelling bird of Southeast Asia. Its head and bill are decorated with red flaps of tissue. Its body feathers range from gold to black. Many centuries ago these birds were domesticated and trained to fight one another, perhaps as the first spectator sport. Through careful breeding, they became a major source of meat. By 1500 B.C. the bird had spread

The modern, domesticated red jungle fowl is grown on farms to supply eggs and meat.

into Central Europe. Today descendants of the red jungle fowl are common barnyard chickens. By New Testament times, the chicken was a common domestic bird in Israel. Probably the best-known Scriptural reference to a rooster is in Matthew 26 in which Peter denied our Lord three times before the cock crowed.

used the dove as a symbol of beauty (Song of Sol. 1:14; 5:12) and gentleness (Matt. 10:16), as an illustration of panic (Hos. 7:11), and as an example of lamenting (because the cooing of a dove sounds like human sighs–Isa. 38:14; 59:11; Ezek. 7:16).

Doves and pigeons are easily raised and were a common food source for the poor in Bible times. They were also sacrificial animals. When Mary and Joseph presented Jesus at the temple, they offered two turtledoves in accordance with their social status and the Law, which states, "If [she] be not able to bring a lamb, then she shall bring two turtles [turtledoves], or two young pigeons; the one for the burnt offering, and the other for a sin offering" (Lev. 12:8).

Water birds

The *water birds* fit into three groups: the *swimming birds,* the *diving birds,* and the *wading birds.*

Ducks and geese, familiar swimming birds, have oval-shaped bodies supported by a pair of short legs with webbed feet. This group includes the *mallard duck* with its distinctive green head; the wood duck with its "hood" of feathers; and the beautiful *mute swan,* a pure white bird with a long, elegant neck.

The *gannet,* a diving bird, can soar to a height of 18-30 m (59-98 ft.), arch over, and plummet headlong toward the water. Open wings perform subtle course adjustments until impact, when the wings fold against the body. The bird pierces the water and snaps

up a fish. The *pelican* is a comical diving bird with a pouch on its lower bill for holding its catch.

The final group contains the wading birds such as the *heron, flamingo, crane,* and *egret.* With long necks and long, stiltlike legs, these birds can see above the plants along the water's edge while they carefully look for fish and other organisms.

Songbirds

Sparrows, wrens, orioles, and robins belong to the largest group of birds, the *songbirds.* Their common names such as chickadee, pewee, chiffchaff, and towhee are actually imitations of the birds' songs. Many songbirds have short bills for eating seeds and berries. Others consume insects, and a few songbirds are predators. Male songbirds attract females with their vocal abilities.

The male *cardinal* is a dazzling red songbird with a bold crest on its head. The female of the species is drably colored. The *mockingbird* has a gray and uninteresting appearance, but its song and mimicry are brilliant. A menace to any

cornfield, the *crow* (a black bird with a long beak) feeds upon the crop, supplementing its diet of insects, berries, young birds, and even small mammals. Unfortunately for farmers, crows are intelligent birds, unintimidated by scarecrows.

Most songbirds are small, but the *raven* sometimes measures 69 cm (28 in.) long. Other members of the same family include the crow, rook, magpie, and jay. Ravens are frequently referred to in the Bible. Noah first sent the raven, a strong flier, from the ark. The raven did not return because it was able to sustain itself: a sign

Elijah Fed by the Ravens by Raphael Camphuysen, Bob Jones University Collection of Sacred Art

that the waters were receding (Gen. 8:6-7). God chose ravens to feed Elijah by the brook Cherith (I Kings 17:2-6). Ravens can often be seen carrying large morsels in their beaks. Jesus chose to teach His disciples not to worry about trivia by saying, "Consider the ravens: for they neither sow nor reap; which neither have storehouse nor barn; and God feedeth them: how much more are ye better than the fowls?" (Luke 12:24).

Review questions on page 436.

Bird Reproduction

For birds the process of reproduction and raising young is quite complicated, usually involving courtship and nest construction. *Courtship* is the male bird's efforts to attract a mate. Some species attempt to catch the eye of a mate with their dazzling appearance; thus, male birds are generally more colorful than the females. The female *peacock* (or peahen), for example, is a dull-brown bird. The peacock (male), however, has an iridescent blue head and neck and has extravagant tail feathers. A more common courtship tool is the bird's song, which enables the animal to call for a mate of its own species.

Birds are oviparous, producing *amniotic eggs*. The male reproductive organs, a pair of *testes*, produce sperm. During mating, the sperm are transferred to the *cloaca* of the female. The female reproductive system usually consists of a single *ovary* for the production of ova and an *oviduct* which transports the ova to the cloaca.

Fertilization occurs within the oviduct. The fertilized egg is coated with a protein-containing substance called **albumen*** (al BYOO min), the egg white, and finally encased in a hard shell by special glands in the oviduct.

Bird Nests

Most birds construct nests to serve as nurseries for their developing young. The bird accomplishes this remarkable feat using only its bill and feet. The design, location, and materials of the nest vary with each species. The *flamingo* nests on the ground by building a large mud mound into which it lays its eggs. The *grebe* builds a floating, raftlike nest on the water. The *burrowing owl* makes its nest in the burrow of a squirrel or prairie dog.

Often the nest design serves to protect the eggs from predators. *Weaverbirds* of Africa construct intricate ball-shaped nests. The entrance to the nest is usually at the bottom to prevent rainwater and predators from entering. As added protection, the nest hangs from a branch too thin for most predators to climb.

The male and female *hornbills* select a suitable hollow tree; the female enters the hollow, and both birds wall up the opening with clay and debris, sealing the female inside. The hornbill lays, incubates, and hatches the eggs within the closed chamber. The male passes food to the female through a tiny hole in the clay "door." After a while the female chisels her way out of the "nursery chamber." The young birds promptly reseal themselves into the chamber where they will remain for weeks.

Not all birds follow typical nest-building, young-raising patterns. In Antarctica, the domain of the flightless *emperor penguin,* the scarcity of materials makes building a nest impossible. The

grebe

penguin with egg on feet

flamingo

weaverbird

penguin, therefore, must carry the egg on its feet, covering it with a fold of skin. The female *brown-headed cowbird* lays its eggs in the nests of other birds. The baby cowbird hatches early and shoves all the other chicks out of the nest. The foster parent bird ends up feeding only the cowbird chick, which may quickly grow to be much larger than the "parent."

---

albumen: (L. ALBUS, white)

17A-10 *A chicken egg*

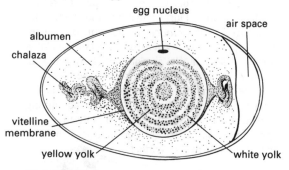

Bird Families

Eggs and young birds require parental care. Most bird eggs must be *incubated* (kept warm) during the development of the embryo. Usually one or both parents accomplish this by sitting on the eggs until they hatch. Depending upon the species, the chick emerging from the egg fits into one of two categories.

❑ **Altricial** (al TRISH ul) **chicks** are incubated in less than two weeks and emerge from the eggs naked, blind, and helpless. When hatched, all they can do is open their large mouths and consume food. The parents supply food until the chicks are feathered and able to fly. Altricial birds, such as robins, thrushes, and sparrows, usually produce fewer than six eggs at a time.

17A-10 *Bird families: a blue jay (left) has an altricial family, and a limpkin (right) has a precocial family.*

❑ **Precocial** (prih KOH shul) **chicks** have longer incubation periods. When hatched, the young are well developed, alert, and able to move and feed themselves. Their bodies are covered with soft down. Though independent compared to altricial birds, these chicks usually stay close to their parents for protection. Christ speaks of the care a

hen, a precocial bird, gives to her brood and compares it to His desire to care for the Israelites (Matt. 23:37, Luke 13:34). Precocial birds, which also include ducks, quail, and most water birds, often have families numbering fifteen to twenty.

Most birds have a reproduction cycle of one year, with a different mate each year. Some birds, however, mate for life. Eagles, for example, usually choose a mate as they reach maturity and remain with that partner until one of them dies, which for some may be 10-20 years. Eagles, like some other birds, usually build only one nest, which they refurbish throughout their lives. For some eagle families, the young birds are still around watching the parents hunt when the next set of eggs is laid.

Bird migrations

Many animals migrate from summer to winter feeding grounds, but few animals make journeys as long and dramatic as those of birds. Nearly half of all bird species travel south in winter and north in summer. The purpose of the migration is twofold.

❑ Migration enables birds to live in a year-round warm climate where food remains abundant enough to supply their enormous needs.

❑ Migration provides the best possible environment for raising young. Most birds nest in northern ranges where the summer days are long, and predators are few.

Jeremiah, when complaining that the Israelites were disobeying God, wrote, "Yea, the stork in the heaven knoweth her appointed times; and the turtle [turtledove] and the crane and the swallow observe the time of their coming; but my people know not the judgment of the Lord" (Jer. 8:7). Today these migratory birds are common passers-by in Israel. The arrival of the *stork,* a large white bird with black-tipped wings and a red bill and legs, is anticipated as a harbinger of spring in the Holy Land, much as the robin's arrival is in the northern United States.

It is well documented that birds monitor the length of days to determine when to migrate. The time, route, destination, and other aspects of bird migration are inborn. These God-given instincts

17A-11 *A flock of migrating ducks*

are necessary for the survival of many bird species. As a bird cannot thrive if it ignores its instincts, so the Israelites could not thrive spiritually if they ignored the promptings of God. The same is true for Christians today.

The mechanisms birds use for navigation during their migrations are not completely understood. Birds may use landmarks to guide them, but some species travel over open water with no such guides. Experiments show that birds have an instinctive sense of direction. Some species appear to be able to detect the magnetic field of the earth, and some use the sun and stars as guides. These guidance systems, though highly efficient, are not perfect. Occasionally, birds can become lost in fog or be blown off course by high winds.

Many birds cover great distances in their yearly journeys. The *arctic tern* covers the greatest distance, traveling 17,700 km (11,000 mi.) from its breeding grounds north of the Arctic Circle to Antarctic in winter and returning the next summer. The *bobolink* breeds in the upper regions of North America. During winter migration it covers 11,000 km (7,000 mi.), finally coming to rest near Argentina.

Not all migratory birds are strong fliers. The *quail,* a weak-flying migratory bird, is always spoken of as food in the Bible. Two months after the Israelites left their bondage, they longed for the "flesh pots" of Egypt, and the Lord gave them quail (Exod. 16:1-13). Following this, the children of Israel had manna daily.

Later they complained and asked for meat again. The Lord again gave them quail, but this time He said, "[I] will give you flesh, and ye shall eat. Ye shall not eat one day, nor two days, nor five days, neither ten days, nor twenty days; But even a whole month, until it come out at your nostrils, and it be loathsome unto you: because that ye have despised the Lord which is among you, and have wept before him, saying, Why came we forth out of Egypt?" (Num. 11:18-20).

The Lord sent a wind to bring an unusually large flock of migrating quail to the Israelites. The next day, near the camp, each person gathered at least 10 homers (about 90 bushels). But while they were eating the meat, "the wrath of the Lord was kindled against the people, and the Lord smote the people with a very great plague. . . . There they buried the people that lusted" (Num. 11:33-34). There is a virus that is sometimes carried by quail which can make people ill (but usually not fatally). It is possible that the Lord miraculously used the wind and the virus to teach the children of Israel, and us, a lesson.

17A-12 *A pair of quail*

Biological Terms

Characteristics of Birds	quill	talon	cloaca	*Bird Reproduction*
class Aves	down feather	keel	syrinx	albumen
vane	contour feather	crop		altricial chick
rachis	flight feather	gizzard		precocial chick

Review Questions 17A-3
1. What are the two most common methods male birds use to attract mates?
2. What is the yolk of a bird's egg? What is the proper name of the egg white, and of what is it made?
3. Describe and give examples of the two major types of bird families.
4. What are the two major reasons a bird migrates?
5. What triggers the migration instinct in birds?

Facet 17A-1: Types of Birds, pages 430-32
1. List three flightless birds, three birds of prey, three game birds, three water birds, and three songbirds.
2. What are the three groups within the birds of prey? Give an example of each.
3. What are the three groups within the water birds? Give an example of each.

Thought Questions 17A
1. List all the characteristics of birds that help them fly. Be sure to include those characteristics which make the birds lighter than other animals of the same size.
2. What types of bird bills usually go with what types of bird legs and feet?
3. Discuss the different abilities and behaviors that a scientist might expect a bird to have, based on size of its brain lobe. Compare these abilities and behaviors to those of representatives of class Osteichthyes, Amphibia, and Reptilia, based on size of their brain lobes.
4. Birds are the first animals we have studied that are endothermic. What advantages and disadvantages does this characteristic present for birds?

17B-Class Mammalia: The Mammals

Most people think that the class Mammalia contains the "real" animals. Dogs, cats, lions, horses, cows, bears, giraffes, elephants, and monkeys are all mammals. Mammals fill our zoos, serve as beasts of burden, are eaten as food, can be trained to do tricks, are loved as pets, and have been written about, photographed, and painted. No single group of organisms has ever affected humans in such diverse ways.

What makes the mammals so useful and popular? The answer partly involves the mammals' warm-bloodedness; since mammals are *endothermic* (maintain a constant body temperature), they, like man, can exist and be active in varied environments. Most of the answer, however, probably involves the mammalian brain.

The mammalian brain is dominated by the *cerebrum,* the center of intellect and instinct, making mammals the most intelligent animals. The tus-

sling of lion cubs or the play of a baby chimpanzee is similar to the activity of young children. The care, protection, and training most mammalian parents give their young have counterparts in human society. Many animals also appear to express emotions such as fear, anger, contentment, excitement, and happiness.

Though these mammal-human comparisons are interesting and in many cases valid, we must be careful not to read too much into them. A mammal, though intelligent, is not capable of the complex emotions and elaborate thoughts that characterize human mental activity. (These contrasts are discussed in Chapter 19A).

Characteristics of Mammals

The **class Mammalia*** (muh MAY lee uh) is one of the smallest vertebrate classes; however, it encompasses animals of great variety which inhabit

---

Mammalia: (L. MAMMA, breast)

virtually every habitat imaginable. The elephant and rhinoceros are giants of the land; whales and porpoises are fishlike mammals. Bats are the mammals of the air. In the trees are the squirrels, on the land are deer and rodents, and underground are the moles. These strikingly different animals share many characteristics.

Hair of mammals

All mammals have hair, even though it is hard to find on some of them. Hair is sparse on elephants and nearly absent on whales and some other aquatic mammals. Hair is a collection of nonliving cells produced by *hair follicles,* structures lodged deep in the skin. Two types of hair usually comprise a mammal's fur coat.

❏ The *underhair* is a soft, insulating fur layer next to the animal's skin.

❏ The *guard hair* is coarser, longer, and found over the underhair. This layer gives the animal its color.

Hair or fur can serve a number of functions. The insulating ability of fur is illustrated by the beaver, which has underhair so dense that water does not penetrate it. Thus, when the beaver enters an icy stream, it never gets soaked to the skin. On cold days many land mammals fluff their fur to trap more insulating air in the underhair.

The hair may also provide camouflage. Some weasels have a dark coat in summer but shed that hair in the fall and grow a new, white coat for the winter. This change enables the animal to remain inconspicuous against its background.

The "whiskers" of animals such as cats, dogs, and seals are enlarged hairs which have follicles supplied with sensory nerves. These "whiskers" permit the animal to detect objects in its path or around its head in total darkness.

Other body hair can be sensory. When a dog is threatened, the neck fur bristles (stands up). This "standing fur" is very sensitive. An unexpected touch to the neck will cause the animal to duck and snap in the direction from which it was touched, a defense reflex that helps the dog protect its vulnerable neck during a fight.

17B-2 *The porcupine (left) and a closeup of a quill (right)*

Hair may also be a means of repelling attackers, as the porcupine aptly demonstrates. This rodent's hair forms long, sharp quills that separate easily from its skin. When approached by a predator, porcupines erect and rattle their quills ominously. Any wise attacker will seek food elsewhere. A predator that ignores the porcupine's warning will probably find itself pierced by the barbed quills. These quills are difficult to remove and tend to work themselves deeper into the victim as he moves.

17B-1 *The hair of many mammals helps to camouflage them. The leopard (left), the black-tailed jackrabbit (center), and the artic fox (right) are good examples.*

Limbs of mammals

Mammals usually possess two pairs of limbs used for locomotion. Their forms, however, are as varied as the animals themselves. The forelimbs of the bat, for example, have elongated fingers that are connected by a thin membrane to form a wing. Short, stout limbs, wide paws, and large claws serve the mole as shovels. The mole can burrow underground at a rate of 3.5-4.5 m (11-15 ft.) per hour. The whale has forelimbs fused into massive swimming paddles. For high-speed travel, the large, heavily-muscled hind limbs of the kangaroo enable it to leap up to 12 m (39 ft.).

The cheetah holds the overland speed record, attaining speeds over 95 kilometer per hour (kmph)(60 mph). The speed is fast when compared to the 69 kmph (43 mph) of a racehorse or the 25 kmph (15 mph) of the sprinting human.

17B-3 *Kangaroos have large hind limbs enabling them to travel rapidly across the "outback" of Australia.*

Limbs can also be feeding tools. The paws of the lion, a major predator of the African grasslands, have needle-sharp retractable claws that tear into prey. The gorilla has heavily-muscled arms, which attain a combined span of almost 3 m (10 ft.) and are powerful enough to bend a 5-cm (2-in.), tempered steel bar. The gorilla, however, is a vegetarian and uses its awesome strength to climb trees and tear down foliage.

Digestion in mammals

If something is edible, there is probably some mammal that eats it. Mammals eat grass, fruits, seeds, leaves, microscopic organisms, invertebrates such as insects and snails, vertebrates, and even each other.

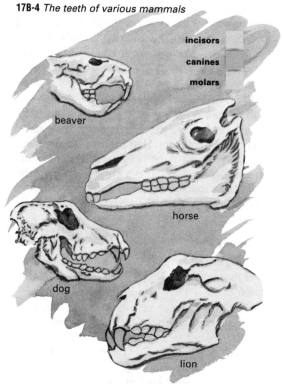

17B-4 *The teeth of various mammals*

incisors
canines
molars

beaver
horse
dog
lion

A scientist can learn a great deal about the diet of a mammal by examining its teeth. There are three basic types of mammalian teeth.

❏ **Incisors*** (in SYE zurz) are flat, thin teeth in the front of the mouth, used in gnawing or biting.

❏ **Canines*** (KAY NINES) are rounded, pointed teeth toward the front of the mouth, used for tearing.

❏ **Molars** (and premolars) are usually thick, squat teeth in the back of the mouth, used for grinding and chewing.

Carnivores such as lions and dogs have enlarged canine teeth. These animals bite into their prey and rip off large pieces of meat to be swallowed whole. Gnawing animals like rats and beavers have large incisors and no canines. Herbivores cut foliage and grind it until it can be easily digested. Thus, the cow, horse, giraffe, and camel have sharp incisors and large, flat molars. Omnivorous animals such as monkeys and bears have well-formed teeth of each type.

incisors: (L. INCISUS, to cut into)
canines: (L. CANIS, dog)

Digestive organs also vary among mammals with different diets. Some herbivorous mammals such as cattle obtain nourishment from cellulose. No vertebrate, however, can digest cellulose without help. Plant material ingested by the cow passes down the esophagus to the **rumen,** a special section of the multi-chambered stomach of certain mammals. Animals that have a rumen, such as the cow and camel, are called *ruminants.* Bacteria maintained within the rumen produce enzymes which digest cellulose.

For improved digestion the ruminants will regurgitate **cud** (partially digested food) into their mouths and chew it a second time, mixing the enzymes with the tough plant materials. They then swallow the food again. Ruminants and other herbivores have long digestive tracts; thus, the digestive system has more time to digest cellulose.

Carnivores such as the seal and wolf eat primarily protein. Protein is easier to digest than cellulose and does not require special stomachs or cultures of digestive bacteria. The carnivore's digestive tract is considerably shorter than the ruminant's and has an unsegmented stomach similar to that of a human.

17B-5 *A diagram of the digestive system in a ruminant*

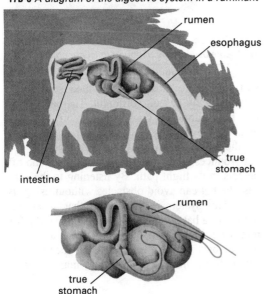

rumen

esophagus

true stomach

intestine

rumen

true stomach

Respiration and circulation in mammals

The major organs of mammalian respiration are a pair of oblong spongy *lungs* in the upper chest cavity. The lungs are separated from the abdominal organs by the muscular **diaphragm.** Air is drawn into the lungs by the contraction of the dome-shaped diaphragm. As air passes down the throat, it goes through the **larynx** (LAIHR inks), or "voice box," a cartilaginous organ containing *vocal cords.* Controlled vibration of these cords enables various mammals to bark, squeal, meow, grunt, or make other sounds.

Like the avian heart, the mammalian heart has four chambers. Mammals have a circulatory system similar to man (see Chapter 21A).

17B-6 *Polar bears have small ears and thick fur to conserve heat.*

Mammals expend energy to maintain a constant body temperature, enabling them to function steadily at a high metabolic rate, even in varying climates. This constant temperature is made possible by various heat-regulating structures in the mammal's body. Mammals in frigid habitats possess mechanisms and behaviors to conserve warmth; mammals in hot environments have mechanisms and behaviors to eliminate excess heat. The polar bear, for example, is designed to conserve heat. Its small head, tiny ears, and compact body shape expose a minimum amount of body surface to the cold. A coat of dense white fur provides heat-conserving insulation.

Many mammals lose excess body heat through their skin, but occasionally, certain mammals must use other methods. A dog pants to cool the

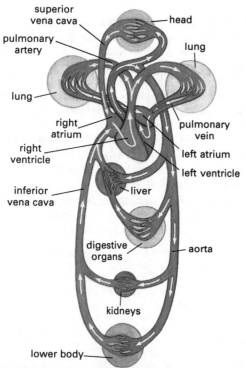

superior vena cava
pulmonary artery
head
lung
lung
right atrium
pulmonary vein
right ventricle
left atrium
left ventricle
inferior vena cava
liver
digestive organs
aorta
kidneys
lower body

17B-7 *Circulation in a mammal*

warm blood which is directed to the tongue and mouth lining when the animal is overheated. The African elephant has a thick skin which not only serves as protection but also holds heat. In the elephant's huge, thin ears, however, the blood is brought near to the body surface and can cool as much as 5° C in a single passage. Bathing and wallowing in mud also cool the elephant.

17B-8 *Blood passing through the vessels of an elephant's ears may be cooled 5° C.*

Many small mammals escape the low temperatures and reduced food supply of winter by entering **hibernation.** Ground squirrels and woodchucks enter a state of true hibernation. After filling itself and its den with food, the mammal gradually reduces its body temperature. Its metabolism slows to a point where the animal becomes unconscious. The mammal's heart and respiration rates drop drastically. Occasionally during this period, the animal will awake to pass its wastes and then quickly return to sleep. An animal in true hibernation needs hours to raise its metabolism back to its normal, active state.

Some large mammals like the bear and badger sleep though the winter but do not truly hibernate. Their heart rate slows, but their body temperature remains close to normal. Unlike true hibernators, these animals will waken if bothered.

Responses in mammals

17B-9 *Bats use echoes of sound to locate objects.*

The sensory organs of mammals are, for the most part, similar to those of man; their sensitivity, however, may be quite different. The bat's hearing, for example, is considerably more sensitive than human hearing. Its large, cup-shaped ears are the receiving devices for its radar system. The bat produces high frequency sounds that echo off objects in its flight path. By listening to the echoes, the bat can avoid obstacles without using its eyes. This system is so accurate that, in an experiment, a bat was able to locate and avoid a 0.1 mm wire in its path, using its radar alone. In nature, bats perform similar feats, locating the small flying insects upon which many species feed.

A familiar example of keen mammalian smell is the legendary bloodhound. These dogs can follow the scant traces left by an animal or person walking through the woods. Trained dogs are used by the police to sniff out and locate hidden explosives and drugs.

The mammalian brain is much larger in proportion to its body than the brain of any other land animal. The cerebrum (the area where voluntary actions are initiated) dominates the brain. The cerebrum is also the seat of the memory and intelligence, which accounts for the trainable nature of most mammals.

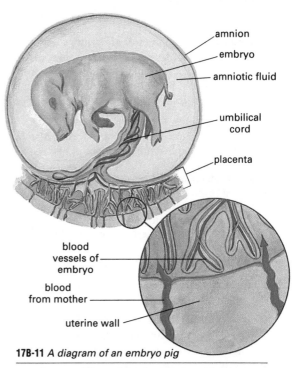

17B-11 *A diagram of an embryo pig*

17B-10 *The brain of a mammal (horse)*

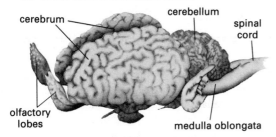

Mammalian reproduction

Periodically the female mammal's paired ovaries produce and release ova, which are guided through a tubular oviduct toward the **uterus.** The uterus is a muscular chamber where the young will develop. When the female's ova are ready to be fertilized, the animal enters a period called "heat." Various odors released by the female at this time attract males of her species. The male's testes produce sperm; fertilization is internal.

In most mammals the sperm fertilizes the eggs in the oviduct. Even before the zygote reaches the uterus, it has divided several times. These first few cells of the new mammal are implanted in the uterine wall. A **placenta,** composed of a portion of the uterine wall and tissues of the embryo, forms. The placenta has a rich blood supply from both the mother and the embryo. The two blood supplies exchange nutrients, gasses, and wastes, even though they do not actually mix.

The blood vessels from the placenta to the ventral surface of the embryo are coated in protective

membranes. These blood vessels and the membranes form the **umbilical*** (um BIL ih kul) **cord.**

While an embryo is in the mother's *womb* (the uterus), it is nourished by her body. This period of pregnancy is **gestation*** (jeh STAY shun). The length of the gestation period varies greatly for different mammals. Generally speaking, the longer the gestation, the more developed the young are when they are born. Most mice have a gestation period of only 21 days; the young are born hairless, blind, and weak. The horse has a gestation period of 335 days; a foal is born with a full coat of hair and can stand, walk, and even run within hours of its birth.

17B-12 *Rodents, like this Norway rat, hold the record for reproductive rates among the mammals. Newborn mammals require extensive care.*

---

umbilical: (L. UMBILICUS, navel)
gestation: (L. GERERE, to carry or to bear)

Parental care continues after the young are born. The first order of parental business is to feed the young. The female supplies milk from **mammary** (MAM uh ree) **glands** usually through a series of nipples along her ventral surface. The mother's milk contains the right nutrients for the development of her offspring. Many mammals train their young to hunt, build shelters, and perform various other actions before they leave the ''family.''

Review Questions 17B-1

1. What characteristics separate the class Mammalia from the other vertebrate classes?
2. What are the two primary types of hair found on most mammals? Of what value is each to an animal?
3. List, describe, and give the functions of the three basic types of teeth found in animals.
4. List several helps certain mammals have in digesting cellulose.
5. Name and describe two structures of the mammal's respiratory system which differ from the bird's respiratory system.
6. List several characteristics which help mammals maintain a relatively constant body temperature.
7. List and describe three structures important during the period of gestation.

Types of Mammals

Living members of the class Mammalia are divided into approximately eighteen orders based primarily on the type of reproduction, the type of teeth, and the design of their limbs. (See Appendix B.) Although 95% of the mammals are placental, two orders are *nonplacental mammals*. One small group of mammals lays eggs; another, having an extremely short gestation period, has abdominal pouches where the young mature. These nonplacental mammals, with a few exceptions, live in and around Australia.

Rodents, the gnawing mammals

Order Rodentia* (the *rodents* or gnawing mammals) is the largest mammalian order, including

duckbilled platypus

Monotremes, the Egg-laying Mammals

The **monotremes** (MAHN uh TREEMZ), or egg-laying mammals, are the exception to many mammalian characteristics. Members of this order are the only mammals to lay eggs and incubate them like birds. Once hatched, the young feed on their mother's milk. Female monotremes, however, do not have nipples. Their mammary glands are scattered along their ventral side. The milk empties onto the skin, and the young lap the milk off the mother's fur.

The best-known monotreme is the *duckbilled platypus*. The platypus reaches about 46 cm (18 in.), including its broad, flat tail which it uses in swimming. It uses its flat, toothless, ducklike bill to dig for invertebrates in the mud and to dig burrows in stream banks. It has webbed, clawed feet. Its hind legs have sharp spurs linked to poison glands, making the platypus one of the few known venomous mammals. In a moss-lined ''nest'' hidden in the burrow, one or two tiny, hairless playtpus young hatch. Sought for its novelty and valuable fur, the platypus was once hunted almost to extinction. Now protected by the Australian government, it appears to be making a comeback.

Rodentia: (L. RODERE, to gnaw)

17B-13 *The beaver is one of the most industrious builders in the animal kingdom.*

such animals as *squirrels, rats, mice,* and *porcupines.* The animals in this order are characterized by the large chisellike incisors in both the upper and lower jaws. The rodent uses these teeth for biting and gnawing. Rodent incisors continue to grow throughout its life, allowing the animal to gnaw almost incessantly. In fact, the rodent must use its incisors, or they grow so long the animal cannot close its mouth. Hard enamel covers the front of the rodent tooth; the back consists of softer material. As the animal gnaws, the back of each incisor wears away faster than the front, keeping the teeth sharp.

Few rodents use their teeth for as large a task as the *beaver* does. This rodent fells trees to construct a safe home for itself. The beaver builds a sturdy dam of trees and mud on a stream, forming a pond. The animal then builds a dome-shaped lodge in the water. The entrance to the lodge is below the water level to prevent predators from entering. Once this monumental job is done, the beaver maintains the dam and lodge, stores bark for food, and digs channels to increase the flow of water to its pond.

Most rodents (with the notable exception of porcupines) are defenseless and frequently fall prey to bird, reptile, and mammal predators. How then do these animals keep from being wiped out? The secret lies in reproduction: rodents become sexually mature sooner, can produce larger litters, and can reproduce more frequently than almost any other mammal. *Field mice,* for example, are *weaned* (stop drinking mother's milk) at 3 weeks, are independent at 4 weeks, and can bear litters at 6 weeks. Captive *meadow mice* can produce 13-17 litters, yielding a total of over 75 offspring, in one year.

Even though they are among the smallest mammals, rodents are an influential group. During the late Middle Ages the Black Death wiped about 25% of the population of Europe (see page 250). The disease was carried by fleas that infested rats. Wherever rats went, the fleas and the Black Death followed. In modern times rodents continue to be a problem. Their constant feeding and gnawing destroy crops and food supplies. Immediately after World War II scientists discovered that the United States was yearly losing more of its crops to rodents than it was sending to other nations.

Biblical Rodents

The Mosaic Law prohibited eating "the mouse" (Lev. 11:29). "Mouse" is probably a term for various small rodents. One of the rodents common in the Bible lands is the Egyptian *jerboa.* Its body is 18 cm (7 in.) long and its tail is 22 cm (9 in.) long. The jerboa's hind legs are 6 times longer than its forelegs, enabling it to jump like a kangaroo.

The common pet *hamster,* often called the *golden hamster* or *Syrian hamster,* is also a Bible land pest. It eats grain and can burrow 2 m (6.5 ft.) into the earth.

In I Samuel 5:2 we read that the Philistines stole the ark of the covenant and placed it in the temple of Dagon at Ashdod. As a punishment, a series of plagues befell the Philistines, one of which was being overrun with "mice." Some Bible scholars feel that the *water vole,* a 15-cm (6-in.) rat which does considerable damage in Syria and Palestine, was the animal the Lord used to force the Philistines to return the Ark. As they did so, however, they sent along a peace offering of five golden mice (I Sam. 6:4).

hamster

jerboa

water vole

Carnivores, the meat-eating mammals

The **order Carnivora** (kar NIV ur uh) are the meat-eating mammals. In a way they are all "kings" of their domains. Most carnivores are

Marsupials, the Pouched Mammals

The **marsupials*** (mar SOO pee ulz), or *pouched mammals,* have a distinct method of development. The fertilized egg begins growing and dividing within the uterus but does not form a true placenta. After a short time the immature offspring crawls out of the uterus and onto the mother's fur. Instinctively this tiny creature crawls toward the mother's pouch, where the nipples are. Often the mother will lick a groove in its fur for the young to follow. Once in the pouch, the young animal will lock its mouth over a nipple. Sustained by the mother's milk, the young marsupial will complete its development within the pouch.

The kangaroo stands erect on two powerful jumping legs and balances with a thick tail. The pouch of the female kangaroo is along its abdomen and serves as both nursery and refuge for the young.

The name "kangaroo" originated with the Australian natives. The first white men in Australia apparently heard the natives cry "kang guru" whenever the animal appeared, only to discover later that the words meant "there he goes."

koala

phalanger

marsupial young require forceful eviction by the mother so that her pouch can be ready for the next offspring.

The koala is a tree-dwelling, tailless animal with a large head, furry ears, and handlike paws. Its resemblance to a teddy bear has endeared it to many people. The koala feeds only on the leaves of eucalyptus trees.

gray kangaroo and joey

Other interesting marsupials include the *wallaby,* which resembles a small kangaroo; the *wombat,* a rodentlike marsupial; and the *phalanger,* which resembles a squirrel. Tasmania, an island south of Australia, has several interesting carnivorous marsupials, including the *Tasmanian devil,* which looks like a raccoon, and the *Tasmanian wolf,* which is like a dog.

It appears that many placental mammals have marsupial counterparts, for there are also some marsupial moles, rabbits, monkeys, rats, and various others. Some speculate that marsupials have survived in and around Australia because they are not in competition with placental mammals, which dominate the rest of the world.

The great gray, largest of the kangaroos, stands about 3 m (10 ft.) tall but is only about the size of a man's little finger when born. It spends the first 6 months in the mother's pouch. In typical marsupial fashion the joey (young kangaroo) will stay with the mother, returning to the pouch for protection and feeding even after it has matured enough to live on its own. Some

Tasmanian wolf

marsupials: (L. MARSUPIUM, pouch)

the largest predators of their areas and need not fear being eaten by other beasts. Not all carnivores are large, however, nor are they monarchs living in ease and safety. Carnivores must often fight with one another over kills or territory. Often the carnivore's prey puts up a vicious fight, resulting in the predator's death.

The structure of the carnivore is very different from that of other animals. Its enlarged *canine* *fangs* and sharp molars are designed for tearing flesh. The carnivore's limbs are usually limber and powerful, providing maximum speed and agility during pursuit. The toes have sharp claws. The most important feature of the mammalian carnivores is their ability to learn behaviors and use intelligence in hunting. To survive, they must know how to catch and kill prey that may be much larger and faster than they are.

Kinds of carnivores

17B-14 *The cat family, including the bobcat (above) and the snow leopard (right), is one of the largest groups of carnivores.*

The cat family, a familiar group of carnivores, ranges in size from the tiny domesticated *cat* to the *Siberian tiger* which averages over 3 m (10 ft.) from the nose to the tip of the tail. Members of the cat family are known for their quiet stalking of prey followed by a high-speed dash and a leap for the kill. Big cats of the Americas include the jaguar, which is a stout-bodied jungle cat, and the *puma,* or *mountain lion,* found in the western United States and in South America.

Bears are the largest land carnivores. The largest is the *Kodiak bear,* which attains a length of 2.5 m (8 ft.) nose to tail, stands 1.3 m (51 in.) at the shoulder, and weighs over 450 kg (990 lb.). Bears are actually omnivorous, eating whatever

The American Marsupial

One of the few marsupials living outside of Australia is the *opossum* a common inhabitant of American woodlands. This mammal, looking much like an overgrown rat, is known for its ability to "play dead." When approached by a potential predator, the animal often flops on its side and appears to be dead–its eyes glassy, its mouth locked in a hideous grimace. When the predator departs, the opossum ambles away. The opossum, however, is a dangerous animal; its sharp teeth can inflict a painful bite. The opossum searches for its mammal, bird, egg, or insect prey at night. The mother opossum produces from 6-20 young which leave the womb after about 2 weeks. They stay in the mother's pouch for about 2 months.

The opossum has a tail that it can use to support its body weight. A view inside the opossum's pouch (bottom) shows tiny embryos attached to their mother's mammary glands.

is available. When they hunt, bears depend upon raw strength and sharp claws.

Cats use stealth, bears use strength, but the *canines* (dog family) use endurance and teamwork. Canines such as *wolves* usually hunt in packs, surrounding their victim, harassing it, tiring it, and finally killing it. These large carnivores often pick older, weaker, or younger animals for their prey and thus help prevent overpopulation. An old Eskimo saying aptly describes this relationship: "The wolf and the caribou are one; the caribou feeds the wolf, but the wolf keeps the caribou strong."

Fearing the loss of his domesticated animals, man has hunted and poisoned many of the larger canines. *Wolves* were once common throughout North America, Europe, the Bible lands, and most of Asia. As man moved in, wolves moved out. Now there are only a few wolves in northern regions. The *coyote*, however, is still common in the American Great Plains. Known for its loud, lonesome howl and mangy appearance, this smaller canine has survived poisoning, trapping, and hunting.

Although the *dog* is often called "man's best friend," most Biblical references to the dog are negative. The stray, unkempt dogs in many oriental cities are considerably different from the well-kept domestic pets found in our own country.

Also in the order Carnivora are several animals that swim better than they run such as seals, walruses, and sea lions. Many smaller animals such as raccoons, mink, otters, weasels, badgers, and wolverines are also carnivores.

17B-15 *Several carnivores*

raccoon

walrus

badger

The Lion in the Bible

The *lion,* one of the best-known carnivores, is described in Proverbs as having a stately tread and courage, for it "turneth not away for any" (Prov. 30:30). The Persian lion, a subspecies of the familiar, slightly larger African lion, is the lion to which the Bible refers. A Persian lion weighs about 180 kg (400 lb.) and is about 1.5 m (5 ft.) long with a 1-m (3-ft.) tail. Since lions are a threat to domesticated animals, shepherds were often called upon to defend their sheep from these large carnivores, as did David (I Sam. 17:36). As often happens, these predators of livestock were killed by man and made almost extinct. Today special animal preserves are keeping many Biblical animals, including the lion, alive in Palestine.

Several times in the Bible the Lord used the lion, which normally avoids humans, to kill men. The disobedient prophet in I Kings 13, the man in I Kings 20:36, and the foreign settlers in Samaria in II Kings 17:25 were killed by lions.

Although the Bible does not call the lion the "king of beasts," it is often compared to strong, majestic things. Judah is described as "a lion's whelp [cub] . . . . Who shall rouse him up?" (Gen. 49:9). Proverbs 28:1 says, "The righteous are bold as a lion," implying that they need fear nothing. Even God Himself is described in terms of lion characteristics, such as "behold, the Lion of the tribe of Judah, the Root of David, hath prevailed" (Rev. 5:5). Satan in his vicious attack on Christians is described as a "roaring lion . . . seeking whom he may devour" (I Pet. 5:8).

Persian lion

Aquatic mammals

Aquatic mammals include the fishlike *whales* and *dolphins*. Unlike the seal and walrus, which are carnivores, these mammals do not come ashore; they even bear their young in the water. Aquatic mammals have flippers; their tails are horizontal flaps, not the vertical tails of true fish.

Whales and dolphins must surface to breathe air. Some have nostrils on the top of their heads. This blowhole is for breathing, although in colder areas the release of warm breath gives the appearance of water being forced out.

17B-17 *A dolphin blowhole*

The largest known living animal is the *blue whale,* which can reach 33.5 m (109 ft.) in length and weigh over 154 metric tons (170 t.). This animal, however, feeds on plankton. The *killer whales,* on the other hand, have sharp teeth and have been known to bite off the tongues and lower jaws of larger whales and to burst through ice to attack seals and men. One specimen had 13 porpoises and 14 whole seals in its stomach.

The *dolphin* has a long snout and a permanent smile. These mammals readily tolerate the presence of man and are easily tamed. They often help wounded dolphins and even drowning humans. Some researchers believe that the dolphin and *porpoises* are among the most intelligent animals since they are easily trained and appear to have an intricate method of communicating by underwater sounds.

17B-16 *Blue whale and human drawn to scale*

Primates, the erect mammals

The members of the **order Primates** (prih MAY teez), the *erect mammals,* include the *great apes,* the *monkeys,* and several smaller animals. Primates share the following characteristics:

- freely moving arms and legs with large hands and feet;
- the thumb and innermost toe usually opposable, enabling the hands and feet to grasp;
- nails on most fingers and toes;
- forward-facing eyes, permitting binocular vision with depth perception;
- a poor sense of smell;
- normally spend their time in trees but can walk erect when on land;
- less specialized teeth than those of most other mammals;
- mostly vegetarian but may supplement diet with eggs, insects, and occasionally other small animals.

The *gorilla,* the largest ape, lives in the dense forests of Africa. Early reports of these apes described terrifying creatures. Indeed, the broad-shouldered gorilla is fearsome in appearance. Its

17B-18 *The mandrill is a primate.*

447

FACETS OF BIOLOGY

Hoofed Animals in the Bible

Horses

The *horse* is an odd-toed mammal which has long served man as a beast of burden and transportation. In the early Bible times, the horse was not used by the Israelites. Pharaoh gave no horses to Abraham (Gen. 12:16), but they were known in Egypt by Joseph's time; as an individual of high rank, he rode in a horse-drawn chariot. The horse was "of Egypt" and was not to be used by God's chosen people. The Lord tells His people, "When thou art come into the land which the Lord thy God giveth thee . . . [the king] shall not multiply horses to himself, nor cause the people to return to Egypt, to the end that he should multiply horses" (Deut. 17:14-16).

Neither King Saul nor King David rode horses. When David's son Absalom "prepared him chariots and horses" (II Sam. 15:1), he was being arrogant and nearing apostasy. King Solomon, however, disobeyed God's directive and purchased horses and chariots from Egypt (I Kings 10:29) and even had them in the army in Jerusalem. As this practice continued, the prophets complained. Isaiah declares, "Woe to them that go down to Egypt for help; and stay on horses, and trust in chariots . . . and in horsemen . . . but they look not unto the Holy One of Israel, neither seek the Lord" (Isa. 31:1). Those who depended on "chariots and horses" were considered materialists and unbe-lievers (Ezek. 17:15; Hos. 1:7; Mic. 5:10; and Zech. 9:10).

Donkeys

The Biblical *donkey,* or ass, is quite different from the small, self-willed animal of the American West. In other lands, including the Middle East, donkeys are sleek and slender and can be beautiful animals. One of the things revealed to us straight from the donkey's mouth is that the donkeys of the Middle East are submissive beasts. When the Lord caused Balaam's ass to speak, it asked its master if it had ever failed to obey. Even Balaam, the wayward prophet, had to answer "nay" (Num. 22:12-30).

donkey

The ass is not as speedy as the horse, but it has more endurance in hot, dry weather and is considerably more surefooted, an advantage in the rugged terrain of the Bible lands. Some people consider the donkey to be smarter than the horse. There are two types of asses spoken of in the Bible: the "strong ass" was a pack animal owned by many people, and the "riding ass" was a stately animal regarded as an indication of wealth. King Saul and King David rode asses. During our Lord's triumphal entry into Jerusalem, He rode an animal not of low estate, but that which was expected of a King of Israel, "a colt the foal [offspring] of an ass" (Matt. 21:5).

Camels

One of man's oldest and most reluctant servants is the *camel*. The camel is ideally designed for desert transport and has been called "the ship of the desert." Long lashes protect its eyes from sun and sand. Its nostrils can pinch closed in a sandstorm. A camel's toes are large and widely separated to distribute its weight over the sand. It also has the ability to travel for long stretches with little water. Before the journey, the camel will drink large amounts of water.

Camels can drink about 30% of their body weight in 10 min. In light of this fact, Rebekah's offer to "draw water for thy camels . . . until they have done drinking" (Gen. 24:19) is an impressive one. During a journey camels will sweat very little, even in high heat, saving the water most other mammals lose. They can survive with elevated body temperatures and can tolerate a water loss of 25% of their body weight. In desert heat they can go a week without drinking, and in cooler temperatures, up to 3 weeks.

toed, hoofed mammals that "chew the cud." Many of man's most beneficial domesticated animals are bovines, including cows, goats, and sheep. Today many people are unfamiliar with the term "ox." An **ox** (plural *oxen*) is any large bovine. What we often label as cattle and similar animals are called oxen in the Bible.

The many types of cattle in domestication today are of uncertain origin. Many of the various wild and domesticated types found in different areas of the world can interbreed. This interbreeding produces a diversity of characteristics, permitting development of strains with particular sets of traits. For example, some are bred for high milk production, while others are bred to live in dry conditions and still produce good beef.

The oxen of the Bible lands were not as "specialized" as our modern cattle. They served primarily as beasts of burden, with milk and meat production being valuable secondary capacities.

In spite of centuries of close association, camels maintain a hearty distaste for man and his demands. The animal grunts and complains loudly when it is being loaded. Even trained camels bite, kick, and spit at their keepers.

Cattle or Oxen

The family Bovidae (BOH vuh dee), the **bovines,** contains even-

A yoke of oxen

Terms for Oxen

Ox (pl., oxen): a collective term for large bovines, both male and female (bulls and cows), usually referring to working animals; often interchangeable with "cattle"

Cattle: a collective term for most large bovines, both male and female, usually referring to animals raised for meat, milk, and leather

Calf: a young ox (under one year old), either male or female

Heifer: a female ox, before it has given birth to its first calf

Cow: a female ox, after it has given birth to its first calf

Bull: a male ox, not castrated, kept for breeding

Bullock: in the Bible, a young male ox; today, a castrated bull being fattened for beef

Steer: a castrated male ox being fattened for beef

Beef: usually a term for oxen meat; sometimes used in the Bible to refer to the animal

Veal: meat of young, usually unweaned oxen

The Heavenly Shepherd by Bartolome Estaban Murillo, Bob Jones University Collection of Sacred Art. The allegory of the Shepherd is one of the most beautiful in the Bible. David wrote of it in Psalm 23.

Males that were not to be used for breeding were castrated (had their testes removed) to make them docile and more willing to pull a plow or cart. A yoke of oxen (a pair used as working beasts) was a valuable possession. Elisha, when he was called of the Lord, was in charge of 12 yoke of oxen (I Kings 19:19), an indication that he was from a wealthy family. Job, with 1000 yoke of oxen (Job 42:12), was very rich.

The size of Solomon's household is shown by their consuming "ten fat oxen, and twenty oxen out of the pastures" daily (I Kings 4:23). When Solomon dedicated the temple, he slew 22,000 oxen for sacrifice (I Kings 8:63). The meat of the oxen became a huge public feast of thanksgiving which went on for days. This was probably the only time some of the poorer Israelites ever tasted beef; their cattle were far too valuable for other purposes.

The domestic *sheep* probably originated from various types of wild, mountain-dwelling species. Abel, Adam's son, was a "keeper of sheep" (Gen. 4:2), which gives sheep the distinction of being the first recorded domestic animal. Most sheep of Bible times were brown, black, or had splotched patterns. Their wool (actually an underhair which grows longer than the guard hair) was one of the sheep's most valuable characteristics to the Israelites. Since white wool is more valuable, sheep have since been bred for white coats.

The domestic sheep is very docile. When its legs are tied together, it will lie quietly on its side while its wool is clipped. Most Palestini-ans knew exactly what was being described when Isaiah compared the Lord's suffering to a sheep, saying, "as a sheep before her shearers is dumb, so he openeth not his mouth" (Isa. 53:7).

The "fat-tailed sheep" was probably the species raised in Palestine during Biblical times. The broad, flat tail of the adult may weigh 4.5-7 kg (10-15 lb.), and some *rams* (male sheep) may have tails weighing 13.5 kg (30 lb.). In the Law, the tails of sheep were to be used in peace offerings, sin offerings, and guilt offerings. For most Israelite families to offer a sheep or a ram was a considerable sacrifice of food and clothing. The Jews were told to sacrifice all of it, even the wool (Lev. 1:13). God paints a perfect picture when our Lord is called "the Lamb of God," for He is the One who sacrificed all for us.

All domestic bovines depend upon man, but the sheep is one of the most dependent, requiring constant attention. Unless they are led to pasture and water and are protected by the shepherd, sheep quickly weaken and fall prey to various parasites and predators. This fact adds special meaning to the relationship between Christ, the "Good Shepherd" (John 10:11), and the Christian, the "sheep of his pasture" (Ps. 100:3). What a comfort for the Christian to know that whatever befalls him, God, the Creator and Sustainer, is his "Good Shepherd."

Review questions on page 452.

Review questions on page 452.

Sheep can still be seen on Jordanian hillsides.

17B-19 *The chimpanzee is considered to be one of the most intelligent of animals.*

large and protruding muzzle give the beast a habitual look of anger. When confronted, the ape rears up on its hind legs and beats its barrel chest in an awesome display. For all this frightening show, however, the ape is a timid creature.

The *chimpanzee* is a smaller ape with arms longer in proportion to its body, a more dome-shaped head, and large ears. Many researchers consider chimps the most intelligent of animals. In the wild, chimpanzees are one of the few groups of animals that use tools. They have been observed to use sticks as weapons and blades of grass to probe ants out of anthills.

In experiments chimpanzees have demonstrated the ability to reason in solving difficult problems. Even more startling research has been done in training chimps to communicate. Using sign language, chimps have learned large vocabularies and appear to be able to communicate effectively and creatively. Just how far this learning and communication can go remains to be seen.

Hoofed mammals

The **hoofed mammals** include a wide variety of animals which spend long hours grazing the available vegetation. Most have toes with enlarged, hardened *hoofs*. Some are large and clumsy, as are the *hippopotamus* and *rhinoceros;* others, like the *gazelle* and *antelope,* are sleek and among the fastest animals on the earth.

The hoofed mammals are divided into two orders based on the type of foot.

❑ *Odd-toed hoofed mammals* (Order Perissodactyla) These mammals have one long-hoofed toe or three enlarged toes and simple stomachs. They include the horses, asses, zebras, and the rhinoceros.

17B-20 *Minor orders of mammals*

Sirenia (aquatic), sea cow

Proboscidea (trunked), elephant

Lagomorpha (rodentlike), rabbit

Edentata (toothless), armadillo

Chiroptera (flying), bat

17B-21 *Swine lack rumens and have divided hoofs. They were considered "unclean" by Old Testament Jews.*

❑ *Even-toed hoofed mammals* (Order Artiodactyla) These mammals have long legs with 2 or 4 functional hoofed toes. Many have antlers or horns. The even-toed hoofed animals are divided into two groups based on whether they have sim-

ple stomachs or rumens. Pigs and hippopotamuses have simple stomachs. Cows, deer, camels, giraffes, antelope, goats, buffalo, and sheep have *rumens* and, using a Biblical expression, "chew the cud" (Lev. 11:4).

In Leviticus 11, the Jewish dietary law describes the even-toed mammals as "cloven-footed." The cloven-footed beasts which "chew the cud" could be eaten. The odd-toed hoofed mammals (uncloven), those with cloven hooves that did not chew the cud, and those that chewed the cud but lacked cloved hooves (as the camel) were not to be eaten by the Jews.

17B-22 *The number of toes is used to classify hoofed mammals.*

horse · pig · even-toed · cow · odd-toed

Biological Terms

Characteristics of Mammals	rumen	placenta	monotreme	*Facets*
class Mammalia	cud	umbilical cord	order Carnivora	bovine
incisor	diaphragm	gestation	marsupial	ox
canine	larynx	mammary gland	aquatic mammal	
molar	hibernation	*Types of Mammals*	order Primates	
	uterus	order Rodentia	hoofed mammal	

Review Questions 17B-2

1. Give an example of a monotreme. What characteristics set the monotremes apart as a separate mammalian order?
2. Give several examples of marsupials. What characteristics set the marsupials apart as a separate mammalian order?
3. List several characteristics and examples of (a) the order Rodentia, (b) the order Carnivora, (c) aquatic mammals, and (d) primates.
4. What are the two major groups of hoofed mammals? Which contains the ruminants? What groups are acceptable as food under the Old Testament Jewish dietary laws?

Facet 17B-1: Hoofed Animals in the Bible, pages 448-50

1. Why was it appropriate for Jesus to ride a donkey during his triumphal entry into Jerusalem (Matt. 21:1-11)?
2. What distinguishes bovine, ox, cattle, bullock, and steer?

Thought Questions 17B

1. Compare gestation length and amount of parental care given by various mammals.
2. Differentiate between true and false hibernation in mammals.
3. Compare and contrast hibernation and estivation.

ECOLOGY

EIGHTEEN

18A - The Ecosystem

In the mid-1800s (about the time Mendel published his findings about inheritance "factors" in peas), the term **ecology*** was first used and defined as "the whole science of the relations of the organism to the environment, including . . . all the 'conditions of existence'." Although it sounds a bit complicated, this is still a good, usable definition of the term.

We need an understanding of the ecology of an area to comprehend what is happening when the environment becomes polluted and to know how to handle potential pollutants or polluted environments. Ecology, however, is not the study of pollution but is the study of what most people would call "nature." It does *not* deal with the individual parts (that is, the individual organisms) but with the whole. How living and nonliving things affect one another is ecology.

In its earliest form, ecology was purely *descriptive*. A scientist would enter a geographical area and describe it. He would find certain organisms in deserts and others in forests. A listing of what

---

ecology: eco- (Gk. OIKOS, house) +
-logy (the study of)

lives where is one of the first steps in any ecological study. As scientists began to ask ''Why?'' ecology really became interesting and, as the answer unfolded, difficult.

Why are polar bears found in the Arctic and not the Antarctic? To answer this question, one must study the polar bear as well as its environment. Polar bears eat seals and fish. They live on the ice floes, swim in ice water, and sleep in caves they dig in the snow. Although they can live in temperate regions (as they do in zoos), they appear to be uncomfortable in the summer heat.

After studying polar bear ecology, scientists conclude that the conditions for polar bear life exist in the Antarctic. There are no polar bears on ice floes around the southern ice cap only because the polar bear has not migrated there, and the perils of the trip through the temperate and tropical regions appear to assure us that they will not.

The polar bear example is a simple one because there are few factors involved. Another example of ecological studies (or more accurately, of a lack of them) will show the importance and a little of the complexity of ecological studies.

18A-1 *A scientist inspecting the teeth of an anesthetized polar bear*

The "Australian" rabbit

Thomas Austin enjoyed rabbit hunting, but on his Australian sheep ranch there were no rabbits. In 1859 he imported 24 rabbits from his native England and released them on the grasslands of his estate. Six years later his land was overrun with 10,000 rabbits. They were destroying the grassland, causing his sheep to starve. He had killed over 20,000 rabbits, enough to satisfy any man's desire for rabbit hunting, but now he was at a loss about what to do.

18A-2 *A fence to prevent the migration of animals in the Australian outback. Note how the vegetation differs on opposite sides of the fence. An "Australian" rabbit (inset).*

In England and Europe the rabbit is a minor pest. Many European animals, ranging from hawks and eagles to cats and snakes, feed on rabbits. In Australia, however, there are no natural predators to check the growth of the rabbit population. The rabbits from Austin's farm were spreading in a circle of destruction. By the early 1900s they had spread over 1,600 km (1,000 mi.) from Austin's farm and had invaded all the major grazing areas of Australia.

In 1883 the Australian government paid thousands of pounds to have the rabbits killed. Poisons were put in the water and in rabbit food, but to little avail. A fence 107 cm (42 in.) high and 1,833 km (1,146 mi.) long was erected across Australia to prevent the spread of the rabbits.

Attempts were made to bring hawks, snakes, and weasels into Australia, but these predators soon died out. (What natural Australian wildlife would these predators have eaten after killing all the rabbits? Today scientists consider Australia fortunate that these predators did not become established.) Most of these rabbit-control attempts met with only minor or temporary success.

A viral disease which causes only mild discomforts for American rabbits was discovered in South America. If European rabbits are exposed to this virus, major swelling of the membranes around the eyes, nose, mouth, and sex organs develops. Within 10 days, 99% of the European rabbits experimentally exposed to the virus were dead. Having seen the effects of introducing rabbits to Australia and Japanese beetles and gypsy moths to America (see pages 383-85), scientists ran extensive tests on Australian animals to see if they would be affected by the virus. By 1937, it was agreed that the virus would affect only the unwanted rabbits. Diseased rabbits were repeatedly released into highly infested areas, but within a few months the disease disappeared and the rabbits remained.

In 1959 a large number of dead rabbits was found in a certain area. They had died of the viral disease. Investigation revealed that the mosquito was the vector of the disease. In the dry areas where the disease was first introduced, mosquitoes could not breed; however, it spread rapidly through the areas where mosquitoes could breed. But it left the numerous Australian grassland rabbits virtually untouched.

Even if mosquitoes could be temporarily induced to thrive in the drier parts of Australia, the viral disease would probably not wipe out the rabbits it infects. Those rabbits capable of withstanding the infection are the ones left to breed, and thus their ability to resist the disease is passed down to a larger and larger portion of the rabbit population.

In addition, the disease spreads effectively only in a dense concentration of rabbits. When the number of rabbits becomes small, fewer mosquitoes come in contact with infected rabbits. In turn, fewer rabbits are bitten by infected mosquitoes, and the disease stops spreading. Although this virus may be a part of the method of rabbit control, it will not restore a rabbit-free Australia.

The role of ecology

In the Australian rabbit example, the scientists were consulted too late. It would have been best to conduct a study to determine the effects of introducing the rabbits rather than to call on scientists to correct the manmade problem.

18A-3 *Scientists tag pelicans (left) to study their behaviors. Swans sprayed with a dye to help scientists track their migration (below).*

Most frequently, ecologists are called upon either to
❑ study the relationships between existing organisms and their environment (example: study Australia before rabbits were introduced);
❑ predict what would happen if some factor were changed (example: predict what effects rabbits would have on Australia); or
❑ recommend steps to change an environment or the organisms in it (example: suggest steps to control the Australian rabbit population).

In the Australian rabbit problem, the first two steps were ignored, necessitating the third step.

Supposedly, if the first two steps are thoroughly completed and man heeds what his intelligence then tells him, there will be no major difficulties such as those in Australia.

The ecologist is not always called upon to correct existing problems. Often the ecologist recommends how to use a natural resource wisely, without destroying it and others. For example, to determine which crop should be planted on what land and what land should be used as pasture or to grow trees is also the work of ecologists.

Making such recommendations may sound simple, but in actuality it is quite difficult. Consider how many organisms and conditions would have to be understood to make a valid prediction in the Australian rabbit example. If the studies are haphazard or if they favor the interests of one group, there may be misuse of the natural resources and disastrous results.

Three hundred years ago man's decisions about how to use a natural resource and other ecological concerns were minor in comparison to current decisions. The wastes of a small town were few and easily dealt with in the environment. When man had to use his own muscle (or that of his animals) to alter the environment, the effect was minor even if he was not wise in his actions. Decisions made today (as with nuclear wastes) can quickly affect the environment on a wide scale for hundreds or thousands of years. Today man can use technology to alter the environment on a major scale. If the decisions he makes are not wise, the results of his actions may be permanent scars. Man's decisions about the use of natural resources and other ecological concerns are, therefore, of major consequence.

In order to make good decisions, the ecological effects of all the possible choices must be accurately determined, and values must be established. For example, the effect of rabbits in Australia could have been determined, and values could have been set on the pleasure and income of rabbit hunting and the worth of raising sheep; then a wise decision could have been made. To help you make wise decisions regarding the use of natural resources, it is advisable for you to know something about how the possible outcomes are determined and what realistic Christian values should be set on natural resources.

The ecosystem

An **ecosystem** is all the living things and all the nonliving factors and their interactions within a limited area. In general terms an ecosystem is everything in any area being studied or discussed. Although Australia is a considerably larger area than most scientists would care to study, in the rabbit example Australia is an ecosystem; it is a limited area which has living and nonliving things interacting. Normally the area spoken of as an ecosystem would be more the size of a pond, a field, or a section of a forest, coastline, or stream.

Even when an ecosystem is small, scientists may divide it into areas which could be considered ecosystems in themselves. In a 100-m stretch of river, for example, there will be different conditions and different organisms near the shore than in the open current. In the quiet backwaters certain organisms will flourish that will only be found as "passers-by" in the rapids.

The Ecosystem	**18A-4**

Physical Environment
❑ Radiation
  • Light   • Heat (temperature)
❑ Atmosphere
❑ Wind (currents in aquatic environments)
❑ Rotation of the earth
❑ Water
❑ Topography (depth of water in aquatic environments)
❑ Soil and geological substrate (mineral concentration in aquatic environments)
❑ Gravity
❑ Fire

Biotic Community
❑ Producers (green plants, algae)
❑ Consumers
  • Feeders (animals, protists)
  • Decomposers (fungi, bacteria)

A major problem with trying to limit an ecosystem is that all ecosystems depend upon the ecosystems around them. To study completely the ecosystem of a river, scientists must study the ecosystems of the banks and even the entire land area that drains into the river. If the surrounding land is forest, the river will have one set of conditions. If the forest burns, is cut down, is changed to farmland, or is converted into a housing subdivision, the water in the river will change; thus, the river ecosystem changes.

Ecosystems are made up of two distinct but interacting parts: the **physical environment** and the **biotic*** (bye AHT ik) **community.** The physical environment is all the nonliving factors in the ecosystem. The biotic community is all the living things within the ecosystem. These two components affect each other. The members of the biotic community affect each other and the physical environment, and the physical environment affects the biotic community.

The Physical Environment

Bananas do not grow in Canada, for it gets too cold in the winter. Neither do they grow in the Sahara Desert; it is too dry. If you want to grow bananas, buy land in the wet tropics. But bananas do not grow everywhere in the wet tropics. Certain areas are too wet or lack certain minerals. In some areas conditions are right for banana tree diseases to thrive. What factors of the physical environment (nonliving parts of an ecosystem) contribute to banana tree growth? To answer that question, one must carefully study the requirements of the organism.

Radiation, winds, and atmosphere

The sun supplies **radiation** as *heat* and *light* to our earth. (Other forms of radiation are sent to earth by the sun. Most of them are either filtered out by our atmosphere or are relatively insignificant.) Plants and algae use light in photosynthesis to produce sugar, which serves as food for the plants and for all other living things.

If the amount or quality of light in an ecosystem changes, then the ecosystem will change. The heat of the sun also affects ecosystems. The heating of large air masses and the *rotation of the earth* cause **winds.** Winds strongly affect the biotic community. Most living things both give off and require certain atmospheric gases. Wind mixes atmospheric gases, keeping them within livable concentrations.

18A-5 *The prevailing wind direction has dramatically affected the growth pattern of these trees (left). The timberline is visible on many mountains (below).*

It is primarily the winds which establish the **timberlines** (lines above which trees will not grow) on mountains. Large plants cannot withstand the heavy blasting of ice and snow. Thus, trees either become stunted or do not grow above the timberline. Trees that grow near the timberline show the effects of heavy winds that move down from the upper, colder regions of the mountain.

In aquatic environments *currents* take the place of winds. The speed at which water moves determines what organisms will live in it. Certain aquatic organisms are found only in rapidly moving streams; others, only in the slower-moving areas; and others, only in standing water.

Currents, or the lack of them, help to determine the concentration and distribution of substances such as dissolved minerals and plankton. A rapidly moving stream contains large amounts of dissolved oxygen, a necessity for some aquatic animals, while standing water may have dissolved oxygen only to a depth of about a meter. Without currents most bodies of water would become stagnant and uninhabitable for most organisms.

biotic: (life)

Water

Water is one of the most crucial environmental factors in any ecosystem. Often the main difference between a lush tropical forest and a desert is the quantity of water, as irrigation of deserts has repeatedly shown.

One estimate indicates that if all the water in the atmosphere were to fall as rain, the entire earth would get about 2.5 cm (1 in.) of rainfall, which is about a 10-day supply. Most areas average about 89 cm (35 in.) of rainfall per year, but some areas of the world have an annual average of over 360 cm (142 in.). Obviously the water which forms clouds and rain originates from some source other than the atmosphere.

Most free water on the earth is **cyclic;** it is in a constantly moving cycle. This movement is called the **water cycle.** Through *evaporation* and *transpiration,* water enters the atmosphere. As the warm, moisture-laden air rises, it cools, condensing the moisture and forming clouds. As clouds become cooler, the water falls as *precipitation.*

Some of the precipitation forms streams which flow toward larger bodies of water (lakes and eventually oceans). Water moving on the surface of the earth is called *runoff water.* Some of the water *percolates** (PUR kuh LAYTS) into the soil. When this water reaches a layer it cannot penetrate, it collects and forms *groundwater.* Groundwater is that which comes out of the ground as springs or that man obtains by digging wells. In time the groundwater also reaches a lake or ocean (Eccles. 1:7).

The water cycle exemplifies the interaction of several parts of the physical environment. If the sun were not warming the atmosphere, evaporation would stop. The heat of the sun and the rotation of the earth cause the winds which move the moisture-laden air, not only so it cools but also so it does not rain only over the oceans where most evaporation takes place. If gravity were not pulling at the rain, runoff water, groundwater, lakes, and oceans would not form.

Other factors in the physical environment

Topography is the "lay of the land"–whether it is flat, hilly, or mountainous. The presence of rocks, lakes, and trenches affects the topography. The slope, height, and expanse of a mountain range determine such factors as winds, temperature, and rainfall hundreds and even thousands of kilometers away. If a rock is placed in a stream, its downstream side will provide an environment suitable for certain organisms that could not exist there while the stream bottom was smooth.

The *soil* and the *geological substrate** (rocks and other substances underneath the soil) are closely related. Often the inorganic parts of the soil are derived from the geological substrate. Together with topography, the soil and geological substrate help determine the amount of precipitation that will become runoff water and, to some extent, the organisms that will be found in an area.

Most aquatic environments receive minerals either by dissolving the geological substrate or from runoff water. Thus the soil, topography, and substrate of the surrounding area affect a body of

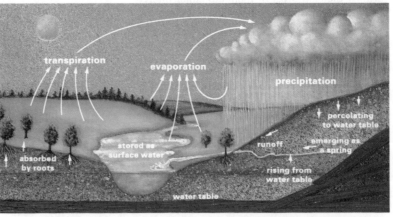

18A-6 *The water cycle*

transpiration

evaporation

precipitation

percolating
to water table

stored as
surface water

absorbed
by roots

runoff

emerging as
a spring

rising from
water table

water table

percolate: per- (L. PER-, through) +
-colate (COLARE, to filter or to strain)

substrate: sub- (under) + -strate
(STERNERE, to spread out flat)

water. The kind and amount of dissolved minerals influence plankton growth.

The *gravitational pull* of the earth of course affects all organisms, but the moon also affects biotic communities. The ocean tides are caused in part by lunar gravity. Certain algae and other organisms which grow along the seashore grow best when they have regular alternating periods of exposure to seawater and air. Ecosystems of thousands of organisms are found in *tidal pools* which are regularly cut off from the ocean as the tide goes out.

Although it can be devastating, *fire* caused by lightning or spontaneous combustion is a normal factor in many ecosystems. In certain forests a regular clearing of small plants, fungi, and insects by a *ground fire* is beneficial. Such fires usually do not kill most vertebrates (for they find shelter)

18A-7 *Fire is a significant, often natural factor in many ecosystems.*

or the large plants. One species of pine produces cones which will not release their seeds unless they are exposed to fire. A fire kills the underbrush that would compete with the pine seedling for light, water, and minerals and thus gives the seedling a better chance of survival.

Review Questions 18A-1
1. Differentiate between ecology and a study of man's pollution of the environment.
2. What functions do ecologists most frequently perform?
3. What are the two components of an ecosystem?
4. List several factors in the physical environment of the grounds of your school.
5. Describe the water cycle.

The Biotic Community

The **biotic community** includes all the living things in an ecosystem. Within the biotic* community are **populations.** A population includes all the members of the same type of living thing (often a species or a similar grouping). The biotic community within the ecosystem of a pond, for example, would include populations of lily pads, cattails, mosquitoes, frogs, and turtles. Each type of fish, alga, and bacterium constitutes a different population.

Some 10-square-meter ecosystems may have only a few dozen populations, yet others of similar size may have hundreds. The ecosystem of a cornfield, for example, is artificially structured to favor the corn population and those other populations which aid the growth of the corn (such as beneficial insects) and to discourage populations which would hamper corn yield (such as weeds, crows, and harmful insects). The biotic commu-

nity of a similar-sized natural swamp, meadow, or forest will have a larger number of more varied populations.

Within an ecosystem the various populations affect one another in different ways. In a pasture the cow population eats the grass population. We may not think that the fungi and bacteria of the soil directly affect the cows, but were it not for these organisms breaking down organic materials, the grass would soon die from lack of usable minerals.

Within the pasture certain birds help the cows by eating grasshoppers and other insects which compete with the cows for food. Some insects, however, help the cows. For example, bees pollinate clover. The roots of clover support bacteria which help to put nitrogen compounds into the soil. Without these compounds the grass would not grow, and the cows would go hungry. Thus

FACETS OF BIOLOGY

18A–1

Biotic Community Relations

When most people think of relationships among the populations that make up the biotic community in an ecosystem, they envision nutritional relationships – who eats whom, or who helps whom get what for dinner. Obtaining energy and material for building and maintaining itself must be high on an organism's priority list. There are, however, other relationships within the biotic community.

Camouflage

For many organisms hiding is almost as important as eating. In fact were it not for their **camouflage** many organisms would either be eaten or not be able to eat. The color and shape of the praying mantis, for example, causes it to look like a branch, as it sits quietly waiting for its prey. Since the vision of insects picks up movement more than shape or color, the mantis is unnoticed as its prey walks within grabbing distance.

A camouflaged insect
(walking stick)

But its camouflage also helps the mantis not be seen by insect-eating birds. Some tropical members

of the mantis family look like brightly colored flower petals and wait for their prey while hiding from insect-eating animals in flowers.

Protective coloration is seen in many insects. They appear as thorns, twigs, buds, flowers, leaves, or rocks. Some butterflies have wings that are brightly colored when opened flat, but when closed over the insect's back, the wings look like a dead leaf. The countershading of aquatic animals is a protective coloration (see page 398). The colors of many young animals help them blend in with their natural surroundings. Stripes on zebras and tigers, which make them seem so obvious when we see them out of their natural habitat, actually help them to blend in with the tall grasses of their normal surroundings.

Animals such as the flounder change colors to blend with their surroundings giving them a protective coloration advantage that most organisms lack.

Warning Coloration

Some animals, rather than blending with their environment, seem to clash with it. These animals have **warning coloration** which appears to be telling potential predators to beware. Most of the poison arrow frogs of tropical regions hunt during the day. Their brightly colored bodies are clear warnings to those who might want to eat them that by doing so they will be eating their final meal.

skunk

The skunk, with its bold white and black markings, sends a clear warning. If an animal comes too close, he quickly learns to avoid animals with the black and white stripes and will often avoid any animal with similar color combinations.

Some insects have "false eyes" which help to ward off predators. The false eyes of some caterpillars are on their back ends. The would-be predator appears to view these as snake eyes and the caterpillar is left alone. Certain butterflies and moths have eye-shaped and colored spots on their wings. To their predators these may appear to be owl eyes, and owls are usually predators to them.

A caterpillar
with false eyes

Mimicry

One of the best known examples of **mimicry** is the common orange and black viceroy butterfly. The monarch butterfly has a bad taste to most insect-eating animals. Once a bird has tried to eat a monarch butterfly, it never again eats an orange and black butterfly. This protects the viceroy butterfly, a

Interdependence of Organisms

Many symbiotic relationships, along with mimicry, protective and warning colorations, and other population relationships, pose problems for the evolutionist. Consider the example of the symbiotic relationship between the *yucca* plant and the *yucca moth*.

The yucca, a native to the American Southwest, produces flowers in which the anthers are isolated from the stigma. Thus, the flower cannot be self-pollinated, nor is it pollinated by wind or any insect except the yucca moth. Both male and female yucca moths are attracted by the fragrance of the yucca flowers and mate within the flower. From the flower in which she mates, the female moth collects pollen and rolls it into a ball. After mating, the female flies to another yucca flower, bores into the ovary of the flower, deposits an egg in it, and then pollinates the flower by placing some of the pollen from the original blossom onto the stigma of the second flower. This sequence is then repeated on other yucca blooms.

Eventually the larvas of the moth hatch and feed upon some of the seeds within the ovary. Then they burrow out and drop to the ground. The development of the moth continues in the soil. A fertilized yucca plant normally produces several hundred seeds in each ovary, and the single larva destroys only a few. The yucca moth cannot complete its life cycle without the yucca, and the yucca cannot produce seeds without the yucca moth.

yucca moth and the yucca flower

Evolutionists often cite the yucca plant and the yucca moth as an example of "evolutionary adaptation between two different organisms." They believe that the ancestors of both the plant and the animal were evolving at the same time, and as they evolved they became ideally suited for the complex mutualism they now exhibit. The yucca could not develop a dependence upon the moth until the moth had developed enough of the specialized structures and behaviors to insure the fertilization of the yucca. Otherwise the plant would have become extinct. Also, the moth could not develop a larva dependent upon yucca seeds until the yucca had developed. The probability of the evolution of two such mutually dependent organisms is virtually impossible.

slightly smaller yet similar orange and black butterfly that does not have a bad taste.

The scarlet king snake (right) and the coral snake (below) exhibit mimicry.

Other examples of mimicry include the harmless scarlet king snake, which has yellow, red, and black stripes, and the highly poisonous coral snake, which has the same colored stripes, just in a different order.

Do not get the idea that these organisms have *become* mimics—that would be evolution. Organisms exhibit mimicry, warning coloration, and camouflage because they were designed with these protective devices.

Review questions on page 467.

bees indirectly help cows. We can assume that, at least indirectly, all the living things affect all the other living things within the ecosystem. In this section we will study some of the ways that populations interact.

Producers and consumers

Some of the most obvious relationships within biotic communities are the *nutritional relationships:* who gets food (energy and building substances) from whom or what. The populations within any biotic community can be divided into two categories based on food sources.

❏ **Producers** These organisms, such as the green plants and algae, manufacture their own food and are the major producers. They carry on *photosynthesis* to produce sugars. (Photosynthetic and chemosynthetic bacteria are also producer organisms, but we will not discuss them here be-

cause of their relative insignificance in most ecosystems.)

❏ **Consumers** Animals, protozoans, fungi, most bacteria, and humans, which consume all or part of other organisms for food, are consumers.

The **productivity** of an ecosystem is the rate of photosynthesis carried on by its producers. As figure 18A-10 shows, only about 50% of the total light energy available to plants is absorbed by the plants. The rest is reflected or lost as heat. Of the light that is absorbed by plants, about 2% (which

18A-9 *This brown bear is a secondary consumer. Bears can also be primary consumers and tertiary consumers, depending on what they eat.*

is about 1% of the total light energy available) is actually converted to sugar. Of that energy stored in sugar, the plants use about 50% in their own metabolism. This means that, of the light energy available to plants, only about 0.5% is available to the first consumer.

Often the nutritional relationships between organisms in an ecosystem are called a **food chain.** A simple food chain might include *algae,* which are eaten by *aquatic arthropods,* which are eaten by *minnows,* which are eaten by *bass.* In this case the algae are the producers, and the other organisms are the consumers. The aquatic arthropods, since they eat producers, are the *primary consumers.* Primary consumers are normally *herbivores.* Minnows are secondary consumers. *Secondary consumers* are usually *carnivores,* often called *first-level carnivores.* Bass are the *tertiary consumers,* often called *second-level carnivores.*

18A-8 *An aquatic food chain consisting of algae, aquatic arthropods, minnows, and a bass*

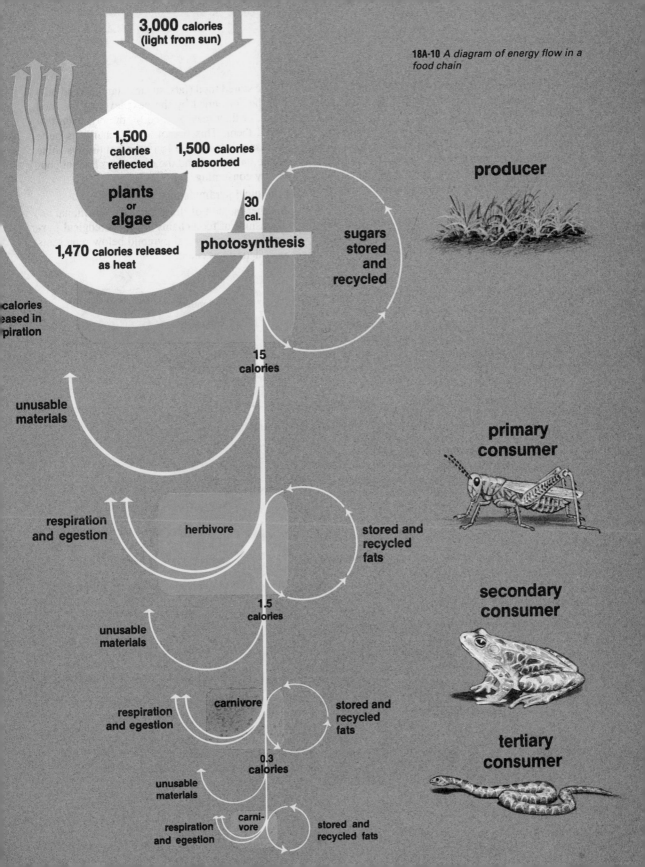

3,000 calories (light from sun)

18A-10 *A diagram of energy flow in a food chain*

1,500 calories reflected   **1,500** calories absorbed

producer

plants or **algae**

30 cal.

1,470 calories released as heat

photosynthesis

sugars stored and recycled

calories eased in piration

15 calories

unusable materials

primary consumer

respiration and egestion   herbivore

stored and recycled fats

secondary consumer

1.5 calories

unusable materials

respiration and egestion   carnivore

stored and recycled fats

tertiary consumer

0.3 calories

unusable materials

respiration and egestion   carnivore

stored and recycled fats

At each step in the food chain there is an 80-90% loss of energy. In other words, for each step up the food chain, a great deal of energy must be invested. Figure 18A-10 shows not only the energy flow in the producers (in this case, grass) but also the energy transfer from producer to primary consumer (grasshoppers), secondary consumer (toads), and tertiary consumer (snakes).

The uneaten blades of grass and the molted grasshopper exoskeletons contain energy which is unusable to the next food chain level; it is lost from this food chain. The respiration of the consumers, as well as the energy contained in materials they give off (excretions and secretions), is energy lost to the next level of the food chain. Much of the energy a consumer ingests is in unusable forms. For example, the exoskeletons of grasshoppers and the bones of toads contain energy that consumers may not be able to convert to a usable form; thus, energy in these forms becomes useless to this food chain.

The stored food (fats, sugars, starches, and oils) may be consumed by the next level of the food chain, or they may be used by the organism that stored them. This use of stored energy is quite necessary because the sun does not always shine on the producers, and the consumers are not constantly consuming.

Ecological pyramids and food webs

Another method of illustrating the nutritional relationships of food chains is with **ecological pyramids.** The ecological pyramid below represents an aquatic food chain.

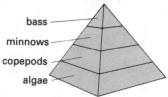

bass —
minnows —
copepods —
algae —

18A-11 *Ecological pyramid* based on energy flow

Detritus Food Chain

Dead organic matter such as fallen leaves, dead trees, dead bodies of animals, or even excrement is **detritus** (dih TRY tus). As you are aware, detritus may be broken down by *decomposer organisms* (bacteria and fungi) to the nutrient substances plants need to grow.

Not all detritus is decomposed directly by bacteria and fungi. Before detritus is decomposed by bacteria and fungi, it is often a part of a separate, but overlapping, **detritus food chain.** A dead leaf, for example, may become the food of a *detritus feeder* such as an insect. Such insects may be eaten by birds, which in turn may be eaten by various other animals. Many insects,

worms, malacostracans (crabs, lobsters, shrimp, and crayfish), and a number of other invertebrates are detritus feeders.

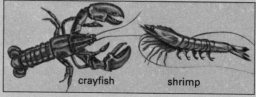

crayfish   shrimp

Many detritus feeders, of course, do not enter food chains which contain progressively larger organisms. All detritus feeders, however, help cycle materials since the foods which pass through their digestive systems are broken into smaller pieces. For example, although most detritus feeders are unable to digest the cellulose of plant cell walls, their digestive systems can break down cellulose into smaller pieces. These smaller pieces are more easily decomposed by bacteria and fungi. Some detritus feeders will eat the same material several times, thus taking advantage of the action of the digestive enzymes secreted by decomposers.

long-horned beetle

The Rabbit and Its Cud

Although not actually a detritus feeder, the rabbit can reingest substances it could not digest the first time. The rabbit passes two types of pellets (feces). One type contains only wastes; the other type contains a great deal of energy in the form of cellulose, a major part of the natural diet of rabbits. Rabbits lack the enzymes necessary to digest cellulose, but bacteria in the pellets do have cellulose-digesting enzymes. In natural conditions rabbits consume these pellets, giving the partially digested cellulose a second trip through their digestive system. The rabbits thus obtain considerably more energy from their food.

For years Bible scholars speculated about the reason God included the rabbit (hare) in the list of unclean animals in Leviticus 11:6 because it

Although the rabbit lacks a rumen, it does the equivalent of "chewing the cud."

"cheweth the cud, but divideth not the hoof." The rabbit's chewing does resemble that of a cow and other bovines, but rabbits lack rumens and do not belch food back to their mouths for additional chewing. Thus, some people felt that Leviticus 11:6 was a clear error in the Bible, while others claimed that "hare" was a mistranslation. The Hebrew word, however, is clearly "hare." Consuming pellets accomplishes the same purpose as chewing the cud, only in a slightly different way.

18A-12 *Ecological pyramid* based on population size

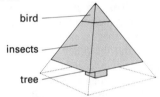

bird
insects
tree

Since it normally takes about ten units of energy to result in one energy unit in the next higher level, ecological pyramids based on energy are always regularly shaped. If the ecological pyramid is based on the number of individuals in a population, however, the pyramid may be misshapen or reversed. For example, a tree (producer) may support thousands of insects (primary consumers) which are the food of only one bird (secondary consumer).

Although food chains and ecological pyramids may be helpful in understanding energy transfer in biotic communities, they oversimplify what actually happens in an ecosystem. For example, a bear may be a secondary carnivore, a primary carnivore, or a herbivore, depending upon what it eats. Birds of prey may be primary or secondary carnivores. Rabbits are eaten by owls, snakes, mountain lions, and many other predators–all of whom will eat different animals if rabbits are not available.

To describe these multiple relationships, ecologists often use **food webs.** Food webs may be simple or extremely complex, depending upon the number of different animals in the ecosystem and their ability to adapt to different foods.

18A-13 *A food web for the edge of a forest*

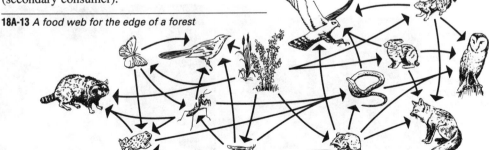

Other relationships between populations

In our discussion of nutritional relationships within the biotic community, we have dealt primarily with **bulk feeders.** A bulk feeder eats either all, or major portions, of its prey. The cow which eats grass is a bulk feeder, as are most carnivores. Even most detritus feeders are bulk feeders. Although bulk feeding and decomposing are the two most obvious nutritional relationships between populations within an ecosystem, there are many others. Ecologists often categorize some of these relationships as follows:

❑ **Neutralism**   Every population in an environment indirectly affects every other population; however, neutralism exists when there is no *direct* relationship. If a toad that eats insects and a bird that eats seeds live in the same area, their relationship could be considered neutralism. Even though, through insects and plants and their relationships, the bird and the toad may affect each other, this relationship is indirect.

❑ **Competition**   If two populations inhibit each other because they depend upon the same resource, they are in competition. Weeds in a carrot patch are competing with the carrots for sun, water, and minerals. Hawks and eagles may compete for the same prey.

❑ **Amensalism*** (AH MEN suh liz um)   When one population is inhibited by a second population, but the second population is not affected by the first, they exhibit amensalism. Certain molds, for example, produce antibiotics that inhibit the growth of certain bacteria. The bacteria are harmed by the mold; but the mold is neither helped nor harmed by the bacteria. The roots of certain plants have been shown to have similar effects on certain soil organisms.

❑ **Predation** (prih DAY shun)   In predation, one organism (the *predator)* eats another organism (the *prey).* A hawk catching a rodent is a good example of predation.

❑ **Parasitism**   In parasitism, the *parasite* depends (often for food) upon a *host.* Usually a parasite is much smaller than its host. Many parasites do not kill their hosts but merely take advantage of a "free meal." Mosquitoes, tapeworms, and many fungi are parasites that usually take little from their hosts. Some parasites, like certain protozoans, flukes, and roundworms, may eventually kill their hosts.

❑ **Commensalism*** (kuh MEN suh LIZ um) If one population benefits from a second population, but the second population is not helped nor harmed by the first population, the relationship is commensalism. For example, vultures "clean up" after the lion has finished eating what it wants of its prey.

❑ **Mutualism*** In mutualism, both populations benefit from the relationship. Some mutualism is *obligatory;* that is, neither organism would survive without the other. The protozoans that live in the digestive tract of the termite are an example. The protozoan supplies the enzymes to digest the cellulose that the termite eats. The termite could not exist without these protozoans, and the protozoans do not live naturally outside the termite. Some lichens are examples of obligatory mutualism, for neither the algae nor the fungi which compose them can exist in the environment of the lichen without the other. Some mutualisms are not obligatory. Barnacles growing on the outside of a sea snail obtain the scraps from the snail's meal; the barnacles camouflage the snail,

18A-14 *What relationships are illustrated by the Harris hawk eating the rabbit it killed (left) and the nurse shark being cleaned by the remora (right)?*

amensalism: a- (without) + -mensal (L. MENSA, table)

commensalism: com- (L. COM-, together) + -mensal (table)

mutualism: (L. MUTUUS, exchanged or reciprocal)

18A-15 *What relationship do barnacles growing on the shell of a mollusk exhibit?*

protecting it from predators. Both barnacles and snails, however, can live without this mutualistic relationship.

Often scientists use the term **symbiosis*** (SIM bye OH sis) to refer to various forms of parasit-

ism, commensalism, and mutualism. Symbiosis, however, can also refer to various other relationships, including competition and amensalism.

Many relationships between organisms cannot be easily classified, and many of them change periodically. Consider the relationship between a berry-eating bird and the berry bush. In the early spring, before the berries are ripe, the bird and the bush may exhibit neutralism. When the berries are ripe, the relationship may appear to be predation, but if the seeds of the berries are dispersed because they pass unharmed through the bird's digestive tract, the relationship could be considered mutualism.

Biological Terms

ecology
ecosystem
physical environment
biotic community

The Physical Environment
radiation
wind
timberline
cyclic
water cycle

The Biotic Community
biotic community
population
producer
consumer
productivity
food chain
ecological pyramid
detritus
detritus food chain

food web
bulk feeder
neutralism
competition
amensalism
predation
parasitism
commensalism
mutualism
symbiosis

Facet
camouflage
warning coloraton
mimicry

Review Questions 18A-2

1. What are the components of a biotic community?
2. What are the two main types of populations (based on their nutritional relationships)?
3. What happens to the radiant energy available to plants? How much of it is available to the first consumer?
4. Construct a food chain using an amphibian, an insect, a bird, and two other organisms.
5. Account for the energy losses between the steps in a food chain.
6. Add four organisms to the food chain established in question 4 and make it a food web.
7. List and describe the nutritional relationships possible between organisms.

Facet 18A: Biotic Community Relations, pages 460-61

1. List and describe several nonnutritional relationships between organisms.
2. Why is it improbable for the relationships between organisms to be the result of evolution?

Thought Questions

1. What, in the ecological sense, is productivity? How would you increase the productivity in an area? What, in terms of energy, are you doing in order to increase productivity?
2. Some ecologists consider the detritus food chain one of the most important in an ecosystem. Why do you suppose this could be true?
3. List three explanations for the description of the rabbit as an animal that "cheweth the cud" in Leviticus 11:6. Which explanations are acceptable, and which are not? Why?
4. Evolutionists sometimes point out the yucca plant and the yucca moth as being a remarkable instance of two species evolving a dependence upon each other. List several reasons why this conclusion (from this and similar examples) is unacceptable.

---

symbiosis: sym- (together) + -bios (life)

Chapter 18B – The Biosphere

Despite certain unexplained phenomena, there is no evidence to support the idea that there is physical life on other planets. The rocks brought back from the moon, as well as the space probes sent to various planets, have revealed no life and no conditions that would support life as we know it. This, however, is not conclusive evidence that there is not life other than that on earth.

Although the Bible states that spiritual beings, including God Himself, dwell in the heavens (which may be just beyond our atmosphere or may be far beyond our world in distance or concept), the Scripture says nothing about physically living beings beyond our planet. Since the Bible gives no information on the topic, we have no way of knowing without investigation–which many people consider a waste of time and money.

The thin shell around our planet in which all known physically living things exist is the **biosphere*** (BY uh SFEER). On land the biosphere goes to the depth of the deepest tree roots. In the ocean most living things exist in the top 150 m (488 ft.) of water, but a few species exist in marine trenches over 9.7 km (6 mi.) deep. While some living things may temporarily fly or be blown a few kilometers into the sky, the lichens growing on the edges of mountain snowcaps are the highest limits of the terrestrial biosphere.

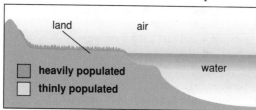

18B-1 *The biosphere*

The limits of the biosphere are thus only about 16 km (10 mi.) apart. The actual thickness of the biosphere at any given spot, however, is much thinner, usually less than 300 m (975 ft.). Within this thin veneer exist vastly different sets of conditions, most of which support some forms of life. Before we discuss how man affects the biosphere, let us examine some of its inner workings.

Interactions in the Ecosystem

Habitat* is a general term for the area where a type of organism lives–its ''address.'' The habitat of the leopard frog is the edges of ponds or the quiet backwaters of streams. If you want to find leopard frogs, look in places like these. ''Habitat'' applies both to the physical environment and to the biotic community in which an organism lives. The physical environment of the leopard frog must include abundant water and a certain range of temperatures. Its biotic community must include insects to serve as prey and predators to keep the frog population in check.

18B-2

These organisms have the same habitat, but their niches differ. How do the niches differ? What other animals with different niches would you expect in this habitat?

Some organisms have wide ranges of habitats, while others have very narrow ones. For example, the raccoon can be found in forests, in meadows,

---

biosphere: bio- (life) + -sphere (L. SPHERA, globe)

habitat: (Fr. HABITAT, natural dwelling place)

or even in suburbs and cities, while the deer leaves the forest and meadows as man converts them to suburbs and cities.

When we discuss *how* the organism affects the ecosystem, we are no longer talking about habitat; what an organism does and how it fits into and affects its habitat is its **ecological niche*** (NICH), often just called *niche*. If the habitat is the "address" of an organism, the niche is its "occupation." For example, the niche of the adult leopard frog is, in part, to serve as a consumer of insects; as a prey of snakes, birds, and raccoons; and as a pet for young boys.

Two organisms may live in the same habitat, but if their niches are different, they are not in direct competition. The ladybug and the grasshopper, for example, may live in the same field. The grasshopper consumes the leaves of the plants, and the ladybug consumes small insects on the plants. They occupy two separate niches in the same habitat.

The niches available within an ecosystem determine what organisms will exist in the ecosystem. Both the physical environment and the other populations within an ecosystem determine what niches are available. To understand how the physical environment and the biotic community interact to determine niches, we will consider some of the cycles found in ecosystems and the concept of limiting factors.

Matter and energy in the ecosystem

Recall that the quantity of available energy in a food chain becomes progressively smaller as it passes from one organism to the next. Finally, the last of the energy captured from the sun by the producer organisms is released in the decomposer organisms; it is no longer in or available for use in the biotic community. Everything alive must constantly have usable energy, but once it has used or released some energy, that energy cannot be reused. It must obtain more.

Even within the physical environment energy merely passes through; it is used, but not reused. For example, the radiant energy that warms a body of water and causes evaporation eventually escapes into the atmosphere. To continue evapo-

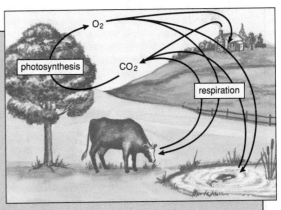

The Oxygen and Carbon Cycles

The **oxygen cycle** is a relatively simple cycle within the ecosystem. Free oxygen (O_2), which is found as an atmospheric gas and dissolved in water, is essential for living things (with the exception of anaerobic bacteria). Organisms use free oxygen predominantly in *respiration*, the breaking down of an energy source such as sugar to obtain the release of energy. Normally during respiration oxygen is used, and carbon dioxide is released. Green plants and algae use carbon dioxide in photosynthesis and produce free oxygen.

Carbon dioxide, an atmospheric gas also found dissolved in water, is the primary source of carbon in living systems and thus is a major part of the **carbon cycle.** In the dark phase of photosynthesis, plants fix carbon dioxide and produce sugars (see pages 94-95). The carbon in these sugars is the primary source of carbon in all other living things. The respiration of sugar (*glycolysis* and *citric acid cycle*; see pages 98-99) converts the carbon of the sugar back into carbon dioxide.

Of course, many carbon-containing compounds are either excreted or remain in the body of the organism when it dies. Decomposer organisms carry on respiration and other processes that convert most organic compounds into carbon dioxide and other substances. The burning of organic substances (be they "fresh" like wood and leaves or fossilized like coal and oil) also converts carbon-containing compounds to carbon dioxide and thus puts carbon back into the atmosphere.

niche: (Fr. NICHE, recess in a wall); *hence,* nest

The Nitrogen Cycle

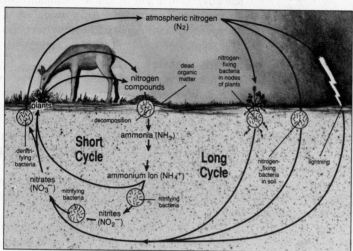

Nodes containing nitrogen-fixing bacteria on legume roots

The nitrogen cycle illustrates interdependence within the biotic community as well as between the physical environment and the biotic community. Although nitrogen comprises only about 0.5-4% (by weight) of living organisms, those compounds that contain nitrogen are crucial. Recall that DNA and RNA contain nitrogenous bases and that many amino acids contain nitrogen.

Nitrogen comprises about 75% of our atmosphere. Gaseous nitrogen (N_2), however, is useless to most living things. Where do living things obtain nitrogen?

Much of the nitrogen found in living things is cyclic within the biotic community (and the soil or water). Although it frequently changes th▪ combinations of its compounds, it remains in **short nitrogen cycle.**

Nitrogen compounds are lost from some the steps in the short nitrogen cycle. Eventually most of these become gaseous nitrogen. To compensate for this loss, the **long nitrogen cycle** converts gaseous nitrogen into usable compounds.

The *short nitrogen cycle* involves decomposer bacteria's breaking down dead organic substances and converting the nitrogen compounds they contain to ammonia (NH_3). Ammonia dissolves in water and converts to ammonium ions (NH_4^+). The conversion of ammonia to ammonium ions hap-

pens spontaneously in the soil. Ammonium ions can be absorbed and used by some plants.

Many ammonium ions are converted into nitrites (NO_2^-), by nitrifying bacteria in the soil; then other nitrifying bacteria convert the nitrites to nitrates (NO_3^-), which can be absorbed by plants. Ammonium ions and nitrates a plant absorbs can be used to form the various nitrogen-containing compounds essential to the plant and to those organisms that consume the plant.

For centuries farmers have known that crops grow better in soil that has grown legumes (clover, beans, alfalfa, or peas) for several years. ▪ly in this century, scientists discovered that ▪ria grew in the small nodules (swellings) on ▪ots of these plants. Later it was discovered ▪t these bacteria were able to convert atmospheric nitrogen into nitrogen-containing compounds, a process called **nitrogen fixation.**

Now it is known that various soil bacteria and several species of algae can also carry on nitrogen fixation. Compounds made by nitrogen fixation can be used directly by plants or algae, and in doing so, enter the short nitrogen cycle. To a much smaller extent, lightning can convert atmospheric nitrogen into compounds that can enter the nitrogen cycle. Therefore, the nitrogen compounds that escape the short nitrogen cycle are offset by the nitrogen fixation of the *long nitrogen cycle.*

ration, more radiant energy is necessary. Thus, energy must constantly be supplied to the environment. Although it may be stored temporarily, energy in the ecosystem is **noncyclic.**

Matter, on the other hand, is **cyclic** – it is used and reused. The carbon, oxygen, and nitrogen cycles and the various other cycles known to scientists show that matter is repeatedly used. Although some matter may escape from the cycle (for example, by falling to the bottom of the ocean or by becoming trapped in a substance like a fossil), there are reserves of most of the elements that living things need. These reserves can be used to add to the amount cycling within the ecosystem. Some of the reserves made available to the biotic community include the water deep in oceans and lakes, the nitrogen in the atmosphere, and elements in the soil and geological substrates.

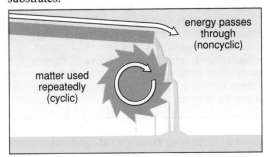

18B-3 *Matter and energy in the biosphere*

Reserves compensate for minor natural losses from the cycles. Occasionally man also uses them for purposes that prohibit their entering ecological cycles (at least temporarily), such as when he uses them as building materials. Other times man uses the reserves to affect the cycles directly. Nitrogen, for example, can be taken from the air, made into nitrogen compounds, and then used as fertilizer. Here man is serving as an agent of nitrogen fixation.

Limiting factors

Whether or not an organism can exist in a particular habitat depends on various **limiting factors**— factors which in some way limit the growth or existence of an organism. Within a lake there may be sufficient dissolved minerals and adequate sunlight to support a large alga population, but not enough carbon dioxide for the algae to carry on photosynthesis. Carbon dioxide is the limiting factor. If the amount of carbon dioxide in the lake were increased, the alga population would grow. But the alga population will not grow larger than the next limiting factor will allow. For example, if the supply of carbon dioxide is increased and the alga population grows, the supply of a dissolved mineral may become depleted. That mineral then becomes the limiting factor.

18B-4 *Limiting factors in a forest include not only how much water there is but also how and when the water is supplied. If the stream were the only source of water, plant growth would be limited. The quantities of snow and ice and the amount of summer rain can limit which trees grow in an area and even how well they grow.*

A limiting factor, however, does not always have to be that which is in short supply. Often the limiting factor is that which goes beyond an organism's *range of tolerance* (see pages 83-84). For example, certain orchids normally grow only in shaded environments because they cannot tolerate the heat of the sun. Put them in bright sun, but keep them cool, and they actually grow better than when kept in the shade. In this example, high

Principles Regarding Limiting Factors

- An organism with a wide range of tolerance for all factors will have a wide distribution. The dandelion and other weed species can tolerate a wide range of environmental factors and can grow "all over."
- An organism with a wide range of tolerance for one factor may have a narrow range for another factor. Many desert plants, for example, have a wide range of tolerance for temperature, but can tolerate water only within certain narrow limits.
- When one factor is not in its *optimal range* (range within which the organism operates best; see page 83), the range of tolerance for another factor may be reduced. For example, certain plants cannot tolerate low quantities of water unless they are receiving sufficient quantities of certain minerals.
- The period of reproduction is the most critical time for limiting factors. Certain plants will grow outside their normal ranges, but often they will not reproduce because of some limiting factor.

Flowering dogwood trees produce beautiful springtime blooms in the South but grow without flowering when planted in the North. In the North, as the days shorten, stimulating the for-

Flowering dogwoods bloom extravagantly in the South.

mation of flower buds, the temperatures drop too rapidly for the buds to form properly.

Limiting factors can also affect the reproduction of animals. Certain crabs thrive in the mouths of freshwater rivers. In these waters, however, crab eggs do not survive. To reproduce, these crabs must return to seawater; salinity is a limiting factor to reproduction but not to the life of the crab.

temperature is the limiting factor. Too much water is often the limiting factor in terrestrial environments. If the soil is too moist, certain plants will not grow well, or not grow at all, as overwatered houseplants demonstrate.

Limiting factors, niches and populations

The niche, the organism to fill the niche, and the size of the population to fill the niche are deter-

18B-5 *Barn owls have stair-step families as demonstrated by these two nestmates. Stair-step families help to limit the size of the owl population.*

mined by limiting factors. Owls and rodents provide an example of limiting factors controlling the size of the population. Owls begin to incubate each egg as it is laid; therefore, there may be chicks at different stages of development in the nest at the same time. This is a *"stairstep" family.*

If the rodent population is up, the parent owls will be able to supply all the food demands of all their chicks. If food is scarce, the parents will be able to meet the food demands of only some of the chicks. Since the older, stronger chicks eat their fill before they permit the younger chicks to have any food, the young chicks may not get enough. The younger chicks may then die or be pushed from the nest. In this way the size of the owl population is limited by the size of the rodent population. In other words, the size of the owls' niche in an area is dependent upon the size of the rodent population.

FACETS OF BIOLOGY

18B-1

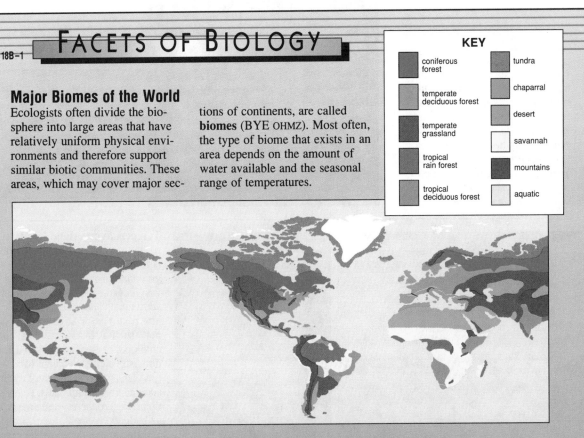

KEY

coniferous forest	tundra
temperate deciduous forest	chaparral
temperate grassland	desert
tropical rain forest	savannah
tropical deciduous forest	mountains
	aquatic

Major Biomes of the World

Ecologists often divide the biosphere into large areas that have relatively uniform physical environments and therefore support similar biotic communities. These areas, which may cover major sections of continents, are called **biomes** (BYE OHMZ). Most often, the type of biome that exists in an area depends on the amount of water available and the seasonal range of temperatures.

Tundra In the tundra the ground remains frozen except for about two months in which the top few inches thaw, permitting a growing season. The predominant vegetation includes lichens, grasses, and dwarf woody plants. The ground holds abundant dead organic material (which decomposes slowly because of the temperatures) and is often waterlogged during the growing season because lower levels of the soil do not thaw. During the growing season, insects thrive, attracting various migratory birds to the area. Caribou, reindeer, musk oxen, lemmings, ptarmigans, and arctic foxes are tundra animals.

caribou

Coniferous forest Pines, spruces, and firs are predominant in coniferous forests; the prevailing temperatures and amount of rainfall determine the species. This biome usually has two major seasons, each lasting about half the year. Coniferous forests support moose, snowshoe hares, squirrels, wolves, and many birds.

bull moose

ground squirrel

bison

Temperate grassland In temperate regions, where the rainfall is too light to support a forest, a grassland grows. Grasses cover vast areas of the interior of many continents. These areas supply natural pastures for large grazing animals such as bison, gazelles, and antelope, or they can be used for domestic cattle or sheep. Most grasslands also have many rodents such as ground squirrels, prairie dogs, and gophers. Predators such as badgers, coyotes, foxes, lions, and tigers also thrive in the grasslands. Wheat and corn grow well in temperate grasslands.

Temperate deciduous forest Abundant rain (40-50 in. per yr.) throughout the year and moderate temperatures characterize the temperate deciduous forest. Plants such as beeches, maples, oaks, hickory, chestnuts, mosses, and ferns dominate. The falling of leaves, a dormant period, a regrowth of leaves, and a growing period are the four different seasons. Animals such as deer, foxes, squirrels, bobcats, wild turkeys, woodpeckers, and wood thrushes are common.

screech owl

black-tailed jackrabbit

Chaparral (SHAP uh RAL)   A chaparral is a region with mild temperatures, abundant winter rainfall but dry summers, and predominant vegetation including trees or shrubs with thick evergreen leaves. Chaparrals can be found extensively around the Mediterranean Sea and in California and Mexico. Rabbits, wood rats, chipmunks, and lizards are common animals. Fire is an important environmental limiting factor in the chaparrals.

African elephants

baboon

Tropical deciduous forest   In a tropical area with ample rainfall in one season and a severe, lengthy dry season, tropical deciduous forests thrive. The "bush" areas in Africa and Australia are tropical deciduous forests. The trees and bushes in these areas lose their leaves during the dry season, often revealing grotesquely shaped branches.

Savanna   (suh VAN uh) *(tropical grassland)*   A savanna is a grassland with a few scattered trees. Savannas are found in warm regions where there are about 50 in. of rainfall per yr., but with a major dry season. Fire plays an important part in this biome. Fire-resistant trees and grasses are the predominant vegetation. Antelope, wildebeest, zebras, giraffes, and their predators are common animals here. In some areas the savannas have been turned into farms and cattle ranches.

warthog

Tropical rain forest Areas with rainfall of over 80 in. per yr., with one or more "dry seasons" (in which there are only about 5 in. of rain per month), and with high temperatures are tropical rain forests. These forests usually do not enter a dormant state, although some of the trees may lose their leaves in the dry seasons. Plants in these areas are greatly diversified; vines and epiphytes are common. Much of the animal life lives in the trees. Monkeys, apes, chameleons, geckos, tree-climbing snakes, frogs, and such birds as toucans, hornbills, birds of paradise, and parrots are common.

poison arrow frog

two Jackson chameleons

saguaro cactus

beavertail cactus

horned toad

Desert Regions where the rainfall is less than 10 in. per yr. are deserts. Most deserts do have sparse vegetation consisting mainly of succulents (such as the cactus) which store water; shrubs which have many short branches from a thick trunk and shed their leaves during longer dry periods; and those annuals that grow, bloom, form seeds, and die within the short growing periods. There are both *hot* deserts and *cold* deserts. Various insects, rodents, and reptiles, and a few birds usually live in the desert, but in *absolute deserts* (such as the central parts of the Sahara) rainfall is so little and infrequent that almost no life exists there.

Aquatic ecosystems Many aquatic ecosystems, such as streams and ponds, are quite small. Others are temporary (such as rivers that change channels, and ponds and lakes that fill with sediment), but their significance cannot be ignored. Plankton, invertebrates, and fish are the predominant populations. Aquatic ecosystems are divided into two groups:

• *Marine ecosystems* The ocean contains ecosystems such as shores, reefs, estuaries (where fresh and salt water mix), open ocean, and others. Different organisms grow in each. Marine ecosystems, such as estuaries and reefs, are among the most productive and most highly populated ecosystems, while others are "watery deserts."

• *Freshwater ecosystems* The depth, temperature, bottom materials, and dissolved materials determine the type of biotic community that will exist in any freshwater ecosystem. Current is also a limiting factor. Streams and rivers will support vastly different populations than will swamps, ponds, or lakes.

marine sponge

freshwater bass

Mountains If you were to travel from the equator to the North Pole, you would notice marked changes in the biomes. Starting with tropical forests and passing through other biomes, you would reach tundra and then ice cap. If you were to start at the base of a tall mountain in the tropics and climb upward, you would pass through the same types of areas, reaching tundra and ice cap at the top. In some mountains this **zonation** occurs in almost distinct lines, whereas between the equator and poles, changes are often gradual with large transition areas between biomes. Zonation in mountains is caused by the predominant temperature, available water, and winds—the same conditions that cause the biomes.

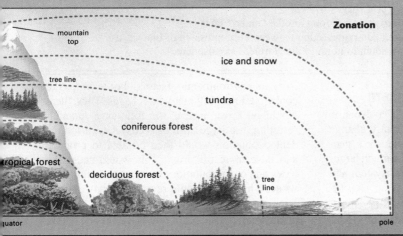

Zonation

mountain top

tree line

ice and snow

tundra

coniferous forest

deciduous forest

tropical forest

tree line

equator

pole

Review questions on page 478.

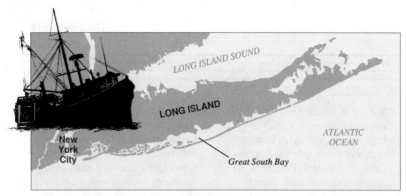

18B-6 *The limiting factors in a body of water are not always obvious. Duck farming on streams leading into the Great South Bay considerably changed this aquatic ecosystem.*

Another example of limiting factors controlling niches involves the Great South Bay in Long Island Sound, New York. Several species of oysters and other shellfish fed on the abundant and diverse phytoplankton of the bay and supported a thriving seafood industry. Then, along the streams feeding into the bay, duck farms were established. The duck feces washed into the bay, greatly increasing the mineral content of the water and thus serving as a fertilizer. The normal phytoplankton in the bay were replaced by several species that thrived in the water with higher mineral content.

Normally, the new species of phytoplankton are uncommon, since conditions for their existence are rare. The oysters and shellfish were unable to digest the new phytoplankton, and their number decreased, spoiling the seafood industry in the bay.

In this example the duck farming altered the available niche of the normal phytoplankton. The new niche was better filled by another species of phytoplankton. The new phytoplankton, however, altered the niche filled by shellfish, and food became a limiting factor for the shellfish.

Review Questions 18B-1

1. Describe the limits of the biosphere.
2. Differentiate between the habitat and the niche of an organism. Choose two organisms and tell the habitat and niche of each.
3. Briefly trace (a) the oxygen cycle, (b) the carbon cycle, (c) the short nitrogen cycle, and (d) the long nitrogen cycle.
4. Why does a closed terrarium constantly need light but does not necessarily need water? Why must a closed terrarium contain sufficient animal life?
5. List at least five possible limiting factors for a squirrel living in a city park.

Facet 18B-1: Major Biomes of the World, pages 473-77

1. List and describe the major terrestrial biomes found in the United States.
2. Account for the zonation of a mountain representing the general progression of biomes, as is seen when one progresses from south to north in the Northern Hemisphere.

Changes in the Biosphere

As we studied in Chapter 1, life is a dynamic equilibrium; all living things constantly change (expend energy) to maintain the homeostasis necessary for their living conditions. In a much larger framework, the same is true of an ecosystem and even the biosphere.

Checks and balances are easily observed between organisms and in the responses of organisms to environmental factors. For example, a cold winter may kill many insect eggs. Thus, there would be fewer insects the following summer, resulting in a large crop of seeds. A well-fed rodent population would then be able to produce and raise more offspring. This would cause the hawk and owl populations to increase. A few mild winters, however, would reverse the process.

Predator-prey relationships are easy to see and understand. Some other obvious changes within an ecosystem and within the biosphere are vital to the survival of the organisms, but are not always so easy to understand. Two of these changes involve *biological rhythms* and *succession*.

Biological rhythms

Biological rhythms (or *biological clocks*) are those mechanisms that cause organisms to regularly change their location, activities, or both. The daily opening and closing of flowers, the flowering of plants in response to photoperiod, and the migration of birds are examples of biological rhythms. Biological rhythms are often classified by the period within which they operate.

❑ **Diurnal*** (dye UR nul) **rhythms** are those cycles that take place within 24 hr. The active and resting phases of most organisms are diurnal. Many biotic communities consist of both **nocturnal*** organisms (those which are active at night) and **diurnal** organisms (those which are active during the day). In the evening certain animals like robins, bees, snakes, and deer begin a period of rest, while owls, cockroaches, rats, raccoons, and others become active.

Even within bodies of water a diurnal rhythm causes different types of plankton to rise or sink to different levels at various times of the day and night. Usually plankton are most active in the warmer, well-lighted surface layers. The cycling of layers (each group having its period near the surface) leaves room for all of them, eliminating crowded conditions at the surface.

❑ **Seasonal rhythms** (or *annual rhythms*) rotate on a yearly cycle. At the North and South Poles there is only one season. In the tundras there may be two seasons, winter and summer. In the tropics there may also be only two seasons, the wet and the dry. In many temperate regions like most of the United States, biologists note six seasons based on the organisms active in each: winter, early spring, late spring, summer, early fall, and late fall. Although seasonal rhythms in temperate regions help organisms withstand temperature fluctuations, most seasonal rhythms are controlled not by temperature but by length of day. Examples include bird migrations, hibernation, and flowering of most plants. Some seasonal rhythms, like the reproduction cycles of birds and fish, depend on a combination of factors, including temperature, day length, and available food.

❑ **Lunar rhythms** Various organisms synchronize their activities with the moon. Certain nocturnal animals, such as a forest rat in Malaysia, have a lunar-based reproductive cycle, with most pregnancies resulting from matings during a full moon. Lunar rhythms are most pronounced along the edges of the oceans, where tides greatly affect the organisms. The palolo worm (phylum Annelida) lives in the coral reefs of various islands. The worms synchronize the release of their reproductive structures (which involves the worm's losing its entire posterior half) with that of other palolo worms, improving the chances of fertilization. In part, this synchronization takes place in

18B-7 *Seasonal changes can be very dramatic as seen in the four seasons of a temperate deciduous forest (left to right: winter, spring, summer, fall). Scientists divide the year of such a forest into six seasons (dividing both spring and fall) based on which populations are active.*

diurnal: (L. DIURNUS, daily)   **nocturnal:** (L. NOCTURNUS, nightly)

FACETS OF BIOLOGY

Succession

A field on a North Carolina farm was purchased and became part of a national park. The first year after the farmer moved, there was no cultivation and the field was covered by quick-growing, sun-loving annual weeds such as ragweed and clover. In the second and third years, perennial plants such as crabgrass, asters, and horseweeds predominated. During these *pioneer periods,* insects like grasshoppers, open-area birds like the meadowlark and the grasshopper sparrow, and small animals like the field mouse inhabited the area.

In about the third year junipers and other sun-loving shrubs took over the field, shading out the pioneer plants but providing suitable conditions for other plants such as the morning glory and honeysuckle vines. In this *shrub period,* animal populations also changed. Rabbits were among the most noticeable animals, and the cardinal and field sparrow became the dominant birds.

The seeds of the shrubs were unable to establish themselves in the shade of the mature plants. Pine seedlings, however, are shade-resistant and were in the field starting about the twentieth year. Twenty-five to thirty years after the field had been farmed, a *pine forest* established itself and began shading out the shrubs. A whole new *understory* (plants growing in the shade of trees) arose, and changes in the animal population took place. Squirrels, raccoons, pine warblers, and towhees thrived in the pine forest.

About 50 yr. after the field had been farmed, hardwood deciduous trees, such as oaks and hickories, were found in the understory of the pine forest. These slow-growing trees eventually began competing for sunlight in the upper story and began to take over as the dominant plants about 100 yr. after the field had been left alone. This produced a hardwood deciduous forest.

Two of the stages in the succession of an old field: pioneer stage (top) and 20 yr. later (bottom)

The accumulation of falling leaves instead of pine needles

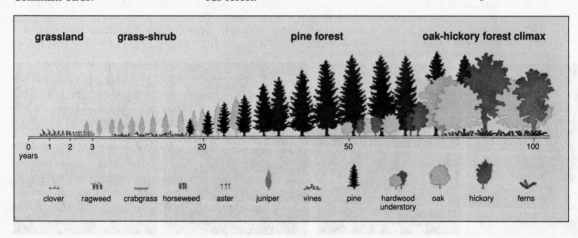

grassland grass-shrub pine forest oak-hickory forest climax

0 1 2 3 20 50 100
years

clover ragweed crabgrass horseweed aster juniper vines pine hardwood understory oak hickory ferns

Comparison of Ecosystems in Succession

Pioneer Stages	Climax Stage
• Few species, large populations of each	• Many species, smaller populations of each
• Smaller organisms	• Larger organisms
• Organisms with higher metabolic rates	• Organisms with lower metabolic rates
• Organisms with short life spans	• Organisms with long life spans
• Organisms with simple forms of reproduction	• Organisms with complicated life cycles
• Large amounts of nutrients needed and large amounts lost from the ecosystem	• Nutrients cyclical within the ecosystem

changed the make-up of the soil, causing a considerable change in the understory. Mosses, ferns, May apples, and orchids began to fill the shaded, moist forest floor. Deciduous trees produced edible leaves, fruits, and nuts, which supported animals like squirrels, deer, raccoons, and wild turkeys. Other animals found in the hardwood forest included foxes and bears.

In many areas of North Carolina, as in many areas of the eastern United States, the hardwood deciduous forest is the **climax vegetation.** The climax vegetation is that plant community normally found in an area free of disturbances by nature (disasters such as fire and flood) or by man (farming, cutting lumber, building structures, and such). A climax vegetation is self-perpetuating. As the plants of a climax vegetation die, they are usually replaced by the same species, not new ones.

The progression of biotic communities described in the North Carolina field is **succession.*** Succession is the predictable, gradual change of a biotic community over a period of time. Normally, succession begins with *pioneer organisms,* progresses through developmental stages, and ends in a stable system called the *climax* (or *climax vegetation*).

As soon as a farmer digs a pond, succession begins to return the pond to the climax of that area. A natural catastrophe (fire, avalanche, earthquake, or others) may change an area, but succession will reclaim it in time.

When a natural disaster happens, scientists are quick to begin observations of succession. In 1883, the volcanic island of Krakatoa, 40 km (25 mi.) from Java, suffered a volcanic eruption. The island was completely covered by molten lava. Nothing survived. Nine months later a scientist discovered the first life to reappear on Krakatoa: a spider (most likely blown from islands near Java) spinning a web. Soon after this, algae spores and fragments were blown to the island; they began forming the base upon which the spores of mosses and ferns and the airborne seeds of other plants could begin to grow.

Within 3 yr. there were 11 species of ferns and 15 species of flowering plants; the island was covered with plants within 10 yr. Some seeds, such as those of the coconut palm and the *Calophyllum* tree, floated to the island. Other seeds, such as the fig, were brought in the digestive system of birds. Birds and insects came to Krakatoa as soon as the plants necessary for their existence had become established. There were 47 species of vertebrates, mostly birds and bats, on the island within 25 yr. Reptiles such as the python and monitor lizards probably swam to the island, while others, such as geckos and skinks, probably came on floating debris. Within 50 yr., the young forest supported over 1,200 species of animals. Almost 100 yr. later, the climax vegetation, a tropical forest, had reestablished itself.

Review questions on page 482.

---

succession: (L. SUCCEDERE, to go after)

response to the moon. At dawn, one week after the full moon in November, the water around certain islands in the South Pacific becomes the consistency of soup as the palolo worms release their reproductive structures.

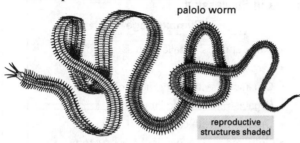

palolo worm

reproductive structures shaded

Once many biological clocks are set, they operate independently of the stimuli by which they are set. For example, the fiddler crab, a common inhabitant of many North American shores, appears a yellowish-white at night but becomes darker around sunrise. It reaches its darkest coloration at low tide, the time when it comes to the shore and feeds. Darker colors may protect the crab from the sun or permit it to hide in dark

fiddler crab

nooks. The cycle of tides occurs every 24.8 hr. (24 hr. 48 min.).

A crab placed in an aquarium (where no tides exist) will still reach its darkest coloration every 24.8 hr. Even crabs kept in dark aquariums for as long as a month still reach their darkest colors in the regular rhythm of the tides and are still synchronized with the crabs on the beach from which they were collected.

18B-8 *The prayer plant closes its leaves at night. Even if it is exposed to a different cycle of light and dark, the leaves close at the accustomed time of darkness.*

Many biological clocks can be reset if the stimuli are changed. The prayer plant normally folds its leaves as the sun sets. When exposed to an artificial pattern of day and night, the plant will slowly adjust its opening and closing of leaves to fit the new pattern. Jet lag, the phenomenon of not being in synchronization with the diurnal cycle of a place to which one rapidly traveled, involves the resetting of biological clocks.

Biological Terms

biosphere	short nitrogen cycle	*Changes in the Biosphere*	lunar rhythm
Interactions in the Ecosystem	long nitrogen cycle	biological rhythm (biological clock)	*Facets*
habitat	nitrogen fixation	diurnal rhythm	biome
ecological niche	noncyclic	nocturnal	zonation
oxygen cycle	cyclic	diurnal	climax vegetation
carbon cycle	limiting factor	seasonal rhythm	succession

Review Question 18B-2

What are the three most common biological rhythm periods? Give an example of each.

Facet 18B-2: Succession, pages 480-81

1. What is the relationship between succession and climax vegetation?
2. Describe a pioneer stage of succession and compare it to a climax stage of succession.

18C–Man in the Biosphere

God created a perfect world. However, we have little knowledge of the original world as He created it. Many Bible scholars agree that before the curse (Gen. 3:14-19) there was no animal death. To say there was no death of any kind would indicate that there was no plant death either. In Genesis 1:29 God informs Adam and Eve that the fruits and plants that bear seeds are to be their food. In the next verse He says that He has given to the animals "every green herb for meat." It is therefore safe to assume that plant cells did die as they were eaten, but it is quite possible that the plant itself did not die.

18C-1 *Today, the lion is a fearful beast, but during the 1,000-year reign of Christ, lions will somehow be different (Isa. 11:6).*

The belief that no animal died before the curse has several interesting implications. Many predators are ideally suited for their roles. A lion, for example, has teeth, claws, and a digestive system designed for its predatory existence. If lions as we know them had existed in the Garden of Eden, the design would have been faulty. If the lion were not a predator then, did it have those structures and instincts equipping it to be a predator? It would be as if God had designed the organisms for life after the Fall, rather than before it.

The Bible does not indicate how long Adam and Eve were in the garden. Archbishop Ussher (who set the 4004 B.C. date of creation) says it was only a day; however, it could have been longer. No matter how long it was, the lion and other predators (if they were like the organisms we

18C-2 *A flea, an external parasite, feeds by sucking blood from its host. Since one flea consumes so little, a healthy host can support many without experiencing significant loss. Would fleas have been the same in the original creation, or were they changed to their present state as part of the curse? No one knows.*

know) would have been "misfits" in the garden. This seems very unlikely.

It is quite possible that lions as well as other predators, detritus feeders, decomposer organisms, and the like were considerably different before the curse. Perhaps the lion was as ideally suited to be a herbivore before the curse as it is now ideally suited to be a carnivore. If parasites and pathogens existed before the curse, what were they doing? The Bible gives no direct answer, Adam did not leave us an account, and we cannot experiment to find out.

If the present predators, detritus feeders, decomposers, parasites, and pathogens were vastly different in the garden, it would mean that extensive changes took place in the creation at the time of the curse. We know that there were great changes in the ground and plant life (Gen. 3:17-18). Any changes must have been, at least in part, genetic in order to have them reproduce the types of organisms we know today. The Bible does not tell us the extent of the curse, but many Bible scholars hold that predation and animal deaths are part of the curse.

18C-3 *The red fox is designed to fill a predatory niche. Foxes and other predators were created for specific purposes.*

This is speculation, and although it is interesting, it is useful only in helping us to realize that God's perfect creation was different from the present imperfect world. How "imperfect" it is we do not know. Romans 8:22 tells us that "the whole creation groaneth and travaileth in pain together until now." Our present world is beautifully designed to show us the power of its Creator (Ps. 104), but it is not as it once was. The intricate design that we see (what some call "the balance of nature") is but a shadow of the perfection God originally created.

The Bible tells us that there will be deliverance for the creation from the effects of the curse (Rom. 8:18-21). Isaiah 11 presents a picture of the physical world during Christ's thousand-year reign on the earth: "The wolf also shall dwell with the lamb, and the leopard shall lie down with the kid; and the calf and the young lion and the fatling together; and a little child shall lead them. . . . They shall not hurt nor destroy in all my holy mountain" (vv. 6, 9). Many Bible scholars assume this to be a lifting of the curse, a change back to the way the creation was originally designed.

Perhaps the changes that God instituted at the curse will be reversed for the Millennium. Perhaps the organisms will be physically changed (but not back to their "original design") and will exist under a "new set of commands." We do know that God will rule the world by direct force, "a rod of iron" (Ps. 2), not by the method used in the Garden of Eden. We do not know the methods God will use to accomplish this prophecy. We should believe what the Bible says and not spend too much time speculating.

Man's Ecological Niche

Most organisms find a niche in an area, migrate, or die. Man may do the same. Organisms affect their environment. Man also affects the environment in which he lives; however, he is intelligent and capable of converting an ecosystem to supply his needs. There is nothing *wrong* with man using his environment, but as with almost anything man can do, there are acceptable and unacceptable ways to use it. The question is not whether man

should use the physical world, but how, when, where, and to what extent.

Man–the consumer-manager

Man affects his environment in two basic ways:

❑ **Consumer** Man can be considered a consumer since he takes materials from the food chain. Man is capable of interrupting at many different points the flow of energy and materials in an ecosystem in order to supply his own needs. Man can be a herbivore and a carnivore, and he can even consume organisms of the detritus food chain (shrimp, lobster, and such).

❑ **Manager** When man begins to change the environment in order to make it meet his needs, he becomes a manager. When man clears ground and plants crops; when he converts land into pasture for domestic animals; when he dams a stream to create a lake or to control flooding; when he constructs a home, a road, an office building, or a factory, man becomes a manager of the environment. When the human population, and therefore man's consumption, increases beyond that which an area can support, man must either move to other areas or become a manager of his environment.

18C-4 *A tuna harvest. Man consumes much that comes from the sea. To a limited degree, man has even begun to manage sections of the ocean.*

There are many ecosystems that, because of their high rates of productivity, can tolerate human "predation" without suffering. For example, the Indians of the American plains killed buffalo to meet their shelter, food, and clothing needs. Seasonally they moved from place to place in order to harvest the natural foods the land provided. As long as their population remained small, they were able to continue this existence as consumers without damaging the ecosystem.

Some people are willing to accept as legitimate man's role as a consumer as long as he only "nibbles." If man consumes so much that he changes the environment or must become a manager of the environment to supply his needs, they feel man has gone too far. They feel that man's management spoils the environment, and he should therefore do nothing but limit his habitat and be only a "light consumer."

The Bible, however, tells us that "in the sweat of thy face shalt thou eat bread" (Gen. 3:19), that man is to "be fruitful and multiply," and that man is to "subdue . . . and have dominion over" the earth (Gen. 1:28). Not everything man wants to do to his environment is acceptable; he must be a good and wise steward of what God has given him. But, the problems of population growth, subduing and having dominion over the earth force man to be a manager.

Man—the manager

Man can carry his consumer-manager role too far and destroy some aspect of his environment. For

18C-5 *The American buffalo at one time formed extensive herds. They were wastefully killed, almost to the point of extinction. Today, small herds are managed in parks and preserves.*

example, when the "white man" came to the American West, he began to prey heavily on the buffalo, often killing hundreds of them by chasing an entire herd off the edge of a cliff and then taking only a few. The rest were left to rot. Other times men shot buffalo for sport, with no intention of using the meat or hides.

Man killed so many buffalo that herds decreased in size, and the buffalo faced extinction. Only through changes in man's practices and through careful management, do we have buffalo herds in a few parks and preserves today. If man had used wisdom in his consumption and management of buffalos, they would not have faced extinction. Many other ecological problems could be avoided if man were a better manager.

Some people feel that almost anything man does to the environment is bad. If a dam is built

18C-6 *A free-flowing stream and a dammed stream. Dams control flooding, generate electrical energy, and create lakes for fishing and enjoyment. But free-flowing streams supply elements which dammed streams cannot. Man must use his God-given intelligence to determine whether or not a dam should be erected.*

on a river and floods a valley, some people feel that too great a sacrifice has been made. God did design a valley there, but man's building a dam may not pervert God's purpose for the valley. There is justification for building dams. Without dams for water storage and flood prevention, certain areas of our land would be uninhabitable and uncultivatable. However, just because some dams benefit man, we cannot conclude that dams should be built anywhere and everywhere.

Every proposed dam must be carefully considered. What would be the losses? What would be the gains? Do the gains outweigh the losses? By how much? Could the needs be met another way? With accurate answers to these and similar questions, the wise and proper decision can be made.

All too often, however, man does not seek these answers, or he ignores them. Sometimes he overrates the importance of one answer in relation to another. Some people feel that killing any animal or forcing any number of people out of their homes is too great a price to pay. On the other hand, killing animals or destroying homes unnecessarily makes little difference to some people if money is to be made. After man gets answers to his criteria questions, he must use his intelligence to weigh those answers.

Man—the user of natural resources

The Los Angeles River runs through Los Angeles in a concrete-lined channel to the Pacific Ocean. During dry seasons it carries little more than a trickle of water. The city uses all the water of this once-large river for drinking, irrigating, and industry and then passes it through sewers and eventually into the ocean.

Long ago, when the water in the river began to be used up, the people of Los Angeles began to dig shallow wells to the water table. As more and more people used this water source, the water table lowered, and wells had to be dug deeper. It became evident that the water, which had seemed so abundant and easily obtained (as most natural resources are at first), was limited.

As Los Angeles grew, its people needed more water. An aqueduct built to the mountains diverted the distant Owens River to Los Angeles, but

in time the city needed still more water. An aqueduct 220 mi. long, which would bring water from the Colorado River, was proposed. But other states and Mexico used water from the Colorado River. A compromise worked out among the various governments permitted dams to be built to form reservoirs during the wet seasons. The Colorado River was channeled to supply water to many areas in the southwestern United States and parts of Mexico.

18C-7 *A section of the concrete-lined Los Angeles River near downtown Los Angeles*

But even with rerouting the water in Los Angeles and nearby areas, there are still shortages in some seasons, and during rainy season there is sometimes too much. What should have been and what should be done? Some possible considerations are the following:

❑ Although it may be loathsome to those who would have everything "natural," perhaps additional channeling of water is part of the answer.

❑ Perhaps areas in the Southwest should have restricted growth—prohibiting new homes, apartments, and water-using industries.

❑ We are now able to recycle water. Recycling may be part of the answer.

There are many avenues of action that can be taken and possibly others of which we are not even aware. The questions are which, when, how, and how far should we go on the chosen avenue. Only through study can man know the answers needed to make wise decisions. But even then the "best" answer often upsets people who are inconvenienced by it.

18C-8 *Man's need of certain materials has resulted in massive environmental manipulation such as this strip mine. Leaving a hole when a desired substance is mined out is poor environmental management. In the past, such mismanagement was common. Today, in many places laws require companies that alter the environment to help the succession of the area to reach its climax vegetation again.*

Stories similar to the Los Angeles water shortage can be told of many of man's uses of natural resources such as minerals, coal, oil, and even the air. For example, during the era of the early American settlers, the forests of our nation were a natural resource so abundant that they could be used without thought of depletion. With the small human population, trees that were taken were replaced naturally before others were needed. In time, the rate of use exceeded the rate of growth. Programs to use the forests wisely should have been instituted *then*. If we had not waited until just a few years ago to begin wise lumber harvesting and reforestation programs, we probably would not have our present lumber problems.

18C-9 *Forests are a renewable natural resource.*

God-supplied natural resources

It is inconceivable that God would have placed man on an earth that did not have natural resources to supply his needs. However, some people think that no matter what man does, he will mess up this world so badly that soon everyone will be starving, wearing gas masks, and drinking water out of cans. These things could happen, but if they do, they will occur because man has misused his environment, not because he used it.

We often hear that because the earth is becoming overpopulated, we will soon run out of food. It is true that the population of the earth in 1700 was just under 1 billion, and the 3 billion mark was reached in about 1970. At this rate of increase, the earth's population will reach more than 6 billion by the year 2000 and nearly 7 billion by about 2010. Will it be possible to feed that many people?

Chart of Population Growth from Noah to A.D. 2100

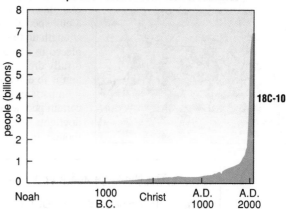

18C-10

History has shown that predictions of population growth are notoriously inaccurate. War and natural disasters, for instance, can stem the tide of population growth. Regarding the food problem, consider this: If only 8% of the earth's land surface, well under the amount that can be cultivated, were farmed using modern techniques, it would be able to produce enough food to support 79 *billion* people. We might not all be able to eat steak daily, but the earth can produce enough food to keep the population of the earth from starving now and in the near future.

FACETS OF BIOLOGY

Modern bullfights are colorful spectacles designed to entertain and thrill the crowds.

Animal Rights and Wrongs

In Europe for hundreds of years bearbaiting was a popular spectacle. A bear, chained to a post or confined in a pen, was whipped or tortured (sometimes its nose was filled with pepper to arouse it). Trained dogs then attacked the bear, trying to seize its nose. Queen Elizabeth of England in 1517 attended a bearbaiting of which a spectator wrote that it was "very pleasant to see," especially "the nimbleness and wit of the dog to take his advantage." The spectator commented favorably about the sight of the bear tearing himself free, "with his blood and the slaver hanging about." Despite the royal presence at bearbaitings, Puritans of the period condemned the spectacles as cruel. Today, bearbaiting is outlawed in most civilized countries.

Other animals including badgers, dogs, apes, and monkeys have often been used in similar spectacles. Today, bullfights are popular events in Mexico, Spain, and several other countries. In a bullfight, a bull specially bred for his strength and aggressiveness is placed in a ring with trained, colorfully dressed people whose main aim is to entertain the spectators.

In parts of the United States certain people find cockfights and dogfights exciting events. Although these events often lack the spectacle of bearbaiting and the ceremony of a bullfight, the results are similar: a provoked animal fights for its life, and after a needless, painful struggle it loses.

Some consider spectator events in which animals are forced to fight and suffer pain as cruel; those who enjoy them are considered sadistic, and those who engage in the event are barbaric. Others consider attending a bullfight or a cockfight an honorable part of their culture and heritage.

An engraving of bullbaiting

The New Age and Animal Rights

The Bible teaches a *dualism:* God and His creation are two separate entities. Scripture teaches that God existed before He created the world and that the world was designed, created, and is sustained by Him. God will also exist after He has destroyed this present world. God's power is revealed to us in the creation, but God is not the world.

Many religions believe in **pantheism**—that the physical world is god. Pantheists speak of the "One" or "Ego" or "Great Spirit," of which every living thing (and for some pantheists, nonliving things as well) shares a part. This spiritual part which all things have in common makes all things related (mother earth, father sea, brother rock, sister flower, cousin bear, aunt cow, and so on). Thus, to destroy or harm anything is to sin against or offend the pantheist's god. But to realize the "spiritual oneness" of everything is to be more aware of that god.

Although pantheism has long been denounced by Bible-believing Christians as a heresy, many Christians are being influenced by pantheism dressed in new clothes—the New Age movement. Teaching doctrines that "sound good" and not publicizing those parts that might be offensive, the New Age movement has gained popularity even among some Christians.

One appealing pantheistic doctrine is "animal rights." Pictures of suffering animals have swayed public sentiment and have caused people to believe the movement was intended only to stop animal cruelty. Certainly bringing unnecessary animal cruelty to people's attention and

Some people argue that events involving animals are less offensive than football or boxing, which involve spectators watching as people inflict pain and occasionally serious injury and death on each other. Human sports are sometimes defended by the argument that the participants have chosen to be involved, whereas the animals in cruel spectator events have not chosen this as their end.

The animal that provided the meat in your last hamburger did not consent to satisfy your hunger, nor did the animal that gave his hide to supply the leather for your shoes volunteer for such a cause. What about those animals used in medical research? Do they choose to be exposed to harmful chemicals so that scientists can learn whether the chemical is safe to use in food or medicines?

What rights do animals have?

When is an animal abused by man? What position should a Christian take regarding the use and the abuse of animals?

In Scripture God gives man control over animals, tells him to use them for food, and gives His approval for using animals for other purposes (see next page). As with every physical blessing that God has placed under human dominion, man can choose to use properly or abuse his authority over the animal kingdom.

If modern Americans tried to feed themselves using only wild game, there would soon be shortages. Man could wipe out every wild species considered desirable for food. This would be an abuse of our dominion over animals. Today, hunting of certain animals is limited to avoid such abuse.

Man has domesticated various animals and through farming

grows enough animals to meet his needs while not destroying wild animal populations. Although

Habitat changes and the killing of elephants have greatly reduced the number of elephants. Although preserves have been set aside, elephants are still killed by poachers for their tusks. Many consider this an abuse since an animal that man is striving to protect is being wastefully killed.

applying pressure to have such abuse stopped can be a legitimate cause.

Many animal rights activists, however, are interested not only in stopping unnecessary cruelty to animals but also in preventing the use of animals for fur. In most civilized countries the fur and leather used in clothing come from domestic animals that were raised either for food (then their hides are used as leather) or for fur. Using animals for those purposes does not violate a Scriptural command, and if the animals were properly cared for while they were alive, the practice cannot be said to involve animal cruelty. Pantheists, however, contend that being raised to die rather than roam free is cruelty and thus intolerable. Clothing made from animals that were taken from the wild, however, has become rare. In some areas people wearing fur coats

have been jeered and have had their coats destroyed by animal rights activists.

Today, there are movements encouraging people to stop eating meat. *Vegetarianism* is the logical end of pantheism. Some people have medical reasons to abstain from eating meat (allergies, digestion problems), but the only religious reason for a Christian not to eat some meats is to prevent spiritual offense to a Christian brother (I Cor. 8:4-13). Vegetarianism, however, is not advocated in the Scripture (I Cor. 8:8; I Tim. 4:3).

To animal rights pantheists, no use of animals by humans is justifiable. They regard animals and humans as parts of the same god. Pantheists say that it is as wrong to hurt an animal as it is to hurt another human and that animals should have the same rights and protection under law as people. Scripture does not support this idea.

techniques differ, the concept of farming was used in ancient times and is not condemned in Scripture. It appears that domestication and farming of animals are wise uses of natural resources and are in keeping with what God ordained.

When man hunts or domesticates an animal, he must assume a portion of the responsibility for the wise use of that animal. As steward of the physical world, man is responsible for altering an animal's habitat. There is nothing wrong with using the physical environment, nor does Scripture directly teach us that animal extinction is wrong. But we must be sure that what we are doing or allowing to be done does not abuse the environment or the animals.

Most people would agree that brutal or cruel treatment of animals, unnecessary scientific experimentation using animals, the wasteful killing of animals, the unnecessary hunting of endangered species, and similar abuses should be condemned. These are abuses of man's position of dominion over animals and cannot be justified with Scripture.

Review questions on page 492.

Man's Relationship with Animals in Scripture

In the Old Testament, animals were sacrificed to God.

On day five of creation, God made birds and fish. On the following day He created the land animals, Adam, and Eve. In God's perfect creation, animals did not suffer, nor was there animal death. God's original plan provided animals as a benefit to man, who was to use and control them (Gen. 1:28). Our present relationship with animals, however, is based not so much on the closeness of when God made man and the animals or the fact that Adam named the animals while he was in the Garden of Eden as much as on God's next act. Following the first sin, God sacrificed animals to clothe Adam and Eve.

As a result of man's sin, God's original purpose and design for all creation changed (Rom. 8:22). In Old Testament times animals were used as beasts of burden and sacrifices. Their skins were used for clothing and for making vessels and tents. Animals also served as food for humans. God told man that he could eat any of the animals (Gen. 9:3). (God limited the kinds of animals that could be eaten by the Israelites in Leviticus 11.) In the Passover feast a lamb was to be sacrificed, cooked, and eaten by every Jewish household (Exod. 12:8). Much of the meat of the Jewish sacrifices was to be eaten by the priests (Exod. 29:32; Lev. 7:19, 8:31). Solomon and his household regularly ate meat (I Kings 4:23).

In the New Testament, Christ ate fish with His disciples (Luke 24:42-43) and miraculously supplied meat to feed over 5,000 people (Matt. 14:15-19). Christ and the disciples kept the Passover, which involved eating lamb (Mark 14:12-18). John the Baptist wore animal skins (Matt. 3:4) and is not condemned in Scripture for doing so. These uses of animals and their skins were done either at God's direct command or without God's condemnation.

Scripture gives some comments regarding the care man should give animals.

❑ We are instructed not to muzzle the ox that treads out the corn (Deut. 25:4). This means that the animal should be allowed to eat of the crop it helps plant and harvest.

❑ Israelites were to help an animal that had fallen into a ditch, even on the Sabbath (Luke 14:5). In other words, care was to be taken for an animal, not letting it suffer just because it was a "special day."

❑ We are told that "the righteous man regardeth the life of his beast" (Prov. 12:10)—that God places the care of animals on a high level.

Animals in Scientific Experimentation:
Diabetes and Dogs

Before the 1920s having *diabetes mellitus* resulted in a period of physical degeneration and eventual death. The disease involves the inability to use food. If a diabetic person ate foods rich in sugar, his blood sugar level could become so high that he could die in minutes. Even if he ate only foods low in sugar, he would gradually lose weight because he would not be able to use the food properly. Many adult diabetics died weighing less than 50 lb. after years of slowly wasting away.

Scientists observed deformed *islets of Langerhans* (small clusters of cells in the pancreas) in the bodies of people who died from this disease, but they did not know whether this condition caused the disease or whether it was a result of the disease. Reports that dogs with their pancreas removed developed diabetic symptoms prompted Frederick Banting, a Canadian physician, to consider that diabetes might be caused by a secretion from the islets of Langerhans.

In the early 1920s Banting, Charles Best, and John Macleod began a series of experiments at the University of Toronto. First they needed to determine whether a lack of materials manufactured by the pancreas caused diabetes. Removing a dog's pancreas and examining its blood confirmed that the blood sugar level increased when the pancreas was removed. If they then injected extracts made from the dog's pancreas, the blood sugar level dropped.

Additional experiments were necessary to determine whether the islets of Langerhans were involved in diabetes. More experiments were needed to isolate the chemicals produced by the islets of Langerhans, and then additional experiments helped to determine which ones were involved in the disease. Additional tests were conducted to determine how this information could be used in the treatment of human diabetics.

Banting and his colleagues used dogs in their experiments, in part, because they were large enough to permit dealing with the pancreas. Today with improved medical techniques, mice or rats would probably be used. Scientists took the lives of a number of dogs to discover, isolate, and test *insulin* (the hormone produced by the islets of Langerhans which is responsible for proper metabolism of sugar) (see page 604). There was, however, no other way that this lifesaving information could have been obtained at the time. These animals were sacrificed for medical information which saved the lives of many people.

Banting (right) and Best (left)

In a war soldiers die so that the people of their nation may live their lives the way they want to. War is not a desirable event, but in this world it is often necessary. (In the Old Testament God commanded the children of Israel to go to war at certain times.) Likewise, in the war against diabetes, dogs died so that many people could live. Using animals in this way may not be desirable, but it is often necessary. We honor those who gave their lives for their country. It might be excessive to honor an animal that gave its life for the advancement of science, but it is also excessive to claim that no animal should be called upon to give its life so that human life may be improved.

Humans are the only organisms God created with an eternal soul. God taught us the worth of human souls by sending His Son to die for them. We must conclude that human life is far more valuable than the life of animals. The sacrifice of animals for medical knowledge is within the guidelines established in Scripture (Gen. 1:24).

Man's unwise actions cause food shortage problems. North America is a "land of plenty" that could produce great quantities of food to export, but the federal government pays American farmers not to cultivate their land. In other areas of the world the land cannot produce enough to feed the local population. Most of us would oppose "feeding the enemy," but we can see that the problem is not a lack of food, but politics! During the thousand-year reign of Christ, people will not die, and we presume the population will grow considerably, but then politics will not keep the producers from producing, and there will be abundance for all (Isa. 35).

Review Questions 18C-1

1. What are the two main aspects of man's ecological niche?
2. In what ways is man the top consumer in the biosphere? How does man differ in his consumption from all other consumers in the biosphere?
3. What types of things does man do to manage the ecology?
4. What is the primary problem regarding man's use of natural resources?

Facet 18C-1: Animal Rights and Wrongs pages 488-91

1. On what basis can bullfighting be condemned while the killing of cattle in a slaughterhouse is accepted?
2. How does New Age pantheism lead to an un-Scriptural view of an animal's rights?
3. List what you consider to be a Christian's view of "animal rights." Give a Scriptural defense of your position where possible.

Pollution

One of the major ecological problems facing us today is pollution. **Pollution*** is man's placing into the environment substances or factors that, either because of their nature or their abundance, make a significant, negative change on the environment. When human population was small, our limited technology did not permit us to contend with many factors or substances that the environment was not able to deal with. With increased population and advanced technology, however, man can now leave things in the environment which will alter it for many thousands of years. With such abilities must come the responsibility to use wisely those abilities.

Pollutants are substances or factors which cause pollution. Pollutants come in various forms.
❑ **Energy pollutants** Energy pollutants are factors that are placed in an environment. Heat is an energy pollutant in aquatic environments. Water from a stream may be used to cool a hot engine, and then is returned to the stream. Although it has no substance pollutants in it, the warm water may alter the stream's ecosystem just as much as

18C-11 *Nonbiodegradable pollutants remain in an ecosystem for many years.*

a chemical pollutant. Noise, another energy pollutant, has recently been listed among pollutants. Its effects on the environment are still largely unknown.
❑ **Substance pollutants** Substance pollutants are objects or chemicals that are placed in the environment. The most familiar can usually be classified into two groups.
• *Substance pollutants–biodegradable** Pollutants that the environment can break down and return to the normal cycling of substances are **biodegradable.** These include sewage, paper,

---

pollution: (L. POLLUERE, to spread plague, pestilence)

biodegradable: bio- (life) + de- (L. DE-, down) + -grad- (GRADUS, rank, or step)

wood products, and many chemicals.

• *Substance pollutants–nonbiodegradable* Pollutants that stay in their original form and that cannot be broken apart in the environment are **nonbiodegradable.** Many chemicals used in insecticides and found in industrial wastes are nonbiodegradable pollutants.

Biodegradable pollutants

If the wastes from the sewers of a city are released into a stream (assuming that the sewage is not from industries that produce nonbiodegradable materials), it is only a matter of time and distance before the normal decomposer organisms in the stream will have converted the sewage into usable materials. Depending upon the amount of sewage and the size of the stream, the polluted area may be only a few feet or a few miles.

If the amount of sewage is large enough to pollute the entire stream for some distance, the pollutants may form an effective barrier to clean water organisms, but it does supply a large niche for the decomposer organisms which normally exist in small numbers.

Problems arise when a large amount of sewage is put into a small stream or when several cities place sewage in a larger stream. The stream may be an open sewer for its entire length. If the stream has any value in fishing and beauty or if cities rely on it for their water supply, severely polluting a large portion of the stream is unacceptable.

We have the technology to convert sewage into pure water. One common practice is to run the sewage through a series of manmade canals, while bubbling air through it. This encourages the growth of the same decomposer organisms that would naturally purify the water in a stream. Rather than polluting a stream, man cleans up the water before returning it to the environment.

Virtually all natural substances are biodegradable; thus most ecosystems can deal with such pollutants. Depending upon the ecosystem and the quantity of pollutant, the time needed to reduce the substance to a state that is no longer considered a pollutant will vary, but it will happen. With biodegradable pollutants, the statement "time heals all wounds" seems to apply.

18C-12 *Pollutants from landfills often enter streams, affecting the quality of the water and causing the death of many organisms.*

Nonbiodegradable pollutants

Time, however, may not heal environmental wounds caused by nonbiodegradable pollutants. The 101 million tons of trash produced by Americans each year may contain many biodegradable materials, but it also contains plastic bags and jugs, glass jars and bottles, aluminum foils and cans, and many other substance pollutants that are not recycled by the environment.

For a long time the saying "the solution to pollution is dilution" seemed to hold true. If you spread out the pollutant far enough it became unnoticeable. A little trash tucked in an unnoticeable place here, or a little trash buried in an out-of-the-way place there was considered acceptable. But when the quantities began to grow and the nearby places became more crowded, the dilution solution became unacceptable. *Landfills* (areas where trash is placed, often with layers of dirt to speed the decomposition of biodegradable material) become full, and new areas for putting trash must be found. But no one wants to live near the trash dump.

Rather than using landfills, many seacoast cities have put their trash in barges and dumped it in the ocean. Some people thought that it would take extreme amounts of trash to really pollute the ocean, and as long as the trash did not interfere with swimming or fishing, there would be no problem. Biodegradable substances are easily recycled by ocean ecosystems.

18C-13 *Barges once dumped New York City's trash into the ocean.*

Recycling

One answer to certain pollutant problems is **recycling.** Recycling also helps reduce the demands upon natural resources. For example, waste water processed in sewage treatment plants provides usable water. (If a city takes water from a polluted stream, it must treat the water using methods similar to sewage treatment to render it fit to drink.) Sewage treatment also reduces the need for finding new water sources.

Substances like paper, glass, and even cloth fibers can be recycled. Recycling is necessary for many metals. Since the amount of readily available metals in the earth is limited, melting them and reusing them, rather than leaving them to pollute the environment, is much to our advantage. Some metals, such as aluminum, are much less expensive to recycle than to mine from the earth.

The nonbiodegradable substances continue to build up, and in recent years swimmers have found such wastes washed up on beaches. The nature of some of these materials has forced the closing of some beaches.

Another solution to the nonbiodegradable trash (such as glass and plastics) problem has been to burn it. But burning creates airborne chemicals and other (often more serious) problems. The soot and other solids released from a small smokestack fall to the ground near the smokestack. The problem has been solved by building taller smokestacks. Atmospheric winds then spread the substances downwind until they are barely noticeable. This works only when a limited amount of chemicals is put into the air. When many tall smokestacks place large amounts of chemicals in the air, all of the downwind air will be affected. *Acid rain* is one example that shows that atmospheric dilution of polluted air is not a good solution (see pages 48-49).

Hazardous wastes

The problem of what to do with nonchemically active (inert) nonbiodegradable pollutants such as plastic and glass is significant. In many ways, however, it is not as significant as what we do with pollutants which are chemically active, especially those that are harmful to living things. Such chemicals are called **hazardous wastes.**

Many of these wastes are chemical by-products from making paints, plastics, textiles, and many other everyday products. Some of them are so strong that a single drop of the chemical in a swimming pool of water could kill anyone who drank the water.

What is to be done with these substances? For a long time factories that made hazardous chemicals put them into metal drums. The drums were then dumped into the ocean, buried underground, placed in caves and old mines, or stacked on land in remote areas. In time, however, the drums rusted or the chemicals inside them ate away the protective lining, and the drums began to leak. These highly poisonous substances were then released into the environment.

For a long time the ''solution to pollution is dilution'' principle was applied to hazardous

"Useful" Pollutants

Not all pollutants are waste products. Man sometimes places substances that are useful in his management of an ecosystem in an area. But when these substances leave the area, they may become pollutants in the next ecosystem.

Such would happen if a farmer put fertilizer (soluble minerals) on his crops to help them grow, and then rain water carried the fertilizer into a pond. Even though there normally are soluble minerals in a pond, added minerals can easily become pollutants. As the pond's physical environment changes, the numbers and kinds of its populations also change. The abundance of algae caused by the added minerals causes the pond to become cloudy. When the algae die, their decomposition can kill fish. The fertilizer that was designed to help the farmer's crop may eventually destroy a pond. Unintentional polluting of the environment has happened to rivers and lakes and in our oceans.

Similar situations often happen with "useful" nonbiodegradable substances. DDT, an effective chemical insecticide (see Chapter 15), does not degenerate rapidly and is not easily broken down by decomposer organisms. Since World War II, huge quantities of DDT have been sprayed on crops; about half of that DDT may still be present in an active form. Tests have revealed that there is DDT in most of the biosphere, even though DDT has never been sprayed in many places. Much of the DDT sprayed on a particular area is carried away by winds and run-off water. The DDT concentration in seawater is still increasing, even though for about ten years laws in many nations have prohibited the use of DDT except in cases of emergency.

Tests show that DDT collects in the fats of organisms. The effect of large amounts of DDT in the fats of most organisms is believed to be minor. In some, however, it is not. **Biological magnification,** a phenomenon first noted in a group of robins that stopped reproducing, can take small quantities of a substance and concentrate it into a harmful dose. For example, in the first observed instance, robins were eating earthworms that had consumed DDT-sprayed leaves. The DDT had collected in the fats of the earthworms and in turn in the fats of the robins. The fats in the yolks of the robin eggs contained large concentrations of DDT that killed the unhatched embryos. The DDT was not applied in amounts sufficient to harm robins directly, but the biological magnification of DDT did harm their offspring.

DDT and other similar nonbiodegradable pollutants are capable of significant, widespread biological magnification. For example, the DDT put on crops eventually collects in the ocean, then in the oil droplets of diatoms. Diatoms are eaten by minute crustaceans, which are eaten by small fish, then larger fish, and finally by fish-eating birds. Fish-eating birds such as American eagles, terns, herons, and pelicans have shown diminished reproduction rates because of the large quantities of DDT in the yolks of their eggs.

DDT has been greatly misused in the past. However, as its use was outlawed, crop losses and insect-related human diseases increased. We should not completely ignore DDT in our warfare against insects. In emergencies DDT may be the only known way to bring certain insects under control and should probably be used at such times. Better nonpolluting ways of insect control are being sought. Our God-given intelligence can help us subdue and dominate the physical world without destroying it.

wastes. Then scientists discovered that many hazardous wastes that seep into the environment can affect humans many miles away. Often these pollutants are carried by the movement of water or by the food chain.

Another category of hazardous wastes is *radioactive substances* made as by-products of nuclear reactors. Exposure to these chemicals causes mutations resulting in cancer, birth defects, radiation sickness, and death. Many of these radioactive wastes will remain radioactive for thousands of years. Containment of them must be in some structure that does not permit radiation to pass through.

18C-14 *The ground was thought to be a good "filter" for nonbiodegradable chemicals. But if placed in the ground, these chemicals actually pass into the water table though the process may take many years. Some pollutants can harm water many miles away from their point of origin.*

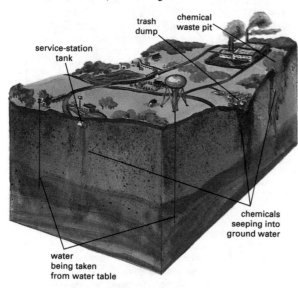

service-station tank

trash dump

chemical waste pit

chemicals seeping into ground water

water being taken from water table

18C-15 *Some Christians believe it would be best if the world were left in its natural state. God's creation, however, is not necessarily violated by a farmer's plow, a rancher's herd, or a family's house.*

Christian Views of Ecology

There are many people, including Christians, who feel that "natural is best." They believe that God wants man to "leave His world alone." It is true that the biosphere is capable of taking care of itself without man's intervention and that man has often misused the environment, misusing natural resources that should still be available to future generations. Should man, therefore, not "touch" the environment at all?

The Bible repeatedly teaches that man is a steward over the physical world. He is to use (manage) it for his purposes under God's will. In the Old Testament God instructed the children of Israel to build a temple, walls, and cities. Although building endeavors may not have disturbed the ecosystem as much in those times as they do now, they *were* departures from the "natural" environment of the area. Clearly, man is to manage the ecosystem.

Man's authority to manage the world does not give him license to misuse it. There is a considerable difference between wise, conservative use and foolish squandering. God has promised to supply a Christian's needs, but not necessarily all of his wants; we can expect that God has supplied all man's needs in his environment, but if man foolishly takes all he wants, someone will eventually have to pay.

Let us consider a common problem. There are people who feel that the energy shortage is merely a contrivance of government and business. Perhaps this is true. If, however, your belief that the energy shortage is phony causes you to waste electricity, make unnecessary car trips, or use energy to heat or cool unused rooms in your home, you are being a bad steward of what the Lord has given you. Does energy cost money? Could money wasted on unnecessary energy be better spent in some aspect of the Lord's work?

In Deuteronomy 22:6 the children of Israel were told that if they came upon a nesting bird, they could take either the bird or the young, but not both. "But . . . let the dam go, and take the young to thee; that it may be well with thee, and that thou mayest prolong thy days" (v. 7). This may speak of God's increasing a man's lifetime, but it may also refer to man's not overtaxing the environment and thus keeping his environment capable of supporting him longer.

Our ecological future

The Bible teaches that our world will be destroyed both by what man does to it and by God's destruction. Man's sin is ultimately responsible for the great trumpets of judgment described in Revelation 8 and the vials of God's wrath poured out upon the earth in Revelation 16. These events cause massive destruction of the physical world and the cataclysmic death of most living things.

Some believe that, because we are told living things will exist in the end times, those living things are going to survive until then, no matter what man may do. Often these people take this belief as license to waste or misuse natural resources. It is true that the Lord will take care of tomorrow, but we sin and let our good (our belief in the Lord's protective care) be evil spoken of if we do not carefully use and protect what God has entrusted to us. The unsaved world should not see us squander the Lord's blessings.

Although a Christian should not be an "ecology nut," screaming about the protection of the environment to the exclusion of its wise use, a Christian must not personally practice nor permit governments to practice unwise environmental management. This is being "a good steward." After all, the Lord has given us not only money and abilities but also the physical world. Using the biosphere wisely is part of a Christian's responsibility.

Biological Terms

Man's Ecological Niche	energy pollutants	hazardous wastes	*Facet*
consumer	substance pollutants	biological magnification	pantheism
manager	biodegradable		
Pollution	nonbiodegradable		
pollution	recycling		

Review Questions 18C-2

1. What are the two main types of pollutants?
2. What are the two main types of substance pollutants?
3. What are hazardous wastes? Give several reasons that they are difficult to deal with.
4. In what ways can a beneficial substance put in an ecosystem become a pollutant?
5. Why is biological magnification a problem with nonbiodegradable pollutants but not with biodegradable pollutants?

Thought Questions

1. What is your opinion regarding the existence of those characteristics that make a predator a predator (or a parasite a parasite) before the fall? What are your reasons?
2. A large swamp is to be drained by constructing a concrete-lined channel for the stream that feeds into the swamp. List some questions that should be answered before work is started. What values must be established before making decisions regarding draining the swamp?
3. Write a paragraph either supporting or refuting the following statement: "Since God has given him the know-how, whatever man wants to do to the environment is within God's will."

• What does it mean to be human? • Hormones: how you control ther.
• Data control: your brain and nerves • Drugs and the Christian • Con

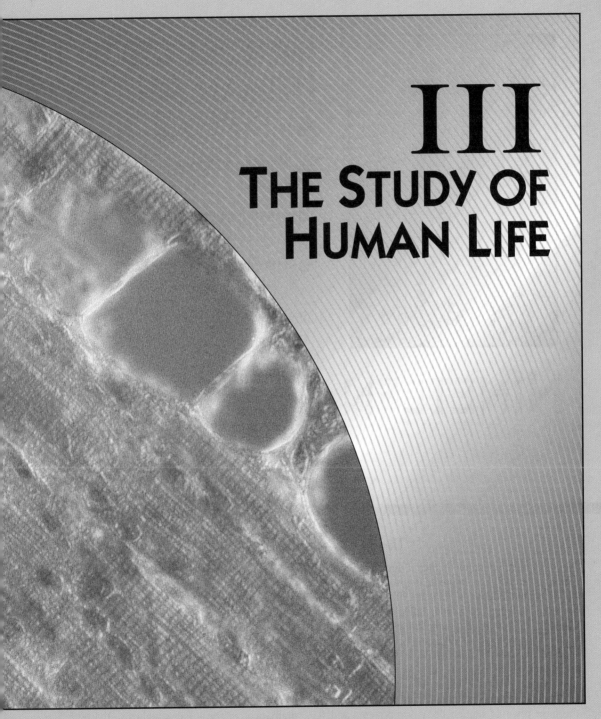

III
THE STUDY OF HUMAN LIFE

how they control you • How much does what you breathe and eat affect you? • Heart and blood: the river of life
of your mind • The marvels of immunity • A Christian view of human relationships

INTRODUCTION TO HUMAN ANATOMY AND PHYSIOLOGY

NINETEEN

19A–What Is a Human?

At one time the value of the human body was estimated to be about $1. The average body contains about 12 gal. (or 100 lb.) of water worth only a few cents. A human body also contains about 25 lb. of carbon which, in the form of coal, also costs only a few cents. As pure carbon it would cost over $20. Still remaining are 9 lb. of nitrogen and small amounts of phosphorus, sulfur, iron, iodine, sodium, and a few trace elements. Inflation and the need for pure forms would force the base price of human body components well above a dollar. However, if you were to purchase all the necessary chemicals, pile them in a heap, and stir, heat, cool, shape, kick, zap with electricity, or do anything else to them, you would not have made a living thing, much less a human body.

The problem seems to be that these chemicals are not in the right form. They are not *organic* chemicals. If, however, you price the organic chemicals that constitute the body, the value rises dramatically. The many starches in the body are expensive; they cost from $15 to nearly $40,000 an ounce. The cholesterol in the membranes of every cell of your body is worth about $27 an ounce.

The proteins of the body are made of amino acids. If you were to purchase them as individual amino acids, you could expect to pay $0.50 an ounce for some and several dollars an ounce for others. If, however, the proteins are already assembled, their value goes up. Collagen, a common structural protein, sells for $2,600 an ounce. Enzymes range from $130 an ounce (for the one found in saliva) to well over $300,000 an ounce.

DNA can be purchased for $210,000 an ounce. This, however, is not *human* DNA. Human DNA would require a special order, and the price would probably be much higher. ATP, the chemical which stores energy in all human cells, costs $750 an ounce. It is very unstable; that is, it breaks apart even as you wiggle the jar. You had better buy a few extra ounces.

One recent estimate says that the chemical value of your body is over $6 million. But still, these chemicals cannot arrange themselves into cells, tissues, organs, and systems. They cannot begin to do what the human body does. No amount of money, work, time, energy, or anything else can cause that heap of chemicals to become alive. Life has no price because it cannot be purchased.

ONE MAN'S TRASH IS ANOTHER MAN'S TREASURE.

In the image of God

The book of Genesis teaches that God took ''the dust of the ground''–a heap of chemicals–and shaped a man and then blew into his nostrils the breath of life. With this act of God, ''man became a living soul'' (Gen. 2:7). Humans are different from animals, for ''God created man in his own image'' (Gen. 1:27).

Even if scientists were able to take inorganic or organic chemicals from the dust of the earth or from a laboratory and somehow force them to exhibit the attributes of life, this ''creation'' would not be human. You are more than the chemicals that form your body. You are even more than the functioning of those chemicals called life. You are a living being created in the *image of God*. Being created in God's image does not mean that men are shaped like God. Man is a special creation of God. Animals were not formed and given life and a soul in the image of God.

What is a soul in the image of God? An easy answer is ''that which makes man different from animals.'' Let us examine what a man is by what he does, to clarify what the image of God is.

Human behavior: innate

Chapter 16 described the three basic *levels of behavior* found in animals: *innate, learned,* and *intelligent*. The lowest level of innate behavior is reflex action which is the only behavior for some animals. Humans also have reflexes. Focusing your eye and pulling your hand away from a source of pain are reflex actions. Other human reflexes and the mechanisms by which they are controlled are discussed in Chapter 22.

The other major type of innate behavior is *instinct*. Instincts, complex reactions to various stimuli, account for much of the behavior of vertebrate animals. In birds parental care is almost all instinct. If a bird egg is separated from other birds before it hatches, the hatched bird (when it matures) will still perform all the normal parental duties of its species as it builds a nest, incubates eggs, and cares for its nestlings. Since it has never seen a nest, been cared for by a parent bird, nor watched other birds care for their young, its parental behavior must be instinctive.

Changing diapers and feeding and bathing babies, however, are all tasks that humans must learn or figure out by using their intelligence. Birds, lacking the intelligence to determine that a nest must be made, that eggs need incubation, and that chirping nestlings need food, must have instincts for parental care.

Is a mother's desire to care for her baby an instinct? Not all mothers want to care for their children. Some mothers find child care rewarding.

19A-1 *The extent of a "mothering" instinct is impossible to determine since many of the activities attributed to it are learned.*

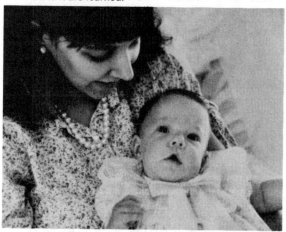

A well-groomed, well-behaved child may be considered a status symbol. Most mothers care for their children because of love. Love, however, is an emotion and is considered part of intelligent behavior, not instinct. It is impossible to say how much of a mother's care for her child is learned from the examples she sees around her and how much is instinct. Experiments cannot be set up to test for human parental-care instincts.

True human instincts are very difficult to determine. The instincts that humans may have are usually so covered over by learned and intelligent behavior that the instinct itself cannot be measured. Even the mating instinct or sex drive of humans, which is supposedly expressed in courtship and marriage, is an intricate set of learned and intelligent behaviors. Human courtship and marriage are not innate, animal instincts.

Human behavior: learned

Humans have learned behaviors, as animals do. Birds have inherited the equipment necessary to fly, but they must learn to do so. Some young birds are reluctant to leave the nest. It is through their parents' encouragement that they learn to fly. Without that parental guidance, learning to fly would take longer. Similarly, a child who is not encouraged takes longer to learn to walk than one whose mother holds his hand and urges him on.

Organisms learn some behaviors by themselves; other behaviors must be taught to them. Crawling and walking are behaviors that humans can learn for themselves. Spelling words, reciting Bible verses, and playing the piano are all behaviors that are learned through teaching and repetition. Some dogs have been taught to sit up, fetch, and roll over. Some dogs perform these learned behaviors better than other dogs, depending on the quality of their training. Likewise, a major factor in the success of man's learning is the quality of the teaching he has had.

Because of human intelligence, much of our learned behavior does not require the extensive trial and error and repetition employed to teach a dog to sit up. Because of our intelligence, once we have been told the goodies are in the refrigerator, we do not need to search the house every time we are hungry.

Human behavior: intelligent

A person can take a test to measure his intelligence. These tests, however, are only *attempts* to measure intelligence. With the test scores, we think we know *how much* a person has, but we are not sure *what it is* he has. Intelligence has not been adequately defined. There are many attributes ascribed to it. Intelligent behavior is based on the ability to reason, to solve problems, to have insight, to see relationships between objects, to recognize causes and effects, to react to something that does not immediately and personally affect oneself, to attach value to something that has no immediate value (such as money), and to react emotionally.

Although animals show some intelligence, we must be careful about attributing human behavior

19A-2 *Intelligence is measured with IQ (intelligence quotient) tests, but scientists disagree about what is being measured.*

to them. Dogs, after they have chewed a slipper or messed the carpet, fear their owners, but is that fear truly intelligent or simply learned from previous whippings? A dog's wagging tail and frisky greeting may be more for the pats and treats he receives than for the highly complex emotion called love. Courting rituals in most animals are necessary instincts, not evidences of love like human love.

It is *not* true, however, that humans are the only organisms with intelligence. An ape, put into a cage with a banana hung from the ceiling above his reach and boxes in the corner, will usually look at the banana, stack the boxes under it, climb upon the boxes, and get the banana. A dog in a

similar situation will tire himself out by jumping, and then he will lie down and eye the food, waiting for something to happen. The ape has shown intelligence in solving his problem; the dog has shown a lack of intelligence.

The more intelligent the organism, the less innate impulses determine its behavior. Monkeys, some of the more intelligent animals, seem to have fewer instincts. For example, parental care in monkeys is largely a learned behavior. A female monkey experimentally brought up in isolation will not know how to care for her offspring. She will likely ignore the infant and leave it to die. Sometimes she harms it by biting off its fingers and toes or even crushing its head. Monkeys have the intelligence to learn by example, but if they have been deprived of the example, they do not have the instinct to know what to do.

Are humans merely highly intelligent animals? Is man a monkeylike organism that merely has enough intelligence to learn a complex communication system using word and letter symbols? It *is* true that the average monkey is more intelligent than some retarded human beings. Then is man merely a very smart animal?

Human behavior: spiritual

Genesis 1:26-27 describes man as being created in the image of God. Does that mean that God has two eyes, a nose, two ears, arms, legs, and

God the Father in Glory of Angels by Francesco Montemezzano, Bob Jones University Collection of Sacred Art

19A-3 *Artists have often portrayed God the Father as a bearded, older man. These human attributes are only artistic conventions.*

man's other physical attributes? Scripture also speaks of God's having feathers and wings (Ps. 91:4), nonhuman characteristics. In Revelation 4 and 5 God's visible form is described very differently from the human form. What is the image of God in that passage?

Intelligence, emotions, and will are often cited as being part of the image of God. These are undoubtedly attributes of God and man; but to limited and varying degrees, animals also possess intelligence, emotion, and will. Some people cite man's dominion over God's creation as part of the image of God. Many Christian scholars, though, agree that the image of God includes the original knowledge, righteousness, and holiness that man lost in Adam's sin.

Many theologians also agree that man's being created in the image of God involves the fact that both God and man are spiritual beings, an attribute not shared by animals. Scripture reveals that God is a spirit (John 4:24; II Cor. 3:17). As a spirit, God can decide and do precisely what He wants to do. Angels, too, are spirits that can decide what they want to do. A group of angels once decided to do wrong and were punished for it (Isa. 14:12-15; II Pet. 2:4).

Whereas angels are spiritual beings with spiritual bodies, man was created "a little lower than the angels" (Ps. 8:5). Man is a spiritual being who now has a physical body. Animals, no matter how intelligent, are not spiritual beings, and

therefore they are not morally accountable to God for their actions. Man is a spirit created in the image of God in that he can make moral decisions and is accountable for them. Men, unlike angels, are limited to physical bodies; men, unlike animals, have spirits with their bodies.

Because man is a *spiritual being,* he has something more than intelligence that directs his behavior. Man is aware that he is more than just a physical body. Animals, on the other hand, are probably not aware of more than the physical realm. Significantly, animals do not make idols, but men who do not know the true God do. Animals are not aware of the significance of their own deaths. Man, in contrast, realizes he must die and, therefore, can prepare physically and spiritually for the inevitable.

Do not look for your spiritual awareness in the four-chambered muscular pump in your chest nor in the gray matter in your skull. For centuries Bible scholars have discoursed, debated, and thought about exactly what constitutes man's spiritual self—and until you are with the Lord, you probably will not know exactly what it is.

Though your spiritual self is not physical, it does affect your physical behavior, and your behavior affects you as a spiritual being. Man can turn to God for salvation and his spirit will spend eternity in heaven (with a glorified body) with the God Who created it, or man can reject Him (Luke 12:8-9) and spend eternity in hell. Man can gain crowns of reward for good deeds done in Christ's name, or he can receive nothing for his selfish efforts (I Cor. 3:12-15).

A spiritual being is aware of God. With spirituality comes the *responsibility* of deciding what to do about God's claims on your life. The *result* of your decision is that you will spend eternity with God's "well done" or under His condemnation. The Bible states that your personal relationship with Christ settles the eternal destiny of your spiritual self (John 3:16).

Review Questions 19A-1

1. List the four levels of human behavior. Describe and give examples of each (if possible).
2. List several possible explanations of the idea that man is created in the image of God.
3. What are the consequences of man's being a spiritual being with a physical body?

Human Tissues, Organs, and Systems

Anatomy* is concerned with how a structure is shaped, where it is found, and of what it is made. **Physiology*** is concerned with the function of a structure. Both are important since one cannot be understood without the other.

Anatomical terms

Human anatomy can be an exacting science. There are names and descriptions of virtually every structure no matter how tiny it is. For most people such detailed knowledge is not necessary, but knowledge of the proper names of major areas of the body is useful. In figure 19A-5 are some terms that you should know.

In order to be precise, people who deal with the human body use terms of direction and area based on the **anatomical** (AN uh TAHM ih kul) **position.** When a person stands erect, arms at his side, with toes, palms, and face forward, he is in the anatomical position. Descriptions of a person's body should be given as if it were in this position. Properly speaking, the left side of a person's heart (or other body part) is the part of his heart on *his* left side when he is in the anatomical position, not the left side of the heart as you are looking at it.

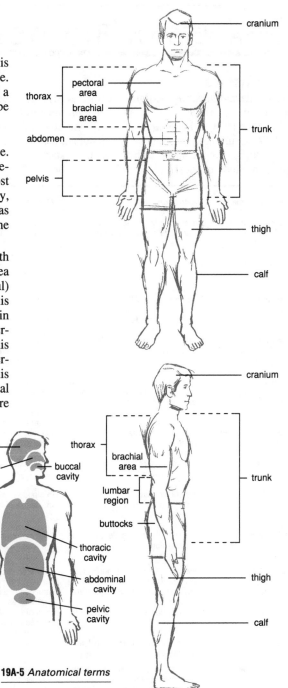

19A-5 *Anatomical terms*

Relative Directions on a Body in Anatomical Position

- **Ventral (anterior):** toward the front (stomach side)
- **Dorsal (posterior):** toward the back
- **Superior:** upward; toward the head
- **Inferior:** downward; toward the feet
- **Superficial:** on or near the surface
- **Deep:** toward the inside
- **Proximal:** toward the main part of the body
- **Distal:** away from the main part
- **Lateral:** toward the side
- **Medial:** toward the middle
- **Transverse:** directly across the body

---

anatomy: ana- (Gk. ANA, up) + -tomy (TOMOS, a cutting)

physiology: phys-, physi-, or physio- (Gk. PHYSIS, nature) + -logy (the study of)

FACETS OF BIOLOGY

Human Tissues

After the development of the light microscope, the primary study of the human body was **histology*** (hih STAHL uh jee), the study of tissues. Now, with advanced techniques, the study of individual cells and even organelles has become prominent. Knowledge of cells and other materials that make up human tissues is important to the understanding of how the tissues function.

Histologists classify tissues into four main groups according to their structure and function.
❏ **Connective tissues** connect, support, cushion, and fill.
❏ **Epithelial** (EP uh THEE lee ul)

Type and Name	Description	Occurrence	Function
Epithelial Tissues	No or very little matrix; avascular; may be a single or multiple layer of cells	The skin; covering internal organs; lining body cavities; lining blood vessels, heart, mouth, nose, throat, esophagus, stomach, intestines, urinary tract, and reproductive tract; found in many glands that secrete substances	Covers and lines to protect; secretes; absorbs; filters
Connective Tissues	Much matrix; usually vascular	Scattered over the entire body	Connects; supports; stores
Bone	Solidified matrix; few cells	The skeleton	Supports rigidly; protects; stores minerals
Cartilage	Matrix of fibers, usually in a gel; avascular	Outer ear; end of the nose; ends of the bones; between the vertebrae; between ends of ribs and sternum; in trachea	Supports firmly but flexibly; cushions; reduces friction in some joints
Dense fibrous connective tissue	Matrix of bundles of fibers which may be arranged all in the same direction or as a membrane	Ligaments; tendons; membrane around bone (continuous with ligaments and/or tendons); the covering of the brain and spinal cord (dura mater); in the dermis of the skin	Joins bone to bone or muscle to bone, permitting flexibility with strength; provides protection; supports
Loose fibrous connective tissue	Fibers (mainly elastic) in a soft matrix	Capsules around organs; beneath facial skin; around the cells of various tissues like muscle	Holds structures flexibly in place
Adipose	Predominantly cells with large lipid-storing vacuoles; some fibers; vascular	Under skin; padding in various areas	Cushions; insulates; supports; stores fats
Blood	Cells in fluid matrix	In blood vessels	Transports substances; protects
Lymph	Mostly fluid with few cells	In vessels of lymphatic system	Bathes cells in fluid to supply substances and remove wastes; protects
Hemopoietic (blood-forming)	Cells supported by a delicate network of fibers	Marrow spaces of bones; lymph nodes; spleen; tonsils; thymus gland	Forms blood cells; filters bacteria; forms antibodies
Muscle Tissues	Vascular; little matrix; other tissues usually in conjunction	Scattered over entire body	Moves and supports
Skeletal	Long (up to 1 1/4 in.), multinucleate, striated cells	Attached to bones, other muscles and structures	Moves bones, eyes, tongue, and other structures
Visceral	Short uninucleate, nonstriated cells	In walls of tubular organs such as blood vessels, intestines, and stomach; in eye; attached to hair follicles	Moves substances in tubular organs; changes size of pupil; focuses lens of eye; causes gooseflesh
Cardiac	Branching fibers; short, uninucleate, striated cells	The walls of the heart	Pumps blood
Nerve Tissues	Cells with long (sometimes several feet) projections; often protected by other cells; avascular; little matrix; most have no further mitosis once maturity is reached	The brain; spinal cord; nerves; in eye; in ear; taste buds; touch receptors	Has irritability; conducts nerve impulses, thoughts, and emotions

histology: histo- (Gk. HISTOS, web; *hence, cells with weblike structure*)+ -logy (the study of)

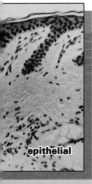
epithelial

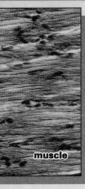
connective

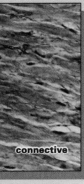
muscle

nerve

tissues cover, line, protect, and secrete.

❑ **Muscular tissues** move the body and substances in the body.

❑ **Nervous tissues** are irritable; conduct impulses; and coordinate movements, thought, and emotions.

Human tissues vary in the amount and type of **matrix** they contain. The cells secrete the non-living matrix that surrounds the cells.

❑ *Solid matrix* Bone is a solid matrix secreted by the cells that are embedded in the matrix.

❑ *Fluid matrix* Blood has a fluid matrix that carries blood cells.

❑ *Fibrous matrix* Ligaments and tendons have a matrix made of fibers. Some fibers are long, others short. Some are elastic.

❑ *Gel matrix* Some tissues have a *gel* or *soft matrix* often mixed with fibers for support. The cartilage of the nose and ear is formed of gel matrix supported by fibers.

Connective tissues have large quantities of different types of matrix and are classified by the types of matrix they contain. Epithelial tissues like your skin, however, have little or no matrices.

Most tissues are *vascular;* that is, blood vessels run through them. Epithelial tissues are usually *avascular,* lacking blood vessels. Avascular tissue must be relatively thin since its food and wastes must enter and exit by diffusion through nearby blood vessels.

Review questions on page 508.

Anatomical Quiz

Try choosing the correct anatomical word or phrase without looking at the charts and diagrams. Answers are on the next page.

1. The brachial area is __proximal/distal__ to the elbow.
2. The abdominal cavity is __superficial/deep__ to the skin.
3. The cervical area is __superior/inferior__ to the lumbar area.
4. Going from __left to right/neck to stomach__ a transverse line crossing the thorax crosses the chest.
5. The calf is __proximal/distal__ to the foot.
6. A __transverse/medial__ line goes from the inferior area of the neck to the shoulder.
7. A line drawn from left lateral area of the abdomen to the right lateral area of the abdomen would be a __medial/transverse__ line.
8. A line drawn from the nose to the navel would be a __transverse/medial__ line.
9. The cranial cavity is __superior/inferior__ to the buccal cavity.
10. The buttocks are __ventral/dorsal__ to the pelvic cavity.
11. The thigh is __superior/inferior__ to the calf.
12. The calf is __proximal/distal__ to the thigh.
13. The pectoral area is __superficial/deep__ to the thoracic cavity.
14. The abdomen is on the __dorsal/ventral__ side.
15. The thumb is __lateral/medial__ to the longest finger.

Organs and systems

The tissues of the body are organized into *organs*. The heart, for example, is an organ made up of several different representatives of the four basic tissue groups. All these tissues work together to accomplish the functions of the heart.

Organs are grouped together into *systems*. This grouping is artificial. The muscular system, it is generally agreed, includes all muscles. But what about the muscles that churn food? They are in the lining of the stomach, and the stomach is an organ in the digestive system. There are many other examples of systems seeming to overlap.

The body was *not* designed to be studied easily; it was designed to carry on life. The systems approach to studying the body, however, is probably the clearest method and will be used in our study. Below is a list of the eleven systems in the group order in which this book will discuss them.

19A-6

The Human Systems

Covering
Integumentary system: skin, hair

Support and movement
Skeletal system: bones, cartilage, joints
Muscular system: muscles

Incoming substances
Respiratory system: nose, throat, trachea, larynx, lungs
Digestive system: mouth, esophagus, stomach, intestines, liver, pancreas, gallbladder

Internal transport
Circulatory system: heart, blood vessels, blood
Lymphatic system: lymph, lymph vessels, lymph nodes, spleen, tonsils

Excretion
Excretory system: kidneys, urinary bladder

Control
Nervous system: brain, spinal cord, nerves, eyes, ears, taste buds, touch receptors
Endocrine system: pituitary gland, thyroid gland, adrenal gland, pancreas

Reproduction
Reproductive system: ovaries, Fallopian tubes, uterus, testes, vas deferens, prostate gland

---

Biological Terms

Human Tissues, Organs, and Systems
  anatomy
  physiology
  anatomical position

Facet
  histology

connective tissues
epithelial tissues
muscular tissues
nervous tissues
matrix

Answers to Anatomical Quiz

1. proximal
2. deep
3. superior
4. left to right
5. proximal
6. transverse
7. transverse
8. medial
9. superior
10. dorsal
11. superior
12. distal
13. superficial
14. ventral
15. lateral (remember anatomical position)

Review Questions 19A-2

1. What is the difference between anatomy and physiology?
2. Write a sentence using all of the following word groups.
      Sentence 1: ventral, dorsal, calf
      Sentence 2: superior, inferior, thoracic cavity
      Sentence 3: superficial, deep, heart
      Sentence 4: proximal, distal, brachial area
      Sentence 5: lateral, medial, shoulder
      Sentence 6: transverse, cranium
      Sentence 7: cervical, thorax, lumbar
3. List the eleven systems of the human body.

Facet 19A-1: Human Tissues, pages 506-7

1. List, describe, tell the function of, and give examples of the four basic types of tissues found in the human body.
2. List eight types of connective tissues and give examples of each.
3. List four different kinds of matrix often found in human tissues.
4. Describe vascular tissues and give an example. Describe avascular tissue and give an example.

Thought Questions

1. Compare and contrast animals and humans in regard to the four basic levels of behavior.
2. Compare and contrast man and angels in regard to their physical bodies, knowledge, and creation in the image of God. Use Scripture to support your comparisons.

19B–The Integumentary System

Approximately 2,800 sq. in. (about 19 sq. ft.) of skin covers the body. Although the thickness varies, it averages 1/8 in. This large but thin system serves the body in a number of varied ways.

❑ *Protection* The skin does not permit significant amounts of substances like water and air to go into or out of the body. Bacteria, viruses, and many common chemicals that you constantly touch would be very harmful if they penetrated into the tissues of the body. Skin is an effective barrier to most of them.

❑ *Sensation* Although distributed unevenly, the nerve receptors for touch, pressure, temperature, and pain are in the skin.

❑ *Heat control* The amount of blood being carried to the surface of skin is regulated to control the amount of heat lost to the atmosphere. The flush of pink after physical exercise is caused by large amounts of warm blood coming to the surface for cooling. The skin turns pale when the body is cold because blood is being withheld from the skin to conserve body heat. When the skin is very cold, blood is sent to it to prevent it from being damaged; hence, one has rosy cheeks after outdoor winter activities. If the body generates excessive heat, the skin secretes large amounts of sweat. Evaporation of sweat cools the skin's surface and thereby cools the blood in the skin's blood vessels.

❑ *Excretion* A small amount of body wastes is excreted with sweat.

❑ *Vitamin and hormone manufacture* The skin produces small amounts of vitamin D and testosterone (the male sex hormone).

❑ *Absorption* The skin can absorb some chemicals, a few drugs, and a small amount of oxygen.

The layers of the skin

The outermost layer of the skin is the **epidermis.*** The epidermis is made entirely of layers of epithelial tissues. The deepest layer of the epidermis is called the *stratum germinativum*. This single cell layer carries on cell division, producing new cells. These new cells are constantly being forced upward as more cells are produced by the stratum germinativum. The older cells of the epidermis fill with a waxy substance called *keratin* and die. These dead cells form the outer layers of the epidermis, called the *horny layer* or *stratum corneum*, and are constantly being sloughed off.

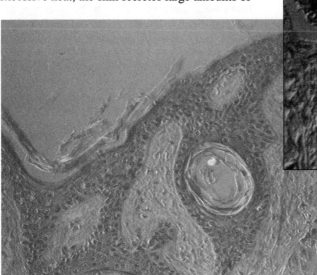
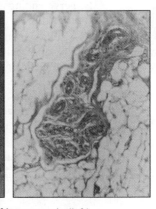

19B-1 *A micrograph of human scalp (left) showing the epidermis, dermis, and a hair follicle; a cross section of human skin (top, left) and a nerve ending in the skin (top right)*

---

epidermis: epi- (upon) + -dermis (skin)

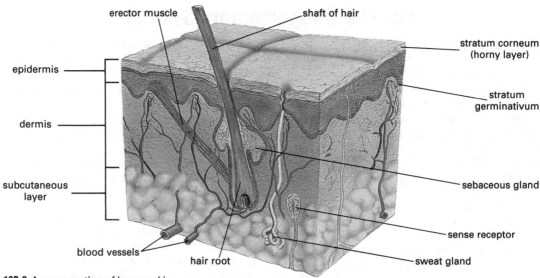

erector muscle — shaft of hair

epidermis

dermis

subcutaneous layer

blood vessels
hair root

stratum corneum (horny layer)

stratum germinativum

sebaceous gland

sense receptor

sweat gland

19B-2 *A cross section of human skin*

About every 25 days (fewer days for some people and some areas of the body) a completely new epidermis covers the body.

The inner, much thicker layer of the skin is the **dermis.*** The dermis is composed primarily of connective tissues. In the dermis are blood vessels, nerve endings, sweat glands, hair follicles, and oil glands.

The **subcutaneous*** (SUB kyoo TAY nee us) **layer** is not actually a part of the skin. It is the portion of the integumentary system that attaches the dermis to the muscles and is composed of connective tissues. Fat deposits found in almost all subcutaneous layers serve to insulate, cushion, and smooth the contours of the body.

Many of the fibers in the connective tissues of the dermis and subcutaneous layers are elastic.

19B-3 *Much of the difference between young and old skin is the elasticity of subcutaneous fibers.*

Just as a rubber band loses some of its elasticity when it is old, so the elastic fibers of the skin lose some of their elasticity with age. Hence, the skin sags and wrinkles. Facelifts surgically shorten some of the major connective tissues of the face, thereby pulling the skin taut and (the patient hopes) wrinkle free.

Hair and nails

Hairs are located on all of the body except the palms of the hands and the soles of the feet. Different body regions, however, have different types of hair. The *root* of a hair lies in a hair **follicle*** (FAHL ih kul), which is in the dermis, or occasionally as deep as the subcutaneous layers. Hair cells are produced at the bottom of the hair follicle and are then filled with keratin and pigments. As the follicle produces more cells, the dead cells are pushed upward and out of the follicle.

The long *shaft* of the hair, above the skin, is actually a collection of these dead, protein-filled cells. Since the shaft of the hair is dead, cutting the hair does not cause it to grow faster or coarser.

Scalp hair grows about 1/2 in. per month. Growth can be affected by diet, hormones, general health, and age. If the follicle is elliptical, the hair is kinky. If the follicle is round, the hair is

---

dermis: (skin)   **subcutaneous:** sub- (under) + -cuta- or -cuti- (L. CUTIS, skin)   **follicle:** (L. FOLLICULUS, little bag)

Skin Diseases and Disorders

Acne: an inflammation of sebaceous glands caused by a blockage of the pore, resulting in the accumulation of oil and white blood cells within the gland. The causes of acne are not completely understood, but cleanliness, bacteria, diet, and heredity are involved.

Blisters: a collection of watery fluid under the epidermis. There are various causes. If the skin is pinched, blood may fill the pinch, and a blood blister may develop.

Boils: rounded, painful inflammation resulting from a localized bacterial infection.

Burns: *first-degree burns* involve damage to the outer epidermal layers only. Cold water on the area, followed by an ointment, is usually the recommended first aid. Mild sunburns are first-degree burns. *Second-degree burns* involve damage to all the epidermal layers and some of the dermis. Cold water and covering with gauze is usually recommended. Severe sunburns can be second-degree burns. *Third-degree burns* involve tissue damage to all the dermis and often into the subcutaneous layer. The area should be covered with a moist, sterile cloth until medical attention can be obtained. Greases should not be applied to second- and third-degree burns unless a physician prescribes them.

Calluses, corns: thickened layers of epidermis caused by pressure and friction.

Cuts: the space where the skin has been cut will fill with fibrous connective tissue and blood vessels. Epidermal cells will grow over the top, but if a large quantity of connective tissue has to form, it will show as a scar.

Psoriasis: red, scaly patches of skin where epidermal cells have fallen off too rapidly. The causes of psoriasis are unknown.

Ringworm: a fungus infection of the skin that appears as a white circle under the skin.

Shingles: a red soreness, followed by blisters, caused by the chicken pox virus.

Warts: layers of hard, dead cells resulting from a localized virus infection.

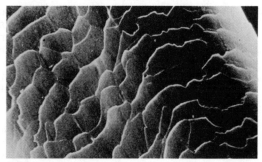

19B-4 *A scanning electron micrograph of human hair (2000X)*

begin to grow again. Diet, chemicals, fever, emotions, and other factors can temporarily shut down large numbers of hair follicles. Baldness, on the other hand, is an inherited trait. When the genes direct the hair to stop growing, little can be done either to prevent hair follicles from shutting down or to start them again.

Attached to most hair follicles is an *erector muscle.* When the muscle contracts, the hair stands on end, and gooseflesh forms. Temperature, as well as emotions such as fear, can trigger contraction of these muscles.

The nails of the fingers and toes are very similar to hair since they develop from the skin and the visible portion is dead cells filled with protein. Whereas fingernails are replaced about every 6 months, toenails require a year.

Oil glands

Every hair follicle has a **sebaceous** (sih BAY shus) **gland,** which produces oil that keeps the hair and skin soft. There are also some sebaceous glands that do not accompany hair follicles, especially if there is only a small amount of hair in that area.

The amount of oil produced by sebaceous glands is inherited. Very oily skin often requires the use of special oil solvents. Removal of too much oil by detergents or oil-soluble soaps can cause skin to become dry and crack and cause hair to become brittle and develop split ends. Washing too often may require the use of conditioners and lotions in order to keep hair and skin supple.

straight. There are varying degrees in between. Straightness, along with texture, color, and other hair characteristics, is inherited.

Periodically a hair follicle stops producing for a time, and the hair falls out. It, however, may

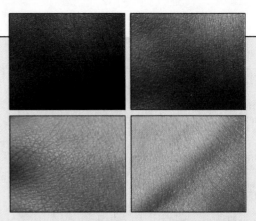

Skin Color

The pink color of a person's skin is his blood showing through; other colors are the result of pigments. **Melanocytes*** are cells in the stratum germinativum of the epidermis that produce **melanin,*** the brown, black, or yellow pigment that colors the skin. Both the number of melanocytes (which determines the amount of melanin that can be produced) and the color of melanin are inherited.

Ultraviolet radiation (one of the forms of radiation from the sun) stimulates melanocytes to produce melanin. When the melanin enters the layers of the epidermis, it causes the skin to appear darker. Melanin in the upper horny layers of the epidermis absorbs ultraviolet radiations before they penetrate and kill skin cells. Thus a person who has inherited many melanocytes that produce dark melanin has a darker skin color and can withstand more of the sun's harmful ultraviolet rays without skin damage than a person with fair skin.

Many people have the idea that sunbathing is good and that a deep tan is an indication of good health. Both ideas are in error. A person with a tan can be very ill, and a fair-skinned person, one who lacks melanocytes and cannot tan, can be in excellent physical condition. When sunbathing to obtain a tan, one actually forces his body to put up a screen against excessive exposure to the sun.

Excessive sunbathing damages or kills skin cells by exposing them to the mutation-inducing ultraviolet rays of the sun. These cells must then be replaced at a rate faster than normal, and the skin consequently ages prematurely. Ultraviolet radiation from the sun can also cause the mutations that cause skin cancer. Tans may be in fashion, but if you have to work at one, it would be better for you to be out of fashion. Although some skin problems can be helped by moderate sunbathing, most people would do better to avoid prolonged exposure to the sun.

Sweat glands

There are approximately 80 **sweat glands** to every square inch of skin. These tube-shaped glands produce *perspiration,* a substance which is about 99% water. Half of the other 1% is salts (primarily sodium chloride), and half is organic substances, including sugars, amino acids, and urea. If a person's kidneys fail, the skin attempts to rid the body of wastes like urea and uric acid. This activity produces an unusual body odor. Skin is a poor excretory organ, though, and a person with kidney failure and without medical treatment will soon die.

Normally, the entire body is constantly sweating and excretes about a half pint of water daily, even if a person remains in a comfortable room and does no strenuous activity. Because this amount evaporates quickly, this perspiration goes unnoticed. On a hot day with strenuous activity a person can lose almost 2 gal. of water (16 lb.).

Sweat itself does not have an odor, but odors are released when sweat combines with substances on the skin and with the waste products of bacteria growing on the dead skin cells that collect on hair and clothing. Washing with warm water to remove the sloughed-off epidermal cells and bacteria and wearing clean clothing minimize body odor resulting from perspiration. Anti-perspirants contain chemicals that stop the sweat glands from producing sweat. Deodorants are usually perfumes to cover body odor, often with a little anti-bacterial substance.

Biological Terms

epidermis	subcutaneous layer	sebaceous gland	melanin
dermis	follicle	melanocyte	sweat gland

---

melanocyte: melan- or melano-
(Gk. MELAS, black) + -cyte (cell)

melanin: (black)

Review Questions 19B

1. List and describe the functions of the human skin.
2. What are the three major layers of the human body covering?
3. Describe the epidermis and give the functions of its parts.
4. Describe a human hair. Tell how it grows.
5. What are sebaceous glands? Where are they found? What functions do they accomplish?
6. List several functions of sweat glands.
7. Describe the tanning process. In what ways does excessive exposure to the sun age the skin?

19C–The Skeletal System

The bones of your body are quite different from the bones of a skeleton that hangs in a science classroom. Such a skeleton is only the nonliving matrix of bone tissue. Embedded in the matrix are bone cells. Bones in your body are living organs that contain blood vessels, nerves, fat tissues, and blood-cell-forming tissues.

The skeletal system serves as a framework for the *support* of the body and for the *protection* of delicate organs such as the brain, spinal cord, heart, and lungs. Bones serve as levers and, with the muscular system, produce *movement*. The bones are also *storage areas* for minerals, especially calcium and phosphorus. Bone marrow is involved in *blood cell production*.

Bone Anatomy and Physiology

The bones of an adult human can be classified according to shape. The bones of the arms and legs are *long bones*, while the bones of the wrists and ankles are *short bones*. Inside the skull are several *irregular-shaped bones*, and the ribs and top part of the skull are good examples of *flat bones*.

A long bone has two basic regions: the **shaft**, which is the long main portion, and the **epiphyses*** (ih PIF ih SEEZ), the ends of the bone. Between the shaft and each epiphysis is a thin internal layer of cartilage tissue called the **epiphyseal** (EP uh FIZ ee ul) **plate** or growth plate.

The surfaces of the epiphyses are covered with a thin layer of smooth, bluish white **articular*** (ar TIK yuh lur) **cartilage.** This cartilage layer provides for smooth movement at the joints when you swim and for cushioning when you return to the gym floor after a jump shot.

The shaft of the bone is covered with a layer of dense, white, fibrous tissue called the **periosteum*** (PEHR ee AHS tee um), which is responsible for muscle attachment and for bone growth

19C-1 *Anatomy of the tibia*

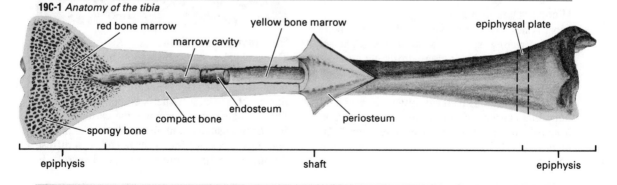

red bone marrow

marrow cavity

yellow bone marrow

epiphyseal plate

endosteum

compact bone

periosteum

spongy bone

epiphysis

shaft

epiphysis

---

epiphyses: epi- (upon) + -physes (Gk. PHYSES, growth)
articular: (L. ARTICULUS, small joint)

periosteum: peri- (around) + -os, -oste-, -osteo-, or osteum (bone)

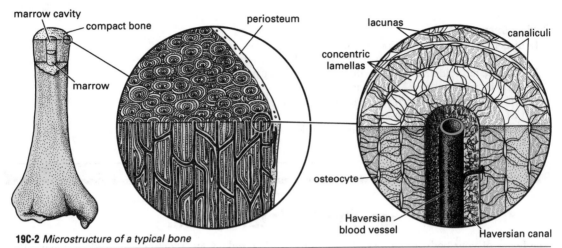

marrow cavity
compact bone
periosteum
marrow
lacunas
canaliculi
concentric lamellas
osteocyte
Haversian blood vessel
Haversian canal

19C-2 *Microstructure of a typical bone*

and repair. Fibers firmly anchor the periosteum to the bone. The shaft of the bone is made of **compact bone** that surrounds a hollow center called the **marrow cavity.** This cavity usually extends the entire length of the shaft. The lining of the marrow cavity is the **endosteum*** (en DAHS tee um) and, like the periosteum, is involved in bone growth and repair. In young people this cavity is filled mostly with **red bone marrow,** a soft tissue that produces red blood cells and certain other blood cells. **Yellow bone marrow** is fatty tissue that gradually replaces the red bone marrow as people grow older.

The ends of a long bone contain **spongy bone.** Spongy bone is sturdy but contains many small spaces that make it look like a sponge. These spaces are filled with red bone marrow and some fat. Red bone marrow in the ends of some long bones retains its blood-producing abilities throughout a person's life.

Microstructure of a bone

Most bones have a thin veneer of compact bone tissue covering spongy bone tissue. Compact bone is more regular in its microscopic arrangement than spongy bone. A common feature of all compact bone tissue is the **Haversian** (huh VUR shun) **system.** A Haversian system is a unit of bone that consists of *Haversian blood vessels* in a *central canal,* surrounded by *concentric* lamellae* (kun SEN trik ◊ luh MEL ee) (layers) of hard matrix.

Between the lamellae are *lucunae* (luh KOO nee) or "pools." These fluid-filled spaces contain the **osteocytes*** (AHS tee uh SITES), which are living bone cells. The osteocytes receive nourishment from the Haversian blood vessels through tiny canals called *canaliculi** (KAN uh LIK yuh LYE). Since several canaliculi open into each lucuna, the osteocytes are continually bathed with nutritive fluid from the Haversian blood vessels.

19C-3 *A micrograph of a hard bone, showing Haversian systems*

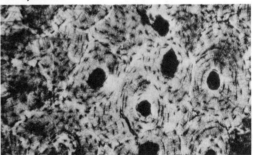

Formation of bone tissue

The skeletal system of an adult human consists of two types of connective tissue: cartilage and bone. Bone gives rigid support, while cartilage is flexible. **Cartilage** tissue is composed of a soft, fibrous matrix that surrounds the cartilage cells. It does not usually contain blood vessels, but the nutrients necessary for cartilage cells can diffuse through the matrix from nearby blood vessels. In

---

endosteum: en- (within) + -osteum (bone)

concentric: con- (same) + -centric (L. CENTRUM, center)

osteocytes: osteo- (bone) + -cytes (cell)

canaliculi: (L. CANALIS, channel)

Broken Bones

A broken bone or cartilage is known as a *fracture*. A fracture also injures the surrounding soft tissues. Sometimes the injury to the soft tissues is even more serious than the fracture itself, especially when an artery is torn or a lung is punctured.

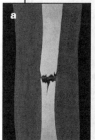

Can you identify these fractures? (Answers at the bottom of the next page.)

The treatment of fractures is twofold. First, the bone must be set in proper alignment, which sometimes requires surgery. *Traction* may also be necessary to keep the bone fragments aligned. In traction, weights are connected to a broken arm, leg, or neck to keep tension on the broken bone. This tension also helps to insure that the fractured bone will be the proper length after healing. Traction is often necessary in comminuted and impacted fractures.

The second part of the treatment is immobilization. Plaster of Paris casts and splints promote healing by holding the bone fragments steady. Some bones naturally heal more rapidly than others. The humerus (upper arm), for example, may

heal in 3 months, but the tibia (lower leg), for a similar fracture, usually requires 6 months. Also, fractures heal faster in a young person. A broken bone in an elderly person sometimes takes years to heal. For this reason artificial bone sections are sometimes surgically substituted for broken bones in older people. This is often done for fractured femurs, a common result of falls among the elderly, and permits the person to walk in a few weeks. Some fractures require metal plates, screws, and pins for proper support.

Often it is unwise to immobilize a mending bone completely. After a long period, certain materials in it will be reabsorbed by the blood for use in bones in areas of high stress. A limited amount of use–but not enough to dislocate the bone piece–actually aids healing. Therefore, "walking casts" or other limited-use devices are often prescribed.

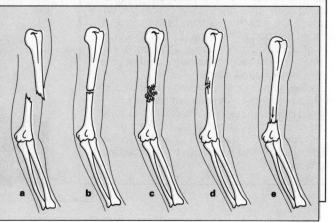

A World War I soldier in traction

Types of Fractures

a. **Complete:** the fracture line extends entirely through the bone, and **open (compound):** the broken bone protrudes through the skin.

b. **Complete** and **closed (simple):** the broken bone does not protrude through the skin.

c. **Comminuted:** the bone is splintered at the site of impact, and smaller fragments of bone are found between the two main fragments.

d. **Incomplete (partial):** the fracture line extends only partially through the bone. Common among young people, a **greenstick** fracture is one in which a side of the bone is broken and the other side is bent.

e. **Impacted:** one bone fragment is firmly forced into the other.

Bone Growth

Bones grow longer at the epiphyseal plate, the last cartilage tissue to ossify. This plate consists of a number of layers of cartilage cells lying between the epiphysis and the shaft. The layer of cartilage cells nearest the shaft divides to produce more cartilage cells and, thus, increases the length of the bone. Meanwhile, the layers of cartilage cells nearest the epiphysis slowly ossify.

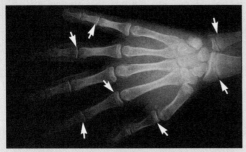

Epiphyseal plates in a 12-year-old's hand

X-rays of the hand and wrist show many epiphyseal plates. Physicians can predict how tall a person will grow by measuring his epiphyseal plates during adolescence. X-rays of teen-agers reveal that illnesses delay the ossification of the epiphyseal plates. In other words, whenever you are ill, your growth rate slows.

As you grow, your body requires an increasingly stronger skeletal system for support. Therefore, as bones increase in length, they must also increase in diameter. This increase in diameter occurs primarily beneath the periosteum, where new bone tissue is added. Specialized osteocytes enlarge the marrow cavity by "eating away" the internal bone tissue. This dissolved bone substance is then used for growth on the outer part of the bone. By this dual process of dissolving and building, a thin bone with a small marrow cavity becomes a thicker bone with a larger marrow cavity.

As they grow, bones continually need calcium in order to form the concentric lamellae of newly-formed Haversian systems. Therefore, you must have calcium in your diet if your bones are to form properly. You also need vitamin D so that the calcium from your food can be absorbed into the blood.

the adult, cartilage is found primarily on the ends of long bones and in the nose and outer ear. It also attaches the ribs to the sternum.

An embryo's tiny skeleton is composed mostly of cartilage, which is gradually changed into bone. This converting of cartilage into bone is called **ossification*** (AHS uh fih KAY shun). Ossification usually begins about the sixth week of embryonic development and is not completed until the late teens, when a person stops growing.

Another gradual change during ossification is the hardening of the cartilage tissue by the addition of *calcium*. Calcium is transported into the changing cartilage by the blood stream. This hardening process usually begins in the middle region of a bone and then spreads outward. Even after ossification is complete, the bone tissue is continually being "remodeled," which accounts for the change in facial features as a person matures physically.

A Separate Plate

During rapid growth (between the ages of 8 and 16) the upper epiphyseal plate of the femur (thigh bone) sometimes separates from the bone because of disease or injury. Often, the plate will slip downward and backward. This condition, if not corrected, can cause one leg to be shorter than the other. Corrective surgery with "stapling" or the insertion of metal pins through the bone may be needed to keep the plate in proper position. These staples or pins can be removed when the epiphyseal plate ossifies.

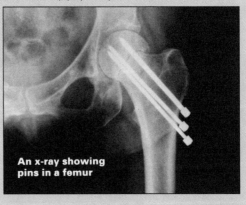

An x-ray showing pins in a femur

Broken bones on page 515: (a) complete (simple), (b) incomplete (greenstick), (c) comminuted

ossification: os- or ossi- (bone) + -fication (L. FICUS, a making or forming into)

FACETS OF BIOLOGY

19C-1

The Human Skeleton

The adult human skeleton consists of approximately 206 bones grouped in two principal divisions:

❏ The **axial skeleton** is based around the imaginary vertical center line of the body (the *axis*). The axial skeleton includes the ribs, the sternum, the bones of the skull and the vertebral column, which total 80 bones.

❏ The **appendicular skeleton** contains the bones of the extremities and the bones of the *pectoral* and *pelvic girdles,* which connect the extremities to the axial skeleton. There are 126 bones in the appendicular skeleton.

Another group of bones, which most humans have a few of, is the *supernumerary bones.* These bones are not numbered because humans are usually not born with them. These bones often develop at joints that are under stress and help protect parts of the body. The patella is a supernumerary bone which protects the knee in virtually everyone. Another example is

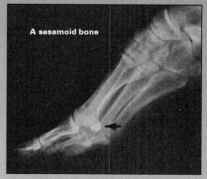

A sesamoid bone

the bone developed in a bunion; it is caused by wearing tight shoes.

Review questions on page 519.

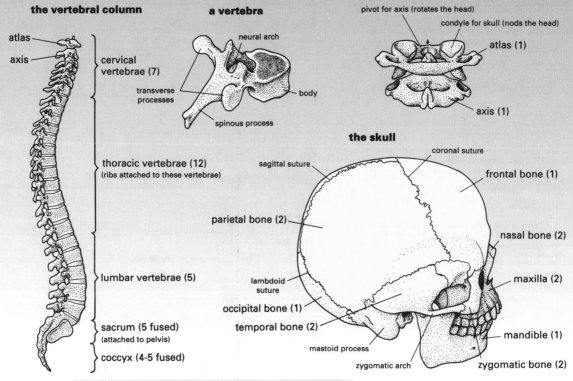

the vertebral column

atlas
axis
cervical vertebrae (7)

thoracic vertebrae (12)
(ribs attached to these vertebrae)

lumbar vertebrae (5)

sacrum (5 fused)
(attached to pelvis)

coccyx (4-5 fused)

a vertebra

neural arch

transverse processes

spinous process

body

pivot for axis (rotates the head)
condyle for skull (nods the head)
atlas (1)
axis (1)

the skull

sagittal suture
coronal suture
frontal bone (1)

parietal bone (2)

nasal bone (2)

lambdoid suture

maxilla (2)

occipital bone (1)
temporal bone (2)

mastoid process

zygomatic arch

mandible (1)

zygomatic bone (2)

Major bones and bone markings of the human skull and backbone. Numbers in parentheses are the number of bones of that type found in the body.

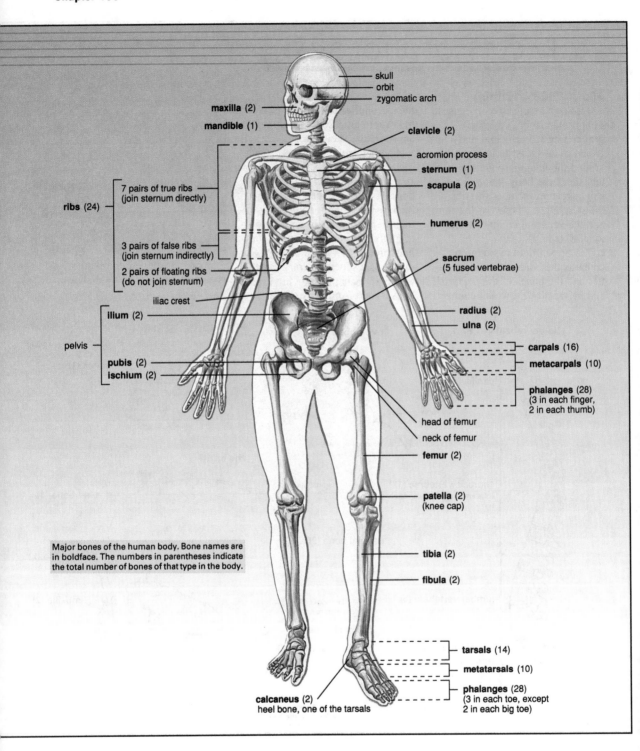

skull
orbit
zygomatic arch

maxilla (2)
mandible (1)

clavicle (2)

acromion process
sternum (1)
scapula (2)

humerus (2)

7 pairs of true ribs
(join sternum directly)

ribs (24)

3 pairs of false ribs
(join sternum indirectly)

2 pairs of floating ribs
(do not join sternum)

sacrum
(5 fused vertebrae)

iliac crest

ilium (2)

pelvis

radius (2)
ulna (2)

carpals (16)
metacarpals (10)

pubis (2)
ischium (2)

phalanges (28)
(3 in each finger,
2 in each thumb)

head of femur
neck of femur

femur (2)

patella (2)
(knee cap)

Major bones of the human body. Bone names are
in boldface. The numbers in parentheses indicate
the total number of bones of that type in the body.

tibia (2)

fibula (2)

tarsals (14)

metatarsals (10)

phalanges (28)
(3 in each toe, except
2 in each big toe)

calcaneus (2)
heel bone, one of the tarsals

Review Questions 19C-1
1. List the functions of the skeletal system.
2. List the four types of bones according to their shapes.
3. Draw a longitudinal section of a long bone and label the parts.
4. Draw two Haversian systems side by side and label the parts.
5. Describe the formation of a bone.
6. List and describe several types of bone fractures.
7. What are the two steps usually taken to treat a bone fracture?
8. Describe how a bone grows in length. Describe how a bone grows in diameter (width).

Facet 19C-1: The Human Skeleton, pages 517-18
1. What are the two main divisions of the human skeleton?
2. What is a supernumerary bone? How does it develop? Give an example.

Joints

A **joint** is a connection between two or more bones or between cartilage and bone. The bones that form a joint are held in position by strong bands of connective tissue known as **ligaments.*** The fibers of the ligaments are actually extensions of the fibers of the periosteum. These continuous fibers secure the joint. Joints are essential in *articulation* (ar TIK yuh LAY shun), one of the most important functions of the skeletal system. Articulation refers to the smooth movement of one bone upon another.

Kinds of Joints

Joints are designed for specific functions and are classified into three groups according to the degree of movement:

❏ *Freely movable joints* Most joints in the skeletal system are freely movable. The ends of the bones at such joints are shaped to provide smooth

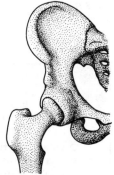

19C-4 *Freely movable joint (hip)*

19C-3	Movable Joints and Their Actions		
Type of Joint	**Description**	**Action**	**Example**
Ball-and-Socket	A ball-shaped head moves within a socket that is "hollowed" to receive the head	Free movement in all directions	Shoulder and hip
Hinge	Two cylindrical surfaces, one concave and the other convex, that fit together to form the joint	Bending only in one direction	Elbow, knee, and between phalanges
Pivot	A ringlike formation at the end of one bone surrounds a toothlike process which functions as an axle	Rotating and swiveling	Between atlas and axis in neck
Gliding	Opposing bone surfaces are slightly convex and concave, respectively, and thereby restrict movement	Limited movement sideways and up and down	Between carpals and between tarsals

ligament: liga- (L. LIGARE, to bind) + -ment (E. suffix indicating action of process)

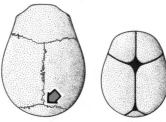

19C-6 *Immovable joint (suture of skull, left) and fonta-nels of the skull of a young child (right)*

articulation. Long bones bear most of the body's weight and, therefore, have large, rounded ends. The bone that receives the rounded end usually has a depression that helps form a sturdy joint. The freely movable joints may be classified according to these ends of the bones that make up the joint and the kind of movement they permit.

❏ *Slightly movable joints* In these joints a pad of cartilage permits limited movement. Slightly movable joints connect the vertebrae. The union between the pubic bones, the *pubic symphysis*, is also classified as a slightly movable joint, even though there is movement only under severe stress, as in childbirth.

19C-5 *Slightly movable joint (vertebra)*

❏ *Immovable joints* In some places where bones meet or where a bone attaches to cartilage, the joints must be rigid. The union of an epiphysis and shaft by the epiphyseal plate is an immovable joint. **Sutures,*** the interlocking margins of skull bones, are also immovable joints. At birth the sutures have not formed, and the spaces between the skull bones are filled with fibrous membranes known as fontanels. These are the ''soft spots'' that allow an infant's skull to be slightly compressed during birth.

Bone and Joint Diseases and Disorders

Arthritis: an inflammation of a joint, usually accompanied by pain and, frequently, changes in the joint structure; three most common types:

❏ **osteoarthritis:** a disease which disintegrates articular cartilage and deposits bony spurs on the exposed bone, limiting mobility;
❏ **rheumatoid arthritis:** a disease in which the fibrous tissue grows into the joint cavity; later the joint may completely ossify;
❏ **gouty arthritis** (gout): a disease which deposits excessive uric acid crystals on the joints.

Bunion: an inflammation and thickening of the bursas of the joint of the great toe, usually resulting in enlargement of the joint and displacement of the toe.
Bursitis: an inflammation of a bursa, especially one located between bones and muscles or tendons as in the shoulder and knee joints.
Clubfoot: any of a number of deformities of the foot present at birth.
Dislocation: the temporary displacement of a bone from its joint; in severe dislocations, ligaments and tendons may be torn; ''popping your knuckles'' is a minor dislocation.
Double-jointed: a joint that is easily dislocated because the ligaments are abnormally long.
Flatfoot: an abnormal flatness of sole and arch of foot often caused by stretching the ligaments of the joints of the tarsals.

Osteoporosis: a bone condition in which calcium is removed more rapidly than it is replaced; common in the elderly; may be caused by several factors including lack of exercise and low intake of calcium, vitamin D, and proteins.
Rheumatism: a general term for various conditions including arthritis; characterized by soreness and stiffness of muscles and pain in joints.
Rickets: a disorder in infants caused by a deficiency of vitamin D; the bones become soft, and legs may become bowed.
Ruptured disc: a disorder in which the central portion of the cartilaginous disc becomes flattened and protrudes outward; commonly called ''slipped disc.''
Sesamoid bones: small, extra bones, most of which develop in tendons, commonly beneath the big toe and above the heel.
Spinal deformity: an abnormal spinal curvature such as the ''humpback'' condition and lateral curvature of the back; may be caused by poor posture, injury, or disease.
Sprain: an injury of ligaments and tendons which causes pain and disability; in severe sprains, the ligaments may be completely torn.
Trick knee: a temporary dislocation of the patella usually due to a previous injury.
Water on the knee: a swelling of the knee in response to torn tissues; water from the blood moves into the joint cavity to dilute toxins and limit movement so that healing can progress.

---

suture: (L. SUERE, to sew)

Anatomy of a typical joint

The joints that allow for free movement are necessarily complicated structures. Movement at a joint such as the knee is governed by the location of the ligaments, the location of muscle attachments, and the presence of other bones that might restrict movement.

The inner surface of the joint cavities is lined with a **synovial** (si NOH vee ul) **membrane** which fills the cavity with a lubricating *synovial fluid*. Synovial fluid also acts as a "shock absorber" between the bones. Ligaments connect the bones of a joint, yet permit free movement. **Tendons,*** which are the fibrous attachments between muscles and bones, often extend across the joint and strengthen it.

Saclike structures called *bursas** (BUR suz), located between tendons, ligaments, and bones, are also lined with synovial membranes that produce synovial fluid. The fluid-filled bursas serve as cushions and reduce friction between moving parts of the joints.

When joints are sprained or dislocated, the fibers of the ligaments and tendons stretch and usually tear. Since these tissues heal rather slowly, it is necessary to restrict their movement. Excessive activity could permanently stretch the ligaments or tendons, resulting in a weak joint which would dislocate easily. However, if the injured person

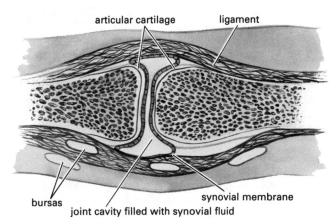

19C-7 *A typical joint*

does not move the joint at all during the healing process, the ligaments or tendons may shorten, greatly restricting the movement of the joint.

Often the doctor will advise a person to walk with the aid of crutches but still "put some weight" on the sprained ankle or knee. He may also give warnings not to engage in any strenuous physical activity that might re-injure the weakened joint since it may not be completely healed even after the pain has subsided. These warnings are a difficult, yet necessary, assignment for young athletes if they expect to be athletes at all when they are older.

Biological Terms

Bone Anatomy and Physiology
shaft
epiphyses
epiphyseal plate
articular cartilage
periosteum
compact bone
marrow cavity
endosteum

red bone marrow
yellow bone marrow
spongy bone
Haversian system
osteocytes
cartilage
ossification

Joints
joint
ligament
sutures
synovial membrane
tendon

Facet
axial skeleton
appendicular skeleton

Review Questions 19C-2

1. List the three types of joints, according to their movability. Give examples of each.
2. Draw a typical movable joint and label the parts.

Thought Questions

1. Describe the process of bone healing. What can be done to speed the process? How would a "walking cast" help bone healing?
2. What, besides proper nutrition, is necessary for proper bone growth?

---

tendon: (L. TENDERE, to stretch)   **bursas:** (L. BURSA, bag or purse)

19D-The Muscular System

The two key words that describe the muscular system are *contraction* and *movement*. Contraction refers to the ability of a muscle tissue to shorten and thereby cause movement. Some muscles, like those which you used to get out of bed this morning, you consciously control. However, the muscles of your stomach and intestines that help digest your breakfast operate without your mental commands. Muscles that cause breathing are under your control when you talk, sing, or take a deep breath, but at other times breathing is automatic. The muscle of the heart, under certain conditions, not only contracts but also tells itself when to contract.

Muscle tissue also possesses three other important characteristics. *Irritability* is the muscle's ability to respond to impulses from the nervous system. After the muscle responds by contracting, it rebounds to its original length. This ability to return to its previous shape is *elasticity*. Muscle tissue also possesses *extensibility:* it can be stretched when it is relaxed. Extensibility is very important because when one group of muscles contracts, sometimes other muscle tissue must passively stretch to allow for movement.

Muscle Anatomy

Muscle tissue, composed of a great number of cells called **muscle fibers,** is supported by layers of connective tissues. In any description of muscle tissue, the words *fiber* and *cell* are synonymous, but in other body tissues the word *fiber* refers to either a part of the cell (nerve fiber) or a nonliving strand of matrix in connective tissues.

Types of muscle tissue

There are three types of muscle tissue in your body. Each type has properties that fit it for particular functions. These muscle types are distinguished by their location, microscopic appearance, and type of nervous control.

The first type, named for its location, is **skeletal muscle** tissue. It is usually attached to bones. It is also called *striated* (STRY ay tid) *muscle* because there are dark and light stripes in its cells. These striations are actually filaments of protein in the muscle cells. Skeletal muscle is also known as *voluntary* muscle tissue because it is primarily controlled by conscious thought. However, the term voluntary does not always apply (for example, when you move while sleeping).

Your **diaphragm** (the primary muscle of breathing) functions under your control when you speak or sing, but at other times it functions involuntarily. Therefore, it is difficult to classify the diaphragm, even though it is skeletal by its location and appears striated. The muscular tissues in the walls of the pharynx (throat) are also classified as striated because of their appearance, but they are neither voluntary nor attached to a bone.

The second type is **visceral*** (VIS ur ul) **muscle** tissue. The term *visceral* refers to internal organs. The name fits well because visceral muscle is located in the walls of internal organs such as the stomach, intestines, blood vessels, and urinary bladder. Visceral muscle is also located in the iris of the eye and causes the pupil (the central dark spot) to enlarge or shrink depending on the brightness of your environment.

19D-1

skeletal muscle

visceral muscle

cardiac muscle

visceral: (L. VISCUS, body organ)

Most of the *sphincters** (SFINGK turz), circular bundles of muscles that regulate the diameter of various tubular organs and openings, are visceral muscles. The muscular valves at both ends of the stomach are examples of sphincters.

Visceral muscle is also called *nonstriated* or *smooth* because it does not have dark and light stripes. All visceral muscle tissue is termed *involuntary* because it is *not* directly controlled by conscious thought. In other words, visceral muscle tissue can function (and, in fact, functions most regularly) when you are asleep.

Cardiac muscle,** the third type of muscle, is located only in the heart. Cardiac muscle tissue is *striated* and *involuntary*. The striations, however, are not as regular and distinct as in skeletal muscle. Cardiac muscle fibers branch and join together. This network of fibers allows nerve impulses to spread quickly through the muscular walls of the heart and produces effective pumping of the blood.

Visceral and cardiac muscle tissue will be mentioned again in connection with other body systems. The remainder of this chapter will deal with skeletal muscle tissue.

Attachments of a muscle
Skeletal muscles produce movements by pulling tendons, which in turn exert force on bones. There is a secure union at the tendon-bone junction because, like the ligaments, the fibers of the tendons are extensions of the fibers of the periosteum. Most tendons of muscles extend over the joint(s) and fasten to the bones that form that joint. When such a muscle contracts, one bone is drawn toward the other. Usually one of the bones involved remains more or less stationary while the other bone moves.

The attachment of the muscle's tendon to the more stationary bone is the **origin** of the muscle. The attachment of the other muscle tendon to the more movable bone is the **insertion.** However, the origin or insertion of a muscle is not always a bone; it can be the skin, a layer of connective tissue, or another muscle.

The movement performed by the muscle when it contracts is called its **action.** For example, the

action of the biceps brachii muscle is the flexing of the arm at the elbow. The fleshy portion between the origin and insertion is the **belly** of a muscle. This is the part of the muscle that you eat as beef steak or see when a strong man flexes his muscles.

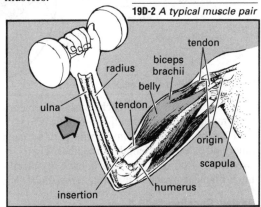

19D-2 *A typical muscle pair*

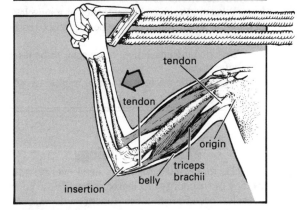

Muscle structure
A skeletal muscle fiber (cell) is barely visible to the unaided eye. Each fiber is cylindrical and is wrapped in a thin sheath of connective tissue. Groups of 10-100 fibers are bound together with other layers of connective tissue to form *muscle bundles.* A thicker connective tissue layer encloses these bundles to form the muscle itself. At the ends of the muscle, the connective tissue merges to form the tendons that attach to bones. The connective tissues not only hold the muscle fibers together but also support blood vessels and nerves that supply the fibers.

---

sphincters: (Gk. SPHINGEIN, to bind tight)   **cardiac:** (heart)

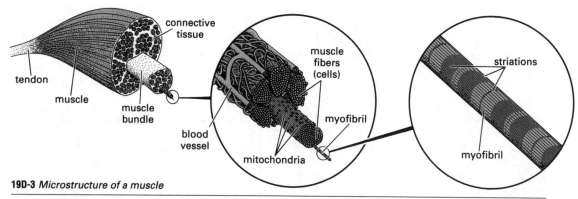

19D-3 *Microstructure of a muscle*

The cytoplasm within each muscle fiber contains numerous tiny, threadlike myofibrils* (MYE uh FYE bruhlz). These myofibrils parallel each other and extend the length of the fiber. There are two kinds of protein filaments in each myofibril—thick filaments made of the protein *myosin* (MYE uh sin) and thin ones made of the protein *actin*. The overlapping arrangement of these filaments is repeated to produce striations. When the fiber is relaxed, the myosin filaments are located primarily in the dark bands and the actin filaments in the light bands.

Review Questions 19D-1

1. What are the five characteristics of a muscle?
2. What are the three basic types of muscle tissue? Describe each and tell where it is located in the body.
3. Describe the attachment of muscles to bones and how muscle action is related to muscle attachment.
4. Describe the microstructures of muscle tissue.

Muscle Physiology

Muscles move. To move, they need energy, and as they move energy is released as heat. How your muscles accomplish these functions is *muscle physiology*.

Muscle contractions

The contraction process begins when impulses from nerve cells stimulate the muscle fiber. The myosin filaments, bearing little extensions called cross-bridges, attach to the actin filaments. Calcium ions and energy cause the cross-bridges of the myosin filaments to merge with the actin filaments. The actin and myosin filaments then slide over each other and cause the muscle to thicken. This thickening pulls on connective tissues around the muscle, drawing the ends toward each other.

Muscle contraction requires the energy derived from ATP molecules. Normally, cellular ATP is derived from the breakdown of glucose to pyruvic acid and then (in the presence of oxygen) to carbon dioxide and water. The amount of ATP in a muscle cell is only enough for a few contractions; therefore, it must be continually replenished by

19D-4 *Muscular action*

myosin filament

myofibril, relaxed

actin filament   cross-bridge

myofibril, contracted

myofibril: myo- (Gk. MUS, muscle) + -fibril (L. FIBRA, fiber)

FACETS OF BIOLOGY

19D-1

Human Muscles and Their Movements

There are nearly 700 skeletal muscles in the human body. These muscles may be tiny, like those that move the lens in the eye, or large, like the trapezius of the upper back which moves the spine, head, and shoulders.

Most body movements are a result of at least two skeletal muscles functioning together. During the flexing of the arm at the elbow, the biceps brachii muscle is the **prime mover** because it performs the action. The triceps bra-

chii, which is relaxed and stretched during this movement, is the **antagonist*** (an TAG uh nist) because it performs the opposite action. When the arm extends, the triceps brachii is the prime mover, and the biceps brachii is the antagonist. Thus, the biceps and triceps of the arm are an *antagonistic pair* because they have opposite actions.

Antagonistic pairs of muscles perform and control most body movements. The muscles that as-

sist the prime mover are the **synergists*** (SIN ur jists), or fixators. A synergist usually contracts at the same time as the prime mover in order to stabilize a particular joint. For example, as the biceps muscle flexes the arm at the elbow, the deltoid and pectoralis major muscles also contract to hold the upper arm and shoulder into a stable position.

Muscles have different roles at various times, depending on the action. During one action a partic-

Characteristics Used to Name Muscles

❏ **Size**
pectoralis major–large muscle in the pectoral (chest) region
pectoralis minor–small muscle in the pectoral region
gluteus maximus–largest (maximum) muscle of the gluteus (buttocks) region

❏ **Shape**
deltoid–triangular-shaped muscle
trapezius–trapezoid-shaped muscle

❏ **Location**
tibialis anterior - muscle located on the anterior region of the tibia
external and *internal oblique* - muscles of the ribs that are on the inside and outside
rectus femoris - muscle near the femur
temporal - muscle near the temporal bone
obicularis oculi - muscle near the eye (ocular organ)
epicranius - muscle that goes around *(epi-)* the head *(-cranium)*

❏ **Action**
masseter (muh SEE tur)–a muscle that is involved in mastication (chewing)
adductor group–adducts thigh
flexors or *extensors* of the hand–flexes or extends hand

❏ **Number of attachments**
biceps brachii–a muscle which has two origins

(bi–, two; *-ceps,* head) and is located in the arm (brachial) region
triceps brachii–three origins

❏ **Direction of fibers**
external oblique–a muscle which is located near the outside of the body and has fibers arranged obliquely (in a slanting direction)

Muscle Actions

Flexor: Decreases angle between bones (biceps brachii, tibiais anterior, rectus femorus)
Extensor: Increases angle between bones (triceps brachii, gastrocnemius, gluteus maximus)
Abductor: Moves bone away from midline of body (deltoid, abductor group)
Adductor: Moves bone toward midline of body (pectoralis major, gastrocnemius)
Rotator: Produces a turning or revolving movement (sternocleidomastoid, longissimus capitis)
Levator: Produces an upward movement (trapezius, masseter, temporal, external intercostals)
Depressor: Produces a downward movement (pectoralis minor, internal intercostals)
Sphincter: Decreases the size of an opening (orbicularis oris, orbicularis occuli)

antagonist: ant-, anta-, or anti- (against) + -agonist (Gk. AGONIZES-THAI, to struggle)

synergist: syn- (together) + -ergist (Gk. ERGON, work)

Major Skeletal Muscles of the Human Body

Muscle	Origin	Insertion	Action
Epicranius	Lower part of occipital	Skin of forehead	Raises eyebrows and wrinkles forehead
Orbicularis oculi	Wall of orbit	Skin around eyelid	Closes eye
Orbicularis oris	Muscle fibers around mouth	Skin at corner of mouth	Draws lips together
Buccinator	Maxilla and mandible	Orbicularis oris	Compresses cheek as in blowing air
Masseter	Zygomatic arch	Mandible	Levates (closes) jaw
Temporal	Temporal bone	Mandible	Levates (closes) jaw
Sternocleidomastoid	Sternum and clavicle	Temporal bone (mastoid process)	Flexes neck; rotates head
Pectoralis major	Clavicle, sternum, and true ribs	Proximal humerus	Adducts upper arm anteriorly
Pectoralis minor	Ribs	Scapula	Pulls shoulder down and forward
Rectus abdominis	Pubic bone	Ribs and sternum	Compresses abdomen; flexes trunk
External oblique	Lower eight ribs	Ilium and pubic	Compresses abdomen
Internal oblique	Ilium and connective tissue in lumbar region	Lower ribs, pubic, opposite internal oblique	Compresses abdomen
Transversus abdominis	Same as internal oblique	Opposite transversus abdominis	Compresses abdomen
External intercostals	Lower border of rib above	Upper border of rib below	Elevate ribs
Internal intercostals	Upper border of rib below	Lower border of rib above	Depress ribs during forceful expiration
Trapezius	Occipital and upper vertebrae	Clavicle and scapula	Raises or lowers shoulders
Latissimus dorsi	Lower vertebrae, lower ribs, and ilium	Humerus	Extends and adducts upper arm posteriorly
Longissimus capitis	Upper vertebrae	Mastoid process	Extends head; rotates head
Deltoid	Clavicle and scapula	Proximal humerus	Abducts upper arm
Biceps brachii	Scapula	Proximal radius	Flex forearm
Triceps brachii	Scapula and humerus	Proximal ulna	Extend forearm
Flexors of hand and fingers	Distal humerus	Metacarpal, carpal, and palm	Flex hand at wrist
Extensors of hand and fingers	Distal humerus	Metacarpals	Extend hand at wrist
Rectus femoris	Ilium	Patella and tibia	Flexes thigh and extends lower leg
Gluteus maximus	Ilium, sacrum, and coccyx	Femur	Extends thigh
Adductor group	Pubic and ischium	Femur	Adducts thigh
Hamstring group	Ischium and femur	Fibula and tibia	Extends thigh
Tibialis anterior	Tibia	Tarsal and metatarsal	Flexes and inverts foot
Gastrocnemius	Lower femur	Calcaneus (Achilles tendon)	Extends foot and flexes lower leg
Soleus	Tibia and fibula	Calcaneus (Achilles tendon)	Extends foot (plantar flexion)

ular muscle may function as a prime mover, but during other actions it may serve as an antagonist or synergist.

Any movement of the body is the result of a muscle *pulling* on its "insertion bone." Muscles *never push;* they only pull. You may be able to push an object, such as your economy-size car, but only because the prime movers, especially of your hips and legs, are pulling on the bones of your legs and feet. In other words, your body is able to push, but your muscles can only pull.

Most of the well-known muscles are described and illustrated on these two pages. As you learn the muscles it may help you to realize that various characteristics of the muscles are used to name them. The boxes on page 525 may help you understand how muscles are named.

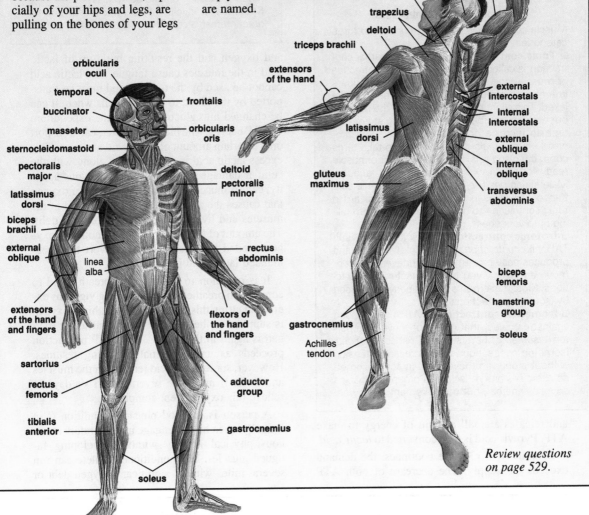

Review questions on page 529.

the numerous mitochondria that are located in the muscle fibers. When glucose and oxygen are converted into carbon dioxide, water, and energy, all the end products are either used by the muscle or released into the blood.

Muscle fatigue and physical condition

When you are resting or moderately active, your skeletal muscles usually have enough glucose and oxygen for energy production. However, after you use your skeletal muscles strenuously for a few minutes, your respiratory and circulatory systems cannot supply enough oxygen to your muscles. Glucose then breaks down to *pyruvic acid*

Types of Muscular Contractions

Muscle contractions may be grouped into three categories:

❑ **Tonic contractions** A continual partial contraction is called a *tonic** (TAHN ik) *contraction* or muscle tone. At any given time, some fibers in a muscle are contracted while others are relaxed. This slight contraction tenses the muscle, but not enough fibers are contracting at any one time to produce obvious movement. Synchronized nerve impulses cause fibers to take turns contracting and relaxing. This keeps the muscle ready for action without its becoming fatigued. Maintaining *posture* is an example of tonic contraction. Muscles in the back of your neck are in tonic contraction to prevent your head from falling onto your chest.

❑ **Isotonic contractions** In *isotonic** (EYE suh TAHN ik) *contractions* the muscle shortens and produces body movement. Whenever you lift or move an object, you perform isotonic contractions. Most movements of your body are caused by isotonic contractions.

❑ **Isometric contractions** When you push against an object that does not move, you perform *isometric** (EYE suh MET rik) *contractions*. Isometric contraction is an increase in tension without producing movement. In some isometric exercises one muscle or a group of muscles opposes another, but no movement is allowed.

Muscle Disorders

Atrophy: a great reduction in muscle fibers and possible replacement by fibrous tissue

Convulsions: violent, involuntary contractions of an entire group of muscles; characteristic of epileptic seizures and drug withdrawals

Cramps: painful, involuntary contractions in those muscles that have been used heavily and have suffered from fatigue

Muscular dystrophy: a progressively crippling disease of unknown cause in which the muscles gradually weaken and atrophy

Paralysis: inability to move a muscle; usually because of some nervous system failure.

Shin splints: a soreness on the front of the lower leg due to straining a muscle; often as a result of walking up and down hills

Spasm: an involuntary contraction of shorter duration than a cramp and usually not as painful

---

and oxygen and the resulting build-up of lactic acid in the muscles cause fatigue. The lactic acid cannot be used by the muscles and must be transported by the blood to the liver cells where it can be changed into glucose through the expenditure of ATP energy. The blood, however, can transport only a certain amount of lactic acid at a time. This excess lactic acid in muscle cells, along with the cellular damage from prolonged strenuous activity, causes muscular soreness. The lack of oxygen that causes the accumulation of lactic acid in the muscles and liver is known as the **oxygen debt.** The amount of oxygen debt is the amount of oxygen needed by these cells to convert the accumulated lactic acid into glucose.

It is common to feel "out of breath" and to continue to breathe deeply following vigorous exercise. During this time of deep breathing, oxygen is supplied to the muscles. When sufficient oxygen is again in the muscles and ATP production proceeds as usual, normal breathing resumes. However, some lactic acid remains in the muscles and liver. It may take several hours or days to relieve this oxygen debt completely.

A person is in good physical condition ("in shape") when he can engage in moderately strenuous physical activity without developing fatigued muscles. The conditioned athlete can run several miles without significant oxygen debt or

and releases a small amount of energy to make ATP. Pyruvic acid is then converted to *lactic acid*.

Eventually, if exercise continues, the demand exceeds the supply. The decrease of both ATP

---

tonic: (Gk. TONOS, tone)

isotonic: iso- (equal) + -tonic (tone)

isometric: iso- (equal) + -metric (measure)

soreness, but the unconditioned athlete cannot. The conditioned athlete's muscles have more fibers and hold more oxygen. His circulatory and respiratory systems function efficiently to get oxygen to the muscles. The "out of shape" person does not have these benefits and soon begins to pant (which does not supply as much oxygen to the lungs as smooth, deep breathing) and to waste energy on excess movements. The person in poor physical condition builds up an oxygen debt much sooner and with much less physical activity than the person in good physical condition.

Your body will build the muscle fibers and oxygen-holding capacity it needs for its normal activities. If you begin jogging daily, you will soon be "in shape" for your usual jog.

Big Muscles, Little Muscles

In a body-building program a person may perform numerous isometric and isotonic contractions to increase the size and strength of his muscles. This increase is an enlargement of individual muscle fibers, not an increase in the number of fibers. The mitochondria within the fibers reproduce, and the number of actin and myosin filaments increases.

Muscle growth is stimulated by using all the muscle fibers in a muscle in a brief period of time. Isometric exercises produce a more rapid increase in muscular strength and size than do isotonic exercises like weightlifting because they can use every fiber more quickly.

Because the strength of a contraction is directly related to the diameter of the muscle fibers, large muscles are strong muscles. Running and other aerobic exercises, however, usually produce only slight increases in the size and strength of the muscles involved. Running benefits the heart, blood vessels, and lungs more than it does the skeletal muscles. The runner may not have the strength or the bulging muscles of the weight lifter, but his endurance is probably greater. A great deal depends, of course, on the individual and his genetic makeup.

The proper motive for participating in any exercise program is to develop and maintain your body's health and strength in order to serve the Lord regularly and efficiently. The desire for bulging biceps to impress people is sinful pride.

A muscle that is not used or is used only to produce weak contractions usually decreases in size and strength. Mitochondria in the fibers and blood capillaries decrease in number. The amount of muscle protein (actin and myosin) also reduces. This is called *muscular atrophy** (AT ruh fee) and happens when a muscle is in a cast or when an active person becomes inactive.

Biological Terms

The Muscular System	diaphragm	origin	belly	*Facet*
muscle fibers	visceral muscle	insertion	oxygen debt	antagonist
skeletal muscle	cardiac muscle	action		synergist

Review Questions 19D-2

1. Describe oxygen debt. Identify its causes, results, and "cure."
2. List the three types of muscle contractions and describe each.
3. When a person exercises, he becomes tired. Why should a person exercise regularly in order not to become tired as easily?

Facet 19D-1: Human Muscles and Their Movements, pages 525-27

1. Compare and contrast the following: prime mover, antagonistic pairs of muscles, synergistic muscles.
2. Give an example of a muscle's name based upon the muscle's (a) size, (b) shape, (c) location, (d) action, (e) number of attachments, and (f) direction of fibers.

Thought Questions

1. How can you push your pencil while the muscles doing the action are not pushing?
2. The ability to build up oxygen debt is essential for humans. Discuss some advantages you have because of this ability.

---

atrophy: a- (without) + -trophy (nourishment)

INCOMING SUBSTANCES

TWENTY

20A–The Respiratory System

"You are what you eat" may not be the best way to express the idea, but food does affect the human body. After your body digests and absorbs the food you eat, it uses the molecules as building materials and as energy for life processes. It needs a constant supply of oxygen to do this properly.

The quality of food and air that enter your body affects your physical condition. To make wise decisions regarding your diet and other habits, you should understand what your body needs and how it uses incoming substances.

Anatomy of the Respiration System

The respiratory system consists of organs that transport oxygen and carbon dioxide to and from the blood: the nose, pharynx, trachea, bronchial tubes, and lungs. Basically the respiratory system brings air from the atmosphere into the lungs. Oxygen in the lungs, however, does most body cells little good. The oxygen in the lungs goes into the blood which then transfers it to the body cells. Carbon dioxide is removed from the cells by the blood and returns to the lungs.

The nose

The term **nose** refers not only to a part of the face but also to the **nasal cavities.** The partition that separates the two nasal cavities is called the *nasal septum.* A *ciliated mucous membrane* lines the nasal cavities and filters bacteria, smoke, and dust particles from the air. If anything irritates your nasal membranes, it stimulates you to sneeze. A sneeze is a deep breathing-in followed by a blast of air up through the nasal cavities. It serves to expel the irritating substance.

20A-1 *Scanning electron micrograph of the ciliated mucous membrane of the nose (5000X)*

The *nasal sinuses* open either into the nasal cavity or into the pharynx. Since the sinuses are lined with ciliated mucous membranes, the mucus continually drains into the nasal cavity and pharynx. If these membranes become infected and swollen, the sinuses become painful and congested.

Air drawn through the nasal cavities is not only filtered but also warmed and moistened before it reaches other parts of the respiratory system. This prevents the delicate linings of these structures from becoming cold and dry when you breathe air that is not particularly warm and moist.

The upper portion of the nose has nerve endings that are involved in sensing odors. The **palate** (PAL it) serves as the "floor" of the nose and roof of the mouth. It has two parts: the anterior *hard palate* and the posterior *soft palate.* The bones of the hard palate grow together during the growth of the embryo and form a suture along the middle. If the bones do not grow together properly, the baby is born with an opening between the mouth and nasal cavity, called a *cleft palate.* This disorder may also include a divided upper lip, a condition called *harelip.*

The soft palate is primarily muscle tissue that ends in a projection called the *uvula* (YOO vyh luh). The uvula moves back and up during swallowing to prevent food entering the nasal cavities.

The pharynx and larynx

The **pharynx,** commonly called the throat, is a muscular tube about 13 cm (5 in.) long, lined with a ciliated mucous membrane. It extends from the back of the nose to the esophagus. The pharynx is sometimes called the "control center" for incoming substances since it serves both the respiratory and digestive systems.

The pharynx has seven openings:

❏ Two posterior openings to the nasal cavities for air flow;

❏ Two passageways to the middle ear called *Eustachian tubes,* for equalizing air pressure;

❏ The posterior opening of the mouth cavity for passage of food and air;

❏ The *esophagus:* passageway to the stomach;

❏ The *larynx:* passageway to the trachea for air.

The **larynx,** or voice box, is a short passageway that leads from the pharynx to the trachea. The walls of the larynx consist of cartilage pieces held together by several muscles and ligaments. The larynx contains a pair of mucous membrane folds

20A-2 *The pharynx is the shaded area.*

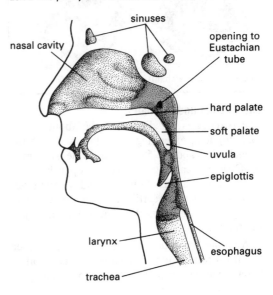

known as the *vocal cords*, or *vocal folds*. The space between the folds is the **glottis**. The closing of the glottis is the last action that the body takes to prevent substances from going to the lungs.

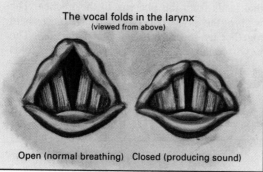
The trachea and bronchi

The **trachea** is a cylindrical tube about 12 cm (4.8 in.) long extending from the larynx to the bronchi. It is about 2.5 cm (1 in.) wide, supported by C-shaped cartilage bands that open back toward the esophagus. Muscular and membranous tissues between the cartilage bands provide flexibility, allowing the neck to move without injuring the trachea.

A ciliated mucous membrane lines the trachea and traps foreign matter such as dust and pollen. Cilia move foreign substances up to the pharynx, where they are swallowed to be destroyed by the stomach.

The trachea ends behind the heart, where it divides into two primary **bronchi*** (BRAHNG kye). The bronchi (sing., bronchus) resemble the trachea in structure but have a smaller diameter. An obstruction or irritation in the bronchi or in the trachea stimulates the *cough reflex*. Coughing involves taking a deep breath and then forcing air from the lungs against the closed glottis. When the glottis opens suddenly, a blast of air is forced through the larynx, pharynx, and mouth, usually carrying with it the substance that stimulated the cough reflex.

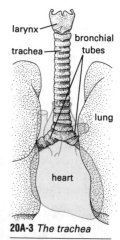

20A-3 *The trachea*

The lungs

Each **lung** is divided internally into nine segments, and each segment receives a separate branch of the bronchus. The bronchi subdivide into smaller **bronchial** (BRAHNG kee ul) **tubes,** which in turn branch to form bronchioles. The bronchioles do not have cartilage tissue in their walls or cilia in their lining. There are more than 250,000 bronchioles in the lungs. All bronchioles end in **alveoli*** (al VEE uh LYE), which are microscopic bubblelike sacs.

Most of the lung tissue, then, is composed of the alveoli. If it were possible to open and flatten

20A-4 *An electron micrograph of lung tissue*

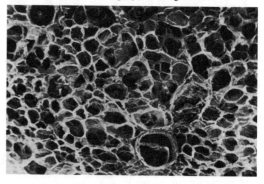

---

bronchi: (Gk. BRONKOS, windpipe)   alveoli: (L. ALVEOLUS, small cavity)

all alveoli, bronchioles, and other tubular passageways of the respiratory system, they would cover about 65 sq. m. (78 sq. yd.).

The alveoli are surrounded by an extensive network of small blood vessels called *capillaries*. The walls of the alveoli and the walls of the capillaries are each made of a single layer of epithelial cells (about 0.005 mm thick). This close physical relationship of alveoli and blood capillaries provides for rapid exchange of carbon dioxide and oxygen.

The **pleura*** (PLOOR uh) is a delicate membrane that lines the thorax and covers the lungs. The *pleural space* is between these two layers and contains *pleural fluid*. This space and fluid reduce the friction between the lungs and walls of the thorax.

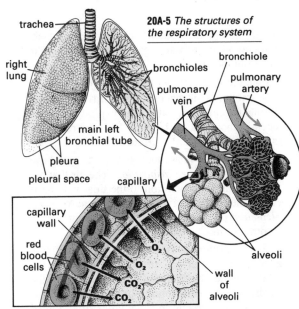

20A-5 *The structures of the respiratory system*

Review Questions 20A-1
1. Name, in order, the structures by or through which a molecule of air passes as it enters the nose and passes to the alveoli.
2. What are the functions of the mucous membranes lining the respiratory system?
3. List the openings of the pharynx and tell where they lead.
4. Describe the pleura, the pleural space, and the pleural fluid.

Respiration

Respiration is usually divided into three phases—external, internal, and cellular. **External respiration** involves the passage of oxygen from the air into the alveoli and then into the blood. **Internal respiration** refers to the passage of oxygen from the blood into the body cells. Cellular respiration refers to the use of oxygen in converting foods to water, carbon dioxide, and energy (see Chapter 4A).

Mechanics of breathing
Breathing involves the movement of outside air into the alveoli and then out again. Filling the lungs is **inspiration,*** and forcing air out of the lungs is **expiration.*** During inspiration the dome-shaped diaphragm muscle contracts, moves down, and becomes more saucer-shaped, while the ribs move upward and outward. These movements increase the chest volume, reducing the pressure in the lungs so that air rushes into them.

When the diaphragm relaxes and the ribs are depressed following inspiration, the tissues of the lungs rebound to force air out. The abdominal organs that were slightly compressed during inspiration spring back and push the diaphragm upward. These body changes constitute expiration. When a person needs to control expiration, as in

20A-6 *The mechanics of breathing*

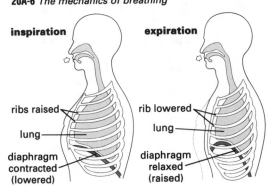

---

pleura: (Gk. PLEURA, rib)   **inspiration:** in- (in) + -spira- (L. SPI-RARE, to breathe)   **expiration:** ex- (out) + -(s)pira- (breathe)

singing, the abdominal muscles squeeze the abdominal organs upward against the diaphragm to force out the air.

Air volumes exchanged in breathing

The amount of air that enters and leaves the lungs during a normal inspiration and expiration during sleep is about 1/2 L (1/2 qt.). This volume of air is known as the **tidal volume.**

If you breathe in as much as you can, you have accomplished *forced inspiration.* The air that enters your lungs in addition to the tidal volume is called the **inspiratory reserve volume** or *complemental air.* Normal adults have about 3 L of inspiratory reserve volume.

Forced expiration is forcing out as much breath as you can, about 1 L of air in addition to the tidal volume. This quantity of air is known as the **expiratory reserve volume** or *supplemental air.* The air that remains in your lungs after forced expiration is the **residual volume** (about 1 L).

The combined total of tidal volume, inspiratory reserve volume, and expiratory reserve volume is the **vital capacity.** This is the amount of air you can exchange between your lungs and the environment. The sum of all lung volumes (vital capacity and residual volume) is called the **total lung capacity** and is nearly 6 L.

Lung volumes and capacities are primarily dependent on the size and physique of the individual and vary considerably. Male athletes usually have greater vital capacities than female office workers. Body position and posture also cause variation in air volumes. For example, the air volumes are greater when you are standing than when you are sitting or lying down. This explains why it is easier to sing when standing.

Transport of oxygen and carbon dioxide

The gases in the blood do not travel as tiny bubbles but are dissolved or are chemically combined with blood substances. Almost all the oxygen in the blood is combined with **hemoglobin,*** the red, oxygen-carrying pigment of the red blood cells.

Hemoglobin is a complex two-part molecule made of *heme* and *globin.* The heme portion of the molecule contains 4 atoms of iron, each of which can combine with 1 oxygen molecule. As oxygen moves from the alveoli into the blood, it combines rapidly with hemoglobin to form *oxyhemoglobin.* Oxyhemoglobin is a brilliant red whereas hemoglobin without oxygen is a dull brick-red color. The chemical bonds that form between oxygen and hemoglobin are rather unstable; therefore, the oxygen can be released quickly to the body cells for use in cellular respiration.

Oxygen diffuses through the alveoli walls into the blood because there is a higher concentration of oxygen in the air inside the alveoli than there is in deoxygenated blood. In the capillaries of the body, oxygen leaves the oxyhemoglobin because there is a greater concentration of oxygen in the blood cells. The blood absorbs the carbon dioxide produced by cellular respiration because, when flowing through the capillaries of the tissues, it has less carbon dioxide in it than do the tissues.

Carbon dioxide is transported to the lungs in three different ways. Most of the carbon dioxide (up to 68%) is transported in the form of bicarbonate ions (HCO_3^-) dissolved in the fluid of the blood. About 25% of the carbon dioxide is also dissolved in the fluid portion of the blood. About 3% of the carbon dioxide of the blood is combined with the hemoglobin. Hemoglobin can carry both oxygen and carbon dioxide at the same time since they do not compete for bonding sites.

20A-7 *Lung volumes*

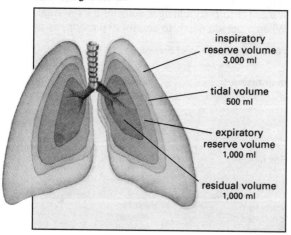

inspiratory reserve volume
3,000 ml

tidal volume
500 ml

expiratory reserve volume
1,000 ml

residual volume
1,000 ml

hemoglobin: hemo- (Gk. HAIMA, blood) + -globin (L. GLOBUS, globe)

As the blood flows through the capillaries that cover the alveoli, most of the carbon dioxide, which is dissolved or attached to the hemoglobin, diffuses into the lungs. The bicarbonate ions, through a complicated process, also release carbon dioxide; however, most of them remain in the bloodstream to help regulate the pH of the blood.

Review Questions 20A-2

1. What are the two main types of breathing?
2. List and compare the amounts of the various respiratory system air volumes.
3. How are (a) oxygen and (b) carbon dioxide carried into the blood?

Control of Breathing

The muscles involved in breathing are controlled voluntarily when you sing, speak, or prepare to hold your breath. Normal breathing, however, is a rhythmic, involuntary activity that continues even when you are asleep or unconscious. The nervous system, in response to several chemical and environmental factors, regulates the rate and depth of respiration.

Respiratory control centers

The *respiratory center,* which controls involuntary respiration, is a group of nerve cells in the lower part of the brain. The respiratory center contains both an *inspiratory* and an *expiratory center.* The inspiratory center stimulates the diaphragm and external intercostal muscles to contract, which causes the lungs to draw in air. The expiratory center interrupts inspiration and thus permits air to be forced out of the lungs. The lung tissue contains specialized nerve cells called *stretch receptors,* which are stimulated as the alveoli expand during inspiration. These stretch receptors tell the brain when to stop inspiration and permit expiration.

During normal, shallow breathing, some of the alveoli are not ventilated, and some may be temporarily closed. The blood that passes over these alveoli, therefore, does not become well-oxygenated. It is believed that this low oxygen level in the blood somehow stimulates *yawning*–long, deep inspirations which supply fresh air to the collapsed alveoli.

Factors affecting breathing: carbon dioxide level in blood

Some brain cells are very sensitive to carbon dioxide. These cells are usually referred to as *chemoreceptors* because they are stimulated by chemicals in the blood. Your muscle cells produce carbon dioxide rapidly during active periods, raising the level of carbon dioxide in the blood above normal.

Excess carbon dioxide dissolved in the blood forms quantities of carbonic acid which causes the blood to become too acidic. Chemoreceptors stimulated by the excess carbonic acid send messages to the brain's respiratory centers. The respiratory centers in turn send impulses to increase

Carbon Monoxide Poisoning

No one should ever work on a car while the engine is running if the area is not properly ventilated. Car exhaust contains carbon monoxide (CO), a colorless, odorless gas that combines with hemoglobin at the same site as oxygen. Competing with oxygen, carbon monoxide is a poison that can cause a great deal of physical damage. Carbon monoxide forms a bond with hemoglobin that is 200 times stronger than the bond with oxygen. Carbon monoxide thus prevents hemoglobin from carrying a normal amount of oxygen, and the person would be stimulated to breathe more deeply.

If he is still inhaling car exhaust, this heavier breathing will result in binding more carbon monoxide onto hemoglobin. The continuing cycle may result in death from *carbon monoxide poisoning* unless the person gets fresh air quickly. Breathing fresh air does not correct the damage done by carbon monoxide, but it prevents more damage from happening. The lowered oxygen-carrying capacity of the blood caused by carbon monoxide poisoning remains until the affected red blood cells are replaced, which may be several weeks later.

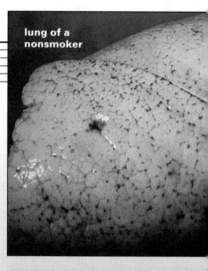

lung of a nonsmoker

FACETS OF BIOLOGY

20A-1

Tobacco Smoking

Tobacco smoking is the major health problem affecting the respiratory system. The effects of smoking, however, are not limited to the respiratory system. Nicotine tars and other harmful substances in the smoke affect the entire body.

In the past 25 yr. intensive studies into the effects of smoking tobacco have led to some startling conclusions:

❑ Of all the lung cancer victims, 99.5% are smokers. There are 1,000% more deaths from lung cancer among smokers than nonsmokers.

❑ The death rate from heart disease is 200% higher among smokers.

❑ Emphysema (EM fuh SEE muh) and chronic bronchitis are 500% more prevalent in smokers.

❑ Death rates from all causes are higher for smokers than for nonsmokers.

In spite of this information and warnings by the surgeon general, the American Medical Association, and other scientific groups, millions of Americans are still using tobacco.

Inhaling tobacco smoke slows down the action of the cilia along the air passageways of the respiratory system. Continued smoking may eventually destroy these cilia. The mucus, normally moved along by the cilia, then collects and acts as an irritant, causing the "smoker's cough." This nonmoving mucus allows smoke particles, bacteria, dust, and other substances to move into the lungs. As smoke particles collect in the alveoli, a person must breathe more deeply to obtain enough oxygen.

Though human lungs are much larger than is necessary for normal, quiet activity, an athlete who smokes experiences shortness of breath because his alveoli are filled with foreign matter. A long-time smoker has often filled so many of his alveoli that he finds it difficult to breathe, especially when suffering from a respiratory disease such as pneumonia, flu, or even a cold.

Emphysema is one of the most crippling diseases often caused by smoking. Emphysema results in degenerated lungs that can no longer transfer oxygen and carbon dioxide between the air and the blood.

The nicotine in tobacco smoke causes the walls of the blood vessels to thicken, restricting the flow of the blood. Nicotine increases the heart rate and blood pressure. Tars and nicotine sometimes stimulate abnormal growth of cell layers in the air passageways. This growth, a type of lung cancer, restricts the air flow. Nicotine is an addictive drug (see pages 622-24.) Once a person's body becomes used to nicotine, it craves more of the drug.

Smokers suffer a variety of symptoms such as shortness of breath; the tendency to tire easily; loss of appetite; inability to sleep; eye and skin irritations; discolorations of teeth, fingers, and lips; difficulty in performing precise

lung of a smoker

movements with the hands; and impairment of vision and hearing. Smokers constantly have a degree of carbon monoxide poisoning. Some people seem willing to live with these problems in order to get the "pleasure" of a cigarette, pipe, or cigar.

Until about 50 yr. ago, the only known evils of smoking were the smell, the ashes, and the fire hazard. Now scientific evidence has revealed that horrible physical problems may result. Yet people continue to smoke. Why?

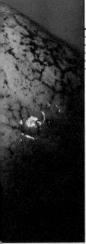

Most smokers began smoking when they were teen-agers. When asked why, people give responses such as the following: "My friends did, and it made me feel like a part of the group"; "It made me feel more mature"; or "Because it was exciting to do something I knew I shouldn't."

When asked why a person who recognizes the hazards of smoking continues to smoke, common answers include the following: "I get nervous if I don't smoke," and "I like the feeling of being accepted by my friends." If asked, many smokers admit they do not like the taste.

Christians cannot accept any of these as valid reasons to smoke tobacco. We are responsible to God for what we do to our bodies. The Bible tells us that we belong to God and that our bodies are His temple (I Cor. 6:19-20). We must not defile what He has given us by knowingly subjecting it to misuse.

Review questions on page 538.

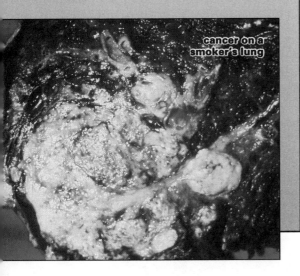

cancer on a smoker's lung

both the depth and rate of inspiration, permitting the blood to lose carbon dioxide more rapidly, restoring the level of carbon dioxide in the blood to normal.

Factors affecting breathing: atmospheric pressure (altitude)

The "flatlander" who visits the mountains finds that he is soon out of breath during relatively mild exercise. The reason for this is the decrease in atmospheric (barometric) pressure at higher altitudes. Although approximately the *same amount of oxygen* is in the air at high altitudes as at sea level, the decrease in atmospheric pressure at high altitudes reduces the amount of oxygen that is inhaled.

This difficulty in breathing, however, can be overcome by *acclimatization** (uh KLYE muh tih ZAY shun). Acclimatization refers to the changes that occur in the body as a person becomes accustomed to different atmospheric pressure. At higher altitudes the primary changes include an increase in the depth of respiration and a speeding of the heart rate and the circulation of blood. These changes cause more red blood cells, with an increased among of oxygen, to pass more rapidly through the blood vessels.

Other factors affecting breathing

Different sensory stimuli can also affect the respiratory system. For example, severe pain usually increases respiration, and sudden exposure to cold can temporarily halt breathing. Physical condition, physical size, and posture also affect the breathing rate.

Age also influences the respiration rate. The more rapid metabolic rate of children demands a higher respiratory rate. This rate gradually decreases until a person reaches old age unless health disorders and inactivity cause the breathing rate to increase slightly.

Respiration Rates (per Minute)	
At birth	40 to 70
1 year	35 to 40
10 years	19 to 24
25 years	16 to 18
Old age	20 or more

acclimatization: ac-, ad- (to) + -clima- (Gk. KLIMA, region of the earth) + -tion

537

Breathing Disorders

Asthma: difficulty in breathing as a result of the bronchioles' becoming constricted; sometimes caused by mold spores

Bronchitis: an inflammation of the bronchi and bronchial tubes

Collapsed lung: failure of the alveoli of the lungs to inflate properly; may be caused by incomplete expansion of lungs in premature babies or by accidental puncture of chest wall

Emphysema: a degenerative condition in which the lungs overexpand and the walls of alveoli lose their elasticity and often rupture; fluids fill the lungs

Hiccuping: irregular contractions of the diaphragm while the glottis is closed; no known useful function for hiccups

Lung cancer: many symptoms; breathing is difficult because abnormal growths of tissues block air passages in the lungs; inhaling tobacco smoke is most common cause

Pleurisy: an inflammation of the pleural membranes which causes painful breathing; usually occurs as a complication of pneumonia and tuberculosis

Pneumonia: an inflammation caused by a bacterial or viral infection; usual symptoms are fever, pain, and a severe cough

Tuberculosis: an infectious disease that can affect any part of the body; the most common type attacks the lungs and results in formation of tubercles (bumps) of abnormal tissue; caused by a bacterium

Biological Terms

Anatomy of the Respiratory System			Respiration		
nose	larynx	lung	external respiration	tidal volume	total lung
nasal cavity	glottis	alveoli	internal respiration	inspiratory reserve volume	capacity
palate	trachea	pleura	breathing	expiratory reserve volume	hemoglobin
pharynx	bronchi		inspiration	residual volume	
			expiration	vital capacity	

Review Questions 20A-3

1. List several respiratory control centers. Tell what they measure and how they affect the breathing rate.
2. Describe how levels of (a) carbon dioxide, (b) carbon monoxide, and (c) atmospheric pressure affect the breathing rate.

Facet 20A-1: Tobacco Smoking, pages 536-37

1. List several harmful effects of tobacco smoking.
2. For what reasons do most people smoke and why are these reasons unacceptable for Christians?

20B–The Digestive System

Knowledge of human digestive processes was very limited until 1833. In that year William Beaumont published the results of the experiments that he had conducted on Alexis St. Martin, whose stomach and body wall had been accidentally perforated by a musket shot. Even after surgical repair and healing, the opening through the body wall and stomach persisted. Beaumont attempted to close it but failed.

Beaumont was able to conduct numerous experiments by inserting food (tied to a string) into the valvelike opening of St. Martin's stomach. Beaumont would then remove the food to determine the extent and speed of digestion. The permanent opening also allowed observation of the churning action of the stomach. Since 1833, scientists have learned much more about the functions of the digestive organs.

Functions of the digestive system

The digestive system provides a means for **ingestion** (food intake) and provides structures and enzymes for **digestion** (breakdown of food to soluble substances). It also allows **absorption** of soluble food molecules into the bloodstream. While the foods are utilized for growth and repair, the large intestine is involved in **egestion** (elimination of undigested, unabsorbed material). Muscle tissue in the walls of the digestive system moves the food material along while these functions are being performed.

Organs of the Digestive System

The organs for digestion are usually divided into the following two groups:

❏ **alimentary*** (AL uh MEN tuh ree) **canal** includes the mouth, pharynx, esophagus, stomach, small intestine, and large intestine;

❏ **accessory organs** include the teeth, tongue, salivary glands, liver, gallbladder, and pancreas.

The alimentary canal, or *gastrointestinal*** (GAS troh in TES tuh nul) tract, is a continuous tube extending from mouth to anus, measuring about 9 m (29 ft.).

The mouth

Food taken into the mouth is mixed with *saliva* from the **salivary glands.** The saliva moistens and lubricates the food for easy swallowing. Three pairs of salivary glands, as well as numerous small glands distributed in the lining of the mouth, secrete saliva. All the salivary glands secrete *salivary amylase*** (AM uh LASE), an enzyme that begins the breakdown of starch to sugar. Taking food into the mouth or even the sight, smell, or thought of food triggers the production of saliva.

During **mastication*** (MAS tih KAY shun), the chewing of food, the *lips* keep food in the mouth cavity, and the *tongue* pushes food toward the teeth. The taste sensations—sweet, salty, sour, and bitter—that you experience as you chew food originate with the **taste buds,** which are located in small bumps called *papillae* on the surface of the tongue. However, because the sense of taste is closely associated with the sense of smell, much of what is defined as taste is actually the detection of odors from the food. Thus, food does not taste the same when you have a cold.

The teeth

Four different types of teeth are involved in mastication. The eight chisel-shaped **incisors** bite, the four cone-shaped **cuspids** tear, and the **premolars** and **molars** have surfaces for crushing and grinding food.

A child's first set of teeth, called *deciduous teeth,* lacks premolars and has only eight molars.

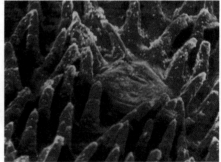

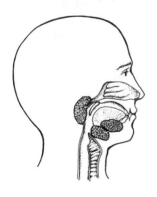
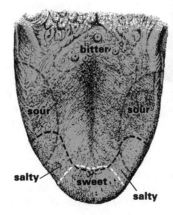

20B-1 The salivary glands are shaded (left). The primary areas of taste on the tongue (middle). A scanning electron micrograph of the papillae of the tongue (above, 100X).

---

alimentary: aliment- (L. ALERE to nourish)

gastrointestinal: gastro- (Gk. GASTER, belly) + -intestinal (L. INTESTINUS, internal)

mastication: (Gk. MASTIKHAN, to grind the teeth)

amylase: amyl- (Gk. AMULON, starch) + -ase (Eng. -ASE, enzyme)

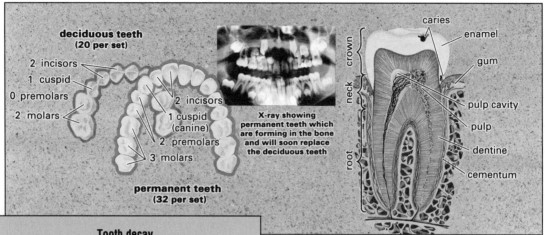

deciduous teeth
(20 per set)

2 incisors
1 cuspid
0 premolars
2 molars

2 incisors
1 cuspid
(canine)
2 premolars
3 molars

permanent teeth
(32 per set)

X-ray showing permanent teeth which are forming in the bone and will soon replace the deciduous teeth

caries
enamel
crown
neck
gum
pulp cavity
pulp
root
dentine
cementum

20B-2 *Human teeth*

Tooth decay

Tooth decay which forms dental caries (cavities) affects about 95% of the population and is most common during the teen-age years. This disease is caused by organic acids produced by bacteria that ferment the sugary film (plaque) on the surface of the tooth.

After these acids break down the enamel, the bacteria and acids may enter the dentin. Spreading rapidly through the dentin, tooth decay may invade the pulp and cause pus formation in the pulp and in the socket between the root of the tooth and the gum. Such a tooth is *abscessed.* A tooth with caries or an abscess should receive professional dental care to prevent the loss of the tooth and/or the spread of infection to the other organs of the body.

People can prevent, or at least slow down, tooth decay by using fluorides and by brushing the teeth properly after every meal. Eating less candy and drinking fewer sugary beverages can also decrease dental caries by reducing plaque formation.

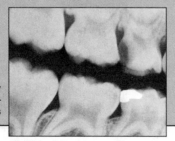

Dental x-ray showing caries and fillings

The *permanent* set of teeth in adults has the same number of incisors and cuspids as the deciduous set but has eight premolars and twelve molars. The last molars, or *wisdom teeth,* frequently fail to erupt or, if they do grow through the gum, are often crooked.

Teeth are set in sockets in the bony ridges of the jaws. These ridges are covered by the fleshy *gums.* The gums merge with the connective tissue that attaches each tooth in its socket. The part of the tooth above the gums is called the **crown,** and the part that is anchored in the socket is called the **root.** Between the crown and the root is the **neck,** the part of the tooth surrounded by the gum.

Each tooth is composed of two layers of hard tissues. **Dentin,** which is similar to bone, forms most of the tooth structure. In the crown portion, the dentin is covered by the **enamel,** the hardest material in the body. The enamel protects the tooth from physical damage and chemical corrosion. A thin layer of bony **cementum** covers the dentin in the root region and is attached to the connective tissue that anchors the tooth. Inside each tooth is a **pulp cavity** filled with blood vessels, lymph vessels, nerves, and connective tissues collectively called the *pulp.*

Review Questions 20B-1

1. What are the four main functions of the digestive system?
2. What are the four types of teeth in a human's mouth?
3. What is the difference in numbers and kinds of deciduous teeth and permanent teeth?
4. What are (a) the three regions of a tooth and (b) the layers of a tooth?

The pharynx, esophagus, and stomach

After the food is chewed, softened, and lubricated, it is swallowed. During swallowing, the tongue pushes upward and backward to direct the food into the *pharynx*. At the same time the *uvula* moves upward, closing the back of the nose to prevent the food from moving into the nasal cavities. The pharynx constricts after receiving the food in order to direct it downward to the esophagus. The *epiglottis* covers the *glottis* of the *larynx* as the food moves into the esophagus, which is stretched open to receive it.

The **esophagus** is a muscular tube that is lubricated by many mucous glands so that the food can be easily pushed downward by peristaltic contractions. Swallowed food takes about 3 sec. to get to the stomach from the mouth.

The esophagus joins the **stomach** at the *cardiac sphincter,* a muscular valve that is closed except when food passes into the stomach. The folds of the stomach lining and the elasticity of the muscular walls enable the stomach to hold about 2 L (2 qt.) of food.

The Walls of the Alimentary Canal

The walls of the organs that form the alimentary canal are typically composed of four layers.

❏ The **mucous lining,** the innermost layer of the alimentary canal, comes in direct contact with the food. This membrane continually secretes mucus that lubricates the interior of the entire canal and protects the lining from acids.

❏ The **submucosa** is composed of loose connective tissue, blood vessels, and many nerve endings. The blood vessels carry away the nutrients that are absorbed, and the nerve endings stimulate the muscle fibers so that the food is continually moving.

❏ The **muscular layer,** consisting of a circular band and a longitudinal band of visceral muscle, is the thickest of the four layers. The main function of the muscular layer is to produce **peristalsis** (PEHR ih STAHL sis), wavelike contractions that move the food along the canal.

❏ The outermost portion of the canal wall is the **serous layer.** It is continuous with the **mesentery,** the connective tissues that attach to the posterior body wall and hold the digestive organs in their proper position.

The thick, muscular walls of the stomach churn the food and mix it with the acidic *gastric juices* which contain enzymes for protein digestion. These enzymes would also digest the walls of the stomach if the walls were not protected by the slimy mucus from the mucous membrane lining of the stomach. The duration of churning may be 4 hr. for coarse foods like celery and spinach, while foods like oatmeal or pudding move rapidly through the stomach. Although the stomach lining does not absorb many food molecules, it does absorb alcohol, water, and certain drugs.

After the food is thoroughly broken down into a semi-liquid state called *chyme* (KYME), the peristaltic contractions propel the food through the *pyloric sphincter* into the small intestine in small spurts. This pyloric valve usually remains closed until the food is converted to chyme.

The small intestine

Most of the digestion and absorption of food occurs in the **small intestine.** The entire small intestine is about 7 m (23 ft.) long and 2.5 cm (1 in.) in diameter.

The **duodenum,** the first section of the small intestine, is about 25 cm (10 in.) long. As the partially digested food passes into the duodenum, the acidity of the food stimulates the intestinal lining to secrete hormones. These hormones stimulate the pancreas, gallbladder, and intestinal lining to secrete enzymes and other materials into the duodenum to convert food into small molecules. **Villi*** (VIL EYE), microscopic fingerlike structures that line the small intestine, then absorb these molecules. The villi increase the surface area of the small intestine and contain blood and lymph vessels which distribute the food molecules throughout the body.

The liver, gallbladder, and pancreas

The **liver,** the largest organ in the body, is in the upper-right part of the abdomen immediately under the diaphragm. It is composed of soft tissue that contains many microscopic spaces called *sinusoids* (SY nyuh SOYDZ). The sinusoids can serve as blood reservoirs. The blood from all digestive organs flows through the sinusoids and comes in contact with the liver cells.

---

villi: (L. VILLUS, shaggy hair)

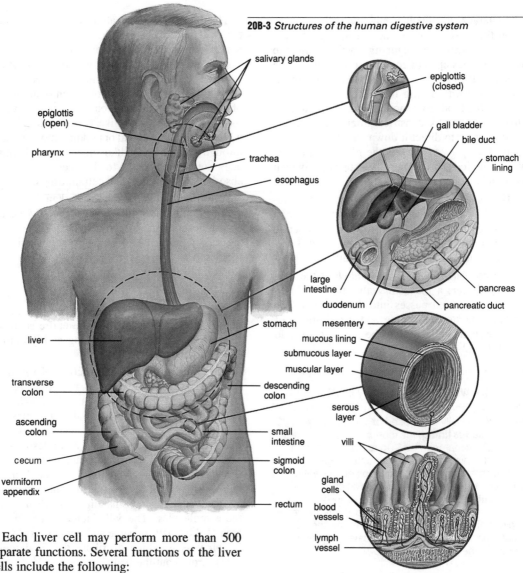

20B-3 *Structures of the human digestive system*

Each liver cell may perform more than 500 separate functions. Several functions of the liver cells include the following:

❑ engulfing bacteria and worn-out red blood cells;
❑ removing many drugs and poisons from the blood;
❑ converting excess glucose into glycogen and storing it;
❑ changing excess glucose into fats;
❑ absorbing amino acids from the blood and using them to manufacture most of the proteins found in the blood; and

❑ storing the fat-soluble vitamins, iron, and copper.

Perhaps the most familiar function of the liver is the formation of **bile,** a greenish fluid that is necessary for the breakdown and absorption of fatty substances in the small intestine. The liver secretes about 1/2 L (1 pt.) of bile a day.

The **gallbladder** is a 7.5-10 cm (3-4 in.), pear-shaped, green sac attached to the liver by the *bile duct*. The gallbladder serves as a reservoir for bile. During a meal, when fatty materials enter the duodenum, the gallbladder contracts and sends bile into the small intestine.

The gallbladder stores bile between meals and concentrates the bile by removing water. If the concentration becomes excessive, cholesterol crystals may form and develop into solids known as *gallstones*. Some gallstones pass unnoticed through the bile duct and into the intestine. Some, however, get into the bile duct and block the flow of bile, causing considerable pain. Occasionally such gallstones must be removed surgically. Often the gallbladder is removed so that the body cannot produce gallstones in the future. After this type of surgery the liver continues to produce bile, and the person usually does not experience any difficulty in digesting fats.

The **pancreas** is a soft, pinkish-white gland 15-25 cm (6-9 in.) long and 2.5 cm (1 in.) wide. About 97% of the pancreas cells produce digestive juices that contain enzymes for digesting carbohydrates, fats, and proteins. These digestive juices flow into the small intestine through the *pancreatic duct*. Often the pancreatic duct merges with the common bile duct before entering the duodenum. Most of the remaining pancreas cells produce hormones involved in regulating the amount of sugar in the blood.

The large intestine

The **large intestine** (colon) is 1.5-2 m (5-6 ft.) long and about 6.5 cm (2.5 in.) in diameter. Its sections are named according to their shape and the direction in which they move food and waste.

Material from the small intestine moves into the *cecum* (SEE kum), which is a pouch about 6 cm (2-3 in.) long. The narrow end of the cecum is the *vermiform* appendix** (VUR muh FORM ◊ uh PEN diks), which secretes mucus for lubrication and harbors certain microorganisms that digest cellulose. Reports indicate that it also forms certain leucocytes and antibodies.

A major function of the large intestine is the removal of *feces* (waste materials) through the *anus*. The *rectum* is the straight, muscular portion that expels the feces.

A second function of the large intestine is the reabsorption of water. In other words, the water in saliva, bile, pancreatic juices, and secretions from the stomach and small intestine is recycled and used again. On a daily basis this amounts to about 7.5 L (2 gal.). If this water were egested with the feces, you would soon become severely dehydrated.

The large intestine also serves as an ideal site for growth of the bacteria and yeasts that produce vitamins B_1, B_2, B_{12}, and K. Minerals (especially sodium, potassium, and chlorine) are also absorbed in the large intestine.

Review Questions 20B-2

1. What structures keep the chyme within the stomach while it is being churned?
2. What prevents the stomach from digesting itself?
3. List several functions of the liver.
4. List and tell the functions of (a) the organs in the alimentary canal and (b) the accessory organs of the digestive system.
5. Describe the formation of gallstones.
6. Describe the location and functions of the vermiform appendix.

Foods and Digestion

Food is any material which contributes to growth and repair or supplies energy. According to this definition, minerals, vitamins, carbohydrates, fats, and proteins are all foods. Abundant water is also needed to use these foods properly.

Most of the meals you eat each day contain something from these groups. The kinds and amount of food you need, however, depend in part upon your physical activities. For example, some people require more of certain vitamins than others; athletes and lumberjacks require food with

---

vermiform: vermi- (L. VERMIS, worm) + -form (FORMA, form) shape

appendix: ap-, ad- (to) + -pendix (L. PENDERE, to hang)

20B-4	Summary of Chemical Digestion				
Location	Mouth	Stomach	Small Intestine		
Digestive Fluid	Saliva from Salivary Gland	Gastric Juices from Stomach Lining	Bile from Liver	Pancreatic Juices from Pancreas	Intestinal Juices from Intestinal Lining
starch	AMYLASE → disaccharides (maltose) / starch			AMYLASE → disaccharides (maltose); (sucrose); (lactose)	MALTASE → mono-saccharides (glucose); SUCRASE → (fructose; glucose); LACTASE → (galactose; glucose)
fat			BILE → emulsified fats	LIPASE → fatty acids and glycerol	LIPASE → fatty acids and glycerol
protein		PEPSIN → protein fragments		TRYPSIN AND CHYMO-TRYPSIN → polypeptides	PEP-TIDASE → amino acids

more calories than office workers and laboratory technicians do.

Because many of the carbohydrates, fats, and proteins you eat are too large for absorption, they must be broken down chemically by the action of **enzymes.** All enzymes are proteins, and many of them require the presence of *coenzymes* in order to function. Many vitamins serve as coenzymes. A few digestive enzymes need minerals to function properly. These coenzymes and minerals, however, are only needed in very small amounts.

Water

Besides oxygen, water is the most important molecule for human survival. A person can live without food for five or more weeks, but without water he can survive only a few days. Most of the normal water loss from your body passes through the kidneys during urine formation. Your body also loses water during expiration, in perspiration, and in feces. The amount of water loss varies, depending upon the level of activity, air temperature, and other environmental conditions. You must replace the lost water as soon as possible.

Water is vital to the body because it dissolves certain foods for easier digestion. It also aids in regulating fluid balance, pH of the blood, and body temperature (through perspiration).

Carbohydrates

The most economical and abundant foods are rich in *carbohydrates*. Carbohydrates include the *sugars*, which are a source of quick energy, and more complex molecules such as *starch* and *glycogen*.

However, carbohydrates are not actually essential in your diet because your body can produce them from fats and amino acids.

Carbohydrate digestion begins in the mouth as the *amylase* from the salivary glands breaks down starches to the disaccharide, maltose. However, all the starch is not converted to maltose primarily because the food is usually swallowed before starch digestion is complete. The highly acidic fluids in the stomach soon stop the amylase digestion of starches.

When the food material moves into the intestine, the pancreas secretes amylase to continue starch digestion. The intestinal lining secretes enzymes that convert *disaccharides* (such as maltose, sucrose, and lactose) into *monosaccharides* (such as glucose, fructose, and galactose). These

---

Food Fiber

Food fiber, often called *roughage* or *bulk,* is primarily the nondigestible cellulose (a complex carbohydrate) of fruits and vegetables. It is the "stringy stuff" in roots, leaves, stems, and fruits that gives the plant physical support. Some good sources of natural food fiber are whole-grain breads and cereals, fruits with the skin, vegetables, nuts, and seeds.

Even though natural food fiber cannot be digested, it is important for moving material through the intestine. It also seems to shield the intestinal lining from irritation by certain harmful substances that may be in food.

Minerals and Vitamins

Your body needs many different kinds of **minerals.** Minerals are inorganic substances found naturally in the soil. They are absorbed by plants and then passed on to animals as they feed on the plants. Humans obtain minerals by eating foods that come from plants and animals.

Although the body needs only small amounts of minerals, they are necessary for it to produce certain compounds. The body does recycle some minerals but not enough to take care of its needs. The minerals you consume, however, must be in usable forms. You cannot get the iron you need by eating rusty nails. Iron in the ferrous (Fe^{+2}) form is absorbed more readily than the ferric (Fe^{+3}) form. Calcium must be consumed with other materials in order to be absorbed and used.

At the beginning of the twentieth century, people thought that the proper amounts of carbohydrates, fats, proteins, and minerals would provide all the needed nutrients. In 1910 scientists began to realize that something more was needed for proper growth and development. These essential organic

Selected Minerals and Their Functions

Mineral	Sources	Functions	Comments
Calcium	Dairy products, egg yolk, and green leafy vegetables	Major part of bones and teeth; necessary for blood-clot formation, nerve cell functions and muscle contractions	Blood calcium level controlled by hormones; deficiency results in muscular twitching, spasms, and poor blood clotting
Phosphorus	Dairy products, meat, fish, poultry, and nuts	Important part of bones and teeth; part of ATP, DNA, RNA, and certain proteins	Deficiency results in poor appetite, retarded growth, and general body weakness
Iron	Meat, liver, egg yolk, beans, peas, dried fruits, nuts, and cereals	Part of hemoglobin and many enzymes	Deficiency results in anemia; mineral most likely to be deficient in diet
Iodine	Iodized salt, seafoods, codliver oil, and vegetables grown in iodine-rich soils	Part of hormone from thyroid gland	Deficiency results in goiter (abnormal growth of thyroid gland)
Copper	Eggs, whole-wheat breads, beans, beef, liver, fish, spinach, and asparagus	Involved in formation of skin pigment and hemoglobin	Some stored in liver and spleen
Sodium	Table salt, meat, seafoods, poultry, milk, and cheese	Important in fluid balance and nerve cell function	Excessive amounts may lead to high blood pressure; too much included in many American diets
Potassium	Avocados, bananas, dried apricots, meats, nuts, and potatoes	Important regulator of muscle contraction and nerve cell function	Excessive or deficient amounts affect heart function and cause muscle weakness
Chlorine	Same as sodium	Important in fluid balance and acid-base balance, and formations of acids in stomach	Closely associated with sodium; most abundant in fluids in brain and stomach
Magnesium	Nuts, legumes, dairy products, and green leafy vegetables	Needed for muscle and nerve cell functions; involved in bone formation; part of many coenzymes	Most abundant in bones

Vitamins: Their Functions and Deficiency Disorders

Vitamin	Sources	Functions	Deficiency Disorders
A	Fish liver oil, milk, butter, yellow and green vegetables	Essential for normal vision, healthy epithelial tissue, proper growth of teeth and bones	Night blindness, scaly skin, poor growth
D	Fish liver oil, egg yolk, fortified milk, butter, and margarine	Essential for absorbing calcium from intestine	Bone disorders such as rickets in children
E	Nuts and wheat germ, oils from seeds, fish, eggs, and liver	Inhibits oxidation; involved in formation of DNA, RNA, and red blood cells	Increased breakdown of fatty acids; may lead to anemia
K	Spinach, cauliflower, cabbage, and liver	Involved in forming prothrombin for blood clotting	Delayed clotting time, resulting in excessive bleeding
B_1 (thiamine)	Eggs, pork, nuts, whole-grain cereals, liver, yeast, and green leafy vegetables	Coenzyme for many enzymes involved in carbohydrate and amino acid metabolism	Beriberi—general body weakness; stunted growth; poor appetite
B_2 (riboflavin)	Yeast, liver, cheese, milk, eggs, asparagus, peas, beets, and peanuts	Used in metabolism of carbohydrates and proteins, especially in cells of eyes, skin, blood, and intestine lining	Eye and skin disorders; anemia; sores in intestines
Niacin	Yeast, liver, meat, fish, cereals, whole-grain breads, peas, beans, and nuts	Essential part of a coenzyme involved in cellular respiration	Pellagra—skin problems; diarrhea; mental problems
B_6 (pyridoxine)	Salmon, liver, meat, cereals, legumes, yeast, tomatoes, spinach, and yogurt	Serves as coenzyme for fat metabolism; involved in production of antibodies	Sores of eyes, nose, and mouth
B_{12} (cyanocobalamine)	Liver, meat, fish, milk, eggs, and cheese	Serves as coenzyme for red blood cell formation; involved in nerve function	Type of anemia and nerve disorders
Pantothenic acid	Kidney, liver, yeast, green vegetables, and cereals	Part of coenzyme involved in cellular respiration and formation of certain hormones	General tiredness; nerve and muscle disorders
Folic acid	Green leafy vegetables, liver, and cereals; also produced by bacteria in large intestine	Part of enzymes that form DNA, RNA, and red blood cells	Type of anemia
Biotin	Yeast, liver, and egg yolk; produced by bacteria in large intestine	Coenzyme in cellular metabolism	Mental depression, muscular pains, tiredness, skin problems
C (ascorbic acid)	Citrus fruits, tomatoes, green vegetables, and strawberries	Needed for connective tissue formation; detoxifies body	Scurvy—slow healing; weak blood vessels and bones

substances became known as **vitamins.**

There are two classes of vitamins:

❑ *Fat-soluble vitamins* Vitamins A, D, E, and K are fat-soluble vitamins and can be stored in your body for future use. The accumulated effects of too much vitamins A or D, however, can be toxic to your body. Many fat-soluble vitamins work with certain molecules in the cell membrane to regulate the movement of substances into and out of cells.

❑ *Water-soluble vitamins* All other vitamins are water-soluble and water-soluble vitamins must be taken in daily to insure good health. If you consume more water-soluble vitamins than your body can use, the excess vitamins will be excreted in the urine. Most of the water-soluble vitamins function as coenzymes, working together with enzymes to regulate certain metabolic reactions.

Under normal conditions, your body needs only small amounts of vitamins. Even though all food groups contain certain types and amounts of vitamins, animal foods (such as milk, meat, fish, and eggs) are rich in fat-soluble vita-

mins, while plant foods contain more water-soluble vitamins.

Some vitamins can be manufactured in laboratories. These *synthetic vitamins* usually have the same effect on your body as *natural vitamins* obtained directly from plant and animal sources. However, if the molecular structure of a synthetic vitamin differs from its natural counterpart or if the natural vitamin is combined with a substance not found with the synthetic vitamin, the body may not be able to use the synthetic vitamin as effectively.

Review questions on page 550.

simple sugars can then be absorbed into the bloodstream and used for energy production, or they can be stored in the liver for future use.

Fats

Fat digestion in humans occurs in the small intestine. As the fats move from the stomach into the small intestine, a hormone stimulates the release of bile from the gallbladder. Flowing into the duodenum, the bile causes the fats to form droplets. The separation of fat into droplets is called **emulsification** (ee MUL sih fih KAY shun). Bile is the **emulsifier.** Since enzymes can work only on the surface of a substance, emulsification greatly speeds fat digestion.

The enzyme *lipase,** secreted by the pancreas, digests fats into *glycerol* and *fatty acids.* The villi

Diseases and Disorders of the Digestive System
Cirrhosis of the liver: a disease characterized by the formation of dense connective tissue and deposits of fatty tissue; may be caused by drinking alcoholic beverages, infections by bacteria and viruses, or breathing certain gases
Diverticulosis: the condition in which sacs or pouches have formed in the wall of the large intestine; usually no inflammation is experienced; commonly occurs in persons who suffer from constipation for long periods
Flatus: a condition of gas in the digestive tract that results from chemical digestion of foods; may also result from drinking too many carbonated beverages or from swallowing air while eating too fast
Heartburn: a burning sensation in the esophagus caused by acidic liquid moving upward from the stomach; called heartburn because the pain seems to come from the heart
Jaundice: a condition in which the skin and white of the eye appear yellow because of excessive bile in the blood; may be caused by diseases of the liver or blockage of bile ducts by gallstones
Mumps: a viral infection of the salivary glands, causing swelling, fever, and painful swallowing
Peptic ulcer: an ulcer (sore) occurring in the lower esophagus, stomach, or duodenum; usually caused by too much acid in the stomach
Vomiting: a rapid emptying of stomach contents through the mouth; usually caused by some irritant to the stomach lining

A Healthy Diet
There is much confusion about the various special diets advocated today. There is also considerable disagreement among authorities regarding what the ideal human diet should be. There are, however, several guidelines that most authorities agree upon.
❑ Your meals each day should include foods from all of the four basic food groups: (1) milk and milk products; (2) meat (including fish); (3) fruits, seeds, and vegetables; and (4) whole-grain breads and cereals. Such meals will supply your body with most of the needed nutrients.
❑ Eat more raw fruits, vegetables, and seeds because they are the best sources of vitamins and minerals. Many nuts and seeds (sunflower and sesame) are also good sources of protein.
❑ Drink more water, fruit juices, and milk and less coffee, tea, and other beverages. Fruit juices are good sources of vitamins and minerals. Milk is a good source of calcium, protein, and certain vitamins.
❑ Greatly restrict your intake of sugars in foods such as candy and carbonated beverages. Avoid foods that contain large quantities of sugar but have little other food value.
❑ Do not overemphasize any one food or group of foods.
❑ If you want to supplement your diet, a multiple vitamin and mineral tablet would be best. The supplement should include the water-soluble vitamins (B-complex and C) because they are not stored in body tissues.
What you eat is important, but a person who talks about little more than what to eat and what not to eat or who makes his favorite diet a doctrine or a principle of his faith is going too far.

of the small intestine, aided by bile, then absorb these smaller molecules. After absorption into the bloodstream, glycerol and fatty acids recombine to form certain types of fat molecules. Two to four hours after a meal rich in fats, the blood reaches its highest concentration of fats which is about 1-2% of the blood volume.

Fats are used to form cell membranes, form protective membranes around certain nerve cells, form certain hormones, cushion delicate structures, and produce energy. Many fats in the body

lipase: lip- (Gk. LIPOS, fat) + -ase (enzyme)

The Calorie and Weight Gain or Loss

The term **calorie*** refers to a measurement of heat produced during oxidation of food. The measurement for caloric value of food (the kilocalorie, cal.) is the amount of heat required to raise the temperature of 1 L of water 1° C. The caloric value of any specific amount of food is determined by burning the food in a special container surrounded by 1 L of water. The increase in water temperature caused by the burning food is measured.

A healthy human body uses carbohydrates as the first source of energy, but fats and proteins can also be used. Fats, however, release more than twice as many calories as the same weight of carbohydrates or proteins. One gram of carbohydrate or protein releases 4.1 cal., while 1 g of fat produces 9.3 cal.

The calories needed to maintain your normal body functions while you are at rest (but not asleep) is called your **basal metabolic rate** (BMR). A person with an abnormally high BMR uses many calories and is overly active. An abnormally low BMR indicates that a person is using few calories and is usually sluggish. Your BMR can be measured by determining the amount of oxygen you use while resting.

Normally the BMR is lower in females than males. Apparently men have more muscle tissue per pound than women and therefore use more oxygen. As you age, your BMR will probably decrease. Emotions such as anger and anxiety as well as physical factors such as a chill, a fever, or an infection will increase the BMR. BMR is generally controlled by a hormone produced in the thyroid gland (see page 600-601).

The total number of calories your body needs daily depends on your BMR and the amount and type of your activity. Scientists have determined that a pound of body fat is equal to 3,500 cal.

When your diet supplies 3,500 calories more than you use for energy purposes, the excess may be converted to fat, and your body weight increases. When you use more calories than are taken in, the body normally breaks down stored fats to supply the energy, and you lose weight.

To lose weight would appear to be a simple matter of eating fewer calories while maintaining your BMR. If the person also increases his expenditure of energy (increasing his usual amount of exercise), he should lose weight even faster. Of course, one must be sure that he maintains a balanced diet and meets his daily requirements of minerals, vitamins, and other nutrients.

Weight gain and loss, however, is not that simple. Some research indicates that people will only gain so much weight, no matter how many calories they consume. It appears that the body has a set weight that it will not normally exceed. The body seems to pass calories that would take it beyond the set weight. The set weight seems to be linked to exercise; within limits, the more exercise, the lower the set weight. Other research indicates that the body can go into "starvation mode" when there is reduction in the number of calories consumed. In "starvation mode" the body gets more calories out of consumed food than it normally would.

do not come directly from the diet but are formed in liver cells from excess sugars or amino acids (that come from proteins).

Fat not used immediately by the body is stored in *adipose** (ADD uh POHZ) *cells*. The conversion of other foods to fats explains why eating any type of food can increase the amount of adipose (fat) tissue in your body. Adipose tissue is found under your skin, between your muscles, behind your eyeballs, on your heart, and between most internal organs. In these locations fat tissue has three general functions: it is a future supply of energy, an insulation from cold, and a layer that protects from physical injury.

---

calorie: (L. CALOR, heat)   **adipose:** (L. ADEPS, fat)

Proteins

Proteins are not only a part of all living cells but also a part of nonliving structures such as hair, nails, and the matrix of connective tissues. All enzymes and some hormones are proteins. About 50% of the body's dry weight is protein, and most of that is in the muscle tissue. Proteins are most important for growth and repair, but they may also be used for energy production.

Protein digestion begins in the stomach. The enzyme *pepsin,** which is secreted by the cells lining the stomach, begins by breaking proteins into smaller fragments. Some proteins, however, are not digested by pepsin. When the food material moves from the stomach into the small intestine, these remaining proteins are exposed to *trypsin* and *chymotrypsin,* enzymes secreted by the pancreas. Other enzymes from the intestinal lin-

Food Fads

Several years ago a well-known scientist stated that large doses of vitamin C could prevent or cure the common cold. Thousands of people increased their orange juice and vitamin C tablet consumption. Many reported having fewer or less severe colds. Many, however, had just as many severe colds as ever.

While people were consuming the vitamin C, some scientists began experiments to determine such things as how much was needed, how long it had to be taken, and in what forms. When the results were in and analyzed, it was discovered that vitamin C has little to do with the common cold.

People want to be healthy. When told by sources they respect that doing something will help their health, many people will alter their actions. Some make significant, permanent changes; most make minor, temporary changes.

Scientists conduct experiments and surveys that seem to reveal information regarding human health or diet. Other scientists, however, often need several years to analyze, set up, and conduct additional experiments or surveys in order to have adequate data to support or disprove the conclusions of the first scientists. Early experimentation and surveys are often limited in scope but seem to point in the same direction. When testing is done on a larger scale, the original findings may melt into insignificance.

While additional experiments are going on, there can be a period of confusion. Those with vested interests can capitalize on this situation. For example, after some preliminary studies showed that oat bran helped to reduce blood cholesterol, food companies quickly added oat bran to almost anything they could and produced commercials saying that oat bran was a food to help make one healthy. After additional studies, however, it became obvious that although oat bran is a good food which would benefit most Americans' diet, it will not magically reduce the amount of cholesterol in a person's blood.

Moderation and caution seem to be the best advice regarding a person's diet. Moderation is advised because too much of anything and not enough of the basic food groups, vitamins, and minerals are not good. You should always have a healthy skepticism regarding a food fad, even a fad that appears to be backed by scientific evidence. Scientists really do change their opinions, but they are often slow in doing so. For example, recent studies shed some doubt on certain levels of cholesterol in the diet and in the blood being as bad as once thought. It will be some time, however, before it is known if these findings are accurate and even longer before physicians will change their practices and food companies stop writing "cholesterol free" in big letters on their labels.

pepsin: (Gk. PEPTEIN, to digest)

Summary of Physical Digestion		20B-5
Structure	**Activity**	
Mouth		
lips and cheeks	Keep food between teeth during chewing	
tongue	Moves food during chewing and swallowing	
salivary glands	Saliva softens and moistens food, covering it with mucus for easier swallowing	
teeth	Masticate food for more rapid digestion and easier swallowing	
Pharynx	Moves food and liquids to esophagus	
Esophagus	Moves food and liquids to stomach	
Stomach	Churns food until semiliquid (chyme); moves chyme into small intestine	
Small intestine	Mixes chyme from stomach with juices from intestine and pancreas and with bile from liver; absorbs most of the foods	
Large intestine	Prepares waste material for egestion; absorbs minerals and vitamins	

ing complete the digestion of the fragments into *amino acids,* which are absorbed and carried to various parts of the body by the blood.

Amino acids are used within the body cells to form various proteins. If your diet does not pro-vide enough amino acids, your body may break down some of your skeletal muscle proteins into amino acids. If your body has an excess of amino acids, they are broken down in the liver cells to release energy.

Biological Terms

ingestion	premolar	muscular layer	*Foods and Digestion*
digestion	molar	peristalsis	food
absorption	crown	serous layer	enzyme
egestion	root	mesentery	food fiber
Organs of the	neck	small intestine	emulsification
Digestive System	dentin	duodenum	emulsifier
alimentary canal	enamel	villi (sing., villus)	calorie
accessory organ	cementum	liver	basal metabolic rate (BMR)
salivary gland	pulp cavity	bile	
mastication	esophagus	gallbladder	*Facet*
taste bud	stomach	pancreas	mineral
incisor	mucous lining	large intestine (colon)	vitamin
cuspid	submucosa layer		

Review Questions 20B-3

1. List the six basic nutritional substances normally found in food. How is each of these substances used by the body? Tell in what form each is absorbed.
2. Describe the digestion processes for (a) a carbohydrate, (b) a fat, and (c) a protein. Tell where each of the steps takes place.

Facet 20B-1: Minerals and Vitamins, pages 545-46

1. What is the difference between a vitamin and a mineral?
2. What are the two main classes of vitamins?

Thought Questions

1. Why are fats a better unit for storing excess energy than carbohydrates?
2. "Calories really do not count in losing or gaining weight." Present evidence either to defend or to contradict this statement.

INTERNAL TRANSPORT

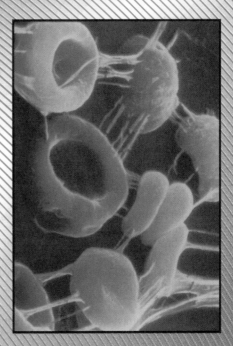

TWENTY-ONE

21A-The Circulatory System

The circulatory system consists of numerous blood vessels through which blood is pumped by the muscular heart. From the time of the Greek Galen (ca. A.D. 100) most scientists believed that the heart produced blood and then pumped it through the vessels to all the parts of the body.

Then William Harvey, an English physician, observed that the heart could not possibly produce as much blood as it pumped and that the structures of the heart and the blood vessels were not designed for blood production. Through careful ob-

servation and experimentation, Harvey clearly demonstrated the circulation of the blood in 1628.

Since that time scientists have learned much about the circulatory system, especially the heart. Many diseases of the circulatory system can now be prevented or controlled by medication, proper nutrition, exercise, and corrective surgery.

Blood

The circulatory system continually transports blood throughout the body. **Blood** is a marvelous

551

"red river" that carries oxygen, food, and hormones for nourishment to all body cells; carbon dioxide to the lungs for expiration; and waste molecules to the kidneys for excretion. Nearly every cell in the body is located next to a tiny blood vessel so that it can exchange these materials with the blood.

Blood seems to be uniform in color, but if you could examine it under a microscope, some cells would be clear while others would be red. When blood is centrifuged, it separates into two distinct parts—the liquid portion (plasma) and the solid portion (blood cells).

21A-1 *Blood separated in a test tube*

Blood plasma

Blood plasma, a straw-colored liquid, is about 90% water. The remaining 10% is mostly proteins but also contains a variety of dissolved gases, minerals, nutrients, hormones, and wastes. The water, minerals, and nutrients in the plasma are absorbed from the digestive organs. Hormones are mostly proteins and lipids secreted into the blood by certain organs. The gases present in the plasma include small amounts of dissolved oxygen, carbon dioxide, and nitrogen. Waste substances such as urea and uric acid that form during protein metabolism are also present in the plasma. Wastes are continuously being filtered from the blood so that they do not reach toxic levels.

21A-2 Major Components of Blood Plasma	
Component	**Amount**
Water	90%
Proteins albumins, globulins, fibrinogen, enzymes, and other proteins	about 8%
Minerals sodium, chloride, bicarbonate, calcium, potassium, magnesium, and phosphate	about 1%
Miscellaneous lipids (fats), sugars, amino acids, vitamins, hormones, dissolved gases, wastes	about 1%

The composition of plasma will vary somewhat, even in a healthy individual. For example, after a meal the plasma may contain many tiny droplets of fat that were absorbed through the intestinal lining. When a person suffers from an illness or a severe injury, the plasma composition usually varies.

A person who is deficient in some substances or who for some reason cannot eat may be given liquid nourishment through a vein of the hand or arm, a process called *intravenous** (IN truh VEE nus) *infusion.* The composition of the fluids that are administered to a patient depends on the condition and needs of the individual as well as the type of disorder he has.

Blood Proteins

Most of the plasma proteins are produced in the liver and accomplish functions only now being discovered by medical scientists. The *albumins** are proteins that control the blood volume by regulating the amount of water that moves into the bloodstream. If there is a decrease in albumins (which may happen during liver diseases), there will be a loss of water from the plasma and the blood cells. If too much water leaves the blood, the body tissues become "waterlogged." This swollen condition is known as *edema** (ih DEE muh).

Globulins (GLAHB yuh linz) are proteins found in the blood plasma. Alpha and beta globulins combine with lipids and certain hormones and transport them where they are needed. *Gamma globulin* functions as an antibody (see pages 570, 572).

Erythrocytes

The term "cell" does not properly describe **erythrocytes** (ih RITH ruh SITES), even though they are often called *red blood cells.* As they develop, erythrocytes contain a nucleus but very little hemoglobin. Shortly before they move into the bloodstream, the amount of hemoglobin increases, but the nucleus decreases in size and is squeezed out. At this point the structure is no longer a true cell.

Erythrocytes contain few cellular structures and do not undergo mitosis; therefore, erythro-

---

intravenous: intra- (within) + -venous (L. VENA, vein)
albumins (L. ALBUS, white)

edema (Gk. OIDEMA, a swelling)
erythrocyte: erythro- (Gk. ERUTHROS, red) + -cyte (cell)

21A-3 *A scanning electron micrograph of erythrocytes (5000X)*

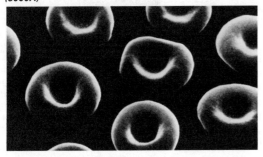

cytes may be described as membranous structures that are filled with hemoglobin and appear as red, biconcave discs. This shape provides the greatest possible surface area for the volume of the "cell" and therefore allows maximum diffusion of oxygen into and out of the erythrocyte. Erythrocytes cannot move by themselves but are carried along by the moving plasma.

Oxygen is bound loosely to the iron-containing heme group in hemoglobin, and the resulting complex, called *oxyhemoglobin,* is a brilliant red color. After oxygen is released into other body cells, the blood becomes a dull brick-red color. It changes again to a brilliant red after it absorbs oxygen while passing through the lungs.

The erythrocytes are the most numerous of all blood "cells," but they will vary in number according to the condition of your body. As you exercise regularly, your body has a greater need for oxygen. The amount of hemoglobin and the number of erythrocytes therefore increase to supply this need. If you changed your place of residence from a low elevation to a mountaintop, the erythrocytes and hemoglobin in your body would increase to insure that you would absorb enough oxygen into your blood.

If you lack iron in your diet, your body cannot form enough hemoglobin. The result is a general decrease in erythrocytes and hemoglobin, a disorder known as *anemia.** Because certain B vitamins also aid in proper formation of hemoglobin, a lack of them also causes anemia. Such anemia is usually corrected by proper diet, rest, and exercise. Some anemias, however, are caused

by exposure to radiation or toxic substances such as benzene, arsenic, and nitrogen mustards. These types of anemias are difficult to correct and are sometimes fatal.

Before you were born, erythrocytes were formed primarily by your spleen, liver, and red bone marrow. At birth only the red bone marrow actively produced erythrocytes. In adults erythrocyte production is restricted to the red bone marrow in the sternum, skull bones, vertebrae, ribs, and ends of long bones. During your life span red blood cells are continually being manufactured. If you weigh about 130 lb., your body forms more than one billion new erythrocytes each day.

Erythrocytes circulate in the blood for 90-120 days. Old erythrocytes are broken down by specialized cells in the liver, spleen, and bone marrow. Also, when the hemoglobin in an erythrocyte is abnormal, these same liver cells will destroy it. Most of the remains of destroyed erythrocytes are recycled to form new erythrocytes.

Leucocytes

The *white blood cells* or **leucocytes*** (LOO kuh SITES) lack hemoglobin. Leucocytes are about twice the size of erythrocytes and possess no def-

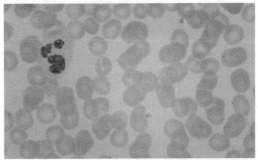

21A-4 *A photomicrograph of a blood smear, showing erythrocytes and leucocytes*

inite shape. Leucocytes have nuclei during their entire life span, and although often carried along in the plasma, they have the ability to move by themselves.

There are various types of leucocytes. Some leucocytes manufacture enzymes for killing microorganisms or digesting toxins in the blood.

---

anemia: an- (without) + hemia or -emia (blood)

leucocyte: leuco- (clear or white) + -cyte (cell)

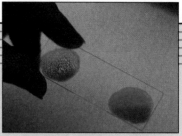

FACETS OF BIOLOGY

21A-1

Blood Transfusions and Blood Grouping

"The life of the flesh is in the blood" (Lev. 17:11). Theologians may dispute the meaning of this passage, but biologically speaking it is true that without the right kind of blood in an adequate supply to flesh, life will be short.

Injuries, illnesses, surgery, and other problems can cause a lack of blood. Without transfusions many people would die. In the past many transfusion recipients suffered violent reactions, usually resulting in death. In a few cases, however, the blood transfusions were successful, and the patients recovered rapidly. Karl Landstiner, an American pathologist, began research to discover why.

He obtained blood samples from workers in his laboratory and mixed the blood in all possible combinations. From this he determined the number of blood groups and which types could be safely transfused. Landstiner speculated that blood should be classified into groups, and in 1901 he proposed the ABO blood group system.

Today we know that **blood types (blood groups)** are determined by the presence or absence of certain molecules in the membranes of the erythrocytes. These molecules, called *antigens,* stimulate the production of *antibodies.* Specialized blood cells produce these antibodies, which are located in the blood plasma. The problems regarding blood transfusions come when antibodies of the recipient's blood react with antigens on the donor's blood cells.

Although human blood may contain many antigens and antibodies causing various blood groupings, the two blood type classifications that are most important in blood transfusions are the ABO group and the Rh system.

ABO blood group

The ABO blood types are determined by the presence or absence of two antigens–A and B–in the membrane of erythrocytes. If a person's erythrocytes have antigen A, then his blood is type A. A person with only antigen B has type B blood, and if a person has both antigens A and B, his blood type is AB. Most people have type O blood because they have neither antigen A nor antigen B.

In addition to antigens, three of these four blood types also possess antibodies. These particular antibodies, however, were not present at birth but were produced between the second and eighth months of life as the body responded to antigens A and B in the person's food, especially meat. Therefore if a person has type A

21A-5 *Antibodies have been applied to samples of the same blood. Anti-A antibodies were placed in the sample on the right; and anti-B antibodies, in the sample on the left. What blood type is being tested?*

blood, his body produces anti-B antibodies; anti-A antibodies do not form because such antibodies would react with his antigens and destroy his erythrocytes. A person with type B blood produces anti-A antibodies. A person with type O has both anti-A and anti-B antibodies. A person with type AB blood has neither antibody.

If type A blood is accidentally given to a person who has type B blood, the individual's body will immediately "recognize" that the A antigen is a foreign substance, and the anti-A antibodies will quickly attack the A antigens. This causes the donor's erythrocytes to **agglutinate*** (clump), becoming stuck together like a roll of coins. The agglutination of incoming cells could block blood vessels and even result in death.

Antigens and Antibodies of ABO Blood Types		
Blood Type	Antigen	Antibody
A	A	anti-B
B	B	anti-A
AB	A and B	none
O	none	anti-A and anti-B

ABO Blood Types for Transfusion		
Recipient	Donor	In Emergencies
A	A	O
B	B	O
AB	AB	A, B, or
O	O	none

agglutinate: ag- or ad- (to) + -glutinate (L. GLUTINARE, to glue)

The Rh System

The **Rh system** (named after the rhesus monkey from which the antigen was first isolated) involves the presence or absence of an antigen in the erythrocyte membrane. Most people are Rh positive (Rh+); they have the Rh antigen in the membranes of their erythrocytes. About 15% of all Americans lack the Rh antigen and are Rh negative (Rh–).

Normally, human blood plasma does not contain anti-Rh antibodies, but these antibodies can be stimulated into production in an Rh– person. For example, when an Rh– person receives Rh+ blood, his body begins to form anti-Rh antibodies. These antibodies remain in his blood plasma. Later, if a second transfusion of Rh+ blood is administered, the anti-Rh antibodies react with the Rh antigens of the donor's blood.

Problems with the Rh antigen occur during pregnancy when blood leaks through the membranes between the unborn child and the mother. If the fetus is Rh+ and the mother is Rh–, the mother's body reacts to the baby's Rh antigen by forming anti-Rh antibodies. The antibodies remain in her blood plasma but pose no danger until she becomes pregnant with another Rh+ baby. If some of the mother's anti-Rh antibodies enter the unborn child's bloodstream, they will react with the child's Rh antigens. The resulting agglutination of the baby's erythrocytes would destroy erythrocytes faster than they could be replaced. Medical researchers have discovered a protein which forms a complex with anti-Rh antibodies in the mother's blood. The kidneys then remove the complex.

When blood is given to a patient, care must be taken to insure that his antibodies will not attack the donor's erythrocytes and cause agglutination. Ideally, donor blood should be the same type as the recipient's blood. If the same blood type is not available, careful matching can determine which other blood type may be transfused. A person with type A (anti-B antibody) blood should never be given type B or AB blood because the erythrocytes of both types would be agglutinated by his anti-B antibodies. For similar reasons a person with type O blood (with anti-A and anti-B antibodies) should never be given type A, B, or AB blood.

If you have type AB blood, you can receive blood of any other type of the ABO grouping. For this reason, people with blood type AB are sometimes called *universal recipients*. Even though types A, B, and O contain antibodies that could cause agglutination of type AB erythrocytes, there is usually no particular problem if the don-or's blood (about 1 pint) is transfused slowly and therefore diluted by the large volume (about 5 qt.) of the recipient's type AB blood.

If you have type O blood, your blood can be received by all other types in the ABO grouping because it does not have antigens A or B. Therefore, people with O blood are often referred to as *universal donors*.

Blood transfusions of the future

There are other antigen and antibody systems found in human blood, but most of them do not cause significant medical problems during transfusions. Today the ABO and Rh labelings on blood are used more as a guideline, eliminating the pouches of blood which are known to be incompatible with a recipient. To be sure that a recipient's blood is completely compatible with blood he is about to be given, a small amount of his blood is usually mixed with a sample of the donated blood. If there are any problems other blood is sought.

Today the naturally occurring substances in donated blood are not as big a problem as the various foreign substances it might contain. Chemical- (drug-) or virus- contaminated blood has caused many people to fear blood transfusions. Many people who face surgery in which they may need additional blood have decided to give their own blood before the surgery to be used if needed.

But some people require blood in an emergency or are too ill to give blood before surgery. In these situations *auto transfusion* is becoming common. The blood a person loses during surgery is collected, filtered, cleaned, and then replaced into his own blood stream.

Despite all the precautions, about 2% of all transfusions have undesirable effects. Scientists have developed "artificial blood." This fluid (kept frozen and warmed in a microwave prior to being put in a person's blood vessels) can match many of the most important properties of blood.

Review questions on page 557.

Summary of Blood Cells			
Blood Cell	**Quantity**	**Where produced**	**Description**
Erythrocytes	4.5-5.5 million per cu. mm.	Red bone marrow	Nonnucleated discs; about 8 μm in diameter; 2 μm thick; flexible; contain hemoglobin and appear red
Leucocytes	6,000-9,000 per cu. mm.	Most formed by red bone marrow; some possibly formed by lymphatic tissues	Nucleated; range from 9-25 μm in diameter; ameboid; some have granules but appear clear (white)
Platelets	250,000-300,000 per cu. mm.	Red bone marrow	Nonnucleated, 2-4 μm diameter; sticky cells for plugging wounds; contain chemicals for clotting

Certain leucocytes engulf large amounts of bacteria and foreign material in the bloodstream and break them down in vacuoles. Many of the white blood cells leave the blood vessels through the capillary walls in order to enter into an area of the body to "wage war" on foreign organisms.

In a healthy person the ratio of leucocytes to erythrocytes is about 1:600. This difference in number makes sense when you recall the functions of these blood cells. Erythrocytes are needed in greater numbers to transport oxygen. The body needs leucocytes to defend itself from bacteria, viruses, and other harmful substances. When the body is in good health, it requires fewer leucocytes. When harmful microorganisms enter the body faster than they can be controlled, however, the number of leucocytes increases drastically.

An *infection* is the invasion of harmful organisms into the body. When the first leucocytes are not successful in stopping the infection, the invading organisms are free to multiply and injure body cells. This results in a swelling and redness called an *inflammation* in the infected part of the body. Chemicals that are released from the injured cells cause additional leucocytes to move out of blood vessels in order to engulf and digest, or to kill, the harmful invaders. Leucocytes digest and remove injured and dead body cells.

The accumulation of dead leucocytes, dead organisms, and broken cells forms a thick fluid called *pus,* which is characteristic of infections. Infections may be rather minor, such as the common cold, or, as with pneumonia, may result in prolonged suffering and death. In all infections, however, the leucocytes are necessary for ultimate victory over the invaders.

Platelets and blood clotting

Platelets develop from large cells in the red bone marrow. A platelet lacks a nucleus and is less than 1/2 the size of an erythrocyte. When you are bruised or cut, the broken blood vessels are plugged by platelets, which tend to stick to the broken edges of the vessels. The platelets release *serotonin* (SEHR uh TOH nin), which causes contraction of the muscles of the vessel walls. This reduces the blood loss from the damaged vessels.

Platelets are also involved in **coagulation*** (koh AG yuh LAY shun), the formation of a blood clot. As the platelets stick to the rough edges of damaged tissue, they release a substance which aids in the formation of *thromboplastin** (THRAHM boh PLAS tin). Together with calcium (which is in the blood plasma), thromboplastin triggers the formation of plasma protein (produced in the liver) into thrombin.

The newly formed thrombin is used to change soluble *fibrinogen** (fye BRIN uh juhn) (another blood plasma protein from the liver) into the insoluble *fibrin.* The fibrin threads then form a microscopic meshwork which entangles the blood

21A-6 *An electron micrograph of blood clotting (5000X). Arrow indicates fibrin fibers.*

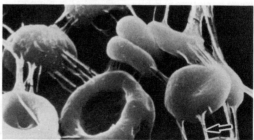

---

coagulation: co- (L. CO-, together) + -agulation (AGERE, to drive)

thromboplastin: thrombo- (Gk. THROMBOS, clot) + -plastin (to mold)

fibrinogen: fibrino- (fiber) + -gen (Gk. GENES, born)

cells to form a *blood clot*. The time required for coagulation varies from 5 to 15 min. Blood clots are gradually dissolved by chemicals in the blood as the vessel wall heals.

A clot that forms within a blood vessel, called a **thrombus**, may cause severe illness or even death. A thrombus readily forms where the blood flow slowly or where the lining of the blood vessel is narrow and rough, as in the disease *atherosclerosis** (ATH uh roh skluh ROH sis). A thrombus that becomes dislodged and floats in the blood

vessels is known as an **embolus*** (EM buh lus). An embolus that becomes wedged in an artery that supplies a vital organ is dangerous. If an embolus plugs a major artery near a person's brain, he may lose consciousness. The loss of blood supply to the brain is called a *stroke* which may result in partial paralysis, depending on the specific brain region that was affected. When a thrombus lodges in a blood vessel going to the heart muscle, it is called *coronary thrombosis* (thrahm BOH sis), one type of heart attack.

Review Questions 21A-1
1. What are the components of blood?
2. List and tell the significance of the components of blood plasma.
3. Describe the shape, size, structure, and function of (a) an erythrocyte and (b) a leucocyte.
4. Describe the size, shape, and function of platelets.
5. Trace the steps in blood clotting.

Facet 21A-1: Blood Transfusions and Blood Grouping, pages 554-55
1. What is a blood transfusion, and why might a blood transfusion be needed?
2. The presence or absence of what substances determines a person's blood type?
3. What is meant by a universal blood donor and a universal blood recipient?
4. Why should blood type compatibility be checked for the donor and the recipient?

The Heart

The **heart** is a hollow, muscular organ that has been described as a four-chambered, double-barreled blood pumper. Approximately the size of a clenched fist and weighing about 12 oz., the heart lies in a slanted position between the lungs with the *apex* (point) directed toward the left.

Sounds of the Heart

The characteristic *lubb-dubb, lubb-dubb* sounds heard through a stethoscope are produced when the atrioventricular and semilunar valves close. When the heart muscle contracts, the blood fills the cups of the valves of the heart which snap together. The atrioventricular (AV) valves snapping closed produce the *lubb*, and the semilunar valves snapping closed produce the *dubb*.

If the heart valves do not develop properly or become scarred by infection, they may not close properly and therefore may allow blood to leak in the reverse direction. The backward flow of blood through the damaged heart valves produces the abnormal hissing sounds known as *heart murmurs*. If the heart murmurs are heard only after strenuous exercise, they are usually no threat to an individual's health; however, if the

murmurs are heard even after a restful night, there is cause for concern. Sometimes it is necessary to replace a defective valve with an *artificial valve*. Many heart murmurs of children correct themselves as the individual matures.

A human heart valve (cross section)   A mechanical replacement valve

---

The heart muscle has greater endurance than any other muscle in the body; it contracts about 70 times per minute. At this rate, the heart beats 100,800 times per day, about 37 million times per year. Every heartbeat pushes about 80 ml (2.4 fl. oz) of blood from the heart; this amounts to 8,000 L (2,100 gal.) per day. In terms of work, the heart exerts enough force each day to raise 907 kg (1 ton) to a height of 12.5 m (41 ft.).

Structure of the heart

A fibrous sac, the **pericardium*** (PEHR ih KAR dee um), loosely covers the heart and prevents it from rubbing against the lungs and chest's wall. A slight space between the pericardium and the surface of the heart contains a slippery liquid, the *pericardial fluid,* which is secreted by the pericardium. This fluid reduces the friction between the heart and the surrounding structures.

The wall of the heart is made up of three layers.
❏ The **epicardium*** is composed of connective tissue that is tightly attached to the muscular tissue of the heart. This tissue keeps the heart muscle from becoming saturated with the pericardial fluid.
❏ The **myocardium,*** the thickest portion of the heart wall, is the muscle tissue that contracts and thereby pumps blood.
❏ The inner surface of the myocardium is lined with a thin layer of epithelial tissue, the **endocardium.*** This layer prevents the blood from saturating the myocardium.

The right and left sides of the heart are separated by a muscular wall called the **septum.** Each half, in turn, is divided into an upper chamber, the **atrium,** and a lower chamber, the **ventricle.** The atria possess a thin myocardium because

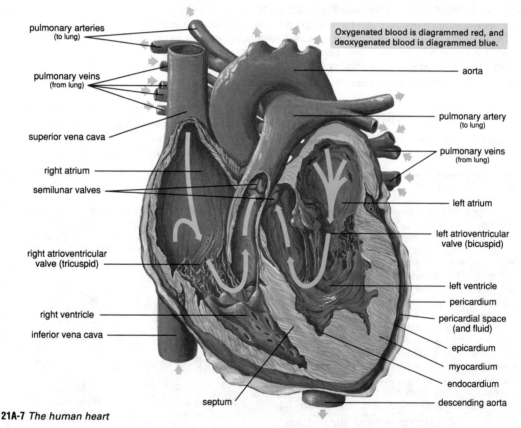

pulmonary arteries (to lung)
pulmonary veins (from lung)
superior vena cava
right atrium
semilunar valves
right atrioventricular valve (tricuspid)
right ventricle
inferior vena cava
septum

Oxygenated blood is diagrammed red, and deoxygenated blood is diagrammed blue.

aorta
pulmonary artery (to lung)
pulmonary veins (from lung)
left atrium
left atrioventricular valve (bicuspid)
left ventricle
pericardium
pericardial space (and fluid)
epicardium
myocardium
endocardium
descending aorta

21A-7 *The human heart*

---

pericardium: peri- (around) + -cardium (heart)

epicardium: epi- (upon or over) + -cardium (heart)

myocardium: myo- (Gk. MYO-, muscle) + -cardium (heart)

endocardium: endo- (within) + -cardium (heart)

these chambers primarily receive blood. The ventricles, in contrast, have a thick myocardium layer because they are responsible for pushing the blood into the blood vessels of the body.

Between the atrium and ventricle in each half of the heart are the **atrioventricular** (AY tree oh ven TRIK yuh lur) **valves** *(AV valves)*. The right AV valve is the *tricuspid* valve,* and the left AV valve is the *bicuspid valve.* The tricuspid valve is composed of three flaps of tissue, and the bicuspid is composed of two. These valves permit the flow of blood from the atria to the ventricles but prevent a reverse flow because the flaps are anchored to the ventricle walls by fibrous strands.

The **semilunar* valves,** located at the exits of the ventricles, have three cup-shaped membranes. They permit the flow of blood into the blood vessels but keep the blood from returning to the ventricles. All heart valves are passive–they do not move by themselves but are moved by the force of the blood during each heartbeat.

Blood flow through the heart

The *superior vena cava* drains deoxygenated blood (traditionally diagrammed as blue) from body parts above the heart, including the arms and hands, and the *inferior vena cava* returns deoxygenated blood from body regions below the level of the heart. As the right atrium fills with blood, it contracts, squeezing the blood through the tricuspid valve and into the right ventricle.

When the right ventricle contracts, the tricuspid valve is forced to shut, and the pulmonary semilunar valve opens to allow the blood to flow into the *pulmonary* artery.* Thus, the right side of the heart pumps only deoxygenated blood.

Each of the two main branches of the pulmonary artery leads to a lung. As the blood flows through the capillaries surrounding the alveoli, oxygen is added to the hemoglobin of the blood.

The richly oxygenated blood (traditionally diagrammed as red) returns to the left atrium through the *pulmonary veins.* The left atrium then contracts, squeezing the blood through the bicuspid valve and filling the left ventricle.

As the left ventricle contracts, the bicuspid valve shuts with considerable force, and blood

rushes through the aortic semilunar valve into the *aorta.* All parts of the body receive blood from branches of the aorta. After the blood flows through the body organs, it eventually returns to the right atrium by way of the superior vena cava and the inferior vena cava.

The heartbeat

A **heartbeat** or **cardiac cycle** is one complete contraction and relaxation of the heart muscle. You can feel your heartbeat by placing your hand over the region of the heart's apex, which for most people is the level of the fifth and sixth ribs, about 3 in. left of the midline.

The contraction of the heart muscle is known as **systole*** (SIS tuh lee). The heart's relaxing and filling with blood are called **diastole*** (dye AS tuh lee).

21A-8 *The conduction system of the heart*

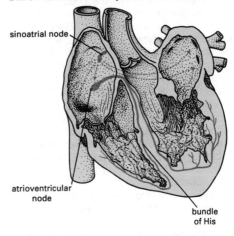

sinoatrial node

atrioventricular node

bundle of His

The regular rhythm of systole and diastole is controlled by the *conduction system of the heart,* specialized tissue embedded in the myocardium. One part of this system, the **sinoatrial** (SYE noh AY tree ul) **node** *(SA node),* starts each systole and thus sets the pace. The SA node has its own rhythm of about 80 electrical impulses per minute. For this reason it has been called the *pacemaker.* The SA node rate, however, can be increased or decreased by the nervous system.

The electrical impulse from the SA node is transmitted through muscle tissue to both atria,

---

tricuspid: tri- (three) + -cuspid (L. CUSPIS, point)

semilunar: semi- (L. SEMI, half) + -luna (L. LUNA, moon)

pulmonary: pulmo- (L. PULMO, lung)

systole: (Gk. SYSTOLE, contraction)

diastole: (Gk. DIASTOLE, expansion)

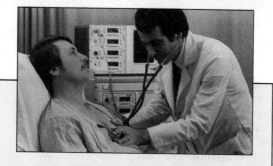

The Electrocardiogram (EKG)

A special apparatus can record on paper the electrical activity of the heart's conduction system. This graphic representation of heart impulses is known as an *electrocardiogram**(ih LEK tro KAR dee uh GRAM)—EKG or ECG. The various peaks or waves of an EKG, designated by the letters (PQRST), represent particular activities of the heart. Any deviation from a normal PQRST wave pattern indicates some defect in the conduction system or in the structure of the heart.

If a portion of the conduction system is injured or diseased, or if the nervous system does not properly regulate the SA node, the impulses do not pass from the atria to the ventricles. This condition is known as a *heart block*. There are different degrees and types of blocks depending on the particular physical defect. For example, in a partial heart block some impulses are missed between the SA node and AV node. This blockage causes the atria to beat somewhat faster than the ventricles.

In a complete heart block there is no communication between the SA and AV nodes, and the atria may beat twice as fast as the ventricles. In heart blocks, the P wave of an EKG will be present, but the QRS wave may be absent for several heartbeats.

Such abnormal rhythms may require surgical implantation of an *artificial pacemaker*. Such a device may be set electronically, or it may stimulate the heart only when the SA node slows in its function. Powered by batteries or nuclear energy, it consists of either a long wire inserted through a vein into the right ventricle or a device implanted in the ventricle wall.

A normal electrocardiogram:
P wave: *atria contracting*
QRS wave: *ventricles contracting*
T wave: *preparing for next contraction*
Variations indicate a possible abnormality.

causing them to contract together. About 1/10 sec. later, the impulse reaches the **atrioventricular node** (AV node), where there is a brief pause to allow for proper emptying of blood from the atria. When the AV node "fires," it sends an electrical impulse down the *bundle of His* to the wall of each ventricle. The fibers of the ventricle walls contract together and efficiently push the blood into the pulmonary artery and the aorta.

The heart rate

The typical resting heart rate of an adult is about 70 beats per minute (bpm); however, during moderate exercise it is commonly about 120 bpm. If the heartbeat is more than 140 bpm, ventricular diastole may be too short for the ventricles to fill

						21A-9
The Cardiac Cycle						
sec.	atria	ventricles	AV valves	semi-lunar valves	sounds	
.1	systole (blood pumped into ventricles)	diastole (blood enters from atria)	open ↓	closed ↓		
.2	diastole (blood enters from body)	systole (blood pumped into arteries)	closed	open	lubb	
.3	↓	↓	↓	↓		
.4		↓	↓	↓		
.5		diastole (blood enters from atria)	open	closed	dubb	
.6	↓	↓	↓	↓		
.7						
.8	↓	↓	↓	↓		

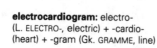

electrocardiogram: electro-
(L. ELECTRO-, electric) + -cardio-
(heart) + -gram (Gk. GRAMME, line)

with blood. Therefore, less blood is pumped at each heartbeat, and the individual begins to tire.

If your heart rate is 72 bpm, about 8/10 sec. is required for one heartbeat. During this brief period of time, the atria are in systole for only 1/10 sec. and then relax and fill with blood for 7/10 sec. The ventricles are in systole for nearly 3/10 sec. and relax and receive blood from the atria for about 5/10 sec.

Heart Attack

To many people the term *heart attack* means that something is seriously wrong with one of the most vital organs. Each year 650,000 people in the U.S. have a heart attack, which is defined as damage or destruction of some of the myocardium. Since the various causes and results of heart muscle damage can be vastly different, the term *heart attack* is somewhat vague. Treatments which help one person recovering from a heart attack may cause one in another person.

Most people who experience a heart attack describe it as a squeezing pain in the chest. This painful sensation may spread to the shoulders, neck, and arms. It may come and go, it may last for two minutes or longer, and it is usually not sharp or stabbing. The person may not appear ill, but he may feel weak, nauseated, short of breath, and sweaty.

If one is suspected of having a heart attack, the best thing he can do is to lie down and try to relax. Put as little strain on the heart as possible. Medical attention should be sought immediately.

21A-10   Factors That Affect the Heart Rate

The following may *increase* the heart rate:
- Increase in body temperature (may increase the heart rate 3-4 bpm)
- Excessive amounts of sodium and potassium
- Certain hormones (may also increase the strength of contraction)
- Caffeine (as in coffee, tea, and cola beverages)
- Increased amounts of blood returning to the heart (increased muscle contractions during exercise force more blood through the veins into the heart)
- Increased acidity of the blood

The following may *decrease* the heart rate:
- Excessive amount of calcium (may cause irregular contractions)
- Extreme deficiency of oxygen (may cause weaker heart contractions)
- Decreased amount of blood returning to heart

The leading cause of heart attacks is **coronary thrombosis,** the blockage of one or both of the coronary arteries by a blood clot. The seriousness of a coronary thrombosis depends on how much of the heart's blood supply is cut off and which area of the heart is being affected. Sometimes chemicals can be put in the blood to dissolve the blood clot. Other times surgery is necessary to remove the blood clot.

Coronary atherosclerosis involves the building up of fatty tissue in the walls of the coronary arteries. As the amount of blood available to the myocardium decreases, the heart tissue may become damaged, and the likelihood of coronary thrombosis increases. Treatment may involve *coronary by-pass surgery* in which a blood vessel (often from the leg) is inserted into the coronary artery going around the affected area.

Heart block is a condition in which the conductive system of the heart does not transmit nerve impulses properly. This usually results in an irregular heartbeat (arrhythmia). It may be caused by a tumor, a coronary thrombosis, or certain drugs.

At one time, having a heart attack meant either death or a very limited lifestyle. Today over 60% of all heart attack victims recover, and many are able to live normal lives.

Cardiac circulation

The myocardium of your heart requires continual nourishment and oxygen. A pair of coronary arteries that branches from the aorta immediately behind the cup-shaped flaps of the semilunar valve meets this need. The coronary arteries carry about 250 ml of blood per minute when you are resting and about 1,000 ml per minute during strenuous exercise. These arteries receive oxygen-rich blood from the left ventricle and carry the blood to the many capillaries in the myocardium.

The flow of blood in the capillaries of the myocardium stops, or nearly stops, each time the heart contracts. When the heart is in diastole, the capillaries open, and blood circulates. About 70% of the blood that flows into the myocardium drains out of the heart by way of the cardiac veins. The remaining 30% passes through the endocardium and into the ventricles.

Review Questions 21A-2

1. List and describe the three layers of the heart's wall.
2. List the heart's valves. Describe their action.
3. Sketch the heart and trace the path of a drop of blood through the heart. Label all the parts of the heart through which the blood passes. Lable the arteries and veins passing into and out of the heart.
4. What causes the sounds of the heart?
5. What are the two main heart structures that determine heart rate?
6. What can be determined by an EKG?

Blood Vessels and Circulations

The heart and blood vessels form a completely closed system. There are three types of blood vessels: **arteries,** which carry blood away from the heart; **veins,** which carry blood toward the heart; and **capillaries,** the tiny vessels which connect arteries to veins.

The Pulse

As your heart beats and the left ventricle forces blood into the aorta, the elastic walls of the arteries expand. This wave of expansion moves down the aorta and along smaller arteries. As the wave passes, the elastic walls of the arteries resume their normal size. This dilation and rebounding of an artery is the **pulse.**

You can measure your pulse rate wherever you can push an artery against a bone. One place is the *radial artery* at your wrist, which can be pushed against the radius. Be sure you use your fingers rather than your thumb because the pulse can also be detected in arteries of your thumb.

There is no pulse in a vein because the force of the heart contraction has been absorbed by the blood flowing through the numerous capillaries.

Usually the arteries of the body are in the deeper muscles and between muscles and bones. Some veins are located near the body surface, and many can be seen under the skin. There are about 50,000 mi. of capillaries in an adult body. Almost every cell of the body is near a blood capillary.

Blood leaves the heart through the strongest arteries in the body: the *pulmonary artery,* which branches into smaller arteries that lead to the lungs; and the *aorta,* which arches behind the heart and continues down the body. The aorta has many branches that carry blood toward all organs of the body except the lungs. The strong, muscular walls of arteries have three layers: an outer elastic layer, a middle muscular layer, and an inner one-cell-thick layer of epithelial cells.

Arteries form smaller vessels known as *arterioles* (ar TEER ee OHLZ), which in turn branch

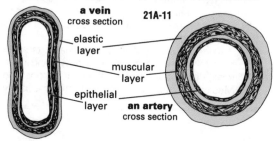

a vein cross section   21A-11

elastic layer

muscular layer

epithelial layer   **an artery** cross section

21A-12 Major Veins and Arteries of the Human Body

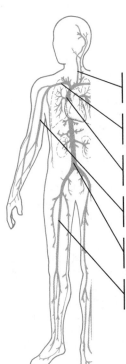

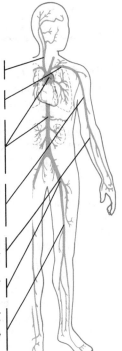

Veins

Jugular Drains blood from brain, skull, scalp, and face; located near surface along neck

Subclavian Drains blood from arms, shoulders, chest, and, in females, mammary glands

Superior vena cava Receives blood from all body regions above the level of the heart

Cephalic Located in upper arm; drains blood from arm into subclavian vein

Inferior vena cava Receives blood from all body regions below the level of the heart

Femoral Located in thigh region; drains blood from legs into inferior vena cava

Arteries

Carotid Supplies neck, head, and brain

Subclavian Supplies neck, shoulders, and arms

Aorta Largest artery in body; receives blood from left ventricles; thickest walls of any blood vessel; extends from top of left ventricle down to hip region

Brachial Located along medial surface of upper arm; where blood pressure is usually measured

Radial Located along lower arm region to the wrist; used to measure pulse

Iliac Supplies urinary bladder and reproductive organs

Femoral Located in thigh region; important "pressure point" to stop blood loss if leg is severely injured

numerously into microscopic capillaries whose walls are only one cell thick. The capillaries are the *functional units of the circulatory system* since through them the diffusion of oxygen, glucose, hormones, and other essential substances occurs. As the blood flows through the capillaries, it also absorbs waste substances and carries them away to the lungs, kidneys, and liver for excretion or conversion into less toxic substances.

The capillaries then merge to form *venules* (VEN yoolz), which join with other venules to form *veins*. Like arteries, all veins have walls with three layers, but the walls are thinner, less elastic, and less muscular. Many veins in your body, especially those in the arms and legs, possess semilunar valves which prevent reverse blood flow. Skeletal muscle contractions

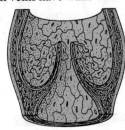

21A-13 *A valve in a vein*

(which squeeze the vessels) and the semilunar valves help force the blood toward the heart.

All veins, except the cardiac and pulmonary, drain blood into the superior and inferior venae cavae. The cardiac veins open directly into the right atrium, and the pulmonary veins return oxygenated blood from the lungs to the left atrium.

Pulmonary and systemic circulations

For the benefit of study, it is convenient to group the entire circulatory system into several divisions or routes. Each of these routes involves the circulation of blood through one or more vital organs and has a definite function. The two main divisions are *pulmonary circulation* and *systemic circulation*.

• **Pulmonary circulation** carries blood from the right ventricle to the lungs for the purpose of absorbing oxygen and releasing carbon dioxide. After passing through the lungs, the oxygenated blood returns to the left side of the heart. At any moment about 1/2 L (1 pint) of blood is in the

FACETS OF BIOLOGY

Blood Pressure and Hypertension

Today a common medical concern is one's blood pressure. Although more of a problem for older people, even children can have blood pressure difficulties. One of the problems is that most people know only that blood pressure consists of two numbers the nurse gets by wrapping a tight band around the arm and listening to the inside of the elbow with a stethoscope.

Blood pressure (BP) may be defined as the pressure of blood against the walls of arteries which causes the pulse. Healthy, elastic artery walls usually expand to absorb this pressure and then rebound to push the blood along.

When the heart beats (systole of the ventricles) BP in the arteries is high; when at rest (diastole of the ventricles) the arteriole blood pressure is lower. Because the standard measurement of blood pressure involves pushing mercury up a thin tube, the numbers used in blood pressure represent millimeters of mercury (mm Hg).

The average pressure the blood of a young adult puts on his blood vessels during ventricular systole is about 120 mm Hg and during ventricular diastole about 80 mm Hg. For convenience such measurements are expressed as 120/80.

Normally your BP rises as you need more blood, as during strenuous activity. To raise the BP, your body increases the amount of blood pumped by the heart, decreases the size of the arteries, and, under extreme stress, thickens the blood by the addition of stored blood cells. Following the need for high BP, a healthy person's BP will quickly return to normal.

Systolic pressures of 140-150 mm Hg and diastolic pressures of 90-100 mm Hg are usually considered the upper limits of normal BP. A person whose BP measurements exceed one or both of these limits suffers from *high blood pressure* or **hypertension.** If the systolic pressure exceeds 200 mm Hg, there is real danger that an artery may rupture. Such a rupture in the brain region is often fatal.

Hypertension is a condition caused by a complex of diseases, disorders and conditions. Some factors that contribute to hypertension include being overweight, eating too much salt (sodium), lack of exercise, anxiety, inability to relax, age, certain drugs (usually taken to deal with some other condition), and build up of fatty substances inside the arteries.

In many cases the BP increases as the walls of the arteries become hardened and thicker. In such cases the arterioles and small arteries are decreased in diameter. The heart is therefore under great stress as it attempts to push adequate amounts of blood through the partially closed, nonelastic blood vessels.

Untreated hypertension can result in death by heart failure, stroke, kidney failure, or closure of the coronary arteries. Treatment or control of hypertension includes proper diet, rest, exercise, and sometimes certain drugs.

Although increasing your BP is essential for you to be able to enjoy normal life, continually high blood pressure is an example of too much of a good thing not being good for you.

Review questions on page 579.

CANDIDATES FOR HIGH BLOOD PRESSURE

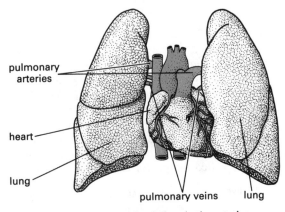

pulmonary
arteries

heart

lung

pulmonary veins   lung

21A-14 *In only pulmonary circulation do the arteries carry deoxygenated blood (blue), and veins, oxygenated blood (red).*

pulmonary circulation. Circulation of this amount requires only a few seconds.

• **Systemic circulation** consists of the flow of blood from the left ventricle to all parts of the body (except the lungs) and then back to the right atrium. Systemic circulation carries oxygen and nutrients to the body tissues and removes carbon dioxide and wastes from the tissues.

There are several special circulations that are part of systemic circulation; some of the familiar ones include the following:

❑ *Coronary circulation* **Coronary circulation** carries blood into and out of the heart muscle.

Diseases and Disorders of the Circulatory System

Anemia: a condition in which there is a decrease in hemoglobin or in the number of erythrocytes
• **aplastic anemia:** caused by improper development of bone marrow or destruction of marrow by certain chemicals or X-rays
• **pernicious anemia:** the erythrocytes are fragile and abnormally large but usually contain less hemoglobin than normal; caused by a lack of certain proteins that are needed for vitamin B_{12} absorption in the stomach.
• **sickle cell anemia:** abnormal sickle- or crescent-shaped erythrocytes are found in the blood stream
• **iron deficiency anemia:** results from a lack of usable iron or other nutrients necessary for the use of iron to make hemoglobin in the diet
Aneurysm: a permanent stretching of an artery or heart chamber; caused by the pressure of blood on muscular walls weakened by disease or injury
Arrhythmia: an irregularity of the heartbeat
Arteriosclerosis: commonly called *hardening of the arteries;* a general term for a variety of conditions which cause the artery walls to become thick and hard and to lose their elasticity
Atherosclerosis: a form of arteriosclerosis with accumulation of fatty material in artery walls
Bruise: an injury of the skin and underlying tissues resulting in broken blood capillaries; the diffusion and breaking down of blood also causes the "black and blue" marks
Endocarditis: inflammation of the lining of the heart; usually caused by bacteria
Fibrillation: the quivering or spontaneous con-

traction of individual muscle fibers in atria or ventricles or throughout the entire myocardium; may be caused by physical injury, a blood clot in coronary arteries, or an overdose of certain drugs
Hemorrhage: a break in a blood vessel resulting in loss of blood; may be due to physical injury or a disease condition
Leukemia: an increase in the number of leucocytes to about 1 million per cubic millimeter (cu. mm.); many immature leucocytes are present in blood; usually fatal but in some cases has been controlled by drugs and proper diet
Leucocytosis: an increase in leucocytes (more than 10,000 per cu. mm.) in response to an infection in the body
Pericarditis: an inflammation of the pericardium; caused by bacterial infection, physical injury to the heart, or tumors
Phlebitis: an inflammation of a vein; the cause is unknown, but it is more common in those people who must stand or walk slowly for long periods of time; weight reduction seems to alleviate the problem
Radiation sickness: an illness caused by too much exposure to radiation; the symptoms include a breakdown of lymphatic tissue, many hemorrhages, immature red bone marrow, and delayed blood clot formation
Stroke: a sudden loss of consciousness caused by a hemorrhage or a blood clot in arteries in or around the brain
Varicose veins: refers to veins that are distended, swollen, and knotted; more common in people who stand for long periods of time

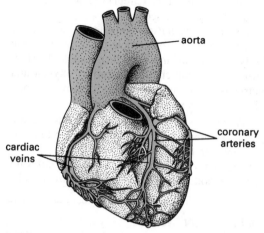

21A-15 *Coronary circulation*

Two coronary arteries that branch off the aorta deliver nutrients to the myocardium of the heart. After passing through many capillaries, the blood flows into the cardiac veins. These veins join to form a large vein called the coronary sinus, which carries the blood into the right atrium.

❏ *Renal circulation* The circulation of blood in and out of the kidneys is known as the **renal*** (REE nul) **circulation.** This route begins with the *renal arteries* that branch from the aorta. These arteries branch extensively into many capillaries to nourish the kidney cells. As the blood flows through the kidneys, the waste materials are removed for excretion as urine. The blood that leaves the kidneys in the *renal veins* is the cleanest blood in the body.

21A-16 *Renal circulation*

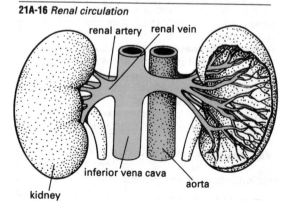

❏ *Portal circulation* The blood from the digestive organs, which is rich in food molecules, is carried to the liver by the *hepatic* portal vein*. The liver also receives oxygenated blood from the *hepatic artery*, a branch of the aorta. These two vessels branch as they enter the liver, and the blood mixes in the liver *sinusoids*. This flow of blood to the liver is called the **portal circulation.** The liver

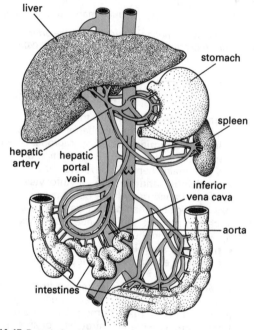

21A-17 *Portal circulation*

cells remove toxic substances from the blood and metabolize foods. The blood leaves the liver through the hepatic veins that merge with the inferior vena cava.

Blood in the portal vein also contains insulin, a hormone from the pancreas which stimulates excess glucose molecules to form *glycogen*, a storage form of carbohydrates. This glycogen can be changed back into glucose when needed, especially between meals. When a person's pancreas does not produce enough insulin, the excess glucose will not be stored for future use but will instead be lost in the urine. Such an individual is suffering from *diabetes mellitus* (meh LYE tus). (See pages 491, 603-4.)

---

renal: (L. RENES, kidneys)   **hepatic:** (Gk. HEPAR, liver)

Biological Terms

Blood	*The Heart*	systole	coronary circulation
blood	heart	diastole	renal circulation
blood plasma	pericardium	sinoatrial node	portal circulation
globulins	epicardium	atrioventricular node	*Facets*
antibody	myocardium	*Blood Vessels and Circulations*	blood types
erythrocytes	endocardium	arteries	(blood groups)
leucocytes	septum	veins	ABO blood types
platelets	atrium	capillaries	agglutinate
coagulation	ventricle	pulse	Rh system
thrombus	atrioventricular valves	pulmonary circulation	blood pressure (BP)
embolus	semilunar valves	systemic circulation	hypertension
	heartbeat (cardiac cycle)		

Review Questions 21A-3

1. Describe and compare arteries and veins.
2. How do pulmonary and systemic circulation differ?
3. List three divisions of systemic circulation and tell what happens to the blood in them.

Facet 21A-2: Blood Pressure and Hypertension, page 564

1. Compare pulse and blood pressure.
2. What is meant by the two numbers usually given as a blood pressure reading?
3. Describe hypertension and list several factors that are believed to help cause the condition.

Thought Question

Why is the concentration of dissolved substances in the materials used for an intravenous feeding important?

21B–The Lymphatic System and Immunity

Your body exists in a hostile environment. Vast numbers of bacteria, viruses, and other microbes would find your body an ideal place to grow and reproduce. And, of course, many of these invaders are pathogenic. The fact that most humans are healthy is a tribute to your body's ability to resist infection. Some mechanisms are *nonspecific* in that they do not distinguish one infectious agent from another. Many of these were discussed in Chapter 9C, but some of the responses of the lymphatic system can be considered nonspecific responses too.

Some body responses to foreign materials are highly *specific*. Each of these mechanisms responds only to a certain foreign substance, such

as a particular protein in a certain virus's coat, a chemical produced by a specific bacteria, or cells that have a certain substance on their cell membrane. The specific defense mechanisms your body employs against invading pathogens can be called your **immune system.**

The structures of the human immune system are not as easy to identify as are parts of the skeletal, circulatory, or other systems. Many of the structures that help you fight off invading pathogens are tiny, and many are parts of other systems and carry on only certain immune system functions. Since much of the actual battle waged against pathogens must be carried on at sites where they invade the body, much of the immune system involves "mobile units" like chemicals and blood cells.

In this section we will deal with the anatomy and physiology of the lymphatic system and then discuss how scientists believe specific human immunities work and are developed.

The Lymphatic System

As blood flows through the numerous capillaries in your body, water and some dissolved substances diffuse out of them into the spaces between cells. Some of this fluid between the cells enters the cells and is used in metabolic reactions, and some is reabsorbed by the capillaries. The remaining fluid between the cells passes into the **lymphatic** (lim FAT ik) **system**. When this fluid finally gets inside these capillaries and ducts, it is called **lymph.***

Lymphatic Organs

The **tonsils** of the pharynx region are composed of several small lymph nodes covered with connective tissue. These masses are found toward the back of the mouth on each side, on the back wall of the throat, and on the back of the tongue. In the past it was a common medical practice to remove the tonsils even if they were healthy; however, today the tonsils are usually removed only if they become infected and progress beyond antibiotic treatments.

The **thymus gland,** located between the aorta and the sternum, is composed of lymphatic tissues. In the thymus many of the cells responsible for specific immunities are developed. This gland also produces a hormone that stimulates the production of lymphocytes. Active in children, the thymus atrophies by adulthood.

The **spleen** is the largest organ of the lymphatic system and is located immediately under the diaphragm on your left side. It is similar to a large lymph node, but it filters blood rather than lymph. A microscopic view reveals growths of lymphocytes and large spaces for storage of red blood cells. If you were cut and lost blood, your spleen would quickly put these stored blood cells into your blood stream. Phagocytic cells of the spleen also destroy old red blood cells.

Although the lymphatic system returns the fluid to the blood stream, it has neither a heart nor arteries. Its tiny "dead-end" **lymph capillaries** are located in almost every region of the body. They absorb the excess fluids and proteins from most body tissues, keeping these tissues from becoming swollen.

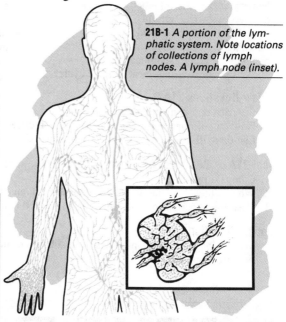

21B-1 *A portion of the lymphatic system. Note locations of collections of lymph nodes. A lymph node (inset).*

The pressure of the between-the-cell fluid is usually greater than in the lymph capillaries. This forces the fluid into the lymph capillaries. The walls of the lymph capillaries are constructed with overlapping cells so that the fluid can enter easily. This mechanism works somewhat like a swinging door that opens inward only. As the volume of fluid increases within the lymph capillary, the cells are pushed together, preventing the outward flow of lymph.

The lymph capillaries combine and form **lymph vessels,** which are structurally similar to veins. The lymph is carried along the lymph vessels by a pumping action of muscle fibers in the walls. The lymph is prevented from flowing backward by tiny one-way valves similar to those in the veins. Lymph is also moved upward by the pressure of skeletal muscle contraction as you

---

lymph: (L. LYMPHA, water)

move your body. After the lymph flows through numerous lymph nodes, it finally drains into two main ducts that join the blood stream where the jugular and subclavian veins meet in the shoulder region.

Lymph nodes

The lymphatic system helps in combating infections in your body. Along the tiny lymph vessels are numerous small masses of tissue called **lymph nodes.** As the watery lymph flows into and through the nodes, bacteria, viruses, and other foreign matter are filtered out and destroyed.

Lymph nodes are composed of a layer of connective tissue surrounding small groups of cells. The size of the nodes may vary from that of a pinhead to that of a large lima bean. Lymph nodes are located in all body regions but are most numerous in the floor of the mouth, the neck region, the armpit, and the groin region.

There are two main types of cells found in lymph nodes: *lymphocytes** (which are primarily involved in specific immune responses and are discussed in the next section) and **macrophages.*** **Macrophages** (sometimes called *monocytes*) are large, phagocytic cells. They ingest virtually any substance which is foreign to the body. There are two basic types:

❑ *wandering macrophages* which travel through the blood and lymph, and

❑ *fixed macrophages* which are found embedded in various body tissues, including lymph nodes.

As the lymph slowly flows through the lymph node, fixed macrophages engulf certain bacteria, viruses, and other foreign substances and digest them in vacuoles. For some minor infections this is all that is necessary to rid the body of the pathogen. If, however, the foreign substance is in large quantity, it may slip by the first lymph node. Rarely, however, will a recognized foreign substance make it past the second or third lymph node along a lymph vessel.

Disorders and Diseases of the Lymphatic System

Edema: a condition in which the body tissues are swollen with excess fluids; lymph vessels may be blocked with a clot or a parasitic worm, as in *elephantiasis*

Hodgkin's disease: a cancer that causes the lymph nodes, spleen, and liver to become abnormally large

Mononucleosis: a disease in which a high concentration of monocytes are present in the blood; caused by a virus but usually occurs in people fatigued, under stress, and lacking proper rest and nourishment

Tonsillitis: inflammation of the tonsils; may be caused by a variety of organisms and viruses

---

The combat between bacteria and lymph node macrophages may result in swollen lymph nodes near the region of the body where the infection occurs. For example, if a person suffers from a sore throat, the lymph nodes in the neck region may become swollen, causing a soreness, especially when he swallows or moves his head.

In severe bacterial infections the bacteria which are carried into the node may become so abundant that they overwhelm the node. The node may swell and become a place where bacteria are growing rather than where they are being destroyed. This infection of the lymphatic system may result in bacteria entering the blood and being carried to other areas of the body.

Some foreign substances cannot be digested by the enzymes produced by the macrophages. For example, macrophages are unable to break down many substances in tobacco smoke. In heavy smokers the lymph nodes fill with smoke particles and become dark gray or black. In time these foreign materials may interfere with the function of the node. Asbestos is another substance which macrophages cannot digest.

Review Questions 21B-1

1. Where does lymph come from? Where does lymph go?
2. Name and describe two types of macrophages.
3. What happens to lymph as it passes through lymph nodes?
4. List three lymphatic organs.

---

lymphocytes: lympho- (water) + -cytes (cell)

macrophages: macro- (large) + -phages (Gk. PHAGEIN, to eat)

Immunity

A person is **immune** to a disease when his body reacts to the presence of a pathogen by destroying it or rendering it harmless. Today, scientists recognize that the mechanisms involved in immunity are often complex. Frequently the body's defense mechanisms deal with the pathogen's products or with some aspect of the human body and not directly with the pathogen itself.

The human immune system's primary function is to search for, recognize, and eliminate antigens. An **antigen** is any foreign substance (usually a protein) to which the body responds by making chemicals or specialized cells which directly or indirectly eliminate that antigen itself. An antigen may be one of many different substances, including a portion of a virus's protein coat, a chemical released by a bacteria, an enzyme produced by a fungus, or even a toxin released by an infected body cell.

Normally antigens cause the body to produce *antibodies* or to increase the number of a specific kind of *T cells*. Although these two processes often work together in fighting a disease, we will discuss them separately.

Humoral immunity

Humoral immunity involves antibodies. **Antibodies** are proteins which travel through the body by dissolving into the blood or lymph. (The word *humor* refers to fluid.) Antibodies are involved in the destruction of antigens.

Within the lymph nodes and spleen are specialized lymphocytes called **B cells.** Each person has thousands of different kinds of B cells in his body. Each kind of B cell recognizes a different antigen. The presence of an antigen stimulates a particular kind of B cell to divide, producing *plasma cells* and *memory B cells*. Plasma cells are responsible for producing antibodies. Some plasma cells produce 2,000 antibody molecules per second for the 4-5 days they live. Even at that rate, the first build up of plasma cells and antibodies needed to fight off a particular infection may take several days to several weeks.

Antibodies may react with antigens in several ways. Some antigens are toxins. Their toxic effect may be *neutralized* when the proper antibody combines with them. Some antibodies neutralize viruses by combining with the viral coat protein which permits the virus to enter its host cell. Other

21B-2 Humorial immunity

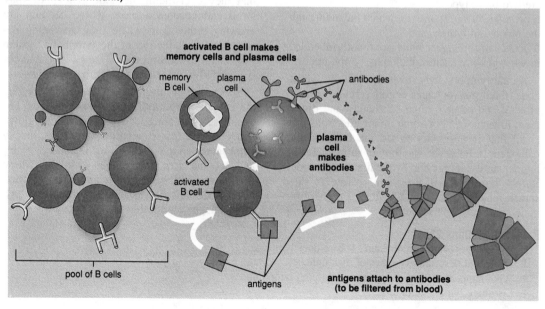

570

FACETS OF BIOLOGY

AIDS: Acquired Immune Deficiency Syndrome

It appears that a few years ago a virus mutated and became a virulent killer. Since the virus caused an infectious disease that severely damaged the immune system, it was named **Acquired Immune Deficiency Syndrome (AIDS)** when it was officially described in 1982. In 1981, in the United States, 266 people were identified as having AIDS. By 1987 the official number had jumped to over 42,000. And by the end of that year only 40% of those people were alive. The actual number of people may be 10% higher than these figures.

This new, rapidly spreading, lethal disease became an international concern. Who has it? How is it spread? What can be done to prevent getting it? What can be done to cure it? Rumors flew rampant. Scientific information was misrepresented, misunderstood, and sometimes inaccurate (often because of haste).

Let us examine some facts about AIDS. Once the virus is in the body, it enters certain helper T cells. It appears that in some people the virus can remain dormant in these cells for a long time. Although some people develop symptoms of AIDS and die within

2 yr. or less, there are people who have lived with the virus in their blood cells for over 8 yr. but have no symptoms of the disease (see "latent viruses," page 241). Once the virus becomes activated and the disease symptoms start, the patient has little hope. Although some drugs can slow the process of the disease, there have been no recoveries or long remissions (based on reports available in 1990).

The virus destroys the helper T cells it invades. Since these cells trigger cell-mediated immunity, the person with AIDS loses most of his ability to fight off new infections. In time, his immunities are impaired, and he is unable to develop new ones. The AIDS virus may initially cause symptoms including fever, night sweats, diarrhea, weight loss, fatigue, rashes, swollen lymph glands, loss of memory, loss of coordination, and even paralysis.

It has been said that no one dies of AIDS. AIDS victims usually die from infections of other diseases which their bodies cannot fight off. Medical science is able to help the person fight many of these diseases. In time, however, the number of infections and the physical strain of the diseases and the medications slowly wear the person down. The immune system of most healthy people easily fights off the pathogens that lead to death for AIDS victims also.

The AIDS virus is normally found in the body fluids of an infected person: blood, semen

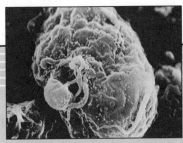

Electron micrograph of an AIDS-infected lymphocyte

(sperm-containing fluid), secretions of the female reproductive organs, and (to a much lesser extent) saliva and tears. For AIDS to be transferred from one human to another, there must be *contact with the passage of body fluids or the transfer of blood.*

In the late 1980s about 90% of the people with AIDS were either homosexuals or users of illegal intravenous drugs. AIDS, however, is not a disease of homosexuals and intravenous drug abusers only. It appears that the primary reason the disease is prevalent among these people is that the disease got into these groups and their activities fostered the rapid spread of the disease.

Anyone who receives body fluids from a person that has the virus can get the disease. For example, some people contracted AIDS as they were given transfusions of blood that contained the virus. (Today donated blood is tested to be sure it does not contain the AIDS virus. The test is reliable, but like all such tests, it is not infallible. There is a slim chance a person can get AIDS from a blood transfusion.) The disease can be transferred from an infected mother to her unborn child. At this time a small number of people have contracted the disease through heterosexual contact with someone who has the virus.
Review questions on page 576

AIDS and HIV

AIDS is a disease caused by the **HIV**, human immunodeficiency virus. (Thus, the *HIV* and *the AIDS virus* are the same thing.) Because the HIV is a latent virus, a person can have HIV, but not yet suffer AIDS. When the HIV becomes active, he will suffer the AIDS symptoms.

FACETS OF BIOLOGY

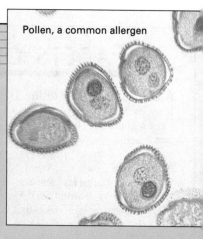
Pollen, a common allergen

Allergies and Tissue Rejection

Sometimes good things can be carried too far, and that is the case with an **allergy**. Normally, pollen, perfume, dog dander, feathers, strawberries, milk, wheat, house dust, and other normal substances in the environment do not stimulate the body to produce antibodies. The immune system of some people, however, after being exposed to these substances, does begin to produce antibodies or helper T cells against them. Then, whenever that person is exposed to that substance, his body reacts against it. This, essentially, is what is called an allergy.

The word *allergy* comes from a Greek word which means "change from the original state." It was first used by an Austrian pediatrician in 1906 when he noted that some people are changed when they encounter a normally harmless substance. Repeated exposures to the substance, he explained, resulted in increased changes until

the person is hypersensitive to the substance.

In the case of allergies the foreign substance that causes the reaction is called an **allergen**. When the antibodies that cause an allergy come in contact with the allergen, the two combine causing certain cells to release *histamine** and other chemicals. These chemicals cause the symptoms of an allergic reaction. Many allergy sufferers find relief by taking *antihistamines.** There are many different antihistamines on the market. Some are potent, others mild. Some work well for certain allergies and do very little for other allergies.

Inhaled allergens (pollen, mold spores, animal dander, and house dust) usually cause a runny nose, sneezing, and itchy eyes. Skin contact with an allergen (such as poison ivy, cosmetics, perfumes, chemicals, and metals) usually causes redness, itching, swelling,

and blisters. Reactions to ingested or injected allergens (foods, drugs, and venoms) can cause problems in almost any area of the body which range from itching and sneezing to diarrhea and vomiting. In exceptionally severe cases the person's blood pressure drops, the air passages become constricted, and the person may collapse and die.

Another condition in which the immune system seems to work against a person involves transplanted tissues and organs. As a result of disease, injury, inherited factors, reactions to drugs, and other causes, various organs and

antibodies cause *precipitation* (the formation of clumps bonded together) of the antigen. Other antibodies cause *agglutination*. In agglutination the antigen is part of the cell, and the antibody causes the cells to form clumps. The precipitated antigens and the agglutinated cells can be removed from the body by phagocytosis or other means. Some antibodies cause *immobilization* of cells by reacting with their flagella. Stopping cellular movement permits the body to deal with the cells more easily.

The memory B cells produced by a stimulated B cell may live for several dozen years. When an antigen which had resulted in memory B cells

being made enters the body a second time, memory cells quickly divide, making plasma cells and additional memory cells. The next time more antibodies are made faster. This more rapid response permits the elimination of the antigen before the person suffers symptoms of the disease.

Cell-mediated immunity

In **cell-mediated immunity** various immune system cells are involved in the destruction of cells involved with the antigen. In some cases the cells destroyed are body cells that have been invaded by a virus or body cells that have become cancerous. Other times cell mediated immunity will be against foreign cells.

histamine: hist- (Gk. HISTOS, web) + -amine (Eng. -AMINE, a group of organic compounds of nitrogen)

antihistamine: anti- (opposite) + -hist- (web) + -amine (organic compounds of nitrogen)

tissues may cease to function properly and need replacement. At present, the major problem with most transplanted organs is **tissue rejection.** Rejection involves the immune system's forming killer T cells which in time destroy the cells of the transplanted organ.

The rejection process usually begins as soon as the organ is transplanted. If the donated organ's chemical make-up is quite similar to that of the person who receives it, the rejection process may be slow and can then be controlled with drugs. The first successful kidney transplant involved identical twin boys in 1954. Each boy was able to live with one kidney and the recipient's body did not reject the transplanted kidney. Both boys lived to be adults.

Not every donated organ can come from a twin. And many organs, like the heart and liver, are vital to the life of the donor and must come from deceased donors.

Speed is essential, and, to be successful, most organs must be transplanted within 24 hr. A person in need of an organ undergoes extensive testing, and the results are put into computer networks. When an organ becomes available, it is quickly tested, and the computer is used to select the patient with the best possible match of characteristics.

The better the match, the less likely the body will be able to find foreign substances to react against. Today doctors prescribe drugs which "suppress" the immune system. These drugs hamper the manufacture of T cells and thus limit cell-mediated immunity. The person must continue his immune-system suppression, or the donated organ will be rejected.

Some of the organs that have "successfully" been transplanted include kidneys, livers, bones, tendons, eardrums, ear bones, corneas, bone marrow, lungs, and

hearts. Costs of transplants range from about $2,500 for a cornea to well over $100,000 for a heart. The average kidney transplant is about $30,000. The major expense, however, is not the transplanted organ, but the drugs needed to suppress the immune system and other drugs necessary to keep the person healthy.

Better matching techniques will improve transplant success. Kidneys are relatively easy to transplant because they require attaching only the renal artery, renal vein, and the ureter.

The most successfully transplanted organ is the cornea, the clear front portion of the eyeball. The cornea does not have blood flowing through it and thus does not stimulate the immune system to react against it. Corneas can also be stored longer than most organs.

Review questions on page 576.

Where Immunity Begins

The cells responsible for your body's immune responses are collectively called *lymphocytes,* a kind of white blood cell. Lymphocytes, like all blood cells, begin in the red bone marrow. At first all lymphocytes are alike, but depending upon where they mature, they develop into one of several different types of lymphocytes.

Some immature lymphocytes migrate to the thymus gland and become *T cells.* (The *T* stands for *thymus.*) In time these cells will be either directly involved in cell-mediated immunity or will stimulate other cells to produce antibodies. Other immature lymphocytes are believed to remain in the bone marrow and mature into *B cells.* B cells are involved with manufacturing antibodies and thus deal with humoral immunity.

While the T cells and B cells are maturing, each develops the ability to recognize one of several specific antigens. Once mature these cells migrate to the lymph nodes and spleen where they await the arrival of their specific antigen. These cells may quietly wait for decades, but when their specific antigen comes, these cells carry on cell division and develop into the army of immune system cells which wage war on the antigen.

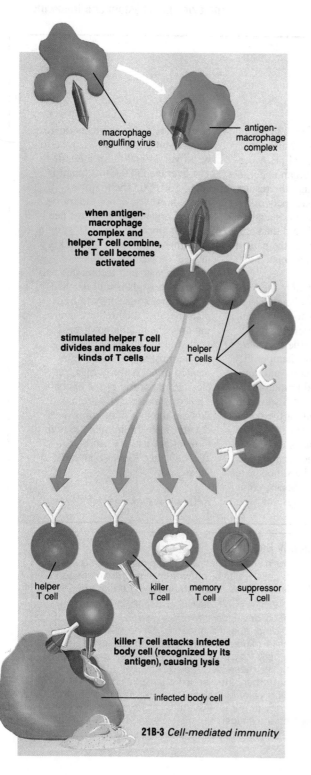

macrophage
engulfing virus

antigen-
macrophage
complex

when antigen-
macrophage
complex and
helper T cell combine,
the T cell becomes
activated

stimulated helper T cell
divides and makes four
kinds of T cells

helper
T cells

helper
T cell

killer
T cell

memory
T cell

suppressor
T cell

killer T cell attacks infected
body cell (recognized by its
antigen), causing lysis

infected body cell

21B-3 *Cell-mediated immunity*

When a macrophage ingests certain antigens, parts of the antigen become bonded on the macrophage's membrane. This *antigen-macrophage complex* may stimulate one of the various kinds of **helper T cells.** (There are many different kinds of helper T cells produced in the body. Each kind recognizes and is stimulated by a different antigen.)

Once stimulated by the antigen-macrophage complex, the helper T cell divides, forming various types of T cells:

❏ **Killer T cells** *(cytotoxic* T cells)* Killer T cells attack body cells which have been affected by the antigen. The killer T cell attaches itself to the affected cell and then releases a protein which forms a hole in the affected cell's membrane. This causes the cell's contents to spill (lysis) and thus kills the affected cell.

❏ **Helper T cells** A helper T cell stimulated by an antigen-macrophage complex will make more of the same kind of helper T cells. A rapid build-up of a specific kind of helper T cell permits the body to fight the infection quickly. Stimulated helper T cells may also cause plasma cells to produce antibodies against the antigen and may produce other chemicals to help the body fight the infection.

❏ **Suppressor T cells** Toward the end of the fight, suppressor T cells are made. These cells stop the activities of the killer T cells, the helper T cells, and the plasma cells, returning the body to normal operations.

❏ **Memory T cells** For many diseases, memory T cells made during an infection will circulate in the blood for dozens of years. When the antigen-macrophage complex of that disease again appears, these cells are ready to divide, rapidly forming killer and helper T cells.

Acquired immunity

The Greek historian Thucydides made one of the earliest known observations of acquired immunity. About 450 B.C. he noted that those who were sick and dying of the plague were cared for by those who had recovered from it, ''for no one was ever attacked a second time.'' That people could develop immunity to certain diseases interested the medical profession for many years. Could a

cytotoxic: cyto- (cell) +
-toxic (poison)

Kinds of Immunity

An immunity can be either active or passive. A person has an **active immunity** when he manufactures the antibodies himself or has activated T cells for a particular antigen. One way a person can acquire an active immunity is, of course, to experience the disease. This is a *natural active immunity*. However, by being inoculated with the antigen that stimulates the production of antibodies or activates T cells, a person can gain immunity without having the disease. In the case of a serious disease such as polio, this method of acquiring an *artificial active immunity* is preferred. In essence, this is what Jenner's vaccination did (see pages 238-39).

A **vaccine** is a weakened form of a pathogen sometimes produced by exposing the pathogen to chemicals, acids, heat, x-rays, or other conditions. Vaccines are used to stimulate the body to produce antibodies or activate T cells which provide just as much protection as those formed as a response to the disease. Some diseases require booster shots (which have the effect of secondary infections), causing the body to produce more memory cells, and thereby increase the level of immunity.

A person can develop a **passive immunity** by being given antibodies that have been formed by another person or an animal. Since the person is not producing the antibodies, these immunities are short-lived. A mother who has an immunity to a specific disease can supply antibodies to an unborn infant through the placenta or to a newborn infant by her milk. In this way antibodies formed in the mother's body can protect the infant for the first 6-12 months of its life. This is called a *natural passive immunity*.

A passive immunity can also be acquired from an immune animal or human. Most often the

In 1894 the effectiveness of serum against diphtheria was announced. By 1895 horses were being inoculated with diphtheria to produce diphtheria serum that saved the lives of thousands of people.

The Common Cold—A Disease Without Immunity

If the human immune system is so effective that when exposed to a virus similar to the smallpox virus it can develop a permanent immunity, why cannot the body develop an immunity for the common cold?

If there were only one common cold virus, it would probably be possible. But the common cold is caused by any one of about a hundred similar viruses. Many of these are believed to be the result of minor mutations, changing only the protein coat of the virus. In the case of the common cold virus, the protein coat appears to be what the immune system recognizes as the antigen.

The many common cold viruses are different enough to require a whole new reaction of the immune system. Thus, although you may be immune to some cold viruses, there are probably still many more you do not have an immunity for.

blood of the organism that has the immunity is used to make a **serum.** A serum is made by removing the blood cells and most dissolved substances from the fluid portion of the blood, leaving specific antibodies. A serum injection results in an *artificial passive immunity* which generally lasts only a few weeks or months. These preformed antibodies can effect full protection from a disease, or in reduced amounts they can cause partial protection. In the latter case, if a person contracts the disease, he will have only a light case and will then develop his own active immunity to it.

Kinds of Immunity

Active immunity The antibodies or the T cells needed for the immunity are being made by the person.
❏ Natural: The person has experienced the disease.
❏ Artificial: The person has been given a vaccine or toxoid.

Passive immunity The antibodies needed for the immunity are being supplied to the person.
❏ Natural: Antibodies are given by the mother to the unborn child or through mother's milk.
❏ Artificial: The antibodies are obtained from the blood serum of other humans or animals.

person become immune to a disease without having the disease? Could people be made to be immune to diseases which were normally contracted repeatedly, like the common cold?

Edward Jenner induced his patients to develop immunity against smallpox without having the disease (see pages 238-39). His success was based on the fact that the cowpox virus and the smallpox virus are quite similar. He had little idea about what the body was doing to become immune.

Neither did Louis Pasteur understand how immunity develops when he accidentally left a culture of chicken-cholera bacteria on a shelf. After a two-week vacation, he remembered the bacteria and decided to see whether it was still pathogenic. He injected it into chickens, and they did not develop the disease. Later, when he exposed these chickens to the cholera pathogen, they did not develop the disease. Pasteur speculated that he

had weakened the bacteria so that it did not cause the disease, but did cause immunity. He experimented with several ways to weaken other pathogens and developed a vaccine for rabies.

Today, we know that when you suffer from certain diseases, your body manufactures *memory B cells* and *memory T cells*. When they are stimulated by the proper antigen, these cells quickly divide and again produce antibodies and reactivate the processes of cell-mediated immunity. Thus, in *secondary infections* (when a pathogen one has experienced before enters the body) the body's defenses can attack more quickly than when the body first had the disease. In secondary infections the disease is usually conquered before you experience the symptoms. During secondary infection of a disease to which you are immune, more memory cells are made. This boosts your immunity to later infections of that pathogen.

Biological Terms

immune system	lymph node	helper T cell	*Facets*
The Lymphatic System	macrophage	killer T cell	Acquired Immune
lymphatic system		suppressor T cell	Deficiency Syndrome (AIDS)
lymph	*Immunity*	memory T cell	allergy
tonsils	immune	active immunity	allergen
thymus gland	antigen	vaccine	tissue rejection
spleen	humoral immunity	passive immunity	
lymph capillary	antibody	serum	
lymph vessel	B cell		
	cell-mediated immunity		

Review Questions 21B-2

1. List two responses of the body to an antigen.
2. Other than being involved with immunity, what do T cells and B cells have in common?
3. How do antibodies react with antigens?
4. List several differences between humoral and cell-mediated immunity.
5. What do memory B cells and memory T cells have to do with acquired immunity?
6. What is the difference between active and passive immunity?
7. List and describe two ways of acquiring an active immunity.
8. List and describe two ways of acquiring a passive immunity.

Facet 21B-1: AIDS–Acquired Immune Deficiency Syndrome, page 571

1. Describe the cause of AIDS.
2. What are the symptoms of AIDS?
3. Why is it possible for a person to have AIDS but not suffer the symptoms?
4. How is AIDS spread?

Facet 21B-2: Allergies and Tissue Rejection, pages 572-73

1. How are allergies and the body's immune system related?
2. How is the immune system involved with transplanted organs or tissues?

21C–The Excretory System

Various organs remove body wastes. The skin's sweat glands (primarily responsible for regulating body temperature) excrete salts, urea, and other wastes. The lungs excrete water and carbon dioxide during breathing. The liver produces bile which contains pigments from broken-down erythrocytes. Because bile flows into the small intestine, these pigments are removed from the body with the feces.

Despite these excretory functions of other organs, the kidneys and associated structures are the primary excretory system of the human body and are vitally important in regulating the blood's chemical composition.

Organs of the excretory system

The **kidneys** resemble two large, purplish brown beans. Their function is to filter metabolic wastes from the blood and excrete these wastes in a liquid called *urine*. As the kidneys form urine, they regulate not only the composition of the blood but also the fluid balance throughout the body tissues.

As the urine forms, it is carried into the collecting basin of the kidney, called the *pelvis*. The urine moves down the muscular **ureters** by peristaltic contractions. About 75 ml of urine per hour is carried down the ureters and is emptied into the **urinary bladder,** the reservoir for urine. The elastic wall of the bladder is composed of muscle layers and a lining.

The **urethra** (*yoo REE thruh*) is the tube that leads from the bladder to the outside of the body. There are two sphincter muscles around the opening of the bladder which remain closed when the bladder is relaxed. During elimination of urine, the muscles of the bladder contract. The resulting pressure forces one sphincter open, but before urine enters the urethra, the other sphincter must be opened voluntarily.

Kidney

Each kidney is about 10 cm (4 in.) long, 6.4 cm (2.6 in.) wide, and 4.8 cm (2 in.) thick. The kidneys are located against the lower back body wall

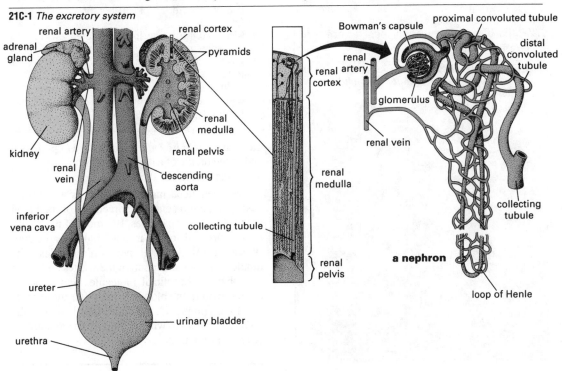

21C-1 *The excretory system*

Artificial Kidneys

If a person has to take certain drugs over long periods of time, one or both kidneys may cease to function. Alcoholic beverages and nicotine (from tobacco) may also contribute to kidney failure. Although a person can survive with less than 1/4 of his nephrons working, if his kidneys fail, an *artificial kidney* will be necessary for his survival. The body cannot tolerate a buildup of wastes or other substances in the blood. An artificial kidney, or *dialysis (dye AL ih sis) machine,* cannot fully duplicate the functions of a normal kidney, but it certainly can prolong life.

In the artificial kidney a cellophane membrane is used to substitute for the glomerulus, and the substitute for the tubule is a large volume of fluid called the *dialysate.* When the machine is in use, the patient's blood flows on one side of the membrane and the dialysate on the other. Thus, as both fluids circulate through the machine, wastes move from the blood into the dialysate, and some substances that are lacking in the blood are absorbed from the dialysate. In this manner the wastes are carried away by the circulating, fresh dialysate.

Today many people who have suffered kidney damage have had a kidney transplant (see pages 572-73) and no longer need the periodic use of a dialysis machine.

This experimental dialysis machine is designed to be worn while the person is engaged in mild exercise.

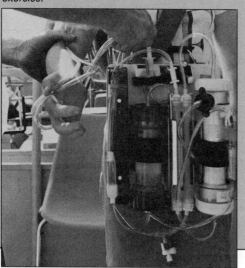

just above the iliac bones. Each kidney is surrounded by a thin protective layer of connective tissue which holds it in place. If you examine a kidney that was sectioned, you could easily distinguish the outer **cortex** region from the inner **medulla.** The medulla consists of several cone-shaped masses of tissue called *pyramids.*

The cortex of each kidney is composed of approximately a million microscopic tubular units called **nephrons,*** which are held together by thin layers of connective tissues that contain blood vessels, nerves, and lymph vessels. If you could untangle all the nephrons in a single kidney and place them end to end, they would be over 70 mi. long.

As the blood flows into the kidney, it passes into a collection of capillaries called the *glomerulus** (gloh MEHR yuh lus). Some of the plasma

Diseases and Disorders of the Excretory System

Floating kidney: a kidney that has been jarred from its usual location and is left movable; may be caused by an injury or blow to the lower back; can occur after an obese person reduces body fat

Kidney failure: an abnormal condition in which the kidneys fail to form urine; may be caused by physical injury, bacterial infections, or exposure to toxic chemicals

Kidney stones: accumulations of various mineral crystals in the pelvis of the kidney; believed to be prevented by drinking sufficient water

then passes into *Bowman's capsule,* a cup-shaped end to the tubule of a nephron. This plasma passes along the *tubules* of the nephron.

Even beneficial molecules such as water, glucose, and amino acids are forced out of the blood in the Bowman's capsules. But most of these substances are reabsorbed into the blood as the substances travel along the nephron's tubules. The tubule is designed to contain the wastes and make sure that the beneficial molecules and minerals are returned to the bloodstream. After these processes are completed, the fluid that flows out the *collecting tubules* (which compose the medulla of the kidney) is urine.

nephron: (Gk. NEPHROS, kidney)
glomerulus: (L. GLOMUS, ball)

21C-2	Normal Components of Urine
Component	**Amount per day**
Water	1200-1500 ml (g)
Urea	25-30 g
Uric acid	0.7 g
Creatinine	1-2 g
Ammonia	0.6 g
Sodium chloride	10-15 g
Potassium chloride	2.5 g
Calcium	0.3 g
Magnesium	0.2 g
Phosphate	1.7 g
Sulfate	2.0 g

Minute amounts: Fatty acids, amino acids, pigments, mucin, enzymes, hormones, and vitamins

21C-3	Abnormal Components of Urine
Component	**Cause**
Glucose	Diabetes mellitus
Proteins	Kidney disease or heart disease
Acetone	Diabetes mellitus, starvation
Erythrocytes	Infections in urinary system
Leucocytes	Large numbers indicate an infection in the urinary system
Casts (deposits of epithelial cells, fat, pus, or blood)	Lesions (sores) in kidney
Amino acid crystals	Severe liver disease
Uric acid crystals	Gout

Urine

Normal **urine** is about 95% water with the rest being solid solutes. *Urea* (yoo REE uh), formed from protein breakdown, is usually the most common organic substance in urine. Uric acid, which forms during nucleic acid breakdown, and *creatinine,* which is produced during muscular contraction, are also common substances in urine. A normal urine sample also contains very small quantities of pigments, hormones, enzymes, vitamins, and various inorganic substances.

A *urinalysis* detects the amounts of normal substances and the presence of any abnormal substances. For example, urine that contains glucose indicates that the pancreas is probably not producing enough insulin. Normal urine may contain small amounts of proteins, but if there is more than a trace, then there must be some tissue breakdown in the nephron that allows these large molecules to be filtered out of the blood. If blood and bacteria are present in a urine sample, the person is probably suffering an infection somewhere in the urinary system.

Drinking enough water (about 8 glasses per day) is helpful in maintaining healthy kidneys. This water is absorbed into the bloodstream and later is used to dilute any toxins in the blood. An abundance of water makes it easy for the kidney to filter out toxins and other unwanted substances. This is one reason for the "drink plenty of liquids" prescription so often recommended when you are sick.

Biological Terms

Excretory System	urinary bladder	medulla
kidneys	urethra	nephron
ureters	cortex	urine

Review Questions 21C-1

1. List the various organs in the excretory system and tell their functions.
2. What are the three primary regions of the kidney?
3. Describe a nephron. Tell the function of each part of a nephron.
4. What are the normal constituents of urine?
5. List several abnormal constituents of urine, and tell what a physician would suspect if he found these substances in a patient's urine.

THE NERVOUS SYSTEM
CONTROL PART I

TWENTY-TWO

22A–The Structure of the Nervous System

One of the great marvels of your body is that it all works together. When you touch something hot, the response of withdrawing your hand is immediate. If you consciously had to feel, see, recognize, think, and then draw away your hand, you could be seriously burned.

The internal workings of your body, so often taken for granted, offer interesting examples of carefully designed control. As your body activity increases, your heart automatically steps up its pace; your respiratory system responds with deeper, more rapid breathing; but your digestive system slows down, while hundreds of other adjustments are made so that you can function properly. When the activity stops, the system automatically reverses itself.

Even a simple movement like taking a step involves thousands of cells, all of which must work with great precision. The intricate control mechanisms which are so vital to your well-being were programmed into your body by the Creator. How else could they be adequately explained?

Two main systems control the body: the *nervous system* and the *endocrine system*. The brain, spinal cord, sensory organs (eyes, ears, taste buds, touch receptors, and others), and the nerves which supply them compose the nervous system. The endocrine system is discussed in the next chapter.

All your voluntary activities, such as speaking and running, and many involuntary activities, such as your heartbeat and digestion, are controlled by the nervous system. The nervous system receives stimulation (possibly from the environment or an internal source such as the level of a blood chemical), interprets it, and responds to it. Scientists understand, at least in part, how the nerve cells are able to perform some of these simple functions.

But the human nervous system performs activities that scientists cannot explain. How does a cell or group of cells in your brain remember a beautiful mountain scene you saw two years ago? Or, for that matter, how does it "store" the concept and the word "mountain"? How do you think? What is a dream? What is an emotion? We all know these are controlled by the brain. But what *are* these things, and how does a group of cells in the skull cause them? These questions are the subjects of many scientific studies. We do know many things about the nervous system, and a basic grasp of them will help you to understand and use the body's controls wisely.

In general terms, the nervous system is composed of the **central nervous system (CNS,** the brain and spinal cord) and the **peripheral nervous system** (**PNS,** nerves that originate from the central nervous system but go throughout the body). Our study will begin with the neuron, the basic cell of the nervous system.

Neurons

Neurons* (NOOR AHNZ) are cells which serve as the functional units of the nervous system. Once mature, neurons never divide by mitosis but are capable of living as long as you do, although many do not. A typical neuron is designed to receive and distribute a *nerve impulse.* The number of impulses and whether or not a particular neuron is stimulated is the essence of the control of the body by the nervous system.

Neurons are composed of three basic parts.

❑ The **dendrites*** of a neuron have many branches that receive and relay impulses along the remainder of the neuron.

❑ The **cell body** contains the nucleus and is the part of the neuron with the greatest diameter. The cell body may also receive an impulse from another neuron.

❑ The **axons** are neuron branches that carry impulses away from the cell body. Axons are usually the longest portion of a neuron. Along your spinal cord some axons may be over 2 ft. long. Axons terminate at another neuron, a muscle fiber, or a gland cell.

Neurons have many different functions. However, all neurons may be grouped into three functional types.

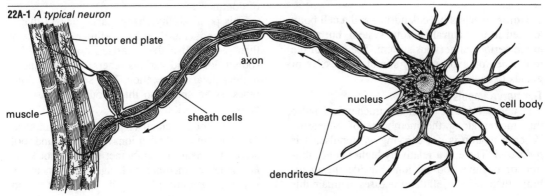

22A-1 *A typical neuron*

motor end plate

axon

muscle

sheath cells

nucleus

cell body

dendrites

---

neuron: (Gr. NEURON, nerve)   **dendrite:** (Gk. DENDRON, tree)

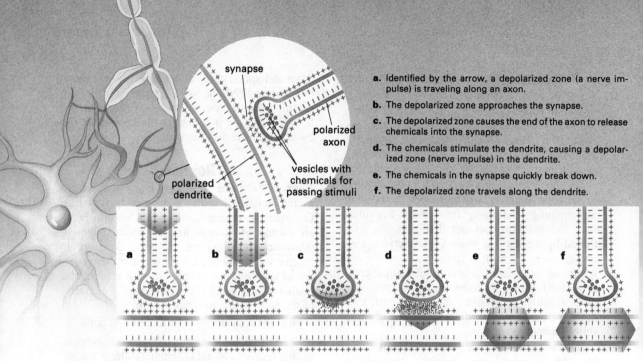

synapse

polarized
axon

vesicles with
chemicals for
passing stimuli

polarized
dendrite

a. Identified by the arrow, a depolarized zone (a nerve impulse) is traveling along an axon.

b. The depolarized zone approaches the synapse.

c. The depolarized zone causes the end of the axon to release chemicals into the synapse.

d. The chemicals stimulate the dendrite, causing a depolarized zone (nerve impulse) in the dendrite.

e. The chemicals in the synapse quickly break down.

f. The depolarized zone travels along the dendrite.

a   b   c   d   e   f

22A-2 *Transfer of a nerve impulse across a synapse*

☐ **Sensory neurons** carry impulses toward the central nervous system and respond only to particular stimuli. For example, the sensations you experience (seeing, hearing, tasting, temperature changes, and others) result from stimulated sensory neurons that transmit impulses to other neurons in the central nervous system. Usually, the cell body of a sensory neuron is part of the central nervous system, but the dendrites are part of the peripheral nervous system.

☐ **Interneurons,** located within the central nervous system, receive impulses from sensory neurons. Interneurons distribute the impulse to other neurons.

☐ **Motor neurons** have dendrites and a cell body located in the central nervous system, but axons in the peripheral nervous system. The ends of the motor neuron axon usually stimulate muscles or glands to cause a response.

The nerve impulse

The **nerve impulse** is an electrochemical pulse that moves along the membrane of a neuron. When a neuron is not carrying an impulse, it is *polarized*. There is a relatively higher concentration of positive sodium ions outside the membrane than inside. Cellular processes maintain this imbalance of various ions. When a neuron is polarized, the sodium ions are in a position to rapidly diffuse into the neuron.

A nerve impulse appears to be associated with a change in a neuron membrane's permeability. When a stimulus affects the neuron membrane, membrane permeability changes, and sodium ions rush into the cytoplasm; that area of the neuron is depolarized. It appears that when one section of neuron membrane is stimulated and changes polarity, this in turn stimulates the next section of membrane to change its polarity. It is a chain reaction somewhat similar to the falling of a row of dominoes.

This permeability change lasts for less than 1 millisecond (0.001 sec.). Cellular mechanisms then re-establish the polarized conditions. The sodium ions, and various others, are "pumped" to their polarized location. This sets up the dominoes, so to speak, so that another impulse can come and knock them down.

Even though scientists know that as impulses travel, sodium and other ions move back and forth across the neuron membrane; they do not know *how* a neuron membrane changes its permeability when it is stimulated. They do know that the polarity of the membrane is disrupted as an impulse travels along the neuron.

Between the end of the axon and the dendrites of the next neuron is a space called the **synapse*** (SIN APS). The impulse cannot "jump" this space. The change in membrane permeability is believed to cause the end of the axon to release chemicals into the synapse. These chemicals then stimulate the next neuron (or other cell), passing on the impulse. Normally other substances in the synapse destroy the chemicals released by the axons just after the impulse is passed.

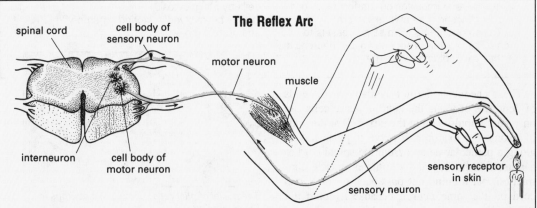

The Reflex Arc

spinal cord
cell body of sensory neuron
motor neuron
muscle
interneuron
cell body of motor neuron
sensory receptor in skin
sensory neuron

The **reflex arc** is a good example of various types of neurons working together. It includes the neurons necessary for a reflex. If a wasp stings you or you cut your finger, the automatic, immediate jerk of your body is a reflex. The nerve impulses travel so rapidly that you actually move without thinking. Let us examine how they operate.

Your skin contains an abundance of receptors, which are actually the dendrites of sensory neurons. Once the sensory neuron is stimulated, the impulse is carried to the central nervous system. There the sensory neuron may form a synapse with only one interneuron, or it may branch and pass the impulse to many interneurons. What happens depends on the particular stimulus and the part of the body involved.

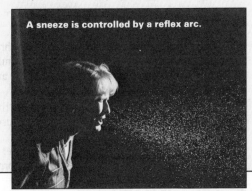

A sneeze is controlled by a reflex arc.

The interneuron passes the impulse to a motor neuron (or motor neurons) which carries the impulse to a muscle; body movements result. At the same time, the interneurons may send impulses to the brain, telling of the stimulus it received. But the muscle action prompted by the motor neuron often happens before you are conscious of the stimulus; thus reflex arcs are involuntary.

The body part that responds to the stimulus is the **effector.*** Effectors may be muscles or glands, depending on the reflex arc. For example, the muscles of your eyelid are effectors when you get something in your eye. Your sweat glands may be the effectors in a reflex arc when you are in a warm room. Many of your movements and most internal responses are controlled by reflex arcs.

There may be only one sensory and one motor neuron or dozens of each in a reflex arc. If only two or three neurons are involved, you are usually unaware of the stimuli, as is the case with those that control internal organs. No matter how many neurons are involved, the central nervous system is the center of each reflex arc. Parts of the brain and spinal cord are *reflex centers* for such actions as eye movement, sneezing, coughing, and breathing.

synapse: (Gk. SUNAPSIS, point of contact)

effector: (L. EFFECTUS, to bring about)

Glial Cells

Dispersed throughout the nervous system are small spider-shaped or ameboid cells called **glial*** (GLEE ul) **cells,** which outnumber neurons about ten to one. Unlike neurons, they are able to divide as long as they live. Glial cells do not conduct nerve impulses but perform the following functions in the nervous system:

❑ Transfer nutrients from blood vessels to neurons. The process is not known, but neurons die if they are separated from glial cells.

❑ Form a protective covering for some nerves.
❑ Line the spaces of the brain and spinal cord and regulate the secretion of the fluid that surrounds the brain and spinal cord.
❑ Destroy dead and diseased nervous system cells by phagocytosis.
❑ May be involved in storing "memory" in RNA and protein molecules.

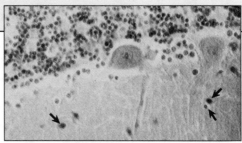

The nuclei of glial cells (arrows) and neurons in the cerebellum

These chemicals are not available at the ends of dendrites or along the neuron; nerve cells can only pass impulses on to the next cell at the ends of axons. For example, a nerve impulse travels along a particular neuron from the spinal cord to a muscle in the leg and stimulates muscle contraction, but it could not pass back to the spinal cord on the same neuron because it could not "jump" the synapse from dendrite to axon.

Review Questions 22A-1
1. What are the two primary systems of body control?
2. Which two main divisions of the nervous system are based on location?
3. List the three main parts of a neuron and describe how they differ.
4. What are the three basic types of neurons?
5. Describe a nerve impulse.
6. Trace a nerve impulse through a simple reflex arc. Name each neuron involved and give its location in the body.
7. List five functions of glial cells.

The Central Nervous System

The brain is one of the first organs that forms in the human embryo. After about 18 days of development, a group of cells forms the *neural plate*. This grows and eventually becomes a hollow, tubular mass of tissue. The anterior region enlarges and forms the major parts of the *brain;* the remainder becomes the *spinal cord.* The inside space increases in size and forms the **ventricles** (spaces inside the brain) and the central canal of the spinal cord.

Coverings of the central nervous system
The brain and spinal cord are covered by three protective coverings called **meninges*** (muhn NIN jeez). Starting with the external covering and moving inward, they are as follows:

❑ **dura mater:*** a thick, tough membrane that may contain blood vessels. In the skull it is fused with the inner-bone surface.

❑ **arachnoid*** (uh RAK noyd) **membrane:** a thin, delicate, cobweblike membrane that forms

---

glial: (Gk. GLIA, glue)
meninges (Gk. MENIX, membrane)

dura mater: (L. DURA MATER, hard mother)

arachnoid: (Gk. ARAKNOIEDES, cobweblike)

many small spaces by its attachment to the pia mater.

❏ **pia mater:*** a thin membrane on the surface of the spinal cord and brain. This membrane contains many small blood vessels.

The **cerebrospinal*** (SEH ree bro SPY nul) **fluid** flows through the spaces between the pia mater and the arachnoid membrane. It also fills the ventricles of the brain and central canal of the spinal cord. The cerebrospinal fluid filters from the blood in the ventricles, passes over the central nervous system, and then returns to the blood. It nourishes the cells of the brain and spinal cord and protects them by suspending these delicate organs in a watery cushion.

The meninges surround the spinal cord down to the level of the coccyx. The cerebrospinal fluid can help to identify infections in the central nervous system. Physicians obtain a sample by a *spinal tap,* an insertion of a syringe needle between the lower lumbar vertebrae. The spinal cord usually ends above this level, and it is not injured. Erythrocytes, bacteria, or viruses in the fluid clearly indicate infection or tissue damage.

The brain

The adult human **brain** accounts for only about 2% of body weight (about 1.36 kg or 3 lb.), but it receives about 20% of the blood pumped by the heart. The natural color of the brain surface is

> ### Lobes of the Cerebrum
> Brains differ in specific features, but the arrangement of the major fissures is quite uniform. Normally the cerebrum is divided by fissures into lobes named for the skull bones that cover those areas.
> ❏ The **frontal lobe** is responsible for mental functions, such as reasoning, planning, and memorizing. It also controls your ability to communicate verbally and starts the commands for your voluntary body movements.
> ❏ The **parietal lobe** is responsible for sensations, such as pain, pressure, touch, and temperature. This information is directed to the frontal lobe, which determines what to do about it. The parietal lobe also responds to muscle tension, sensing the position of your body. For example, an expert diver knows his body position while he moves in the air because of impulses sent to his parietal lobe.
> ❏ The **occipital lobe** is involved primarily in vision and memory of objects and symbols. A severe blow to your head may cause the sensation of seeing "stars" because it stimulates the neurons leading from the eyeballs to the occipital lobe. Nerve impulses from these fibers are interpreted as visual impulses by the occipital lobe.
> ❏ The **temporal lobe** perceives the sensations of hearing and smell. It also provides the ability to remember the pronunciation of words and the melody of songs that you have heard and stores memories of both sight and sound.

pinkish-gray and red. Blood gives the red color. The gray is characteristic of tissue composed primarily of cell bodies and dendrites and gives the *gray matter* its name. The deeper tissue of the brain is mostly *white matter* composed of axons covered with protective white, fatty membranes called the **myelin sheaths.**

The brain is subdivided into seven regions: the cerebrum, thalamus, hypothalamus, midbrain, pons, medulla oblongata, and cerebellum.

The **cerebrum** appears as two large, irregularly folded lumps. Each half of the cerebrum is a *hemisphere.* The hemispheres are connected by a thick layer of white matter, which allows communication between them. The ridged or raised areas of the brain are *gyri* (JY RYE; singular, *gyrus*). The deeper, depressed areas are *fissures.*

22A-3 *Structures of the human brain*

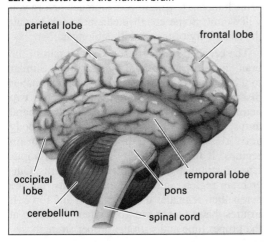

- parietal lobe
- frontal lobe
- occipital lobe
- temporal lobe
- pons
- cerebellum
- spinal cord

pia mater: (L. PIA MATER, tender mother)

cerebrospinal: cerebro- (L. CEREBRUM, brain) + -spinal (SPINA, the human spine)

The gray-matter surfaces of the *cerebral hemispheres* appear "wrinkled," making it possible to have more neurons in the gray matter. The **cerebral cortex** (outer gray matter) is 2.5-4 mm (0.1-0.2 in.) thick but contains 12-15 billion neurons. Generally speaking, the cerebral cortex is responsible for our conscious activities. Researchers have mapped the various lobes according to their specific functions. Neurosurgeons use such information to determine which regions are diseased.

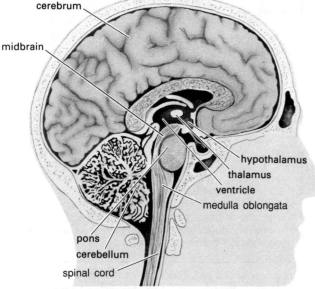

cerebrum
midbrain
hypothalamus
thalamus
ventricle
medulla oblongata
pons
cerebellum
spinal cord

22A-4 *Cross-sectional view of the human brain*

The **thalamus*** is composed of two oval, gray masses near the center of the brain, connected at the middle by a bundle of white matter. The thalamus receives general sensations and quickly decides which impulses are important enough to be relayed to the parietal lobe. The thalamus is the first part of the brain that is aware of changes in the environment. The thalamus also helps to keep us awake and alert.

The **hypothalamus*** weighs only about 4 gm (0.14 oz.), yet it controls many involuntary activities, such as regulation of body temperature, blood volume, fluid balance, and some control of your appetite and emotional expressions. It also controls hormone release by the *pituitary gland* and forms two hormones itself. The hypothalamus functions in both the nervous system and endocrine system.

The **midbrain** is located between the thalamus and the pons. Many motor impulses transmitted from the pons and the cerebellum to the cerebrum pass through the midbrain. In it are centers for controlling body movements and posture, especially controlling the head in relation to the rest of the body and space. Other midbrain centers are involved with vision and hearing reflexes.

The **pons*** is a bulging structure located between the medulla and the midbrain. It is composed almost entirely of white matter that carries information from one side of the brain to the other. With the medulla, it controls involuntary respiration. It also contains reflex centers which control chewing, facial expressions, response to sounds, and eyeball movement.

The **medulla oblongata** is continuous with the spinal cord and functions primarily as a relay center between the spinal cord and the brain. Centers for the control of respiration, blood vessel diameter (blood pressure), and heart rate are in the medulla. Therefore, injuries to the medulla may result in a *coma** (unconscious state) or death. Its reflex centers control sneezing, coughing, swallowing, and vomiting. Other factors, however, stimulate these actions. For example, something has to irritate your stomach before you will vomit. Some cough medicines seek to dull the sensitivity of the medulla oblongata.

The **cerebellum,** the second largest part of the brain, is below and behind the cerebrum. Similar to the cerebrum, it possesses folds of gray matter that cover a mass of white matter and has two hemispheres that join in the middle. In general terms, the cerebellum monitors and adjusts body activities that are stimulated by other brain regions. It functions totally at the subconscious level; it stimulates no voluntary movements. Other brain regions initiate the movements, but the cerebellum regulates their quickness and force. It insures that a movement goes where it should at the proper time and with the proper strength.

---

thalamus: (Gk. THALAMOS, inner chamber)

hypothalamus: hypo- (Gk. under) + -thalamus (inner chamber)

pons: (L. PONS, bridge)

coma: (Gr. KOMA, deep sleep)

The spinal cord

The **spinal cord,** the second major division of the central nervous system, is continuous with the medulla and usually extends down to the first or second lumbar vertebra. It carries messages between the peripheral parts of the body and the brain. It is a cylindrical mass of nervous tissue composed of 31 segments with 1 pair of spinal nerves originating from each segment.

In a transverse section the spinal cord appears as two masses of tissue joined by a narrow bridge of tissue with a tiny canal in the middle. The abundant nerves that branch from the cervical and lumbar regions make these areas of the spinal cord the thickest.

The spinal cord is white matter in outer regions and gray matter in the center. The H-shaped or butterfly-shaped central gray matter is mostly interneurons and the cell body portions of the sensory and motor neurons. The white matter is myelinated axons arranged vertically. It is like a mass of communication cables, all insulated by the myelin sheaths. Some of the axon bundles carry impulses to the brain; others carry impulses only away from the brain. For example, pain impulses pass only along certain axons, while impulses to muscles pass along other neurons.

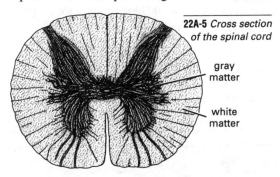

22A-5 *Cross section of the spinal cord*

gray matter

white matter

The Peripheral Nervous System

The *peripheral nervous system* (PNS) includes all the neurons that function as sense receptors, the neurons that link these receptors with the central nervous system (brain and spinal cord), and the neurons that connect the central nervous system with muscles and glands.

The portions of the peripheral nervous system that regulate your body movements are under your conscious control and are therefore voluntary. The voluntary portion of the peripheral nervous system includes most of the fibers in the cranial and spinal nerves. The involuntary portion of the peripheral nervous system is, in part, the autonomous nervous system.

Cranial nerves and spinal nerves

22A-6 Summary of Cranial Nerves
Number, Name, Type, Function
I. Olfactory: *Sensory*–smell
II. Optic: *Sensory*–vision
III. Oculomotor: *Motor*–movement of eyelid and eyeball (adjusts lens to focus vision, constricts pupil)
IV. Trochlear: *Motor*–movement of eyeball
V. Trigeminal: *Motor*–chewing; *Sensory*–face and teeth
VI. Abducens: *Motor*–movement of eyeball
VII. Facial: *Motor*–facial expressions, secretion of saliva; *Sensory*–taste
VIII. Auditory: *Sensory*–hearing, equilibrium
IX. Glossopharyngeal: *Motor*–swallowing, secretion of saliva; *Sensory*–taste
X. Vagus: *Motor*–controls movements of most digestive and respiratory organs, regulates heart actions; *Sensory*–carries sensations from organs it supplies
XI. Spinal accessory: *Motor*–head and shoulder movements
XII. Hypoglossal: *Motor*–tongue movements

The twelve pairs of peripheral nerves that originate from the brain are the **cranial* nerves.** Most of these control the sensations and movements of the head and neck, and a few supply muscles and other organs in the trunk. Scientists classify cranial nerves by their general function–*sensory, motor,* or *mixed* (containing both sensory and motor fibers)–and name them according to their size, location, function, and distribution.

Thirty-one pairs of **spinal nerves** attach to the spinal cord. These are mixed nerves that deliver the stimuli for most voluntary movements of the body. All impulses enter the spinal cord through the sensory neurons in spinal nerves.

---

cranial: (L. CRANIA, head)

FACETS OF BIOLOGY

22A-1

The Body on "Automatic Pilot"

All internal organs (glands, blood vessels, the heart, and the smooth muscle tissue in the walls of internal organs) are under the control of the **autonomic* nervous system (ANS),** the involuntary part of the peripheral nervous system. These parts function automatically without conscious control.

The ANS helps maintain a steady internal condition in the body. For example, the ANS carefully regulates the internal body temperature (keeping it an almost constant 98.6° F) and the pH of the blood (keeping it within the narrow range of 7.35-7.45). It also regulates the heartbeat, perspiration, breathing rate, and other body activities.

There are two divisions of the autonomic nervous system: the *sympathetic* and the *parasympathetic*. These divisions have generally opposing influences on body organs. While both divisions function at all times, one usually dominates at a time, depending on the environmental stimuli.

The **sympathetic nervous system** is composed of neurons whose fibers originate in the thoracic and lumbar portions of the spinal cord. It helps the body adjust to stressful or frightening experiences. In other words it is "sympathetic" to problems during times of emergency; it helps a person "gear up" in order to survive and be successful.

For example, if a person suddenly sees a snake move across his trail while he is hiking, his sympathetic division instantly activates his body. Primarily, the adrenal glands release a rapid surge of the hormone epinephrine (adrenalin). The adrenalin stimulates a quick increase in heart and breathing rates and causes a rise in the blood sugar needed for muscle action. The pupils of the eyes dilate quickly so that he can see where he is running. His digestive system is "shut off." ("I can finish digesting food later; now I must save the body.") His entire nervous system is put on emergency standby, making him jumpy.

The **parasympathetic nervous system** is composed of neurons from the brain stem and the sacral portion of the spinal cord. Its overall function opposes that of the sympathetic nervous system. It serves the "business as usual" functions of the body. It stimulates proper digestion, absorption of food, and elimination of wastes. It also maintains slower, normal heart and breathing rates as well as lower blood pressure. These functions are performed best when a person relaxes in a pleasant, peaceful environment. The best example of the control of the parasympathetic system is its control over a person who sleeps after eating a delicious meal.

The sympathetic and parasympathetic nervous systems are both necessary, but both can be misused. A person who is almost constantly in stressful situations, stimulating the sympathetic nervous system and having the body on alert most of the time, may damage his body. If a person is constantly "tense," he may not be able to meet the demands of an emergency because he has exhausted his supply of reserves. Peace and rest are necessary for a properly functioning human body.

When many people are told that they must relax, they may respond that they cannot because their lives are too stressful. How can a person have peace in the "high-pressure" world in which he lives? The Creator knows the needs of the body and has supplied a "divine escape." The Bible tells you to "[cast] all your care upon him, for he careth for you" (I Pet. 5:7).

Review questions are on next page.

IT APPEARS THAT TENSION IS YOUR PROBLEM, MR. HYDE.

autonomic: auto- (Gk. AUTO, self) + -nomic (L. NOMEN, name)

Diseases and Disorders of the Nervous System

Cerebral palsy paralysis from improper development of the brain or from damage to the brain at birth

Coma abnormal state of deep unconsciousness caused by disease, injury, or poison; the patient cannot be aroused

Encephalitis inflammation of the brain; caused by a virus; symptom of other diseases

Epilepsy disturbed brain function often causing convulsions and loss of consciousness

Headache general pain in different portions of the head; may be caused by infection, chemicals, injury, or stress

Hydrocephalus abnormal increase in the amount of cerebrospinal fluid; may result in brain damage and the enlargement of the skull in children

Mental illness any condition that adversely affects the mind

Meningitis inflammation of the membranes surrounding the brain and spinal cord; caused by bacteria, viruses, or other organisms

Multiple sclerosis patches of hardened tissue in the brain and spinal cord with deterioration of myelin sheaths; may result in paralysis and jerking muscle contractions

Parkinson's disease chronic nervous disorder that usually affects the elderly; characterized by rigidity of muscles and tremors of arms and legs

Phobia abnormal fear of a particular object, group of objects, or situation

Senility loss of mental abilities as a result of age

Shock sudden reduction in vital processes that control blood volume and blood pressure; results in critically low blood pressure; often caused by severe injuries, or emotional trauma

Biological Terms

central nervous system (CNS)
peripheral nervous system (PNS)
Neurons
neuron
dendrite
cell body
axon
sensory neuron
interneuron
motor neuron
nerve impulse
synapse

reflex arc
effector
glial cell
The Central Nervous System
ventricle
meninges
dura mater
arachnoid membrane
pia mater
cerebrospinal fluid
brain

myelin sheath
cerebrum
cerebral cortex
frontal lobe
parietal lobe
occipital lobe
temporal lobe
thalamus
hypothalamus
midbrain
pons
medulla oblongata

cerebellum
spinal cord
Peripheral Nervous System
cranial nerves
spinal nerves
Facet
autonomic nervous system (ANS)
sympathetic nervous system
parasympathetic nervous system

Review Questions 22A-2

1. What are the main divisions of the central nervous system?
2. List, describe, and tell the functions of each of the meninges of the CNS.
3. What is the structural difference between gray matter and white matter in the CNS?
4. List the lobes of the cerebrum and tell which bodily functions each controls.
5. List the major divisions of the brain and tell what each controls.
6. What are the two main divisions of the peripheral nervous system?
7. List several cranial nerves and tell their functions.

Facet 22A-1: The Body on "Automatic Pilot," page 588

What are the two main divisions of the autonomic nervous sytem? What is the general function of each?

Thought Questions

1. Compare the electricity in a wire to a nerve impulse traveling on a neuron.
2. In our world many people suffer from hypertension. Some, however, claim that no Christian should have this disorder. Is this a legitimate position? Why or why not?

Chapter 22B–The Sense Organs

It is commonly thought that humans have five senses: sight, smell, taste, touch, and hearing. You would have great difficulty if your body had only five senses. For example, you not only see your hand as you move it in front of you but also "sense" its moving. By extremely complicated mechanisms you see thousands of shades of color clearly. Skin not only relays to your brain the fact that you have touched something but also senses the texture and temperature of objects.

Your "sense of balance" seems to be two separate senses functioning together. You are able to sense not only when *you* move your body but also when some external force moves it. Further, you can sense the relative positions of parts of your body even when they are not moving. Scientists surmise that humans are somehow able to sense humidity, atmospheric pressure, and even the presence of static electricity.

All known sense organs contain **receptors,** specialized dendrites of sensory neurons. Receptors are stimulated by various external and internal conditions and inform the body of changes. Usually a receptor is sensitive to only one type of stimulus. The neurons of the eye, for example, are sensitive to light, but not to sounds or odors. Changes in temperature and chemicals in the air stimulate other neurons in other locations.

The sense organs also contain structures and tissues that support and assist the receptors. For example, the back of the eyeball contains light receptors. Other structures of the eyeball direct and focus the light entering the eye while they support and protect the receptors.

Minor Senses

Those senses that are not exceptionally active in humans and that most people do not greatly depend on are the *minor senses.* They include the senses of the skin (such as temperature, touch, and pain) and the senses of smell and taste.

Often people who do not have use of one of their major senses (sight or hearing) are said to develop special powers in their other senses. A person deprived of one sense may become more aware of the changes noted by his other senses, but there is little evidence to suggest that a person who is blind, for example, can smell or hear significantly better than other people.

Senses of the skin

Receptors for cold, heat, pain, pressure, and touch are primarily in the skin; these are the **cutaneous sensations.** (Other regions of the body also have pain receptors.) Each sensation has different receptors.

22B-1 *The five types of cutaneous receptors and their locations*

touch
near exterior of skin (most numerous in finger tips, palms, soles); around roots of hairs

heat
deeply embedded in dermis

pain
nearly every tissue of the body

cold
dermis and subcutaneous regions of skin; cornea of eye; tip of tongue

pressure
below the skin; membranes of abdominal cavity; around joints and tendons

Referred Pain

The term **referred pain** is used when pain seems to be in one area of the body but actually originates in a different body organ. A diseased liver or gall bladder often causes pain in the right shoulder region. A decreased blood supply to the heart may cause pain along the left shoulder and arm. One cause of referred pain is that the neurons that supply the damaged organ originate from the same area of the spinal cord as the neurons supplying the skin area that seems to be in pain. The brain does not distinguish the pain originating from the internal organ from pain impulses coming from the skin area. Automatically it assigns the pain to the skin, which usually senses pain, rather than to the organ, which may never before have sent sensations to the brain up those nerves.

Cutaneous receptors are more numerous in certain areas. For example, touch receptors are densely arranged in the tip of the tongue but are few in number on the back of the neck. Other neurons transport the impulses from the receptors to the brain. A stimulated heat receptor in your finger sends impulses up a set of neurons and stimulates a particular area of your brain, making you aware of that stimulus. You feel the heat in your brain, not in your finger.

Taste and smell

There are about 10,000 **taste buds,** the receptors for taste, in the average adult. Children, however, have considerably more. Most taste buds are on the *papillae* of the tongue, but some may be found on the inner surface of the cheek, roof of the mouth, tonsils, and epiglottis. All portions of the tongue and all taste buds are sensitive to all four sensations (sweet, sour, bitter, and salty). Various areas of the tongue, however, respond most to certain tastes.

The cells that form the taste buds are not neurons, but they are attached to nerve endings. These cells have a short life span and must be replaced continually. This replacement decreases with age; older people cannot taste substances as well as children. This may explain a child's objection to certain foods which he enjoys as an adult. Exceptionally hot or spicy foods damage taste buds, explaining why some older people require more seasonings in order to enjoy foods.

The *olfactory sense* (sense of smell) is one of the least-understood senses. The **olfactory receptors** consist of numerous cells in the mucous membrane that line the upper region of the nasal cavities. Olfactory cells are neurons; so if they are injured (as during infection), they do not regenerate. Even under normal conditions, these neurons decrease in number with age; thus, the older we become, the less sensitive our sense of smell becomes.

Humans apparently can distinguish several thousand different odors. However, these odors can be detected only if the molecules stimulate the olfactory receptors. Since the olfactory receptor areas are poorly ventilated, the ability to detect odors is greatly increased by sniffing. Your sense of smell is less acute when you have a cold because odors cannot reach the olfactory receptors. Your sense of taste is also affected because much of taste is actually smell.

Receptors for smell reach a point of **accommodation** more rapidly than other sense receptors. Accommodation means that after a short period of stimulation, the receptors become insensitive to that specific stimuli.

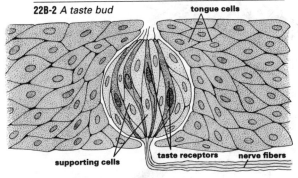

22B-2 *A taste bud*

tongue cells

supporting cells

taste receptors

nerve fibers

Review Questions 22B-1

1. List several cutaneous sensations.
2. Why can children taste more than adults?
3. What is accommodation to a sensation? Give several common examples.

The Ear: Hearing and Balance

Normally we think of the skin-covered flap of cartilage on either side of the head as our hearing apparatus. Embedded within the temporal bone is a small chamber and beyond that a tiny, bony structure shaped like a snail shell. These areas inside the bones of our skull are a small fraction of the size of the outer flaps, but they are actually responsible for our sense of hearing and most of our sense of balance.

Within the inner structures of our ear are thousands of nerve endings which are indirectly stimulated by sound waves (vibrations). By poorly understood mechanisms, these nerve endings transform an almost limitless variety of sound waves into impulses, which travel along neurons to the brain where we ''hear'' them.

The ear

The **outer ear** consists of the *auricle,** an outer flap of tissue designed to collect sound waves, and the **external auditory* canal,** a tube which goes into the head and ends at the **tympanic membrane** (eardrum). The skin lining the canal contains *ceruminous glands* (wax glands). The skin continually loses dead surface cells, which combine with ear wax and gradually move out of the ear. It is unnecessary and even dangerous to the delicate tissues of the ear to use any object other than a washcloth to clean the outer ear. (A physician shoud be consulted if the ear wax becomes impacted.)

The **middle ear** is a moist, air-filled chamber containing three **ossicles*** (AHS ih kulz, bones): the *malleus* (MAL ee us, hammer), *incus* (ING kus, anvil), and *stapes* (STAY peez, stirrup). Joints between the bones are movable. These bones form a lever system that picks up vibrations of sound waves hitting the tympanic membrane and transfers them to the **oval window,** a membrane-covered opening of the inner ear.

Two small muscles attach to the ossicles and modify their movements. When exposed to sudden loud noises, they respond by limiting the vibrations, protecting the delicate membranes of the inner ear. In contrast, they also respond to soft sounds by increasing the movement of the ossicles, enabling us to hear better.

The middle ear connects with the pharynx by the *Eustachian tube*. This tube makes it possible for the air pressure within the middle ear chamber to remain the same as the atmospheric pressure.

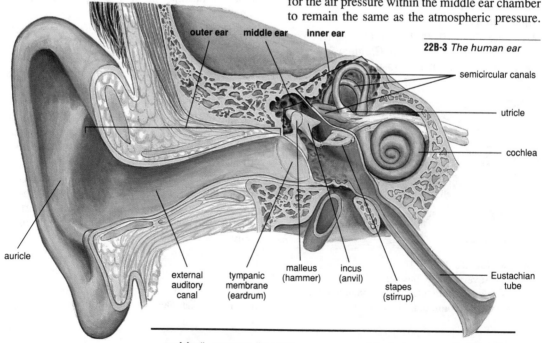

22B-3 *The human ear*

outer ear   middle ear   inner ear

semicircular canals

utricle

cochlea

auricle

external auditory canal

tympanic membrane (eardrum)

malleus (hammer)

incus (anvil)

stapes (stirrup)

Eustachian tube

auricle: (L. AURICULA, little ear)
auditory: (L. AUDIRE, to hear)

ossicle: (L. OSSICULUM, small bone)

As you drive in high mountains, the atmospheric pressure decreases, but the middle ear pressure remains the same, causing the eardrum to bulge outward. The Eustachian tube opens (when you blow or yawn), allowing the air pressure within the middle ear chamber to equalize with the atmospheric pressure. As the eardrum snaps back to a flat position, you may feel and hear a "popping" sensation in your ears.

The **inner ear** consists of a *bony labyrinth* enclosing a *membranous labyrinth*. The bony labyrinth consists of channels and cavities within the temporal bone. The inner membranous labyrinth closely duplicates the shape of the bony channels. It is a tube-within-a-tube arrangement. The spaces between the bony and membranous labyrinths are filled with two slightly different fluids necessary for the sensations of hearing and equilibrium.

Hearing
The **cochlea*** (KOH klee uh), a snail-shaped division of the inner ear labyrinths, receives sound. Along the full length of the cochlea's inner surface runs the actual sound receptor, the *organ of Corti* (KAHR tye). Over the Corti is a membranous flap, the *tectorial membrane,* which is in contact with "hair cells" of the organ of Corti.

The sound waves in the atmosphere hit the eardrum, moving the bones in the middle ear. The vibrations of the stapes move the oval window in and out. At the same time the stapes pushes the oval window in, another membrane-covered

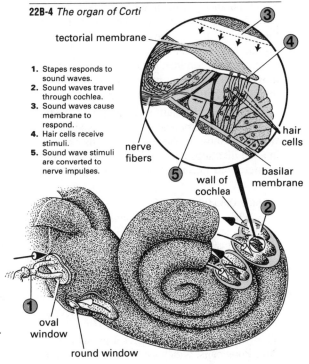

22B-4 *The organ of Corti*

tectorial membrane

1. Stapes responds to sound waves.
2. Sound waves travel through cochlea.
3. Sound waves cause membrane to respond.
4. Hair cells receive stimuli.
5. Sound wave stimuli are converted to nerve impulses.

nerve fibers
hair cells
basilar membrane
wall of cochlea
oval window
round window

opening of the cochlea, the **round window,** moves out, and vice versa. This sets up "ripples" in the cochlear fluids, causing the tectorial membrane to bend certain of the cilialike processes of the hair cells, producing nerve impulses. These impulses are carried to the temporal lobe of the cerebrum, where they are perceived as different sounds.

The sense of balance
The body maintains balance by two different senses, the sense of *static* equilibrium* and the sense of *dynamic* equilibrium*. Static equilibrium refers to the sense of body position when the body is not moving. Sensory hair cells within the walls of the fluid-filled *saccule* and *utricle** (YOO tri kul), which are part of the inner ear, perform this function.

The hair cells of the utricle and saccule are embedded in a jellylike substance that contains mineral crystals. When the head moves, the crystals slide, pulling the jelly. This movement bends the hairs, stimulating nerve impulses which travel

Deafness

There are two major types of deafness.
❑ **Conduction* deafness** is caused by anything blocking transmission of the vibrations to the inner ear and can often be corrected by surgery or a hearing aid. Common causes include blockage of the auditory canal, stiffness or fusion of joints between ossicles, and middle-ear infections.
❑ **Nerve deafness** occurs when the cochlea, the auditory nerve, or the brain does not function properly. Nerve deafness may be either partial or complete. Surgery usually does not help this type of deafness but hearing aids often do.

cochlea: (L. COCHLEA, snail shell)
conduction: (L. CONDUCERE, to escort)
static: (Gk. STATOS, standing)
equilibrium: equi- (L. AEQUUS, level) + -librium (L. LIBRA, balance)
dynamic: (Gk. DUNAMIS, power)
utricle: (Gk. UTRICULUS, little leather bottle)

along a branch of the auditory nerve to the temporal lobe of the cerebrum. The brain interprets the impulses as head movements. Violently shaking the head can set the jelly and crystals in motion; this may continue after the head has stopped moving, and the head may seem to be still "going" even though it is not moving.

Dynamic equilibrium is the ability of the body to respond automatically to positional changes when it is moving. Sensory hair cells embedded in a jellylike substance in the enlarged ends of the **semicircular canals** of the inner ear detect these changes.

The three semicircular canals are at right angles to each other. Thus, all possible head movements and positions may be sensed. During walking, running, and other dynamic activities, the fluid in the semicircular ducts flows over the gelatinous material, bending the hair cells. The movement of the hairs stimulates nerve impulses that pass along a branch of the auditory nerve to the temporal lobe and cerebellum. Impulses from the cerebellum adjust muscle actions, producing coordinated movements for each position change. Imagine all the impulses that a basketball player experiences during a game!

Review Questions 22B-2

1. What are the three main divisions of the ear? What structures are in each division? What structures separate each division from the other?
2. What is the primary function of the Eustachian tube?
3. Describe the process of hearing in the inner ear.
4. What are the two main types of equilibrium? What are the primary organs for sensing each type?

The Eye and Sight

Your eyes are a set of spheres a bit smaller than Ping-Pong balls, which supply you with a continuous series of color pictures for at least 16 hr. per day and then operate repair and maintenance systems while you sleep. Normal eyes can focus on a hair as near as a few inches and large objects as distant as several miles.

The brain controls muscles that move and focus your eyes so that both eyes work together in harmony, providing you with a stereoscopic image that permits depth perception. You can see only silhouettes in near darkness, but you can distinguish minute variations in color in bright light. Scientists have not been able to explain completely how our eyes operate. The beauty and wonder of the eye is that it is perfectly designed to permit us to see. "I will praise thee; for I am fearfully and wonderfully made" (Ps. 139:14).

Structure of the eye

The eyeball has three tissue layers. The outer layer, known as the **sclera,** * is "the white of the eye." This white fibrous tissue maintains the shape of the eyeball. The transparent, anterior portion of the sclera, the **cornea** (KOHR nee uh),

allows light to enter the eyeball. The cornea lacks blood vessels but receives nourishment from the fluid underneath it in the eyeball.

The middle layer, the **choroid** (KOHR OYD), is fragile and thin with many blood vessels for nourishing the retina. The anterior portion of the choroid, the **iris*** (EYE ris), contains muscles and is the colored part of the eye. The circular opening in the iris is the **pupil** and lets light into the eyeball. Muscles in the iris change the diameter of the pupil, regulating the amount of light entering the eye. In bright light the pupil is almost closed, protecting the retina from too much light. In dim light, however, it dilates (opens), permitting all the available light to enter.

The third and innermost layer of the eyeball is the **retina,** composed of thousands of specialized neurons and their fibers. The neurons of the innermost layer are *photoreceptors** that can be stimulated by light. The impulses from the photoreceptors are transmitted to the occipital lobe of the brain by way of the *optic nerve.*

There are no photoreceptors where the optic nerve fibers leave the eye to form the optic nerve. This area is the *blind spot* or *optic disc.* In people with normal eyes, the blind spot of each eye af-

---

sclera: (hard)   **iris:** (L. IRIS, rainbow)   **photoreceptor:** photo- (light) + -receptor (L. RECEPTARE, to receive)

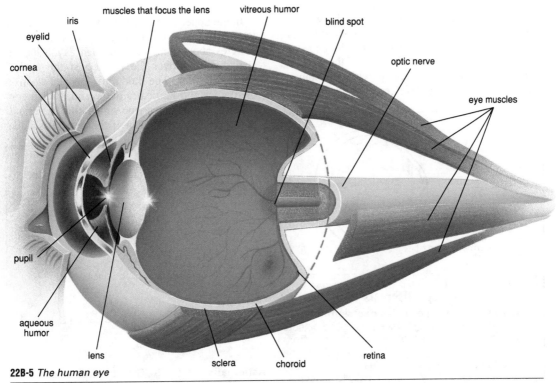

eyelid
iris
muscles that focus the lens
vitreous humor
blind spot
optic nerve
eye muscles
cornea
pupil
aqueous humor
lens
sclera
choroid
retina

22B-5 *The human eye*

fects a different area of vision; therefore, the total field of vision is unbroken.

The **lens** of the eye is a biconvex, semisolid substance supported by the **ciliary*** (SIL ee UHR ee) **muscles,** which change the shape of the lens. When looking at a close object, the muscles contract, making the lens thicker (more convex) and focusing the image on the retina. When looking at a distant object, the muscles relax and the lens flattens to focus the image.

The ability to focus on objects at different distances from the eye is *visual accommodation.* The lens is elastic in children but becomes more rigid

with age. Therefore, at about age 40 some people have difficulty in focusing on things closer to them; they hold reading material farther from their eyes. Lenses in glasses can compensate for the hardened natural lenses.

There are two cavities in the eyeball: one in front of the lens and one behind. The anterior cavity is filled with the **aqueous** (AY kwee us) **humor,*** a transparent, watery fluid that diffuses

22B-6 *The thickness of the lens changes, permitting the eye to focus on objects at different distances.*

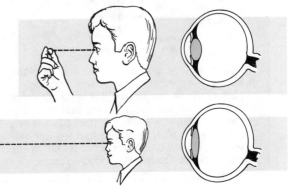

---

ciliary: cili- (L. CILIUM, eyelash) + -ary (Eng. -ARY related to)

aqueous humor: (L. AQUA, water) + (M.E. HUMOUR, fluid)

from blood vessels located near the ciliary muscles. This fluid nourishes the cornea and diffuses into the blood by way of canals on the edge of the cornea. The posterior chamber of the eyeball contains a clear, permanent, jellylike substance called the **vitreous*** (VIHT ree us) **humor.**

In the upper lateral region of each eyelid is the *lacrimal** (LAK ruh mul) *gland* (tear gland). It secretes about 1 ml of fluid each day, which is spread evenly over the surface of the eyeball when you blink. The fluid moistens and cleanses the cornea and lubricates the eyelid. It also contains *lysozyme,* an enzyme which kills bacteria. If the eyeball is irritated or if the person is under

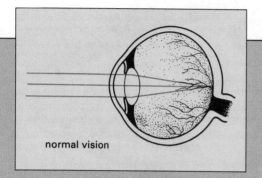

normal vision

Eye Disorders

Myopia (mye OH pee uh) or **nearsightness** is a condition in which light rays from close objects can be focused on the retina, but those from distant objects are focused in front of the retina and therefore are not seen clearly. The problem is usually caused by an abnormally long eyeball, which is an inherited trait. Eyeglasses with concave lenses may compenstate for myopia.

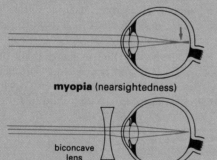

myopia (nearsightedness)

biconcave lens

Hyperopia (HYE puh ROH pee uh) or **farsightedness** is a condition in which light rays from far objects can be focused on the retina but those from near objects focus behind the retina. Hyperopia may be caused by an inherited short eyeball or by hardening lenses. Eyeglasses with convex lenses may help a farsighted person to see close objects. Occasionally *bifocal glasses,*

which have lenses for farsightedness in the lower portion and other lenses in the upper portion, are necessary.

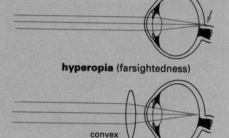

hyperopia (farsightedness)

convex lens

Astigmatisms* (uh STIG muh TIZ ums) occur when either the cornea or lens or both are uneven or unequally curved and the light rays from an object are not focused properly on the retina. This results in an area of the person's vision being out of focus. Sometimes the other eye will compensate for mild astigmatisms.

Cataracts, or clouded lenses, may be caused by old age, overexposure to bright sunlight, or diseases such as diabetes. Treatment may involve the surgical removal of the lens and the implant of an artificial one. Sometimes special eyeglasses are used to compensate for the loss of the lens. Clouded corneas can be removed and replaced with transplants.

Glaucoma is the buildup of aqueous humor resulting in abnormal pressure within the eye. This causes a decrease of circulation to the retina and may damage the retina and cause blindness.

Night blindness results from a lack of a pigment (visual purple) in the rods of the eye. Using cones, the person can see clearly in bright light but in dim light the person cannot see well. To form the pigment, one must have enough vitamin A in his diet.

---

vitreous: (L. VITRUM, glass)
lacrimal: (L. LACRIMA, tear)

astigmatism a- (without) + -stigma- (Gk. STIGMA, spot) + -ism (Eng. -ISM, indicating a condition)

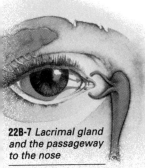

22B-7 *Lacrimal gland and the passageway to the nose*

emotional stress, the lacrimal gland secretes more fluid, often resulting in tears.

Several sets of muscles control the movement of the eyeballs so that both eyeballs are directed toward the same object. In some individuals muscles that are not equal in length or strength, or are paralyzed, cause the eyes to cross.

Vision

There are more than 100 million photoreceptors in each eye, most of which are shaped like *rods*.

Rods, which are responsible for night vision, are scattered over the retina. They are sensitive to low intensity light and produce a shadowed or silhouette image. They cannot determine color but can rapidly discern movements.

Cone-shaped photoreceptors detect colors. The *cones* are especially concentrated at the *fovea** (FOH vee uh), a small depression in the central region of the retina. Therefore, you see the sharpest color image of an object when you look directly at it in a lighted environment; in dim light the image would not be clear because there are no rods at the fovea.

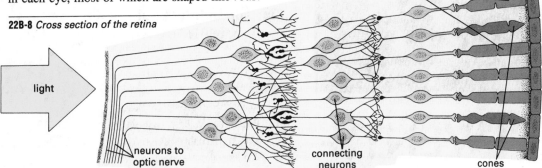

22B-8 *Cross section of the retina*

light

neurons to optic nerve

connecting neurons

rods

pigment layer

cones

Biological Terms

receptors

Minor Senses
cutaneous sensations
referred pain
taste buds
olfactory receptors
accomodation

The Ear
outer ear
external auditory canal
tympanic membrane
middle ear
ossicles
oval window
inner ear

cochlea
round window
conduction deafness
nerve deafness
semicircular canal

The Eye and Sight
sclera
cornea

choroid
iris
pupil
retina
lens
ciliary muscle
aqueous humor
vitreous humor

nearsightedness
farsightedness
astigmatism
myopia
hyperopia
glaucoma
cataract

Review Questions 22B-3

1. List and describe the functions of the three main layers of the eye.
2. How is the amount of light that enters the eye regulated?
3. How is the eye focused?
4. Where are the lacrimal glands? What do they produce?
5. Differentiate between the functions of the rods and the cones of the eye.
6. Describe myopia and hyperopia.
7. Differentiate between cataracts and astigmatism.

Thought Question

Occasionally when a body part is amputated, the person can still feel sensations in the missing limb. This is called a phantom limb. What could explain these sensations?

---

fovea: (L. FOVEA, pit)

HORMONES AND THE HUMAN MIND
CONTROL PART II

23A – The Endocrine System
page 598

23B – The Control of the Mind
page 611

TWENTY-THREE

23A – The Endocrine System

The **endocrine*** (EN duh krin) **system** consists of the *ductless glands* of the body. These glands lack *ducts* (tubes) to transport the substances they secrete. Instead, the endocrine glands release the substances they manufacture into the blood, which transports these substances to the body's tissues and cells. One endocrine gland, for example, produces a substance which affects every hair follicle in your body. This particular gland does not need a system of ducts to every hair follicle; the circulatory system reaches them.

The endocrine glands help to control the body, but they do it differently than the nervous system. The nervous system connects directly with individual muscles and internal organs throughout the body to regulate movements. The endocrine system is composed of glands located throughout the body. The secretions of these glands affect cells, tissues, or organs in other areas of the body through the blood. The effects of the endocrine system are slower and longer lasting than the effects of the nervous system.

---

endocrine: endo- (within) + -crine
(Gk. KRINEIN, secrete)

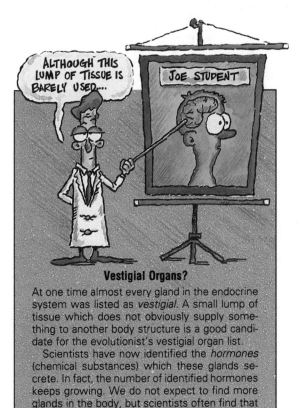

Vestigial Organs?

At one time almost every gland in the endocrine system was listed as *vestigial*. A small lump of tissue which does not obviously supply something to another body structure is a good candidate for the evolutionist's vestigial organ list.

Scientists have now identified the *hormones* (chemical substances) which these glands secrete. In fact, the number of identified hormones keeps growing. We do not expect to find more glands in the body, but scientists often find that cells in a gland known for one particular function also produce hormones for a different function.

Hormones

Hormones* are chemical messengers produced in one area of the body and carried by the blood to affect cells in other areas of the body. Hormones are often difficult to separate from other blood substances, and once a scientist isolates a supposed hormone, determining its exact function may be difficult.

To understand how the endocrine system works, you must understand hormones. Here are some of their major characteristics:

❏ *Organic chemicals produced by the endocrine glands* Hormones are either proteins, amines (similar to amino acids), or sterols (fats).

❏ *Carried and distributed by the blood* Small amounts of over thirty different hormones can be found in the blood at any time.

❏ *Specific chemical messengers* Most hormones stimulate or speed up processes in body cells, but some slow them down. While hormones pass through the blood, they are exposed to all body cells. However, they affect only specific *target tissues*.

❏ *Secreted in small quantities* Usually only small amounts of hormones are produced, and only a tiny amount is needed to affect the target tissue.

❏ *Constantly filtered out of the blood by kidneys or deactivated by the liver or other glands* This forces the endocrine glands to constantly produce hormones.

❏ *Quantity is usually self-regulated* Most hormone secretion is controlled by **negative feedback** mechanisms. When the hormone level gets too high, it affects the secretion of another hormone, which controls the secretion of the first, and vice versa.

An example of negative feedback is the control of the thyroid hormone by a hormone secreted by

23A-1 *The negative feedback mechanism that controls the secretion of the thyroid hormone*

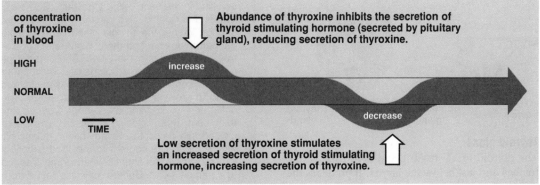

concentration of thyroxine in blood

Abundance of thyroxine inhibits the secretion of thyroid stimulating hormone (secreted by pituitary gland), reducing secretion of thyroxine.

HIGH

increase

NORMAL

LOW

decrease

TIME

Low secretion of thyroxine stimulates an increased secretion of thyroid stimulating hormone, increasing secretion of thyroxine.

hormone: (Gk. HORMON, to stir up)

the pituitary. If the level of the thyroid hormone gets too high, the amount of the pituitary hormone decreases. This decrease causes the thyroid to produce less. If the amount of thyroid hormones becomes too low, the pituitary is stimulated, and the thyroid in turn is stimulated. Hormone production varies within rather narrow limits because of a **dynamic equillibrium** maintained by negative feedback.

The Endocrine Glands

Most of the endocrine glands produce hormones that are essential throughout an individual's life. Some hormones are released in quantity only at specific times, such as puberty, pregnancy, or periods of stress. In a system as complex and as sensitive as the endocrine system, it is not uncommon for hormone levels to have temporary fluctuations within the body or for the levels to differ between individuals.

Occasionally there may be major problems. If a disease or injury affects an endocrine gland, the production of its hormone may decrease, resulting in **hyposecretion*** (HYE poh see KREE shun), or increase, resulting in **hypersecretion*** (HYE pur see KREE shun). These abnormal amounts of hormones eventually produce physical and, occasionally, mental and psychological abnormalities, some of which can cause death. As we discuss some of the major endocrine glands and their hormones, we will examine a few of these disorders.

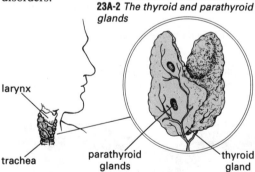

23A-2 *The thyroid and parathyroid glands*

larynx

trachea

parathyroid glands

thyroid gland

Thyroid gland

The thyroid (THY royd) gland is in front of the trachea and just below the larynx. It produces the

hormone **thyroxine** (thye RAHK sin). Several weeks' supply of thyroxine can be stored in follicles of the thyroid gland until it is needed. Thyroxine is synthesized from an amino acid (tyrosine) and iodine.

Thyroxine increases oxygen use, stimulates heat production in most body tissues, and indirectly affects growth. Thyroxine secretion is regulated by the negative feedback mechanism between the anterior pituitary and thyroid gland. The amount of *thyroid stimulating hormone* (TSH) produced by the pituitary depends on the amount of thyroxine, and vice versa. Exposure to cold weather increases metabolism by increasing production of TSH which then increases the amount of thyroxine produced.

Too Much or Too Little Thyroxine

A person who has hyposecretion of thyroxine during the early years of his life may be physically and mentally retarded. This type of person is called a *cretin** (KREET in). When there is extreme hyposecretion of thyroxine in an adult, the individual develops the condition called *myxedema* (MIK sih DEE muh). In this condition, a general swelling of body tissues (edema) develops and cholesterol levels increase, possibly leading to hardening of the arteries. Cretinism can be prevented and myxedema treated by taking thyroxine pills.

Hypersecretion of thyroxine may increase the body's metabolism by 60% or more. The metabolic rate often exceeds the food intake, causing weight loss. Such a person also tends to be nervous, irritable, and emotionally unstable. His thyroid gland usually becomes enlarged, causing a swelling in the neck called a **goiter*** (GOY tur).

Iodine deficiency also causes goiter. Without enough iodine, the thyroid gland cannot make enough thyroxine, and the concentration of thyroxine decreases in the blood. The anterior pituitary secretes large amounts of TSH in an attempt to correct this lack. This causes the thyroid gland to grow, sometimes to a large size. The enlarged thyroid gland still cannot produce thyroxine until there is iodine in the diet. The use of iodized salt helps to prevent goiter, especially where the iodine content in the food supply is low. Often a goiter shrinks when iodine is added to a person's diet. Goiters may also result from other illnesses; most goiters can be corrected.

---

hyposecretion: hypo- (under) + -secretion (L. SECRETIO, separation)

hypersecretion: hyper- (exceeding) + -secretion (separation)

cretin: (Fr. CRETIN, idiot)

goiter: (L. GUTTER, throat)

Major Endocrine Glands and Their Hormones

23A-3

Gland	Hormone	Function
Thyroid	Thyroxine	Stimulates an increase in use of foods, resulting in increased metabolism (body heat)
	Calcitonin	Stimulates a movement of calcium from the blood into bone tissue
Parathyroids	Parathyroid hormone (PTH)	Stimulates an increase in blood calcium
Anterior pituitary	Thyroid stimulating hormone (TSH–thyrotropic hormone)	Stimulates thyroid follicles to synthesize and secrete thyroxine
	Adrenocorticotropic hormone (ACTH)	Stimulates adrenal cortex to secrete cortisone
	Growth hormone (GH)	Stimulates growth in general, especially bone and muscle tissue
	Gonadotropic hormones	
	• Follicle-stimulating hormone (FSH)	Stimulates development of gametes
	• Luteinizing hormone (LH)	Female: stimulates ovulation and development of corpus luteum; Male: stimulates production of androgens (especially testosterone)
	Prolactin (PRL)	Stimulates the formation of milk during and following pregnancy
Posterior pituitary	Antidiuretic hormone (ADH)	Stimulates reabsorption of water from kidney tubules
	Oxytocin	Stimulates contraction of uterus for birth; movement of milk to nipples for sucking infant
Islets of Langerhans	Insulin	Stimulates movement of glucose from the blood to liver and muscles; decreases blood sugar level
	Glucagon	Stimulates liver to convert glycogen to glucose; raises the blood sugar level
Adrenal medulla	Glucocorticoids (cortisone)	Stimulates many aspects of carbohydrate metabolism
	Epinephrine (adrenalin) and norepinephrine (noradrenalin)	Stimulates body for overcoming stressful situations
Adrenal cortex	Mineral corticoids	Stimulates reabsorption of sodium from kidney tubules; regulates blood volume
Ovaries		
follicles	Estrogens	Stimulates growth and development of the female secondary sex characteristics
corpus luteum	Progesterone	Stimulates development of uterus for possible pregnancy; stimulates mammary gland growth
Testes (interstitial cells)	Androgens (especially testosterone)	Stimulates growth and development of the male secondary sex characteristics

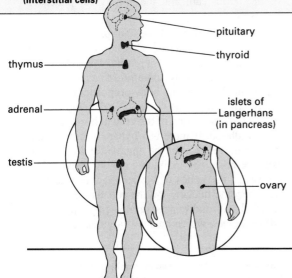

pituitary
thyroid
thymus
adrenal
testis
islets of Langerhans (in pancreas)
ovary

Calcitonin (KAL sih TOH nihn), a hormone secreted by the cells between the follicles of the thyroid gland, is released when the calcium level of the blood gets too high. It causes calcium to move from the blood to the bone tissue, stabilizing the blood calcium level.

Parathyroid glands

The **parathyroid*** (PAR uh THYE ROYD) **glands** are brownish-yellow clusters of cells embedded in the connective tissue around the sides of the thyroid gland. The *parathyroid hormone* regulates the calcium and phosphorus levels of the blood and body fluids. The function of the parathyroid hormone is opposite that of calcitonin: it

---

parathyroid: para- (Gk. PARA, beside) + -thyroid (shield) moves calcium from the bone to the blood. It makes sure there is enough calcium in the blood for normal nerve and muscle function and for blood clot formation. The blood calcium level may decrease as it is used by the bone tissue or when the diet is deficient in calcium. In response, the parathyroid secretes more hormone to raise the calcium level of the blood.

Review Questions 23A-1

1. List several characteristics of hormones.
2. Why is the circulatory system significant in the function of the endocrine glands?
3. Describe the negative feedback mechanism that controls the secretion of many hormones. Why is this significant?
4. Describe the thyroid gland. What do its hormones control? What symptoms characterize hyposecretion and hypersecretion of thyroxine in (a) young children and (b) adults?
5. What does the parathyroid gland control?

Pituitary gland–anterior lobe

The **pituitary*** (pih TOO ih TEHR ee) **gland,** or *hypophysis* (hye PAHF ih sis), is about the size of a small marble, weighs about 1/2 g (0.018 oz.), and hangs at the base of the brain. It has two lobes. The anterior lobe is epithelial tissue, but the posterior lobe is nervous tissue. Blood vessels connect the anterior lobe to the hypothalamus of the brain. The posterior lobe connects directly to the hypothalamus by the pituitary stalk. The *hypothalamus* controls both lobes.

The anterior pituitary produces several hormones, each synthesized by a different type of cell. Chemical secretions from the hypothalamus control anterior pituitary hormone secretions.

23A-5 *Giants over 8 feet tall and 42-inch midgets, such as the circus performers of a previous age, were frequently the result of growth hormone imbalances. Today such imbalances are usually corrected before the condition becomes permanent.*

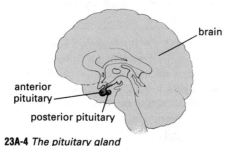

23A-4 *The pituitary gland*

Body height and size are determined largely by the action of the **growth hormone** produced in the anterior pituitary. This hormone increases the uptake of amino acids for protein synthesis, stimulates the breakdown of fats, increases the level of sugar in the blood, and stimulates the formation of the periosteum and the epiphyseal plates of bones.

If the pituitary gland does not produce enough growth hormone during childhood, the person will be a dwarf. Usually a *pituitary dwarf,* unlike dwarfs or midgets by some other causes, is normal in intelligence and body proportions. Abnormally tall individuals (''giants'') develop if they have a hypersecretion of the growth hormone during childhood. If there is a hypersecretion of the growth hormone after the epiphyseal plates have become bone, the individual cannot grow taller. However, the bones of the hands, feet, and face may become thicker, and the soft tissue may enlarge. This condition is *acromegaly** (ACK roh MEG uh lee), which means ''large extremities.''

pituitary: (L. PITUITA, phlegm; *from the belief that the gland secreted phlegm*)
acromegaly: (Fr. ACROMEGALIE, enlargement of extremities)

adrenocorticotropic: ad- (L. AD-, near) + -reno- (RENES, kidneys) + -cortico- (CORTEX, bark) + -tropic (Gk. TROPOS, turn, change)

gonadotropin: gonado- (L. GONAD, primary sex gland) + -tropin (Gk. TROPIN, changing)

The anterior pituitary secretes three groups of **tropic hormones,** which stimulate growth and function of other endocrine glands. Following are the tropic hormones:

❏ *Thyroid stimulating hormone* (TSH) or thyrotropic hormone, which regulates the thyroid gland;

❏ *Adrenocorticotropic** (uh DREE noh KAWR ti koh TROH pik) *hormone* (ACTH), which acts on the adrenal cortex; and

❏ *Gonadotropins** (go NAD uh TROH penz), which control the hormones secreted by the reproductive organs. The gonadotropins are the *luteinizing** (LOO tee in IZE ing) *hormone* (LH) and the *follicle stimulating hormone* (FSH), which are discussed in the next chapter.

*Prolactin** stimulates cells of the breast to produce milk. This special hormone is produced by the pituitary during pregnancy. After birth, the breast-feeding infant stimulates a continual release of prolactin from the pituitary gland. When the baby stops nursing, milk production ceases in about a week.

Pituitary gland–posterior lobe

The posterior pituitary stores and releases two hormones, which are actually made by cells in the hypothalamus. One of these hormones, *oxytocin** (AHK sih TOH sin), stimulates the smooth muscles of the body to contract. Its greatest effect is on the uterus, causing the birth of the baby.

The second hormone released by the posterior pituitary is *antidiuretic* (ant tih DYE yuh RET ik) *hormone* (ADH), which is regulated by the volume and water content of the blood. It helps the body to conserve water by stimulating reabsorption of water from the kidney tubules. A hyposecretion of ADH causes an increase of water in the urine; this condition called *diabetes insipidis* increases urine volume and thirst.

Islets of Langerhans

There are more than a million small groups of cells known as **islets of Langerhans** (LAHNG ur AHNZ) scattered throughout the **pancreas.** The islets of Langerhans contain two different kinds of cells, one which secretes glucagon, and one which secretes insulin.

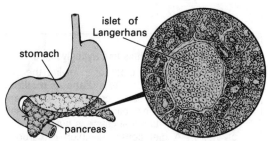

23A-6 *The islets of Langerhans*

Insulin is a hormone that stimulates body cells to take glucose from the blood, lowering the blood glucose level. Insulin also stimulates the conversion of glucose to glycogen, which is stored in the liver. Insulin also affects protein synthesis by increasing the movement of amino acids into body cells. Therefore, normal growth requires proper levels of insulin.

Glucagon performs functions basically opposite to those of insulin. Primarily, it raises the blood sugar level by stimulating the liver to convert glycogen to glucose. It also stimulates the breakdown of fats to form glucose.

The secretion of insulin and glucagon is controlled by and helps to control the blood sugar level. Soon after a meal, the increased sugar content of the blood stimulates the secretion of insulin. Then, as the body cells take up the glucose, the blood sugar level decreases. This results in a decrease in insulin secretion. Several hours after a meal, the blood sugar level begins to drop. The lower blood sugar level stimulates the secretion of glucagon. This stimulates the liver to produce more glucose, and return the blood sugar concentration to its normal level.

Adrenal glands

The **adrenal** (uh DREE nul) **glands** are small yellow masses of tissue enclosed in fat tissue on top of each kidney. Each gland consists of an inner portion, the **adrenal medulla,** and a larger outer region, the **adrenal cortex.** The two portions function as two different endocrine glands.

The cells of the adrenal medulla secrete **epinephrine** (EP uh NEF rin) (also called **adrenaline**) and **norepinephrine** (NAWR ep uh NEF rin) (also called **noradrenalin**). The secretions of the adrenal medulla are controlled by the sympathetic

---

luteinize: lutein- (L. LUTEUM, egg yolk; *referring to corpus luteum*) + -ize (Eng. -IZE, to cause)

prolactin: pro- (before) + -lactin (L. LACTO-, milk)

oxytocin: oxy- (Gk. OXUS, sharp, quick) + -tocin (TOKOS, childbirth)

insulin: (L. INSULA, island)
adrenal: ad- (near) + -renal (L. RENES, kidneys)

Diabetes Mellitus and Hypoglycemia

The most common disorder involving the hormones from the pancreas is **diabetes mellitus.** It is the third most common cause of death and is the leading cause of blindness, kidney disease, and gangrene. Its usual cause is hyposecretion of insulin. A diet continually high in carbohydrates may cause the islets of Langerhans to slow down or stop their production of insulin. This decrease in insulin secretion appears to be partly hereditary.

The decrease in insulin causes three major metabolic disturbances:

❏ Most of the glucose remains in the blood, largely unavailable to body cells. The liver cells are unable to store glucose.

❏ The body cells must rely on fats for energy. The release of fats into the blood may multiply the fat level five times. As fats are broken down, certain substances (ketone bodies) are produced that decrease the pH of the blood. Without insulin treatment, this condition may result in coma and death.

❏ The body breaks down proteins to amino acids. The liver cells then convert amino acids into glucose, compounding the blood sugar level problems. Normally, there is a balance of protein synthesis and protein breakdown, but an untreated diabetic may become thin and emaciated as his body uses its proteins for energy.

The diabetic's blood sugar level usually becomes so high that sugar is present in the urine. As the sugar in the urine increases, more water is also lost, and the diabetic has a constant thirst.

Treatment involves regulating the diet to reduce carbohydrates and increase proteins, minerals, and vitamins. If the condition is severe,

A diabetic using a blood testing device to determine her blood sugar level

insulin injections may be necessary. Insulin is not effective when taken orally because it is a protein, and the body digests it before the blood absorbs it. However, some drugs which help to stimulate insulin production are not digested and may be taken orally. The use of some of these drugs has been reevaluated since prolonged use may injure the heart.

A person with diabetes mellitus suffers from too much blood sugar. A person with too little blood sugar has **hypoglycemia*** (HYE poh glye SEE mee uh). One cause of hypoglycemia is an overproduction of insulin. If the blood sugar level drops too low, the person will feel extremely drowsy or become uncoordinated or unconscious.

Hypoglycemia may also result if a diabetic injects too much insulin. This severe reaction, known as *insulin shock,* requires a quick supply of sugar because the overdose of insulin has drastically reduced the glucose supply to the brain. If untreated, the person may lose consciousness, suffer brain damage, or even die.

---

nervous system and help to prepare a person for emergencies or threatening situations.

You may have read of someone who saved a life by actually lifting a car off an injured person. An abundant release of epinephrine and norepinephrine, which greatly increase the metabolic rate, can make such physical feats possible. The hormones rapidly increase the heart rate, blood pressure, blood sugar level, and breathing rate, providing the brain, heart, and muscles with a maximum of sugar, oxygen, and hormones and

permitting the individual to exert the strongest possible muscle contractions to lift the car.

The adrenal cortex secretes several hormones, one group of which is the glucocorticoids (GLOO koh KAWR tih koydz). These hormones primarily promote the conversion of fats and amino acids to glucose. They insure that the body cells are well supplied with energy when the body is under stress. The adrenal cortex therefore supplements the functions of the adrenal medulla. Stress causes the anterior pituitary to produce abundant ACTH,

---

hypoglycemia: hypo- (under) + -glyc- (Gk. GLUKOS, sweet) + -emia (Gk. HAI-MA, blood)

FACETS OF BIOLOGY

23A-1

Anabolic Steroids–Instant Muscle

Proverbs 20:29 says "The glory of young men is their strength." Most young men are pleased with what they are physically able to do (play sports, do some activity well, accomplish some feat). In times past if a young person were not able to do physically what he wanted to do, he would work at it. Depending upon the quality and the amount of effort and his inherited characteristics, he may have been able to obtain the glory of doing what he set out to do. And if not, he at least learned and developed by trying. Today, some young people seek a short cut to achieving a physical goal through the use of anabolic steroids.

About 25 yr. ago Communist athletes dominated some international sports. It was learned that these athletes had been taking the male hormone, testosterone. The athletes won many victories, but at great expense. Some of the men were unable to urinate without having a tube inserted into their urinary bladder. Women appeared to be so masculine that chromosome tests had to be conducted to prove they were females.

Synthetic versions of testosterone, called **anabolic steroids,** were developed in the 1960s. Anabolic steroids have been used as a medical drug for people who have lost their hormone-producing glands by injury, cancer, infection, or rare diseases. At first it was thought that steroids might promote healing of joint, bone, and muscle injuries, but it has been demonstrated that they do not help significantly.

What steroids do

The adult male body produces about 2.5-10 mg of testosterone a day. The quantity normally fluctuates in a slow cycle. Testosterone stimulates development of the male secondary sex characteristics (see page 609).

Anabolic steroids are taken by some young men in order to increase their muscular strength and size. Depending upon the amount of steroids taken, the amount and quality of physical exercise engaged in, their diet, and the persons' inherited potential, the gain in muscle mass can be rapid and significant. In a few weeks the gains made by a person taking steroids can equal gains made by a person using only exercise for a number of months or years.

The dosage taken by athletes seeking to gain physical size and strength is many times the normal daily supply, which can create significant physical and emotional problems. Some of the side effects men notice when taking anabolic steroids appear to them to be minor: acne, water retention (swelling of the feet and legs) changes in blood cholesterol levels, and frequent or continuing erections.

Other known side effects, however, are significant. Because testosterone is produced in response to a negative feedback mechanism, high levels of anabolic steroids

cause the body to stop producing natural testosterone. The testes then shrink and stop producing sperm, resulting in sterility. Other known significant physical effects of large doses of steroids include cancer, heart disease, jaundice, liver diseases and tumors, prostate enlargement, stunted growth, and death. There are many other suspected side effects.

Some female athletes have also sought to increase their muscular size and strength by taking steroids. The physical side effects they experience include many of the male symptoms as well as baldness, hairiness of the body, and improper functioning of their reproductive system, resulting in damage to their unborn children or sterility.

Not all effects of steroids are physical. Large doses of steroids cause a person to feel strong and powerful and also make him prone to moodiness, depression, and irritability. Some mild-mannered people using steroids have periods when they become extremely angry and aggressive (commonly called "roid rages"). They are often obnoxious, provoke fights, and do such things as ram their fists through walls for no apparent reason. People who have taken steroids report that one minute they feel so good and strong that they believe they could "take on the whole world, like the muscular comic book heroes," and the next minute they are extremely depressed and contemplating suicide.

Many young people plan to take steroids just long enough to build their physical size and strength and then stop before the undesirable side effects develop. The feeling of strength and the increase in muscle size often cause them to want more strength and size, which usually results in their increasing the dosage. Also, the bulging muscles quickly fade after the chemical that induced their growth is withdrawn. The feeling of macho strength also fades when the steroids are stopped; thus, some people continue to use steroids to keep from "feeling weak."

A Christian perspective

The Bible does not condemn a person for seeking to be strong or skilled at something that is proper and acceptable. Playing sports and seeking to be good at them can be fine. However, most Christians agree that if one does not take the proper care of his physical body, he sins (Rom. 12:1). The same principle would apply to a person who knowingly harms his body's future by taking steroids for present gain.

The Bible does not condemn young men for their physical strength when it says that their "glory is their strength." The Bible, however, clearly condemns pride (Prov. 16:18, I John 2:15-17; Mark 7:22-23). Many people do not take steroids to improve their athletic ability, but merely to achieve the "big, strong look." One steroid user said that he did not mind if steroids killed him as long as he "looks big in the coffin." Besides all the physical problems, the person who takes steroids merely to develop a muscular build has sinful pride.

Review questions on page 611

Anabolic Steroids and Athletics

Most sports are riddled with anabolic steroid users. Olympic gold medalists have been stripped of their awards when tests revealed that they had used steroids. Many professional sports now periodically test their players and either fine or suspend them if they are found to have used steroids. Some college teams forfeit games and are not permitted in league competition if members of their teams test positive for steroid use. Even high school athletes use steroids and face disqualification if caught.

Desire to win and excel must be strong if a person is going to put in the long, hard hours of practice necessary to become good at any athletic endeavor. This desire to win has led many athletes to seek all the help they can. For many, "help" has come in the form of anabolic steroids. It is one thing to sacrifice time and energy for the goal of winning, but something else to make the physical and emotional sacrifices that anabolic steroid use demands.

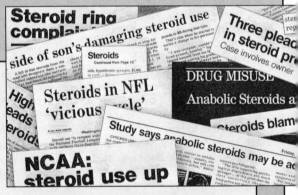

It also gives an unfair advantage to those who use them. What once was a contest involving quality of coaching, level of training, and inherited characteristics of the athlete now becomes a competition of how much anabolic steroids a person's body can take before some part of it deteriorates or the person kills himself. Although the "breaking of records" and the spectacle of "big athletes battling it out" may be obtained with the use of steroids, this is not a good, true athletic competition. With the use of anabolic steroids all sense of sport and sportsmanship in athletic competition is lost (I Tim. 2:5).

Cortisone and Cushing's Syndrome

Glucocorticoids, such as *cortisol* and *cortisone,* are used to reduce pain in allergic reactions, infections, arthritis, and certain types of cancer.

After several years of use, serious side effects known as *Cushing's syndrome* may develop. In this syndrome, fat is gradually redistributed from arms and legs to the trunk region, the face appears swollen, and the number of lymphocytes often decreases, making it difficult for the patient to fight infections. The skin becomes thin and internal bleeding is common.

Hormonal Disorders in Humans

Growth hormone
  Hyposecretion–dwarfism
  Hypersecretion–
    Child: giantism
    Adult: acromegaly

Thyroxine
  Hyposecretion–
    Child: cretinism
    Adult: myxedema, goiter
  Hypersecretion–goiter

Parathyroid
  Hyposecretion–spasms, tetany
  Hypersecretion–weak, brittle bones;
    kidney stones

Insulin
  Hyposecretion–diabetes mellitus
  Hypersecretion–hypoglycemia

Cortisone
  Hyposecretion–Addison's disease
  Hypersecretion–Cushing's syndrome

which stimulates glucocorticoid secretion. This is vital in supplying the abundant energy needed quickly during times of stress.

The gonads and sex hormones

From birth the **gonads** (the reproductive organs) produce small amounts of the *sex hormones*. In males the *testes* produce hormones called **androgens** (AN druh jenz), the most familiar of which is **testosterone** (tes TAHS tuh RONE). In women the *ovaries* produce hormones called **estrogens** and another hormone called **progesterone** (proh JES tuh RONE).

Gonadotropic hormones secreted by the pituitary act as a feedback mechanism, controlling the hormonal secretion of the gonads. During childhood, little or no gonadotropic hormones are produced, and the small amounts of sex hormones secreted by the gonads barely affect the body.

In the early teens, however, there are great increases in the secretion of gonadotropic hormones. Additional gonadotropins stimulate the *testes* to begin to produce sperm and the *ovaries* to continue the maturation of ova. The increase also causes comparatively large quantities of sex hormones to be produced and released.

Sex hormones cause the body to mature and activate genes which cause the body to develop **secondary sex characteristics.** Most secondary sex characteristics are *sex-limited characteristics;* that is, the genes for these characteristics are present in both sexes but are not expressed until the gonads produce adequate amounts of the necessary sex hormones. Tumors or hormone treatments for other disorders (such as cancer) can cause hormonal imbalance, causing the opposite secondary sex characteristic to develop.

Other Endocrine Glands

Some scientists agree that the **pineal gland,** a small, oval structure located in the head, secretes the hormone *melatonin* (MEL uh TOH nin), but its function in humans is unknown. Experimental evidence from animals indicates that the pineal gland affects the regular rhythms of the body and possibly pigmentation. In humans the pineal gland begins to decrease in size before puberty.

The **thymus** (THYE mus) **gland,** located between the lungs, is large in young children but shrinks after puberty. It secretes *thymosin* (THYE muh sin), a hormone which activates most of the lymphocytes formed in the red bone marrow. The thymus gland is associated with the body's ability to develop immunities (see pages 570, 572-76).

The **placenta** (pluh SEN tuh), the tissue that joins the mother and fetus during pregnancy, is also a source of certain hormones. They function to continue the pregnancy (see pages 333-35).

FACETS OF BIOLOGY

Puberty and Maturity

The time during which the secondary sex characteristics develop is called **puberty*** (PYOO bur tee). Girls may show signs of puberty anytime between 10 and 16 yr. of age, but between 12 and 13 yr. is average. In females the beginning of *menstruation* is considered the start of puberty. Menstruation, a monthly discharge of the lining of the uterus, is a normal part of a woman's life until she is about 45 (see Chapter 24). Actually, the hormonal and bodily changes of a developing woman begin months or sometimes years before the first menstruation.

In boys puberty usually begins sometime between 11 and 17 yr. of age, but 14 is average. The exact start of puberty in young men is not as obvious as it is in young women.

Puberty: physical growth

For many teen-agers, growth during puberty is slow and regular. About 50% of all teen-agers, however, have a *growth spurt* in which they grow about 15 cm (6 in.) in a year, and a few may even grow 20-25 cm (8-10 in.) in a year. Girls normally experience a *prepubertal growth spurt* and grow rapidly when they are about 11 yr. old, just prior to entering puberty. Boys usually have a *pubertal growth spurt* at about age 14.

The brain does not always adjust to the body's new height and strength during a growth spurt. The person is clumsy, often when he wants most to be coordinated. Spilling things and running into

doors does little to help a self-image, but it is a normal part of growing up.

Puberty: hormonal and emotional imbalance

Puberty is also a time of hormonal imbalance. The body develops in response to the new hormone levels, but the hormone release is not steady. This unsteadiness may cause temporary emotional imbalance.

An exciting activity (such as a big game, a big date, a performance, or a trip to an amusement park) stimulates the body to release various hormones. Levels of epinephrine (adrenaline) and other hormones are increased, and the teen-ager experiences a "hormonal high": he feels good, as if he could conquer the world. This hormonal high, however, is short-lived. Negative feedback mechanisms begin to operate, and soon hormone levels drop; the person may have a "hormonal low." He is discouraged, feels everybody hates him, and is ready to either pout or "fly off the handle" at the slightest provocation.

Puberty is not only a time of physical and emotional change, but also a time of *self-identification*. A young child is concerned about himself and cares little about other children. The teen, however, begins to be concerned about what others think of him, as well as what he thinks of himself.

The desire for acceptance by friends of the same age reflects itself in many ways. For example,

teens become concerned about their clothes. They want to dress to reflect "themselves." Actually, most reflect the styles of those whom they want to accept them. Dressing to imitate rock stars or those who follow rock stars is not "being yourself" but is "being like someone else" to gain acceptance, something a teen may later regret.

Peer pressure (the compulsion of wanting to be accepted by the group) is strong during the teen years. Some teens will do things that they know are wrong just because their friends do them. For example, some teen-agers steal, not because they need the items or money but because their friends are stealing and it is "exciting." The excitement is in part a hormonal high. Later, when the depression comes, they feel it is time to steal again because it was "fun" (they were accepted by the group) and "exciting." Stealing

puberty: (L. PUBER, adult)

may be a drastic example, but the principle holds true in other areas too. This is one reason that Christian teens need Christian friends.

Satan has other, more subtle ways of using your body's changes to cause you to sin. Your body, especially during a time of change, greatly affects your mental attitudes. Hormonal highs and lows, however, are not an excuse to sin. For example, suppose Bob's mother asked him to take out the trash, but because Bob has had a "rotten day" (partly caused by a hormonal low), he does not "feel like it." He tells her that if she wants the trash taken out, she can take it herself. She then scolds him for disrespect and not doing what he should. Bob feels like screaming, socking someone in the jaw, running out of the house and never coming back. But he takes out the trash, goes to his room, and plops down, all the while thinking how bad his lot is and what it is going to be like when he can "get out of here."

Some people would say that Bob's thoughts and actions were justified because he was having a hormonal low, which is "natural" during puberty. However, Paul says, "I keep under my body" (I Cor. 9:27). Satan is tempting Bob to the sin of rebellion (I Sam. 15:23) and is using his body to get him to sin. No matter how a Christian *feels*, sin is sin. Part of a Christian's growing up is learning to submit himself to Christ's will, no matter what he may feel like (I Cor. 10:13; II Cor. 10:4-5).

Maturity

In some cultures a teen-age boy performs a task (such as hunting and killing a certain animal or traveling a distance alone), after which he is considered a man. Literature often portrays a teen going

---

Human Secondary Sex Characteristics

Male:

Body hair Hair on the scalp becomes coarser. The beard begins to grow. Hair grows on chest, arms, legs, under the arms, and in the pubic region.

Body fat The child's subcutaneous layer of body fat diminishes, resulting in a more muscular, trim appearance.

Muscular growth Stimulated muscular growth causes broader shoulders, thicker arms and legs, and a deeper chest.

Bone growth The person grows to his adult height.

Voice The vocal folds and other speech mechanisms become larger, causing the voice to become deeper. As this happens, difficulty in controlling the "new voice," especially in times of stress, often results in vocal "cracking."

Skin The skin is stimulated to become thicker and tougher. During the time of adjustment, the oil glands often overproduce, causing acne or other skin problems.

Reproductive glands: The reproductive glands enlarge as they prepare for reproduction and for producing functional gametes.

Female:

Body hair Hair on the scalp becomes coarser. Hair on the legs, under the arms, and in the pubic region begins to grow.

Body fat The child's subcutaneous layer of body fat is retained, resulting in a smooth appearance.

Muscular growth The muscles are stimulated to grow, but to a lesser extent than in the male.

Bone growth The person grows to her adult height. The pelvis spreads and rotates to supply a wider base for supporting a child during pregnancy.

Voice The voice deepens slightly, but this usually happens over a long period. Young ladies, therefore, usually do not have the problem of their voices "cracking."

Skin Same as in the male. The retained layer of subcutaneous body fat gives the skin a smoother, somewhat translucent appearance.

Reproductive glands As they prepare for reproduction, the gonads and accessory sex organs enlarge. Menstruation begins, and the breasts (mammary glands) develop.

through a difficult experience; at the end he is "grown up."

Maturity, however, is not something that happens when you reach a certain height or age, or accomplish some feat. Circumstances work together to cause a person to mature, but maturity is not achieved all at once. In fact, some people *never* achieve it.

Maturity is a difficult concept to define. Some of the major characteristics are as follows:

❏ *The mature person can control himself.* He thinks things through, makes wise decisions, and then disciplines himself to do what he knows to be best, no matter what his whim or another person's wishes may be. A mature person has control of his anger, love, hate, and other emotions. He does not "fly off the handle" but tempers his actions with good judgment.

❏ *The mature person recognizes true value.* Mature people make good value judgments. For example, they waste little time or money on unprofitable activities. They do not buy what they do not need or cannot afford. They give their time to valuable activities that are not necessarily "fun," such as homework, practicing the piano, or visiting the sick.

Mature Christians do not sacrifice their prayer and Bible reading even for a good television program, nor do they skip church so that they can have a full day at the beach. Mature, spiritual Christians realize that thrills like those obtained by hormonal highs or pure-

ly physical excitement (such as watching a game or enjoying a ride at an amusement park) have their place, but are second-rate compared to the thrill of leading a person to Christ or spending time alone with the Lord.

❏ *The mature person works for deferred goals.* A mature person realizes that there is value in preparation for the future. Mature students study not just for grades but to prepare for their future goals. Mature people practice (sports, piano, or sewing, for instance) not only to have fun but also to acquire a valuable skill to use in the Lord's service.

Mature Christians realize that giving money to missionaries is not just performing a duty, but helping to advance their Lord's work. They are "laying up treasures in heaven" (Matt. 6:20). Witnessing is a normal part of the mature Christian's life, for he recognizes his long-range *goal.*

Acting mature–being mature

Although it is easy to find people who *act* in mature ways, it is not always easy to find a person who *is* mature. All too often *incentives* cause him to do the right thing. One who responds to a "big prize" (an all-expense paid trip to Hawaii for the family who brings the most people to church in the next month) but does not seek "the prize of the high calling of God" by giving the same effort when there is no contest is not completely mature. Usually, when a mature person is convinced of the value of an action, he is self-

motivated in ways that are in keeping with the Scripture.

How do you become mature? Your physical body grows and matures as you exercise and eat proper food. A baby's share of food and exercise would be of little profit to an adult. You mature emotionally as you stop depending upon your parents to do everything for you and begin to assume responsibility wisely. If your parents still have to tell you to do the things you know you should do, you lack maturity.

Likewise, if your only spiritual food is supplied in Sunday school and your only spiritual exercise is an occasional prayer, you are a babe in Christ. Hebrews 5:12-14 discusses Christian maturity. There are Christians who, because of the length of time they have known Christ, ought to be living examples and teachers of the Christian faith. But instead, they need to be taught the principles of Christianity again. They keep needing the "milk" of the Word rather than "strong meat [which] belongeth to them that are of full age, even those who by reason of use have their senses exercised to discern both good and evil" (Heb. 5:14).

Here is the key to Christian growth: "by reason of use." Only when you begin to assimilate the Word of God and exercise your faith in prayer, witnessing, and a daily walk in the path of righteousness can you become a mature Christian.

Review questions on next page.

Biological Terms

endocrine system
hormone
negative feedback
dynamic equilibrium
The Endocrine Glands
hyposecretion
hypersecretion
thyroxine
goiter
parathyroid gland
pituitary gland (hypophysis)
growth hormone

tropic hormone
islets of Langerhans
pancreas
insulin
glucagon
adrenal glands
adrenal medulla
adrenal cortex
epinephrine (adrenaline)
norepinephrine (noradrenalin)
diabetes mellitus
hypoglycemia

gonad
androgen
testosterone
estrogen
progesterone
secondary sex characteristics
pineal gland
thymus gland
placenta
Facets
anabolic steroids
puberty

Review Questions 23A-2

1. Describe the pituitary gland. What hormones does it produce, and what do they control?
2. Describe the significance of hyposecretion and hypersecretion of the pituitary growth hormone in (a) children and (b) adults.
3. Why would a hyposecretion of insulin cause an increase in the amounts of sugar in the urine? What is the name of this disorder? What is the usual treatment of severe cases?
4. Describe the adrenal gland. What hormones does it produce, and what do they control?
5. In what way are the adrenal glands the "glands of emergency"?

Facet 23A-1: Anabolic Steroids—Instant Muscle, pages 605-6

1. What natural chemical do anabolic steroids imitate in the body?
2. What do some people hope to gain by taking anabolic steroids?
3. What are some of the side effects of taking anabolic steroids?

Facet 23A-2: Puberty and Maturity, page 608-9

1. List several characteristics of (a) physical maturity, (b) emotional maturity and (c) spiritual maturity.
2. List the secondary sex characteristics for (a) males and (b) females.

Thought Questions

1. What type of temptations are typical during puberty? Does the fact that these are normal temptations justify yielding to them? Give Scriptural support for your answer.
2. How does one mature (a) emotionally, and (b) spiritually?

23B–Control of the Mind

The body's responses are not all automatic reactions to physical stimuli and hormones. If they were, we would be little more than machines. The brain, a physical organ, is the seat of the consciousness (awareness) of the physical self. All of us, however, have a *mind*. The mind is the seat of the **will,** which enables all of us to make decisions about what to do or not to do.

The mind is in the brain just as the federal government is in Washington, D.C. We could not point to "the government" if we were in Washington; we cannot point to our minds in our

23B-1 *The Federal government of the U.S. may be in Washington D.C., but where in that city is it? Government is bigger than the Capitol building (above) or any other physical reality. Our mind is bigger than our brain.*

brains. The government is bigger than Washington; our minds are more than the sum of the parts of our brains or bodies.

Two people in love speak of giving their hearts to each other. People greatly involved with their hobbies have "given their hearts" to it. Actually, their hearts are still in their bodies pumping blood. These people have *willed* their conscious activity toward what they love. They cannot truly love something without thinking about it, being concerned about it, and sacrificing themselves for it. All these activities involve not the heart or brain, but the mind. People will to do these things.

You have heard of "giving your heart to the Lord." This phrase does not refer to giving Him the muscular pump in your chest, but to giving Him your very essence, your will. Giving the Lord your will means that you have decided to do what He wants, not what you want.

The Bible says that when you do your own will rather than the Lord's will, you allow Satan to control you (Rom. 6:16). When you daily deny Satan the use of your will and do the will of God, you become a strong, dedicated Christian. It is God's will that you believe and obey His revelation of Himself in Scripture. This task would be impossible if He did not promise you the strength that you need to do His will (Ps. 73:26). Salvation is the miracle of a moment, but living the Christian life obedient to the will of God is the work of a lifetime.

"Not my will"

It sounds easy. All you need to do is say, "Not my will, but Thine." You then place your life in the control of a loving, all-powerful God who has promised to meet all your needs, to bless you, and to take you to heaven when you die. Although victory is assured, the battle to give yourself to God is not always easy. You have a powerful adversary who "as a roaring lion, walketh about, seeking whom he may devour" (I Pet. 5:8).

One of Satan's most powerful weapons is tempting the Christian to take the control of his life back from God. Satan has won a victory if he can make you believe that God's will is not as good or as necessary as what you want to do and can get you to violate the Lord's will. He would like you to think that *you are in control,* when you have really taken some aspect of your life from God and yielded it to Satan's use.

Satan is in control of the physical world around us. He has manipulated the world to make his will look good, appealing, and fun–in other words, tempting. This situation seems grim, but it is, in fact, the best possible for us. Christians need the opportunity to choose to do God's will. If we do not have that choice, we are robots, not men. Christians have the assurance, however, that God will not permit us to be tempted beyond what He enables us to endure (I Cor. 10:13). We choose either to sin or to serve God. God promotes our growth by allowing us to make these decisions.

The Conscious and the Subconscious

When you are awake, you are **conscious;*** that is, in control of your physical, mental, and spiritual self. You can will to act or not to act, to think certain thoughts or not to think certain thoughts, to serve God or not to serve God. However, you can also become **unconscious** and would then not be in control of yourself.

Several aspects of consciousness-unconsciousness concern the Christian life. One normal, natural example of being unconscious is sleep. Your body is put under automatic control: your heart rate, breathing, and other body functions are stimulated by impulses from the nervous system and other control mechanisms within the body. Because you use much of your physical energy in physical activities while you are awake, your body does most of its growth, repair, and healing when you are asleep. This is one of the reasons that physicians prescribe "plenty of rest" for almost every illness.

Sleep and dreams

We can sin by choosing to sleep when we should be doing something else. We do not, however,

control what happens in our minds or to our physical bodies while we are asleep. The subconscious part of the brain takes control, and the conscious mind–the will–is somehow at rest. Since we are not in control, we do not sin while asleep.

Often Christians are concerned when they dream of a sinful situation. Are these "sins from within"? Should we attach any significance to those normal sometimes silly or fearful dreams that people experience most of the time? Where do these contortions of reality come from? (Dreams are discussed on pages 10-11.)

Most dreams stem from thoughts or experiences in the dreamer's conscious time. A terrifying experience often causes nightmares for days, weeks, or longer. A vivid experience is often relived in dreams. Sometimes things dreamed about together do not belong together in reality. Experiences from the past may combine with a contemporary factor to form an unusual dream. It seems that the mind is rapidly remembering various things and recombining them.

Although we dream about half the time we are asleep, only those dreams happening when we wake up (when our consciousness crosses over subconsciousness) are remembered. Exceptionally frightening dreams wake us up, and we remember them. Some unusual sound or happening may also disturb us enough to wake us up enough to remember a dream.

Some scientists speculate (since experimental data is hard to obtain) that people are "thinking" about the happenings of their day, sorting them

---

Dreaming to Forget

Some Christian psychologists believe that the "playback" function of the dreaming mind is a way of "erasing" or "bleeding off" thoughts and experiences. It is known that after a period of dreaming about a terrible experience, a person will settle down, accept the situation, forget it, and go on about his normal life. This idea seems to support the "erasing" theory.

This function may be significant for Christians because it enables us to "dream away" some of the corruption that we are exposed to by living in this world. Our minds are cleansed by "dreaming out" the corruption we hear or see. This cleansing may be the reason that Christians often dream of sinful situations which they would not even consider when they are conscious. If this concept of dreams is true, then it is not wise to remember and dwell on dreams, for that is merely putting back in what has been "bled off." Although there is no Scripture to back up or contradict this idea and little experimental evidence relating to it, it is an interesting theory.

---

conscious: con- (L. COM, together) + -scious (SCIRE, to know)

out, and storing them in their memory as they sleep. Dreams are believed to be part of this process. Many people have noticed that after a good night's rest they have the solutions to problems that troubled them the day before. Some scientists believe that a person actually dreams about the problem. Without the distractions of the world around him, he is able to "think it over" (try various solutions) and find an answer. The next day, when the problem presents itself, he "remembers" the solution without even realizing he dreamed it. This theory lacks scientific evidence, but "sleeping on it" does help many people solve problems.

Some students find that their best study time is the few moments before they go to sleep. Those who have to memorize material often find it easier if they work on it just before bed. Many Christians have found that meditations on a passage of Scripture just before retiring yields much fruit the next day.

Although we may be able to "program" our dreams somewhat by directing our just-before-sleep thoughts, we are not in control of what we dream. Most Bible scholars agree that we do not commit a sin unless we will to do it. Since our dreams are not in our conscious control, we do not sin while dreaming even though we may dream of sinful situations.

Hypnosis

Hypnosis* is a little-understood phenomenon which became popular about 300 yr. ago as an amusing parlor trick. The *hypnotist* (one who

places the subject in the trance) uses verbal suggestions to cause the helpless hypnotized person to do funny things. During a *hypnotic trance,* the subject gives up control over his mind and body, his conscious will, to the hypnotist. The mind of a person in a trance operates on the subconscious level, but is able to communicate with the world around him. Since he is not in control, he usually follows the hypnotist's suggestions unless they violate one of the subject's deep moral principles.

In a hypnotic trance a person will often recall and reveal things which he does not will to recall or reveal. The hypnotist can make suggestions to a person in a hypnotic trance that can influence him even when he is no longer hypnotized. These aspects of hypnosis have fascinated physicians and psychologists.

Could hypnosis be a method of finding out what sins we need to confess or what temptations we need to pray about? No, the Bible tells us what God expects of us. We can see temptations and sins if we know the Word. The Bible teaches that the Holy Spirit convicts of sin (John 16:7-11). A Christian who wants what God wants will have no trouble knowing what sins stand between him and God. We also know that no man stands between a Christian and God. We do not approach God to ask forgiveness through a priest or a psychologist, "for there is . . . one mediator between God and men, the man Christ Jesus" (I Tim. 2:5).

Could hypnosis be a method of helping Christians avoid sins? Could a hypnotist make suggestions that will cause a Christian not to fall into a sin that has become a problem for him? No, the Bible clearly teaches that we are to look to God for the strength needed to withstand Satan's temptations (I Cor. 10:13) and that only Christ has the power to overcome Satan (Eph. 6:10-11). To look to a hypnotist–or even to look to ourselves–for such power will not produce a lasting victory.

A Christian does not need hypnosis to recognize and seek forgiveness for sins nor to help him overcome temptations. He may need to talk to other Christians or be instructed from the Word of God. Hypnosis, however, is completely unnecessary for a Christian's emotional health, for we

hypnosis: (Gk. HUPNOS, sleep)

may speak directly to the Mighty Counselor and Prince of Peace, who shows us our problems and offers us the only remedy.

Hypnotism is more than just unnecessary for the Christian. Because hypnotism is an act of the will, to be hypnotized a Christian must consciously take his will away from God and give it to the hypnotist. The Bible teaches that we are to yield ourselves to God and that taking back any part of life for ourselves is wrong (Rom. 6:11-23).

Transcendental meditation

In many Eastern religions various forms of transcendental meditation are taught (and often called various things). **Transcendental meditation** focuses the will upon the self and attempts to make man the master of his mind and body. The person is encouraged to relax, think peaceful thoughts (often about nature), and look into himself to "cleanse" himself by becoming one with nature. Such a person is seeking "inner peace" through his own strength. This effort cannot succeed. Man

is too small to conquer Satan. Satan may give a temporary peace, fooling man into thinking he is going the right way, but in time the "father of lies" will reveal his true self. Man can obtain the inner peace he seeks only when he is at peace with his Creator. Only the Creator Himself can give that peace (John 14:27; 16:33).

Note that the same principle that makes hypnosis wrong also makes transcendental meditation wrong. When a Christian takes control of his life and looks to himself for peace he is not yielding to God what is rightly His—the Christians's will.

Some Christians try to "blend" some aspects of transcendental meditation into their Christian life. We are told to meditate on God and His Word (Ps. 119:9-16), not to nature or ourselves. God, who knows us better than we know ourselves, has promised to supply *all* our needs (not just physical needs). We do not need to look to ourselves for strength, peace, or joy. And if we do, we will not find real, lasting strength, peace, and joy, but only Satan's counterfeits.

Review Questions 23B-1
1. How can a Christian use his will to sin? How does he will to grow spiritually?
2. Give two hypotheses regarding the content of dreams.
3. Describe transcendental meditation and tell why it is unacceptable for a Christian.

Drugs

The Greek word *pharmakon,* which can mean either a healing drink or a deadly drink, has supplied the English language with many words. "Pharmacy" (the place where we purchase drugs) and "pharmacology" (the study of drugs and their effects) are both derived from *pharmakon.* So are the words "poison" and "potion."

It is true that "all drugs are poisons, and all poisons are drugs." A **drug** can be defined as any chemical that causes an alteration in the function or structure of a living tissue. Any poison will also fit this definition. Even the *medical drugs,* such as penicillin and aspirin, can be considered poisons in the sense that they can kill if they are taken in sufficient doses. Lest we seem to be building a case against medicine, consider that

23B-2 *In the 1700s, shops like the Marshal Apothecary prospered in America's larger cities. This one thrived for over 100 yr. and was a retail store, chemical manufacturing plant, and school for pharmacists.*

Miraculous Healing

The Bible teaches us that God controls sickness and health and works His will through both. Sometimes He accomplishes His will through healing, other times through death. He sometimes accomplishes His will through healings that take a long time and other times through miraculous healings.

The Scripture tells us that Christ healed people instantly and that apostles and prophets were instruments of miraculous healings. We can make several observations from Scripture about miraculous healing:

❑ The faith of the prayer, not necessarily that of the sick, is important (Acts 3:1-11).
❑ The ability to heal is not a sign of salvation or of spiritual power (Matt. 7:21-23).
❑ Christians are told to pray for the sick (James 5:15), asking for God's will.

The Scripture does not condemn the use of medicines. If anything, it supports their use. (James 5:14-16, olive oil was a principal medi-

"Christ Healing the Blindman" by Cornelis van Haarlem

cine in New Testament times; see also Luke 10:34). Drugs have their place and purpose. If God wants to heal miraculousIn He will. The will of God, however, often includes man's using his intelligence. Most medical drugs are tools that God uses to effect His will.

---

under this definition even water is a drug. Pure water, consumed in large amounts, can cause the body to reduce its salt content. Children who have rapidly consumed large quantities of water have died of ''water poisoning.''

Medical drugs

A **medical drug** is one taken to prevent, treat, or cure a disease or disorder. Today, literally thousands of medical drugs are available. Some are legally obtained only by a *prescription* written by a physician, but some may be purchased ''over-the-counter,'' without a prescription.

Medical drugs can be grouped according to their sources, the compounds they contain, and the body parts they affect. The following classifications are designed to help explain what medical drugs are. This simple grouping, however, does not include all of the drugs in medical use today.

❑ *Dietary supplement* If the diet is insufficient in a nutrient (like a vitamin or mineral), that nutrient must be added to the diet as a supplement most often in the form of a drug. Some people,

because of injury, disease, or their metabolism, may require more of certain nutrients than their diet supplies and must take them as dietary supplements.

❑ *Supplement of body chemical* Some people's bodies cannot make necessary chemicals. Hemophiliacs, for example, cannot make a certain blood chemical which can be injected into their blood permitting them to live a nearly normal life (see pages 138-39, 155). Many diabetics are not able to make sufficient insulin for their needs and must receive it as a drug (see pages 163, 604).

❑ *Agent to treat infections* Some drugs either kill pathogens directly or help the body in its war against the pathogen. Antibiotics are drugs which help to destroy bacteria and some other pathogens. Other chemotherapy treatments deal with pathogenic bacteria, fungi, protozoans, and worms. Some topical (surface) medications contain drugs to prevent infections.

❑ *Agent to induce immunity* Physicians give vaccines or similar drugs to stimulate T cells or to cause the body to produce antibodies and thus develop immunities (see page 575).

❏ *Substances that decrease a body function or relax muscles* During an asthmatic attack people are often given drugs that relax the muscles of the trachea to permit breathing. Physicians use drugs to relax the muscles of the blood vessels to lower blood pressure. Some drugs slow the heart rate to restore a regular heartbeat. Some drugs control the amounts of chemicals the body produces. Many young people take drugs to control the quantity of oil their skin produces.

❏ *Substances that increase a body function or stimulate muscles* Sometimes a heart attack patient needs drugs to stimulate his heart. Some people are able to make hormones but need drugs to stimulate their bodies to do so. Some drugs are used to stimulate the kidneys to remove extra quantities of a substance from the blood. Drugs are used to stimulate the muscles of the blood vessels, increasing blood pressure.

❏ *Pain relievers* The most common over-the-counter drug purchase involves pain relievers. Several effective pain relievers (such as aspirin and ibuprofen) can be used to relieve minor pains. Several stronger pain relievers are available as prescription drugs when the pain is extreme. Minor pain relievers have few harmful side effects on most people (see page 619). Some relievers, however, are psychotropic drugs, and some are addictive drugs.

❏ *Psychotropic drugs* A **psychotropic*** (SY kuh TROH pik) **drug** is one that alters the emotional state or the sense of reality or both. Many of the more commonly used psychotropic drugs are listed in table 23B-3. The psychotropic drugs include the following main groups:

• **Narcotics** The narcotics produce euphoria, a chemically-induced emotional state. They are *physically addictive* (see pages 622-24).

• **Depressants** These drugs slow down the central nervous system, usually removing the ability to focus attention on problems. Often memory is impaired, and the person may go to sleep. Some depressants are physically addictive.

• **Stimulants*** The stimulants increase the action of the central nervous system and often step up body metabolism. The person feels alert and

has increased physical energy. Usually these drugs cover the body's sense of fatigue, but do not remove it. The stimulants are not usually physically addictive, but some people rely on them for the "boost" they need to face life.

• **Hallucinogens*** (huh LOO suh nuh jenz) Taking hallucinogens usually amplifies a person's

---

Physical Effects of Alcohol

• Dehydrates and numbs membranes of the mouth and throat, causing thirst.
• May inflame and irritate the esophagus, stomach, and duodenum. This inflammation may extend to rawness, ulceration, hemorrhage (bleeding), and perforation (holes in the walls) of these organs.
• Inactivates the centers of judgment in the brain. Progressive anesthesia of the whole nervous system ensues, causing sleep and, depending on the amount consumed, coma. Large doses lead to poisoning of the respiratory center and circulatory center of the brain, causing death. Long-term abuse of alcohol leads to brain atrophy. The brain of a heavy drinker is actually much smaller than a normal brain.
• Inactivates the antidiuretic hormone (ADH) when alcohol is present in the blood and causes excretion of excessive amounts of water.
• Lowers blood pressure by dilating (enlarging) blood vessels near the skin. This causes body heat to be brought to the surface. The immediate effect is a feeling of warmth. This effect can be harmful in cold climates. In time the effect, especially on the nose and face, is permanently enlarged blood vessels which give the skin a redness.
• Increases the work load of the heart.
• Decreases surface tension in the alveoli of the lungs, interfering with lung function.
• Poisons the sensitive cells of the liver that metabolize alcohol in small amounts in order to eliminate it from the body. This elimination process is only temporary. Large amounts or continual amounts of alcohol lead to fibrosis, fatty degeneration, and distortion of the liver–a condition know as *alcoholic cirrhosis*. Eventually, cirrhosis of the liver causes death. Food and vitamins help to protect the liver (and other body parts as well) against some of the toxic effects of alcohol.
• Causes physical and psychological addiction.

---

psychotropic: psycho- (Gk. PSYCHE, principle of life) + -tropic (turning, changing)   **stimulant:** (L. STIMULARE, to excite)   **hallucinogen:** (L. HALLUCINARE, to wander mentally, rave)

FACETS OF BIOLOGY

23B–1

The Drug Alcohol

Alcohol affects many body tissues. For normal people all the physical effects of alcohol are undesirable. Although the body appears to be able to tolerate small amounts of alcohol, major physical problems are experienced by those who repeatedly consume even small amounts of alcohol. Alcohol's most immediate and pronounced effect is on the brain. Those who consume alcohol want their brain to be affected; they are willing to tolerate the physical effects of alcohol on other body tissues in order to gain the mental effects.

Alcohol acts as a *depressant*–it slows down brain activity. The degree of this effect depends on the dosage. In small quantities, alcohol produces a feeling of **euphoria** (yoo FOHR ee uh), a state of mental well-being. It decreases tension by causing a disorganization of mental processes. A person who has had a few drinks cannot concentrate on his problems. One reason that people drink at social gatherings is to become "loosened up" by false euphoria.

Increasing the dosage causes a loss of muscular control. The slowed mental activity results in a brain that is no longer able to control the body. The person staggers, cannot focus his eyes, and becomes sleepy. It is easy to see why alcohol is responsible for more traffic fatalities than any other cause. After only one or two drinks, the person feels he is capable of driving well and can usually pass police sobriety tests. Even so, his reaction time is slower and his

Although strict laws seek to deter drunk driving, alcohol is still the leading cause of automobile related accidents and deaths.

judgment is poorer than when he is sober.

Larger doses of alcohol cause more disorganization: the person loses his ability to reason and his mood changes from euphoria to irritation and anger. Larger doses cause complete loss of body control, and sleep comes. If the dosage is large enough, the drinker will enter a coma.

Alcoholism is the dependence upon the drug alcohol. An alcoholic is a person who, once he has started drinking alcohol, does not stop until his body forces him to. Some claim that alcoholism is a disease and that alcoholics cannot help themselves–they have to drink. There is no conclusive scientific data to support this position. A person must *will* to take a drink and *will* to keep drinking to be an alcoholic.

It is easy to understand why an unsaved person in our high-pressure society would turn to something that would permit him to "forget, relax, and sleep." Friends and alcohol advertisements tell him that "this is the way to go." Many people know of no better way to escape their problems than to drown them in alcohol. Unfortunately, drowning problems does not remove them; it just preserves them until later. At the same time, the alcohol creates many additional problems.

Knowing these things, the writer of Proverbs reminds us that strong drink is deceitful (20:1). Scripture condemns drunkenness repeatedly (Luke 21:34; Rom. 13:13; Gal. 5:19-21). Besides the fact that we should not abuse our bodies, we, as Christians, are told to bring our burdens to the Lord, for He will take them away or give us the grace and strength to bear them. A Christian disobeys God if he depends on strong drink to relieve or solve his troubles.
Review questions on page 626.

Aspirin

In the early nineteenth century a bitter fluid said to be effective in reducing fevers was produced from the bark of the willow tree. By 1852 *salicylic* (sal ih SIL ik) acid was isolated and methods of preparing it in large quantities were available. Doctors used it to relieve the pain of rheumatism and found it effective on types of *gout** (caused by excess uric acid in the body) because the drug increased the amount of uric acid in the urine.

Salicylic acid was given with great care, however, because it irritated membranes in the mouth, throat, and stomach. Pharmacists found that adding sodium to the acid made *sodium salicylate* (suh LIS uh LATE). The new drug was effective and not so irritating, but it tasted so bad that some patients could not take it.

Scientists sought other derivatives and formulated *acetylsalicylic* (uh SEET ul sal ih SIL ik) *acid* which was much more effective and produced cheaply. It reduced fever, pain, swelling of the joints, and increased the excretion of uric acid. In small doses it is relatively safe and can be purchased "over the counter." Acetylsalicylic acid is the scientific name for *aspirin*.

Most people consider aspirin a relatively safe pain reliever. There are, however, more than two dozen possible dangerous side effects if aspirin is taken in large doses or for prolonged periods.

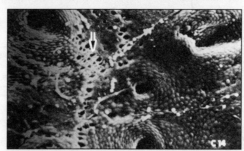

Scanning electron micrograph of stomach ulcerations caused by aspirin. Sixteen minutes after the person took aspirin, tiny ulcers (small arrow) become apparent (500x).

Even though it has been tested extensively, scientists still do not know *how* it works. It affects the sensation of pain in the brain; it affects inflamed areas and stimulates the kidneys to secrete uric acid (although it is no longer used for treating gout).

For most people aspirin is an effective, safe drug when taken occasionally in small doses for minor pain. Larger doses are prescribed by doctors for various conditions.

Good Drugs–Bad Drugs

No drug can be called truly good because all drugs can be misused and, thus, could be called bad. Some drugs can be considered good because they are useful and their wise use is acceptable. In the same sense, some drugs can be called bad because their use is neither wise nor acceptable. Let us compare aspirin and alcohol.

❑ Aspirin is taken to relieve physical pain. Alcohol is a poor pain reliever, except when taken in large doses.

❑ Aspirin does not significantly impair the mental or emotional processes. Alcohol produces multiple mental and emotional side effects.

❑ A dose of aspirin in sufficient quantity to relieve most minor pains has only minor physical side effects in most people. Even a small dose of alcohol has significant physical effects on most people.

❑ Aspirin has significant, potentially harmful side effects in some people (those who are allergic to it or consume too much of it over a long period of time, for instance). Alcohol has significant, harmful side effects in all people.

❑ Few circumstances besides great physical pain would cause one to take large quantities of aspirin. Alcohol's depressant qualities and temporary euphoria-producing effect cause many to consume it in large, harmful quantities.

We cannot say absolutely that aspirin is a good drug. Although it has good uses when taken in proper doses for the proper conditions, has few side effects, and does not affect the will, aspirin does have its drawbacks. Alcohol, on the other hand, is easily classified as a bad drug. Its harmful side effects, altering of emotions, and impairment of self-control are dangerous and undesirable.

senses and distorts his judgment. Some of the stronger drugs make him feel things and experience smells, tastes, and visions that are not really there (hallucinations). He is not in control of himself and cannot exercise his will. These drugs are not usually physically addictive.

gout: (L. GUTTA, drop; *from the belief that gout was caused by drops of morbid humors*)

Some Psychotropic Drugs and Their Effects

Class	Name	Effective Duration	Source	Short Term Effects
Narcotics	Morphine	6 hr.	Derived from opium (the dried sap of the opium poppy)	Causes lack of feeling (pain killer) and euphoria followed by sleeplessness and anxiety
	Heroin	4 hr.	Synthetically derived from morphine	Causes euphoria, followed by sleepiness and anxiety
	Cocaine*	Varies	Derived from leaves of coca plant (not the cola nut used in cola beverages)	*External application*–deadens skin sensations *Internal application*–stimulates nervous system, causing euphoria, excitement, talkativeness, and shakes
	Methadone	24 hr.	Synthetically produced	No mental or emotional effects; same physical effects as opiates (therefore prevents withdrawal symptoms)
	Codeine	4 hr.	Derived from the opium poppy	Same as morphine, but milder
Stimulants	Amphetamines	4 hr.	Synthetically produced	Increases heart rate and blood pressure; decreases feeling of fatigue (the person thus feels awake); causes feeling of self-confidence; permits easier breathing; decreases appetite
	Caffeine	4 hr.	Derived from many plants (and found in beverages made from them: cocoa, coffee, cola) and synthetically produced	Causes slight increases in heart rate; sense of wakefulness
Depressants	Barbiturates	Varies	Synthetically produced	Causes quiet stages, followed by sleep; memory is impared; physical coordination and reflexes are impaired; anxiety is curbed
	Tranquilizers	Varies	Synthetically produced	Dampens feelings a person has about life's situations; relieves anxiety; affects ability to concentrate on a situation
	Alcohol	Depends on dose	Derived from fermentation	Dampens feelings; increases blood pressure; produces mild euphoria, followed by sleep; large doses can cause coma and death.
Hallucinogens	LSD (lysergic acid diethylamide)	10 hr.	Synthetically produced	Senses amplified; judgment is affected; hallucinations; person feels "out of himself" (experiencing himself and other phenomena in a distorted way); extreme emotions; may be pleasing or a terrifying experience, depending on mood and environment when taking the drug
	DMT (N, N-dimethyl-tryptamine)	45 min.	Synthetically produced	
	STP	72 hr.	Synthetically produced	
	Mescaline	12 hr.	Derived from a cactus	Senses amplified; hallucinations; pupils dilate; extreme emotions
	Psilocybin	6-8 hr.	Derived from a mushroom	About same as mescaline
	Marijuana (Cannabis)	4 hr.	Derived from species of *Cannabis* leaves, shoots, etc.	Senses feel amplified; slows speech; affects judgment; may make anxious or relaxed; hallucinations are very rare.

*Concentrated forms, such as crack, produce intensified effects more rapidly.

Some Psychotropic Drugs and Their Effects (continued)

Long Term Effects	Medicinal Uses	Addiction Characteristics
Same as short term	Used as a powerful pain killer, in extreme cases	As short term effects wear off, physical withdrawal begins (cramps, internal pain, chills, shakes, vomiting, diarrhea). Severity depends on dosage and length of time the drug has been taken. Rarely fatal. Body does build up tolerance; larger doses must be taken to prevent withdrawal and maintain the euphoric state.
Loss of appetite, constipation	None	
External–none known; *internal*–after early symptoms, person becomes depressed; body may enter convulsions; large doses may cause other effects	Used as local anasthetic on mucous membranes (nose and throat)	
Same as short term	Taken to prevent withdrawal symptoms from narcotics	
Same as short term	Used as an easily administered mild pain killer; often found in cough syrups	Physical addiction with withdrawal symptoms is questionable. Body does build up tolerance.
False sense of energy causes people not to take care of themselves. Large doses over periods of time cause headaches, insomnia, confusion, panic, circulatory collapse, nausea.	Often prescribed as "pep pills" for those who lack energy or to counteract depression caused by other drugs; used to treat some mental disorders; for appetite control	No physical withdrawal. A person may, however, develop a psychological addiction. Body does build up tolerance; increasingly larger doses must be taken to produce effects.
Doses of the equivalent of ten cups of coffee result in insomnia and the jitters in some people; larger doses may cause various other effects	Used as a stimulant in conjunction with other drugs	
Relaxing the heart and muscles of breathing can cause death; some people experience wakefulness after using	Sedatives; inducing sleep or hypnotic trance	Physical withdrawal begins 24 hr. after last dose and lasts up to 7 days; weakness, visual distortion, sleeplessness, tremors, low blood pressure, delirium and convulsions are common.
Varies; often loss of interest in life and responsibilities	Used to prevent symptoms of mental illness; used to help people "cope with their problems"	Usually no physical withdrawal; however, a person may develop a psychological addiction.
Loss of motor and mental control; deterioration of brain, liver, and other organs	Solvent for other drugs	Physical withdrawal from prolonged, larger doses involves cramps, shakes, hallucinations, insomnia, indigestion–a condition known as d.t.'s (delirium tremens).
Can cause psychosis, panic; chromosome damage not confirmed; time distortion; flashbacks to bad experiences while taking the drug may happen weeks to years later	Not used today (was used to treat mentally ill)	No physical withdrawal; however, a person may develop a psychological addiction, feeling the dream world is better and more "real" than the real world; such a person was really mentally disturbed before he began using the drug; body does build up a tolerance and may require increasingly larger doses to produce similar effects.
Cramps, vomiting, increased heart rate, anxiety or euphoria; time distortion	None	
Same as mescaline	None	
Can cause abnormal emotional behavior; various physical problems have been linked to sustained use	None	Psychological addiction common; body builds up tolerance and may require larger doses for similar effects.

FACETS OF BIOLOGY

23B–2

The Narcotics

A **narcotic*** is a drug which dulls the senses, induces sleep, and becomes addictive with prolonged use. Most narcotics also soothe the mind, producing **euphoria,** a chemically-induced "good feeling." Some narcotics are used as medical drugs to relieve pain. People who use narcotics for non-medicinal reasons do so because the euphoria obscures their problems.

The body builds up a **tolerance** to narcotics; that is, the next time the drug is consumed, the size of the dose must be increased to obtain the same euphoria. No matter what the dosage, the euphoria lasts only a few hours. When the person no longer takes the drug, he enters **physical withdrawal,** experiencing actual physical symptoms. If he has taken a single small dose, the period of withdrawal may take place while he is asleep and may not even wake him. Estimated thousands of "weekenders" take narcotics occasionally on weekends and "sleep it off" before going to work on Monday.

If a person has taken narcotics over a longer period of time and has built up a tolerance to large doses, the physical withdrawal may be severe. Cramps, leg jerking (from which comes the term "kicking the habit"), shakes, chills ("cold turkey"), vomiting, diarrhea, fitful sleep, insomnia, and other painful side effects are common symptoms of narcotics withdrawal. These symptoms stop once the body has become *detoxified** (no longer has the poison in it). The time needed for detoxification varies according to the amount of narcotics taken and the duration of use.

Although everyone agrees that narcotics are *addictive drugs*, few authorities agree on what **addiction*** actually is. Part of the addiction problem is that tolerance to the drugs requires consuming larger doses to maintain the desired effects; the person must continue these large doses to prevent withdrawal.

There is more to addiction than just maintaining euphoria and preventing withdrawal. Even after detoxification, an unexplained craving for the drug remains. Many studies have shown that even after detoxification and years of "rehabilitation,"* over 95% of the people who have taken them in large quantities for a period of time will return to the use of narcotics. This return to drug abuse is scientifically unexplainable, yet a very real part of addiction.

Some people feel that the high rate of return to abuse of narcotics (as well as alcohol, barbiturates, nicotine, and other addictive drugs) is caused by some type of "biological need" created in the body by the drug itself. Other than the fact that most people return to taking drugs, there is little scientific evidence to support this view. Others think that the reason for returning to the drug is merely a desire for previous euphoria feelings (psychological reasons). Some feel

Cocaine–Crack

A concentrated form of cocaine called "crack" or "rock cocaine" has become popular in the drug culture. Cocaine, which is usually sniffed, is a narcotic stimulant that slowly dissolves into the blood stream and causes euphoria.

Crack, however, is smoked. This strong stimulant enters the blood stream and reaches the brain in about 10 sec. Thus, the user gets an immediate reaction. The euphoria from crack lasts only 5-20 min.

Crack causes a person to be active, excited, and even aggressive. Since all of the drug taken enters the body at once, almost all of it passes from the body at one time. Withdrawal comes immediately after the euphoria, and because of the large amount of the drug involved, symptoms are severe. A person addicted to crack needs more of the drug within minutes. A powerful addiction can be built up within 2 wk.

Because crack enters the blood quickly in a concentrated form, a lethal overdose is easy. Some people have died from a single smoke of crack, with over 5 times a lethal dose of cocaine in their bodies.

narcotic: (Gk. NARKOTIKOS, numbing)

detoxified: de- (reversal) + -toxi- (L. TOXICUM, poison) + -fied (making)

addiction: (L. ADDICTUS, one awarded to another as a slave)

rehabilitation: re- (again) + -habilita- (L. HABILITAS, ability) + -tion (process)

that social reasons are the cause (when the person returns to his life among drug users, he returns to using the drug himself). No matter what the reason may be, the person must *will* to take the drug.

The temptation to take a drug again is a powerful weapon in Satan's arsenal. Satan has convinced many people that these addictive drugs control them, while Satan is really the primary influence. Temptation comes from outside the will (although it may be inside the body), but it is the will that yields to temptation. Christians are promised strength from God so that they do not have to yield to temptations. Non-Christians do not have this strength and must rely on their own willpower to resist taking the drug again. Human willpower cannot match the strength of Satan's will, and it is easy to see why most unsaved people return to drugs.

Narcotics and the law

In 1920 the U.S. passed the 18th Amendment to the U.S. Constitution and established *Prohibition*. During Prohibition the manufacture, transportation, and sale of alcoholic beverages was prohibited. A **black market** (illegal manufacture, buying, and selling) for alcohol grew. Major criminal groups made fortunes in the black market for alcohol. The laws were difficult to enforce, and the criminal activities associated with the black market were rampant. In 1933 the 21st Ammendment to the Constitution repealed Prohibition.

In 1914 the legal supply of narcotics was stopped. A minor black market for narcotics quickly developed. Following Prohibition the narcotic black market started to grow. In the 1960s, the use of narcotics became rampant. Once a person becomes addicted, he is

A photograph of the police inspecting equipment found in an illegal brewery during Prohibition

willing to pay high prices to "support his habit." To supply the money, many must become criminals because while they are taking large doses of narcotics they cannot keep most jobs. By the 1980s, the narcotics black market had made fortunes for drug suppliers and had filled many streets with crime.

Today the narcotics black market has three major results affecting the user:

❑ The high price of narcotics forces many people to commit crimes to support their addiction.

❑ The purity of the narcotics is unknown. A person who purchases the drug on the black market has no idea what its strength is. Accidental lethal overdoses are common.

❑ Drug use is often unsanitary. Many narcotics users "mainline," injecting the drug into their veins. Using makeshift equipment and improper techniques, many drug users become infected with various diseases.

The effects of narcotics addiction are bad enough without the problems added by the black market. Narcotics laws have not eliminated the supply of narcotics, but have compounded the problems associated with the use of drugs and have cost billions of tax dollars spent in attempts to enforce almost unenforceable laws.

As Christians, we realize that legislation against sin or man's weakness does not prevent him from sinning, but having such laws does set a certain moral standard and discourages some people from taking drugs who might otherwise do so. Someday, however, lawmakers may consider these laws futile and repeal them as they did Prohibition. This would open

and creative thinking. Scientific research has since shown that these drugs do not improve mental or creative abilities, although the user may think so—especially while he is taking them. In Sir Arthur Conan Doyle's famous detective stories, Sherlock Holmes used cocaine to occupy his mind while not on a case (although Dr. Watson condemned the practice). Samuel Coleridge, a famous poet, was addicted to narcotics and was frustrated with his inability to stop using them.

In nineteenth-century America, opiates were legal, sold without prescription, and used as widely as aspirin. Many of the popular *patent medicines,* recommended for everything from "teething babies" to "women's troubles," from "coughing and diarrhea" to "arthritis and gout," contained opiates. Much of this opium was imported, but it became profitable to grow opium poppies in America (a practice that did not become illegal until 1942). In 1906 the Pure Food and Drug Act required the proper labeling of the patent medicines containing opiates. Later the amount had to be specified.

In 1914 Congress passed the Harrison Narcotic Act, which stopped the legal supply of opiates. The reasons for this legislation appear to have been politically tied to our foreign policy with England and the Orient. The addictive quality of narcotics was, unfortunately, not a major issue.

Narcotics in History

Narcotics have been used almost as long as alcohol to relieve pain and induce euphoria. In the Orient the lower classes of people have used opiates for thousands of years to escape the reality of their hard life. Narcotics were used in Bible times. Some Bible scholars think that the gall offered to Christ as He was suffering on the cross was a pain-relieving drug, quite possibly a narcotic. Note that when Christ tasted the substance, He refused to drink it (Matt. 27:34).

In the 1800s narcotic use became fashionable in certain social groups. At that time, narcotics were used not only to reduce pain and produce euphoria but also to stimulate mental abilities

the way for the legal sale of narcotics. What would happen then?

Most of the reasons for not taking narcotics result from the black market sale of drugs. Legal narcotics could be obtained inexpensively (opiates could be as inexpensive as aspirin), eliminating the need to commit crime to support the habit. The purity of the drug could be

controlled and the means for sanitary use could easily be provided. Some "experts" feel that, with the exceptions of those effects brought on by the black market, there are fewer physical problems involved with the use of narcotics than there are with the use of alcohol.

For many non-Christians, the major reasons for not taking nar-

cotics are the ones that result from the black market. If narcotics were legalized, we could expect a nation of narcotics addicts to even a greater extent than we now have a nation of alcoholics. (See *Psychotropic drugs and the Christian* on the next page.)

Review questions on page 626.

Psychotropic drugs and psychological addiction

Although some of the psychotropes cause physical withdrawal and addiction, most of them are psychologically addictive. In **psychological addiction** the person does not experience actual physical symptoms of withdrawal but may go through a period of emotional withdrawal. After a time, a person who has taken stimulants to be alert, tranquilizers to remain calm, and sedatives to go to sleep usually becomes dependent on the drugs to help him function "normally." If he is deprived of the drug, he *thinks* he cannot function normally and therefore cannot function normally without the drug. This "thinking" that he needs the drug is psychological addiction.

Thousands of "normal" people in the United States are psychologically addicted to tranquilizers, sleeping pills, or stimulants. These people are usually not criminals obtaining their drugs on the black market, although there is an active black market in these drugs. Many psychotropes are available as over-the-counter drugs. Thousands are prescribed by physicians to help their patients sleep, calm down, wake up, or "cope" with their problems. Many such prescriptions are made merely to satisfy the patient, rather than for legitimate medical reasons.

Psychotropic drugs and the Christian

Some psychotropic drugs have legitimate medical uses. Some of them are strong pain killers; others increase or lower blood pressure; some are the only known treatment for various *physical* conditions. The vast majority of the psychotropic drugs are taken to alter the person's emotional state and sense of reality, to give him the euphoria, sleepiness, alertness, escape, or other "feeling" he thinks he needs.

There is good evidence that pharmaceutical companies will soon be able to produce various psychotropic drugs that will lack most side effects but will chemically cause particular moods. For example, if a person needs to be industrious, he could take a purple pill; when going to a party, take a pink one; to be physically active, take a yellow one; to relax, take a green one; to sleep, take a blue one; and so on. In time, according to some authorities, we will be able to control our moods completely by taking drugs.

Sound good? You could be happy when you should be, energetic when you should be, and sleepy when you should be. But what of God? When the still small voice (I Kings 19:11-13) begins to speak to a Christian, teaching him faith by permitting a sorrow in his life, but the Christian takes a pill rather than turning to the Lord, what has he done? When God wants a person to wake up in the night and wrestle with a sin in his life and pray and grow spiritually strong, but he takes another sleeping pill because the last one has worn off, what is he really doing? In reality a Christian who takes psychotropes merely to al-

BREAKFAST OF DRILL SERGEANTS

ter his moods to fit his own wishes is disobeying God. Such a Christian is willfully taking the control of his mind and body away from God.

"But the Bible doesn't tell us not to take drugs," chimes back the immature Christian. "If drugs aren't going to hurt us physically, why not enjoy their benefits?" How can these benefits compare with God's promise to give peace of mind and heart (Phil. 4:6-7)? The Christian does not need a psychotrope to help him through life's problems. The unsaved may seek peace of mind and escape from his burdens with a bottle of drugs, but a Christian has a far better source of strength and relief. A chemical relief is temporary; a spiritual relief is eternal. Christians should not yield their minds and wills to anything but the Lord. If we take back control and give it even to a bottle of "harmless" drugs, we sin.

Biological Terms

will	*Drugs*	*Facets*
The Conscious and the Subconscious	medical drug	euphoria
	psychotropic drug	alcoholism
conscious	depressant	narcotic
subconscious	stimulant	tolerance
hypnosis	hallucinogen	physical withdrawal
transcendental meditation	psychological addiction	addiction
		black market

Review Questions 23B-2

1. Compare *drug* and *medical drug*. List and give examples of the kinds of medical drugs.
2. Why can aspirin be considered a good drug? Why can it be considered a bad drug?
3. List several points that should be considered about miraculous healings.
4. List the four groups of psychotropic drugs. List three drugs in each group.
5. List several differences between psychological and physical addiction. List several similarities.
6. List several reasons why psychotropic drugs are unacceptable for Christians.

Facet 23B-1: The Drug Alcohol, page 618

1. What are some of the physical effects of alcohol?
2. How does alcohol produce euphoria? Why does this euphoria fade as large quantities of alcohol are consumed?
3. Why do many Christians consider it unacceptable to view alcoholism as a disease?

Facet 23B-2: The Narcotics, pages 622-23

1. What characteristics of narcotics make them so desirable that many people will seek to obtain them on the black market?
2. Distinguish between opium, morphine, heroin, cocaine, and codeine. Comment on the medical uses of each.
3. What are the three major results of narcotics being sold on the black market?
4. What two main characteristics of narcotics contribute to their addictive qualities?

Thought Questions

1. List the characteristics of good drugs and the characteristics of bad drugs. What Christian principles can you cite to substantiate your position? How would penicillin and LSD fit into your classification of drugs. Why?
2. "If a physician prescribes it, it's all right to take it." Why is this an unacceptable position for a Christian?

HUMAN REPRODUCTION

24A – The Reproductive System
page 627

24B – Human Relationships–
A Christian Perspective
page 638

TWENTY-FOUR

24A–The Reproductive System

It is natural for young people to be interested in the subject of human reproduction. As a child becomes a teen-ager, his interest changes from the curious "Where did I come from?" to an awareness that his body and mind are being prepared for possible marriage and parenthood. Such changes are part of God's plan. To insure that mankind would continue, God created us with strong feelings of love, desire, and a need for security and companionship (Gen. 2:18, 23-24).

These feelings motivate a man and a woman to unite in the inconvenience, heartache, yet fulfillment and joy that are part of rearing a child. In part, God established marriage to fulfill these needs and accomplish this purpose. He ordained marriage and the intimate relationship between man and wife (Heb. 13:4) and commanded Adam and Eve to reproduce (Gen. 1:28). When looking for an example of the close relationship between Himself and the saved, God found nothing better than the relationship between a man and his bride (Eph. 5:25).

As is often the case, Satan took something good–sex–and perverted it. Satan subtly uses the normal drives and processes of the body to entice people to sin. These sins have become increasingly accepted and widespread.

Christians must be careful in their stand against evil not to condemn the good also. We should not condemn knowledge of human reproduction simply because some people misuse reproductive processes and thereby sin. It is good for Christian young people to understand their bodies and the basics of the human reproductive processes. If we understand these things, we are better able to see how Satan can use them to tempt us to sin. When we are aware of the traps Satan has set for us, we can better avoid them and be good stewards of the bodies God has given us.

Unlike any other body system, the functions of the reproductive system are not necessary for the survival of an individual. But its functions are vital for the continuation of the human race. Although many of the hormones and substances produced by the reproductive system make us "normal," life does not depend upon them.

In this chapter we will deal with the physical structures of the human reproductive system and their functions as we have dealt with the other structures of the body. We will also examine what the Word of God tells us about various related topics.

Male Reproductive System

The organs of the male reproductive system produce sperm and transfer them into the body of the wife. The primary organs of the male reproductive system are the **testes** (singular, *testis*). Normally a man has two testes and produces sperm and the male sex hormones continuously, though not always at a constant rate, from puberty to death. The other structures of the male reproductive system are the *accessory organs*.

The testes and the sperm

The testes develop in the abdominal cavity of the male embryo, but about two months before birth they descend into the **scrotum** (SKROH tum). The scrotum is a skin pouch which develops from the abdominal wall. In the scrotum the testes are kept at the ideal temperature for sperm production: about 2° C (3.6° F) less than in the abdominal cavity. To maintain the testes at this temperature, the muscle tissue of the scrotal wall relaxes in hot weather so that the testes are positioned farther from the body. In cold weather, the muscles contract, drawing the testes closer to the abdomen, where they are kept warm.

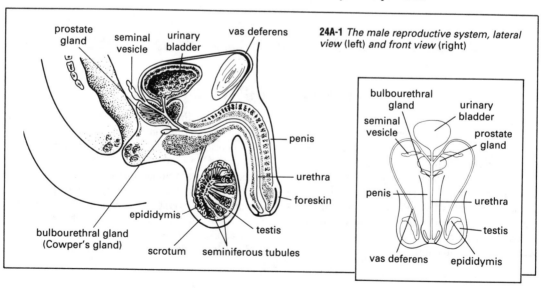

24A-1 *The male reproductive system, lateral view* (left) *and front view* (right)

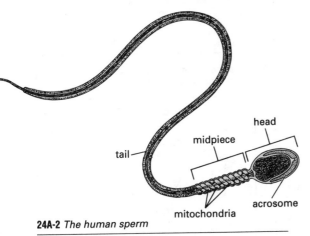

24A-2 *The human sperm*

Each testis is shaped like a flattened, 4 cm (1 in.) long egg and is covered by connective tissue. Most of the testis consists of tiny **seminiferous*** (SEM uh NIF ur us) **tubules,** where the sperm are produced. Between the seminiferous tubules are clusters of cells that secrete the male sex hormones.

Each day in the adult male, cells lining the seminiferous tubules carry on meiosis to produce millions of immature, nonmotile sperm. Also in these tubules are cells that produce jellylike secretions to nourish the sperm. This sperm-containing jelly is carried along the tubes and then enters the sperm-storing **epididymis*** (EP ih DID uh mis). Each epididymis is a thin coiled, 6 m (37 ft.) long tube that is tightly packed upon the testis within the scrotum. After at least 18 hr. in the epididymis, the sperm can become mature. Mature sperm are motile and can fertilize an ovum.

Although sperm are able to live for over 6 wk. in the ducts of the male reproductive tract, they normally survive less than 2 days after they are released from the body. A sperm has three basic parts:

❑ A *head* contains the haploid nucleus. At its front tip is an *acrosome* (ACK ruh SOHM), which contains enzymes, apparently to help the sperm enter the ovum.

❑ A *midpiece* of the sperm contains many mitochondria (see pages 77-78, 99-100) that are wrapped into a tight coil. They provide the energy needed for the swimming action of the sperm.

❑ A *tail* is a modified flagellum capable of whip-like movements which propel the sperm. The flagellum is not activated until just prior to its leaving the body.

Semen* is the fluid containing the sperm. Semen is an alkaline fluid and is rich in substances that nourish the sperm. The alkalinity activates the sperm and protects them from the acidic environment in the female's body.

The accessory organs

The accessory organs of the male reproductive system carry the sperm from the testes to the outside of the body and produce about 95% of the semen. The epididymis is an accessory organ. As each epididymis leaves the testes, it continues as a straight tube, the **vas deferens*** (VAS ◊ DEF ur enz), or *seminal duct*. The vas deferens, which carries the sperm by muscular contractions, passes into the abdominal cavity and around the urinary bladder.

The **seminal vesicle,** located near the urinary bladder, produces a fluid and adds it to the fluid of the semen. The vas deferens then passes through the doughnut-shaped **prostate gland,** which produces the largest part of the seminal fluid. The sperm can then be deposited into the **urethra.** The urethra serves as a common passageway for both sperm and urine. However, the action of certain muscles makes it impossible for the urine and sperm to mix together.

The *bulbourethral* (BUL boh yoo REE thrul) *glands* (Cowper's glands) are two pea-sized structures located below the prostate gland. Their ducts open into the urethra. These glands secrete a clear, sticky, alkaline fluid that neutralizes the normal

---

Circumcision

When a boy is born, the tip of the penis is covered by a loose-fitting fold of skin often called the *foreskin*. This is usually surgically removed soon after birth, a process known as *circumcision.**

For the Jews, circumcision is part of the Law (Gen. 17:10-14) to be performed on all male children 8 days after they are born. Early Jewish Christians felt that the Gentiles converted to Christianity should be circumcised. In I Corinthians 7:19 Paul points out that circumcision is part of the Law and is not necessary for salvation. Circumcision is still practiced in most civilized areas for sanitary reasons.

---

seminiferous: semini- (L. SEMEN, seed) + -ferous (FERRE, to carry, bear)

epididymis: epi- (near) + -didymis (Gk. DIDUMOS, testicle)

semen: (seed)

vas deferens: (L. VAS DEFERENS, vessel for carrying off)

circumcision: circum- (L. CIRCUM, around) + -cision (CAEDERE, to cut)

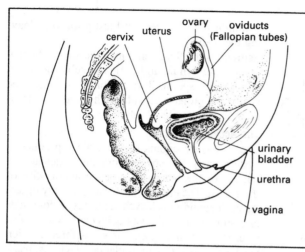
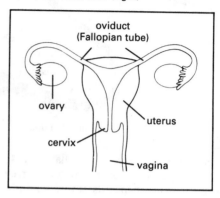

24A-3 *The female reproductive system, lateral view* (left) *and front view* (right)

acids along the urethra. The urethra passes through the **penis** and opens outside the body. The penis is designed to transfer the sperm into the wife's body during sexual relations.

Female Reproductive System

The female reproductive system is designed to produce ova (eggs), to receive the sperm, and to provide protection and nourishment for the developing embryo. The reproductive organs also are important in the birth of the baby and in nourishing the baby after birth. The principal organs of the female reproductive system are the ovaries. The accessory organs include the oviducts, uterus, vagina, and the mammary glands (breasts).

The ovary and the ovum

Human **ovaries** (sing., *ovary*) are solid organs about the size and shape of large almonds. They are held against the lower side walls of the pelvic cavity by ligaments. Unlike sperm production, which begins at puberty and continues throughout life, at birth there may be 200,000 immature ova in each ovary. At the rate of a few each month for about 35 years of the woman's adult life, these will begin to mature. Most often the two ovaries alternate, one producing an ovum one month and the other the next.

Each immature ovum with the surrounding cells constitutes a **follicle.** When puberty begins, the *follicle-stimulating hormone* (FSH) (see pages 601, 603) secreted by the anterior pituitary gland stimulates several follicles to develop each month. As the follicles grow, the process of meiosis (oogenesis) (see pages 122-23) continues. At a certain point in their development, one or two developing ova are selected by unknown mechanisms to continue development. The others usually degenerate. The follicles that continue to develop, enlarge, and form a cavity which fills with a clear fluid. Within each follicle the ovum is nourished and protected by the fluid.

Eventually, the mature follicle appears like a blister on the surface of the ovary. At this stage the immature ovum has not yet completed the second division of meiosis. After about 2 wk. of development, the wall of the mature follicle ruptures and releases the ovum, a process called **ovulation** (OH vyuh LAY shun). The released ovum is surrounded by follicle cells which secrete a gelatinous coating to protect it. When released, it is barely visible to the unaided eye.

24A-4 *A cross section of an ovary: developing follicle (1-4), ovulation (5), growth and degeneration of the corpus luteum (6-7)*

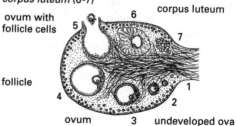

Other female reproductive organs

The **oviduct** or *Fallopian tube* is a tube with one end attached to the uterus and with a funnel-shaped free end with fingerlike projections which partially encircle the ovary. The inner surface of the oviduct is lined with a ciliated mucous membrane. The cilia beat, creating a current that draws the released ovum, which cannot move by itself, into the oviduct. The ovum is carried toward the uterus by the action of the cilia and peristaltic contractions of the oviduct walls. Fertilization normally occurs if the ovum and sperm meet and fuse in the oviduct. The resulting *zygote* then begins its early development as it moves along toward the uterus. If fertilization does not occur, the ovum degenerates.

The **uterus** is a 7 cm × 5 cm (3 in. × 2 in.) hollow, pear-shaped organ held in place by ligaments. The neck of the uterus, where it narrows and joins the vagina, is called the **cervix*** (SUR viks). The wall of the uterus consists of muscle tissue, but the inner surface is lined with ciliated

---

Cervical Cancer

A common disease of women is cancer of the cervix, which often spreads to the uterus and results in the deaths of thousands each year. This type of cancer, however, can easily be detected at early stages by a simple test (Pap smear) in which a few cells are removed from the cervix and microscopically examined.

Cancer of the uterus was once a major cause of death in females. Today most cases are found early enough to remove the cancerous portion of the cervix and uterus. Often the woman can still become pregnant. Sometimes a *hysterectomy,* (HISS tuh REHK tuh mee)(removal of the uterus) is needed because the disease has spread.

---

epithelial cells. The lining becomes thicker in preparation to receive the tiny embryo. If an embryo becomes implanted in the uterine lining, the membranes remain enlarged, and the uterus serves as the **womb,** a protective, nourishing place for the unborn baby.

The **vagina*** (vuh JYE nuh) is the short, elastic canal that leads from the outside of the body to the cervix of the uterus. It receives the semen and is the *birth canal* (the way the baby leaves the womb). Folds of tissue called the *labia* provide protection for the delicate tissues around the opening of the vagina and urethra.

Female reproductive cycles

In the female both the ovary and the uterus must be prepared in proper sequence if reproduction is to take place. Two cycles prepare these organs:

❑ *the ovarian cycle* The ovary prepares and releases an ovum.

❑ *the menstrual cycle* The uterus prepares its lining to receive an embryo.

If an ovum is prepared but the uterus is not ready to receive it, a pregnancy will not develop, and vice versa. It is essential, therefore, that these two cycles coordinate precisely.

Hormones released by the anterior lobe of the pituitary gland control the ovarian cycle. These hormones stimulate the ovary to produce other hormones that control the menstrual cycle. Thus, a negative feedback mechanism (see page 599) regulates these two cycles.

A relatively large amount of follicle-stimulating hormone (FSH) released by the pituitary gland starts the **ovarian cycle** by stimulating a follicle to begin to develop. For about 2 wk. the amount of FSH diminishes, and then ovulation takes place. During these 2 wk., the pituitary increases the production of *corpus luteum stimulating hormone* (luteinizing hormone, LH).

At ovulation the luteinizing hormone is being produced in large quantities. After ovulation the luteinizing hormone causes the follicle to develop into a yellow structure called the **corpus* luteum*** (KOHR pus ◊ LOO tee um). Over the next 2 wk., the amount of luteinizing hormone decreases, causing the corpus luteum to degenerate.

Hormones produced by the follicle and the corpus luteum control the **menstrual* cycle.** The follicle produces **estrogens** (a group of hormones) which stimulate the growth of the uterine lining. While the follicle grows, additional estrogens are produced, and this stimulates even more growth of the uterine lining.

---

cervix: (L. CERVIX, neck)　　corpus: (L. CORPUS, body)　　menstrual: (L. MENSIS, month)
vagina: (L. VAGINA, sheath)　　luteum: (L. LUTEUM, yellow)

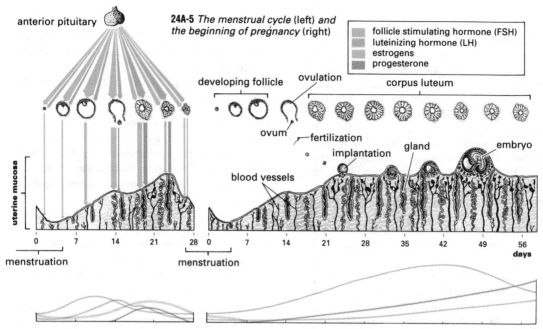

anterior pituitary

24A-5 *The menstrual cycle* (left) *and the beginning of pregnancy* (right)

follicle stimulating hormone (FSH)
luteinizing hormone (LH)
estrogens
progesterone

developing follicle   ovulation   corpus luteum

ovum   fertilization
implantation   gland   embryo

blood vessels

uterine mucosa

0   7   14   21   28   0   7   14   21   28   35   42   49   56
days

menstruation   menstruation

Just prior to ovulation, the follicle begins to produce **progesterone.** Once ovulation has taken place, the corpus luteum starts to produce large quantities of progesterone. Progesterone stimulates the growth of blood vessels in the uterine wall and causes the glands of this membrane to produce substances which prepare the uterus to receive a fertilized ovum. About 7 days after ovulation, the amount of progesterone is at its peak, and about 10 days after ovulation, the uterine lining is at its thickest.

At this point, one of two things happens. If an ovum has been fertilized in the oviduct and the tiny embryo has been carried to the uterus, it is *implanted* in the uterus. The nourishing fluids produced by the glands sustain the embryo as the *placenta* develops. The placenta produces a hor-

mone which stops the degeneration of the corpus luteum, and pregnancy begins.

If, however, no ovum has been fertilized, no placenta is formed. As the corpus luteum degenerates, it produces less and less progesterone. Decreasing progesterone causes the uterine lining to shrink, and about 4 weeks after it started to grow (about 14 days after ovulation), the uterine lining is shed from the body.

The several days that the uterine lining is being shed is known as **menstruation.** Hormone levels cause the uterine muscle to contract, often causing it to cramp, resulting in varying degrees of discomfort. The dramatic change in hormone levels just prior to and during menstruation, coupled with the discomfort, often temporarily affects the moods of the woman.

Review Questions 24A-1

1. List and give the functions of (a) the primary organs and (b) the accessory organs of the male reproductive system.
2. What are the three main parts of a human sperm?
3. What is circumcision? What was the significance of circumcision to an Old Testament Jew? What was Paul's objection to circumcision for New Testament Gentiles?
4. List and give the functions of (a) the primary organs and (b) the accessory organs of the female reproductive system.
5. What are the two primary female reproductive cycles? What happens during each cycle?

Human Embryology and Birth

The implantation of a human embryo and its development into a baby that is ready to be born is an orderly process of changes controlled by genes. Some genes express themselves only at certain stages of development and may be repressed during the remainder of the individual's life. For example, certain genes stimulate the formation of the eyes, but after this process is completed, these genes may not express themselves again, even if an eye is removed or lost.

Although scientists have only vague ideas regarding the "hows" of human **embryology*** (the study of the time between fertilization and birth), a great deal is known about descriptive embryology, some of which is presented in the following sections.

Fertilization and implantation

Fertilization takes place in the oviduct a few hours to a few days after ovulation. Semen, containing the sperm, is deposited in the vagina during sexual relations. Once within the vagina, the sperm travel into and through the uterus rapidly and reach the upper portion of the oviducts in a few minutes.

When the sperm reaches an ovum, it moves through the follicular cells and the transparent gel that surrounds the ovum. Biologists believe that an enzyme secreted by the acrosome in the sperm head helps the sperm through these barriers. Many sperm may reach an ovum. But after one sperm penetrates the ovum, there is a change in the ovum membrane, after which no other sperm can pass through the membrane.

During fertilization the sperm loses its tail, and its head swells. At this time the immature ovum nucleus divides, completing meiosis. The nuclei of the ovum and the sperm come together near the center of the cell, their nuclear membranes disappear, and their chromosomes combine.

Shortly after it is formed, the zygote undergoes mitosis, giving rise to 2 daughter cells. These cells in turn divide into 4 cells, which divide into 8 cells, and so forth. With each division, the resulting daughter cells are smaller. For this reason, this phase in development is termed *cleavage*.

It takes about 3 days for the young embryo to reach the uterus, and by then the embryo consists of a solid mass of about 16 cells. Once inside the uterus, the embryo remains free within the uterine cavity for about 3 additional days. Before the tiny embryo attaches to the mother's uterus, the energy needed for growth is supplied by its own cytoplasm and nutrients secreted by the uterus.

Cell divisions continue, and a fluid-filled sphere of cells known as the **blastocyst*** (BLAS tuh sist) forms. In the blastocyst stage the embryo is implanted. **Implantation** takes place as the outer cells of the embryo, together with the cells of the uterine wall, form the *placenta*. This organ transfers nutrients and wastes between mother and child.

The baby makes its own blood, and under normal circumstances none of the mother's blood cells enters the child. Substances dissolved in the blood plasma, however, easily diffuse between the blood vessels of the mother and child in the placenta. Thus, nutrients, oxygen, and antibodies diffuse into the baby's blood. Other substances dissolved in the mother's blood, such as drugs, alcohol, and toxins (from diseases and the like) can also diffuse into the child's blood. These substances affect the mother's body in relatively minor ways when compared to the effects they have on the rapidly growing and dividing cells of the unborn child. Babies born addicted to drugs and deformed by substances they have unnecessarily been exposed to are the innocent victims of a mother's neglect.

24A-6 *Stages in a human embryo*

zygote   cleavage   blastocyst

The embryo

By the third week of development, the cells of the embryo are arranged into three distinct layers known as the *embryonic germ layers*. These layers develop into the various adult tissues.

---

embryology: em- (in) + -bryo- (Gk. BRUEIN, to grow) + -logy (the study of)

blastocyst: blasto- (Gk. BLASTOS, shoot, bud) + -cyst (KUSTIS, bladder, pouch)

❑ The **ectoderm** (outer layer) forms the epidermis and associated structures such as nails and hair and also much of the nervous system.

❑ The **mesoderm** (middle layer) forms the muscles, blood, and bones.

❑ The **endoderm** (inner layer) gives rise to the epithelial lining of the digestive tract, respiratory tract, bladder, and urethra.

Special membranes develop around the embryo but are not considered part of it. Since they protect, help obtain nourishment, and eliminate wastes of the developing child, they are vital to the survival of the baby inside the womb but are discarded at birth.

❑ The *amnion* begins to develop even before the first structures of the embryo take form and eventually expands to surround the entire embryo. The amniotic cavity is filled with a clear *amniotic fluid* which bathes the embryo. This sterile fluid serves to keep the embryo moist, functions as a shock absorber, maintains a uniform temperature, and provides room for the embryo's movements.

❑ The *yolk sac* forms during the second through the sixth weeks of development. There is no yolk in the human ovum, but this sac (along with the spleen) functions in blood cell formation.

❑ The *allantois* consists of numerous blood vessels that converge to form the **umbilical cord.** This cord contains the umbilical arteries and veins which carry the blood of the fetus to the placenta where food, wastes, oxygen, and carbon dioxide are exchanged.

❑ The *chorion* grows rapidly along a section of the uterine wall after the embryo is implanted, forming the child's part of the placenta.

At the end of the first month, the embryo is cylindrical in shape. It is about 5 mm (0.2 in.) long and weighs about 0.02 gm (0.001 oz.), about 10,000 times as heavy as the zygote. The embryo has a large head in proportion to the rest of its body because the brain develops rapidly. The head and jaws have begun to develop, and the arm and leg buds have appeared. The heart is tubular and S-shaped and beats about 60 times per minute. The nervous system and the heart are the first major structures to develop.

At the eighth week, all major internal organs are present. The first 8 weeks are the most critical stage of development. While he is less than an inch long and the major organs are forming, the embryo is susceptible to injury. Quantities of

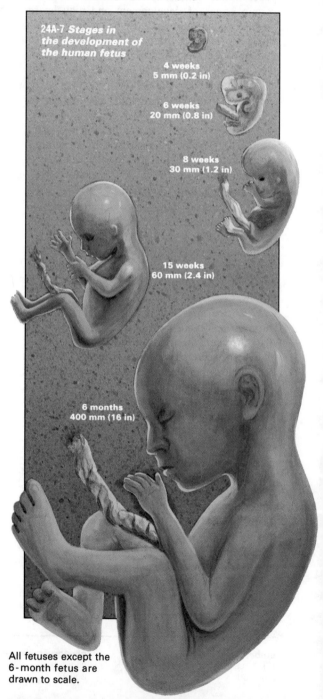

24A-7 *Stages in the development of the human fetus*

4 weeks
5 mm (0.2 in)

6 weeks
20 mm (0.8 in)

8 weeks
30 mm (1.2 in)

15 weeks
60 mm (2.4 in)

6 months
400 mm (16 in)

All fetuses except the 6-month fetus are drawn to scale.

drugs, and disease-caused toxins in the mother's blood, which would have little or no effect on the mother, can greatly hamper the development of the child. At 2 months the embryo is 30 mm long and weighs about 1 gm (0.04 oz.), the weight of a paper clip.

Review Questions 24A-2

1. In what organs do (a) fertilization and (b) implantation take place?
2. List the three primary germ layers. Into what adult structures do each of these embryonic tissues develop?
3. List and tell the functions of the four embryonic membranes that develop around the embryo but are not considered part of the embryo.
4. What structures make up the umbilical cord?
5. How long is the embryonic stage of human development? What is the child like at the end of the embryo stage?

The fetus

At the end of the second month, the embryo is clearly recognizable as a human. From this point until its birth, it is called the **fetus,** which means offspring. The face becomes humanlike with development of the nose, lips, and eyelids. The muscle tissues are beginning to differentiate, and the fetus is capable of some movement. The cartilaginous skeleton is being transformed into bone. The liver enlarges and takes over the function of blood cell formation from the spleen. The brain begins to send impulses to regulate the functions of other organs.

By the end of the third month, the fetus is about 56 mm long (2.2 in.) and weighs about 14 g (0.5 oz.). During the third month, reproductive organs are distinguishable as male or female. The ears and eyes have moved to their final positions, but the eyelids are fused. The fetus "practices" sucking and begins breathing movements by inhaling and exhaling amniotic fluid.

During the fourth month, the fetus grows rapidly, but the rate of growth decreases somewhat during the fifth month. During the fifth month, the baby becomes active and strong enough that the mother may feel the movements. At this stage the fetus has grown to about 250 mm (10 in.), about half the length that it will be at birth, and weighs slightly more than 1 lb. Its heart beats about 150 times per minute and can be heard with a stethoscope.

During the fifth and sixth months, hair begins to appear on the head, and eyelashes and eye-

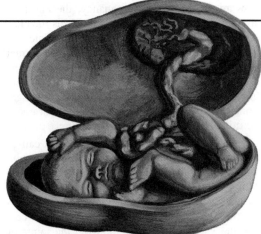

24A-8 *Model of the human fetus, with umbilical cord and placenta enclosed in the uterus*

brows begin to grow. The skin becomes covered with a mixture of oil from the sebaceous (oil) glands and dead skin cells. This "cheesy" layer protects the baby's skin from the amniotic fluid. In the sixth month the arms and legs reach the relative proportions they will have at birth.

During the last three months of development, the fetus grows rapidly and gains a layer of fat tissue under the skin. If the baby is born at the beginning of the seventh month, it is able to move and cry, but unless given special help, it often dies because the brain is not developed enough to control breathing and maintain body temperature. The eyelids open during the seventh month, and the baby begins to appear chubby. When ready to be born, the fetus is usually positioned upside down with its head toward the cervix.

Birth

Toward the end of the pregnancy, the uterus is stretched to the maximum, and the fetus thus has outgrown its home. This stretching stimulates reflexes that cause the uterine muscle to contract occasionally. In the final weeks the contractions become more frequent but are still weak. A few hours before the birth of the baby, the contractions become quite strong and occur about every 30 min. This is the beginning of **labor.**

During labor the stretching of the cervix causes the pituitary gland to release more *oxytocin,* which stimulates stronger uterine contractions. This cycle of positive feedback is repeated until strong contractions cause the baby to begin moving through the **birth canal.** The birth canal (cervix and vagina) is elastic, and even the joints of the bones of the mother's pelvis are prepared to stretch, helping the baby to pass through. The flexible bones of the baby, and the fact that the skull bones of the child are not yet fused (permitting the head to be compressed slightly) help the child in passing through the birth canal.

As the pressure increases in the uterus, the amnion bursts, releasing the amniotic fluid through the vagina. Often referred to as "breaking of the water," this sometimes occurs before labor. The strong uterine contractions, aided by the pushing of the mother, move the baby through the birth canal, and he is born.

In about 90% of the births, the head of the fetus is positioned downward. This is the ideal position so that the head acts as a wedge to open the birth canal as the baby emerges. This position also allows the baby to breathe safely even before it is completely born.

In about 3% of the births, the baby is positioned with his posterior end toward the birth canal. This type of delivery is a *breech birth.* Breech births are difficult in that the baby's neck is sometimes trapped in the birth canal or the umbilical cord may become pinched or wrapped around the child's neck. Breech births require special procedures by the physician.

When the baby is born, the umbilical cord still connects the baby with the placenta. Most physicians clamp and cut the cord immediately after the baby is born. The baby, deprived of its oxygen supply, builds up carbon dioxide in his blood. This is a powerful stimulant to the respiratory center of the brain, and the baby begins to breathe. Thus, the baby may begin to breathe before the physician "slaps his bottom" (or, more frequently now, taps the bottom of his foot), causing him to take his first breath.

After delivery of the baby, the uterus begins to contract again, and the placenta and remains of the umbilical cord are expelled. Generally, this "afterbirth" occurs within 20 minutes after the birth of the baby. About 5-6 weeks after the birth of a baby, the uterine wall has healed, the uterus has returned to its normal size, and the normal ovarian cycles resume.

If the space between the mother's pelvic bones (which can be measured before the time of labor) is too small, if the baby's head is unusually large, or if complications threaten the baby's life, the baby may need to be delivered by performing a *Caesarean** (sih ZEHR ee un) *section*. This is a surgical procedure, delivering the baby by opening the mother's abdominal and uterine walls.

Caesarean: (after Julius Caesar who was reputedly born this way)

Beyond maintaining general good health and a proper diet, the mother has no control over the unborn child's development, much of which takes place before she is even aware of the child. At

24A-10 *Today, babies that are born early can be nurtured in incubators until they are strong enough to survive in the natural world.*

birth the baby leaves a protected place where all needs are supplied and enters a more demanding but more interesting world, where he can develop into an adult.

Father and mother gave the baby physical life; the mother nurtured that life inside her; and normally the newborn baby's own body is capable of sustaining that life. Now the parents must support the new life physically, mentally, emotionally, and spiritually. In God's sight the child is the "heritage of the Lord" (Ps. 127:3) and not the property of the parents. The child will grow, but it is the parents' responsibility to rear the child to love and fear the Lord (Deut. 6:2-5; Eph. 6:4).

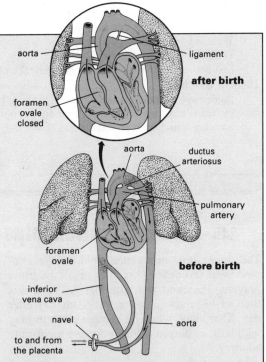

The Newborn Baby

Soon after birth, major changes take place within the circulatory system of the infant. Since before birth the fetus did not use his lungs for breathing, there was only a small quantity of blood circulating through them. Before birth about half of the blood that entered the right atrium flowed through the **foramen ovale*** (fuh RAY mun ◊ oh VAL ee), an opening into the left atrium. The blood that flowed into the right ventricle was pumped into the pulmonary artery, but only a small amount of that blood reached the lungs. Most of it was sent through the **ductus arteriosus*** (DUHK tus ◊ ar TIHR ee OH sus), a short blood vessel that connects the pulmonary artery with the aorta.

When the baby is born and takes his first breath, the lungs quickly inflate. The foramen ovale begins to close, and the ductus arteriosus closes and eventually becomes a ligament. These changes divert blood to the lungs so that oxygen may be absorbed. If one or both of these fetal structures fail to close, the blood supply to the lungs is not adequate, and the blood lacks sufficient oxygen. Thus, poorly oxygenated blood circulates throughout the body, resulting in *cyanosis** (SYE uh NO sis), a blue condition of the skin. Babies in this condition are commonly called "blue babies." In minor cases the condition corrects itself in a short time. In major cases surgery may be required.

The remaining umbilical cord on the baby's abdomen withers and eventually drops off, leaving a scar called the *navel*. Since the infant now obtains oxygen from his own lungs, obtains nutrients from his own digestive tract, and eliminates his own wastes, the umbilical blood vessels atrophy and become ligaments.

foramen ovale: (L. FORAMEN OVALE, oval opening)

ductus arteriosus: (L. DUCTUS ARTERIOSUS, arterial duct)

cyanosis: cyan- (Gk. KUANOS, blue color) + -osis (sickness)

Biological Terms

Male Reproductive System
testes (sing., testis)
scrotum
seminiferous tubule
epididymis
 (pl., epididymides)
semen
vas deferens
seminal vesicle
prostate gland
urethra
penis

Female Reproductive System
ovary
follicle
ovulation
oviduct
uterus
cervix
womb
vagina
ovarian cycle
corpus luteum

menstrual cycle
estrogen
progesterone
menstruation

Human Embryology and Birth
embryology
blastocyst
implantation
ectoderm
mesoderm
endoderm

umbilical cord
fetus
labor
birth canal
foramen ovale
ductus arteriosis

Review Questions 24A-3

1. List a few of the things that characterize the unborn child: (a) during months 3-4; (b) during months 5-6; and (c) during the last three months of pregnancy.
2. List three conditions that help the baby to pass through the birth canal.
3. What is a breech birth?
4. What is a Caesarean section?
5. List two circulatory system changes that take place within the newborn infant.

Thought Question

Some have said that parental care begins long before pregnancy, is crucial during pregnancy, but is most important from birth on. Support each of these concepts from the physical, emotional, and spiritual standpoints.

24B–Human Relationships–A Christian Perspective

The story is told of a young child who was encouraged to confess his sins in his bedtime prayers. The child was sure that the Lord was tired of his confessing the same sins day after day. That night, when his mother came to pray with him, he prayed, "Please forgive me for my adultery."

His mother was a little stunned, and following the "Amen," she asked why he had confessed that particular sin. "Well, it is a sin. I heard the preacher say it was," he replied. Mother agreed that it was a sin. She then asked when the child had committed adultery, to which he replied, "Oh, I act like an adult every so often." Relieved that her child did not know what he was talking

about, the mother decided she would have a talk with her son in the morning after she had a chance to prepare a few remarks.

Frequently young and even older adults are uninformed about what sin actually is. Scripture defines sin as "the transgression of the law" (I John 3:4). It is evident that sin is the failure to put God in the proper place in one's life (Matt. 22:36-38). Paul says that he would not have us to be ignorant lest Satan should get the advantage of us (II Cor. 2:11). Too often, in attempts to shun evil, some Christians become naive to the extent that they do not even recognize evil when it confronts them. Satan has an easy time tempting and causing the downfall of such Christians.

It is essential, therefore, that we understand what is right and what is wrong. To "understand" does not mean to experience. You do not have to steal to know that stealing is wrong. However, a child does have to be told what stealing is before he can consciously refrain from doing it. Likewise, a Christian does not have to stumble upon witnessing to know it is good. Witnessing is one of God's commands for Christians.

Satan is a master of deceit. He has so clouded people's understanding that often it is difficult for them to see that certain things are actually sins. God, however, is clear concerning what He wants of His children. That Christians be informed about what is right and wrong is, in part, the purpose of the Bible (Matt. 28:20).

The next few pages describe some modern practices and philosophies and compare them to the standards set forth in God's Word. The following sections do not present a complete discussion of the issues raised, nor are all related issues mentioned. The issues presented here are considered basic, those that Christians often confront and about which all Christians should be informed.

The Control of Life

Human life is different from other forms of life. Although it may be difficult to distinguish certain major biological differences between man and some mammals, none can deny that man is unique among living things.

The Bible clearly states that man is a special creation. Not only is man's intelligence superior

to the "intelligence" of animals, but man also has a God-breathed soul. The principle of the **sanctity of human life** (that human life is of high value) appears repeatedly in the Bible. After Abel was killed, God cursed Cain, his murderer. To make sure there was no blood feud, God said He would inflict Cain's punishment sevenfold on whoever killed Cain (Gen. 4:15). "Thou shalt not kill" is one of the Ten Commandments, written directly by the hand of God. God's condemnation falls on anyone who murders another human, and the Bible teaches that murderers are to be put to death (Gen. 9:6; Exod. 21:12).

Christians agree that a man's spiritual life is important. After all, God's Son was sent to die to redeem man. It is in our physical bodies, however, that we accomplish our earthly ministry. A Christian's physical life is special because it, too, belongs to Christ. A Christian who does not yield all of his physical self to Christ is sinning. Our physical lives belong to God and are His to direct.

God holds human life as special, something of high value. This concept establishes the principle of the sanctity of human life. Let us now consider two aspects of medical practice—*abortion* (the killing of an unborn child) and *euthanasia* (the killing of a suffering, infirm, or elderly person)—which directly concern the sanctity of human life.

Abortion

Many people believe a pregnant woman has the right to decide whether she wants the child inside her to live. If she does not want the child, it is now legal for her to have the child killed. The killing of an unborn child is called **abortion.***

The Increase of Legally Performed Abortions in the United States 24B-1

Year	Abortions
1969	22,670 (legal in 10 states)
1970	193,500 (legal in 24 states)
1971	495,800 (legal in 25 states)
1972	586,800 (legal in 28 states)
1973	745,000 (legal in all 50 states)
1974	780,800
1975	1,034,200
1976	1,179,300
1977	1,316,700
1978	1,409,600
1979	1,497,700
1980	1,553,900
1981	1,577,300
1982	1,573,900
1983	1,575,000
1984	1,577,200
1985	1,588,600

abortion: (L. ABORTARE, to die, miscarry)

Most abortions in the United States are performed before the baby is 16 weeks old. The most common method involves a physician's placing sharp instruments into the womb through the vagina. The walls of the womb are then scraped, and the baby's body is cut into pieces. As the material is removed from the uterus, tiny arms, legs, or other parts of the unborn child are often recognizable.

In later stages of pregnancy, the physician will inject a strong salt solution into the fluid-filled bag that protects the baby. As the baby breathes and swallows the salt, his outer layer of skin is burned off by the salt, and the baby dies in about an hour. About a day later the woman enters labor and delivers a dead baby.

If the pregnancy is past the time when the child can be poisoned by salt, it is removed from the woman much the same way a baby is taken by Caesarean section. The baby is alive, but is usually left unattended and dies a few moments after it has entered the world. Often, when aborted in the final stages of pregnancy, the child would have lived if proper care had been given.

Except in certain laboratory conditions, human sperm and ova have no chance of reproduction or even a lengthy survival outside the body. Under normal circumstances, however, when they are together, they are fully capable of becoming a complete human. A human's physical life is a continuing existence that begins when the sperm fertilizes the ovum and progresses through devel-

---

The Bible and Abortion

The Bible is quite clear that before birth the contents of the womb are human.

❏ "Thus saith the Lord that made thee, and formed thee from the womb. . . ." (Isaiah 44:2).
❏ When God called Jeremiah to be a prophet, He said, "Before I formed thee in the belly I knew thee; and before thou camest forth out of the womb I sanctified thee. . . ." (Jer. 1:5).
❏ Psalm 139:13-16 declares, "For thou hast possessed my reins: thou hast covered me in my mother's womb. I will praise thee; for I am fearfully and wonderfully made: marvellous are thy works; and that my soul knoweth right well. My substance was not hid from thee, when I was made in secret, and curiously wrought in the lowest parts of the earth. Thine eyes did see my substance, yet being unperfect; and in thy book all my members were written, which in continuance were fashioned, when as yet there was none of them."

Some people argue that God would not mind if a deformed baby were aborted. A growing number of techniques now permit us to tell if an unborn child is normal. Some people feel that God does not want "abnormal" babies. It is true that the *genetic screen* (see page 160) kills deformed children and then naturally aborts them. These natural abortions are often called *miscarriages* or *stillbirths*. But God is sovereign; He is in control of everything. He decides whether what we would call an abnormal baby will naturally abort or will be born.

Despite what we may call "best," God makes what we call "perfect" and also what we call "imperfect." Both are within the realm of His intention and, for Christians, will "work together for good" (Rom. 8:28). Although we may consider something "deformed" or "wrong," God's ways are beyond our ability to understand (Isa. 55:8). For example, when God spoke to Moses in the burning bush, Moses claimed he was not fit to lead the children of Israel out of Egypt, for he could not speak well. We do not know the extent of Moses' handicap, but God's response is significant: "Who hath made man's mouth? or who maketh the dumb, or deaf, or the seeing, or the blind? have not I the Lord?" (Exod. 4:11).

God has ordained what we call handicapped or deformed. When it comes to deliberately killing a human that we feel is not physically or mentally "normal," we are ignoring the Bible's teaching about the sovereignty of God and the sanctity of human life. Some parents who suspect a possible deformity (perhaps inherited) can use prenatal testing to see if the child is afflicted. This information can often be used to help the parents (and physicians) prepare wisely for the child, but the information should have nothing to do with a decision to kill the child before or after its birth.

Madonna and Child with Elisabeth and Young John by Lubin Baugin, Bob Jones University Collection of Sacred Art

The unborn John the Baptist leaped for joy when his mother was greeted by Mary while she was carrying Jesus in her womb (Luke 1:39-44). Here the French painter Lubin Baugin (1610-1663) depicts a later meeting of these mothers and their sons.

opment, birth, growth, maturity, and death. Few people would argue that a newborn baby is not a complete human and that killing the infant is not murder. Some feel that the unborn child is not human and that killing him or her is not murder. People may try to redefine the terms and may pass laws to the contrary, but abortion is killing a human—and that is murder.

Euthanasia

A dictionary defines **euthanasia*** (YOO thuh NAY zhuh) as "an easy and painless death, or an act or method of causing death painlessly so as to end suffering; advocated by some as a way to deal with victims of incurable diseases." The Euthanasia Society of America defines euthanasia as "termination of human life by painless means for the purpose of ending severe physical suffering." In common usage, euthanasia is "mercy killing."

Often euthanasia is divided into two types:

❏ **Active euthanasia** In active euthanasia, a person's life is terminated either by something that will kill him (overdose of a drug, poison, or the like) or by removing a life-sustaining apparatus (a respirator, an intraveneous feeding tube, a cardiac pacemaker, or the like).

❏ **Passive euthanasia** In passive euthanasia, treatment is not begun or treatment that could sustain life is withheld from a person. For example, if a person diagnosed as terminally ill with cancer also develops heart trouble, the heart may not be treated. If this lack of treatment results in his earlier death, those who withheld the treatment may have practiced passive euthanasia.

Legally, active euthanasia when a person is not clinically dead is murder. A physician who practices active euthanasia may face a malpractice suit. A person is *clinically dead* if he has stopped breathing, has no heartbeat, and has no (or exceptionally subnormal) brain waves.

Many people feel that for a person with abnormal brain waves whose breathing, heartbeat, or other bodily function is being maintained by a life-support apparatus, active euthanasia is justified. They feel that since the person's life is probably not going to be "meaningful" because of the abnormal brain waves, he should be killed (probably by "pulling the plug" on his life-support apparatus). Many Christians argue that active euthanasia of this type is unacceptable because of the principle of the sanctity of human life. God can enable people with abnormal brain-wave patterns to recover. If it becomes acceptable practice to kill someone who faces an "abnormal" life, all of us face being killed.

Passive euthanasia, in the minds of many Christians, presents a different situation. With modern life-sustaining apparatus, drugs, and medical techniques, people who are about to die can often be kept alive for additional hours, days, months, or even years. Many Christians would accept passive euthanasia in cases where the person is not conscious, or is of considerable age,

---

euthanasia: eu- (well, good) + -thanasia (Gk. THANATOS, death)

Should Treatment Be Terminated?

Below are some factors that must be considered when making a decision about euthanasia, whether as a policy, a conviction, or even for an individual case. Just because, in a specific case, there are more reasons on the "yes" side than on the "no" side does not mean that a person should be killed.

Yes, if:

■ there is informed consent of all relevant parties (patient, physician, hospital, and family).

■ there is a permanent loss of all cognitive function, all ability to understand; when the family and attending physicians agree there is no hope of regaining the capacity to think or experience normal human consciousness.

■ there is "irrefutable" evidence that biological death is imminent. (AMA [American Medical Association] House of Delegates Declaration)

❑ there is great suffering or unrelievable pain.

■ there is a lack of the will to live, total demoralization, or wishing for death.

❑ continued hopeless treatment involves unconscionable cost to the family or society; if it places grave burdens, such as potential impoverishment, on those who care for the hopelessly dying.

■ there is an immediate limited availability of life-sustaining equipment or heavy stress on intensive care facilities. This situation is similar to the procedure of triage, where combat casualties are divided into hopeless cases who get no medical attention and more hopeful cases who receive medical attention.

❑ the next of kin are unwilling to provide long-term care for a hopelessly ill patient.

No, because:

■ all parties could agree to an unjust or unwise termination; for example, a limited physical impairment, such as hearing loss, would not justify termination even if all parties consented. Although consent is important, it does not stand alone as an absolute indicator of discontinuing life.

■ there is always the possiblity of misdiagnosis ("It's happened before"–citing cases). Prognosis, the predicting of the future of an illness, is a notoriously inexact science. Besides, if you terminate "low quality of life" patients, where do you draw the line? Would not senile, retarded and genetically handicapped patients be endangered by the same rule?

■ imminent death is a difficult and predictive calculation that differs from physician to physician. The simple fact that death is near would not, by itself justify termination of treatment in every case. You would not, for example, withhold respiration from a fully conscious dying patient who wishes to remain conscious.

❑ medications can relieve the pain. Counseling and supportive therapies can help with mental anguish. In the Western religious experience, suffering is understood as a potential means of special grace and spiritual learning.* Further, if suffering justifies the ending of life, then obviously suicide is morally acceptable. This cannot be.

■ every doctor knows that some patients face periods of depression. The patient does not always use the best judgment during such low periods. The physician's duty extends to protecting the patient from poor judgment during depression.

❑ at what point does the value of life become a budget item? Anyway, most cases are covered by insurance arrangements, which should be humanized in the light of newer life-sustaining technologies.

■ in most cases nearby medical facilities are available in crises. Anyway, triage is an ethic of exceptions under emergency conditions of warfare. Do not build a set of general guidelines on exceptions.

❑ the value of the patient's life does not depend, according to law and common moral decency, on whether his relatives are willing to care for him.

From *Should Treatment Be Terminated?* by Thomas C. Oden (New York; Harper and Row Publishers, 1976), pp. x-xiii. Used by permission.

This table is included because of its broad scope and does not necessarily reflect the views of the author of *Biology for Christian Schools* or of Bob Jones University Press.

*Mr. Oden probably refers to Judaism, Catholicism, and Protestantism. Bible-believing Christians, who usually resent being lumped with "Western religions," would nonetheless agree that illness can potentially be a means of blessing for the saved person.

and death is merely postponed. These Christians feel that it is not always in God's will to use all the apparatus, drugs, and techniques at the physician's disposal to keep alive a person in such advanced stages of age and illness.

Making decisions about passive euthanasia asks people to make decisions regarding the quality of the patient's life. Factors such as the patient's age, possibility of regaining consciousness, and even spiritual condition must be taken into account. Other Christians feel that one who advocates passive euthanasia is neglecting to use the knowledge God has given and is "playing God" by deciding when a person will die.

Christians must also consider the euthanasia "stopping point." If active euthanasia becomes legal, at what point will a person's life be "safe"? Where will euthanasia stop? If we give to doctors, "next of kin," or anyone to whom God does not give the *death authority* (the authority to terminate life), what will stop that authority from growing and (if it has not already done so) in time violating the sanctity of life principle?

The brief comments made here oversimplify this involved topic. An in-depth discussion is beyond the scope of this book. Various cases pose so many different situations that even Christian authorities disagree on possible guidelines.

Review Question 24B-1

1. Give five Biblical supports for the sanctity of life principle.
2. List three abortion methods.
3. List three Biblical references supporting the concept that an unborn child is a human.
4. List the two main types of euthanasia and define each.
5. What is clinical death?

Sexual Purity

Read Proverbs 5. In this divinely inspired passage the wisest man who ever lived advises his sons regarding sexual relationships. In definite terms he tells them to stay away from the "strange woman." In this passage the "strange woman" is any woman who would entice him into sinful sexual relationships. Verses 4-13 tell of the consequences to the people who do not heed this advice, and verses 20-23 tell of God's condemnation of those who ignore this warning. The young man is also told to "rejoice with the wife of [his] youth," and to be "ravished always with her love."

The basic themes of emotional and physical love between a husband and wife and the condemnation of sexual relationships between those who are not husband and wife are repeated frequently in Scripture. There is no doubt about God's standards: He demands sexual purity. **Sexual purity** means that a person does not enter into sexual relationships with anyone other than his or her marriage partner.

Adultery and fornication

A heterosexual relationship between a married person and anyone other than that person's spouse (marriage partner) is **adultery.*** Scripture tells us repeatedly that adultery is sin (Matt. 5:27-28). Even one of the Ten Commandments is "Thou shalt not commit adultery" (Exod. 20:14).

Most agree that unfaithfulness in marriage causes severe problems between the marriage partners, and, therefore, many agree that adultery is wrong. Although adultery may cause marital difficulties, this in itself does not make it sin. Adultery is not a sin merely because it harms a person or harms his relationship with others; but it is sin because it is disobedience to God's Word.

Fornication as used in the Bible is a general term referring to any form of heterosexual license. Fornication may be adultery, premarital sexual relationships, or any sexual relationships other than between a man and his wife. Fornication is condemned in Scripture (Gal. 5:19-21). Today many forms of fornication are considered permissible by worldly people. If God says something

adultery: (L. ADULTERARE, to pollute, commit adultery)

is sin, no amount of human rationalizing or action can make it right. God's condemnation cannot be removed by man.

Sexual purity, however, means more than just having refrained from physical sexual relations with someone else; it means also that one's *thought life* is pure. Proverbs 12:20 and Psalm 41:6 tell us that sin is committed in the heart (mind, will). Therefore, even looking at others and wishing to have sexual relationships with them is to have "sinned already" in your mind (Matt. 5:28). An evil thought life, in God's sight, is as bad as life filled with evil physical acts.

Some Christian young people, after having had impure thoughts about another person, feel that since they have "sinned already," they may as well go ahead with the physical act. This is illogical; the person is sinning again. The Bible tells us that we are to turn from sin, not to go on sinning (Rom. 6:1-2; I John 3:6-9).

Sexual temptations

Today, advertisers try to sell everything from clothing to toothpaste by using "sex appeal." To get our attention and to convince us to purchase an item, they tell us that using the product will make us more attractive to the opposite sex. Many times advertisements contain enticing-looking people who are there merely to stir up "youthful lusts" and have us sin in our minds. The manufacturer hopes we will be favorably impressed and purchase his product. Buying trends show that such techniques often work. They have appealed to man's sinful nature and have won by helping him temporarily satisfy his lusts.

Humans do have an inborn, natural instinct to engage in sexual relationships and reproduce.

FACETS OF BIOLOGY

24B–1

Sexually Transmitted Diseases

For many years people condemned sexual immorality because it spread certain diseases. These **sexually transmitted diseases (STD, *venereal diseases, VD)*** are the most widespread, contagious diseases in America. Some STDs are minor infections, but some can cripple a person for life and if not treated, can kill. One STD, AIDS, has no known cure.

All STDs can be transferred by various means, but the vast majority of the cases are the result of sexual relationships among infected people. Many STDs can be passed from an infected mother to an unborn child; some can be transferred during blood transfusions, and some can be transmitted by contact between a cut on an uninfected person's skin and the blood of an infected person. These other methods of transfer, however, account for only a tiny percentage of the cases of STDS.

Physicians can treat most STDs. Both syphilis and gonorrhea can be cured by antibiotics. The damage they have caused the body, however, often cannot be corrected even when the disease is cured. A few STDs cause only minor discomfort for the person with the disease, but some of these cause problems for the child in the womb. Many babies are born suffering from the STD their mother has; others are born deformed because of their mother's disease.

Sexual purity before and during marriage virtually prevents the spread of all STDs. Thus, in times past a person with an STD was considered to have been "caught in his sin." This changed as medical science found cures for many STDs. Prior to the AIDS epidemic modern attitudes toward sexual relationships permitted various forms of fornication in part because STDs were not considered a major problem. To people who did not know God, it appeared as though He no longer considered fornication a sin since there was no longer a punishment for it.

When the AIDS epidemic started, some people said that the disease was God's judgment on the sins of homosexuals and fornicators since at the time they were the primary ones affected by the disease. Individuals may suffer in this life because of their sins, but God does not promise a particular

This inclination is fulfilled in marriage as the man is "joined unto his wife, and they two [become] one flesh" (Eph. 5:31). The extent to which this behavior is inborn and the extent to which it is an acquired inclination is difficult to discern.

One thing is certain: we are to be in control of our sexual instincts. Satan would have us think it is so strong that we cannot control it. Satan wants us to believe that we are not normal (not "real men" or "real women") if we do not desire sexual relationships so strongly that we give in and commit sin, at least mentally if not physically. No matter how strongly a person may desire to engage in sinful sexual relationships, "[God] will not suffer you to be tempted above that ye are able; but will with the temptation also make a way to escape, that ye may be able to bear it" (I Cor. 10:13).

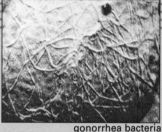

syphilis spirochete   gonorrhea bacteria

physical punishment for a particular sin.

The statement that the sin of homosexuality will result in God's judging a person by his contracting AIDS or any other STD cannot be supported by Scripture. God's judgment on sin is eternity in hell, and everyone who does not have his sins washed away by Christ's blood will be so condemned by the righteous Judge (Rev. 20:12-14). It is misleading to claim that any particular physical condition is God's judgment upon a person. Particular sins may tend to lead to certain physical sufferings. God will condemn to hell the soul that has not been washed clean of sin in His Son's blood, but Scripture does not tell us any particular physical punishment that is attached to any particular sin. If AIDS were to be the punishment for homosexuality, God would be an unjust judge if all homosexuals did not contract AIDS. Only those homosexuals exposed to the AIDS virus will contract the disease. Also there are nonhomosexuals who have been exposed to the virus and have AIDS (and some of these people were exposed in nonsinful ways, such as blood transfusions).

Review questions on page 647.

Syphilis and Gonorrhea—Two Common STDs

Syphilis (SIF uh lis), a common STD, is caused by a spirochete. From 21-90 days after a person has been exposed to the syphilis spirochete, he may develop a *canker* (an open sore or lesion producing a fluid discharge). The cankers usually form on the soft skin of the reproductive organs near the place where the spirochete entered the body; however, they may also form on the mouth or near the eyes. The fluid from these cankers contains the spirochetes. When the fluid comes in contact with other skin, the syphilis organism may enter the body, and the disease spreads.

In about three weeks the canker disappears, but unless medically treated, the person is not cured of the disease. A few days to a few weeks later, secondary symptoms, such as a general body rash, fever, headaches, or sore throat develops. In time, these symptoms disappear, but the spirochetes still live in the bloodstream.

The third stage of syphilis may happen immediately after the second stage, or it may not be evident for 10-25 yr. During the third stage, the spirochete affects various internal organs. In untreated syphilitic patients, 1 in 200 becomes blind, 1 in 25 becomes permanently crippled as the organism affects the brain, and 1 in 13 develops heart or blood disorders. Syphilis may also affect the liver, bones, or almost any other organ, causing various symptoms. Infected women can pass the syphilis organism to their unborn children, causing the death of the child or causing it to be born blind, deaf, or in other ways deformed.

Gonorrhea (GAHN uh REE uh), another common STD, is caused by a species of bacteria. Although these bacteria can spread through the body and cause serious complications, gonorrhea often infects only the reproductive organs causing pain and sterility. An infected mother may have deformed children.

Homosexuality

Homosexuality* is sexual relations among members of the same sex; men with men, women with women. Romans 1:25-28 says, "Who changed the truth of God into a lie, and worshipped and served the creature more than the Creator, . . . For this cause God gave them up into vile affections: for even their women did change the natural use into that which is against nature: And likewise also the men, leaving the natural use of the woman, burned in their lust one toward another; men with men working that which is unseemly, and receiving in themselves that recompence of their error which was meet. And even as they did not like to retain God in their knowledge, God gave them over to a reprobate mind, to do those things which are not convenient."

God calls homosexuality a sin, and those who engage in this act are reprobates. (They are sinning against God, and they know it.) Thus, God condemns them for it (Rom. 1:32). I Corinthians 6:9-10 places homosexuality ("abusers of themselves with mankind") with adultery, fornication, idolatry, and other sins.

Despite these and other passages condemning the sin of homosexuality, today many people claim that homosexuality is not sin because they consider it a "normal, natural" way for some people to be. Extensive tests have revealed no biological difference between homosexuals and **heterosexuals*** (those who engage in normal sexual relations between men and women).

Homosexuality is "normal and natural" for people just as greed, stealing, hate, murder, and all other forms of sin are "normal and natural." Such feelings permit homosexuals to *justify their sin in their minds*. But Christians are to follow God's precepts, not those of the world. We are to "walk in the Spirit, and [we] shall not fulfil the lust of the flesh" (Gal. 5:16).

Today Satan has convinced people that adultery and fornication are so much a normal part of life (since everybody is doing it) and so natural (since humans do have a reproductive inclination) that such acts are not really sins. God's Word tells us that the pleasures of sin are for a season (Heb. 11:25) and that we should not sin under any circumstances (Rom. 6:12-13). God's purpose for the Christian on earth is not temporal, physical "pleasures." We are here to glorify God by doing His will. Obedience to God results in blessings such as love, joy, and peace, which are pleasures the sinner cannot really know (Gal. 5:22-23; I Cor. 2:14). Also, God promises the Christian the pleasures of heaven for eternity, while the unsaved will spend their eternity in the torment of hell (I Cor. 6:9-10; Rev. 21:7-8).

A Christian view

One of today's attitudes toward sexual relationships appears to be, "If it doesn't hurt anybody, or if the people involved all agree, anything is acceptable." Abortion or various other measures can be used to prevent illegitimate children (those born to parents who are not married to each other) or even unwanted children. Antibiotics or other treatments can prevent or cure most sexually transmitted diseases. Therefore, some people feel that the reasons not to engage in any sexual relationship they desire are "outdated psychological hang-ups [like guilt or pressure] from people who are not with it."

God, however, calls any sexual relationship other than that between husband and wife sinful. Even though it may *appear* that man has devised ways to remove the "results" of a sin, nothing can be done to make a sin no longer a sin. Nothing can make disobedience acceptable.

Some Christian young people cannot understand why God calls these sexual relationships sin. It appears to them that God is a "big bully trying to stop us from having fun like everybody else." That is exactly what Satan wants young people to think. Satan wants them to rebel against God, His Word, and His instruments in their life (such as godly parents, pastors, Christian teachers) so that Satan can have his way with them.

If you are inclined toward a rebellious attitude because you feel God has "limited you," consider the following two points:

❑ God is an all-powerful and all-knowing God.

---

heterosexual: hetero- (Gk. HETEROS, other) + sexual

homosexuality: homos- (Gk. HOMOS, same) + sexuality (also called *sodomy* after Sodom–see Gen. 19:5).

We are His, not our own. We were made by Him, were bought by Him, are kept by Him, and will be delivered by Him. He can do with us what He wants to do with us. He may test our obedience in any way He cares to. He could destroy us in an instant and replace us in the next. Who are we that we should think that God is doing wrong (Job 40:2)? Although it is hard for a proud man to accept, it is nonetheless a Biblical truth that we belong to God and are accountable to Him.

❑ God has promised us blessing if we keep His commandments (Deut. 28:1-2; I Cor. 6:17-20). There is no way that doing things contrary to His commandments can bring blessing. Satan has set up this world so that it *appears* that keeping God's commandments is "wrong and unnatural," and that those who obey God are not "enjoying themselves." God's Word tells us that those who disobey Him (sin) are the ones who will be judged; but those who follow God's commands are the ones who will be blessed.

"Choose ye this day whom ye will serve." Yourself and Satan? Or will you join with those who answer, "As for me . . . [I] will serve the Lord" (Josh. 24:15). "Whatsoever ye do, do all to the glory of God" (I Cor. 10:31).

24B-3 *The family is not only the basic unit of all societies but also the model God uses to illustrate His close personal relationship with man (Hos. 12:12, Rom. 8:14-17; Rev. 21:2). The bonds within the Christian family are ordained of God and should be strengthened.*

Biological Terms

The Control of Life	*Sexual Purity*	*Facet*
sanctity of human life	sexual purity	sexually transmitted diseases
abortion	adultery	
euthanasia	fornication	
active euthanasia	homosexuality	
passive euthanasia	heterosexuality	

Review Questions for 24B-2
1. Distinguish between the terms adultery and fornication.
2. List three Scriptural passages that condemn homosexuality.

Facet 24B-1: Sexually Transmitted Diseases, page 645
1. What separates sexually transmitted diseases from other forms of contagious diseases? What is another name for STD?
2. Give two examples of sexually transmitted diseases.

Thought Questions
1. In a few paragraphs, summarize your opinion on active and passive euthanasia.
2. What are Satan's two basic tenets to convince people that adultery and fornication are acceptable? Why are these two tenets illogical?
3. In what way can unregenerate people consider homosexuality "natural"? Does this justify a person's being a homosexual?
4. In a paragraph, summarize what you believe to be the Biblical position on sexual relationships.

Appendix A
A History of Scientific Thinking

It is easy to point to the beginning of science. Adam was the first biologist: he tended and dressed the Garden of Eden and named the animals (Gen 2:15, 19-20). However, we do not know the processes which Adam used. Did he group the animals and give them names within the groups? What botanical knowledge was involved in caring for the Garden, and how did Adam obtain the knowledge? We have no way of knowing.

We, likewise, have very little way of knowing the scientific processes used by most other Biblical characters or ancient peoples. On rare occasions God gave certain people specific skills for special purposes (Ex. 35:30-35). Presumably they taught others this knowledge. With these exceptions, the Bible tells us only that some people had knowledge of certain skills (Gen. 4:20-22; I Chron. 15:22; II Chron. 2:13-14); it does not tell us how they obtained this knowledge.

We know that ancient people had various kinds of scientific knowledge (such as how to build a pyramid, grow certain crops, make certain metals, calculate the seasons, etc.). We do not know how much of this knowledge was passed on to them or what methods they used to discover these things. Although much of their scientific knowledge was accurate and impressive, much of what they thought they knew was inaccurate. For example, ground-up pearls do not help people bear children, nor does mustard on the nose cure deafness.

Today, both Christians and non-Christians assume that the scientific method is a good way to determine valid, workable solutions to many physical problems. This has not always been the case. As you consider how people in different ages have determined what they thought was true regarding the physical world, you will understand better what a Christian should believe regarding the relationship between science and the Scripture.

The ancient Greeks

The Greek culture flourished about 500 yr. before Christ. Although known for sculpture, architecture, and literature, the most significant Greek contribution to society was *philosophy*. Philosophy is a system of values which affects how a person thinks and what he does. The ancient Greeks were "natural philosophers" because they sought logical explanations of nature. They wanted to explain physical phenomena without resorting to supernatural explanations, such as "the gods did it" or "an evil spirit caused it."

Anaximander (uh NAK suh MAN dur) (ca. 500 B.C.) imagined a physical substance called "boundless" which made up all things. "Boundless" was a concept that stated that something was slowly becoming: this something used to be something else, but now it is what we can experience with our senses; and it is "boundless" in what it can be-

come. Anaximander realized that his speculations needed observations to back them up, but he also believed that making observations was not a philosopher's job. Because he felt observations were needed to support his theory, Anaximander is called "the Father of Science" even though his "boundless" theory was forced into the philosophical "junk heap" due to the lack of observable proof.

Empedocles (em PEHD uh KLEEZ) (ca. 425 B.C.) changed "boundless" into four substances which he called *humors* (fluids): fire, air, water, and earth. Different combinations of these humors made up everything from matter to weather, and living things consisted of special forms of these humors. Empedocles' concept was later known as the Doctrine of Humors.

Hippocrates (ca. 400 B.C.), a physician-philosopher, used the four humors idea to explain sickness and health (see pages 4-5). The idea that physical health is controlled by a mixture of four fluids seems unscientific today. Before Hippocrates, however, most people believed that sickness was caused by evil spirits and that good health was a result of pleasing the gods. Because he explained health and sickness in natural rather than supernatural terms, Hippocrates is called "the Father of Modern Medicine."

As far as science is concerned, one of the greatest of the Greek philosophers was *Aristotle* (ca. 350 B.C.). Aristotle believed that reality (that which is true) was found in nature, not in some far-off ideal as some of his predecessors had claimed. Since reality is the objects, to know truth one needs to know the objects. To Aristotle, if someone observed, grouped, and described natural phenomena, he could arrive at the truth about them. Aristotle was an early biologist because he described and grouped over 500 organisms.

Paul speaks of the Greeks seeking wisdom but says that God will "destroy the wisdom of the wise and bring to nothing the understanding of the prudent." Even today, those who look for explanations of physical phenomena and ignore the God who created all things lack true wisdom. Christians who believe in the truth of Christ, which is "to the Greeks foolishness," recognize that Christ is the power and wisdom of God (I Cor. 1:18-24).

Science of the Romans and the early Christians

Rome conquered Greece and then "borrowed" Greek culture and philosophy. Most of the Roman scientists were like *Pliny* (PLIHN ee) (ca. A.D. 50) who wrote a 37-volume encyclopedia of real and fictitious descriptions of physical phenomena. Many of these descriptions were based on stories of travelers; only a few were the direct result of Pliny's own observations.

Galen (ca. A.D. 175) was a Roman physician (see page 551) who believed the Doctrine of Humors; dissected sheep, apes, and other large mammals; and applied his observations to humans. His observations led to some accurate conclusions and some inaccurate ones. For example, he said that the liver made blood, which the heart warmed and sent out through the blood vessels.

A stated Christian philosophy of science from this period is difficult to find. Most Christians were too busy with more pressing problems than scientific pursuits. The periodic persecutions by the Romans not only kept the Church strong but also left its members little time for significant scientific activities.

In A.D. 313 the Emperor Constantine embraced Christianity, which in time became the state religion. By then, however, political Rome was in decline, and a short time later it was completely destroyed. The "official church" (the Roman Catholic church) stepped in to become not only a religious organization but also a form of government. Some of its beliefs and practices were based on what was best to maintain its political control rather than what was Scripturally correct.

The Dark Ages and scholasticism

The time between the 5th and the 9th centuries is sometimes called the Dark Ages because during this time culture and science stagnated. Only a few of the nobility and some of the church leaders were educated. It was relatively easy for the educated minority to keep the ignorant in submission with tales and threats.

One concept they found convenient was a perversion of the doctrine of faith. A person's salvation is all of faith in Christ's atoning death on the cross; however, they went so far as to say that everything should be of faith. This grew to mean that there is no truth outside of Scripture. Thus, knowledge of sacred things was considered good while knowledge of physical things was considered "worldly" (meaning both "of the physical world" and "of the sinful world"). If a person had an abundant knowledge of physical phenomena, he must have been very worldly, perhaps a sorcerer or witch. He was, perhaps, a dealer in the "black arts" and in league with the "prince of the power of this world," Satan himself. A philosophy that equated knowledge of the physical world with evil made it a truly dark age for science.

In time, the absurdity of this philosophy became apparent, and even the Roman Catholic church began looking beyond Scripture for knowledge of the physical world. Scholars rediscovered the writings of the ancient Greeks and in doing so created much controversy. Many recognized the Greeks as anti-God in that they tried to explain everything in "natural terms" and did not wish to recognize a supernatural God. Others believed that the Greek writings were an interesting new source of knowledge.

Thomas Aquinas (uh QWINE us) (ca. 1200), a Catholic theologian-philosopher, developed strong arguments supporting the idea that Aristotle and Scripture did not contradict each other. Aristotle was, of course, a pagan and also erred in many of his observations and conclusions. "The

Philosopher" was the name that Aquinas gave to Aristotle, and in order to justify and "Christianize" him, Aquinas often misrepresented Aristotle and even occasionally contradicted the Bible.

The practice of seeking truth in ancient writings, along with Scripture, and the teachings of the Roman Catholic church is called *scholasticism* (skuh LASS tuh SIZZ uhm). Scholastics even believed that if some point of knowledge were not revealed by the ancients or Scripture, it was either not worth knowing or could not be known.

An Example of Scholastic Thought

The following anecdote shows how scholastics thought problems should be solved:

In the year of our Lord 1432, there arose a grievous quarrel among the brethren over the number of teeth in the mouth of a horse. For thirteen days the disputation raged without ceasing. All the ancient books and chronicles were fetched out . . . [and consulted]. At the beginning of the fourteenth day, a youthful friar . . . asked his learned superiors for permission to add a word, and straightway, to the wonderment of [all] . . . he beseeched them . . . to look in the open mouth of a horse and find answer to their questionings. At this, their dignity being grievously hurt, they waxed exceedingly wroth; and . . . they flew upon him and smote him hip and thigh, and cast him out forthwith. For, said they, surely Satan hath tempted [him] to declare unholy and unheard-of ways of finding truth contrary to all the teachings of the fathers. After many days more . . . [they declared] the problem to be an everlasting mystery because of [lack] of historical and theological evidence thereof, so ordered the same writ down. (Francis Bacon, cited by C.E. Kenneth Mees in "Scientific Thought and Social Reconstruction," *Electrical Engineering*, March 1934, pp. 383-84.)

Aristotle, who was probably one of the ancient writers consulted, would have agreed with the procedure suggested by the friar.

One argument the scholastics used to support their looking to old writings for knowledge used this logic:
- Adam was perfect before he sinned.
- Part of being perfect is to know all things.
- When Adam sinned, he was no longer perfect.
- When Adam was not perfect, he began forgetting things he had known.
- Adam's offspring could not know things Adam had forgotten.
- The more generations one is removed from Adam, the less is remembered.
- The ancient writers were many generations closer to Adam than we are.
- Thus, the ancient writers know more about things than we do.

Appendix

The awakening of science

The age of scholasticism was not without its critics. *Roger Bacon* (ca. 1250) was an English Franciscan monk who had a few chemicals and some crude apparatus. To satisfy his curiosity, he conducted some experiments and wrote about the results. He was accused of witchcraft and other related evils, tried, condemned as a heretic, and imprisoned for his crime. In his papers he claimed that observation and experimentation were better methods for understanding nature than blind devotion to the past.

Although ahead of his time, his voice was heard. During the 1500s and 1600s many people found more fault with the ancients and began to look to their own ability to solve problems. The awakening of science began when people stopped looking to the past and started trying to figure things out for themselves.

It was one thing to question the authority of Aristotle and demonstrate his errors in light of observation. It was quite another to challenge the Roman Catholic church, which claims to have Divine guidance and authority. A major controversy developed over the belief that the earth was the center of the universe. Using ancient writings and a couple of Scripture passages that do not directly deal with the topic, the Catholic church taught that the heavenly bodies rotated around the earth. Some even used logic to support this belief: a perfect God would not send His sinless Son to a planet that was off center.

Galileo (ca. 1600), a respected Italian scientist, had studied the physics of falling bodies, tried to describe light, and used the newly invented telescope to observe the night sky. In one of his early books, Galileo denounced the scholastic view saying that those who look only to the ancients were acting as if "nature had written this great book of the world to be read by none beside Aristotle."

Galileo, after many observations and calculations, wrote an interesting and popular book which stated that the sun was the center of the universe, and the earth and other planets revolved around it. Galileo was warned by church officials that he was bordering on heresy: the church was right because of its great authority, and his observations or calculations could easily be inaccurate. He was warned to keep quiet about this matter unless he had "undeniable proofs." Galileo was sure of his observations and calculations, and, with the blessing of some in the church, continued to write about the earth going around the sun.

Galileo, a loyal Roman Catholic, defended his position, saying that "The book of nature and the Scriptures have the same author." In other words, accurate observations of the physical world will not contradict the Scripture since both were created by God. Galileo wanted the church leaders to change their opinions regarding what they believed the Scripture said. The controversy was not so much over whether the sun or earth was at the center of the universe, but whether the church had the right to interpret Scripture and force reason, logic, and observations to go along with its interpretations.

At the time, the Roman Catholic church was troubled by what it considered the heresy of the Protestant reformers. Since Galileo was a well-known scientist, the church could not tolerate his rebellion against church authority. To do so would have seemed like weakness and would have encouraged others to challenge the church. Thus, Galileo was summoned before a church tribunal and told that if he did not recant, the church would condemn him to death and hell as a heretic. Galileo, at this time an old, blind, and sick man, recanted and agreed to not spread his heresy. The church was merciful; it did not imprison him but, instead, confined him to his house for the rest of his life.

Some believe that at his recantation, Galileo, after disavowing that the earth went around the sun, got up from his knees and said under his breath, "But it does." Although somewhat in keeping with Galileo's character, it is doubtful that he did this. It is also doubtful that Galileo really believed what he was forced to say. It was 300 yr. later (in the 1980s) that the Roman Catholic church changed its position regarding the universe and recognized that Galileo had been right.

Experimental biology

Biology, because it deals with living things which are more difficult to measure and experiment with, is often far behind the physical sciences. Although he was ahead of his time, *William Harvey* (ca. 1615), an English physician, introduced observation and experimentation into the biological sciences.

While Galileo was observing the heavens, Harvey was observing the human heart and blood vessels. He respected the ancients and often cited them in support of what he believed. He also believed that experimentation, observation, and reason could prove them wrong. Galen's theories about the heart and circulation had been the basis for medical practice for over 1,400 yr., but to Harvey, they did not make sense.

Harvey observed that the valves of the heart permitted blood to flow only in certain directions, not back and forth. He observed that blood which leaves the heart goes only into certain blood vessels (arteries). Other blood vessels (veins) have valves in them which permit blood to flow only toward the heart. He also demonstrated that there were no holes in the wall between the two sides of the heart (needed for Galen's theory to work). He measured the amount of blood forced from the heart in a single beat and then calculated how much blood would have to be made in order to keep the heart pumping. It is impossible for a body to contain that much blood.

Based on his observations and experiments, Harvey described the *circulation* of the blood. A complete theory of blood flow lacked only an explanation of how blood moves from the arteries to the veins. He speculated about tiny blood vessels which attach arteries and veins and demonstrated that they must exist. But since the microscopes available to him were not strong enough to see the tiny capillaries, he could not observe them. Because of his pioneering work, Harvey is often called the "Father of Experimental Biology."

Harvey was heavily criticized and a number of his colleagues were rude to him because of his beliefs. However, he was not imprisoned or threatened with death and hell for his scientific work and beliefs. England was no longer under the control of the Roman Catholic church, and the intellectual world was turning its back on scholasticism.

The Age of Modern Science

Although Bacon, Galileo, and Harvey were at the forefront of scientific developments, many other scientists followed their example. By the 1800s the scientific method was the primary method of learning about the physical world. The ancient Greeks are still considered as wise masters of many things, but it is laughable to cite them as scientific authorities.

Man's use of science has flourished. Observation and experimentation have allowed man to be able to control many aspects of the physical world. Diseases have been conquered; abundant food, clothing, and comfortable housing have been supplied; and, in general, life has been made easier through scientific advances. Science has become man's tool to supply his physical needs with less effort.

But where does God fit? For many, He does not. Today, some people look to science for everything. To them, man will improve through science. In fact, science is man's only hope of ever improving. This is *scientism*, the worship of science. A Christian, however, knows that science cannot make a man truly good. Only Christ can forgive sin; only Christ can give him the strength to live a life that is pleasing to Him.

Scientism is quite similar to the "natural philosophy" of the ancient Greeks. They sought to explain natural phenomena without resorting to supernatural explanation. Those who believe in scientism refuse to recognize God as Creator and Sustainer of the physical world and as the only Saviour of men. (See Chapter 1A and B for a modern definition and philosophy of science and pages 25-29 for a Christian philosophy of science.)

Review Questions

1. Describe the scientific philosophy of the ancient Greeks.
2. Describe the scientific philosophy of the scholastics.
3. Would Galen be considered a good scientist today? Why?
4. On what basis did the scholastics base the idea that the ancients knew more about natural phenomena than they did?
5. Identify the following as to historical period and contribution to scientific thought: (a) Anaximander, (b) Aquinas, (c) Aristotle, (d) Roger Bacon, (e) Empedocles, (f) Galen, (g) Galileo, (h) William Harvey, (i) Hippocrates.
6. What was the crime that brought Galileo before the Roman Catholic tribunal?
7. Describe William Harvey's work and its significance.
8. Of the men listed in question 5 which holds a position most like the Christian philosophy of science described in Chapter 1 (especially pages 9, 12, 25-29)? Explain your answer.

Appendix B

A Modern Classification System

Listed below are the major divisions of the classification system along with their main characteristics, examples, and their location in this book. This listing is to be used for summary and review of the text material. Several additional divisions and examples are listed for reference purposes. The classifications are presented in the order they are covered in the text with supplemental classifications listed alphabetically unless otherwise noted.

The term *phylum* is used for uniformity throughout this classification system. The term *division* is technically correct in the kingdom Plantae and is sometimes used in the kingdoms Monera, Protista, and Fungi.

Kingdom Monera[1] (Chapter 9)

Cellular Structure
- Cells procaryotic (lack organized nucleus; lack membrane-bound organelles)
- Most have cell walls with capsules or sheaths; unicellular or simple colonial organisms

Nutrition
- Most heterotrophic; some photosynthetic; some heterotrophic and photosynthetic; some chemosynthetic
- Some parasitic
- Some pathogenic

- Most use oxygen when available but can also carry on fermentation; some require oxygen; some carry on only fermentation

Reproduction
- Simple fission (forms of genetic recombination are known in some species)
- Some form endospores

Motility
- Many nonmotile; some motile by simple flagella; some have gliding movement

Subkingdom Eubacteria (The True Bacteria)

Phylum Gracilicutes

Thin cell walls that stain Gram-negative (pages 226-36)
Many true bacteria: *Escherichia coli, Salmonella*; phototrophic bacteria
Cyanobacteria (blue-green algae): *Nostoc, Oscillatoria, Anabaena* (page 233)
Rickettsias (page 234)
Spirochetes (page 235)

Phylum Firmicutes

Thick cell walls that stain Gram-positive; many form endospores (pages 226-36)

Many true bacteria: *Bacillus, Staphylococcus, Streptococcus*

Phylum Tenericutes

Lacks cell walls (page 235)
Mycoplasmas

Subkingdom Archaebacteria

Phylum Mendosicutes

Unusual cell walls and capsules; makes methane gas; lives in very salty or hot, sulfurous environments; many have unique metabolic pathways
Methanobacterium

Kingdom Protista (Chapter 10)

<table>
<tr>
<td>

Cellular Structure
- Cells eucaryotic (have an organized nucleus and membrane-bound organelles)
- Many unicellular, many are colonial; some form large multicellular structures; none have tissues

Nutrition
- Some heterotrophic (either ingesting material or absorbing substances); some are photosynthetic; some can be either heterotrophic or photosynthetic

</td>
<td>

- Some parasitic
- Some pathogenic

Reproduction
- Most carry on simple fission
- Colonies often reproduce by fragmentation or budding
- Many have sexual reproduction either by conjugation or gametes

Motility
- Many float, others sessile (grow attached to surfaces)
- Many move by cilia, flagella, or pseudopods

</td>
</tr>
</table>

Subkingdom Protozoa[2] (Chapter 10A)

Motile in at least one phase of its life cycle; heterotrophic (some are heterotrophic and photosynthetic)
"Animallike" protists, protozoans

Phylum Sarcodina[3]

Unicellular; no pellicle; moves by pseudopods; heterotrophic (engulfs food by phagocytosis); some form tests, some form cysts; reproduction usually by fission; salt water and freshwater forms; some parasitic, some pathogenic (pages 260-63)
Sarcodines: ameba, foraminiferans, radiolarians

Phylum Ciliophora

Unicellular; has pellicle; moves by cilia; heterotrophic; some form cysts; many have macronucleus and micronucleus; salt water and freshwater forms; some parasitic, some pathogenic (pages 263-64)
Ciliates: paramecium, stentor, *Vorticella*

Phylum Mastigophora[3]

Unicellular or colonial; has pellicle; moves by flagella; heterotrophic, but some can be either photosynthetic or heterotrophic; salt water and freshwater forms; some parasitic, some pathogenic (pages 264-65)
Flagellates: *Euglena, Trypanosoma, Volvox*

Phylum Sporozoa[4]

Unicellular, rarely colonial; no structures for locomotion; forms spores; all parasitic, many pathogenic (pages 265-67)
Sporozoans: *Plasmodium*

Subkingdom Protophyta[2] (Chapter 10B)

All are photosynthetic with chlorophyll and other pigments in plastids
"Plantlike" protists, algal protists

Phylum Chlorophyta[5]

Unicellular or colonial forms; motile, free-floating and sessile forms; food stored as starch; cell walls of cellulose; salt water and freshwater forms (pages 270-71)
Green algae: *Spirogyra, Ulothrix, Protococcus,* desmids, *Oedogonium, Chlamydomonas*

Phylum Chrysophyta

Unicellular and colonial forms; motile and free-floating forms; food stored as oils and complex carbohydrates; cell walls often contain silicon; salt water and freshwater forms (pages 272-73)
Diatoms, yellow-green and golden algae: *Vaucheria, Dinobryon*

Phylum Pyrrophyta

Unicellular with two flagella; food stored as starch or oil; mostly salt water forms (page 273)
Dinoflagellates: *Gymnodinium*

Phylum Phaeophyta[5]

Colonial (usually large thallus); sessile; food stored as oil and complex carbohydrates; cell walls of cellulose; mostly shallow salt water forms (page 273)
Brown algae: *Fucus,* kelp, *Sargassum, Laminaria*

Phylum Rhodophyta[5]

Colonial; nonmotile, usually sessile; food stored as carbohydrates; cell walls of cellulose; mostly deep salt water forms (page 274)
Red algae: *Chondrus, Lemanea, Polysiphonia*

Kingdom Fungi (Chapter 11)

Cellular Structure
- ❑ Cells eucaryotic
- ❑ Has cell walls which usually contain chitin
- ❑ Some unicellular, some colonial; some form large structures of intertwined hyphae; none have tissues

Nutrition
- ❑ All heterotrophic with external digestion
- ❑ Some parasitic
- ❑ Some pathogenic

Reproduction
- ❑ Some carry on simple fission; many form various kinds of spores
- ❑ Most have sexual reproduction by conjugation or gametes

Motility
- ❑ Many sessile, some float, a few are motile
- ❑ Some produce motile gametes

Phylum Zygomycota[6]

Hyphae are nonseptate; sexual reproduction by conjugation (pages 282-83)
Common molds: *Rhizopus, Pilobolus, Glomus, Entomopthora*

Phylum Ascomycota[6]

Hyphae are septate; forms sexual spores in an ascus; many produce asexual spores on conidia (pages 283-84)

Sac fungi: cup fungi, yeasts, fruit molds, powdery mildews, morel, *Penicillum, Aspergillus, Neurospora*
Imperfect fungi:[7] athlete's foot fungus, ringworm, thrush

Phylum Basidiomycota[6]

Hyphae are usually septate; mycelia often produce large, fruiting bodies; produces spores on a basidium (pages 284-86)
Club fungi: mushrooms, puff balls, earthstars, shelf fungi, rusts (wheat rust, apple cedar rust), smuts (corn smut)

Phylum Myxomycota[8] (Myxomycophyta)

A plasmodium (multinucleate cellular structure) that often moves with pseudopods and produces sporangia
Slime molds

Phylum Oomycota[8]

Water molds, downy mildews, *Saprolengnia*

Phylum Acrasiomycota[8]

Cellular slime molds

Kingdom Plantae[9] (Chapters 12-13)

Cellular Structure
- ❏ Cells eucaryotic
- ❏ All have tissues; most have organs
- ❏ Most have chlorophyll and other pigments in plastids
- ❏ Has cell walls made of cellulose

Nutrition
- ❏ Most autotrophic (photosynthetic), some parasitic

Reproduction
- ❏ Reproduces sexually
- ❏ Many have asexual forms of reproduction

Motility
- ❏ Most sessile, some float
- ❏ Some produce motile gametes

Part 1: Nonvascular Plants

Phylum Bryophyta

Lacks vascular tissues; plants small; no true leaves, roots, or stems; gametophyte plant dominant; sporophyte is a parasite on the gametophyte (pages 289-91)
Bryophytes

- ❏ **Class Musci**   (pages 289-91)
  Mosses: *Bryum, Polytrichum, Musci*

- ❏ **Class Hepaticae**   (page 291)
  Liverworts: *Marchantia*

- ❏ **Class Anthocerotae**
  Hornworts

Part 2: Vascular Plants Without Seeds

Phylum Psilophyta

Has vascular tissue (xylem and phloem); lacks roots; has scales instead of leaves; reproduces by spores (page 293)
Whiskferns

Phylum Lycophyta

Has vascular tissue; usually has creeping and erect stems; reproduces by spores (page 293)
Ground pines: *Lycopodium*

Phylum Sphenophyta

Has vascular tissue; thick perennial underground stem with erect annual stems; leaves in whorls from nodes on the stem; conelike spore-producing structures on top of stems (page 293)
Horsetails, scouring rushes: *Equisetum*

Phylum Pterophyta

Has vascular tissue; has roots, stems, and leaves; leaves have sori which produce spores; sexual reproduction by sperm swimming to ovum on small gametophyte plant; sporophyte plant dominant; has fiddleheads (pages 292-94)
Ferns: *Osmunda, Pteris, Polypodium*

Part 3: Vascular Plants with Seeds

A. Gymnosperms
(nonflowering plants that produce seeds not enclosed in an ovary wall)

B. Angiosperms
(flowering plants that produce seeds enclosed in an ovary wall)

Phylum Coniferophyta

Has vascular tissue; woody plants with needles or scalelike leaves; produces cones containing seeds (pages 295-97)
Conifers (cone-bearing plants)

> **Family Pinaceae**   Usually has needles (pages 295-96)
> Pine family: pines, firs, hemlocks, cedars
>
> **Family Taxaceae**   Waxy, green needles; fruit looks like open-ended berries (pages 296-97)
> Yew family: yews
>
> **Family Cupressaceae** Usually has scales (page 296)
> Cypress family: cypress, junipers, arborvitae
>
> **Family Taxodiaceae**   (page 297)
> Redwood family: redwoods, giant sequoia, bald cypress

Phylum Cycadophyta

Has vascular tissue; often looks like a palm tree; some have fiddleheads; produces seeds in a single, large conelike structure (page 296)
Cycads, sego palms (mostly extinct)

Phylum Ginkgophyta

Has vascular tissue; has a fan-shaped leathery leaf (page 296)
Ginkgo (one living species, *Ginkgo biloba*)

Phylum Anthophyta

Has vascular tissue; produces flowers; seeds develop inside an ovary wall (page 297)
Angiosperms

❏ **Class Monocotyledoneae**   Seeds have one cotyledon and one seed leaf; parallel leaf venation; roots usually fibrous; flower parts usually in threes or sixes; young stems have scattered vascular bundles and usually become hollow as they mature (page 297)
Monocots

> **Family Arecaceae (Palmae)**
> Palm family: coconut palm, date palm, palmetto, royal palm
>
> **Family Iridaceae**
> Iris family: iris, flag
>
> **Family Liliaceae**
> Lily family: lily, onion, tulip, hyacinth, garlic, crocus
>
> **Family Orchidaceae**
> Orchid family: orchids, lady's slipper
>
> **Family Poaceae (Graminae)**
> Grass and grains family: corn, wheat, rice, grass, sugar cane, bamboo, timothy, oats, crabgrass
>
> **Family Typhaceae**
> Cattail family: common cattail

❏ **Class Dicotyledoneae** Seeds have two cotyledons and two seed leaves; netted leaf venation; usually has a taproot; flower parts usually in fours, fives, or multiples of these numbers; young stems have vascular bundles in a ring and are usually solid (pages 297-98)

Dicots

Family Aceraceae
Maple family: maple

Family Apiaceae
Parsley family; parsley, dill, carrot, celery, Queen Anne's lace, parsnip

Family Asteraceae (Compositae)
Composite family: dandelion, sunflower, marigold, thistle, zinnia, chrysanthemum, dahlia, ragweed, sagebrush, daisy

Family Brassicaceae (Cruciferae)
Mustard family: mustard, radish, turnip, cabbage, cauliflower, sweet alyssum

Family Cactaceae
Cactus family: cactus, prickly pear

Family Caryophyllaceae
Pink family: pink, carnation, sweet William, baby's breath

Family Ericaceae
Heath family: rhododendron, azalea, heather, blueberry, cranberry, mountain laurel

Family Fabaceae
Pea family, the legume family: pea, bean, peanut, soybean, alfalfa, vetch, clover, redbud

Family Fagaceae
Beech family: beech, oak, chestnut

Family Juglandaceae
Walnut family: walnut, hickory, pecan

Family Malvaceae
Mallow family: marsh mallow, hollyhock, cotton, hibiscus

Family Nymphaeaceae
Water lily family: water lily

Family Papaveraceae
Poppy family: poppy

Family Rosaceae
Rose family: rose, apple, hawthorn, blackberry, raspberry, strawberry, pear, plum, cherry, peach, apricot, almond

Family Solanaceae
Nightshade family: potato, tomato, green pepper, tobacco, eggplant

Kingdom Animalia (Chapters 14-17)

Cellular Structure
- ❏ Cells eucaryotic
- ❏ Cells lack cell walls and plastids

Nutrition
- ❏ All heterotrophic
- ❏ Some parasitic
- ❏ Some pathogenic

Reproduction
- ❏ All reproduce sexually, but many reproduce both sexually and asexually

- ❏ All have embryonic stages, but some have both embryonic and larval stages

Motility
- ❏ Most motile with muscles
- ❏ Some sessile

Phylum Porifera

Sessile adults; supported by a system of interlacing spicules and/or spongin fibers; body bears many pores; feeding accomplished by collar cells and intracellular digestion; no respiratory or excretory structures; response to stimuli mainly on the cellular level; asexual reproduction by budding, gemmules, or regeneration; sexual reproduction by eggs and sperm; either asymmetrical or radially symmetrical (pages 342-43)
Sponges: *Grantia*

Phylum Cnidaria (Coelenterata)

Movement using a system of musclelike fibers; body consists of two cell layers forming a gastrovascular cavity with a single opening; jellylike tentacles for obtaining food; digestion is first extracellular within the gastrovascular cavity and then intracellular; no respiratory or excretory structures; nervous system consists of a nerve net with limited sensory capabilities; asexual reproduction by budding and regeneration; sexual reproduction by gametes; life cycle includes either a sessile polyp or a free-swimming stage or both; usually radially symmetrical (pages 344-46)
Cnidarians (coelenterates)

- **Class Hydrozoa** (pages 344-46)
  hydras, obelias

- **Class Scyphozoa** (pages 345-46)
  jellyfish

- **Class Anthozoa** (page 346)
  corals, sea fans

Phylum Platyhelminthes

Movement using layers of muscles; body consists of three cell layers; several organs of mesodermal origin; dorsal and ventral body surfaces flattened; some degree of cephalization; body covering of ciliated epidermis or tegument; digestion is extracellular and intracellular within an intestine that has a single opening; some adults lack digestive structures; no respiratory or circulatory organs; excretion using flame cells and a system of tubules; nervous system with nerve mass and two longitudinal nerve cords joined by transverse nerves; some have sense organs such as eyespots; asexual reproduction by division with regeneration; sexual reproduction usually by cross-fertilization between hermaphroditic adults; bilateral symmetry (pages 347-53)
Flatworms

- **Class Tuberllaria** Free-living; body covering of ciliated epidermis used for motion; usually has eyespots; usually aquatic, some terrestrial (pages 347-48)
  Planarians

- **Class Trematoda** Parasitic; body covered with a tegument; adults have digestive system; adults have few sense organs (pages 349-50)
  Flukes

- **Class Cestoda** Parasitic; body covered with a tegument; adult is composed of a scolex and proglottids; lacks a digestive system; lives in host's intestines; few sense organs (pages 350, 352-53)
  Tapeworms

Phylum Nematoda

Longitudinal muscles only, permitting thrashing movements; body covering of cellular epidermis with a protective cuticle; tubular digestive system with mouth and anus; no respiratory or circulatory organs; excretion using special cells or tubules; anterior nerve ring with dorsal and ventral nerve cords; sexes are separate; bilateral symmetry (pages 350-51, 353-54)
Roundworms: trichina worm, *Ascaris,* pinworm, hookworm, whipworms

Phylum Annelida

Movement by two layers of muscles; setae for locomotion present in most; distinct external and internal segmentation; three cell layers; each layer may develop into various tissues or organs; body covered with an epidermis and moist cuticle; digestive system is complete (mouth and anus); respiration by skin or gills; closed circulatory system; excretion using paired nephridia in each body segment (except first and last few segments); nervous system has anterior ganglia and a ventral nerve cord with a ganglion in each segment; asexual reproduction by regeneration in some; sexual reproduction involving hermaphroditic adults or separate sexes; bilateral symmetry (pages 355-57)

Segmented worms: earthworms, sandworms, leeches, clam worms, feather worms

Phylum Mollusca

Movement by muscular foot; body covering of ciliated epithelium; most with cephalization; has a mantle; many have a shell secreted by the mantle; digestive system is complete (mouth and anus); respiration by gills or lungs which are formed by the mantle; circulatory system with heart and colorless blood; nervous system made up of ganglia and nerve cords; many have sense organs for vision, taste, touch, smell, and balance; no asexual reproduction; sexual reproduction involving a trochophore larval stage; bilaterally symmetrical or asymmetrical (pages 358-60)

Mollusks

- **Class Bivalva (Pelecypoda)** (pages 359-60)
  Bivalves, Hatchet-footed animals: clams, oysters, scallops

- **Class Gastropoda** (pages 360-61)
  Gastropods, Stomach-footed animals: snails, slugs, nudibranches

- **Class Cephalopoda** (page 361)
  Cephalopods, Head-footed animals: squids, octopuses, nautiluses

- **Class Polyplacophora (Amphineura)**
  Chitons

- **Class Scaphopoda**
  Tooth shells

Phylum Echinodermata

Locomotion by a water-vascular system and tube feet; supported by a system of hardened plates beneath the epidermis; digestive system complete (mouth and anus); respiration usually by skin-gills; no well-organized circulatory or excretory organs; asexual reproduction by regeneration; sexual reproduction involving separate sexes and external fertilization; life cycle involves free-swimming larval stage; salt water; radial symmetry in adults, bilateral symmetry in larvas (pages 362-63)

Echinoderms, spiny-skinned animals

- **Class Stelleroidea** (pages 362-63)
  starfish, brittle stars

- **Class Echinoidea** (page 363)
  sea urchins, sand dollars

- **Class Holothuroidea** (page 363)
  sea cucumbers

- **Class Crinoidea** (page 363)
  sea lilies

Phylum Arthropoda[10]

Movement by jointed appendages moved by muscles; body segmented, usually with head, thorax, and abdomen; sometimes body segments are fused; body covered by exoskeleton containing chitin; exoskeleton secreted by epidermis and periodically molted; digestive system complete (mouth and anus); circulatory system open, with a dorsal heart; respiration by gills, tracheae, and book lungs; excretion by green glands or Malpighian tubules; nervous system with anterior ganglia and ventral nerve cord with ganglia; sense organs include antennas, sensory hairs, compound and/or simple eyes; sexes usually separate; parthenogenesis in some (Chapter 15)

Arthropods, joint-footed animals

- **Class Malacostraca (Crustaceae)** Cephalothorax and abdomen; two pairs of antennas; one pair mandibles, two pairs maxillae and one to three pairs of maxillipeds (mouthparts); one pair of legs or less per body segment; respiration by gills; usually has larval stages; usually aquatic, few terrestrial (pages 366-68)
  Malacostracans (crustaceans): crayfish, crabs, barnacles, shrimp, lobsters, pill bugs

- **Class Arachnida** Cephalothorax and abdomen; no antennas; chelicerae and pedipalps (mouthparts); four pairs of walking legs attached to thorax; respiration by book

lungs or tracheae; no larval stages (except for ticks); usually terrestrial (pages 369-73)
Arachnids: spiders, ticks, mites, scorpions

❑ **Class Chilopoda** Head and many body segments; one pair of antennas; one pair of mandibles and one or two pairs of maxillae (mouthparts); has poison glands; carnivorous; one pair of walking legs per body segment; respiration by tracheae; no larval stages; terrestrial (page 372)
Centipedes

❑ **Class Diplopoda** Head, short thorax, and many body segments; one pair of antennas; one pair mandibles and one pair maxillae (mouthparts); eats dead plant material; two pairs of walking legs per body segment; respiration by tracheae; no larval stages; terrestrial (page 372)
Millipedes

❑ **Class Insecta**[11] Head, thorax, and abdomen; one pair of antennas; one pair mandibles, one pair maxillae, one labium, one labrum (mouthparts); three pairs of legs on thorax; may have one or two pairs of wings on thorax; respiration by tracheae; usually has larval stages; mainly terrestrial (Chapter 15B)
Insects

• **Order Coleoptera** (sheath wing) Complete metamorphosis (larva called a grub); one pair horny wings covering a pair of membranous wings; chewing mouthparts (page 386)
Beetles, weevils: Japanese beetle, lady bugs, rice weevils, blister beetles, cotton boll weevil

• **Order Diptera** (two wings) Complete metamorphosis (larva called a maggot); one pair of membranous wings; piercing or sponging mouthparts (page 386)
Flies, mosquitoes, gnats

• **Order Hymenoptera** (membranous wing) Complete metamorphosis; two pairs of membranous wings; chewing or siphoning mouthparts; many have stinger in last abdominal segment; many are social insects, forming colonies (pages 380-82)
Ants, bees, wasps

• **Order Lepidoptera** (scale wing) Complete metamorphosis (larva called a caterpillar and has chewing mouthparts); two pairs of scale-covered wings; adults have siphoning mouthparts (pages 382, 386)
Butterflies, moths, skippers

• **Order Orthoptera** (straight wing) Incomplete metamorphosis on land; one pair of membranous and one pair of leatherlike wings; chewing mouthparts (page 387)
Grasshoppers, crickets, cockroaches, mantids

• **Order Anoplura** (unarmed tail) No metamorphosis; no wings; piercing and sucking mouthparts
Sucking lice

• **Order Thysanura** (tassel tail) No metamorphosis; no wings, chewing mouthparts
Silverfish, firebrats

• **Order Dermaptera** (skin wing) Incomplete metamorphosis on land; one pair of leatherlike wings; chewing mouthparts
Earwigs

• **Order Hemiptera** (half wing) Incomplete metamorphosis on land; forewings have a leatherlike anterior half and a posterior membranous half; hind wings are membranous; many lack wings and sucking mouthparts
True bugs: bedbugs, stinkbugs, water bugs, water striders, chinch bugs

• **Order Homoptera** (same wing) Incomplete metamorphosis on land; two pairs of membranous wings; piercing and sucking mouthparts
Cicadas, aphids, leaf-hoppers, scale insects

• **Order Isoptera** (equal wing) Incomplete metamorphosis on land; two pairs of membranous wings shed at maturity;

chewing mouthparts
Termites

- **Order Ephemeroptera** (lasting-only-a-day wing) Incomplete metamorphosis in water; two pairs of membranous wings; adults do not feed
Mayflies

- **Order Odonata** (toothed) Incomplete metamorphosis in water; two pairs of membranous wings; chewing mouthparts
Dragonflies, damselflies

- **Order Neuroptera** (nerve wing) Complete metamorphosis; two pairs of membranous wings; chewing mouthparts
Dobsonflies, ant lions, lacewings

- **Order Siphonaptera** (siphon, without wings) Complete metamorphosis; no wings; sucking mouthparts
Fleas

- ❏ **Class Merostomata**
Horseshoe crabs

Phylum Acanthocephala

Spiny-headed worms

Phylum Brachiopoda

Brachiopods, lampshells

Phylym Ectorprocta (Bryozoa)

Bryozoans (sea mosses)

Phylum Chaetognatha

Arrow worms

Phylum Ctenophora

Comb jellies

Phylum Nematomorpha

Horsehair worms

Phylum Nemertea

Proboscis worms, ribbon worms

Phylum Phoronidea

Phoronis

Phylum Rotifera (Trochelminthes)

Rotifers

Phylum Chordata

Has a dorsal notochord which is replaced by vertebrae in many; has dorsal tubular nerve cord; has pharyngeal pouches during embryonic development (Chapters 16 and 17)
Cordates

Subphylum Cephalochordata

Retains notochord throughout life (page 389)
Amphioxuses

Subphylum Urochordata

Notochord as larva only (page 389)
Tunicates or sea squirts

Subphylum Vertebrata

Internal vertebral column supports body; usually two pairs of limbs (pelvic and pectoral); skeleton of cartilage and/or bone; body divided into head, trunk, and usually a neck and tail; closed circulatory system; muscular heart is ventral to vertebral column and has two, three, or four chambers; red blood cells contain hemoglobin; digestive system complete with an alimentary canal composed of esophagus, stomach, and intestines located ventral to vertebral column; liver and pancreas attached to alimentary canal; brain consisting of several lobes; nerve cord (spinal cord) dorsal to vertebral column; most have projections from vertebrae surrounding and protecting the nerve cord; most have eyes, ears, and nostrils on head; paired cranial nerves branch from brain and serve major sensory organs of the head, and they affect many body movements and functions; paired spinal nerves branch from spinal cord and serve sensory organs of the trunk and appendages, and they affect many body movements and functions; kidneys filter wastes from blood; sexes usually sep-

arate, each individual usually having a pair of either ovaries or testes (pages 389-93)
Vertebrates

❑ **Class Agnatha**[12]   Scaleless body; no jaws; circular, sucking mouth; no stomach; skeleton of cartilage; unpaired fins; respiration by gills (no operculua); two-chambered heart; ectothermic; external fertilization; oviparous development (page 395)
Jawless fish: lampreys, hagfish

❑ **Class Chondrichthyes**   Skin with mucus-producing glands and placoid scales; mouth usually on ventral surface; jaws with teeth; skeleton of cartilage; fins both paired and unpaired; respiration by gills; two-chambered heart; ectothermic; fertilization generally internal; development usually ovoviviparous or viviparous (pages 398-99)
Cartilaginous fish: sharks, rays, skates

❑ **Class Osteichthyes (Pisces)**   Skin with many mucus-producing glands; usually covered by scales; mouth with jaw located in the front of the head; skeleton chiefly of bone with some cartilaginous parts; fins both paired and unpaired; respiration by gills covered with opercula, two-chambered heart; often an air bladder for controlling depth in water; ectothermic; fertilization generally external; development usually oviparous, but some ovoviviparous and viviparous; eggs usually minute and numerous (pages 394-403)
Bony fish: perch, eels, salmon, coelacanth, guppy

❑ **Class Amphibia**   Skin smooth with many glands and chromatophores (pigment cells); no scales; large mouth; nostrils open into mouth cavity; skeleton chiefly of bone; two pairs of limbs usually present (some lack limbs); no claws, feet often webbed; respiration by gills, lungs, mouth lining, and skin—either individually or in combination; three-chambered heart as adult, two-chambered heart in larva; ectothermic; fertilization generally external (except salamanders); development usually oviparous; eggs surrounded by jellylike coat (Chapter 16C)
Amphibians

• **Order Apoda**   Legless (pages 406-7)
Caecilians

• **Order Caudata**   Has head, trunk, and tails; most have two pairs of identical legs; internal fertilization (page 407)
Salamanders: tiger salamanders, newts

• **Order Anura**   Wide head fused with short body; no tail; front pair of legs short; hind pair of legs long with webbed toes (pages 406-7)
Frogs, toads

> **Genus *Rana***   (page 406)
> Common frogs: leopard frog *(R. pipiens)*, bullfrog *(R. catesheiana)*, green frog *(R. clamitans)*, pickerel frog *(R. palustris)*

> **Genus *Bufo***   Has poison glands behind tympanic membrane (page 406)
> Common toads: American toad *(B. americanus)*, oak toad *(B. quercicus)*, giant toad *(B. marinus)*

> **Genus *Hyla***   Has sticky pads on enlarged toes (page 406)
> Tree frogs: spring peeper *(H. crucifer)*, green tree frog *(H. cinerea)*

❑ **Class Reptilia**   Body covering of tough, dry scales; limbs, if present, paired; clawed toes; respiration by lungs; most have three-chambered heart with partial division of ventricle, but some have four-chambered heart; predominantly ectothermic; fertilization internal; oviparous, producing amniotic eggs with a leathery shell; some ovoviviparous (Chapter 16D)
Reptiles

• **Order Rhynchocephalia**   (page 417)
Tuataras (one living species: *Sphenodon*)

• **Order Squamata**   Sheds scales; jaws have teeth; detached quadrate bone (pages 417-21)
Snakes, lizards

> **Suborder Serpentes**   No limbs; no eyelids; no ear openings (pages 417-20)
> Snakes

Suborder Sauria Two pairs of limbs; movable eyelids; ear openings (pages 420-21)
Lizards

- **Order Testudinata** Has an upper and lower shell of fused bones and scales; jaws with no teeth (page 421)
Turtles, tortoises

- **Order Crocodylia** Has a four-chambered heart; scales grow and are not molted (pages 421-22)
Alligators, crocodiles, caimans

❑ **Class Aves** Body covering of feathers; body spindle-shaped with head, neck, trunk, and tail; neck usually long and flexible; skeleton composed of porous, lightweight bones; forelimbs (wings) used for flight in most species; lower section of hind limbs usually covered with scales; body supported on hind limbs only; toothless bill; four-chambered heart; respiratory system with air sacs; endothermic; excretory system usually lacks bladder; oviparous reproduction with egg enclosed in lime-containing shell; female with only one developed ovary and oviduct (Chapter 17A)
Birds

- **Order Sphenisciformes** Flightless birds that swim (page 430)
Penguins

- **Order Struthioniformes** Flightless birds that run (page 430)
Ostriches, rheas, emus

- **Order Falconiformes** Birds of prey; daytime hunters (pages 430-31)
Falcons, eagles, hawks, vultures

- **Order Stringiformes** Birds of prey; nighttime hunters (pages 430-31)
Owls

- **Order Galliforme** Game birds (pages 431-32)
Quails, pheasants, ptarmigans, partridges, turkeys

- **Order Columbiformes** Game birds (pages 431-32)
Pigeons, doves

- **Order Anseriformes** Waterbirds that swim (page 432)
Ducks, swans, geese

- **Order Pelecaniformes** Waterbirds that dive (page 432)
Pelicans, gannets, cormorants

- **Order Ciconiiformes** Waterbirds that wade (page 432)
Herons, bitterns, storks, flamingos

- **Order Passeriformes** Songbirds (page 432)
Skylarks, nightingales, finches, mockingbirds, swallows, crows, ravens, cardinals, robins

- **Order Apodiformes**
Hummingbirds

- **Order Caprimulgiformes**
Whippoorwills

- **Order Charadriiformes**
Gulls, sandpipers, terns

- **Order Coraciiformes**
Cuckoos, roadrunners

- **Order Piciformes**
Woodpeckers, flickers, toucans

- **Order Psittaciformes**
Parrots, parakeets

❑ **Class Mammalia** Body covering of hair; usually has teeth in both jaws; two pairs of limbs (one pair in some) designed for running, climbing, digging, grasping, or flying; respiration by lungs; diaphragm used to assist in breathing; four-chambered heart; endothermic; reproduction viviparous with young sustained within mother by a placenta (all except Monotremata and Marsupialia); some ovoviviparous (Monotremata); some lack placenta (Marsupialia); young nourished by milk from mammary glands (Chapter 17B)
Mammals

- **Order Monotremata**   Lays eggs in leathery shell; lacks nipples (page 442)
Egg-laying mammals: duckbilled platypuses, spiny anteaters

- **Order Marsupialia**   No placenta; young born immature and develop in an abdominal pouch where nipples are located (pages 444-45)
Pouched mammals: kangaroos, koalas, opossums

- **Order Rodentia**   Two sets of chisel-shaped incisors (teeth) which continue to grow throughout the animal's life; generally herbivores (pages 442-43)
Gnawing mammals: rats, squirrels, mice, porcupines, beavers, hamsters, jerboas, water voles

- **Order Carnivora**   Large, pointed canine teeth for ripping and tearing meat (some omnivores); short digestive system (pages 443-46)
Meat-eating mammals: lions, tigers, bears, dogs, weasels, seals, raccoons, wolves, coyotes

- **Order Cetacea**   Born and lives entire life in the water; pectoral limbs usually flippers; pelvic limbs often a "tail flipper"; echolocation for underwater guidance (page 447)
Marine mammals: whales, dolphins, porpoise, sea lions

- **Order Primates**   Limbs permit erect (or nearly erect) walking; five fingers or toes, with most having nails (not claws); eyes face front; often has social heirarchy; has incisors, canines, and molars (omnivores) (pages 447-48)
Erect mammals

  Family Callitrichidae
  Marmosettes, tamarins

  Family Cebidae   Tail used for climbing (prehensile)
  New world monkeys: spider monkeys, squirrel monkeys, howler monkeys

  Family Cercopithecidae   Tail which is not used for climbing (nonprehensile)

Old world monkeys: baboons, rhesus monkeys, mandrills

  Family Hylobatidae   Forelimbs twice as long as hind limbs; tree dwellers
  Lesser apes: siamangs, gibbons

  Family Lemuridae
  Lemurs

  Family Pongidae   No tail; long hindlimbs; lives in trees and on land
  Great apes: gorillas, chimpanzees, orangutans

- **Order Perissodactyla**   Legs have either a single toe with a curved hoof or three toes, each with a hoof; herbivores (pages 448-52)
Odd-toed hoofed mammals: horses, zebras, rhinoceroses

- **Order Artiodactyla**   Stands on two or four toes each with a hoof; herbivores with long digestive systems (pages 448-52)
Even-toed hoofed mammals

  Suborder Ruminantia   Has rumens (chews the cud)
  Ruminants

  Family Bovidae   Many have horns (pages 449-50, 452).
  Bovines: cattle, sheep, goats, antelopes

  Family Cervidae   Most have antlers.
  Deer, elk, reindeer, wapiti

  Family Giraffidae
  Giraffes, okapi

  Suborder Suina   Lacks rumens
  Swine (pigs), hippopotamuses, peccaries

  Suborder Tylopoda   Has rumens; four toes
  Camels, llama

- **Order Chiroptera**   Forelimbs are wings; most nocturnal; many sense objects by echolocation
Flying mammals: bats

- **Order Insectivora**   Lives under ground; eats small invertebrates
Insect-eating mammals: shrews, hedgehogs, moles

- **Order Edentata** Small or no teeth
Toothless mammals: sloths, anteaters, armadillos
- **Order Lagomorpha** Has chisel-shaped front teeth; hind limbs used for running and jumping
Rodentlike mammals: rabbits, hares, pikas

- **Order Proboscidea** Large herbivores; flexible trunks
Trunked mammals: elephants, tapirs
- **Order Sirenia** Aquatic; front limbs as flippers; hind limbs usually absent
Aquatic mammals: sea cows, manatees

Footnotes

1. At one time the kingdom Monera was divided into two phyla: Schizomycophyta (Schizophyta)–containing all bacteria, mycoplasmas, rickettsias, and spirochetes (none of which contained true chlorophyll)–and Cyanophyta–containing the blue green algae (which do contain true chlorophyll).
2. Some classification systems have a third subkingdom, "the fungal protists," which includes the slime molds and similar organisms.
3. Some classification systems use phylum Sarcomastigophora which contains subphyla Sarcodina and Mastigophora.
4. Some classification systems divide phylum Sporozoa into several phyla: Apicomplexa, Microspora, Ascetospora, Myxozoa.
5. Some classifications place phyla Chlorophyta, Phaeophyta, and Rhodophyta in the kingdom Plantae.
6. Some classification systems list phylum Eumycophyta which contains class Phycomycetes (Zygomycota and Oomycota), class Ascomycetes (the sac fungi of phylum Ascomycota), class Deuteromycetes (the imperfect fungi of phylum Ascomycota), and class Basidiomycetes (Basidiomycota).
7. The imperfect fungi, those that lack a known form of sexual reproduction, are placed in phylum Ascomycota, awaiting observation of the sexual reproduction many scientists believe they have.
8. In some classification systems Myxomycota, Oomycota, and Acrasiomycota are placed in the Kingdom Protista.

9. An older classification system for the Kingdom Plantae:
   Phylym Bryophyta
   Phylum Tracheophyta
     Subphylum Psilosida
     Subphylum Lycopsida
     Subphylum Sphenopdisa
     Subphylum Pteropsida
       Class Filicineae (ferns)
       Class Gymnospermae
       Class Angiospermae
         Subclass Monocotyledoneae
         Subclass Dicotyledoneae
10. The phylum Arthropoda can be divided into subphyla Crustacea (class Malacostraca), Chelicerata (classes Arachnida and Merostomiata), and Uniramia (classes Diplopoda, Chilopoda, and Insecta).
11. The first five orders in the class Insecta are the ones discussed in the textbook in alphabetical order. The next orders are listed in the following groups, alphabetically within the group: those with no metamorphosis, those with incomplete metamorphosis on land, those with incomplete metamorphosis in water, and those with complete metamorphosis. These are the fifteen most common of the twenty-six insect orders.
12. Some classification systems make Agnatha into a superclass containing Class Cephalaspidomorphi (the lampreys) and Class Myxini (the hagfish).

Appendix C

Metric System Conversion Table

Metric Unit	Appropriate English System Equivalent	Metric Conversion	Handy Comparisons
Length			
kilometer (km)	1090 yards	1000 m	11 football fields
meter (m)	1 yard 3 inches; 39 inches	0.001 km	a yardstick and 3 inches
centimeter (cm)	0.4 inch	0.01 m; 10 mm	a nickel is about 2 cm in diameter
millimeter (mm)	0.04 inch	0.1 cm	the thickness of a penny
micrometer (μm)	0.00004 inch	0.001 mm	a red blood cell is 7.5 micrometers
nanometer (nm)	0.00000004 inch	0.001 μm	a polio virus is 25 nanometers
Angstrom (Å)	0.000000004 inch	0.1 nm	1/2 size of a hydrogen atom
Weight			
kilogram (kg)	2.2 pounds; 35 ounces	1000 g	2/3 the weight of this book
gram (g)	0.035 ounce	0.001 kg	the weight of 24 drops of water; a dime weighs 2.3 g
milligram (mg)	0.000035 ounce	0.001 g	the weight of 0.2 of a drop of water
Volume			
liter (L)	1 quart and 1/4 cup	1000 ml	1/4 gallon
milliliter (ml)	0.004 cup; 1000 μl	0.001 L	the volume of 24 drops of water, about 1/5 teaspoon
microliter (μl)	0.000004 cup	0.001 ml	the volume of 0.024 of a drop of water
liter dry (L)	0.03 bushel		the volume of about one quart

Temperature

On the Celsius (centigrade) scale 0° is the freezing point of water, and 100° is the boiling point of water at sea level. On the Fahrenheit scale, 32° is the freezing point of water, and 212° is the boiling point of water at sea level. Normal body temperature is 37°C or 98.6°F.

The following formulas can be used to convert one to another:

- °F to °C: subtract 32, multiply by 5, divide by 9.
- °C to °F: multiply by 9, divide by 5, add 32.

Unit Abbreviations

Å   Angstrom(s)

A.D.   anno Domini (after the death of Christ)

B.C.   before the birth of Christ

bpa   bushels per acre

bpm   beats per minute

bps   beats per second

bu.   bushel(s)

C   Celsius

Cal   kilocalorie(s)

cm   centimeter(s)

F   Fahrenheit

g   gram(s)

gal.   gallon(s)

gm   gram(s)

in.   inches

kcal   kilocalorie(s)

kg   kilogram(s)

km   milometer(s)

kmph   kilometer(s) per hour

L or l   liter(s)

lb.   pound(s)

m   meter(s)

mg   milligram(s)

mi.   mile(s)

ml   milliliter(s)

mm   millimeter(s)

mm Hg   millimeters of mercury

μl   microliter(s)

μm   micrometer(s)

nm   nanometer(s)

oz.   ounce(s)

pH   acidity scale (see pages 47-49)

pt.   pint(s)

qt.   quart(s)

sec.   second(s)

sq. m.   square meter(s)

sq. mi.   square mile(s)

sq. yd.   square yard(s)

wk.   week(s)

X   times larger, power (enlargement)

yd.   yard(s)

yr.   year(s)

Glossary

abdomen A body region posterior to the thorax.

abscisic acid A plant hormone that stimulates the formation of the abscission layer.

abscission layer A layer of cells at the base of leaf petioles and fruits which die, causing the separation of the leaf or fruit from the stem.

absorption The movement of food molecules from the alimentary canal into the bloodstream.

accommodation The ability of the eye to focus on objects at different distances.

acetyl coA (acetyl coenzyme A) A two-carbon substance found in many cellular metabolisms.

acid Any substance that yields hydrogen ions when dissolved in water; a substance that neutralizes a base.

Acquired Immune Deficiency Syndrome (AIDS) A viral disease which affects the human immune system.

activation energy The initial energy necessary to start a reaction.

active absorption The process of taking water into root epidermal cells; the result of differences in ion concentration.

active site The area of an enzyme that combines with the substrate.

active transport The movement of molecules across cellular membranes against the concentration gradient; requires cellular energy expenditure.

adaptation According to evolutionists, the change of an organism that enables it to survive in a new environment.

addiction The continued use of habit-forming drugs; the inability to stop using a drug for physical or psychological reasons or both.

adenosine diphosphate (ADP) The molecule that is produced when ATP is split to yield energy.

adenosine triphosphate (ATP) A compound that serves as a temporary energy storage molecule in all cells.

ADP (See **adenosine diphosphate**.)

adrenal cortex The larger outer region of the adrenal glands; secretes the sex hormones, mineralcorticoids, and glucocorticoids.

adrenal glands Endocrine glands located on each kidney; composed of cortex and medulla regions.

adultery The act of sexual relations between a married person and anyone other than that person's marriage partner.

adventitious roots Roots that grow from a stem, petiole, or leaf.

aerial hyphae Hyphae of a fungus that grow above the substrate.

aerobe, obligate An organism that can live only in the presence of free oxygen.

aerobic Processes that require oxygen.

aerobic cellular respiration The oxygen-requiring process of breaking down a food substance to obtain cellular energy.

agar A gelatinous substance obtained from red algae; used as a culture medium in microbiology.

agglutinate The clumping together of blood cells that occurs when blood types are not matched properly in a transfusion.

AIDS (See **Acquired Immune Deficiency Syndrome**.)

air bladders Structures in algae and many fish that enable them to float.

albinism A genetic abnormality resulting in a lack of pigmentation.

albumen The white of an egg.

albumins Blood proteins that are primarily responsible for maintaining the blood volume.

alcoholic fermentation The formation of alcohol and carbon dioxide from glucose; performed by yeast cells.

algin A purified carbohydrate obtained from brown algae.

alimentary canal A group of digestive organs arranged in a continuous tube extending from mouth to anus.

allantois An embryonic membrane in an amniote egg that serves for respiration and excretion for the embryo; in humans, becomes part of the umbilical cord.

alleles A pair of genes that has the same position on homologous chromosomes.

allergy A disorder caused by the body's producing antibodies when stimulated by natural, nonpathogenic substances.

alternation of generations The reproductive cycle in which the asexual reproductive stages give rise to sexual reproductive stages that, in turn, give rise to asexual reproductive stages.

atricial chicks Birds that are immature and helpless when hatched.

alveoli (sing., **alveolus**) Small bubblelike structures of the lung where gases are exchanged between the atmospheric air and the blood.

amebocytes Amebalike cells in a sponge's mesenchyme that produce spicules, transport food, and eliminate waste.

ameboid movement A constant change in shape by an ameba or similar cell by the formation of pseudopodia.

amensalism The situation in which one population in an environment is inhibited by another, while the other is not affected by the first.

amino acid The basic "building block" of a protein molecule.

amniotic egg An egg that has a leathery or hard shell in which the embryo is enclosed by an amnion.

amplexus The physical contact of a male and a female amphibian that stimulates the female to release eggs into the water.

amylase An enzyme secreted by the salivary glands and pancreas to digest starches into sugars.

anabolism The phase of metabolism that builds molecules and stores energy; the constructive part of metabolism.

anaerobe, obligate An organism that cannot live in the presence of free oxygen.

anaerobic Processes that do not require oxygen.

anatomical position A standing position of the human body with the arms at the sides and the palms turned forward.

anatomy The science that deals with the structure of organisms.

androgens Male sex hormones produced by the testes.

aneuploid An organism in which the chromosome number is not an exact multiple of the haploid number.

annual plant A plant that grows from a seed, produces more seeds, and dies during one growing season or within one year.

annual ring In woody stems, one layer of xylem that forms during one year.

ANS (See **autonomic nervous system**.)

antagonist The muscle that performs an action opposite to that of the muscle acting as the prime mover.

antediluvian Before the Flood.

antenna (pl., **antennas**) Elongated, movable sensory appendage on the head of various invertebrates.

antennules Sensory appendages responsible for the sense of balance in some arthropods.

anther The structure on a stamen in which pollen is produced.

antheridium (pl., **antheridia**) The reproductive structure that produces sperm in certain plants.

anthropology The study of the origin, races, and cultural development of man.

antibiotics Chemicals, produced by living organisms, that naturally kill or inhibit the growth of other organisms.

antibodies Protein substances produced to eliminate antigens that have entered the body.

anticodon The triplet of nucleotides on transfer RNA that will pair with the codon of the messenger RNA to line up amino acids during protein synthesis.

antigens Foreign materials in the body that stimulate antibody production or begin cell-mediated immunity.

anus The posterior opening of the alimentary canal for egestion of feces.

apical dominance A condition in plants in which the terminal bud suppresses the growth of lateral buds.

apparent age A feature of God's creation; man, plants, and animals created in their mature forms; earth created with the appearance of age.

applied science Using pure science to solve practical problems.

aquaculture The farming of aquatic environments.

aqueous humor A transparent, watery fluid in the eyeball that nourishes the cornea.

arachnoid membrane A thin membrane surrounding the brain and spinal cord; between the dura mater and pia mater.

archegonium (pl., **archegonia**) Female reproductive structure in algae, fungi, and some plants.

artery Any blood vessel that carries blood away from the heart.

articular cartilage A cartilage layer covering the epiphyses of bones; provides cushioning and smooth movement at the joints.

artificial insemination The mechanical placement of a male's sperm into a female's reproductive organs.

ascus The structure in which the haploid ascospores are formed in the molds of the class Ascomycota.

asexual reproduction Producing a new organism without the fusion of a sperm and an ovum.

assimilation The conversion of nutrients into living cells; a process of growth.

aster A collection of microtubules radiating from the centriole; some of these microtubles form the spindle during cell division.

astigmatism A condition in which the cornea or lens or both are unequally curved and the light rays from an object are not equally focused on the retina.

asymmetrical In organisms, those whose body parts are unlike in size, shape, or structure and cannot be divided into like halves.

atom The smallest unit of an element that can exist either alone or in combination.

ATP (See **adenosine triphosphate.**)

atrioventricular node (AV node) A mass of specialized cardiac tissue located in the right atrium; responsible for the contraction of the ventricles.

atrioventricular valve One of the membranous structures between the atria and ventricles in the heart that prevent backflow of blood into the atria.

atrium (pl., **atria**) One of the heart chambers that receives blood from different parts of the body.

auricle An outer flap of ear tissue leading to the auditory canal.

autonomic nervous system (ANS) The involuntary portion of the peripheral nervous system.

autophagy A process whereby a cell forms a membrane around some of its own cellular parts and digests them.

autosomes Any chromosome other than a sex (X or Y) chromosome.

autotrophs Organisms that are able to make their own food.

auxin A growth-regulating hormone in plants.

avascular Human and animal tissues in which there are no blood vessels.

AV node (See **atrioventricular node.**)

axial skeleton The portion of the skeleton that supports and protects the organs of the head, neck, and trunk.

axon The portion of a neuron that carries impulses away from the cell body.

bacillus (pl., **bacilli**) A rod-shaped bacterium.

bactericidal Capable of killing bacteria.

bacteriophage A virus that parasitizes a bacterial cell.

bacteriostatic Preventing the multiplication of bacteria.

basal body The action-controlling structure at the base of a cilium or flagellum.

basal disc The flattened structure at the lower end of certain cnidarians; used for attaching to objects and for locomotion.

basal metabolic rate (BMR) The amount of calories needed to maintain normal body functions while at rest.

base A substance that releases hydroxyl ions when dissolved in water; neutralizes an acid.

basidia (sing., **basidium**) The microscopic structures in Basidiomycota that produce the asexual basidiospores.

B cells Cells involved in humoral immunity.

benign tumor A tumor characterized by localized growth.

Biblical kind The natural groupings of organisms established by God.

biennial plant A plant that sprouts and grows in one season but does not flower and produce seeds until the following growing season.

bile A greenish fluid produced by the liver; necessary for the breakdown and absorption of fatty substances.

binomial nomenclature A system of naming organisms in which each organism is given a genus and species name.

biodegradable Capable of being broken down by the environment and returned to the normal cycling of substances.

biogenesis The concept that life comes only from pre-existing life.

biological father The man who supplies the sperm for the zygote of a child.

biological key An arrangement of descriptions and illustrations used to identify an organism.

biological magnification The process that concentrates small quantities of a substance into larger quantities as it is passed in a food chain.

biological mother The woman who supplies the ovum for the zygote of a child.

biological rhythm (biological clock) Periodic recurring changes in organisms; the mechanism that causes organisms to change regularly either their location or activities or both.

biology The science that deals with living organisms and vital life processes.

biome A major biotic community with populations of climax species.

biopsy The removal of a sample of a tissue to be observed for abnormalities.

biosphere The part of the world in which life can exist.

biosynthesis The formation of a chemical compound by a living organism.

biotic community All the living things (populations) in an ecosystem.

birth canal The cervix and vagina; very elastic at time of delivery to allow passage of the baby.

blastocyst A fluid-filled sphere of embryonic cells.

blood plasma The liquid portion of the blood.

blood pressure The pressure of the blood against the walls of arteries caused by contraction of the heart ventricles.

bloom (bloom condition) A rapid, seasonal reproduction of a particular organism in an optimal environment.

BMR (See **basal metabolic rate.**)

body tube The cylindrical part of the microscope between the eyepiece and the objectives.

bone marrow, red A tissue that makes red blood cells and that is located in the marrow cavities of some bones.

bone marrow, yellow Fatty tissue that gradually replaces red bone marrow as humans become older.

Bowman's capsule The end of the nephrons of the kidney where blood plasma is absorbed from the blood vessels.

bracts Brightly colored leaves on plants that appear to be showy flowers; leaflike structures.

breech birth A delivery in which the baby is positioned with his posterior end toward the birth canal.

bronchi (sing., **bronchus**; adj., **bronchial**) The two branches of the trachea which carry air to the lungs; the bronchial tubes.

Brownian movement The movement of molecules caused by the heat they possess.

budding A type of asexual reproduction in which portions from the parent form a new individual; in plants, a method of grafting in which a bud is placed under the bark of another plant.

buffer A dissolved substance which makes a solution resistant to a change in its pH (the concentration of hydrogen ions).

bulk feeder An organism that eats either all or major portions of its prey.

bundle of His The specialized heart muscle tissue which transports impulses from the AV node in the heart to each ventricle.

bursas (sing., **bursa**) Saclike structures between tendons, ligaments, and bones that cushion and reduce friction.

calcitonin A thyroid hormone that lowers the blood calcium level.

calorie A measurement of heat produced during oxidation of food.

calyx The collective name for all the sepals of a flower.

canines Pointed teeth generally used for tearing; members of the dog family.

canker An open sore or lesion producing a fluid discharge.

canopy theory The theory that states that a canopy of water vapor surrounded the earth during the time before the Flood.

capillaries Blood vessels that have walls one cell thick where diffusion of nutrients and exchange of gases occur.

capillarity The property of water that causes it to cling to surfaces.

capsule A cellular secretion surrounding certain algae and bacteria.

carapace The portion of the exoskeleton that covers the cephalothorax in some arthropods; dorsal part of a tortoise's body shell.

carbohydrates Organic compounds that contain only carbon, hydrogen, and oxygen.

carcinogens Cancer-causing substances.

cardiac cycle The series of physical events that transports blood through all four heart chambers during one heartbeat.

carnivorous animals Animals that eat other animals.

carrier A heterozygous organism that is normal for a trait but which also has a recessive gene for an undesirable trait and can transmit that gene to offspring.

cartilage A flexible connective tissue found in the nose, outer ear, between ribs and sternum, and on the ends of long bones.

catabolism The phase of metabolism which breaks down a molecule or releases energy; the destructive phase of metabolism.

catalyst A substance that affects the rate of a reaction but is not changed in the reaction.

cataract An opaqueness of the lens of the eye.

catkins Male flowers found in some plants.

cecum A blind pouch which forms the first portion of the large intestine; its lower end forms the appendix.

cell The unit of function and structure of life.

cell body The part of the neuron with the greatest diameter; contains the nucleus.

cell-mediated immunity An immunity to disease involving activated cells.

cell membrane (plasma membrane) The outermost boundary of a cell.

cell specialization Genetically identical cells developing differently to become the various structures of the adult organism.

cell theory The theory that all living organisms are made up of microscopic units called cells.

cellular membrane The structures made of lipids and proteins which form thin membranes around and in cells.

cellular respiration The breakdown of foods (glucose) to release energy including both aerobic and anaerobic cellular respiration.

cellulose Chains of glucose molecules; found in plant cell walls.

cell wall A rigid structure manufactured by the cell; located outside the plasma membrane; often made of cellulose, silica, or other substances.

cementum An external bony layer on the roots and the neck of a tooth; it anchors the tooth in the socket.

central nervous system The part of the nervous system consisting of the brain and spinal cord.

centrioles Organelles composed of microtubules and located near the nucleus; doubles before cell division to establish the poles.

centromere The attachment point of two sister chromatids; also serves as point of attachment of spindle fibers during mitosis.

cephalization The presence of a "head" region, usually containing nerve tissue and supplied with sense organs.

cephalothorax A body region consisting of a fused head and thorax.

cerebellum A part of the brain; monitors and adjusts body activities involving muscle tone, body posture, and equilibrium.

cerebral cortex The gray matter of the cerebrum.

cerebrospinal fluid The fluid which nourishes and protects the brain and spinal cord and that flows between the two inner meninges.

cerebrum The part of the brain containing major motor and sensory centers; controls voluntary muscle activity; the area of conscious activity.

ceruminous glands Wax glands in the external auditory canal.

cervix The neck of the uterus where it narrows and joins the vagina.

chelicerae The first pair of appendages in arachnids; used for feeding; poisonous fangs in certain spiders.

chelipeds "Pinchers"; arthropods' appendages.

chemical change A change in which a substance loses its characteristics and changes into one or more new substances.

chemosynthesis A process whereby certain organisms obtain cellular energy from the breakdown of inorganic chemicals.

chemotherapy The use of chemical agents to treat a disease.

chemotropism Growth movement of a plant toward or away from certain chemicals.

chitin A chemical component in the exoskeletons of arthropods.

chlorophyll The green pigment of plant cells that is necessary for photosynthesis.

chloroplast An organelle that contains chlorophyll for photosynthesis.

cholesterol A common sterol found in the membranes of animal and human cells.

chorion In an amniotic egg, an embryonic membrane that becomes closely joined to the inner surface of the egg membrane; in humans, becomes part of the placenta.

choroid The thin middle layer of the eyeball; contains blood vessels for nourishing the retina.

chromatid, sister One of the two DNA duplicates that comprise one chromosome (when the chromosome is not separated).

chromatin material A complex of DNA and surrounding proteins in the nucleus of a cell.

chromatophores Skin cells that contain pigments.

chromosomes Strands of DNA complexed with proteins; usually found within the cell's nucleus.

chrysalis A protective sack found in the pupa stage of metamorphosis of some insects.

chyme The semiliquid mixture of partly digested food and digestive juices in the stomach and small intestine.

ciliary muscle A muscle that supports the lens of the eye and can change shape of the lens.

ciliate A protozoan that possesses cilia.

cilium (pl., cilia) One of numerous short extensions of the cell's plasma membrane; aids in movement.

circumcision The surgical removal of the foreskin.

classify To assign an organism to a particular classification group.

cleavage The division of a cell; the phase in development of an embryo during which the zygote divides.

climax vegetation The predictable plant community that would normally be found in an area if it were not disturbed.

clitellum The swollen region in the anterior of an earthworm; secretes the cocoon that contains the eggs.

cloaca The terminal portion of the digestive tract in certain vertebrates that serves as a common passageway for the elimination of urine and feces.

clone A group of organisms produced asexually; the process of reproducing organisms asexually.

coagulation The formation of a blood clot.

coccus (pl., cocci) A spherical bacterium.

cochlea A snail-shaped division of the inner ear that functions in sound perception.

codon A triplet of nucleotides that forms the code for a particular amino acid on messenger RNA.

coelom The body cavity.

coenzyme A nonprotein substance that helps to form the active portion of an enzyme.

cohesion The force that holds molecules together; characteristic that causes water to move up plant stems.

colchicine A poison that disrupts the spindle fibers during cell division, resulting in polyploid cells.

collar cells Flagellated cells that line the inner cavity of a sponge.

collenchyma A strengthening tissue in plants.

colloid A mixture of fine particles, often including protein molecules; these particles do not settle out.

colonial organism An organism that consists of a group of similar cells living together. Each cell functions like a unicellular organism.

columnar A type of growth in plants typified by a crown of leaves atop a nonbranching stem as in palm trees.

commensalism A relationship in which one population benefits from a second population, but the second population is not harmed nor helped by the first.

common ancestor A hypothetical organism that supposedly gave rise to two or more types of organisms.

communicable disease A disease that can be spread from one organism to another.

competition The relationship in which two populations inhibit each other because they both depend upon the same resource.

complex tissue A tissue that is made up of different types of cells.

compound A substance composed of two or more elements combined in definite proportions.

compound eyes Eyes composed of many individual lenses.

compound leaf A leaf having several blades on a single petiole.

concentration gradient The difference between the number of molecules in one area as opposed to the number of the same molecules in an area nearby.

conditioned behavior A behavioral response learned by experience.

conidiophore A fungus sporophore that forms asexual conidia by repeated divisions at its tip and not in an enclosure.

conjugation A temporary union of two organisms or cells for the one-way transfer of genetic material; type of sexual reproduction.

connective tissues Tissues of the body that connect, support, cushion, and fill spaces around organs.

conservation, law of The concept that the quantities of matter and energy in the universe are constant, not being created or destroyed.

constriction A method of suffocating prey by squeezing it.

consumer An organism that takes materials from the ecosystem.

contact infection A disease spread by direct contact with a sore, lesion, or mucous membrane of an infected person.

contamination infection A disease that enters the body by way of a contaminated food or water source.

contractile vacuole A vacuole, found in some cells, which collects water and expels it from the cell.

control group The group in an experiment that is not exposed to the experimental variable.

controlled experiment An experiment testing two identical groups for a single variable.

cork cambium A layer of cells under the epidermis that produces cork cells for protecting the stem of woody plants.

corm A short, upright, underground stem that produces aerial leaves at its top.

cornea The transparent anterior portion of the sclera of the eye.

corolla The collective name for the petals of a flower.

coronary thrombosis A thrombus (blood clot) in the coronary arteries that supply the heart muscle.

corpus luteum The structure formed in the follicle of the ovary after ovulation; forms several hormones.

cortex The region of thin-walled parenchyma cells that stores food just inside the epidermis of a root or stem.

cotyledon The leaf in a seed; the first leaf or leaves that emerge through the soil during germination.

countershading A form of camouflage coloring in certain animals; one color on the top side of the animal and another color on the bottom side of the animal.

covalent bond A chemical bond formed between atoms as a result of sharing a pair of electrons.

cranial nerves Nerves originating from the brain.

creationist One who believes the Bible account of creation.

cristae The folds of the inner membrane of the mitochondria; contain enzymes necessary for cellular respiration.

crop A portion of the digestive tract that temporarily stores food.

crossing over The exchange of segments between homologous chromosomes during meiosis.

cross-pollination The process of fertilizing a flower with the pollen from another flower.

cud In ruminants, partially digested food regurgitated from the rumen for additional chewing to aid in digestion.

cuspids The cone-shaped teeth used for tearing food.

cutaneous sensations Sensations of cold, heat, pain, pressure, and touch received from receptors located primarily in the skin.

cuticle The protective, waxy covering found on the outer surface of the epidermis of plants; a dead layer of skin; noncellular covering of certain parasitic invertebrates.

cyclic Recurring in a series; that which can be used and reused in a recurring series of events.

cyst A structure similar to a spore that is formed as part of the life cycle of some organisms or when conditions become unfavorable; protective shell formed by parasite larvas.

cytokinesis The division of the cytoplasm in a dividing cell.

cytokinin (kinin) A substance that affects plant cells in many ways including stimulation of the division of cells.

cytology The study of cells.

cytolysis The bursting or disintegration of a cell.

cytoplasm All the material inside the plasma membrane of a cell, excluding the nucleus.

cytoplasmic matrix The colloid portion of the cytoplasm.

cytoplasmic organelles Specialized structures in cells, such as mitochondria, that accomplish various cellular functions.

cytoplasmic streaming A flowing of the cytoplasm inside the boundaries of the cell for moving the cell's contents.

cytoskeleton The internal structure of cytoplasm; made of microfilaments and microtubules.

dark phase (dark reactions) The phase of photosynthesis that does not require light.

data The recorded information from an experiment or survey.

daughter cells The two cells that result from a mitotic division.

daughter chromosomes The separated sister chromatids in a dividing cell.

deciduous Plants that shed their leaves before a period of dormancy.

deciduous teeth A child's first set of teeth.

decomposer An organism that breaks down dead organic matter into forms that can be used by other organisms.

deductive reasoning The process of beginning with known facts and predicting a new fact.

deficiency disease A disease caused by improper nourishment such as a lack of vitamins or minerals.

degenerate code A code in which there is more than one way to indicate something.

degeneration, law of In all natural processes there is a net increase in disorder and a net loss of usable energy.

dehumanization Ignoring the essential quality of man as a living, eternal soul.

dehydration synthesis The process whereby two molecules combine and a water molecule is released.

deliquescent A growth pattern of shrubs and trees in which the main stem branches repeatedly to form many small branches.

deluge The Genesis Flood (Gen. 6-8).

deluge fossil formation theory The belief that most fossils were formed by the Genesis Flood.

dendrite Part of the neuron that receives nerve impulses and transmits them toward the cell body.

dentin Bonelike tissue that forms the root of the tooth and the portion of the inner crown.

deoxyribonucleic acid (DNA) The nucleic acid that is located primarily in the nucleus; carrier of genetic information.

depressants Drugs that slow down the central nervous system; they may cause drowsiness and sleep.

dermis The thick inner layer of the skin.

detritus Dead organic matter.

diaphragm The muscle that separates the thoracic and abdominal cavities in mammals and man; the device under the stage of a microscope that regulates the amount of light on the specimen.

diastole The phase of the cardiac cycle during which the myocardium is relaxed and the heart chamber fills with blood.

diatom One of the unicellular algae of phylum Chrysophyta that have silicon in their cell walls.

diatomaceous earth Soil composed mostly of diatom cell walls.

dicot A plant in the class Dicotyledonae.

diffusion The random movement of atoms, ions, or molecules from an area of higher concentration to an area of lower concentration.

diffusion pressure The pressure for diffusion that is produced by the concentration gradient.

digestion The process of breaking a large molecule down into its component parts.

dihybrid cross A genetic cross dealing with two characteristics at the same time.

diploid The condition of having homologous pairs of chromosomes.

disaccharide A sugar composed of two monosaccharides.

Glossary

dispersed particle   The dispersed solid in a colloid.

dispersion medium   The liquid medium in a colloid.

diurnal   Active during the day.

division plate   A structure formed by plant cells during cytokinesis to divide the cytoplasm.

DNA   (See deoxyribonucleic acid.)

dominant generation   The stage that is most often seen in the life cycle of a plant.

dominant trait   The characteristic that is expressed even in the presence of the recessive genes.

dormancy   A period of greatly reduced activity in organisms.

dorsal   On or near the upper surface (the backs of bilaterally symmetrical animals and humans).

Down's syndrome (mongoloidism)   A genetic disorder caused by a trisomy of the twenty-first chromosome.

drone   A haploid reproductive male in a bee colony.

droplet infection   A disease transmitted through the air by pathogens suspended in water droplets.

drug   A chemical that causes a change in the function or structure of a living tissue.

ductus arteriosus   A short blood vessel in the unborn and newborn baby that connects the pulmonary artery with the aorta.

duodenum   The first section of the small intestine.

dura mater   A tough membrane covering the brain and spinal cord.

dynamic equilibrium   An organism's maintaining a steady, balanced living state by expending energy; the ability of the body to respond automatically to position changes while it is moving.

dystopia   A wicked, oppressive society resulting from man's corrupt use of knowledge.

ecological niche   What an organism does and its relationship to and effect on its habitat.

ecology   The whole science of the relationships between an organism and its environment.

ecosystem   The total system of interactions between living organisms and nonliving things and factors within a limited area.

ecotype   A subgroup of a species that survives best in a particular environment; often will not interbreed with other ecotypes.

ectoderm   The outer germ layer in an embryo; the outer tissue layer in some animals.

ectoplasm   The thin cytoplasm on the outer perimeter of a cell.

ectothermic   Animals that are not able to maintain a constant body temperature; body temperature varies with the temperature of the environment.

effector   A body part (such as a muscle or gland) that responds to a stimulus as a result of a nerve impulse transmitted along neurons.

egestion   The elimination of nonsoluble, undigested wastes.

electrocardiogram (ECG or EKG)   A tracing made by an apparatus that records the impulses produced by the conduction system of the heart.

electroencephalogram (EEG)   A tracing made by an instrument used to measure brain waves.

electron   That part of the atom that has a negative charge and that moves in a shell-like orbit around the nucleus.

element   A substance that cannot be broken down into simpler substances by chemical reactions.

elongation region   The area of a plant where cells extend in length.

embolus   A blood clot, debris, or foreign matter floating in the blood stream.

embryo   In animals, the young of an organism in early stages of development; the young before hatching; the time when organs and systems are developing; in plants, the plant within the seed.

embryology   The study of the development of the embryo.

embryonic membranes   The amnion, yolk sac, chorion, and allantois.

embryo sac   The sac in a plant ovule that contains the haploid cells resulting from the division of the megaspore mother cell.

emulsification   The process by which liquid fats are made into small droplets within another liquid.

endocardium   The inner lining of the heart chambers.

endocrine system   A system of glands which secrete hormones.

endoderm   The inner germ layer in an embryo; forms lining of digestive and respiratory tracts, bladder, and urethra.

endodermis   The single cell layer inside the cortex of a young root or stem; regulates the passage of substances into the vascular tissues.

endoplasm   The dense cytoplasm found in the interior of a cell.

endoplasmic reticulum   A cellular structure consisting of a complex network of fine, branching tubules.

endoskeleton   An internal skeleton usually composed of bone and cartilage; characteristic of vertebrates.

endosperm   The stored food that is used by the embryo in a mature seed.

endospores   An asexual spore that forms within a bacterium.

endosteum   The lining of the marrow cavity in a long bone; involved in bone growth and repair.

endothermic   Maintaining a constant body temperature; an energy-consuming chemical reaction.

endotoxin   A toxin produced by a cell; released only after the death and disintegration of the cell.

energy   The ability to do work.

energy, kinetic   The energy of motion.

energy, potential   Stored energy.

entropy   A measure of the unusable energy that escapes when energy is being converted from one form to another; an increase in disorder and degeneration.

environmental determinism   The concept that the environment determines an individual's characteristics.

enzymes   Protein molecules that are produced by living cells to catalyze specific reactions.

epicardium   Connective tissue covering the muscular tissue of the heart.

epicotyl (plumule)   The portion of the plant embryo above the point of attachment to the cotyledons that becomes the stem and leaves.

epidermis   In plants, the outer layer of cells which usually lack chlorophyll and serve for protection; in animals and humans, a tissue that usually covers or lines a structure.

epididymis (pl., epididymides)   A coiled tube that stores sperm.

epinephrine   Adrenalin; a hormone secreted by the adrenal medulla that stimulates reactions needed in an emergency.

epiphyseal plate (growth plate)   A thin, internal layer of cartilage tissue between the shaft and each epiphysis in a long bone.

epiphyses   The ends of a long bone.

epiphyte   A plant which grows on another plant but is not parasitic.

epithelial tissue   A tissue of the body that covers or lines a body part; functions in absorption, secretion, and protection.

erythrocyte   A red blood cell.

esophagus   The tube connecting the pharynx and stomach.

estivation   A period of inactivity and slowed metabolism whereby some animals escape unfavorably hot weather conditions.

estrogens   Female sex hormones that stimulate the development of secondary sex characteristics.

etiolated   The condition of a plant when grown in the absence of light; thin, elongated stems with small, pale leaves.

eucaryotic cells   Cells that possess both organelles and a nucleus that is surrounded by a nuclear membrane.

eugenics   The science that deals with improvement of the human race by applying principles of genetics.

euphoria   Feeling of well-being caused by a slight disorganization of mental processes, often induced by drugs.

euploidy   A chromosomal change that involves the addition or loss of entire genomes.

Eustachian tubes   Tubes leading from the pharynx to the middle ear space to equalize air pressure.

euthanasia   "Termination of human life by painless means for the purpose of ending severe physical suffering" (from the Euthanasia Society of America).

euthanasia, active   Ending a person's life by either administering something that will kill him or removing a life-sustaining apparatus.

euthanasia, passive   Ending a person's life by withholding treatment that could sustain life.

evolution, theory of   A composite of ideas involving the philosophy of evolution, the theory of beginnings, and biological evolution.

evolution, theory of biological (organic evolution) The theory of the beginning of life and the slow process of organisms becoming more complex.

evolution, philosophy of The theory that all things are progressing toward a future perfection.

evolve To change; to become more complex.

excretion The elimination of soluble wastes.

excurrent A cone-shaped branching pattern in trees and shrubs.

excurrent pore The osculum, the opening of the sponge's body that expels water.

excurrent siphon The tube that expels water from the body of a mollusk.

exon A section of RNA that is kept when forming messenger RNA.

exoskeleton A system of external plates that protect and support.

exothermic Giving off energy by a chemical reaction.

exotoxin (soluble toxin) A toxin that diffuses from a microorganism into the surrounding tissue while the pathogen is still alive.

experimental group The group in an experiment that is exposed to the experimental variable.

experimental variable The factor being tested in an experiment.

expiration Breathing air out of the lungs.

expiratory reserve volume The amount of air that can be forced out of the lungs after a normal expiration.

external auditory canal The canal from the outer ear to the eardrum.

external digestion The process in which enzymes are secreted to digest food outside the organism.

external fertilization The uniting of the sperm and egg outside the organism.

external respiration The passage of oxygen from the air in the alveoli into the blood.

extracellular digestion The breakdown of substances that occurs in spaces outside the cells such as within the stomach or intestine.

eyespot A light-sensitive area of some organisms.

fallacy A false idea; that which is contradicted by scientific evidence or God's Word or both.

fang Needlelike teeth of a reptile used to inject poison into prey.

fat The most abundant type of lipids; composed of glycerol and fatty acid.

feces Waste material of an organism.

fermentation, cellular The anaerobic breakdown of carbohydrates to pyruvic acid, and then to alcohol and carbon dioxide or lactic acid.

fertilization The process of forming a zygote; the union of gametes.

fetoscope A fiber optic device which can be inserted into the womb to take pictures of the unborn child.

fetus The term applied to an embryo; in humans, the unborn child from the second month of development until birth.

fibrin An insoluble protein involved in blood clotting; forms a fine, interlacing network of filaments that traps blood cells.

fibrinogen A protein produced by the liver; involved in blood clotting.

fibrovascular bundle In herbaceous plants, a bundle composed of vascular tissues surrounded by fibrous tissue.

filament A chain of cells; the stalk of the stamen.

flagellate An organism with one or more flagella.

flagellum (pl., flagella) A long, tubular extension of a cell's plasma membrane that aids in movement.

flame cells Cells that possess tufts of cilia; part of the planarian's excretory system.

follicle A small saclike structure in the ovary that encloses an immature ovum; the tube from which a hair grows.

fontanel One of the fibrous membranes that fills the spaces between the skull bones at birth, forming the "soft spot."

food chain The nutritional relationships between organisms in an ecosystem.

food web A method of illustrating multiple nutritional relationships and interactions between populations in an ecosystem.

foramen ovale An opening between the right atrium and left atrium of a newborn baby's heart.

fornication Any act of sexual relations between people not married to each other.

fossil Any evidence or remains of an organism.

fovea A small depression in the central region of the retina; contains a concentration of cones.

fragmentation A form of reproduction caused by the breaking of a colonial organism by a physical disturbance.

frond A leaf of a fern or a palm; a thallus that resembles a leaf.

frontal lobe The region of the brain that controls reasoning, communication, and commands for voluntary body movements.

fruit A ripened plant ovary with or without seeds.

fungicide A chemical substance used to kill or inhibit the growth of fungi.

gallbladder The pear-shaped sac on the underside of the liver; concentrates and stores bile.

gamete A haploid cell which can unite with another gamete to form a zygote.

gametophyte The stage that produces gametes in the life cycle of a plant.

ganglion (pl., ganglia) A mass of nerve tissue.

gap theory An interpretation of the Genesis creation account which states there was a long period of time between Genesis 1:1 and 1:2.

gastric ceca Finger-shaped organs, attached to an insect's stomach, that secrete enzymes for digestion of foods.

gastrovascular cavity The internal cavity of cnidarians where digestion and food circulation occur.

gastroderm The inner cellular layer of the digestive tract of cnidarians.

gel The semisolid state of a colloid.

gemmules In a sponge, internal dormant cluster of cells encased in a tough spicule-reinforced covering.

gene A segment of DNA capable of producing a specific amino acid chain (polypeptide) resulting in a particular characteristic.

gene linkage Genes arranged in a definite order on a chromosome.

gene mutation A changing of the gene itself, which alters the sequence of nucleotide bases within a gene.

gene pool All the genes (possible alleles) in a population of a given organism.

genetic disorder (inherited disorder) Any undesirable phenotype caused by genetic defects in an individual.

genetic engineering The manipulation of chromosomes or genes by methods other than normal reproduction.

genetic load The number of mutations in a given organism.

genetics The study of heredity.

genetic screen A mechanism that prevents badly deformed or genetically defective individuals from living and/or reproducing.

genome A complete haploid set of chromosomes of an organism.

genotype The genetic makeup of an individual organism.

genus A group of organisms that has one or more common characteristics; includes one or more species.

genus-species name The scientific name for an organism.

geotropism Growth movement of a plant in response to gravity.

germination The beginning of growth by a seed, spore, bud, or other structure following a state of dormancy.

germ mutation A mutation that affects the gamete-producing cells.

gerontology The science of aging.

gestation The period of pregnancy.

gibberellin A plant hormone that causes rapid elongation of stems.

gill A respiratory structure in aquatic organisms through which oxygen and carbon dioxide are exchanged; the thin, spore-producing membrane of certain fungi.

girdling Removing a ring of bark from a woody stem.

gizzard A thick-walled digestive organ that grinds food.

glial cell A type of cell dispersed throughout the nervous system which performs beneficial functions for neurons.

globulins Proteins found in the blood plasma.

glomerulus Blood capillaries found in the Bowman's capsule of the nephron.

glottis The space between the vocal folds.

glucagon A hormone that raises the blood sugar level; also stimulates breakdown of fats to form glucose.

glucose A common six-carbon simple sugar.

Glossary

glycogen A polysaccharide; animal starch; branching chains of glucose molecules.

glycolysis The breakdown of glucose to pyruvic acid.

goiter A swelling of the thyroid gland.

Golgi body A membrane-bound organelle that deals with synthesis and packaging of materials.

gonad A reproductive organ.

grafting The joining of two plant parts, usually stems, so that their tissues grow together.

granum (pl., grana) Structures within chloroplasts that contain the chlorophyll and other pigments involved in photosynthesis.

gray matter Brain tissue composed mainly of neuron cell bodies and dendrites.

green glands Organs that excrete wastes in some malacostracans.

guanine A pyrimidine base in a nucleic acid molecule.

guard cell One of the cells surrounding a stoma that controls the opening and closing of the stoma.

gullet A food passageway into the digestive tract of an animal.

guttation The process whereby drops of water are forced through pores at the tip and edges of a leaf.

habitat Where an organism lives; the "address" of an organism.

half-life The length of time necessary for a radioactive substance to decay to half its original amount.

hallucinogen A drug that amplifies the senses, affects a person's judgment, and can produce hallucinations (visions).

halophyte A plant that grows in soil that has high salt concentrations.

haploid The condition of having only one member of each homologous pair of chromosomes; characteristic of gametes.

haustoria Hyphae of parasitic fungi which enter the host's cells to obtain nourishment.

Haversian system A unit of bone in compact bone tissue.

hemoglobin The red pigment of erythrocytes that transports oxygen and carbon dioxide.

hemophilia Bleeder's disease; a genetic disorder in which a blood chemical for blood clotting is not produced.

hemotoxin A type of venom that affects blood cells.

hepatic portal vein The vein that carries food-rich blood from the digestive organs to the liver.

herbivore (adj., herbivorous animal) An animal that eats plants.

hermaphrodite An organism that has both male and female reproductive organs.

heterocyst A large colorless cell in the filaments of certain cyanobacteria.

heterogametes Gametes which differ in size and shape.

heterosis (hybrid vigor) An increased capacity for growth or strength in a hybrid.

heterotroph An organism that depends upon other organisms for food.

heterozygous Having two different alleles at the same position (locus) on homologous chromosomes.

hibernation A state of extremely slow metabolism by which certain animals survive unfavorable conditions.

hilum The point where a seed (ovule) is attached to the ovary wall.

histology The study of tissues.

HIV (See **Human Immunodeficiency Virus.**)

holdfast The special structure that anchors an organism.

homeostasis The equilibrium or internal "steady state" that every living organism must maintain.

homologous pair of chromosomes Two chromosomes that have the same kinds of genes (alleles) in the same order.

homologous structures Organs that are similar in structure between two organisms; once thought to show evolutionary relationships.

homologue One member of a homologous pair of chromosomes.

homosexuality Sexual desire for members of the same sex.

homozygous Condition in which both alleles in one organism are the same.

hormone A chemical regulator; in plants, produced in meristematic tissues, effecting cell maturation; in animals, produced in ductless glands, carried in blood, affecting metabolism.

horny layer (stratum corneum) The dead outer cell layers of the epidermis, sloughed off by the body.

host An organism in or on which a parasite lives.

Human Immunodeficiency Virus (HIV) The AIDS virus.

humoral immunity An immunity to disease involving antibodies.

humus Dark material in the soil; composed of dead organic matter.

hybridization The crossbreeding of two genetically unrelated individuals.

hydrogen and electron transport system A series of aerobic reactions that gives off energy and combines hydrogen and oxygen to form water.

hydrolysis A reaction whereby a substance is split apart by the addition of a molecule of water.

hydrophilic Attracted to or having an affinity for water.

hydrophobic Not having an affinity for water.

hydroponics Growing plants in mineral solutions.

hyperopia An eye condition in which it is easy to focus on distant objects but not on near objects.

hypersecretion Excessive production of a substance.

hypertonic solution A solution in which the concentration of solutes is greater than in the cytoplasm of living cells.

hypha (pl., hyphae) The slender filaments that compose the mycelium of a fungus.

hypnosis State of being in a subconscious trance and submissive to the will of a hypnotist.

hypocotyl The stem portion of an embryonic plant in a seed.

hypoglycemia Low blood sugar; often caused by an overproduction of insulin.

hyposecretion Insufficient production of a substance.

hypothalamus That region of the brain that controls involuntary activities, emotional expressions, appetite for food, and release of certain hormones.

hypothesis An educated guess about the solution to a problem; when supported by sufficient facts, it may become a theory.

hypotonic solution A solution in which the concentration of solutes is less than in the cytoplasm of living cells.

identify To determine the group in which an organism belongs.

immune carrier An individual who transmits pathogenic organisms but does not show symptoms of the disease.

immunity (adj., immune) The ability to resist infection or to overcome the effects of infection.

implantation The process whereby the tiny embryo attaches to the uterine wall and forms the placenta.

inborn behavior A pattern of reaction and response that the organism has inherited and does not need to learn.

inbreeding The mating of closely related organisms.

incisors Flat, thin teeth used in gnawing, biting, and cutting food.

incomplete dominance The type of inheritance in which the alleles for expressing characteristics are neither dominant nor recessive.

incomplete flower A flower that lacks petals or sepals or either the stamen or pistil.

incubation period The time between infection by a pathogen and the appearance of the first symptoms.

incurrent pores Tiny openings in the sponge's body for the intake of water.

incurrent siphon The tube that draws water into a mollusk.

independent assortment, concept of The Mendelian idea that the separation of one set of alleles during gamete formation is not affected by the separation of another set of alleles.

index fossil The remains of an organism that was believed to have lived only at a certain time in evolutionary history.

indicator organism An organism that is characteristic of a particular environment.

individual characteristics Characteristics that differ among members of a species; variations.

inductive reasoning A process of beginning with many facts or assumptions in order to reach a general conclusion.

infection The condition of the body after it has been invaded by harmful organisms.

infectious disease A disease caused by a pathogen.

inflammation The reaction of tissues to injury or infection; characterized by increased flow of blood, redness, pain, and swelling.

infusion A nutrient-rich solution in which microorganisms can live.

ingestion The intake of food.

inherited disorder (See **genetic disorder.**)

inhibitor gene A gene that prevents the expression of other genes.

initiator codon A codon that codes for amino acids that bond in only one direction; starts the polypeptide chain of amino acids.

innate behavior Inborn behavior; includes reflexes and instinct.

innoculate To expose to a substance.

inorganic Substances that lack carbon (with few exceptions); usually derived from non-living material.

insecticide A chemical or agent that destroys insects.

insectivorous plants Plants that capture and digest insects.

inspiration Filling the lungs with air.

inspiratory reserve volume The amount of air that can be forced into the lungs beyond a normal inspiration.

instinct Elaborate, often highly complex inborn behaviors.

integuments The protective folds over a plant ovule.

intelligent behavior Behavior marked by analysis, thought, emotion, reasoning, use of tools, and use of symbols; motivated by reasoning or intelligence.

interferon A protein substance or substances produced by cells exposed to viruses; acts to slow the spread of a virus.

intermediate host An animal that temporarily harbors an immature form of a parasite.

internal cellular membranes The cellular membranes found inside the cell forming the boundaries of organelles and other cellular structures.

internal fertilization The fertilization of the ovum inside the female's body.

internal respiration The passage of gases between the blood and the body cells.

interneuron A neuron located in the central nervous system; transmits an impulse from a sensory neuron to another neuron.

interphase A period of time between cellular divisions.

intestinal flora Nonpathogenic microorganisms that live in the intestines and function to protect the body against pathogens.

intestine A section of the digestive system where most of the digestion and absorption of foods usually occurs.

intracellular digestion The breakdown of substances within cells.

intracellular parasites Organisms that live inside the cell.

intron A section of RNA that is cut out when forming messenger RNA.

invaginate To pinch in; the method of cytokinesis in animal cells.

invertebrate An animal that lacks a backbone or vertebral column.

ion An atom or group of atoms that has a positive or negative charge as a result of losing or gaining electrons.

ionic bond A chemical bond between ions of opposite charge.

iris The colored portion of the eye.

irritability The ability to respond to changes in the environment.

islets of Langerhans Endocrine glands that consist of small groups of cells in the pancreas that secrete the hormones glucagon and insulin.

isogametes Gametes that are similar in shape and size.

isometric contraction A muscular contraction in which there is no change in the length of the muscle.

isotonic contraction A muscular contraction in which a body part is actually moved.

isotonic solution A solution that has the same concentration of solutes as the cytoplasm of living cells.

isotope One of the forms of an atom produced by having different numbers of neutrons in the nucleus.

Jacobson's organs Sensory pits used by a reptile in the sense of smell.

karyotype An illustration in which the chromosomes of a cell are arranged according to their size.

keel The ridge on a bird's sternum.

kinetosome A basal body.

labial palp A sensory appendage on the labium of an insect.

labium Lower mouthpart of an insect.

labrum Upper mouthpart of an insect.

lacrimal gland The tear gland in the eye.

lactic acid fermentation The formation of lactic acid from glucose.

large intestine (colon) The part of the alimentary canal that extends from the small intestine to the anus.

larva An immature stage in the life cycle of many animals, usually different from the adult.

larynx The short passageway that leads from the pharynx to the trachea; the sound-producing organ; the voice box.

latent virus A virus that enters a cell and may remain inactive for long periods of time.

lateral buds Buds at the base of the petiole; buds on the sides of a branch.

lateral line A canal that runs the length of a fish's body that detects vibrations in the water.

layering A method of vegetative reproduction in which a branch is exposed to the soil, allowed to form roots, and then separated from the parent plant.

leaflets The blades of a compound leaf.

leaf scar A layer of cork cells left on the stem after a leaf falls.

leaf venation The pattern of the veins of a leaf.

leafy shoot A stem-and-leaf-like arrangement that lacks water conducting tissues.

learned behavior Conditioned behavior, learned by repetition and often motivated by reward or punishment.

lenticel Small openings in the cork layer of older woody roots and stems through which air is admitted into the plant.

lethal Causing death.

leucocyte A white blood cell.

leucoplast Colorless plastid used as a storehouse in a cell.

life A highly organized cellular condition which is derived from pre-existing life; requires energy to carry on processes such as growth, movement, reproduction, and response, and faces death.

ligaments Bands of connective tissues that hold a joint together.

lignin A substance that makes a secondary cell wall rigid.

limiting factor Something that in some way restricts the growth or existence of an organism.

lipids Organic compounds that are insoluble in water but soluble in certain organic solvents.

liver The largest organ in the body; secretes bile, purifies blood, metabolizes food molecules, and stores minerals and vitamins.

loam A soil mixture of sand, silt, and clay.

locus (pl., **loci**) The specific location of a gene on a chromosome.

logical reasoning A process of arriving at a conclusion through a series of ordered steps.

long-day (day-age) theory An interpretation of Genesis that states that each day of the creation week was actually a long time period.

lunar rhythm A cycle of activities that synchronizes with the moon.

lung A structure for the exchange of gases between the atmosphere and the blood of an organism.

lymph The fluid found between body cells; absorbed in the lymphatic system and returned to the bloodstream.

lymph node A small mass of tissue through which lymph passes and in which lymphocytes are produced.

lymphocyte A type of cell that produces antibodies that destroy foreign matter in lymph and blood.

lysis The rupturing of a cell.

lysosome A membrane-bound organelle that contains various hydrolytic enzymes.

lytic cycle The sequence of events whereby a virus replicates within a cell and eventually destroys the cell.

macronucleus An organelle found in certain protozoans; contains multiple copies of the cell's genetic material.

malignant tumor A tumor characterized by rapid and chaotic growth; often spreads and may be fatal.

Malpighian tubules Numerous threadlike tubules in insects that extract wastes from the blood and empty them into the intestine.

Glossary

mammary glands   Organs of mammals and humans which produce milk to nourish the young.

mandible   Chewing mouthpart of an insect; lower jaw in vertebrates.

mantle   The sheath of tissue that covers the body of a mollusk; also secretes the shell.

mantle cavity   The space between the mantle and the body of a mollusk.

mass selection   The method for selecting breeding stock in which only the desirable organisms are selected.

mastication   The chewing of food.

matrix   Nonliving material in a tissue; secreted by the tissue's cells.

matter   Anything that occupies space and has mass (weight).

maturation region   The area of a young root or stem in which the primary tissues are developed; area of cell differentiation.

maxilla   Mouthpart that assists in chewing.

maxilliped   One of the "jaw feet" that holds the food in place in some arthropods.

medulla   The inner region of an organ.

medulla oblongata   A part of the brain; the relay center between spinal cord and brain; contains several reflex centers.

medusa   The free-swimming, umbrella-shaped stage in the life cycle of cnidarians; reproduces sexually.

meiosis   Cell division in which the chromosome number is reduced from the diploid to the haploid state.

melanin   A dark brown or black pigment.

melanocytes   Cells in the human epidermis that produce melanin.

meninges   The protective coverings of the brain and spinal cord.

menstrual cycle   The process by which the uterine lining is prepared to receive an embryo.

menstruation   The time during which the uterine mucosa is shed.

meristematic region   An area in a plant containing young, rapidly-dividing cells.

meristematic tissues   Plant tissues that are able to reproduce and become other plant tissues.

mesenchyme   A noncellular, jellylike matrix between cell layers of a sponge; contains the amebocytes.

mesenteries   The transparent membranes that surround body organs and attach them to the body wall.

mesoderm   The middle germ layer in an embryo; the middle tissue layer in some animals.

mesoglea   The jellylike layer found between the ectoderm and the endoderm of the cnidarians.

mesosome   An organelle that appears as invaginations of the cell membrane in procaryotic cells; has enzymes attached to it.

messenger RNA (mRNA)   The RNA molecule that carries the code for a polypeptide chain from the DNA.

metabolism   The sum of all reactions that occurs in a living organism.

metamorphosis   A change in shape or form that an animal undergoes in its development from egg to adult.

microbe   A microscopic organism.

microfilaments   Flexible, rodlike assemblies of protein molecules found in cells.

micronucleus   The small reproductive nucleus in some protozoans.

micropyle   A small opening between the integuments where the pollen tube may enter the ovule.

microtome   A device used to cut thin sections of a substance.

microtubules   Hollow, spiral assemblies of protein molecules that comprise flagella, cilia, mitotic spindles, and other cellular structures.

middle lamella   A layer between two adjacent cell walls; composed primarily of pectins.

midline (median)   Dividing into right and left halves (only for animals with bilateral symmetry).

midrib   A large, central vein going to the tip of a leaf.

milt   The sperm of certain aquatic animals; released into the water.

mimicry   An organism's appearing like another organism; form of protective coloration.

miracle   A direct act of God which sets aside natural laws or processes.

missing link   A hypothetical organism that would fit between existing organisms listed on a phylogenetic tree.

mitochondria   Membrane-bound cellular organelles responsible for the respiration of foods to release usable energy.

mitosis   The duplicating and separating of a cell's chromosomes.

mixture   A material that contains two or more substances.

model   An explanation or representation of how something works.

molecular formula   A description of a molecule that indicates the number and kinds of atoms in the molecule.

molecule   The smallest possible unit of a substance that consists of two or more atoms.

molt   To shed an exoskeleton, scales, feathers, or fur.

monocot   Any flowering plant whose embryo has only one cotyledon. (Class Monocotyledonae)

monohybrid cross   A genetic cross that deals with only one set of characteristics.

monosaccharide   A simple sugar.

monosomy   A condition in which there is only one of a homologous chromosome pair.

mother cell   Any cell that is ready to begin cell division.

motor neuron   A neuron that receives impulses from the central nervous system and stimulates muscles or glands.

mRNA   (See messenger RNA.)

mucous membrane   The thin membrane lining of many internal structures of the body; produces mucus.

mucus   A slimy substance on the surface of mucous membranes and on the exterior of many fish and aquatic animals.

mulch   Decomposing organic matter; often added to the soil to enrich its mineral content or texture and to preserve soil moisture.

multicellular   An organism, organ, or tissue that consists of many cells.

multiple alleles   The possible arrangement of three or more genes (alleles) for a trait at a single locus.

multiple gene interaction   When two or more genes produce a cumulative effect on the same trait.

muscle fiber   A muscle cell.

mutagen   A substance that induces mutation.

mutation   A random change in a DNA molecule.

mutation-selection theory   (See Neo-Darwinism.)

mutualism   A form of symbiosis in which the organisms depend on each other for protection and nourishment.

mycelium (pl., mycelia)   All of the hyphae in a fungus plant.

mycoplasma   A type of bacteria that lacks a cell wall.

myelin sheath   The white, fatty membrane that protects neurons.

myocardium   The muscular tissue of the heart.

myopia   An eye condition in which only light rays from close objects can be focused accurately on the retina.

naiad   An aquatic insect nymph that possesses gills.

narcotics   Addictive drugs that induce a sense of euphoria, sleepiness, and anxiety; derived from opium or manufactured synthetically.

nastic movement   Movements of some plants due to the loss of turgor in cells, such as the opening and closing of petals.

natural system of classification   A taxonomy based on characteristics such as genetic similarities and reproductive capabilities.

nematocyst   A stinging cell, characteristic of cnidarians, that contains poisonous barbs, coiled threads, or a sticky substance.

Neo-Darwinism (mutation-selection theory)   An evolutionary theory proposing that mutations produce variations and that natural selection determines which variations will survive in order to produce biological evolution.

nephridia   Tubelike structures that filter wastes from blood.

nephron   A microscopic tubular unit of a kidney.

nerve impulse   An electrochemical pulse that moves along the membrane of a neuron.

nerve net   A nervous system which lacks a brain and major ganglia.

nervous tissue   Body tissue capable of responding to changes and conducting electrical impulses.

neural arch   The part of the vertebra that encloses the spinal cord.

neuron   The functional unit of the nervous system; the cell that receives and distributes nerve impulses.

neurotoxin   Venom that affects the nervous system.

neutralism   The state in which there is no direct relationship between populations in an environment.

nictitating membrane A thin, transparent membrane that protects the eye and keeps it moist.

nitrifying bacteria Soil bacteria that carry on nitrogen fixation.

nitrogen fixation The process of converting atmospheric nitrogen to nitrogen-containing compounds.

nocturnal Active at night.

node The place where a leaf, root, or flower attaches to the stem.

noncyclic Not recurring in a series; that which is not used again.

nondisjunction The failure of a pair of homologous chromosomes to separate during meiosis.

norepinephrine (noradrenalin) A hormone secreted by the adrenal medulla; functions with adrenalin during stressful situations.

notochord A tough, flexible rod of cartilage, usually located along the dorsal side of an animal; supports the animal's body.

nuclear area A nonmembrane-bound mass of DNA and proteins in a procaryotic cell.

nuclear envelope (membrane) The double membrane forming the surface of the nucleus in eucaryotic cells.

nucleic acids Organic compounds in living cells that are responsible for passing on hereditary information; DNA and RNA.

nucleolus A spherical body in the nucleus that has a high concentration of RNA and proteins.

nucleotide The basic component of a DNA or RNA molecule; each is made up of a sugar, a phosphate, and a base.

nucleus The positively charged central portion of an atom; the region of a eucaryotic cell that contains the chromosomes.

nymph One of the stages of incomplete (gradual) metamorphosis in an insect.

objective The part of a light microscope that is near the specimen and contains lenses; that which forms an image of an object.

occipital lobe The brain region responsible for vision and memory.

ocular The eyepiece of a microscope; contains lenses.

olfactory lobe A part of the brain that receives impulses from smell receptors in the nostrils.

omnivorous animal An animal that eats both plants and animals.

oogenesis The meiosis process that forms ova.

oogonium (pl., oogonia) The structure that produces the ovum.

operculum (pl., opercula) A plate that covers the gills of a fish.

opium The dried juice of the unripe capsule of the opium poppy; an addictive drug that gives the user a sense of euphoria.

optic disc (blind spot) The area where the nerve fibers leave the eye to form the optic nerve; contains no photoreceptors.

optic lobe A division of the brain that receives impulses from the eyes.

oral groove The funnel-shaped indentation in the body of the paramecium; lined with cilia to sweep food into the mouth pore.

organ Tissues grouped together to perform a specific function.

organic Naturally derived from living organisms.

organic evolution (See **evolution, theory of biological.**)

origin The point of attachment of a muscle's tendon to a more stationary bone.

osculum The excurrent pore, the opening of the sponge's body that expels water.

osmosis Diffusion of water molecules through a semipermeable membrane.

ossicles The bones in the middle ear.

ossification The process of converting cartilage tissue into bone.

osteocyte A living bone cell.

ova (See **ovum.**)

oval window A membrane-covered opening of the inner ear.

ovarian cycle The process by which the ovary prepares and releases an ovum.

ovary In plants, the part of the pistil containing the ovules that mature into the fruit containing the seeds; in animals and humans, the primary sexual reproductive organ in females; produces ova.

oviduct Fallopian tube; tube transporting the ovum from the ovary to the uterus.

oviparous A method of reproduction in which young develop within eggs that are laid and hatched outside the body of the parent.

ovipositor An insect organ used to deposit eggs.

ovoviviparous A method of reproduction in which young develop within the egg that hatches in the body of the parent.

ovulation The release of ova from the ovary.

ovule A structure in a plant ovary that contains the egg cell and will mature into a seed.

ovum (pl., ova) A gamete formed by a female; usually nonmotile and larger than a sperm.

oxygen debt The amount of oxygen that must be supplied to change lactic acid to glucose during physical exercise.

oxyhemoglobin A molecule that forms as oxygen combines with hemoglobin in the blood.

oxytocin A hormone released by the posterior pituitary; stimulates the smooth muscle of the uterus to contract during birth.

palate The structure serving as the floor of the nose and the roof of the mouth.

palisade mesophyll The primary photosynthetic tissue in plant leaves that has the cells lined up side by side.

palp A structure near an organism's mouth, usually used in obtaining food.

pancreas An organ that secretes enzymes into the duodenum to perform digestion; also secretes hormones.

papilla (pl., papillae) A small bump on the tongue surface in which a taste bud is located; a tiny bump on the skin of a bird from which a feather protrudes.

parasite An organism that obtains its nourishment by living in or on another organism.

parasympathetic nervous system The neurons that help the body return to normal processes after a stressful situation.

parenchyma The tissue in plants comprising the pith, cortex, spongy tissue of leaves, and major parts of fruits.

parietal lobe The brain region responsible for most sensations, such as pain, pressure, touch, and temperature.

parthenogenesis Reproduction in which organisms develop from unfertilized ova.

passive absorption The process of water entering root epidermal cells because of differences in water concentrations.

passive mediated transport Passive transport that requires the presence of a protein factor in the cellular membrane.

passive transport The movement of substances through a cellular membrane without the expenditure of cellular energy.

pathogen An organism that causes a disease.

pathologist One who studies diseased tissues.

pectin A jellylike substance that helps solidify a cell wall.

pectoral girdle The part of the appendicular skeleton designed to support and provide attachment for the arms.

pedicel The stalk that supports the flower.

pedigree A diagram to show the characteristics of several generations of organisms.

pedipalps The second pair of arachnid appendages; used for sensory perception and sperm transfer.

pellicle A firm yet flexible covering outside the cell membrane of certain protozoans.

pelvic girdle The hip bones; designed to support and provide attachment for the legs.

penis The organ that transfers sperm from male to female.

perennial plant A plant that lives for many years.

pericardium A fibrous, slippery sac covering the heart and protecting it from rubbing against the lungs and chest wall.

pericycle A layer of meristematic tissue in a root.

periosteum A layer of fibrous tissue covering the shaft of a long bone; serves for muscle attachment and bone growth and repair.

peripheral nervous system The division of the nervous system containing the nerves that originate in the central nervous system and the sense organs.

peristalsis Muscular movements that move food in the alimentary canal.

petiole The stalk connecting the blade of a leaf to the stem.

PGA (See **phosphoglyceric acid.**)

PGAL (See **phosphoglyceraldehyde.**)

Glossary

pH A symbol that is used with numbered values from 1 to 14 to indicate the concentration of hydrogen ions in a solution.

phagocytic vacuole A vacuole made by phagocytosis (cellular eating); a type of food vacuole.

phagocytosis The process of a cell engulfing a substance.

pharyngeal pouches Folds of skin along the neck region of vertebrate embryos that develop into either structures of the lower face, neck, and upper chest, or into gill openings.

pharynx The portion of the digestive tract that connects the mouth cavity and the esophagus; also serves as passageway for air from nose to larynx.

phenotype The physical expression of an organism's gene.

phloem A vascular tissue that usually carries water and dissolved foods downward in plants.

phosphoglyceraldehyde (PGAL) A three-carbon sugar produced during the dark phase of photosynthesis; also found in glycolysis.

phosphoglyceric acid (PGA) A three-carbon acid that forms from RuDP during photosynthesis; also forms during glycolysis.

phospholipid A molecule consisting of two fatty acid molecules and a phosphate group attached to a glycerol molecule.

phosphorescent Light-producing.

photolysis The breaking apart of a water molecule by energized chlorophyll.

photoperiodism The responses of a plant to changes in light intensity and length of days.

photo phase (light reactions) The phase of photosynthesis that requires light; consists of photolysis, hydrogen fixation, and the manufacture of ATP.

photosynthesis The process whereby simple sugars are formed from carbon dioxide and water in the presence of light and chlorophyll.

phototropism Growth movement of a plant in response to light.

phylogenetic tree A diagram that demonstrates the supposed stages of evolution.

physical change Altering a substance in its state of matter and appearance, without changing it into a new substance.

physical environment All the nonliving factors in an ecosystem.

physical withdrawal Actual physical symptoms that occur when a person stops taking a physically addictive drug.

physiology The science that deals with the various processes and activities that occur within a living organism.

phytoplankton Plankton that are photosynthetic organisms.

pineal gland A small structure in the brain which secretes melatonin.

pinocytosis The process whereby a cell takes in fluid by forming vesicles.

pistil The female reproductive structure that produces seeds in a flower.

pith The central area of a woody stem.

pith rays Plant tissues in young woody stems that extend laterally from the central pith to the xylem and phloem.

pituitary gland (hypophysis) An endocrine gland attached to the lower part of the brain.

placenta In plants, the structure that holds the ovule to the ovary wall; in animals and humans, the structure that consists of a portion of the uterine wall and chorion of the embryo: allows nutrient and waste exchange between mother and embryo.

plankton A tiny floating aquatic organism.

planula The free-swimming larval stage of some cnidarians.

plasma membrane The cell membrane; the cellular membrane that forms the outermost boundary of a cell's cytoplasm.

plasmodium A multinucleate mass of protoplasm that forms the vegetative body of a slime mold.

plasmolysis The shrinking of a cell's protoplasm when the cell loses water.

plastids Membrane-bound organelles found in plants, algae, and a few other organisms, but not in animals. (See also **leucoplast** and **chloroplast**.)

plastron The ventral part of the tortoise's bony shell.

platelet A small, colorless body found in the blood; lacks hemoglobin and a nucleus; involved in blood clot formation.

pleura A delicate membrane that lines the thoracic cavity and covers the lungs.

polar body A cell produced by meiotic division in oogenesis.

pollen A haploid cell that contains the tube and sperm nuclei of plants; produced in the anther.

pollen cone A structure on a conifer that produces pollen.

pollution Contamination of the environment with substances or factors that change the environment significantly.

polyp A sessile, tubular cnidarian with a mouth and tentacles at one end and a basal disc at the other; reproduces asexually.

polypeptide chain A chain formed by many peptide bonds, as in the formation of a protein by many amino acids being bonded by peptide bonds.

polyploid Any cell or organism that has multiple genomes.

polysaccharide A large, complex carbohydrate composed of many monosaccharides.

pons A rounded portion of the lower brain that relays information from one side of the brain to the other; contains reflex centers.

population All the members of the same type of living things within an area.

population genetics The study of the types and frequencies of genes in a given population.

portal circulation The flow of blood from the digestive organs to the liver.

postdiluvian After the Flood.

precocial chicks Birds that have a long incubation period and are usually able to care for themselves when they hatch.

predator An organism that eats another organism.

preening An activity in which a bird uses its bill to apply oil to its feathers and also to arrange them.

preformationist One who believes that completely formed organisms exist within sperm.

premolar The teeth in front of the molars used for crushing and grinding food.

primary growth The increase in length of a root or stem.

primary root The original root that sprouts from a seed.

primary tissue A plant tissue formed by the apical meristem; the plant tissues that result from primary growth.

procaryotic cell A cell that lacks a nuclear membrane and has only indistinct organelles; found only in kingdom Monera.

producer An organism that produces its own food; photosynthetic and chemosynthetic organisms are producers.

productivity The rate of photosynthesis carried on in an ecosystem.

proglottid A segment of a tapeworm's body.

prop root An adventitious root that helps to support the plant.

prostate gland A structure that produces a portion of the semen.

protein An organic compound that is composed of amino acids.

protein coat The structure which covers the nucleic acid core of a virus.

prothallus The heart-shaped gametophyte generation in ferns.

protonema A branched filamentous structure.

protoplasm All the living substances within a cell.

protozoan The general term given to microscopic organisms within the phyla Sporozoa, Ciliophora, Sarcodina, or Mastigophora.

pseudopod (pl., **pseudopodia**) A cytoplasmic extension of a cell; used for locomotion or engulfing substances.

psychotropic drug A drug that alters the emotional state of the user and often affects his sense of reality.

puberty The period of hormonal-induced change during which the secondary sex characteristics develop.

pulmonary circulation The flow of blood from the right ventricle to the lungs and back to the left atrium.

pulp cavity The central region of a tooth; filled with blood vessels, lymph vessels, nerves, and connective tissues.

punctuated equilibrium The theory that evolution occurs rapidly for a period of time followed by a long period of nonevolving before another period of rapid evolution.

Punnett square A diagram used to visualize genetic crosses.

pupa One of the stages of incomplete metamorphosis of an insect.

pupil The circular opening in the iris of the eye.

pure science Knowledge obtained through scientific activities.

pure strain An organism that is homozygous for certain traits.

pus A thick yellowish fluid composed of leucocytes, bacteria, and broken cells; characteristic of infections.

pyloric valve   A muscular valve at the end of the stomach.

pyrenoid   A protein-containing structure present in the chloroplasts of algae; center for starch storage.

pyruvic acid   The organic acid formed during glycolysis.

quadrate bone   A snake bone loosely attached to the skull and the jaw that enables the snake to open its mouth widely.

quarantine   Strict isolation to prevent the spread of disease or pests.

quill   The shaft portion of a feather that extends below the vane; the part of the feather in the skin.

rachis (shaft)   The slender, central part of a bird's feather from which the barbs protrude.

radicle   The portion of a plant embryo that will become the root.

radiocarbon dating method (carbon-14 dating method)   A method of determining the age of fossils using the half-life of carbon-14 as a basis.

radiometric dating method   A method of determining the age of an object by measuring the amount of a radioactive substance that is part of the object.

radula   A platelike structure in the pharynx of certain mollusks; composed of rows of tiny teeth.

ray   A cartilaginous or bony support in the fins of fish; the arm of a starfish.

receptacle   The enlarged end of the pedicle; bears the flower parts.

recessive trait   The characteristic that is only expressed in the homozygous recessive condition.

recombinant DNA   DNA which has had a section of DNA that contains gene(s) spliced into it.

rectilinear movement   Movement used by snakes; movement in a straight line with the aid of abdominal scutes.

rectum   The muscular portion of the large intestine that contracts in order to rid the body of feces.

referred pain   Pain that seems to be in one area of the body but actually originates in a different area.

reflection   The image caused by light rays bouncing off an object.

reflex   An automatic, involuntary response to a stimulus.

reflex arc   A series of neurons which produces a single reaction in response to a stimulus.

refraction   The bending of a light ray when it passes from one medium to another at an oblique angle.

renal circulation   The flow of blood in and out of the kidneys.

replication   The process whereby a DNA molecule duplicates itself and forms a new DNA molecule.

reproduction   The formation of another organism that has characteristics and limitations similar to the original.

research   An investigation into a topic often carried on by reading, inquiry, or scientific observation.

research method   Using the scientific method to obtain knowledge.

residual volume   The amount of air in the lungs after all of the vital capacity has been expired.

resolution   The characteristic that allows a microscope to form a clear image of detailed structures.

respiration   The release of energy from a food source.

retina   The innermost layer of the eyeball; composed of specialized neurons and their fibers.

revealed truth   The information that God has recorded in His Word.

rhizoid   A rootlike structure that lacks water-conducting tissue.

rhizome   A thick, fleshy, horizontal underground stem which produces leaves or leaf-bearing branches.

ribonucleic acid   The type of nucleic acid that forms from DNA and functions with ribosomes to form protein molecules. (See also **messenger RNA, ribosomal RNA, and transfer RNA.**)

ribosomal RNA (rRNA)   The RNA molecule that combines with proteins to form a ribosome.

ribosome   A nonmembrane-bound cellular organelle associated with protein formation.

ribulose diphosphate (RuDP)   A five-carbon sugar diphosphate that serves as a carbon dioxide acceptor in photosynthesis and then splits to form two molecules of PGA.

rickettsias   A group of obligate parasites in the kingdom Monera.

ring canal   A circular canal within the water-vascular system of an echinoderm.

RNA   (See **ribonucleic acid.**)

root cap   Thick-walled cells which cover and protect the delicate root tip.

root hair   An outgrowth of epidermal cells of the root.

root pressure   The pressure that causes water to move up the stem of a plant; caused by active absorption.

round window   A membrane-covered opening of the cochlea.

rRNA   (See **ribosomal RNA.**)

RuDP   (See **ribulose diphosphate.**)

rumen   The first of four chambers of the stomach of a ruminant.

salivary gland   A gland in or near the mouth; secretes saliva to break down starches.

sanctity of human life   The Biblical principle that human life has high value.

saprophyte   A plant that obtains its nourishment from dead organic matter.

scale   An epidermal plate on reptiles and fish; the small overlapping leaves of some gymnosperms.

science   A body of facts that man has repeatedly observed about the physical universe around him.

scientific method   A logical method of problem solving that involves observing and reaching a conclusion.

scientism   An exaggerated trust in science; the "worship" of science.

scion   The unrooted portion that is grafted into the stock; may be a bud or twig.

sclera   The outer layer of the eye; "the white of the eye."

scolex   The anterior end of a tapeworm.

scrotum   A skin pouch within which the testes are located.

scute   One of the broad scales on a snake that aids in movement.

sebaceous gland   A gland of the skin that produces oil.

secondary growth   The increase in diameter of stem and roots.

secondary sex characteristic   A body characteristic caused by the sex hormones.

secondary tissue   Any tissue that is manufactured in a plant after primary growth.

sedimentary rock   Layers of rock formed by sedimentation.

sedimentation   The settling out of materials due to the action of water or wind.

seed   A mature plant ovule that consists of embryo and stored food enclosed by a coat.

seed cone   The structure on conifers which produces the seeds.

segregation concept   The Mendelian concept that only one gene for each characteristic may be carried in a particular gamete.

selection   Nonrandom mating; may occur naturally or artificially.

selectively permeable membrane (See **semipermeable membrane.**)

semen   The fluid that contains sperm.

semicircular canal   A structure in the inner ear that maintains dynamic equilibrium.

semilunar valve   A membranous structure located at the exit of each ventricle; permits one-way flow of blood.

seminal receptacle   The storage vessel in an organism that receives sperm from another organism.

seminal vesicle   An organ that produces a fluid that activates sperm.

seminiferous tubule   One of the tiny tubes that produces sperm within the testes.

semipermeable membrane   A membrane that is permeable to certain molecules or ions but not to others.

sensory neuron   A neuron that carries impulses toward the spinal cord or the brain.

sepal   An outermost flower structure; usually encloses the other floral parts in the bud.

septum (pl., septa)   A wall that separates individual cells in fungi; the muscular wall separating the chambers of the heart.

serpentine movement   A movement used by snakes for swimming and crawling; winding in a series of "S" curves.

Glossary

serum   The clear fluid (obtained from blood) that contains antibodies; used to transfer immunity to another person or animal.

sessile   In organisms, growing while attached to something else; non-motile; in leaves, lacking a petiole.

seta (pl., **setae**)   A stiff bristle on a segmented worm; used for locomotion and sensation.

sex chromosomes   Special chromosomes (in humans X and Y) that determine whether an organism will be male or female.

sex-limited characteristic   A trait expressed in only one sex even though the genes are present in the autosomes of both sexes.

sex-linked   Determined by genes located on the sex chromosomes.

sex-linked traits   An inherited characteristic for which there is a gene on the X chromosome but not on the Y chromosome.

sexually transmitted disease (STD)   A contagious disease spread by sexual contact with an infected person.

sexual reproduction   The union of haploid gametes that results in a diploid zygote which develops into a new individual.

sheath   A thick capsule that surrounds a colony of bacteria.

shoot apex   The rapid-growing region of a stem where cells begin to differentiate into leaves, branches, and flower parts.

short-day theory   An interpretation of Genesis which states that each day of the creation week is a literal 24-hr. period.

sickle cell anemia   A genetic abnormality that causes the production of abnormal hemoglobin which is unable to carry oxygen and that causes sickle-shaped red blood cells.

sidewinding   Movement used by snakes; shuffling sideways by continually looping forward.

simple eye   An eye with only one lens.

sinoatrial node (SA node)   A small mass of specialized cardiac muscle located in the right atrium; performs the job of starting each systole; the pacemaker of the heart.

sinus venosus   A thin sac at the back of the heart; receives deoxygenated blood and empties it into an atrium of the heart.

siphon   A tube in a mollusk used to draw in or expel water.

sister chromatid   Each single strand in the pair of DNA duplicates that is part of a chromosome ready to go through cell division; becomes a daughter chromosome during mitosis.

skeletal muscle   Muscle tissue that is attached to and moves the skeleton.

skin gills   Fingerlike projections on the surface of echinoderms; used for respiration.

small intestine   The digestive organ where most of the digestion and absorption of food occurs.

sol   The liquid state of a colloid.

solute   The dissolved substance in a solution.

solution   The uniform dissolving of one substance into another substance.

solvent   The substance (often a liquid) in which a solute is dissolved.

somatic mutation   A mutation that affects only body cells (not gametes).

sonography   (See **ultrasonic scanning**.)

soredium (pl., **soredia**)   An asexual reproductive structure in lichens; consists of a group of algal cells enclosed in fungus hyphae.

sori (sing., **sorus**)   Groups of sporangia attached to the underside of fern fronds.

spawn   The laying of eggs by aquatic animals.

species   A population of organisms that are structurally similar but do have a degree of variation; those organisms that interbreed and produce fertile offspring.

sperm   A gamete formed by a male; often motile.

spermatogenesis   The meiosis process of sperm formation.

spicules   Sharp, pointed, supporting structures in sponges; composed of silicon or calcium compounds.

spinal cord   The nervous tissue that conducts messages between the brain and the peripheral body parts.

spinal nerve   A mixed nerve attached to the spinal cord.

spindle   Fibers that form between centrioles during cell division.

spine   In plants, a stiff, hard, pointed outgrowth on stems; in animals, bony supports in fins; projecting part of a bone.

spiracles   Small pores in an insect's body that function in breathing.

spirillum (pl., **spirilla**)   A spiral-shaped bacterium.

spirochete   A group of spiral-shaped organisms in the kingdom Monera.

spleen   A lymphatic organ which filters blood, stores red blood cells, and destroys old red blood cells.

spongy bone   The type of bone that contains many small spaces; located in the ends of a long bone.

spongy mesophyll   The photosynthetic tissue in leaves that is formed of irregular-shaped cells and many airspaces.

spontaneous generation   The formation of organisms from nonliving materials.

spontaneous mutation   A chromosomal and gene mutation that occurs naturally.

sporangiophore   A fungus sporophore that produces its asexual spores within an enclosure.

sporangium (pl., **sporangia**)   A structure in which spores are produced.

spore   A cell with a hard protective covering that is capable of producing a new organism.

sporophore   A spore-producing hypha of a fungus mycelium; spore-producing stage in the life cycle of a plant.

stamen   The male reproductive structure of a flower.

starch   A polysaccharide; often used for energy storage.

statocyst   An organ of equilibrium in Malacostracans.

STD   (See **sexually transmitted diseases**.)

sternal sinus   The collecting chamber for blood in some open circulatory systems.

stigma   The expanded tip of the pistil that receives the pollen.

stipe   The stalk of a mushroom.

stipule   A structure at the base of the petiole of a leaf; often leaflike.

stock   The rooted plant onto which a scion is grafted.

stolon (runner)   In fungi, an aerial, horizontal hypha that produces new fungi asexually; in plants, a slender, branched, underground stem that produces new shoots.

stoma (pl., **stomata**)   An opening between the guard cells of a leaf that permits exchange of gases.

stratum germinativum   The deepest layer of the epidermis; carries on cell division.

stroma   The fluid in a chloroplast.

structural defenses   The body's first line of defense in preventing pathogens from entering the body, such as skin, tears, and stomach acid.

structural formula   An expanded drawing that shows the arrangement of atoms and bonds within the molecule.

style   The elongated portion of the pistil that supports the stigma.

subcutaneous layer   The layer of fat and connective tissues below the dermis of the skin.

submucous layer   The second layer of the alimentary canal.

substrate   The chemical or chemicals an enzyme will affect.

succession   The predictable, gradual change of a biotic community over a period of time.

succulent leaf   A thick leaf with a tough cuticle; capable of storing water.

sucrose   A common disaccharide; table sugar; made of one glucose molecule and one fructose molecule.

surrogate mother   A woman who nurtures and brings to birth from her womb a child for which she did not provide the ovum.

survival of the fittest   Part of Darwin's evolutionary theory; only the organisms best suited to their environment will survive.

suspension   The state of a substance when its particles are mixed but are undissolved.

suture   An interlocking margin of skull bones.

symbiosis   Two organisms of different species that live together in close association.

symmetry   A likeness in size, shape, or structure of parts of an organism.

sympathetic nervous system   A system of neurons that helps the body adjust to stressful situations.

synapse   A space between an axon and a dendrite or between the end of an axon and the body structure it affects.

synovial fluid   A lubricating fluid in joints.

synovial membrane   The lining of a joint cavity which fills the cavity with a lubricating fluid.

synthesis The process of putting things together in order to make new things.

syrinx The song box of a bird.

system A group of body organs that works together to perform one or more vital functions.

systematics The science of classifying organisms.

systemic circulation The flow of blood from the left ventricle to all parts of the body, except the lungs, and back to the right atrium.

systole The phase of the cardiac cycle when the myocardium contracts and the heart chamber pumps blood.

talons Long curved claws found on birds of prey.

tannic acid The product of the chemical breakdown of plant cell contents that causes a brownish color; found in tea.

taproot system The plant root system in which the primary root continues to grow as the main root.

taste buds Groups of cells near the tongue surface that produce taste sensations.

taxes (sing., **taxis**) An organism's response to a single stimulus.

taxonomy The science of classifying organisms.

T cell Any of several types of cells involved in cell-mediated immunity.

technical method The use of prescribed techniques to gain knowledge about a specific case.

tectorial membrane The membranous flap over the organ of Corti.

tegument A protective body covering.

telson The last abdominal segment of some arthropods.

temperate phage A virus which enters and replicates within a cell but may never destroy the cell.

template RNA Messenger RNA.

temporal lobe The brain region responsible for hearing and smelling.

tendon The connective tissue that attaches muscles to bone.

terminator codons Codons that end a chain of amino acids.

testa Seed coat.

test cross The mating of an organism that possesses a dominant phenotype but unknown genotype with an organism that possesses a recessive phenotype to determine the genotype of the dominate individual.

testes The primary male reproductive organs, which produce sperm and male sex hormones.

testosterone The male sex hormone that promotes the development of secondary sex characteristics; one of the androgens.

test-tube fertilization Under scientifically controlled conditions, the uniting of a sperm and an ovum to form a zygote outside the female's body.

tetraploid Having four complete sets of chromosomes (genomes).

thalamus The brain region that receives general sensations and relays impulses to the parietal lobe.

thallus (pl., **thalli**) A leaflike or plantlike structure in algae, fungi, and plants; not differentiated into true leaves, roots, or stems.

theistic evolution The interpretation of the Bible according to evolutionary theories.

theory An idea supported by many observations.

theory of evolution (See **evolution.**)

theory of inheritance of acquired characteristics An evolutionary theory that states that a characteristic acquired by an organism can be passed on to its offspring.

theory of natural selection A process that supposedly results in the survival of the organisms that are best suited for their environment.

theory of need An evolutionary theory which states that an organism must have a need for a structure in order to evolve it.

theory of recapitulation An evolutionary theory which states that all organisms go through their evolutionary history as they develop from a zygote to a mature organism.

theory of use and disuse An evolutionary theory which states that if an organ is used, it will keep evolving; if not, it will degenerate.

thigmotropism Growth movement of a plant in response to contact.

thorax A body region between the head and the abdomen.

thrombin A substance involved in blood clotting.

thromboplastin A substance released by platelets; triggers the conversion of prothrombin to thrombin during blood clotting.

thrombus A blood clot lodged in an unbroken blood vessel or the heart.

thylakoids Flattened sacs in a chloroplast that form grana.

thymus gland A mass of lymphatic tissue thought to produce hormones; this degenerates prior to puberty.

thyroxine The thyroid hormone that regulates the metabolic rate.

tidal volume The amount of air that enters the lung during a normal inspiration or leaves the lung during a normal expiration.

tissue Many similar cells grouped together to perform a similar function.

tissue rejection The condition of a transplanted tissue or organ in which it stimulates the body's immune system to react.

tonic contraction A continual partial contraction of a muscle; muscle tone.

tonsil One of the masses of lymph nodes in the pharynx region.

topography Land features.

torsion A twisted body arrangement unique to gastropods.

total lung capacity The vital capacity and the residual volume.

toxoid A weakened form of a toxin used to stimulate immunity.

trachea A tube that extends from the larynx to the bronchi.

transcription The process of forming messenger RNA from DNA.

transfer RNA (tRNA) The RNA molecule that carries (transfers) a specific amino acid to the ribosome during protein synthesis.

transformation The genetic change that is produced when DNA from one bacterium is taken up through the membrane of another bacterium.

translocation The movement of water and dissolved substances in a plant; the transfer of a chromosome segment to a nonhomologous chromosome.

transpiration The release of water through the leaves of a plant.

transpiration-cohesion theory Possible explanation for water translocation in a plant; as water is released from the leaves, additional water molecules must enter the roots.

trichocyst An organelle in a paramecium which discharges a thread-like filament in response to stimuli.

triplet A series of three bases in DNA that has the code for one specific amino acid molecule during protein synthesis.

triploid Consists of three complete sets of chromosomes (genomes).

trisomy An abnormal condition in which there are three chromosomes in a set instead of two.

tRNA (See **transfer RNA.**)

trochophore The ciliated, free-swimming, larval stage of mollusks.

tropic hormone A hormone that stimulates the growth and function of other endocrine glands.

tropism A growth response of plants to external stimuli such as light, gravity, and touch.

tube feet Small soft, tubular structures in echinoderms; used for locomotion and food capture; part of water-vascular system.

tuber A storage stem which produces roots and often has "eyes" (buds) to produce aerial stems.

tubule A tiny tube.

tumor An abnormal growth of cells.

turbidity Cloudiness of water.

turgor (adj., **turgid**) The presence of water inside a plant or protist cell in quantity sufficient to give the cell stiffness.

turgor pressure The added pressure within a plant cell that results from the movement of water into the central vacuole.

tympanic membrane A circular membranous structure that serves to transmit sound vibrations to an ear cavity; the eardrum.

ultrasonic scanning (sonography) The use of sound waves to produce a computer-generated picture of internal structures.

umbilical cord The flexible structure that contains blood vessels and that conducts the blood of the fetus to the placenta for exchange of food, wastes, oxygen, and carbon dioxide.

understory Plants that grow in the shade of trees.

unicellular Consisting of a single cell.

unit characteristics concept One of the Mendelian theories which states that each characteristic of an organism is determined by a single gene.

universal flood A flood that covers the entire earth; the Genesis Flood, Noah's Flood.

Glossary

unrevealed truth Natural laws that God has established but has not revealed in His Word.

unsaturated fat A fatty acid molecule in which some of the carbon atoms are double bonded to each other.

unviable Not able to germinate.

uracil The base in RNA that is comparable to thyamine in DNA.

ureter One of the tubes that conducts urine into the bladder.

urethra A passageway for urine; also the passageway for sperm in the male.

urinary bladder An organ designed as a reservoir for urine.

urine A liquid excreted from the body; contains the metabolic wastes from the blood.

uropod The flipper-shaped tail appendage of arthropods.

uterus A reproductive organ for storing ova until they are fertilized or laid; the womb; in most mammals and in humans, the organ in which the embryo develops.

utopia An ideal society.

vaccination A method of exposing a person to a controlled amount of a disease-causing factor to develop an immunity.

vaccine A weakened form of a pathogen used to build immunity by stimulating the body to produce antibodies or activate T cells.

vacuole A membrane-bound sac in a cell.

vacuole, contractile A cellular structure used to collect water molecules and keep cells from bursting.

vagina The elastic canal that leads from the outside of the body to the cervix of the uterus.

valid Anything that is meaningful, accurate, and reliable.

valve A mollusk shell.

vane The flat part of a feather; composed of parallel rows of barbs.

variable The factor in an experiment that is subject to change and is therefore the one being tested.

variations The differences between different individual organisms of the same kind; difference based on genotype; the expression of different individual characteristics in organisms of the same kind.

varieties Different forms or types of organisms within a species.

vascular cambium A layer of meristematic tissue between the xylem and phloem; produces secondary xylem and phloem.

vascular cylinder The central area of the young root or stem; contains xylem and phloem.

vascular tissue Tissues (xylem and phloem) that conduct water and dissolved materials in a plant.

vas deferens (seminal duct) The tube which carries the sperm from the testes to the urethra.

vector An insect or other arthropod that carries pathogens to other host organisms.

vegetative organ A leaf, root, or stem of a plant.

vegetative reproduction Asexual reproduction in plants.

vein Any blood vessel that carries blood toward the heart; fibrovascular structure for strengthening and conduction in plants.

venation The pattern of veins in a leaf.

ventral On or near the lower surface (or at the front of some organisms).

ventricle The chamber of the heart that pushes blood into the arteries; space within the brain.

vermiform appendix The narrow end of the cecum.

vertebrae (sing., vertebra) The bones or cartilaginous segments of the vertebral column.

vertebral column Bony or cartilaginous structures that are used in supporting an organism; the backbone.

vertebrate An animal that possesses a backbone or vertebral column; members of subphylum Vertebrata.

vesicle A small vacuole.

vestigial structure An organ which supposedly no longer has any function.

viable Capable of growing and developing.

villi (sing., villus) Microscopic fingerlike structures that line the small intestine.

viper A poisonous, long-fanged snake of the Old World.

virulence The ability of a virus or other pathogen to cause a disease.

virus A submicroscopic, noncellular particle, composed of a nucleic acid core and a protein coat; obligate parasite.

visceral Relating to internal organs.

visceral hump The portion of a mollusk's body that contains internal organs.

visceral muscle Muscle tissue that forms the walls of internal organs.

vital capacity The sum of the tidal volume, inspiratory reserve volume, and expiratory reserve volume.

vitalism The theory that the activities of living organisms are controlled by a vital force.

vitamin An organic substance other than proteins, fats, and carbohydrates that is necessary for normal metabolism, growth, and development.

vitreous humor A clear, jellylike substance in the eyeball.

viviparous A method of reproduction in which the young are born alive after being nourished in the uterus through a placenta.

vocal sacs A pair of sacs in the mouth region of male frogs.

vomerine teeth A set of inconspicuous teeth that protrude from the roof of the mouth of some animals.

water-vascular system A series of canals and tubules that are used for locomotion and food capture in echinoderms.

womb A place where the unborn baby is protected and nourished; the uterus.

workability A characteristic of scientific knowledge that allows its practical application.

wound infection A disease caused by pathogens entering the body through wounds.

xylem A vascular tissue that carries water and dissolved minerals upward in a plant.

yolk Food material stored in an egg to nourish the embryo.

yolk sac The membrane that contains the yolk in an amniotic egg.

zoology The study of animals.

zooplankton Plankton which are tiny animals or protozoans.

zoospores A motile, swimming spore; possesses cilia or flagella.

zygospore A zygote surrounded by a hard, protective covering to survive unfavorable conditions.

zygote A diploid cell formed by the union of two haploid gametes.

Index

abdomen 365, 369, 374, 378, 533, 659

abdominal cavity 505

abductor 525-27

abortion 639-41; natural, 156

abscissic acid 324

abscisson layer 304

absorption 70-77, 539; passive, 317

acclimatization 537, 553

accommodation 591, 595

acetyl coenzyme A 98-99,105-6

acid 47-48, 65; rain, 3, 48, 494

acne 511

acromegaly 602

acrosome 629

actin 79, 524

activation energy 54-57

active site 59, 65

adaptation 224

addiction 620-22

Addison's disease 607

adductor 527

adenine 103-8

adipose 506, 548

ADP (adenosine diphosphate) 91, 94-95

adrenal glands 601, 603

adrenaline 588, 603-4

adultery 638, 643-44

adventitious root 308

aeciospore 285

aerobic 97, 279, 238; bacteria, 235, 652; cellular respiration, 97-99; exercises, 529; molds, 231

African sleeping sickness 266

agar 274, 322-23

age, aging 537; 255-56; apparent, 188; of the earth, 174, 184-91

agglutinate 554-55

Agnatha (class) 394-95, 662

AIDS (acquired immune deficiency syndrome) 2-3, 571, 644-45

air, bladders, 269, 273, 397, 400, 662; pollution, 494; sacs, 428; volumes, 534

albinism 153-54

albumen 433

albumin 552

alcohol 63, 84, 106, 227, 235, 283, 289, 617-21, 633

alcoholic fermentation 100

alcoholism 618

algae 71, 80, 90, 102, 117-18, 122, 260-61, 268-76, 286-88, 459, 462, 470-71, 495, 653-54; blue-green, 223, 275; colonies, 269

algin 273

alimentary canal 390, 539

allantois 416, 634

allele 127-41, 153

allergen 572

allergy 163, 572

alligator 417, 663

aloe 307

alternation of generations 291

altitude 537

altricial bird 434

alveoli 532-33, 617

ameba 34, 203, 260-61, 653

amebocyte 342, 362

ameboid movement 261

amensalism 466

amino acid 89, 102, 106, 113, 155, 164, 501, 550

amino 65

amniocentesis 161

amnion 416, 634

amniotic, eggs, 416, 433-34; fluid, 441

amphetamine 620-21

Amphibia (class) 143, 212-13, 340, 391, 404-12, 429, 662; classification, 406-7; skin of, 405. See also frog

amphioxus 389, 661

amplexus 410

amylase 60, 539, 544

Anabeana 233

Anacystis 233

anabolic steroids 605-6

anabolism 109

anaerobic 97, 235, 279, 469; bacteria, 235, 251

anaphase 114-15, 122

anatomical position 505

anatomy 505

Anaximander 648

androgen 601, 607

anemia 553, 565

aneuploidy 143, 146-48; in humans, 147

aneurysm 565

angelfish 403

angiosperm 289, 294, 297, 656

Angstrom 35

animal 63, 212-15, 337-52, 462, 657-64; in Scripture, 490; on the Ark, 182-83

animal rights 488-91

Annelida (phylum) 347, 340, 355-57, 658-59

annual 293, 299, 309, 476; rings, 312

ant 377, 380-82, 660

antagonist 525

antediluvian 175, 177, 293

antenna 129, 365-66, 369, 374, 378, 382, 659

anterior 505

anther 331

antheridia 271, 272-73, 275, 290-93

anthocyanin 304

Anthophyta (phylum) 289, 297

anthropology 199-202

antibiotic 227, 252, 279

antibody 251-52, 258, 554, 570, 572, 575, 633

anticodon 103-4, 107-8

antigen 554, 570, 573

antihistamine 572

Anura (order) 407

anus 354, 359, 362, 367, 369, 375, 400, 658-59

aorta 401, 410, 558, 562-63, 566

aortic arch 356

Apatosaurus 413-15

apes 393, 447, 476, 503

apical, bud, 310; dominance, 310; meristem, 310

Apoda (order) 406-7

appendage 347, 365

appendix 204, 542-43

apple 119, 294, 297, 303, 657

aquaculture 268

aquatic, leaves, 307; mammals, 447; roots, 308

Aquinas, Thomas 649, 651

Arachnida (class) 212-13, 340, 366, 369, 659-60

arachnoid membrane 584

arborvitae 296

archegonia 271-72, 290-93

Aristotle 8, 112, 211, 341, 648-49

Ark 180, 182-83, 222-23

arrhythmia 561, 565

arteriole 562, 564

arteriosclerosis 565

artery 390, 401, 410, 562-63, 650

arthritis 235, 520, 624

Arthropoda (phylum) 212-13, 340-41, 364-87, 462, 659-61

articulation 513-14, 519

Ascaris 353-54, 658

Ascomycota (phylum) 281, 283-84, 654

ascus 283

asexual binary fission 264

asexual reproduction 118-20, 229, 261, 269-75, 271-74, 281-84, 328-30, 345

aspirin 617, 619, 624

assimilation 30

aster 79, 114-15

asthma 538, 617

astigmatism 596

atherosclerosis 557, 561, 565

athlete's foot 281, 654

atlas 517

atmospheric pressure 537

atom 35, 43-45

ATP (adenosine triphos-

phate) 91, 94-101, 106, 109, 501, 524, 528

atria 401, 409, 558, 561, 565

atrioventricluar node 560

atrophy 528-29 617

attributes of life 30-32

Australia 391, 454

Australopithecus 200

autophagy 110

autoradiography 40

autosome 136

autotroph 90, 96, 230, 260, 264; bacteria, 234

auxin 323, 335

avascular 506-7

Aves (class) 212-13, 423-36

avoiding reaction 263-64

axis 517

axolotl 220

axon 581-83

B cell 570, 572-73

bacillus 226, 228

Bacon, Roger 650-51

bacteria 34-35, 63, 96, 117, 163-64, 225-37, 239, 248, 250-52, 320, 439, 459, 462, 464, 466, 469, 470, 538, 567, 570, 596, 616, 645, 652-53; colonies, 226, 228; control of, 231; growth, 229-32; nutrition, 230

bacteriochlorophyll 230

bacteriophage 239-40

balance, sense of 592-94

ballooning 372

banana 118, 315-16, 329

Banting, Frederick 491

barberry 285

barbiturate 620-21

barb (feather) 424

barbule (feather) 424

bark 312

barnacle 366, 368, 466

barometric pressure 537

basal, body, 75, 79-80; disc, 344; metabolic rate (BMR), 548

base 47-48, 66-68

basidia 285-86

Basidiomycota (phylum) 280, 284, 654

basidiospore 284-86

basidium 284-86

bass 462, 477

bat 200, 205, 437, 440, 664

bat moth 211

bean 327, 470, 657

bear 350, 436, 439, 445, 454, 462, 664

bearbaiting 488

Beaumont, William 538

beaver 438, 443

bee 373, 380-81, 660; killer, 380

beetle 158, 374, 376, 379-81, 386, 464

Index

Photograph Credits